HUDSON'S
HISTORIC HOUSES AND GARDENS
including HISTORIC SITES OF INTEREST

Duff House, Banff

Published by

NORMAN HUDSON & COMPANY

High Wardington House, Upper Wardington, Banbury, Oxon OX17 1SP
Tel: 01295 750750   Fax: 01295 750800

Project Co-ordination: Joyce Binns
Design and Typesetting: K.C. Graphics
Electronic Pre-Press: Catalyst Publishing, Leamington Spa
Printed in Great Britain by BPC Magazines (Dunstable) Ltd.

Cover Picture: Scotney Castle, Kent
A National Trust Property.

Johansens has been successfully publishing accommodation guides for fifteen years. The quality and value of the recommendations made by their inspectors are acknowledged by discerning, independent travellers in Britain and throughout the world. The Johansens inspectorate search for only the very best establishments to include in the four guides. Each property is individually inspected prior to inclusion and the team are looking for those places which offer the highest standards of cuisine, accommodation and service. Properties recommended by Johansens are not chain hotels. The majority are privately owned and independently run, many by the owners themselves. They all boast that special ambience, so often lacking in larger, more impersonal hotels.

Johansens guides are printed on quality art paper, displaying each recommendation in full colour on an A4 large page format. There are clear maps and at-a-glance facilities, for example, golf or fishing on site.

JOHANSENS RECOMMENDED
guides...

Recommended Hotels in Great Britain and Ireland 1996:

Featuring over 430 excellent hotels, ranging from restored medieval castles to grand country manor hotels set in acres of grounds and elegant town houses. This guide is an essential source of reference for regular travellers, or those seeking an occasional weekend away at a special venue.

Published at £17.95 + P&P

Recommended Country Houses and Small Hotels in Great Britain and Ireland 1996:

This attractive guide will particularly appeal to readers seeking somewhere small and usually very beautiful in which to stay. With over 200 entries, this guide contains a selection of out-of-the-way farm houses, fine country mansions and interesting town house hotels. Most recommendations are family-run properties with few bedrooms in rural surroundings..

Published at £9.95 + P&P

Recommended Inns with Restaurants in Great Britain 1996:

Now in its eighth year this is a guide to places where excellent hospitality and a traditional welcome are the qualities that have established their reputation. There are centuries old coaching inns, peaceful hostelries nestling by unspoilt village greens and some fine restaurants to discover. These inns are ideal for a relaxing short break away from the hustle and bustle of daily life.

Published at £9.95 + P&P

Recommended Hotels in Europe 1996:

The launch of Recommended Hotels in Europe has added an exciting dimension to the Johansens portfolio, certain to appeal to overseas travellers. The guide contains 127 of the most excellent hotels selected from more than 20 European countries. Recommendations include French Chateaux, German Castles, Italian Palaces and Belgian Town Houses.

Published at £9.95 + P&P

FREE (Recommended Hotels in Europe 1996) when you purchase the set of 3 UK guides. Offer available on our Freefone line only

DIVERSITY AND EXCELLENCE FOR THE DISCERNING TRAVELLER

INTRODUCTION

Hudson's Directory, now in its 10th year, has developed from a specialist publication for the travel trade into the principal and most comprehensive guide fully reflecting the growing range of activities taking place at historic properties.

The market place has also grown, and we have grown with it. Our aim is to provide professionals, group organisers and individuals, both in the UK and worldwide, with the information they need, in a 'user friendly' form. To do this we have kept in touch with the many changes taking place.

We particularly value the encouragement of the Historic Houses Association, The National Trust, and English Heritage with whom we share an interest in securing a useful and valuable future for this part of Britain's built heritage.

Norman Hudson

CONTENTS

Meaning of Symbols

Historic Houses Association member offering access under HHA Friends Scheme

Property owned by the National Trust

Property in the care of English Heritage

Property owned by the National Trust for Scotland

Property in the care of Historic Scotland

Property in the care of CADW - Welsh Historic Monuments

PUT IDEAS INTO YOUR HEAD?

NOW TALK TO THE OTHER AUTHORITY ON COUNTRY HOUSES.

Hudson's Directory is synonymous with beautiful and historic houses.
But sadly, you can only visit them.

But if they've fired your imagination, there's someone else you should be talking to.

Knight Frank.

We too are synonymous with country houses. From cottages to castles we offer a wealth of knowledge and expertise backed by a century of experience in buying, selling and valuing. And with over 90 Knight Frank offices in 20 countries around the world, you can rely on the best advice wherever you are.

If you are considering a move, or would like the opportunity to discuss anything relating to country houses, just call us on 0171 629 8171.

What's New ...

Hudson's Choice
'Up-Market B&B'

House of Urrard, Scotland.

A growing number of private owners of beautiful and stylish country houses are now offering accommodation, effectively bridging the gap between ordinary B&Bs and top class hotels. Over 50 of these delightful and varied houses have been selected on the basis of their likely appeal to those who appreciate and visit historic buildings and gardens. They can be found in the accommodation section (yellow edged pages) towards the rear of this book.

Since when were mince pies illegal as well as fattening ?

A Tudor "Delia Smith" at Sulgrave Manor shares some intriguing and often stomach turning secrets of the kitchen.

Did you know it was actually illegal to eat mince pies ?
Or that the tradition of decking a house with holly and ivy at Christmas comes from an old yuletide ritual to destroy evil ?

These are just two of the amazing facts to be gleaned from the Tudor Christmas events that will be held at Sulgrave Manor, Northamptonshire - ancestral home of George Washington. The great hall of the Manor is bedecked with seasonal greenery, with the log fire burning, and beeswax candles glowing. Visitors meet the 'Tudor Lord of the Manor' and his cook, enjoy a warming wassail and sweetmeats, and hear of the customs and traditions of early Christmases. Mince pies - or shred pyes - were a popular part of yuletide feasting and were oval to represent the crib. In 1650 Oliver Cromwell passed an Act of Parliament to ban them and this Act has never been repealed.
In the 16th century people believed evergreens, which did not die in autumn, housed evil spirits so they hung boughs inside to dry and on Twelfth Night burned them on their huge log fires. The proof of the demons destruction was in the squealing and shrieking of the blazing wood. A Tudor Christmas at Sulgrave will take place in 1996 on December weekends and December 27th - 31st, 10.30am - 1pm and 2pm - 4.30pm.

Hire an historic setting for special occasions

Wrotham Park, Hertfordshire.

The right setting for any occasion can make a great deal of difference to a special event. In *Hudson's* we are trying to draw attention not only to those places that are open to view but also to those houses that either in addition, or separately, offer a stylish, relaxing and gracious setting for social functions, board meetings and client entertaining.

Duff House Restored

Duff House (see frontispiece) a masterpiece by the great Scottish architect William Adam is being opened to the public following restoration. Designed by Adam for William Duff, 1st Earl of Fife, it is set in parkland between the towns of Banff and Macduff, 167 miles north of Edinburgh. The £2.5 million restoration was a joint effort by Historic Scotland, Local Authorities and the National Galleries of Scotland - which has provided 200 paintings, many previously unseen, and period furniture. Duff House was the home of The Earls of Fife until 1906 and then had a chequered career - it was an hotel, then a sanitorium and in World War II housed first German prisoners then Norwegian and Polish troops.

Get married in an Historic House

The Marriage Act 1995 opened the way for Civil Weddings to escape from the dreary surroundings of registry offices and to be held in more agreeable surroundings including historic houses. A number of houses are already officially registered as places where Civil Wedding ceremonies can be performed. Many more provide the venue for receptions. An index of places to hold Civil Weddings can be found towards the back of the book.

Meet George, aged 1,700

The skeleton of a mystery man affectionately known as George has been reunited with his coffin at Lullingstone Roman Villa in Kent. He was buried in 300AD in a vault below a large Pagan temple. George was parted from his coffin because the latter was on the verge of collapse and had to be given stainless steel reinforcement. Experts believe he was in his mid-twenties and was possibly a member of the family that owned the villa. Lullingstone Roman Villa, an English Heritage property, is open daily. (See page 106).

A Stylish Way of Life

by Knight Frank

The British people have a great affection for traditional domestic architecture. We cherish our cottages and farmhouses, manors and mansions, lavishing time and money on them in a way that would probably surprise their original occupants. Interest in authentic style has never been greater than it is today; every opportunity to renovate and restore is grasped, and our appetite for period interior decoration appears insatiable.

Hinton Lodge, Berkshire ~ a classic Queen Anne house.

Authenticity, however, is a relative term in the modern architectural lexicon. Life as portrayed in the pages of Anthony Trollope or Jane Austen may make the reader long for a Small House at Allington or Mansfield Park - but surely not without central heating, electricity and an efficient plumbing system ? Only a fanatic, obsessed with historical accuracy and oblivious of comfort, would be prepared to forgo such modern amenities.

Given these modern adaptations, however, it is possible to enjoy the different characteristics of each period of buildings without suffering from their deficiencies. If you are lucky enough to find a relatively unspoilt medieval house, for example, you can appreciate its great hall without having to endure the throat-burning conditions created by an open fire smoking its way up to a hole in the roof.

Medieval and Tudor architecture on a domestic scale is difficult to find nowadays. The hovels of the poor have not survived, and better houses have mostly been replaced or altered almost beyond recognition, but even if it were more widespread, would it be popular ? The small windows that were once necessary, to defend occupants from attack, are now often regarded as a nuisance. And making alterations to such houses can be a difficult business in the

face of restrictions imposed by the inevitable preservation orders.

Better, perhaps, to choose an architectural style that suits a modern way of life. The classical forms that first appeared in Britain in the work of Inigo Jones (1573 - 1652) have endured for hundreds of years and are still used in building design today. During the 17th century, the unstructured appearance of earlier architecture began to look old fashioned. Anyone who could afford it was rebuilding or extensively altering his home with a grander and more comfortable style in view.

Of course, new styles took different forms in different parts of the country and regional variations account for much of the appeal of period houses. An example of Jacobean taste in the brick and timber framing of East Anglia might bear little resemblance to an interpretation of the same idea in Dorset limestone. And since prosperity could be regional too, not all parts of the country are equally well endowed with houses of particular periods. In upland areas of Britain, for example, where farming has always been the dominant occupation but where few have made their fortunes, building styles were conservative and reacted only slowly and slightly to changing architectural fashions.

1 Hampstead Square, London NW3 ~ built in 1721

Elsewhere, however, large glazed windows, panelled rooms and decorative plasterwork were all the rage and happily, much remains to delight property owners today. During the Georgian period, houses of basically classical design sprang up all over the country. And it is a fact that, however picturesque the earlier vernacular regional styles, it is these Georgian buildings that provoke the fiercest competition amongst buyers of country houses in the late 20th century. Light and well proportioned rooms, and 'dolls house' façades, have an enduring appeal - as is clear from the neo Georgian designs of many modern house-builders.

The flights of fancy that followed during the Victorian period were a reaction to all the classical restraint. 19th century house design reflected the eclectic tastes of home owners who were happy to throw together styles of differing periods. This could result in some rather eccentric houses. Every architectural style has its followers today, however, and eccentricity is a valuable commodity in the context of modern mass production and volume house building. Despite being built of factory made materials which rob it of regional character, the Victorian country house has proportions and space which compare favourably both with farmhouse style dwellings and with what was to follow in our own century.

Cobweb, Haddenham, Buckinghamshire ~ a fine example of a Tudor Yeoman's house. Once owned by Juliana Force, Founder Director of the Whitney Museum in New York.

The basic, vernacular appearance of Arts and Crafts houses influenced much of the mass house building that went on in Britain between the two World Wars. Modern architecture made some inroads, but its appeal was always limited and few country house builders employed its ideas, despite the fact that large areas of glass and raised living areas are ideal for admiring a rural view. It is no accident that the name of Edwin Lutyens, the best known exponent of the Arts and Crafts style, is far more familiar today than any of the Modern architects.

We are traditionalist through and through, it seems, in architecture as in much else. Even the internationally recognisable and ever popular characteristics of Georgian buildings are having to compete today with designs based on regional vernacular styles. As modern life becomes ever more cosmopolitan, appreciation of the localised and the familiar grows stronger, making our houses, cottages and castles more prized and popular than ever.

Trafalgar House, Wiltshire ~ a Grade I listed Georgian house now thought to have been designed by John James of Greenwich, one of the most respected architects of his time, being surveyor to the Dean and Chapter of St. Paul's and Westminster Abbey.

Victorian architecture has lacked *cachet* during the 20th century, not least because there is a lot of it about. But the Victorian period spawned some minority architectural movements whose houses are consequently full of historical interest. The Queen Anne style, epitomised by Richard Norman Shaw's work in Bedford Park, West London, was an attempt to fuse classical rigour with Victorian romanticism and resulted in a small number of very pretty country houses.

Similarly, the Arts and Crafts movement of the turn of the century aimed to regain the simplicity of a vanished age. Its architects employed craftsmen to produce by hand every detail of construction. But their approach was already an anomaly since, already, the cost effectiveness of mass production meant the hand crafted buildings were affordable only to the rich. These houses command high prices in the market today, too, beautifully sited as they often are, and possessing features of a quality that is now barely attainable.

Hadley Lodge, Hertfordshire ~ a recently completed Lutyens style house.

Knight Frank - but no more Rutley.
Leading estate agent Knight Frank and Rutley has changed its name this year - and dispensed with the 'Rutley' exactly 100 years after the firm was founded.

Illustrated are some of the houses that Knight Frank have recently been instructed to sell.

Caption Competition

Sir Humphry Wakefield Bt. with his dog Brigand photographed at his home,
Chillingham Castle, Northumberland (see Northumberland section).

Brigand is deep in thought.
A bottle of champagne goes to the supplier of the caption judged to be the wittiest.

Send your caption (max. length – 20 words) to;
Caption Competion, Hudson's Directory,
High Wardington House, Upper Wardington,
Banbury, Oxon OX17 1SP.
(Closing date 31 August, 1996)

A day out

BLICKLING HALL, N.T.P.L.

SOUTER LIGHTHOUSE, N.T.P.L.

with the National Trust can come in all shapes and sizes.

captivating views of Stowe Landscape Gardens - widely regarded as Britain's largest work of art - rival anything a gallery has to offer.

In fact, with over 300 historic properties, 547 miles of coastline and over half a million acres of countryside, we have something for everyone.

From proud stately homes to modest country cottages, celebrated works of art to working industrial heritage sites, the National Trust cares for properties great and small. Each different from the last.

Each significant in its own right. And each offering the visitor a vastly different experience and endless ways to spend their days.

For further information telephone **0181-315 1111.**

The towering perspectives of Souter, the country's first reliable working lighthouse, are an imposing sight.

Impressive, yet no more outstanding than Blickling Hall in Norfolk, the first major country house to come to the National Trust. A property whose medieval origins date back to Anne Boleyn, Henry VIII's ill-fated second wife.

And, whilst English landscape art is celebrated the world over, the

FELBRIGG HALL, N.T.P.L.

The National Trust

Experience a day out that will stay with you for the rest of your life …

No memory will remain with you for quite so long as a visit to one of English Heritage's 400 historic sites. Whether you're holidaying at home, or visiting from abroad, English Heritage has something for everyone.

From a family day out in the country houses and gardens created for kings and queens, to historic re-enactments in the castles of feudal barons. With many more events throughout the year for all ages, especially children. All of our larger sites have experienced staff, restaurants and souvenir and literature shops. And as you're about to discover, the richness of our heritage can be experienced from Prehistory, to the Second World War.

Everyone will want to experience the world's greatest prehistoric monument, **Stonehenge**. Quite simply, it's an amazing feat of 5,000 year old engineering.

If the mind boggles at Stonehenge, your imagination can run wild at **Tintagel**, Cornwall's castle of legends. Was King Arthur born there? Visit Tintagel and you'll believe it.

Built on historic fact is the reason for a 73 mile long wall from the East to the West coast of England. In AD 130, **Hadrian's Wall** kept the wild tribes of the North apart from civilised Roman society. But there's more than a mere wall to explore; causeways, forts, settlements, temples and turrets bring Roman Britain within your experience.

Further south, at **Whitby Abbey**, the ruins left by Vikings in 876 AD were restored by a Norman Knight, Reinfred. But Henry VIII razed it again, providing a dramatic setting for scenes in Bram Stoker's 'Dracula'.

Another Abbey marks the spot of the most famous date in history; 9am, 14th October 1066. **Battle Abbey** was built by William the Conqueror in 1070, and the high altar placed where King Harold fell.

Dover Castle has been in constant military use for 800 years. At last, previously top secret Second World War tunnels and rooms, including the 'Hellfire Corner' underground hospitals, are open to view.

If you're in need of a breath of fresh air, you'll find plenty at **Kenilworth Castle**, one of Britain's largest ruins. Kenilworth saw better days under Robert Dudley, Earl of Leicester. It was here that he presented Queen Elizabeth I with a magnificent 19 day pageant.

The Hundred Years War. The Spanish Armada. The imprisonment of Charles I. Now you know why **Carisbrooke Castle** on the Isle of Wight is a renowned backdrop to some of history's most famous moments. While you soak them up, the children can watch the donkeys' working on the wheel in the 16th century well house.

Also on the Isle, the whole family can enjoy a Victorian horse and carriage ride at **Osborne House**, Queen Victoria's favourite seaside retreat.

While 'Palace' is usually only associated with royalty, **Audley End** is a 17th century palace in all but name. Built by Thomas Haward, Earl of Suffolk, later owners had rooms designed by Robert Adam and landscaping by 'Capability' Brown. A perfect parkland setting for a picnic.

A feast for the eyes can be found at English Heritage's latest acquisition, **Brodsworth Hall**. Opened for the first time in 1995, this is a very special Victorian country house with much of its contents amazingly intact since the 1860's. A visit not to be missed.

For further information about all of our sites call English Heritage Customer Services on 0171 973 3434, or write to English Heritage Customer Services Department, PO Box 9019, London W1A 0JA.

DOVER CASTLE

BATTLE ABBEY

BRODSWORTH HALL

TINTAGEL

STONEHENGE

AUDLEY END

ENGLISH HERITAGE
A Legendary Day Out

Subscribe!

Informative, lively and controversial, **Perspectives** is the beautifully illustrated magazine about architecture, conservation and the environment.

Published in association with the Prince of Wales Institute of Architecture, **Perspectives** provides a voice for those concerned with traditional architectural values. Each issue brings you news, comment and opinion, features on the best buildings in the world – new and old, and information on suppliers and craftsmen.

You can save over 10% off the cover price by subscribing. Simply complete the form below and enjoy **Perspectives** delivered to your door.

Perspectives ON ARCHITECTURE

I would like a subscription for

❏ **One Year**
❏ **Two years**

Name _____

Address _____

_____

_____

Postcode_____

Country_____

❏ *Please tick this box if you do not wish to receive promotional material from other companies.*

Subscription rates for one year
(6 issues)

UK £15

Europe and Eire £24

Rest of World £30

North America .... US $38

Subscription rates for two years
(12 issues)

UK £30

Europe and Eire £48

Rest of World £60

North America .... US $75

Payment information

I enclose a cheque for _____ *payable to* **Perspectives Ltd**

Please charge my Access/Amex/Mastercard/Visa for _____

Card number _____ Expiry date _____

Signature _____ Date _____ 96HH1

Send to: **Perspectives**
PO Box 426, Freepost WD 4260, Woking, Surrey GU21 1BR

or call: **01483 733883**
with your credit card details

Modelled with a free hand

Ornamental plasterwork modelled by hand was a lost art until a few years ago. **Joanna Watt** *meets Trevor Proudfoot, a pioneering spirit behind its revival. Photograph by* **John Millar**

TRACKING DOWN TREVOR PROUD-foot for an interview is not an easy job. If he is not at his workshop in Berkshire, he might be found at any number of National Trust properties, or in Westminster Cathedral (where he has just completed a conservation project) or even in Turkey (where he has been studying sculptures from the first century). Proudfoot is one of those energetic people who seems to achieve in a week what you or I would in two. He met me at a running pace, and throughout our encounter talked at speed. This is a man for whom time is precious but also for whom work has no limits. He habitually works until three in the morning.

I caught him between Turkey and Waddesdon Manor, in Buckinghamshire, deep in the woods of the Cliveden estate, at the Cliveden Conservation Workshop. Proudfoot established the workshop in 1991 after nine years with the National Trust as one of its sculpture conservators. Since then, he has broadened his horizons, and has about 40 conservators working for him.

Renowned for his work in stone, he has more recently become something of a pioneer in the conservation and restoration of ornamental plasterwork – in particular plaster modelled by hand, rather than cast. Far more lively and less pedantic designs were achieved throughout the seventeenth and eighteenth centuries using this method. But it was an art that had, by and large, been lost until only a few years ago. It died out around the middle of the eighteenth century, when plasterers discovered that it was quicker and cheaper to produce moulds from which casts could be made. Many plaster companies in Britain (a few of which were established in the last century or earlier) are renowned for their designs and restoration techniques, but virtually none model plaster by hand. Most of them work in fibrous plaster, rather than the natural and original material, lime.

By a strange twist of fate, it was a tragedy that initiated the revival of freehand modelling. The infamous fire at the National Trust's Uppark in West Sussex has led to arguably the largest and most ambitious restoration this century, providing hundreds of craftsmen with the monumental challenge of recreating an eighteenth-century house down to its last detail. But, as Proudfoot says, "nobody knew how Uppark's eighteenth-century ornamental plaster ceilings were made, not even the most experienced plaster companies. The whole art of freehand modelling in lime had been lost."

Until, that is, conservationists such as Proudfoot sifted through 2,000 dustbins of debris like detectives, carefully piecing together the few remains. "Through the vision of Martin Drury, the trust's historic building secretary, and the architect Paul Drury, of the Conservation Practice," he says, "we gradually worked out how the ceilings were put together." Proudfoot and his team worked on four ceilings: the Rococo ceilings of the Red Drawing Room, Small Drawing Room and Staircase Hall; and the Neo-Classical Saloon and Little Parlour. They were then faced with the laborious task of working out what exactly was in the lime mixture. "We weren't too sure," he admits. But all sorts of concoctions soon bubbled from the cauldron on the Cliveden estate. "People tried throwing in beer, and even sugar to get the right mix." Once satisfied, the Cliveden conservation team applied it directly to each ceiling where it was modelled, upside down of course, on site.

With Uppark under his belt, Proudfoot has a number of other ornamental plaster commissions in the pipeline. He has also been repairing plasterwork at Chastleton in Oxfordshire and a decorative ceiling at Newton House in South Wales, all thanks to the knowledge gained at Uppark. "Before Uppark, I saw no evidence of anyone working in freehand modelling. But this is a very exciting time. I believe that for the first time since the eighteenth century, there are now plasterers who are are good as or even better than their eighteenth-century predecessors."

This interest still has to filter through the ranks of specialist conservationists, though.

Grand country houses may be getting the attention they deserve from the country's leading plasterers, but what about more modest houses, most of whose plaster is cast from moulds but is no less interesting for that? Walk into any Georgian or Victorian house, and the chances are that the ceiling friezes and cornices will be hidden beneath layers of paint. Even the proudest home-owners leave their plaster hidden. But, as Proudfoot says, restoring such features is possible, and it makes all the difference to a room's character. "We are hungry for smaller commissions, particularly since plasterers are so much more knowledgeable now."

And what of new designs fashioned from freehand modelling? "It is my wildest dream to design a new ceiling," says Proudfoot enthusiastically. "But," as he admits, "they can be pricey." What better way though to celebrate the revival in an art that has been dead for so long than to take it one step on and commission your own, unique ceiling? Mr Proudfoot is your man. ☐

The Cliveden Conservation Workshop, The Tennis Courts, Cliveden Estate, Berkshire (0628 604721)

Gallery of Family Portraits

◀ The Duke and Duchess of Argyll with their son, the Marquess of Lorne and daughter Lady Louise Campbell at **Inveraray Castle**, Argyll. The Duke is hereditary master of Her Majesty's household in Scotland and keeper of the Great Seal of Scotland. The fairytale exterior of the castle belies the grandeur of its interior.

▼ Mrs Farquhar Ogilvie in her garden at **House of Pitmuies**, by Forfar, Tayside. Adjacent to the 18th century house are walled gardens with long borders leading down to a river. The massed delphiniums and other perennials in July must be one of the most memorable displays of its type to be found in Scotland.

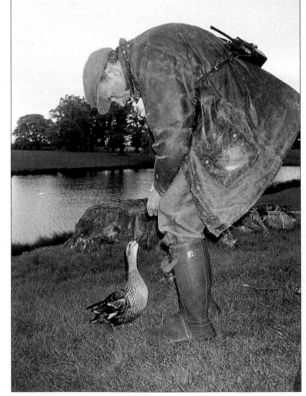

▼ Lord and Lady Inglewood at **Hutton-in-the-Forest**, Cumbria where his family have lived since the beginning of the 17th century. The house is built around a medieval pele tower with 17th, 18th and 19th century additions.

Lord Inglewood, who is qualified as both a barrister and a chartered surveyor, was formerly a Member of the European Parliament for Cumbria and Lancashire. He is now a Government Minister in the House of Lords. Lady Inglewood is a talented photographer with work published under her maiden name of Cressida Pemberton Pigott.

▲ Lord Barnard at **Raby Castle**, Co Durham. He is a direct descendant of the Nevilles who built the Castle in 1370 having occupied the site since the 12th century. Lord Barnard is keen on wildlife conservation and is President of the Durham Wildlife Trust. He is seen here with Mathilda, a wild duck which came to join a group of domestic East India Ducks originally bought for Lord Barnard by his daughter Sophia.

◄ A portrait of the Duke and Duchess of Sutherland at **Mertoun** in the Scottish Borders. The focal point of the 20 acre garden overlooking the River Tweed, is the 3 acre walled garden with its box hedges, neat rows of vegetables and flowers, and well-tended glass houses ~ just as one always imagines an ideal kitchen garden should be.

Mr and Mrs Francis ► Grant with their daughter Elizabeth and labrador Musky at **Kingston Bagpuize House** in Oxfordshire which Francis Grant was given by his mother Lady Tweedsmuir in November 1995. They hope to use the house and gardens to host a variety of events in future years.

▲ Robert Byng, owner of **Wrotham Park**, Hertfordshire, took over the management of the estate in 1991. Whilst the house has for many years been frequently used as a location for films and TV he is now promoting Wrotham as a venue for private and corporate occasions. One of his first bookings last year was to host the pre-wedding ball for Crown Prince Pavlov of Greece and his fiance Miss Marie-Chantal Miller which was attended by 1,300 guests including Royal Families from throughout Europe.

▲ Lord Digby, Lord Lieutenant of Dorset, whose gardens at **Minterne** lie up the valley from the Cerne Abbas Giant. The Minterne landscape was created in the 18th century but it is the woodland garden with its rhododendrons and azaleas towering over small lakes and cascades that astonishes. Here can be found some of the most interesting and impressive rhododendrons in the country.

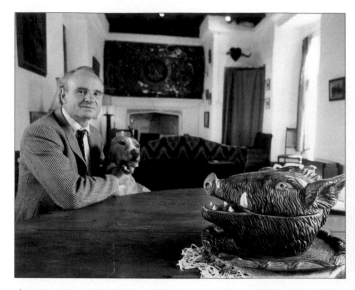

▼ Major Tom Wills at **Misarden Park,** Gloucestershire, with his son Nicholas, daughter Camilla and black labrador Tulip. The gardens at Misarden have wonderful views over the famous Golden valley and is noted in spring for its bulbs and flowering trees and in mid-summer for the large double herbaceous borders.

▲ Sir Humphry Wakefield, and his dog Brigand at **Chillingham Castle**, Northumberland. He is a specialist in reproducing works of art. The hog's head tureen is a copy of a late 18th century original held by the Duke of Argyll. In recent years Sir Humphry has worked marvels in restoring the great Border fortress of Chillingham Cattle and its splendid garden and grounds which were laid out by Sir Jeffrey Wyatville fresh from his triumphs at Windsor Castle.

◄ Mr and Mrs Robert Hasell-McCosh with their children Hermione, George and Beatrice, their grand father Bryce McCosh and dog Lizzy at **Dalemain**, Penrith, Cumbria. The imposing Georgian facade of Dalemain conceals a fine mixture of Medieval, Tudor and early Georgian architecture with an interesting collection of furniture, pictures and objects typical of a well established family house. The late Mrs McCosh revitalised the gardens replanting many of the borders introducing rare and exotic plants.

Mr and Mrs Alexander McEwan, at **Bardrochat**, ► Ayrshire, the house built by Sir Robert Lorimer for Mr McEwan's grandfather. Bardrochat is featured in the "Where to stay" section of this book because while it can be viewed by appointment it is also possible for groups of people to stay. Many do so because it forms the ideal base from which to tour the many fine gardens in south west Scotland.

Bardrochat is used frequently for fashion photography. The interiors by Lorimer are particularly photogenic and the clear light of the surrounding countryside with every sort of location from beaches, ruined castles, moorland and hills make it particularly suitable.

In the pre-Beatles era of the late 50s and 60s Alex McEwan and his brother Rory were well known as a guitar playing and singing duo. They had a regular spot on the BBC Tonight programme singing topical songs and Scottish folk music, appeared in four Edinburgh festivals, and in 1963 filled London's Festival Hall.

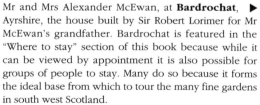

◀ Mr and Mrs Antony Jarvis with their daughters Sophie, Claire and Catherine in front of **Doddington Hall,** Lincolnshire. Victoria Jarvis is Chairman of the newly formed Lincolnshire Gardens Trust. Externally Doddington with its perfectly symmetrical front elevation is one of the most appealing of Elizabethan houses. In 1760 it was rescued by Sir John Delaval after a period of neglect. This restoration resulted in the present Georgian rooms, and 200 years ahead of its time, a system of double glazing to try and exclude draughts.

▼ Mr and Mrs Ian Pasley-Tyler are the third generation of the same family to live at **Coton Manor**, Northamptonshire and run the garden which opened to the public in 1969. Since they took over in 1991 Ian and Susie have added a restaurant and established a gardening school (The Gardener's Academy). Sales of unusual plants, all propagated from the garden, have been greatly expanded and developments in the garden include a formal herb parterre, a wild flower meadow and an orchard specialising in many varieties of old English apples. Susie is President of the Northamptonshire Gardens Trust.

▲ Mr Edmund and The Hon Mrs Brudenell with their granddaughters Sophie and Victoria at **Deene Park**, Northamptonshire. A famous member of the family was James Brudenell, 7th Earl of Cardigan who led the Charge of the Light Brigade at Balaklava.

▲ The Earl and Countess of Sandwich in their garden at **Mapperton**, Dorset. Lord Sandwich works in connection with Third World development, especially India and parts of Africa, and on advocacy for Christian Aid and Save the Children Fund. Lady Sandwich, as Caroline Montagu, is a writer who has specialised in Gulf and Saudi Arabian business and economics. For fifteen years she was Chairman of a housing association. She is currently Chairman of the Dorset Gardens Trust and of the HHA Gardens Committee. The garden at Mapperton, notable for its layout, has been allocated a whole chapter in Christopher Lloyd's new book *Other People's Gardens*. The garden will be seen on cinema screens this year in the new feature film of Jane Austen's Emma and in the 17th century romance, Restoration, with a star studded cast including Hugh Grant and Meg Ryan.

▲ Capt and Mrs Beauchamp Blackett of **Arbigland**, Dumfries & Galloway on his 50th birthday with Annabel, Jamie, Edward, Flora and Letitia and dogs Bolly and Brodie. The gardens which have evolved over three centuries make an ideal place for a family outing. Having seen the gardens younger visitors (and dogs) can run down to a sheltered sandy bay on the Solway Coast and let off steam.

▲ Mr James Hunter Blair whose home **Blairquhan**, Ayrshire is one of the finest houses by the architect William Burn. This welcoming house with its original furniture is open to the public for a month each summer or more extensively available for small conferences, corporate hospitality and accommodation.

Photo: Clive W Couch

▲ The Earl and Countess of Glasgow with their son David, Viscount of Kelburn and their daughter Lady Alice Boyle in the main drawing room at **Kelburn Castle,** Ayrshire, situated on the picturesque north Ayrshire coast. Lord Glasgow is a documentary film producer and regularly speaks in the House of Lords on broadcasting matters. He is a keen builder of "follies" and recently his energies have been directed to enhancing the Kelburn Country Centre. Here the newest attraction, *The Secret Forest*, enthuses both adults and children with the 35ft Pagoda, Mysterious Grotto, the Green Man Maze and the Giant's Castle. In some of the purely architectural conceptions he has been aided by the architect Vernon Gibberd. In various places interesting sculptures are discovered as if by chance including a surrealist tree with fish climbing up it.

◀ Sir Arscott and Lady Molesworth St Aubyn at **Pencarrow**, Bodmin, Cornwall, a handsome Georgian house with 50 acres of gardens. Pencarrow is not far from the main A30 artery through Cornwall or from the popular coastal resorts of Rock, Polzeath and Padstow and provides a marvellous antidote to a surfeit of sea, sand and surf. Children are invariably captivated by the way the house is shown and the appealing and uncontrived things to see and on which they can play in the courtyard behind the house, particularly the slate hung 'Wendy House' on staddle stones.

Captain Nigel Thimbleby riding ▶ from the gatehouse at **Wolfeton House**, Dorset following a meeting of the South Dorset Hounds. Wolfeton is a fine Medieval and Elizabethan Manor House much embellished around 1580 and with splendid plaster ceilings, fireplaces and panelling of that date. Captain Nigel Thimbleby is a representative for Christies in the Dorset area.

▲ Mr and Mrs James Lowther, owner of **Holdenby House**, Northamptonshire, once the largest house in England and prison of Charles I, with their children in the Elizabethan Garden. The existing house was adapted from the remains of the Elizabethan house by Mr Lowther's great great grand-mother. Mr Lowther is the creative director of M&C Saatchi having moved with Maurice and Charles Saatchi when they formed their new agency. He is particularly keen on heritage education and this year Holdenby has received the rare accolade of a 3rd Sandford Award.

Baroness Strange and her husband Capt Humphrey ▶ Drummond in their garden at **Megginch Castle**, Errol, Perthshire. Lady Strange is a regular attender in the House of Lords where she took her seat in 1984 and has a special interest in defence matters and foreign affairs. She is President of the War Widows Association which has achieved several successes in obtaining better treatment of war widows.

The gardens at Megginch are noted for their 1,000 year old yews and doubled walled kitchen garden against which are grown outside tender fruit including white peaches, nectarines and apricots. A recent addition, the Astrological Garden, planted in accordance with 16th century herbals, fascinates visitors who are keen to discover and see plants associated with different signs of the Zodiac (see Tayside).

▲ Ms Catherine Maxwell Stuart, The Lady of Traquair and 21st Laird (with hands together behind the terriers) with members of the family, staff and craftworkers at **Traquair**. Traquair, the oldest inhabited house in Scotland, has been occupied for over 1,000 years and visited by 27 Scottish Kings. The Stuarts have been there for over 500 years. Last year Catherine Maxwell Stuart married Mr John Grey but each will retain their own name.

Traquair has strong Jacobite associations. To commemorate the 250th anniversary of the 1745 Rising, a special limited edition Jacobite Ale was brewed. So popular was this ale, based on an 18th century recipe flavoured with coriander and with 8% alcohol, that it is being repeated this year. It is available from selected outlets or by mail-order from Traquair.

The Earl and Countess of Harrowby at **Sandon ▶ Hall**, Staffordshire with their daughter Lady Rosalthé Rundall and grand children Tom, Mark and Jack Rundall. The family has been prominent in legal and Parliamentary affairs for 250 years with seven generations in Parliament, three successive ones in the Cabinet. While Sandon Hall its grounds, park and arboretum are open throughout the year for pre-booked parties, Lord Harrowby is successfully encouraging ancillary use of the house for functions and other events.

▲ Christopher Lloyd of **Great Dixter**, East Sussex (on holiday in Turkey). Great Dixter is one of the outstanding gardens of the 20th century. It is primarily the inspiration of four people: Nathanial Lloyd who bought the old manor house in 1910, his wife, and his friend Edwin Lutyens and more recently his son Christopher.

Christopher Lloyd's outstanding achievement is the inspired planting that harmoniously complements the older framework created by his father and Lutyens.

Photo: Tony Weaver, Express Newspapers.

◀ Lord and Lady St Levan, at **St Michael's Mount**, Cornwall. Lord St Levan's father gave St Michael's Mount to the National Trust in 1954, not for financial reasons but to ensure its long term protection from the possibility of any unsuitable heir. He retained a 1,000 year lease of the Victorian wing in which Lord and Lady St Levan live today. Lord St Levan has continued to top up the endowment fund so that unusually for a National Trust property it has an endowment fund in surplus. Last winter St Michael's Mount was a location for the filming of Twelfth Night with Nigel Hawthorne, Ben Kingsley and Helena Bonham-Carter in leading roles.

▲ The Earl and Countess of Wemyss and March in the celebrated marble hall at **Gosford House**, East Lothian having their portrait painted by Stephen Stephen. Gosford, a model of which can be seen in the photograph was designed by Robert Adam. It has a striking coastal situation. The two wings were subsequently re-built in 1890. Lord Wemyss is President Emeritus of the National Trust for Scotland and has been a prominent figure in Scottish conservation circles for many years. His first wife died in 1988. Last year he married Shelagh Kennedy well known for her work with the National Trust for Scotland and in particular in connection with The Georgian House, Charlotte Square in Edinburgh. Lord Wemyss' son, Lord Neidpath, lives at Stanway, Gloucestershire.

House of Lords

Highclere Castle
is an extravagant Victorian
dream in which
tales of mystery and hidden
treasures entwine,
says **Siân Ellis.**

Main picture: Lord Carnarvon stands beneath a portrait of the 5th Earl. Right: The pretty gardens. Below: A walk in the grounds. The Jackdaw's Castle folly can be glimpsed in the far distance.

The splendour of Highclere Castle near New-bury in Berkshire is reminiscent of an exuberant burst of fireworks captured on a magnificent photograph and so imbued with a motionless elegance. Ornate, soaring pinnacles shoot upwards to the skies, sweeping the tall, central tower to some Italianate heaven. It is the epitome of Victorian ostentation.

It is also strangely familiar, even to the first-time visitor, for despite its setting amidst peaceful parkland studded with follies and lakes, Highclere Castle bears a striking resemblance to the Houses of Parliament. Even the 7th Earl of Carnarvon, whose family has lived here ever since it was built, admits: "It is quite funny going to the House of Lords, because when I arrive it looks so like Highclere. It is quite incredible."

Sir Charles Barry was asked by Henry Herbert, 3rd Earl of Carnarvon, to alter his plain Georgian house in the 1830s, for he desired a grand mansion at Highclere more befitting his increasing wealth and importance. At the time the architect was about to embark on the design of the Houses of Parliament, which explains their similarities.

Although Barry retained the square shape of the 3rd Earl's original home, he clad it with fantastic stonework and carvings which transformed it into an extravagant Victorian dream, the apogee of which was its central tower — the result of the architect's guile.

"Barry was quite cunning about the tower," Lord Carnarvon explains. "My ancestors had told him that there was not enough money around to build a tower, so he wrote to Prince Albert and asked him what he thought of the plans for the house he was designing for Lord Carnarvon, adding: 'I hope you like the tower.'

"The Prince Consort wrote back saying he thought it absolutely majestic and that the tower was the crowning glory. My ancestors were cornered and had to build it!"

So pleased was Barry with his masterpiece that he always considered it one of his greatest accomplishments and liked it better even than the Houses of Parliament.

Three characteristic Victorian qualities are immediately apparent at Highclere: a sense of ancestry, of the past and of extravagance.

The Carnarvon family claims ancestry with the great Christian Emperor Charlemagne and the family motto, written in Norman French, can be found on the castle's façade: *Ung ir serviray* (one only will I serve).

But the story of the Herbert family at ▶

Main picture: The Saloon. Right: The Smoking Room. Below left: The 3rd Earl of Carnarvon. Below right: Preparing the grand Dining Room.

HIGHCLERE.

▶ Highclere begins in the 17th century.

In 1692 the lawyer Sir Robert Sawyer bequeathed a stuccoed mansion at Highclere to his only daughter Margaret, Countess of Pembroke. However, Margaret lived at Wilton House in Wiltshire, which in turn would be inherited by her first son, so it was her second son, Robert Herbert, who inherited Highclere.

Portraits of Sir Robert Sawyer and his daughter hang in the Dining Room and an old family legend relates that disaster will strike the Herberts if ever the portrait of Margaret is displaced. "My father would never allow it to be moved," Lord Carnarvon affirms.

It is also believed that the ghost of Sir Robert used to wander the castle during the 19th century, until "Grumpus," as he was known, was banished for 100 years. "He is due to come back any time now!" Lord Carnarvon says. Nor are these the only legends and "curses" which lend an air of mystery to the Carnarvon family and their home.

After Robert Herbert's death, Highclere was inherited by his nephew, Henry, who was created Baron Porchester and 1st Earl of Carnarvon by King George III in recognition of his help in preventing the spread of the Gordon Riots of 1780, when a furious mob terrorised London for a week in opposition to a Bill to give equal rights to Catholics.

Both the 2nd and 3rd Earls were active

in politics, but it was the 4th Earl who scored the greatest success: as Secretary of State for the Colonies and Lord Lieutenant of Ireland, he occupied a position of considerable power throughout the reign of Queen Victoria, helping to expand the British Empire worldwide.

The 4th Earl was also responsible for increasing the flamboyant richness of Highclere by completing its interiors after his father's death. In the process he created a magnificent social stage on which to entertain visiting friends and politicians, including the Prime Minister Disraeli.

The architect Thomas Allom used both Barry's original designs and his own for Highclere's interiors. The result is perhaps the most impressive range of styles to be found in any one house. This

is due not so much to the fact that more than one designer was involved, more to the Victorian fashion fearlessly to mix styles of different eras in order to produce a larger-than-life effect.

Walk into the Entrance Hall, designed by Sir George Gilbert Scott, and you might be admiring a church ornate with fan vaulting and columns; the Library exudes an air of opulence and masculinity reminiscent of a gentleman's club; the Music Room, by contrast, with its baroque ceiling from the old Georgian house, is gently feminine.

With another leap of imagination you come to the rococo revival of the Drawing Room, furnished with a wonderful mix of commodes and cabinets ranging from 1730 to 1900. But the most breathtaking scene is the theatrical ▶

RICHARD GREENLY.

HIGHCLERE.

RICHARD GREENLY

 *ain picture:*
The ornate staircase.
Left: The Drawing
Room. Below: The 5th
Earl and an Egyptian
painted wooden coffin
of the 7th century B.C.

been discovered there — two of his finest racehorses were killed in separate incidents. Was this coincidence, or the return of Tutankhamun's curse? It is all part of the mystery of the Herberts!

Although the 5th Earl never saw the mummified Boy King Tutankhamun and it was left to Howard Carter to complete the clearance of the tomb, his name will forever live on in history and legend.

Unfortunately, the Egyptian Government would not permit the treasures of Tutankhamun to be shared. Such *partagement* had previously existed, but a new law rendered all treasures from complete royal tombs the property of the Government. So the treasures remained in Cairo and only the artefacts from previous expeditions came to Highclere, although most of these were sold by the widowed Lady Carnarvon to the Metropolitan Museum in New York.

The 6th Earl fought unsuccessfully to overturn the *partagement* ruling — and subsequently took no further interest in Egyptology.

"My father never discussed it," Lord Carnarvon recalls. "My sister and I were told by our governess not to raise the subject and I never dreamed there might be hidden treasures here."

But there were. Another extraordinary twist to the tale of the 5th Earl's explorations came in July 1987 when Lord Carnarvon unblocked a door — closed for many years — between the Drawing Room and Smoking Room at ▶

▶ Gothic of the Saloon at the heart of the castle, rich with tapestry and decoration.

Such vivacity and exotic taste was influenced both by the times and by the Herbert family's passion for foreign travel. The 3rd Earl was an adventurer who journeyed through Europe, Greece, Turkey and North Africa and was deeply interested in Moorish architecture. His love of distant lands and cultures was inherited by the 5th Earl, who turned to Egypt for the adventures which were to make him famous: the discovery of the tomb of Tutankhamun.

The present Lord Carnarvon holds him in great admiration. "He was a yachtsman, one of the first drivers of a car and clever with his racing and breeding of horses. He was also a good photographer, very well read and a classical scholar."

It was a motor racing accident which led the 5th Earl's doctors to recommend that he recuperated in a warm climate, so in 1907 he took himself off to Egypt. Thus began a fascination in the lost civilisation of the Pharoahs and almost every winter for 15 years was spent excavating and exploring. Working with the Egyptologist Howard Carter, the Earl's searches culminated in the remarkable discovery in 1922 of the richest burial site ever found: the treasures of Tutankhamun.

Tales of legend and curse romanticise the adventure. A mosquito bite and blood poisoning brought a tragic end to the Earl's life in Cairo in 1923. At the moment he died, the lights of Cairo went out and at Highclere his favourite dog suddenly died. Was it coincidence or was it the curse of the Pharoahs, placed upon any royal tomb to protect it?

The present Lord Carnarvon brings the intriguing story up to date. When excavation work was being carried out at Highclere last year — the estate is rich in early artefacts and a medieval village has

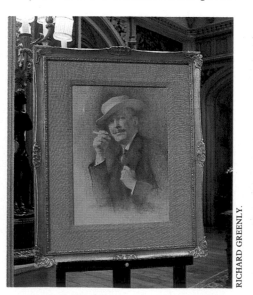

RICHARD GREENLY.

RICHARD GREENLY.

RICHARD GREENLY.

RICHARD GREENLY.

▶ Highclere. Inside the thickness of the wall he discovered tiny pigeonholes containing carefully wrapped packages. They were the forgotten artefacts from the 5th Earl's early expeditions: miniature tools and vessels, jewellery and pottery.

Further discoveries of treasure in other rooms of the house, which Lord Carnarvon was preparing to open to the public, led to the creation of an exhibition in the cellars at Highclere. Lord Carnarvon has since added items he has found at auctions, and the exhibition is a popular attraction for visitors.

A third passion besides politics and travel has motivated the Herberts of Highclere — horse racing — and the present Lord Carnarvon can claim to be the most distinguished member of his family in this sphere.

The 5th Earl had established a stud at Highclere in the late 19th century and the 6th Earl was a great amateur rider. The present Earl is Racing Manager to H.M. The Queen, and has bred many of his own winners at Highclere. It is an interest which he shares with his wife, who comes from an American ranching family in Wyoming, and their three children, all of whom are involved with the running of the farms, stud and castle which make up the Highclere estate.

Although Lord and Lady Carnarvon no longer live in the castle, but in a house nearby, it is still very much their family home. Something is always happening here — dinner parties, shooting weekends, concerts and cricket matches on Highclere's own pitch.

"There is a very cosy atmosphere," says Lord Carnarvon. "I think it is a wonderful home. It is something which has meant a lot to me — and certainly when I came back after the war. Thinking of home when things were pretty horrible meant an awful lot and after the war one wanted to see that the estate was kept and

*A*bove: *Egyptian treasures on display in the Highclere cellars. Below: The opulence of the Library.*

properly looked after."

Highclere is, and will remain, a fascinating stage on which history and mystery have together created a magical tale of a remarkable family. ●

For further details about Highclere including opening times, see page 76. This article first appeared in Heritage magazine also published as Realm in the USA (see inside back cover). **Photographs by Richard Greenly tel: 01488 685256**

RICHARD GREENLY.

1 ROYAL CRESCENT
Bath

NUMBER 1 was the first house to be built in the Royal Crescent, John Wood the Younger's fine example of Palladian architecture. The Crescent was begun in 1767 and completed by 1774.

The House was given to the Bath Preservation Trust in 1968 and both the exterior and interior have been accurately restored.

Visitors can see a grand town-house of the late 18th Century with authentic furniture, paintings and carpets.

On the ground floor are the Study and Dining Room and on the first floor a Lady's Bedroom and Drawing Room. A series of maps of Bath are on the second floor landing. In the Basement is a Kitchen and a Museum Shop.

❖

ADVICE TO COURIERS & DRIVERS
Please make sure you are familiar with restrictions in The Royal Crescent and parking regulations in the centre of Bath.

FACILITIES FOR THE DISABLED
The house is not suitable for the disabled.

CATERING
There is no restaurant or tea room, but there are many facilities in Bath.

GUIDED TOURS
There are guides in every room. Tours in French and Italian are available on request. Average time taken is 45 minutes.

GIFT SHOP
The Gift Shop is open at the same time as the house, and sells such items as classical creamware and books.

GUIDE BOOKS
A full-colour guide book is available. French, German, Spanish, Italian, Japanese, Chinese, Danish and Dutch translations available on request.

SCHOOL VISITS/CHILDREN
School visits are welcome. The cost per child is £2.00 and guides can be provided. New Education Officer.

CONTACT

Mrs Elizabeth Grant
Curator/Administrator
1 Royal Crescent
Bath
Avon
BA1 2LR

Tel: (01225) 428126
Fax: (01225) 481850

LOCATION

Exit 18 from the M4, then the A46 to Bath
2½ hours from London

Rail: Bath Spa Railway Station (1hr, 20 mins from London)

Taxi: Streamline

OPENING TIMES

Summer
13 Feb - 27 October
Daily except Mondays.
10.30am - 5.00pm
Closed Good Friday.
Open Bank Hols and Bath Festival Mondays.

Winter
29 Oct - 1 December
Daily except Mondays.
10.30am - 4.00pm

Last admissions 30 mins before closing. Special tours by arrangement with the administrator.

ADMISSION

All Year
Adult	£3.50
Child*	£2.50
Student	£2.50
OAP	£2.50
Family	£8.00

Groups
Adult	£2.50
School*	£2.00
Student	£2.50

*Aged 5 - 16yrs.

BATH ABBEY

Tel: 01225 464930   **Fax:** 01225 429990

Bath, Avon BA2 6RP

Contact: Canon Richard Askew

England's last great medieval church, begun 1499 as monastery, dissolved 1539. Now a parish church. Fine perpendicular architecture, fan vaulting, windows. On site of Saxon monastery and Norman Cathedral. Heritage Vaults Museum.

Location: Centre of Bath, adjacent to Roman Baths.

Opening Times: Easter - 31 Oct: 9am - 4.30pm. Sunday services: 8am Holy Communion, 9.15am Parish Communion, 11am Choral Matins, 12.15pm Holy Communion, 3.15pm Choral Evensong, 6.30pm Evening Service.

Admission: Adult £1.50 (Voluntary contribution)

BECKFORD'S TOWER

Tel: 01225 338727   **Fax:** 01225 481850

Lansdown Road, Bath, Avon BA1 9BH

Owner: Bath Preservation Trust   **Contact:** Vicky Harmer

Built in the 1820s for the eccentric William Beckford, the Tower is a striking feature of the Bath skyline. Two museum rooms tell the story of Beckford's life, while climbing the 156 steps to the top will give fine panoramic views.

Location: Lansdown Road.

Opening Times: March - October: Sat, Sun, Bank Holiday Mondays 2 - 5pm.

Admission: Adult £1.50, Child 10-16/OAPs 75p, Children under 10 free. Groups by arrangement.

BLAISE CASTLE HOUSE MUSEUM

Tel: 01179 506789   **Fax:** 01179 593475

Henbury Road, Henbury, Bristol, Avon BS10 7QS

Owner: Bristol City Council   **Contact:** The Curator

18th century mansion, now Bristol's Museum of Social History.

Location: 5 miles NW of Bristol city centre, off B4057.

Opening Times: All Year. Tues - Sun 10am - 1pm & 2 - 5pm. Also Bank Holiday Mondays.

Admission: Free.

BRISTOL CATHEDRAL

Tel: 01179 264879   **Fax:** 01179 253678

College Green, Bristol, Avon BS1 5TJ

Contact: Mrs J Coupe

Founded in 1140 as an Augustinian monastery, the building has developed in a variety of styles over the centuries and became a Cathedral in 1542. The Norman Chapter House and colourful early English Lady Chapel and unique enclosed garden should not be missed.

Location: Central Bristol.

Opening Times: All Year: 8am - 6pm. Sunday services: 8am, 10am and 3.30pm. Weekday services: 8.40am, 12.30pm, 3.30pm and 5.15pm.

Admission: Donation.

CLAVERTON MANOR

OPEN

23 Mar - 3 Nov
Grounds: 1 - 6.00pm

Museum: 2 - 5.00pm
(except Mondays)

Bank Hol Weekends,
Suns & Mons.
11.00am - 5.00pm

Special weekend
openings Nov/Dec.
apply to the Secretary.

Tel: 01225 460503
Fax: 01225 480726

THE AMERICAN MUSEUM, BATH, AVON BA2 7BD

Owner: The Trustees of the American Museum in Britain   *Contact: Mrs S Ford*

Situated overlooking the valley of the River Avon and housed in a Georgian mansion, the Museum has 18 period furnished rooms from the 17th to 19th centuries. Special sections devoted to the American Indian, the Pennsylvania Germans, the Shakers etc. New Gallery with seasonal exhibitions. Many exhibits in beautiful gardens. A replica of George Washington's garden at Mount Vernon. American arboretum.

Location: Off the A36 (not suitable for coaches), other route via Bathwick Hill, Bath.

Admission: Adult £5.00, OAP £4.50, Child £2.50.

CLEVEDON COURT

Tel: 01275 872257

Tickenham Road, Clevedon, Avon, BS21 6QU

Owner: The National Trust   **Contact:** The Administrator

Home of the Elton family, this 14th century manor house, once partly fortified, has a 12th century tower and 13th century hall. Collection of Nailsea glass and Eltonware. Beautiful terraced garden.

Location: 1½m E of Clevedon, on B3130, signposted from exit 20 of M5.

Opening Times: 3 Apr-29 Sep:Wed, Thur, Sun & BH Mon, 2 - 5pm. Last adm: 4.30pm.

Admission: Adult £3.50, Child £1.70. Children under 17 must be accompanied by an adult. Parties of 20+ by prior arrangement, no reduction.

DYRHAM PARK

NR. CHIPPENHAM, AVON SN14 8ER

Owner: The National Trust   *Contact: The Administrator*

Tel: 0117 937 2501

Built for William Blathwayt, Secretary at War and Secretary of State to William III between 1691 and 1710. The rooms have been little changed since they were furnished by Blathwayt and their contents are recorded in his housekeeper's inventory. Surrounding the house, the 263 acre ancient parkland with herd of fallow deer, overlooks the Severn valley.

Location: 8m N of Bath, 12 miles E of Bristol. Approached from Bath - Stroud road (A46), 2 miles S of Tormarton interchange with M4, exit 18.

Admission: Adult £5.00, Child £2.50, Family (2 adults & 3 children) £12.50.

Opening Times: Park: All year (except Christmas Day) 12 Noon - 5.30pm, last admission 5pm/dusk. 1 Apr - 20 Oct: 11am - 5.30pm (except Wed & Thur, 12 Noon - 5.30pm). House: 1 Apr - 29 Oct: Daily except Wed & Thur 12 noon - 5.30pm. Last admission 5pm or dusk if earlier.

GATCOMBE COURT

OPEN

Open by written
appointment.
Please apply to
Mr Charles Clarke,
Gatcombe Court,
Flax Bourton,
Bristol,
BS19 1PX.

Tel: 01275 393141
Fax: 01275 394274

GATCOMBE COURT, FLAX BOURTON, BRISTOL BS19 1PX

Owner: Mr & Mrs Charles Clarke   *Contact: Mr Charles Clarke*

A Somerset Manor House, dating from early 13th century, which has evolved over the centuries since, it is on the site of a large Roman village, traces of which are apparent. There is a garden terraced by old stone walls, with many climbing roses, yew hedges and a herb garden.

Location: 5 miles west of Bristol, north of the A370, between the villages of Long Ashton and Flax Bourton.

Admission: By arrangement (see above).

HORTON COURT

Tel: 01985 843600

Horton, Near Chipping Sodbury, Bristol, Avon B17 6QR
Owner: The National Trust   **Contact:** The Administrator
A Cotswold manor house with 12th century Norman hall and early Renaissance features. Of particular interest is the late perpendicular ambulatory, detached from the house. Norman hall and ambulatory only shown.
Location: 3m NE of Chipping Sodbury, ³/₄m N of Horton, 1m W of A46.
Opening Times: 3 Apr - 30 Oct: Wed & Sat, 2 - 6pm or dusk if earlier.
Admission: Adult £1.50, Child 80p

JOHN WESLEY'S CHAPEL

Tel: 0117 926 4740

36 The Horsefair, Broadmead, Bristol, Avon BS1 3JE

Contact: Rev J.A. Newton

The oldest Methodist chapel in the world.
Location: 36 The Horsefair.
Opening Times: Summer; Mon - Sat, 10am - 4pm, Living Rooms closed 1 - 2pm but the chapel remains open. Winter; same as summer except closed on Wednesdays. Closed Bank Holidays.
Admission: Groups £2 ea. (includes talk by warden). Others free - donations appreciated.

LEIGH COURT

Tel: 01275 373393   **Fax:** 01275 374681

Abbots Leigh, Bristol, Avon BS8 3RA
Owner: J T Group   **Contact:** Mrs Sally Barker
The style of the building is Greek Revival and it stands in 25 acres of parkland.
Location: 2 m from J19 on M5.
Opening Times: As Leigh Court is used as a conference centre prior booking to view is advised.

MUSEUM OF COSTUME & ASSEMBLY ROOMS

Tel: 01225 477789   **Fax:** 01225 428184

Bennett Street, Bath BA1 2QH
Owner: National Trust (leased by Bath & NE Somerset Council) **Contact:** Mrs P Ruddock
Location: Near city centre.
Opening Times: All year from 10am (Sun 11am) - 5pm. Not open Christmas and Boxing Day. Last admission 30 minutes before closing.
Admission: Adult £3.50, Child under 18yrs £2.20, under 8yrs free. Family (2 adults - up to 4 children) £10.00. Group (20+): Adult £3.00. Child over 8yrs in summer £1.50 / in winter £1.30. No reduction for NT members. Note. Open all year, but Assembly Rooms may be closed for booked functions. Check availability in advance.

1 ROYAL CRESCENT, BATH

See Page 1 for full page entry.

ROMAN BATHS AND PUMP ROOM

Tel: 01225 477000   **Fax:** 01225 477709

Stall Street, Bath, Avon BA1 1LZ
Owner: Bath & North East Somerset Council   **Contact:** Mr S Clews
Location: Central Bath.
Opening Times: Oct - Mar: Mon - Sat, 9.30am - 5pm, Sun 10.30am - 5pm. April - Sept: Daily 9am - 6pm. Aug: also open 8pm - 10pm. Not open Christmas & Boxing Day. Last admission 30 minutes before closing.
Admission: Adult £5, 8 - 18yrs £3, under 8yrs free, Family (2 adults + 1 - 4 children) £13. Group (20+), Adult £4, Child over 8 in summer £2 / in winter £1.50. Prices after 31 March 1996 are unconfirmed.

SHERBORNE GARDEN

Tel: 01761 241220

Litton, Bath, Avon BA3 4PP
Owner: John Southwell Esq   **Contact:** John Southwell Esq
Location: 7m N of Wells on B3114, off A39.
Opening Times: June - September: Sun & Mon, 11am - 6pm.
Admission: Adult £1.50, Child free.

WESTBURY COLLEGE GATEHOUSE

Tel: 01985 843600

College Road, Westbury-on- Trym, Bristol, Avon
Owner: The National Trust   **Contact:** Rev G M Collins
The 15th century gatehouse of the College of Priests (founded in the 13th century) of which John Wyclif was a prebend.
Location: 3m N of the centre of Bristol.
Opening Times: Visitors to collect the key by prior written arrangement.
Admission: Adult £1.00, Child 50p.

Where to Stay

For Private Accommodation and Johansens recommended Hotels, see Accommodation Section

---

SPECIAL EVENTS

◇ **CLAVERTON MANOR (THE AMERICAN MUSEUM IN BRITAIN)**   **11 – 12 MAY**
American Civil War Camp & Drill Displays

◇ **CLAVERTON MANOR (THE AMERICAN MUSEUM IN BRITAIN)**   **15 – 16 JUNE**
North American Indian Weekend

◇ **CLAVERTON MANOR (THE AMERICAN MUSEUM IN BRITAIN)**   **6 – 7 JULY**
American Independence Day Displays

For National Trust and English Heritage Events see separate section.

LUTON HOO
Luton

LUTON HOO is famous for housing the world famous Wernher Collection, formed primarily by Sir Julius Wernher, who purchased the mansion in 1900, and altered the House with opulent Edwardian interiors by the designers of the Ritz Hotel in London.

There is also a large collection of Russian Fabergé jewellery and jewelled objects in addition to mementoes of the Russian Imperial family. This is the only collection of work by Carl Fabergé on public view in the country.

Recent additions to the collection included memorabilia of the Tsarevitch, which are displayed in the beautifully restored Chapel, now consecrated as a Russian Orthodox Church to the memory of Tsar Nicholas II and the Imperial Family.

Visitors can view the full splendour of the 18th century 'Capability' Brown landscape from the terraces, together with the formal gardens by Romayne Walker from earlier this century. In addition, the most peaceful area is the Rock Garden, a quiet retreat, always with some colour and a variety of most interesting plants.

---❖---

SUITABILITY FOR OTHER EVENTS
Conferences/Seminars/Functions and Wedding Receptions all year.
CONFERENCES/FUNCTIONS
All modern conference facilities and services can be provided. Banqueting facilities include the Pillared Hall, Dining Room, Ballroom, Drawing Room and Small Conference Room.
EXTRA FACILITIES
Grounds available for Marquee events, eg Family Days/Corporate Days/Clay Shoots etc. (No motorised activities).

ADVICE TO COURIERS & DRIVERS
Guided Tours at least 1¹/₂ hours (can be 2 hours).
FACILITIES FOR THE DISABLED
Toilets. Ramp access to Coffee Shop. Lift internally.
PARKING FOR COACHES & CARS
Ample parking.
CATERING
Self-service Coffee Shop.
GUIDE BOOKS
A colour guide book is available.
GUIDED TOURS
Monday-Thursday, morning or afternoon, by arrangement.
GIFT SHOP
Gift shop open at the same time as the house.
SCHOOL VISITS/CHILDREN
Age 12 and over.

CONTACT

The Administrator
Luton Hoo
Luton
Bedfordshire
LU1 3TQ

Tel: (01582) 22955
Fax: (01582) 34437

LOCATION

Road: M1, Exit 10.
London 30 miles
Birmingham 85 miles.

Rail: Kings Cross
Thames link to
Luton/Harpenden.

Bus: Green Line 747
Jet Link.
London Country 321
from Watford.
United Counties X1, X2
or X3 from Bedford.

Air: Luton Airport 1 mile.

CONFERENCE AND FUNCTION FACILITIES

ROOM	DIMENSIONS	CAPACITY	LAYOUT	POWER POINTS	SUITABLE FOR A/V
Ballroom	24' x 69'	200	Theatre	3	3
Dining Room	38' x 24'	50	Any Function	3	3
Pillared Hall	57' x 37'		Any Function	3	3
Conference Hall	25' x 25'	35	Any Function	3	3
Sitting Room		50	Any Function	3	3

OPENING TIMES

Summer
1 April - 13 October

Fris, Sats & Suns
House: 1.30pm - 5.45pm
Gardens & Restaurant:
Open at 12 noon

Bank Holiday Mondays
10.30am - 5.45pm

Mons - Thurs
Open for Coaches and
Groups only, by prior
arrangement.

Winter
Closed.

Conference/Function
Facilities available
all year.

ADMISSION

Summer
HOUSE & GARDEN
　Adult £5.50
　Child* £2.50
　OAP/Student . . .£5.00
Groups**
　Adult £5.00
　Child* £2.00
　OAP £4.50
** Min. 25 persons pre-paid
within 14 days.

GARDEN ONLY
　Adult £2.50
　Child* £1.00
　OAP/Student . . .£2.25
*Must be of school age

Winter
Closed

WOBURN ABBEY
Woburn

THE ABBEY, home of the Dukes of Bedford for over 350 years, was built on the site of a Cistercian Monastery, founded in 1145. During the 17th century, it was restored, with further re-designing and rebuilding by Henry Flitcroft and later Henry Holland in the 18th century. Today the house is more or less as Flitcroft and Holland left it, with the exception of the East Wing which was demolished in 1950 along with the huge Indoor Riding School and Real Tennis Court.

The interior is richly decorated and furnished and has one of the most important private art collections in the world, with English and French furniture; paintings by many of the world's famous artists, including 21 views of Venice by Antonio Canale in the Canaletto Room; English, Continental and Oriental porcelain, and silver by some of the famous Huguenot silversmiths.

Within the 3,000 acre Deer Park landscaped by Humphrey Repton there are nine species of deer, including the Milu, better known as Père David, which was saved from extinction by the 11th Duke of Bedford. Nearby is the 350 acre drive-through Safari Park.

❖

SUITABILITY FOR OTHER EVENTS
Fashion shows, product launches, wedding receptions (Civil Licence held) and filming. Company 'days out' can be arranged.

EXTRA FACILITIES
Use of parkland and garden. Lectures on the property, its contents, gardens and history can be arranged.

ADVICE TO COURIERS & DRIVERS
No unaccompanied children. No photography in House. Dogs in park on leashes. Guide dogs only in House. Special 'out of hours' tours can be pre-booked during either summer or winter - special rates apply.

FACILITIES FOR THE DISABLED
Wheelchairs can be accommodated in the Abbey by prior arrangement (max 8 per group). There are toilet facilities for the disabled.

PARKING FOR COACHES & CARS
There is a very large hardstanding and grass area for coaches and cars.

CATERING
Day to day catering in the Flying Duchess Pavilion Coffee Shop, whenever the Abbey is open to the public. Conferences, banqueting, luncheons, dinners etc can be arranged in the Sculpture Gallery, Lantern and Long Harness Rooms.

GUIDED TOURS
By arrangement, maximum per guide is 15. Tours can be conducted in French, German and Dutch. There is an additional charge of £7.50 per guide. Audio tape tour available - £1 per person.

GIFT SHOP
There are two gift shops, one in the Abbey, the other in the grounds. Both offer a wide variety of attractive and useful gifts.

GUIDE BOOKS
Colour, 48 page guide book, £3.50.

SCHOOL VISITS/CHILDREN
Groups are welcome. Special schools programme is available on request. Cost per child £2.50 (group rate).

CONTACT

Peter A Gregory
Woburn Abbey
Woburn
Bedfordshire
MK43 0TP

Tel: (01525) 290666
Fax: (01525) 290271

LOCATION

From London, either M1 exit 12/13, or A5 turn off at Hockliffe.

Rail: Euston to Leighton Buzzard, Bletchley or Milton Keynes.

Air: Luton 14 mls
Heathrow 39 mls

OPENING TIMES

Summer
24 March - 3 November

Mon - Sat 11am - 4pm
Sundays & Bank
Holidays 11am - 5pm

Winter
1 Jan - 23 March 1996

weekends only
11am - 4pm
(last entry 4pm)

Abbey closed between
28 Oct - 27 Dec

ADMISSION

All year
HOUSE
(including Private Apts)
  Adult £6.80
  Child* £2.50
  OAP £5.80

Groups (15 persons min.)
  Adult £5.80
  Child** £2.50
  OAP £4.80

* 12 - 16 years
** 7 - 16 years

Reduced rates apply to Deer Park only if private apartments not available.

CONFERENCE AND FUNCTION FACILITIES

ROOM	DIMENSIONS	CAPACITY	LAYOUT	POWER POINTS	SUITABLE FOR A/V
Sculpture Gallery	130' x 25'	400	Reception	3	3
		300	Theatre		
		250	Dinner/Dance		
Lantern Room	24' x 21'	100	Reception	3	3
		80	Theatre/Dinner		
		20	Boardroom		

WREST PARK & GARDENS ⊞
Silsoe

The great gardens of Wrest Park provide a serene backdrop to the house, a 19th century mansion built in the style of an 18th century French chateau. Several rooms can be visited, as well as the grand staircase. Other 19th century additions include the formal Parterre gardens of flowers and clipped hedges and a vast orangery. The woodland gardens flanking the Long Water invite you to long tranquil walks, and the gardening style of 'Capability' Brown has left wide open spaces for playing or picnicking in. Horse and carriage rides available.

❖

OPENING TIMES

1 April - 30 September

Weekends and
Bank Holidays only.

10.00am - 6.00pm

CONTACT

Ms Pauline Carter
Wrest Park
Silsoe
Luton
Bedfordshire
MK45 4HS

Tel: (01525) 860152

ADMISSION

Adult £2.50
Child* £1.30
OAP/Student/UB40
holders £1.90

15% discount on groups
of 11 or more

* 5 - 15 years.
Under 5's free

LOCATION

Wrest Park House is
³/₄ mile East of Silsoe
off the A6, 10 miles
South of Bedford.

Rail: Flitwick

Bus: United Counties
X1,X2, X5

ADVICE TO COURIERS & DRIVERS
Tour leader and Coach driver have free entry. 1 extra place for every 20 additional people.

PARKING FOR COACHES & CARS
There are free coach parking facilities. Drop off point at entrance.

CATERING
Refreshments are available.

GUIDED TOURS
Personal stereo tours are included in the admission price.

SCHOOL VISITS/CHILDREN
School visits are free if booked in advance. Contact the Administrator.

BUSHMEAD PRIORY ⊞

Tel: 01230 62614

Colmworth, Bedford, Bedfordshire
Owner: English Heritage   **Contact:** The Custodian
A rare Survival of the medieval refectory of an Augustinian priory, with its original timber-framed roof almost intact and containing interesting wall paintings and stained glass.
Location: On unclassified road near Colmworth, 2 m E of B660.
Opening Times: 1 Apr - 30 Sept: 10am - 6pm. Jul - Aug weekends only.
Admission: Adult £1.50, Child 80p, Conc £1.10.

CECIL HIGGINS ART GALLERY

Tel: 01234 211222

Castle Close, Bedford, Bedfordshire MK40 3NY
Owner: Bedford Borough Council & The Trustees of the Cecil Higgins Art Gallery
Contact: Halina Graham
Original home of Cecil Higgins this award winning Victorian mansion has rooms displayed to give a lived in atmosphere. Adjoining Gallery housing watercolours, prints, drawings, ceramics and glass. Gardens leading down to the river embankment.
Location: Centre of Bedford, just off the river embankment
Opening Times: All year (except 25, 26 Dec and Good Friday); Tues - Sat, 11am - 5pm. Sun and BH Mon 2 - 5pm.
Admission: Free.

DE GREY MAUSOLEUM ⊞

Tel: 01536 402840

Flitton, Bedford, Bedfordshire
Owner: English Heritage   **Contact:** Mr Stimpson
A remarkable treasure-house of sculpted tombs and monuments from the 16th to 19th centuries dedicated to the de Grey family of nearby Wrest Park.
Location: Attached to the church on unclassified road 1¹/₂ m W of A6 at Silsoe.
Opening Times: Weekends only.

HOUGHTON HOUSE ⊞

Tel: 01234 824195

Ampthill, Bedford, Bedfordshire
Owner: English Heritage
Reputedly the inspiration for "House Beautiful" in Bunyan's "Pilgrim's Progress", the remains of this early 17th century mansion still convey elements which justify the description, including work attributed to Inigo Jones.
Location: 1m NE of Ampthill off A421, 8m S of Bedford.
Opening Times: Any reasonable time.

LUTON HOO 🏛

See Page 4 for full-page entry.

SWISS GARDEN

Tel: 01767 627666   **Fax:** 01234 228921

Biggleswade Road, Old Warden, Bedfordshire
Owner: Bedfordshire County Council
Laid out in the early 1800's and steeped in the indulgent romanticism of the time, Swiss Garden combines all the elements of high fashion: formal walks and vistas, classical proportions, tiny thatched buildings, woodland glades and, hidden away, a fairytale grotto with a brilliant glazed fernery, magnificent trees and a network of ponds and bridges.
Location: 1¹/₂ miles West of Biggleswade A1 roundabout, signposted from A1 and A600.
Opening Times: Mar - Sept: Sat, Sun & Bank Hols 10am - 6pm; weekdays 1.30 - 6pm (closed Tuesdays). Jan, Feb & Oct: Sundays & New Year's Day 12 noon - 3.30pm. Parties at any time on request.
Admission: Adult £2.50, Conc. £1.50, Family £5.00. Season ticket available. Special rates for parties and Guided Tours.

WOBURN ABBEY

See Page 5 for full-page entry.

WREST PARK & GARDENS ⊞

See Page 6 for full-page entry.

Wrest Park.

Where to Stay

For Private Accommodation and Johansens recommended Hotels, see Accommodation Section.

SPECIAL EVENTS

✦ **LUTON HOO** Craft Fair	**9 – 10 MARCH**	
✦ **LUTON HOO** Antique Fair	**15 – 17 MARCH**	
✦ **WOBURN ABBEY** Trafalgar House Run	**27 APRIL**	
✦ **WOBURN ABBEY** Spring Craft Fair	**4 – 6 MAY**	
✦ **WOBURN ABBEY** Dog Show	**12 MAY**	
✦ **WOBURN ABBEY** Stationary Engines	**2 JUNE**	
✦ **WOBURN ABBEY** Angling Fair	**8 – 9 JUNE**	
✦ **WOBURN ABBEY** Flower Show	**8 – 9 JUNE**	
✦ **WOBURN ABBEY** Model Helicopters	**14 JULY**	
✦ **LUTON HOO** Country Day	**14 JULY**	
✦ **LUTON HOO** Firework Music Concert (2 programmes)	**20 – 21 JULY**	
✦ **WOBURN ABBEY** Weekend at Woburn Music Festival. Classical and contemporary music	**20 – 21 JULY**	
✦ **WOBURN ABBEY** Weekend at Woburn Music Festival. Classical and contemporary music	**27 – 28 JULY**	
✦ **WOBURN ABBEY** Radio Society of Great Britain	**4 AUGUST**	
✦ **WOBURN ABBEY** Tiger Moth Fly In	**17 – 18 AUGUST**	
✦ **LUTON HOO** Antique Valuation Day	**27 SEPTEMBER**	
✦ **LUTON HOO** Interior Design Exhibition	**18 – 20 OCTOBER**	

For National Trust and English Heritage Events see separate section.

DORNEY COURT
Windsor

"One of the finest Tudor Manor Houses in England." Dorney Court is an enchanting, many gabled pink brick and timbered manor house with more than just a taste of history.

The Grade 1 listed Dorney Court offers a most welcome, refreshing and fascinating experience. Built about 1440 and lived in by the present family for over 400 years.

The rooms are full of the atmosphere of history: early 15th and 16th century oak, beautiful 17th century lacquer furniture, 18th and 19th century tables, 400 years of family portraits, stained glass and needlework. Here Charles II once came to seek the charms of Barbara Palmer, Countess of Castlemaine, the most intelligent, beautiful and influential of ladies. St James' Church, next door, is a lovely, cool, cheerful and very English village church.

"The approach to the house is through ancient Buckinghamshire woodland which transports the visitor into a dreamland. Suddenly the early Tudor house, a ravishing half timbered vision in gabled pinkish brick, comes into view, prettily grouped with a church. This is Dorney Court, a surprisingly little known manor house ... happily genuine...an idyllic image." *Daily Telegraph*

❖

CORPORATE HOSPITALITY
Dorney Court is a privately owned and lived in family house and because it is in no way a 'tourist attraction' hotel or commercial banqueting hall, is the perfect place for an 'upmarket' group visit or for exclusive private functions for companies and tourist groups from overseas.

Dorney offers exclusivity and privacy combined with a superbly convenient rural location, only 25 miles west of London.

The house is ideal for private dinners etc., often matched into conferences held elsewhere, and makes a complete change from the work environment.

Catering can either be done by the best of outside caterers or by ourselves. We farm the surrounding land as we have for centuries, producing some of England's best lamb, growing strawberries, raspberries and other delicious fruit and vegetables. As far as possible we use fresh home-produced food such as lamb and asparagus in spring but if not appropriate then the best available fresh ingredients such as summer salmon, grouse or partridge in autumn, with venison or beef in winter.

On a cold and dark winter's night, the Great Hall flickers in candlelight and the large wood fires glow with warmth. In summer you can stroll the lawns with a cooling cocktail. The cocktail might be the famous Palmer cocktail, winner of the Grand Prix in Paris in 1934, the secret recipe given to the family by an Hungarian barman in Budapest, the only recognisable ingredient being the topping up champagne, cooling and refreshing.

SUITABILITY FOR OTHER EVENTS
Activity and family fun days, product launches, spouses programmes and garden parties, overseas tourist groups, filming, photography. No private family parties, weddings or dancing.

GENERAL ADVICE
No facilities for disabled, unaccompanied children, dogs or photography in the house.

SCHOOL VISITS
£2.00 per child plus £16 per guide required. No charge for accompanying adults.

PICK-YOUR-OWN FRUIT
June - August every day. 10% discount Mons - Weds 10.00am - 5.00pm.

GIFT SHOP
Open for visitors to the House. Guide Book £2.00.

GUIDED TOURS
Are available for private visits: 1½hrs.

CONTACT

Peregrine & Jill Palmer
Dorney Court
Windsor
Berkshire
SL4 6QP

Tel: (01628) 604638
Fax: (01628) 665772

LOCATION

25 miles West of
London
via M4, 40 mins.
depending on traffic.

Rail: Windsor 5 miles,
Burnham 2 miles.

Air: London Airport
(Heathrow) 20 minutes

OPENING TIMES

Summer

Easter: Good Friday, Sat, Sun & Mon.

May: Sundays and Bank Holiday Mondays.

June - September: Suns, Mons & Tues.

2.00 - 5.30pm.
Last admission 5pm.

Open at other times for groups by arrangement.

Winter

October - Easter
Pre-booked tours only.
(1997 dates will change)

ADMISSION

HOUSE & GARDEN
  Adult £4.00
  Child** £2.00
  OAP £3.60
Groups* on open days
  Adult £3.60
  Child £2.00

Private Visits £5.50
10% discount NT,
NADFAS and OAP's

* Minimum 10 people
**Age 10-16 years

CONFERENCE AND FUNCTION FACILITIES					
ROOM	DIMENSIONS	CAPACITY	LAYOUT	POWER POINTS	SUITABLE FOR A/V
Great Hall	33' x 24'	65	Various	3	✓
Dining Room	20' x 20'	18	Various	3	✓

BASILDON PARK

OPEN
30 Mar - 31 Oct
Wed - Sat: 2 - 6.pm
Sun and
Bank Hol Mons
12 noon - 6pm
(closed Good Fri &
Wed after Bank Hol)
Grounds: 9 - 29 Mar
Sat, Sun
12 noon - 5pm
(Sats 6pm)
30 Mar - 31 Oct
same as house.
Last adm: 5.30pm.

Tel: 01734 843040

LOWER BASILDON, READING RG8 9NR

Owner: *The National Trust*   ***Contact:*** *The Administrator*

A fine Georgian house overlooking the Thames Valley, with important pictures, furniture and plasterwork. Attractive Octagon Room and Decorative Shell Room, garden and woodland walks. Home-made teas in house; shop in stable-yard. Free car park.
Location: 2¹/₂ miles NW of Pangbourne on the A329, 7 miles from M4 junc. 12.
Admission: Adult £3.70, Child £1.85, Family Ticket £9.
Park & Gdn only £1.50, Family £3.75.

THE SAVILL GARDEN

OPEN

Mar - Oct
10.00am - 6.00pm

Nov - Feb
10.00am - 4.00pm

Tel: 01753 860222
Fax: 01753 859617

WINDSOR GREAT PARK, BERKSHIRE SL4 2HT

Owner: *Crown Property*   ***Contact:*** *Mr. J. Bond*

World-renowned woodland garden of 35 acres, providing a wealth of beauty and interest in all seasons. Spring is heralded by hosts of daffodils, masses of rhododendrons, azaleas, camellias, magnolias and much more. Roses, herbaceous borders and countless alpines are the great features of summer, and the leaf colours and fruits of autumn rival the other seasons with a great display.
Location: Wick Lane, Englefield Green. Clearly signposted from Ascot, Bagshot, Egham and Windsor. Nearest station: Egham.
Admission: Adult £3.50, OAP £3.00, Parties of 20+ £3.00. Under 16's free. Accom.

DONNINGTON CASTLE   **Tel:** 01179 750700

Newbury, Berkshire.

Owner: English Heritage   **Contact:** The South West Regional Office
Built in the late 14th century, the twin towered gatehouse of this heroic castle survives amidst some impressive earthworks. The remainder was destroyed during one of the longest sieges of the Civil War, lasting nearly two years.
Location: 1 m N of Newbury off B4494.
Opening Times: Any reasonable time
Admission: Free.

DORNEY COURT   See Page 8 for full page entry.

ENGLEFIELD HOUSE   **Tel:** 01734 302221   **Fax:** 01734 303227

Englefield, Theale, Reading, Berkshire RG7 5EN
Owner: Sir W Benyon   **Contact:** Sir W Benyon
A 7 acre garden, herbaceous and rose borders, fountain, stone balustrades and staircases, woodland and water garden, set in Deer Park. Large variety of trees, plants and shrubs, children's garden, plant sales.
Location: 4m W of Reading off A4.
Opening Times: Garden only: all year, Mon 10am till dusk. Apr - Jun: Mon, Tues, Wed and Thur 10am till dusk. Sun, 12 May and 14 July: 2 - 6pm.
Admission: £2.00.

ETON COLLEGE   **Tel:** 01753 671177   **Fax:** 01753 671265

Windsor, Berkshire SL4 6DW
Owner: Eton College   **Contact:** Mr Howard Eaton
Eton College, founded in 1440 by Henry VI, is one of the oldest and best known schools in the country. The original and subsequent historic buildings of the Foundation are an integral part of the heritage of the British Isles and it is with pleasure that visitors are invited to experience and share the beauty and traditions of the environs which include the magnificent College Chapel, a masterpiece of the perpendicular style.
Location: Off junction 5/M4.
Opening Times: 30 Mar - 6 Oct: Times vary, best to check with the Visits Manager.
Admission: £2.50. Groups by appointment. Rates vary according to type of guided tour.

ST GEORGE'S CHAPEL, WINDSOR   **Tel:** 01753 865538   **Fax:** 01753 620165

Windsor, Berkshire SL4 1NJ
Owner: The Dean & Canons of Windsor   **Contact:** Lt Colonel N J Newman
Opening Times: Mon - Sat, 10am - 4pm, Sundays open for services only.
Admission: Free admission on payment of entry charge into Windsor Castle.

SWALLOWFIELD PARK   **Tel:** 01734 883815

Swallowfield, Reading, Berkshire RG7 1TG
Owner: Country Houses Association   **Contact:** Mrs Glaister
Built in 1678 by the second Earl of Clarendon.
Location: In Swallowfield, 6 m SE of Reading. 4m S of J11/M4.
Opening Times: 1 May - 30 Sept, Wed and Thur, 2 - 5pm.
Admission: Adult £2.50, Child £1.50, Groups by arrangement.

WELFORD PARK   **Tel:** 01488 608203

Newbury, Berkshire RG20 8HU
Owner: Ms A C Puxley   **Contact:** Ms A C Puxley
A Queen Anne house, with attractive gardens and grounds.
Location: On Lambourn Valley Road. 6 miles from Newbury West.
Opening Times: 2 Aug - 28 Aug and 29 May, 2.30 - 5pm.
Admission: House by prior arrangement; Adult £3.00, Child Free, Conc. £2.00. Grounds free.

WINDSOR CASTLE   **Tel:** 01753 868286

Windsor, Berkshire SL4 1NJ
Owner: H M The Queen   **Contact:** The Information Officer
Windsor Castle has belonged to the Sovereigns of England for over 900 years. Enquiries for the Castle tel: 01753 831118, for St George's Chapel tel: 01753 865538.
Location: 3 m off J6 of M4.
Opening Times: Mar - Oct: Daily 10am - 5.30pm (last adm. 4pm).
Nov - Feb: Daily 10am - 4pm (last adm. 3pm). Closed 1 Jan, 5 April, 25/26 Dec. Please telephone for additional closing dates.
Admission: Adult £9.50, Over 60's £7.00, Under 17's £5.50, Family (2+2) £21.50.
Sundays: Adult £7.50, Over 60's £5.50, Under 17's £4.50, Family (2+2) £17.50.
Group rates available.

SPECIAL EVENTS

❖ **THE SAVILL GARDEN**   **11 MAY**
Spring Plant Fair: 10.00am - 5.30 pm
Many specialist nurseries, garden crafts and old gardening books.
Free admittance to Plant Fair. Car Park Charge.

❖ **THE SAVILL GARDEN**   **24 AUGUST**
Autumn Plant Fair: 10.00am - 5.30 pm
Many specialist nurseries, garden crafts and old gardening books.
Free admittance to Plant Fair. Car Park Charge.

For National Trust and English Heritage Events see separate section.

MENTMORE TOWERS
Nr. Leighton Buzzard

MENTMORE TOWERS is an example of the Victorian 'Jacobethan' revival at its best. Built in 1855 for Baron Meyer Amschel de Rothschild, this grand romantic house is a reminder of the enormous wealth and power of the Rothschilds in the 19th Century.

The architect was Sir Joseph Paxton, designer of the Crystal Palace, whose early experience designing greenhouses is reflected in the liberal use of glass to open up Mentmore's glittering interior. The main rooms of the House are grouped around the vast Entrance Hall dominated by the magnificent white marble Grand Staircase. The use of marble in the reception rooms contrasts with the ornate gilded style of the living rooms. De Rothschild plundered Europe for his great house, the gilded boiseries in the Dining Room were from the early 18th Century Hotel de Villars in Paris and the striking black and white marble fireplace in the Hall is reputed to have been designed by Rubens for his home in Antwerp.

The House is now the administrative Headquarters of Maharishi University of Natural Law.

SUITABILITY FOR OTHER EVENTS
Corporate hospitality, archery, shows, filming, sales exhibitions, fairs, concerts, conferences, product launches.

EXTRA FACILITIES
Parkland. Tables for 100 and chairs for 200 people. Lectures can be given on the property, contents, gardens and history. The Lecture Room has a max. capacity of 250 people. Cost of hire of the room and lecture negotiable. Projector and screen can be provided.

VIDEO FACILITIES
We can now offer 3 machine high-band editing, including time-coded computer list editing. Cameras (Sony DXC3000PK), a prompter, and portable and studio high-band recorders are also available for hire.

Standard conversion and VHS duplication from low-band, high-band and one inch are also available at very competitive rates.

ADVICE TO COURIERS & DRIVERS
Do not enter grounds through front gates. Use South Entrance. No dogs except guide dogs. No smoking. No unaccompanied children.

FACILITIES FOR THE DISABLED
Disabled and elderly visitors may alight at the entrance to the property. Vehicles can then be parked in the allocated area. There are no toilet facilities for the disabled.

PARKING FOR COACHES & CARS
Capacity of the car park - 100 cars and 10 coaches, near to the House.

GUIDED TOURS
Up to 40 people per tour. Average tour time is 45 minutes.

GIFT SHOP
Postcards are available.

SCHOOL VISITS/CHILDREN
Groups of children are welcome. A guide can be provided on request.

CONTACT

The Events Manager
Mentmore Towers
Mentmore
Nr Leighton Buzzard
Bedfordshire
LU7 0QH

Tel: (01296) 662183
Fax: (01296) 662049

LOCATION

M1 to junction with M25. M25 west to A41. A41 north to Tring. Follow signs from Tring to Pitstone, Cheddington and Mentmore.
London: 1hr (40 miles)

Rail: Cheddington Station 2 miles, Leighton Buzzard 4 miles

Taxi: Valcars (01296) 661666

OPENING TIMES

April - October
Bank Hol Mons
1.45 - 4.00 pm.
Last tour 3.15pm

Tues - Sat : Groups by appointment only.

Sun. 1.45 - 4pm
last tour 3.15pm

November - March
Closed

ADMISSION

Adult £3.00
Child* £1.50
OAP £2.00
Student £2.00
Groups**
Adult £2.50
Child* £1.00
OAP £2.50

* Aged under 14
** Min. 20 People

CONFERENCE AND FUNCTION FACILITIES

ROOM	DIMENSIONS	CAPACITY	LAYOUT	POWER POINTS	SUITABLE FOR A/V
Grand Hall	34' x 43'	35 - 250	Various	8	✓
Dining Room	36' x 27'	35 - 125	Various	6	✓
Gold Room	22' x 30'	26 - 110	Various	18	✓
Conservatory	21' x 55'	35 - 150	Various	6	✓

STOWE SCHOOL
Buckingham

STOWE owes its pre-eminence to the vision and wealth of two owners. From 1715 to 1749 Viscount Cobham, one of Marlborough's Generals, continuously improved his estate, calling in the leading designers of the day to lay out the gardens, and commissioning several leading architects - Vanbrugh, Gibbs, Kent and Leoni - to decorate them with garden temples. From 1750 to 1779 Earl Temple, his nephew and successor continued to expand and embellish both Gardens and House. The House has now become a major public school.

Around the mansion is one of Britain's most magnificent landscape gardens. now in the ownership of the National Trust. Covering 325 acres and containing no fewer than 6 lakes and 32 garden temples, it is of the greatest historic importance. During the 1730's William Kent laid out in the Elysian Fields at Stowe, one of the first 'natural' landscapes and initiated the style known as 'the English Garden'. Capability Brown worked there for 10 years, not as a consultant but as head gardener, and in 1744 was married in the little church hidden in the trees.

CONTACT

The Commercial Director
Stowe School
Buckingham
MK18 5EH

Tel: (01280) 813650
House only
or (01280) 822850
Gardens

LOCATION

From London, M1 to Milton Keynes, 1^1/$_2$ hrs or Banbury 1^1/$_4$ hrs

Bus: from Buckingham 4 miles

Rail: Milton Keynes 15 miles

Air: Heathrow 50 miles

SUITABILITY FOR OTHER EVENTS
Venue for international conferences, prestige exhibitions, weddings and private functions.

EXTRA FACILITIES
Indoor swimming pool, sports hall, tennis court, squash courts, parkland, cricket pitches and golf course.

FACILITIES FOR THE DISABLED
Disabled and elderly visitors may alight at the entrance to the property. Vehicles can then be parked in the allocated areas. There are toilet facilities for the disabled in the gardens. 'Batricars' are available.

PARKING FOR COACHES & CARS
There is extensive parking for coaches and cars.

CATERING
The National Trust Restaurant /Tea Room can cater for up to 100 people. Parties should book in advance.

GUIDED TOURS
At an additional cost, parties can be given a guided tour in groups of 30. Average time taken for a tour of the house and garden 2^1/$_2$ hours. House only - 30 minutes.

GIFT SHOP
During term time, open Monday - Friday 9.00am - 12 noon, 12.50pm - 5.00pm; Saturdays 1.00pm - 5.00pm. During school holidays, open Monday - Friday 9.00am - 5.00pm; Saturday and Sunday 11.00am - 5.00pm; Items include postcards, books, gifts, souvenirs and prints.

GUIDE BOOKS
Guide book £1.20 and £6.00. There is also a guide to the gardens.

OPENING TIMES

Summer

HOUSE
23 March - 14 April and
7 July - 8 Sept
Daily: 2 - 5pm
Suns: Noon - 5pm

GARDENS
23 March - 14 April and
7 July - 8 Sept
Daily 10am - 5pm

15 April - 5 July and
9 Sept - 3 Nov
Mon, Wed, Fri & Sun.
Daily 10am - 5pm

Winter

House closed.
(Sundays by appointment only).

GARDENS
27 Dec - 5 Jan 1997
Daily 10am - 5pm/dusk

NB: It may be necessary to close the house at times when it is being used for private functions. Please telephone first to check.

ADMISSION

Summer
HOUSE ONLY
Adult £2.00
Child £1.00
OAP £2.00
Student £2.00

10% discount for parties of more than 30.

GARDENS ONLY
Adult £4.00
Child £2.00
OAP £4.00
Family £10.00

CONFERENCE AND FUNCTION FACILITIES

ROOM	DIMENSIONS	CAPACITY	LAYOUT	POWER POINTS	SUITABLE FOR A/V
Roxburgh Hall	–	460	Theatre	✓	✓
Audio Visual Room	–	50	Theatre	✓	✓
Music Room	–	120	Various	✓	✓
Marble Hall	–	150	Various	✓	✓
State Dining Room	–	180	Various	✓	✓
Garter Room	–	200	Various	✓	✓
Memorial Theatre	–	120	Theatre	✓	✓

Photo: J. Bethell. National Trust, Waddesdon Manor.

WADDESDON MANOR
The Rothschild Collection, Waddesdon

WADDESDON MANOR, designed in the style of a French Renaissance chateau, was built in the 1870s by Baron Ferdinand de Rothschild from the Austrian branch of the famous Rothschild banking family.

The interior evokes 18th Century France and is furnished with panelling, furniture, carpets and porcelain, many of which have a royal French provenance. There is an important collection of English 18th Century portraits by Gainsborough and Reynolds and of 17th Century Old Masters.

In addition to the State Reception rooms and the bedrooms there are rooms devoted to Sèvres porcelain, an exhibition on the Rothschild family and important rooms on the first floor recently mounted with more of Baron Ferdinand's 18th century panelling. The family's association with wine is illustrated by the newly remodelled wine cellars.

In the garden the rococo-style Aviary houses exotic birds. The garden includes the formal parterre (with a lavish 19th Century planting scheme), acres of parkland and woodland walks.

SUITABILITY FOR OTHER EVENTS
The Manor is an outstanding setting for private events and important occasions. Rothschild Wine Tasting days are available. Wedding Ceremonies can be booked at The Dairy. Film location use may also be possible. There are regular Special Events held, contact the Special Events Manager for further details.

EXTRA FACILITIES
Extensive parklands, woodland walks, aviary, formal gardens, children's play area. Nearby nursery & plant centre where many of the plants found in the Manor garden can be purchased. The award winning Five Arrows Hotel can be found near the entrance to the Manor.

ADVICE TO COURIERS & DRIVERS
Coaches are advised to book in advance.

FACILITIES FOR THE DISABLED
Wheelchair and ramp access to ground floor, restaurant, shops, toilet, garden. Limited access to 1st floor. No access to wine cellars. Guide dogs in garden only. Some wheelchairs available.

PARKING FOR COACHES & CARS
Car parking and coach park within short walking distance of the House.

CATERING
Licensed Old Kitchen restaurant and The Stables Tearoom. Large groups are encouraged to pre-book. Catering for special events and private parties can be discussed with the Special Events Office.

GUIDED TOURS
Entry to the House is strictly by timed ticket, sold on a first come first served basis. Visitors may not gain immediate entry to the House as early slots are quickly filled. Special group visits in the morning can be arranged.

GIFT SHOP
The Gift & Wine Shop offers an unusual range of stationery, gifts, toys, books, toiletries and a wide selection of Rothschild wines and presents for wine lovers.

GUIDE BOOKS
Garden, Aviary, Wine Cellars leaflets and a Garden and House Guide can be purchased in the Gift & Wine Shop.

CONTACT

Special Events Office
Waddesdon Manor
Nr Aylesbury
Buckinghamshire
HP18 OJH

Tel: (01296) 651282
Fax:(01296) 651293

LOCATION

On the A41 between Bicester & Aylesbury, approx 90 mins from London.

From Junc 9, M40 follow signs to Bicester then Aylesbury on A41. Approx 7 miles from Bicester, Waddesdon Manor is in village of Waddesdon on the right.

From Junc 8, M40 follow signs to Thame A329 then Aylesbury A418, then Long Crendon B4011. Manor entrance is 1st turning left after the Five Arrows Hotel.

Rail: From Marylebone to Aylesbury.

Buses: From Aylesbury bus station. take 1, 15, 16.

OPENING TIMES

House
28 March - 13 October
Thursday - Saturday
12.30 - 6.00pm

House also open on Sundays, Bank Hol Mons and Good Friday
11.00am - 6.30pm

July & August
Weds 12.30 - 6.00pm

**Grounds,
Restaurant,
Gift and Wine Shop,
Wine Cellar**
28 Feb - 22 December

Wednesday - Sunday
11.00am - 5.00pm
(6pm when house is open)
Private Tours of the house by special arrangement.

ADMISSION

HOUSE £6.00
(Including children
6 - 17yrs)

BACHELORS' WING
(Open Thurs only)
an extra £1.00

GARDEN TICKET
with access to carpark,
Shops, Restaurant,
Aviary & Wine Cellars

Adult £3.00
Child (5 - 17yrs) . . .£1.50

FAMILY GARDEN
TICKET
2 Adults &
2 Children £7.50

ASCOTT

Tel: 01296 688242

Wing, Leighton Buzzard, Buckinghamshire LU7 0PS
Owner: The National Trust   **Contact:** The Administrator
Anthony de Rothschild collection of fine pictures, French and English furniture and exceptional oriental porcelain. The garden contains unusual trees, flower borders, naturalised bulbs, water-lilies and a topiary sundial.
Location: 1/2m E of Wing, 2m SW of Leighton Buzzard, on A418.
Opening Times: House & Garden: 2 Apr - 5 May and 3 - 29 Sept: Tue - Sun, 2 - 6pm (open Good Friday but closed BH Mon) last admission 5pm. Garden only: 8 May - 28 Aug: every Wed and last Sun in month, 2 - 6pm.
Admission: House & Garden: £5.00. Grounds only: £3.00. No reduction for parties, which must book.

BOARSTALL TOWER

Boarstall, Aylesbury, Buckinghamshire HP18 9OX
Owner: The National Trust   **Contact:** The Administrator
The stone gatehouse of a fortified house long since demolished. It dates from the 14th century, and was altered in the 16th and 17th centuries, but retains its crossloops for bows. The tower is almost entirely surrounded by a moat.
Location: Midway between Bicester and Thame, 2m W of Brill.
Opening Times: By written appointment to Administrator. May - end Sept: Wed, 2- 6pm.
Admission: £1.00, no reduction for parties.

BUCKINGHAM CHANTRY CHAPEL

Market Hill, Buckingham, Buckinghamshire
Owner: The National Trust   **Contact:** The Administrator
Rebuilt in 1475 and retaining a fine Norman doorway. The chapel was restored by Gilbert Scott in 1875, at which time it was used as a Latin or Grammar School.
Location: On Market Hill.
Opening Times: Apr - end Oct: by written appointment with the Buckingham Heritage Trust, c/o The Book Barn, Church Way, Whittlebury, Northants NN12 8SX..
Admission: Free.

CHENIES MANOR HOUSE

Tel: 01494 762888

Chenies, Buckinghamshire WD3 6ER
Owner: Lt. Col. A A MacLeod Matthews   **Contact:** Lt. Col. A A MacLeod Matthews
Early Tudor Manor House with contemporary furniture, tapestries, secret passages and hiding places. Lovely gardens.
Location: Off A404 between Amersham and Rickmansworth.
Opening Times: 2 April - 31 Oct. Please telephone for times.
Admission: Adult £4.00, Child £2.00.

CHICHELEY HALL

Tel: 01234 391252   **Fax:** 01234 391388

Newport Pagnell, Buckinghamshire MK16 9JJ
Owner: The Hon Nicholas Beatty   **Contact:** Mrs V Child
Fine 18th century house specialising in residential conferences of up to sixteen delegates.
Location: 10 m from Milton Keynes, 5 mins from Junction 14, M1.
Opening Times: 2.30 - 6.30pm Easter Sun and Mon, May Bank Hol Sun & Mon, and all Sundays and Bank Holidays in August.
Admission: Adult £3.50, Child £2.00, Groups: Adult £3.00/Child £2.00.

CHILTERN OPEN AIR MUSEUM

Tel: 01494 871117   **Fax:** 01494 872163

Newland Park, Gorelands Lane, Chalfont St Giles, Buckinghamshire HP8 4AD
Owner: Chiltern Open Air Museum Ltd.   **Contact:** Dr. J Moir
A museum of historic buildings showing their original uses including a blacksmith's forge, stables, barns etc.
Location: At Newland Park, Chalfont St Giles, 4 1/2 m from Amersham. 3m from J17/M25.
Opening Times: Apr - Oct: Tues - Fri 2 - 6pm, Sat, Sun and Bank Holidays 11am - 6pm.
Admission: Adult £3.50, Child (5-16yrs) £2.00, Child under 5yrs Free, Over 60's £3.00, Family £10. 10% discount for pre-booked groups of 20+.

CLAYDON HOUSE

OPEN

30 Mar - end Oct
Sat - Wed & Bank
Holiday Mondays
1.00 - 5.00pm

(closed Good Friday)

Last admission
4.30pm

Tel: 01296 730349
or 01296 730693

MIDDLE CLAYDON, NR. BUCKINGHAM MK18 2EY

Owner: The National Trust   *Contact: Custodian*

A fine 18th century house with splendid rococo carvings in the state rooms. Florence Nightingale often visited Claydon. Her bedroom and museum with mementoes of her life are on show. Home-made teas available. Free car park.
Location: In Middle Claydon, 13 miles North-West of Aylesbury, signposted from A413, A421 and A41.
Admission: Adult £3.70, Child £1.85, Family ticket £9.00.

COWPER & NEWTON MUSEUM

Tel: 01234 711516

Home of Olney's Heritage, Orchard Side, Market Place, Olney, Bucks MK46 4AJ
Owner: Board of Trustees   **Contact:** Mrs E Knight
Once the home of 18th c. poet & letter writer William Cowper and now containing furniture, paintings & belongings of both Cowper & his ex-slave trader friend, Rev John Newton (author of "Amazing Grace"). Attractions include re-creations of a Victorian country kitchen & wash-house, two peaceful gardens and Cowper's restored summerhouse. Costume gallery, important collections of dinosaur bones and bobbin lace & local history displays.
Location: On A509, 6m N of Newport Pagnell (leave M1 at junction 14).
Opening Times: Apr - Oct: Tues - Sats, & Bank Hol Mons 10am - 1pm and 2 - 5pm. Feb - Mar & Nov - 14 Dec: 1 - 4pm.
Admission: Adult £2.00, Conc. £1.50, Child & Students (with card) £1.00, Family £5.00.

DORNEYWOOD GARDEN

Dorneywood, Burnham, Buckinghamshire SL1 8PY
Owner: The National Trust   **Contact:** The Administrator
The house was given to the National Trust as an official residence for either a Secretary of State or Minister of the Crown. Garden only open.
Location: SW of Burnham Beeches. 2m E of Cliveden.
Opening Times: Wed 10 & 17 Jul & Sat, 10 & 17 Aug. 2 - 5.30pm. By written appointment only to Dorneywood Trust.
Admission: £2.50. No reduction for parties.

HUGHENDEN MANOR

OPEN

2 - 31 March
Sat and Sun only
3 Apr - end Oct
Wed - Sun & Bank
Holiday Mondays.
1 - 5pm

Last adm: 4.30pm

Tel: 01494 532580

HIGH WYCOMBE, HP14 4LA

Owner: The National Trust   *Contact: The Property Manager*

Victorian Gothic home of Disraeli from 1847 until his death in 1881. The house contains much of his furniture, pictures, books and other relics. Shop and tearoom in stable yard. Free car parking.
Location: 1 1/2 miles north of High Wycombe on the A4128.
Admission: Adult £3.70, Child £1.85, Family ticket £9.00, Garden only £1.00.

JOHN MILTON'S COTTAGE
Tel: 01494 872313

21 Deanway, Chalfont St. Giles, Buckinghamshire HP8 4JH

Owner: Milton Cottage Trust   **Contact:** Mr E A Dawson

The XVIth century cottage where John Milton lived and completed 'Paradise Lost', and started 'Paradise Regained', contains many relics and exhibits of interest. Three museum rooms and attractive cottage garden open to the public. Free car park.

Location: ½ m W of A413. 3m N of J2 / M40.

Opening Times: 1 Mar - 31 Oct: Wed - Sun, 10am - 1pm & 2 - 6pm. Closed Mon / Tues except BH Mons. Coach parking by prior arrangement only.

Admission: Adult £2 entry, under 15's 60p, Groups of 20+ £1.50.

MENTMORE TOWERS
See page 10 for full page entry.

NETHER WINCHENDON HOUSE
Tel: 01844 290101

Aylesbury, Buckinghamshire HP18 ODY

Owner: Robert Spencer Bernard Esq   **Contact:** Mr R Spencer Bernard

Medieval and Tudor manor house with 18th century additions.

Location: 2m N of A418 equidistant between Thame & Aylesbury.

Opening Times: 1 - 28 May and 25 / 26 Aug. 2.30 - 5.30pm (last party at about 4.45pm).

Admission: Adult £2.50 (HHA members free), Child £1.50, Senior citizens £1.50 (not weekends or Bank Holidays). Groups by prior arrangement.

PITSTONE WINDMILL

Ivinghoe, Buckinghamshire

Owner: The National Trust   **Contact:** The Administrator

One of the oldest post mills in Britain; in view from Ivinghoe Beacon.

Location: ½m S of Ivinghoe, 3m NE of Tring. Just W of B488.

Opening Times: June - Aug: Sun & Bank Holidays in May. 2.30 - 6pm. Last adm. 5.30pm.

Admission: £1.00.

PRINCES RISBOROUGH MANOR HOUSE

Princes Risborough, Aylesbury, Buckinghamshire HP17 9AW

Owner: The National Trust   **Contact:** The Administrator

A 17th century red-brick house with Jacobean oak staircase.

Location: Opposite church off market square.

Opening Times: House and front garden by written arrangement only with Administrator. Wed 2.30 - 4.30pm last admission 4.00pm. Hall, Drawing room and staircase shown.

Admission: £1.00. No reduction for parties.

STOWE LANDSCAPE GARDENS

OPEN

23 Mar - 14 Apr &
7 July - 8 Sept &
27 Dec - 5 Jan (1997)
Daily

15 Apr - 5 Jul &
9 Sept - 3 Nov
Mon, Wed, Fri, Sun.

10am - 5pm or dusk if earlier. Last adm. 1hr before closing.

Tel: 01280 822850
Fax: 01280 822437

NR. BUCKINGHAM MK18 5EH

Owner: The National Trust   *Contact: The Administrator*

One of the supreme creations of the Georgian era. The first formal layout was adorned with many buildings by Vanbrugh, Kent and Gibbs. In the 1730's Kent designed the Elysian Fields in a more naturalistic style, one of the earliest examples of the reaction against formality leading to the evolution of the Landscape Garden. Miraculously this beautiful garden survives; its sheer scale must make it Britain's largest work of art.

Location: 3 miles north west of Buckingham via Stowe Avenue off A422 Buckingham/Banbury road.

Admission: Gardens: Adult £4.00. Family ticket £10.00. Parties by prior arrangement with administrator.

STOWE SCHOOL
See page 11 for full page entry.

TAPLOW COURT

OPEN

House and Grounds open Sundays 2.00pm - 6.00pm from Easter to the end of July. Please telephone to check.

Tel: 01628 773163
Fax: 01628 773055

BERRY HILL, TAPLOW, NR. MAIDENHEAD, BERKS SL6 0ER

Owner: SGI-UK   *Contact: Robert Samuels*

Set high above the Thames affording spectacular views. Refurbished mid-19th century by William Burn. Earlier neo-Norman Hall. 18th century Home of Earls of Orkney & more recently of Lord & Lady Desborough who entertained "The Souls" here. Tranquil gardens & grounds. Anglo-Saxon burial mound. Permanent & temporary exhibitions, cream teas, gifts, guided tours. Entrance ramp & lift.

Location: J7 of M4, off Bath Road towards Maidenhead. 6 m off J2 of M40.

Admission: No charge. Free parking.

WADDESDON MANOR
See page 12 for full page entry.

WEST WYCOMBE PARK
Tel: 01494 524411

West Wycombe, High Wycombe, Buckinghamshire HP14 3AJ

Owner: The National Trust   **Contact:** The Administrator

A Palladian house with frescos and painted ceilings fashioned for Sir Francis Dashwood in the mid 18th century. The landscape garden and lake were laid out at the same time as the house with various classical temples including some by Nicholas Revett.

Location: At W end of West Wycombe S of the A40.

Opening Times: Grounds only: April & May, Sun & Wed, 2 - 6pm. Easter May & Spring BH Sun & Mon, 2 - 6pm. House & Grounds: Jun, Jul & Aug, Sun - Thur, 2 - 6pm. Last admission 5.15pm.

Admission: The West Wycombe Caves and adjacent cafe are privately owned and NT members are liable to admission fees. House & Grounds £4.00, Family £10.00. Grounds only £2.50. Parties must book.

WINSLOW HALL
Tel: 01296 712323

Winslow, Buckinghamshire, MK18 3HL

Owner: Sir Edward Tomkins   **Contact:** Sir Edward Tomkins

William and Mary house generally attributed to Wren. Virtually unchanged structurally and mostly original interiors. Good period furniture, pictures and Chinese objets d'art. Attractive garden with unusual trees and shrubs.

Location: In the town of Winslow on the A413.

Opening Times: Bank Hols (except Christmas), Weds & Thurs in Jul & Aug. 2.30 - 5.30pm. Any other time by appointment.

Admission: £4.50. Children under 12 free.

Where to Stay

For Private Accommodation and Johansens recommended Hotels, see Accommodation Section.

SPECIAL EVENTS

❖ **WADDESDON MANOR**   THROUGHOUT 1996
Rothschild wine tastings, lectures, tours of the Victorian Water and Rock Garden.
Musical events and dinner theatres. Please contact the Special Events Office.

❖ **MENTMORE TOWERS**   5, 6, 7 JULY
Fireworks concert.

❖ **MENTMORE TOWERS**   24, 25, 26 AUGUST
Design For Living Show.

For National Trust and English Heritage Events see separate section.

ELTON HALL
Peterborough

ELTON HALL, home of the Proby family for over 300 years, stands in the midst of unspoilt landscaped parkland on a site where there has been a house since the Norman Conquest. Sir Peter Proby, Lord Mayor of London and Comptroller of the Royal Household, was granted land and property at Elton by Queen Elizabeth I. His grandson, Sir Thomas Proby, completed the main House in 1666. In the 18th Century John Proby was created the first Earl of Carysfort. He and his successors enlarged it to the 18th Century character that it has today.

Elton is a fascinating mixture of styles. Every room contains treasures - magnificent furniture from many countries and fine paintings from early 15th Century Old Masters to the remarkable Pre-Raphaelite work of Alma Tadema and Millais. Great British artists are well represented by Gainsborough, Constable and Reynolds. The Library is one of the finest in private hands containing some 12,000 books. The collection includes the unique Henry VIII's Prayer Book in which can be seen the writing of the Tudor King and two of his wives.

GARDENS

The formal gardens have been carefully restored in recent years. The Victorian Rose Garden contains some 1,000 roses including many old fashioned varieties whose fragrance in the summer months is quite memorable.

New herbaceous borders provide great interest to gardeners and non-gardeners alike. An arboretum has recently been planted. Picnics may also be taken in this pleasant area.

CONTACT

The House Manager
Estate Office
Elton Hall
Elton
Peterborough
PE8 6SH

Tel: (01832) 280468
Fax: (01832) 280584

LOCATION

From London, A1(M), A605 to Elton. 86 mls.
From Leicester, A47, B671, A605 to Elton.

Bus: Peterborough Kettering bus passes the Hall.

Rail: P'borough 8mls.

Air: Private Airport 3mls.

Taxi: Norwood, Oundle 273585.

SUITABILITY FOR OTHER EVENTS
Corporate Entertaining, product launches, promotions, photographic and film location work

EXTRA FACILITIES
Parkland for rallies etc. Clay Pigeon shoots can be arranged. Special lecture tours of Hall. Please apply for details.

ADVICE TO COURIERS & DRIVERS
Elton Hall is not suitable for disabled visitors because of the steps. It is, however, of great interest to art lovers. No dogs in Hall, or formal gardens. No photography in Hall. Ploughmans suppers and buffet suppers are available for parties being taken on a guided tour. Parking for 200 cars and 10 coaches, 50 yards from the house.

FACILITIES FOR THE DISABLED
Disabled and elderly visitors may alight close to the entrance. Vehicles can then be parked in the allocated areas. There are no toilet facilities for the disabled and there are steps at the entrance and in the Hall.

CATERING
The State Dining Room is available for Banquets, Receptions etc. Up to 70 can be seated or 100 for buffet-type functions. Menus and prices on application. The Billiard Room seats 50 people. Prices on application. Meals can be booked in advance and menus are available on request.

GUIDED TOURS
Parties of up to 100 people can be split into groups of 20, except on Bank Holidays. Average time taken for a tour ³/₄ hour.

SCHOOL VISITS/CHILDREN
Elton Hall is suitable mainly for 5th and 6th formers. There is a special question sheet with a competition for younger children. Grassed picnic area available. Guided tours available; please apply to House Manager for costs.

CONFERENCE AND FUNCTION FACILITIES

ROOM	DIMENSIONS	CAPACITY	LAYOUT	POWER POINTS	SUITABLE FOR A/V
Billiard Room	38' x 28'	60	Buffet Lunch/Dinner	3	3
State Dining Room	38'6" x 23'6"	100	Banquets/Receptions Product Launches	3	3
Old Laundry	21' x 20'	40	Product Launches Receptions	3	3
Conference Room	21' x 20'	20	Conferences	3	3

OPENING TIMES

Summer
Easter Monday
2.00 - 5.00pm

May and August
Bank Hols
Sun & Mon
2.00 - 5.00pm

July
Wed & Sun
2.00 5.00pm

August
Wed, Thurs & Sun
2.00 - 5.00pm

Winter
Private parties by appointment.

ADMISSION

Summer
HOUSE & GARDEN
Adult £4.00
Child* £2.00
OAP £3.80
Student £1.90

GARDEN ONLY
Adult £2.00
Child* £1.00
OAP £1.90
Student £0.95
Groups**
Adult £3.80
Child* £1.90

Free ticket to all party organisers.

* Aged 5-15
** Over 20 people. Over 50 people gain additional 10% discount.

Winter
Private Parties by appointment only.

ANGLESEY ABBEY

OPEN

House
23 Mar - 13 Oct: 1 - 5pm
(closed Good Fri)

Garden
23 Mar - 7 Jul
and 11 Sept - 3 Nov
Wed - Sun: 11am - 5.30pm
8 Jul - 8 Sept
Daily: 11am - 5.30pm.

Lode Mill
23 Mar - 3 Nov
Wed - Sun & BH Mons:
1 - 5pm.

Tel: 01223 811200

LODE, CAMBRIDGE, CAMBRIDGESHIRE CB5 9EJ

Owner: The National Trust　　　*Contact: The Administrator*

Dating from 1600, the house, built on the site of an Augustinian abbey, contains the famous Fairhaven collection of paintings and furniture. Surrounded by an outstanding 100-acre garden and arboretum, with a wonderful display of hyacinths in spring and magnificent herbaceous borders and a dahlia garden in summer. A watermill in full working order is demonstrated on the first Saturday in each month.
Location: In Lode village, 6m NE of Cambridge on B1102. Signposted from A14.
Admission: NT members free. House & Gdn: Adult £5.50, Family £11, (Sun & BH Mon £6.50, Family £13.00). Parties 15+: £4.50. Gdn only: Adult £3.20, Child half price. Lode Mill free on entry to the garden. Parties please book with SAE to Administrator. (No reductions Sun & BH Mon).

DENNY ABBEY

Tel: 01223 860489

Ely Road, Chittering, Waterbeach, Cambridgeshire CB5 9TQ
Owner: English Heritage　　　　**Contact:** The Custodian
What at first appears to be an attractive stone-built farmhouse is actually the remains of a 12th Century Benedictine abbey which, at different times, also housed the Knights Templar and Franciscan nuns.
Location: 6m N of Cambridge on A10.
Opening Times: 1 Apr - 30 Sept: 12 noon - 5pm.
Admission: Adult £1.50, Child 80p, Conc. £1.10.

ELTON HALL

See page 15 for full page entry.

ELY CATHEDRAL

Tel: 01353 667735　　**Fax:** 01353 665658

Ely, Cambridgeshire CB7 4DL

Contact: Ms. Jan Pye

A wonderful example of Romanesque architecture. Octagon and Lady Chapel are of special interest. Superb Medieval domestic buildings surround the Cathedral. Guided tours, Cathedral Shop, Refectory snack bar and Almonry Restaurant. Stained Glass Museum.
Location: On A10, 15m N of Cambridge.
Opening Times: Summer: 7am - 7pm. Winter: Mon - Sat, 7.30am - 6pm, Sun and week after Christmas, 7.30am - 5pm. Sunday services: 8.15am, 10.30am and 3.45pm. Weekday services: 7.40am, 8am, and 5.30pm (Thursday only also 11.30am and 12.30pm).
Admission: Adult £3.00, Child (12+) £2.20, Conc £2.20, Group concessions (15 or more).

ISLAND HALL

Tel: 0171 491 3724

Godmanchester, Huntingdon, Cambridgeshire PE18 8BA
Owner: Mr Christopher & The Hon. Mrs Vane Percy　**Contact:** Mr. Christopher Vane Percy
Location: 15m NW of Cambridge A14.
Opening Times: 30 June, 7, 14, 21, 28 July, 2.30 - 5pm. Last admittance 4.30pm.
Admission: Adult £3.00, Grounds only, £1.50 Child £1.
May - Sept: Group rate £2.50 (by appointment only).

KIMBOLTON CASTLE

Tel: 01480 860505　　**Fax:** 01480 861763

Kimbolton, Huntingdon, Cambridgeshire PE18 OEA
Owner: Governors of Kimbolton School　　　　**Contact:** T F Hayward Esq
A late Stuart House, an adaptation of a 13th century fortified manor house, with evidence of Tudor modifications. The seat of the Earls and Dukes of Manchester 1615 - 1950, now a school. Katherine of Aragon died in the Queen's Room - the setting for a scene in Shakespeare's *Henry VIII.* A minor example of the work of Vanbrugh and Hawksmoor; Gatehouse by Robert Adam; the Pellegrini mural paintings on the Staircase, in the Chapel and in the Boudoir are the best examples in England of this gifted Venetian decorator.
Location: 7 miles NW of St. Neots on B645.
Opening Times: Easter, Spring and August BHs Sun and Mon 2 - 6pm.
August, Sundays only 2 - 6pm.
Admission: Adult £1.00, Child 50p, Conc 50p, Groups by arrangement.

KING'S COLLEGE

OPEN

Grounds
Mon - Sat
9.30am - 4.30pm
Sun 10am - 5pm

Chapel: In Term
Mon: 9.30am - 4.30pm
Tues - Fri:
9.30am - 3.30pm
Sat: 9.30am - 3.15pm
Sun: 1.15 - 2.15pm
5 - 5.30pm (BST only)

Out of Term
Grounds: as above

Tel: 01223 331212
Fax: 01223 331315

KING'S PARADE, CAMBRIDGE, CB2 1ST

Contact: Mr D. Buxton

Visitors are welcome to see the Chapel and the Grounds, but are reminded that this is a working College. Please respect the privacy of those who work, live and study here. The Chapel houses an exhibition, included in the admission fee, giving information on religion, history and architecture. The Chapel is often used for services, recordings, broadcasts, etc, and ideally visitors should check before arriving. Recorded message for services, concerts and visiting times: 01223 331155.
Admission: Adult £2.50. Child (12-17), Student (ID required) £1.50. Child under 12 free if part of a family unit.

LONGTHORPE TOWER

Tel: 01733 268482

Peterborough, Cambridgeshire.
Owner: English Heritage　　　　**Contact:** The Custodian
The finest example of 14th century domestic wall paintings in northern Europe. The tower, with the Great Chamber that contains the paintings, is part of a fortified manor house. Special exhibitions are held in the upper floor.
Location: 2m W of Peterborough on A47.
Opening Times: Jul - Aug: weekends only: 10am - 6pm.
Admission: Adult £1.00, Child 50p, Conc 80p.

THE MANOR HEMINGFORD GREY

OPEN

All year but only
by appointment

Tel: 01480 463134

HUNTINGDON, CAMBRIDGESHIRE PE18 9BN

Owner: Mr and Mrs P.S. Boston　　*Contact: Diana Boston*

Built about 1130 and made famous as Green Knowe by the author Lucy Boston. The Manor is reputedly the oldest continuously inhabited house in the country and much of the Norman house remains. Visitors are offered the unique chance to walk into the books and to see the Lucy Boston patchworks. The garden features topiary and old roses.
Location: Off A14, 3 miles SE of Huntingdon. 12 miles NW of Cambridgeshire
Admission: Adult £3.00, Child £1.50. Garden only: Adult £1.50, Child 50p.

OLIVER CROMWELL'S HOUSE

Tel: 01353 662062   **Fax:** 01353 668518

29 St Mary's Street, Ely, Cambridgeshire CB7 4HF
Owner: East Cambridgeshire District Council   **Contact:** Mrs Alison Curtis-Smith
Location: 15m NW of Cambridge A14.
Opening Times: 1 Oct - 31 Mar: Mon - Sat 10am - 5.15pm. 1 Apr - 30 Sept: Daily 10am - 6pm.
Admission: Adult £2.30, Conc. £1.80, Family £5.00. Please apply for group rates.

PECKOVER HOUSE & GARDEN

Tel: 01945 583463

North Brink, Wisbech, Cambridgeshire PE13 1JR
Owner: The National Trust   **Contact:** The Property Manager
A town house, built c.1722, with fine plaster and wood rococo decoration, and a collection of the Cornwallis family portraits. The notable 2 acre Victorian garden includes an orangery and the recently restored Reed Barn.
Location: On N bank of River Nene, in Wisbech B1441.
Opening Times: House & Garden: 30 Mar - 31 Oct, Sat & Sun, Wed & BH Mon, 2 - 5.30pm. Garden only: as house, but also open Mon & Tues, 2 - 5.30pm. Parties on house open days by appointment.
Admission: Adult, £2.50 (£1.50 on garden only days), party £2.00.

PETERBOROUGH CATHEDRAL

Tel: 01733 343342   **Fax:** 01733 52465

Peterborough, Cambridgeshire PE1 1XS

Contact: Canon Higham
West front unique in Christendom. Painted Nave Ceiling (c.1220) unique in England. Pure Romanesque interior. Exquisite fan vaulting (c.1500) in retro-choir. Burial place of Katherine of Aragon. Former burial place of Mary Queen of Scots. Saxon sculptures. Monastic Remains. Visitor Centre.
Location: 4 m E of A1, in City Centre.
Opening Times: Mon-Sat 7am - 6.15pm. Sun 7.30am - 5pm. Weekday services: 7.30am, 8am, 5.30pm (3.30pm Sats). Sunday services: 8.15am, 9.30am, 10.30am, 3.30pm.
Admission: Donation suggested.

PRIOR CRAUDEN'S CHAPEL

Tel: 01353 662837   **Fax:** 01353 662187

King's School, Ely, Cambridgeshire CB7 4DB
Owner: Kings School   **Contact:** The Bursar
Early 14th century chapel recently restored to show glimpses of coloured walls and wall paintings.
Location: The College Ely Cathedral. In Cathedral Precincts.
Opening Times: Normal working hours, 9am - 5pm on weekdays.
Admission: Free.

Elton Hall.

RAMSEY ABBEY GATEHOUSE

Tel: 01263 733471

Abbey School, Ramsey, Cambridgeshire
Owner: The National Trust   **Contact:** The Curator
Remains of a 15th century gatehouse of the Benedictine Abbey.
Location: At SE edge of Ramsey at point where Chatteris road leaves B1096, 10m SE of Peterborough.
Opening Times: 1 Apr - end Oct: Daily 10am - 5pm, other times by written application.
Admission: Donation.

UNIVERSITY BOTANIC GARDEN

Tel: 01223 336265 **Fax:** 01223 336278

Bateman Street, Cambridge, Cambridgeshire CB2 1JF
Owner: University of Cambridge   **Contact:** Mrs B Stacey Administrative Secretary
40 acres of outstanding gardens with lake and glasshouses, near the centre of Cambridge, incorporating nine National collections, including Geranium and Fritillaria. Tea room and shop in the Gilmour Building.
Location: 1 mile S of Cambridge city centre, off A1309 (Trumpington Road).
Opening Times: Daily (except Christmas Day & Boxing Day), 10am - 6pm (Summer), 10am - 5pm (Spring and Autumn) 10am - 4pm (Winter).
Admission: Admission charged weekdays March to October inclusive and weekends and Bank Holidays throughout the year.

WIMPOLE HALL & HOME FARM

ARRINGTON, ROYSTON, CAMBRIDGESHIRE SG8 0BW

Owner: The National Trust   *Contact:* Graham Damant

Tel: 01223 207257   **Fax:** 01223 207838

Largest country house in Cambridgeshire. An 18th Century mansion set in landscaped parkland by 'Capability' Brown and Repton. Architects include Gibbs, Flitcroft and Soane. Model Farm with many thatched buildings designed by Soane. Farm houses, many rare breeds of cattle, sheep and pigs. Miles of walks in parkland. Colourful parterres in the garden.
Location: Off A603 signposted 7 miles SW of Cambs (junct. 12 on M11).
Opening Times: Hall: 23 Mar - 3 Nov: Daily except Mon & Fri, 1 - 5pm. Open Bank Holiday Sunday and Monday 11am - 5pm. Open Fridays in August. Park: open all year. Farm: 16 Mar - 3 Nov: Daily except Mon & Fri 10.30am - 5pm. Open Bank Holiday Monday and all week during Aug. Open weekends throughout the winter.
Admission: Hall: Adult £5.00, Child £2.20. Farm: Adult £3.90, Child £2.50. Hall/Farm Ticket: Adult £6.50, Child £3.25. Party rates available.

Where to Stay
For Private Accommodation and
Johansens
recommended Hotels,
see Accommodation
Section.

KEY TO SYMBOLS: THE NATIONAL TRUST    ENGLISH HERITAGE   HISTORIC HOUSES ASSOCIATION

ADLINGTON HALL
Macclesfield

ADLINGTON HALL, the home of the Leghs of Adlington from 1315 to the present day, was built on the site of a Hunting Lodge which stood in the Forest of Macclesfield in 1040. Two oaks, part of the original building, remain with their roots in the ground and support the east end of the Great Hall, which was built between 1480 and 1505.

The Hall is a Manor House, quadrangular in shape, and was once surrounded by a moat. Two sides of the Courtyard and the east wing were built in the typical 'Black and White' Cheshire style in 1581. The south front and west wing (containing the Drawing Room and Dining Room) were added between 1749 and 1757 and are built of red brick with a handsome stone portico with four Ionic columns on octagonal pedestals. Between the trees in the Great Hall stands an Organ built by 'Father' Bernard Smith (c.1670-80). Handel subsequently played on this instrument, and now fully restored, it is the largest 17th century organ in the country.

GARDENS
The Wilderness was landscaped in the style of 'Capability' Brown in the mid 18th century and incorporates both earlier 17th century plantings and sympathetic Victorian additions. The formal French style has given way to an apparently wild, but very carefully cultivated informality. Dotted about the circuitous paths are a number of decorative buildings.

❖

SUITABILITY FOR OTHER EVENTS
Suitable for corporate activity events, clay pigeon shooting, product launches, business meetings, conferences, concerts, fashion shows, garden parties, shows, rallies and filming.

CONFERENCE/FUNCTION FACILITIES
The Great Hall and Dining Room available for use when the Hall is not open to the public.

ADVICE TO COURIERS & DRIVERS
Special requests are considered.

FACILITIES FOR THE DISABLED
Disabled and elderly visitors may alight at the entrance to the Hall. No toilets for the disabled.

PARKING FOR COACHES & CARS
Capacity of the car park - 100 cars and 4 coaches, 100 yards from the Hall.

CATERING
Teas and light refreshments in the Hall.

GUIDED TOURS
Tours are available.

SCHOOL VISITS/CHILDREN
School parties are welcome. Cost per child £1.50. A guide can be provided for the tour.

CONTACT

The Guide
Adlington Hall
Macclesfield
Cheshire
SK10 4LF

Tel: (01625) 829206
or (01625) 820201

LOCATION

5 miles north of Macclesfield (A523), 13 miles south of Manchester. London 178 miles.

Rail: Macclesfield and Wilmslow stations 5 miles.

Air: Manchester airport 8 miles.

CONFERENCE AND FUNCTION FACILITIES

ROOM	DIMENSIONS	CAPACITY	LAYOUT	POWER POINTS	SUITABLE FOR A/V
Great Hall	37' x 26' x 38'	125	Theatre	5	✓
		60	Schoolroom		
		60 / 80	Buffet		
		80 / 100	Dinner/Dance		
Dining Room	35' x 23' x 18'	50	Theatre	3	✓
		25	U-Shape		
Hunting Lodge	60' x 30' x 28'	150	Theatre	15	✓
	40' x 30' x 20'	70/80	U-Shape		
		130	Dinner/Dance		
		150	Lunch/Dinner		

ARLEY HALL & GARDENS
Northwich

ARLEY HALL, the home of Lord and Lady Ashbrook, was built about 1840 by the owner's great great grandfather, Rowland Egerton-Warburton, to the design of the Nantwich architect, George Latham. An important example of the Victorian Jacobean style, it has fine plasterwork and wood panelling as well as interesting furniture, pictures and other contents. Adjoining Arley Hall is a large private Chapel designed by Anthony Salvin.

An impressive range of activities can be held both in the Hall and in the grounds, from corporate conferences of any size to cocktail parties and ambassadorial receptions. Arley Hall offers all its visitors an elegant setting combined with the professional approach to top class management. Catering to the highest standards.

GARDENS
Overlooking beautiful parkland, and providing great variety of style and design, the Gardens extending over 12 acres rank among the finest in the country. Winner of the Christie's HHA 'Garden of the Year' award in 1987. The features include the Double Herbaceous Border, one of the earliest to be established in England 1846, unique avenue of clipped Quercus Ilex, collection of Shrub Roses, fine Yew hedges, Herb Garden, Walled Garden, Woodland Garden with exotic trees, Shrubs, Azaleas and a collection of over 200 varieties of Rhododendrons.

❖

SUITABILITY FOR OTHER EVENTS
Business Meetings & Conferences, Corporate Activity Events, Receptions & Dinner Parties, Concerts, Filming.

EXTRA FACILITIES
100 acres parkland, grass, cricket pitch. Grand piano in Gallery.

ADVICE TO COURIERS & DRIVERS
Free entry and refreshments for courier and coach driver. Photography only in the gardens.

FACILITIES FOR THE DISABLED
Disabled and elderly visitors may alight at the entrance to the Hall, before parking in the allocated areas. Toilets for the disabled, and access to restaurant, shop and Chapel.

PARKING FOR COACHES & CARS
Unlimited parking for cars, 250 yds from Hall and 6 coaches may be parked 100 yds away. Special arrangements can be made for function parking 50 yds from the Hall.

CATERING
The Restaurant/Tea Room seats up to 100 people for light refreshments, lunches and evening meals. Prices range from £1.00 to £12.00.

GUIDED TOURS
Tours of up to 25 people per guide are conducted round the Hall. Guided tours of the Gardens can be arranged for £2.50 per head per tour. Average time taken for a tour of the Hall 1 hour, and for the gardens 1½ hours.

GIFT SHOP/SPECIALIST PLANT NURSERY
Open when the Gardens are open to the public, also at other selected times.

GUIDE BOOKS
Colour Guide Books on House and Gardens.

SCHOOL VISITS/CHILDREN
Guided tours of Hall and Gardens. Environmental and Heritage Trails. Picnic area. Wet weather cover. Mondays and Fridays only.

CONTACT

Eric Ransome
Arley Hall and Gardens
Nr Northwich
Cheshire
CW9 6NA

Tel: (01565) 777353
Fax: (01565) 777465

LOCATION

Car: Knutsford, 5 miles
Northwich, 5 miles
M6 Juncs 19 + 20 5miles
M56 Juncs 9 +10 5miles

Rail: Knutsford, 5 miles
Northwich, 5 miles

Air: Manchester
Airport 16 miles

OPENING TIMES

Summer
31 March - 29 September

Grounds, Gardens, Chapel:
Tues - Suns and Bank Holiday Mons

Apr, May, Sept
12 noon - 5.00pm

June, July, August
11am - 5.00pm

Hall opening times vary: open weekends only in April and September

Winter
Open by arrangement only for groups and on special advertised occasions.

ADMISSION

GARDENS, GROUNDS & CHAPEL
Adult £3.30
Child (5 -16) £1.70
Child (under 5) . .FREE*
OAP £2.90
Groups (min. 15 people)
Adult £2.70
Child £1.35
OAP £2.10

HALL (Extra)
Adult £2.30
Child (5-16) £1.15
Child (Under 5) . .FREE*
OAP £2.00
Groups (min. 15 people)
Adult £2.00
Child £1.00
OAP £1.80
*When part of a family group only

FAMILY (2 + 2)
Gardens £8.00
Hall £5.00
Season . . . .£15.00 ea.

Friends of Arley Assoc. contact 01606 891754 Membership secretary.

CONFERENCE AND FUNCTION FACILITIES

ROOM	DIMENSIONS	CAPACITY	LAYOUT	POWER POINTS	SUITABLE FOR A/V
Drawing Room	38' x 22'	110	Theatre	Ample	✓
		70	Schoolroom		
		22	Boardroom		
		100	Finger Buffet		
		70	Lunch/Dinner		
Gallery	41' x 25'	100	Finger Buffet	Ample	✓
Front Hall	35' x 22'	22	Boardroom	Ample	✓
		22	Lunch/Dinner		
Tudor Barn	56' x 22' +	200	Theatre	6	✓
		120	Finger Buffet		
		100	Lunch/Dinner		

CAPESTHORNE HALL
Macclesfield

CAPESTHORNE HALL has been the home of the Bromley-Davenport Family and their ancestors since Domesday times when the appointment of Chief Forester carrying the responsibility of law and order in the Forests of Macclesfield and Leek was granted to them. Since then many generations have served in Parliament, the Bromley side providing both a Chancellor and Speaker. The present owner is H.M. Lord Lieutenant for Cheshire.

The existing Hall dating from 1719 was originally designed by the Smiths of Warwick, then altered by both Blore in 1837 and Salvin in 1861, the latter rebuilding the centre section following a disastrous fire.

The Hall contains a great variety of paintings, sculptures, furniture and tapestry including a collection of Colonial furnishings brought over by the late Lady Bromley-Davenport from her former American home in Philadelphia.

The park and gardens extend to some 60 acres and feature a beautiful Georgian Chapel dating from 1720 where services are still held, a chain of man-made lakes the central one being spanned by a multi-arch brick bridge. A pair of 18th century Milanese gates, and a nature trail and woodland walk where an old Ice House and Water Cascade can be seen.

❖

SUITABILITY FOR OTHER EVENTS
Capesthorne's situation makes it the ideal venue for functions aimed at the Manchester and North West corporate sector. Facilities are available for clay pigeon shooting, product launches, filming, still photography, shows, wedding receptions, fishing, caravanning, equestrian events (own cross-country course), garden parties, rallies, barbecues, survival games, murder mystery evenings, firework displays, son et lumière etc.

EXTRA FACILITIES
The Theatre is used as a Lecture Room and seats up to 150 people. Cost of hire of the room, audio-visual facilities and lecture negotiable.

ADVICE TO COURIERS & DRIVERS
Rest Room and free meal provided for drivers. No photography in the Hall. Dogs in Park only.

FACILITIES FOR THE DISABLED
Compacted paths, ramps and toilet facilities available.

PARKING FOR COACHES & CARS
Parking for 100 cars/20 coaches on hard-standing and for 2,000 in the park, 50 yds from the house.

CATERING
Capesthorne has its own in-house catering staff providing a wide variety of meals from afternoon tea to banquets. Garden Restaurant, Bromley Room and the ornate Saloon and Queen Anne Rooms available. Special arrangements for corporate functions and weddings

GUIDED TOURS
Can be arranged for up to 50 people at any one time Also available in Italian. The owner can meet tours visiting the house. Average time taken for tour 1 hour.

GIFT SHOP/GUIDE BOOKS
Open when Hall is open and by request at other times. Various brochures on the house, park and garden are available.

CONTACT

Jacquie Caldwell
Capesthorne Hall
Siddington
Macclesfield
Cheshire
SK11 9JY
Tel: (01625) 861221
Fax: (01625) 861619

LOCATION

30 mins South of
Manchester on A34
Near M6, M63 and M62.
Airport: Manchester
International 20 mins.
Helicopter:
(051) 427 1609.
Rail: Macclesfield 5mls
(2hrs from London).
Taxi: (01625) 533464.
Air Taxi: (061) 499 1447.

OPENING TIMES

Summer
March - October

Bank Hol Mons,
Weds & Suns

HOUSE, GARDENS
& CHAPEL
Open at 1.30
Last admission 3.30pm

GARDENS &
CHAPEL ONLY
12noon - 6.00pm

Groups welcome by appointment.

Caravan Park also open March to October.

Corporate enquiries welcome all year.

ADMISSION

Summer

HOUSE AND GARDEN
Adult £4.00
Child* £1.50
OAP £3.50

GARDEN ONLY
Adult £2.25
Child* £1.00
OAP £2.00
Family Ticket . . .£8.50

Groups**
Please telephone for details.

* Aged 5 - 16yrs.
**Min 25 people

CONFERENCE AND FUNCTION FACILITIES

ROOM	DIMENSIONS	CAPACITY	LAYOUT	POWER POINTS	SUITABLE FOR A/V
Theatre	120' x 25'	155	Theatre	Ample	✓
Garden Restaurant	100' x 20'	100	Theatre	Ample	✓
		80	Schoolroom		
		50	Boardroom		
		100	Buffet		
		80	Lunch/Dinner		
Saloon	40' x 25'	100	Theatre	Ample	✓
		80	Schoolroom		
		50	Boardroom		
Queen Anne Room	38' x 26'	80	Schoolroom	Ample	✓
		100	Theatre		

TATTON PARK
Knutsford

TATTON is one of the most complete historic estates in Britain. Five separate features, special events and private functions attract over 700,000 visitors each year.

Man's occupation of Tatton began 10,000 years ago. The Landscape History Trail guides walkers through time from a prehistoric camp to the wartime dropping zone for new recruits to the 1st Parachute Regiment. The trail's explanatory boards are also in the reception barn at Old Hall where visitors are guided through four centuries, from the smokey shadows of the 15th century great hall lit by flickering candles to the home of a 1950's estate employee. The Old Hall was leased to his cousin by Thomas Egerton, Lord Chancellor of England during the reign of Queen Elizabeth I and James I.

At the other side of the park the Palladian Mansion by Wyatt is the jewel in Tatton's crown. The Egerton family collection of fine paintings, porcelain and furniture is found in the splendid setting of the magnificent staterooms.

In stark contrast, the Victorian kitchens and cellars give a fascinating insight into life "downstairs".

The Home Farm is still working with traditional breeds of animal, estate workshops, a steam engine and regular demonstrations. "Horses at Tatton" explains the use of horses for work and pleasure.

GARDENS

These are immaculately maintained by a staff of 12. The superb gardens are full of delightful surprises from all parts of the globe. Successive generations expanded the range of features and specimen plants according to their own taste and style of the times. Extending to 50 acres, including the arboretum, the gardens are considered to be amongst the most important in England. Attractions include the famous Japanese garden with a tea house and Shinto temple, newly restored orangery, New Zealand tree fernery, Italian terraced garden and maze. There's also an African hut and a Greek monument.

Alongside man, deer have roamed the landscape since 8000 BC. Roughly 800 red and fallow deer can still be seen when walking or driving in the Parkland and around the two meres.

Tatton Park is maintained, managed and financed by Cheshire County Council on lease from the National Trust to whom the Mansion and Gardens were bequeathed in 1958 by the late Right Honourable Maurice, Baron Egerton of Tatton, "for the benefit of the Nation".

CONTACT

Conferences, exhibitions, social occasions:
Karen Hay, Functions/Events Manager

Party Visits:
Sylvia Williams,

Tatton Park, Knutsford, Cheshire WA16 6QN

Tel: (01565) 654822
or (01565) 750260

Fax: (01565) 650179

LOCATION

From M56, junct. 7, follow signs.
From M6, junct. 19, signed on A56 and A50.

Rail: Knutsford or Altrincham Stn, then taxi.

OPENING TIMES

Summer
1 April - 30 September and October half-term.
Closed on Mondays, except Park.

Park: 10.00am - 7pm
Gardens: 10.30am - 6pm
Last Admission 5.00pm
Mansion & Farm:
12 - 5pm
Old Hall: weekends
12 - 5pm, weekday tours
at 3pm and 4pm.
Last Admission 4pm.
Groups advised to book early visit to Old Hall (from 10am) at no extra charge.

Winter
1 October - 31 March
Closed Mondays.
Park: 11 am - 5pm
Gardens: 11 am - 4pm
Farm: Suns 12 noon - 4pm
Restaurant,
Shops: 11.30am - 4 pm
All attractions open weekends in Oct. Mansion, Farm open weekends in Dec before Xmas.

ADMISSION

All Attractions
                     Single   Group*
Adult . .£8.00 . . . .£6.40
Child** .£5.00 . . . .£4.00

Any two attractions
Adult . .£4.00 . . . .£3.20
Child .£2.50 . . . .£2.00
MANSION, GARDEN, FARM OR OLD HALL
Adult . .£2.50 . . . .£2.00
Child** .£1.50 . . . .£1.50
PARK
Per car £2.50
Coaches . . . . . . .Free

*Minimum 12 People.
** Aged 5 - 15yrs.
•Mansion & Gardens only, £4.00.

OAP rate as Adult

Tours available outside normal opening times £6.

TATTON PARK CONTINUED...

SUITABILITY FOR OTHER EVENTS

A new reception building provides Tatton with a purpose-designed service area and bar for conferences, trade exhibitions, presentations and product launches in the Tenants Hall. Entry is still possible via the Mansion staterooms and Gardens. A total of 8000 sq ft is now available for hire in the Tenants Hall Event Wing. Other uses include dinners, dances, receptions, concerts, fashion shows, weddings and computer training workshops. Syndicate rooms are nearby.

Special family days can be arranged to run alongside conferences and exhibitions.

For smaller functions Lord Egerton's Apartment has been converted for meetings, dining and receptions. From the covered balcony delegates enjoy an unrivalled view of the Italian garden and Parkland with its lakes to the peaks of Derbyshire beyond. The apartment, like the Tenants Hall, is self-contained and away from the envious eyes of day visitors. The Entrance Hall is available for champagne receptions.

Over 60 public special events are held annually outside in the Park and Gardens, from the Halle with Fireworks to large gatherings of vintage cars.

The 9 hole Knutsford Golf Club borders the Park.

EXTRA FACILITIES

Spotlights, catwalk, dance floor, full public address system, sailing, parkland, shuttle service and marquee hire. The pillarless Tenants Hall has 2 sources of 3 phase power, a scaffold tower and can seat up to 400 for presentations. Projector and screens can be provided. Quads, pilots and grass karts can now be accommodated as can clay pigeon shooting. The new Tatton Outdoor and Sailing Centre if fully equipped with dinghies, windsurfers, canoes and mountain bikes.

ADVICE TO COURIERS & DRIVERS

Visitors now benefit from recent investment in major new services and facilities. Additions and conversions include new lavatories, shops, group dining room, restaurant and a reception/information point adjacent to the coach park. The Privilege Coach Club scheme entitles members and passengers to vouchers.

PARKING FOR COACHES & CARS

Parking for 4,000 cars, 300 yds from the Mansion and for 50 coaches, 200 yds from the Mansion.

VOUCHERS

These are accepted and invoices sent after the visit has been made.

CATERING

There is a self-service restaurant and adjacent tuck shop for snacks and ice-cream.

Less comprehensive catering facilities at Old Hall May-Aug. Prices range from £3.50, special rates apply to groups. Lunches & dinners in Lord Egerton's Apartment from £17, max 40 people.

Booked groups in Harness Room, capacity 80. Menus include pork with cider, beef bordelaise, venison masterchef, buffets. Enquire for availability of Tenants Hall Bar.

GUIDED TOURS

Everyone is taken on a guided tour of Old Hall where "A Story for every Age" begins. Tours of other attractions can be arranged during and outside normal opening times from £1.50 per person. Tours available in Japanese, German, French, Spanish, Italian. Average time taken 1½ hours per attraction.

GIFT SHOP/GARDEN SALES

Open 11.30am-5.30pm. Local crafts, books, children's souvenirs, film, home-grown plants, farm produce. The newly opened Housekeeper's Store stocks English cheeses, wines and estate produce including venison.

GUIDE BOOKS

Colour guide books from £1.

SCHOOL VISITS/CHILDREN

Tatton's award-winning educational programmes are available all year round by prior arrangement with the Education Department. Environmental days with the Rangers in the Park, scrubbing pigs down on the farm or scrubbing floors as a Victorian servant in the Mansion are just some of the activities available. You can even spend the day as an Anglo-Saxon! Flexibility and imagination are the watchwords at Tatton - we can also arrange fishing tuition, windsurfing and sailing instruction, orienteering, photo safaris or any combination of exciting activities suitable for all ages (including adults!) and tastes. An adventure playground is also available.

CONFERENCE AND FUNCTION FACILITIES

ROOM	DIMENSIONS	CAPACITY	LAYOUT	POWER POINTS	SUITABLE FOR A/V
Tenants Hall (Excluding new reception and yard)	125' x 45'	330 - 400	Various	34	✓
Tenants Hall Event Wing – total of 8,000 sq.ft. available					✓
Servants Hall	22' x 15'	30 - 50	Various	4	✓
Lord Egerton's	20' x 16'	16 - 30	Various	4	✓
Apartment	24' x 18'	19 - 35	Various	4	✓
Stables Block Function Room	31' x 20'	80	Various	4	✓

ADLINGTON HALL

See page 19 for full page entry.

ARLEY HALL & GARDENS

See page 20 for full page entry.

BEESTON CASTLE

Tel: 01829 260464

Beeston, Tarporley, Cheshire CW6 9TX
Owner: English Heritage   **Contact:** The Custodian
Standing majestically on sheer, rocky crags which fall sharply away from the castle walls, Beeston has possibly the best views of the surrounding countryside of any castle in England and the rock has a history stretching back over 2,500 years.
Location: 11m SE of Chester on minor road off A49, or A41.
Opening Times: 1 Apr - 30 Sept: 10am - 6pm. 1 Oct - 31 Mar: 10am - 4pm (6pm/dusk in Oct)
Admission: Adult £2.30, Child £1.20, Conc £1.70.

CAPESTHORNE HALL

See page 21 for full page entry.

CHESTER CATHEDRAL

Tel: 01244 324756 **Fax:** 01244 341110

12 Abbey Square, Chester, Cheshire CH1 2HU

        Contact: Mr N Fry
Founded in 1092 as a Benedictine monastery, it became an Anglican cathedral in 1541. All styles of architecture are represented as well as spectacular medieval woodwork.
Location: Chester city centre.
Opening Times: 7am - 6.30pm daily.
Admission: Donation.

CHESTER ROMAN AMPHITHEATRE

Tel: 0191 2611585

Vicars Lane, Chester, Cheshire
Owner: English Heritage   **Contact:** The North Regional Office
The largest Roman amphitheatre in Britain, partially excavated. Used for entertainment and military training by the 20th Legion, based at the fortress of Deva.
Location: On Vicars Lane beyond Newgate, Chester.
Opening Times: Any reasonable time.
Admission: Free.

DORFOLD HALL

Tel: 01270 625245 **Fax:** 01270 628723

Nantwich, Cheshire CW5 8LD
Owner: R C Roundell Esq   **Contact:** R C Roundell Esq
Early 17th century house with good plaster ceilings and panelling. Gardens.
Location: 1 m W of Nantwich on A534.
Opening Times: Apr - Oct : Tuesdays 2 - 5pm.
Admission: Adult £3, Child £1.50. Parties on other days by appointment.

DUNHAM MASSEY HALL

Tel: 0161 9411025 **Fax:** 0161 9297508

Altrincham, Cheshire WA14 4SJ
Owner: The National Trust   **Contact:** The Property Manager
Georgian house with Edwardian additions set in a 250-acre wooded deer park. Until 1976 this was the home of the 10th and last Earl of Stamford. Over 30 rooms are open, with fine furniture, paintings and outstanding Huguenot silver of the second Earl of Warrington; also a fine library, kitchen, laundry and stables. The moat provides power for a working Jacobean mill. The large garden contains an 18th century Orangery, a Victorian Bark House and Well House; all set amongst mixed shrubs, herbaceous borders, mature trees and waterside plantings. There is also a collection of rare, late flowering azaleas.
Location: 3 m SW of Altrincham off A56.
Opening Times: House: 30 Mar - 27 Oct: Sat - Wed, 12 noon - 5pm, last admission 4.30pm. Garden: 30 Mar - 27 Oct: Daily, 11am - 5.30pm, last admission 5pm. The Mill machinery will normally operate on Wed & Sun. Park: Daily throughout the year.
Admission: House & Garden: Adult £4.50, Child £2, Family £11.00. House only: Adult £3, Child £1.50. Garden only: Adult £2.50, Child £1. Discount for pre-booked parties.

HARE HILL

Over Alderley, Macclesfield, Cheshire SK10 4QB
Owner: The National Trust   **Contact:** The Head Gardener
A woodland garden surrounding a walled garden with pergola, rhododendrons and azaleas; parkland: link path to Alderley Edge (2m).
Location: Between Alderley Edge and Prestbury, turn off N at B5087 at Greyhound Road.
Opening Times: 3 Apr - 31 Oct: Wed, Thur, Sat, Sun and BH Mon 10am - 5.30pm. Special opening to see rhododendrons and azaleas: 13 May - 2 Jun: Daily, 10am - 5.30pm. Closed Nov - Mar.
Admission: £2.50 ea. Entrance per car £1.50 refundable on entry to garden. Parties by written appointment c/o Garden Lodge, Oak Road, Over Alderley, Macclesfield, SK10 4QB. Not suitable for school parties.

CHOLMONDELEY CASTLE GARDENS

MALPAS, CHESHIRE SY14 8AH

Owner: The Marchioness of Cholmondeley *Contact:* The Secretary

Tel: 01829 720383 **Fax:** 01829 720519

Extensive pleasure gardens dominated by romantic Gothic Castle built in 1801 of local sandstone. Imaginatively laid out with fine trees and water gardens, it has been extensively replanted since the 1960's with rhododendrons, azaleas, cornus, acer and many other acid loving plants. As well as the beautiful water garden, there is a rose and lavender garden and herbaceous borders. Lakeside picnic area, rare breeds of farm animals, including llamas. Ancient private chapel in the park.
Location: Off A41 Chester/Whitchurch Road & A49 Whitchurch/Tarporley road.
Opening Times: Good Friday, 7 April - 29 Sept, Weds & Thurs 12 noon - 5pm; Suns, BH Mons & Good Friday, 12 noon - 5.30pm. Other days for coach parties (25+) by prior arrangement, at reduced rates.
Admission: Adult £2.50, OAP £2.00, Child 75p.

LITTLE MORETON HALL

CONGLETON, CHESHIRE CW12 4SD

Owner: The National Trust *Contact:* The Property Manager

Tel: 01260 272018

Begun in 1450 and completed 130 years later, Little Moreton Hall is regarded as the finest example of a timber-framed moated manor house in the country. The drunkenly reeling South Front topped by its Elizabethan Long Gallery opens onto a cobbled courtyard and the main body of the Hall. The Chapel, Great Hall, wall paintings and Knot Garden are of particular interest.
Location: 4 m SW of Congleton on E side of A34.
Opening Times: 23 March - 27 Oct: Wed-Sun, 12 noon - 5 .30pm or dusk if earlier. BH Mon 11am - 5.30pm. Last admission 5pm. 2 Nov - 22 Dec, Sat & Sun, 12 noon - 4pm (access to Great Hall, Parlour, Gardens, Shop and Restaurant). Special openings at other times for pre-booked parties.
Admission: Adult £3.60, Family £9.00, pre-booked parties £2.80. A joint ticket available with Biddulph Grange Garden is available for £6.00, Family £15.00. 2 Nov - 22 Dec: free admission.

LYME PARK

DISLEY, STOCKPORT, CHESHIRE SK12 2NX

Owner: *The National Trust*   ***Contact:*** *The Property Manager*

Tel: 01663 762023   **Fax:** 01663 765035

Legh family home for 600 years. Part of the original Elizabethan house survives with 18th and 19th century additions by Giacomo Leoni and Lewis Wyatt. Four centuries of period interiors - Mortlake tapestries, Grinling Gibbons carvings, unique collection of English clocks. Historic gardens with conservatory by Wyatt, a lake and a 'Dutch' garden. A 1,400 acre park, home to red and fallow deer. New catering and retail facilities. Exterior featured as 'Pemberley' in BBC's 'Pride and Prejudice'.

Location: Off the A6 between Stockport & Buxton.

Opening Times: Park: Apr to Oct : Daily 8am 8.30pm & Nov - Mar 8am - 6pm. **Gardens:** 30 Mar - 31 Oct: Daily 11am - 5pm. Nov - Mar: Weekends 12 noon - 4pm. Closed 23, 24, 30, 31 Dec. **House:** 30 Mar - 4 Sept: Sat - Wed 1.30 - 5pm, last entry 4.30pm. BH's 11am - 5pm. Early closure due to major internal work this year. NB. From April 1997 the house, tea room and gift shop will change its open days to Wed - Sun (closed Mon & Tue).

Park Shop & Coffee Shop: Apr - Oct: Daily 11am - 5pm, Nov - Mar: Weekends & local school hols 12 noon - 4pm. **Hall Tea Room & Gift Shop:** 30 Mar - 4 Sept: Sat - Wed 11am - 5pm, Sept - Mar: Sat & Sun 11am - 4pm. Closed 23, 24, 30 & 31 Dec . Ice Cream Kiosk: Serving a selection of speciality ice-cream. Apr - Oct: Sat & Sun and local school hols 12 noon - 4pm.

Admission: House & Garden: Adult £3.00, Family £7.00, Park only £3.00/car.

NESS GARDENS
     Tel: 01513 368733   **Fax:** 01513 531004

Ness, Neston, Cheshire L64 4AY

Owner: University of Liverpool   **Contact:** Dr. E J Sharples

Location: Off A540. 10m NW of Chester.

Opening Times: 1 Mar - 31 Oct: 9.30am - dusk. Nov - Feb: 9.30am - 4pm.

Admission: Adult £3.60, Child £2.60, Family £8, Concessions £2.60, Groups £3.00.

NETHER ALDERLEY MILL
     Tel: 01625 523012

Congleton Road, Nether Alderley, Macclesfield, Cheshire SK10 4TW

Owner: The National Trust   **Contact:** The National Trust

A fascinating overshot tandem wheel watermill, dating from the 15th century, with a stone-tiled low pitched roof. The machinery was derelict for 30 years, but has now been restored to full working order, and grinds flour occasionally for demonstrations.

Location: 1¹/2m S of Alderley Edge, on E side of A34.

Opening Times: 3 Apr - end May & Oct: Wed, Sun & BH Mon, 1 - 4.30pm. Jun - Sept, Tues - Sun & BH Mon 1 - 5.00pm.

Admission: Adult £1.80, Parties (max 20+) by prior arrangement.

NORTON PRIORY WALLED GARDEN & MUSEUM
     Tel: 01928 569895

Tudor Road, Manor Park, Runcorn, Cheshire, WA7 1SX.

Owner: Norton Priory Museum   **Contact:** Norton Priory Museum

Site of Medieval priory set in beautiful woodland gardens.

Location: 3 m from J11/M56.

Opening Times: Every afternoon from 1 Mar - 31 Oct (museum open all year).

Admission: Adult £2.60, Child £1.40, Family £6.95, Concessions £1.40, Group £1.30.

PEOVER HALL

OPEN

House, Stables
& Gardens:
May - Sept
Mondays except
Bank Holidays.

2.30 - 4.30pm.

Stables & Gardens only:
Thursdays
2..00 - 5.00pm.

Tel: 01565 722656

OVER PEOVER, KNUTSFORD

Owner: *Randle Brooks*   ***Contact:*** *J. Stocks*

An Elizabethan House dating from 1585. Fine Carolean stables. Mainwaring Chapel, 18th century landscaped park. Large garden with topiary work, also walled and herb gardens. Refreshments are available in the Stables on Mondays.

Location: 4 miles S of Knutsford off A50 at Whipping Stocks Inn.

Admission: House, Stables & Gardens: Adult £2.50, Child £1.50. Stables & Gardens only: Adult £1.50, Child 50p.

QUARRY BANK MILL & STYAL COUNTRY PARK

     Tel: 01625 527468   **Fax:** 01625 539267

Styal, Wilmslow, Cheshire SK9 4LA

Owner: The National Trust   **Contact:** Quarry Bank Mill Trust Ltd.

A major Georgian cotton mill restored as Europe's largest working textile museum, powered by a 50 ton water wheel. Work is underway to restore steam power with an 1840s beam engine. The story of cotton is brought to life by demonstrations and costumed interpreters. The original Apprentice House recreates the 1830s atmosphere of the lives of the pauper apprentice child workers. The picturesque village of Styal completes this uniquely preserved 18th century factory colony.

Location: 1¹/2 miles N of Wilmslow off B5166. 2¹/2 miles from M56, Junction 5.

Opening Times: Apr - Sept: Daily 11am - 6pm, last entry 4.30pm. Oct - Mar (closed Mons): 11am - 5pm, last entry 3.30pm.

Admission: Mill & Apprentice House: Adult £4.50, Child/Conc. £3.20, Family £10.00. Mill only: Adult £3.50, Child/Conc. £2.50, Family £9. Apprentice House & Garden: Adult £3.00, Child/Conc. £2.30, Family £8. Groups by prior arrangement.

RODE HALL
     Tel: 01270 873237

Church Lane, Scholar Green, Stoke-on-Trent, Cheshire

Owner: Sir Richard Baker Wilbraham   **Contact:** The Owner

18th century country house with Georgian stable block. Later alterations by L. Wyatt and Darcy Braddell.

Location: 5 miles SW of Congleton between A34 and A50. Rail: Kidsgrove (2¹/4 miles)

Opening Times: 8 Apr - 25 Sept: Wed and Bank Hols 2 - 5pm.

Admission: House, Garden & Kitchen Garden: £3.50. Garden & Kitchen Garden: £2.00. Refreshments available from the Bleeding Wolf Restaurant, Scholar Green.

STAPELEY WATER GARDENS LTD
     Tel: 01270 628628   **Fax:** 01270 624188

London Road, Stapeley, Nantwich, Cheshire CW5 7LH

     Contact: Reception

Home of the national collection of Nymphaea (Water Lilies) with over 350 varieties. The world's largest water garden centre with over three acres of display gardens, aquatic plants, pools and fountains. Expert advice and ideas. The Palms Tropical Oasis - a 1.3 acre pavilion: home to piranhas, parrots, monkeys and exotic plants. The Stapeley Yesteryear Museum houses restored memorabilia.

Location: 1 m S of Nantwich on A51 to Stone. Follow brown tourist signs from J16/M6.

Opening Times: All year except Xmas Day from 10am. Yesteryear Museum: Easter - end Oct.

Admission: Charges to the Palms Tropical Oasis and the Yesteryear Museum only. Special Group Rates.

KEY TO SYMBOLS: THE NATIONAL TRUST   ENGLISH HERITAGE   HISTORIC HOUSES ASSOCIATION

TABLEY HOUSE

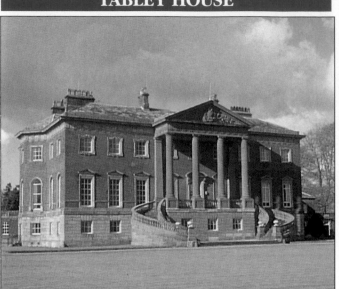

KNUTSFORD, CHESHIRE WA16 0HB

Owner: *Victoria University of Manchester*   **Contact:** *The Administrator*

Tel: 01565 750151

Magnificent Palladian Mansion, Grade I, by John Carr of York completed 1769 for the Leicester family who lived at Tabley for over 700 years. Fine collection of English works of art, furniture, memorabilia can be seen in the State Rooms. Private chapel 1678. Tea Room, Gift Shop. Access for wheelchairs. Civil Wedding Licence.

Location: M6 junction 19, A556. S then on to A5033.

Opening Times: April - October inclusive: Thursdays, Fridays, Saturdays, Sundays and Bank Holidays 2.00 - 5.00pm

Admission: Adult £3.50. Child £1.00. Group bookings on application.

TATTON PARK    See pages 22-23 for full page entry.

Where to Stay

For Private Accommodation and Johansens recommended Hotels, see Accommodation Section.

Lyme Park. Featured in the BBC's 'Pride and Prejudice' (1995).

SPECIAL EVENTS

◇ **ARLEY HALL AND GARDENS** Antiques Fair	**15 –17 MARCH**	◇ **ARLEY HALL AND GARDENS** Arley Garden Festival
◇ **ADLINGTON HALL** Craft Fair	**5 – 6 MAY**	◇ **ADLINGTON HALL** Craft Fair
◇ **ARLEY HALL AND GARDENS** Outdoor orchestral concert	**6 JULY**	◇ **ARLEY HALL AND GARDENS** Antiques Fair
◇ **ARLEY HALL AND GARDENS** Shakespeare at Arley	**20 JULY**	◇ **ARLEY HALL AND GARDENS** Victorian Christmas days at Arley
◇ **ARLEY HALL AND GARDENS** Brass Band Concert	**21 JULY**	◇ **ARLEY HALL AND GARDENS** Victorian Christmas evenings at Arley

Right column dates:
- **27 – 28 JULY**
- **11 – 12 AUGUST**
- **11 – 13 OCTOBER**
- **7, 8, 14, 15 DECEMBER**
- **7, 14 DECEMBER**

For National Trust and English Heritage Events see separate section.

ANTONY HOUSE & GDN. & ANTONY WOODLAND GDN.
Torpoint

Antony House and Garden: A superb example of an early 18th century mansion. The main block is faced in lustrous silver-grey stone, flanked by mellow brick pavilions. The ancestral home of the Carew family for nearly 600 years, the house contains a wealth of paintings, tapestries, furniture and embroideries, many linking the great families of Cornwall. Set in parkland and fine gardens overlooking the Lynher river. An 18th century Bath House in the grounds can be viewed by arrangement. Tea room and shop.

Antony Woodland Garden: The woodland garden was established in the late 18th century with the assistance of Humphrey Repton. It features over 300 varieties of camellias, together with magnolias, rhododendrons, azaleas and other flowering shrubs, interspersed with many fine species of indigenous and exotic trees. A further 50 acres of natural woods bordering the tidal waters of the Lynher provide a number of delightful walks. No dogs.

❖

CONTACT

ANTONY HOUSE
(The National Trust)
The Administrator
Antony House & Gdn
Torpoint
Cornwall
PL11 2QA

Tel: (01752) 812191

ANTONY WOODLAND GARDEN
(Carew Pole Gdn Trust)
Mrs. Valerie Anderson
Torpoint
Cornwall
PL11 2QA

Tel: (01752) 812364

LOCATION

ANTONY HOUSE AND ANTONY WOODLAND GARDEN
5 mls west of Plymouth via Torpoint car ferry, 2 miles north-west of Torpoint.

OPENING TIMES

ANTONY HOUSE AND GARDEN
1 April - 31 October
Tue, Wed, Thur &
Bank Holiday Mondays
plus Suns in June,
July & Aug
1.30 - 5.30pm

Guided tours at less busy times.

Last tour 4.45pm

ANTONY WOODLAND GARDEN
1 Mar - 31 Oct
Daily
11.00am - 5.30pm

ADMISSION

ANTONY HOUSE
Adult £3.80
Parties £3.00

Antony Woodland Garden:
Adult £2.00

Joint Gardens only ticket to NT owned garden and Antony Woodland Garden
Adult £3.00
Child £1.50
Parties £2.00

MOUNT EDGCUMBE
Torpoint

Since 1553 Mount Edgcumbe House has stood at the head of a splendid tree lined avenue looking down across the Tamar river and Plymouth to the Dartmoor hills beyond.

The Tudor walls of the ancestral home of the Earls of Mount Edgcumbe survived a direct hit during the 1941 bombing of Plymouth. The sixth Earl and the architect Adrian Gilbert Scott restored the interior in 1958. The House and 800 acres of parkland are now owned jointly by Cornwall County and Plymouth City Councils.

Today the Edgcumbe family paintings and furniture can be seen once more in the House. They include land and seascapes by Gérard van Edema and van de Velde and portraits by Sir Joshua Reynolds and R. Stanhope Forbes. Amongst the furnishings are boulle desks, Bronze Age horns, Chinese and English porcelain, and for the sharp-eyed, unicorns, mermaids, wild boar and bears can be tracked down.

GARDENS

Next to the House the two acre Earl's Garden created in the 18th century has a restored Victorian terrace garden, and many notable trees including a 400 year old lime, a Lucombe oak and a rare Mexican pine. A beautiful Shell grotto, c.1790, sparkles with minerals, shells and fossils; and summer houses with striking views of the sea enhance the unique character of this secret garden.

In the Park in the 17th and 18th centuries, the Edgcumbe family created gardens, temples and summer houses in the Italian, French and English styles; and recently an American plantation and a New Zealand garden complete with geyser, have been established.

Forts, follies, wild fallow deer and the National camellia collection can be found while exploring the beaches, hillsides and woods of the wider parkland.

❖

SUITABILITY FOR OTHER EVENTS
Filming, promotions, conferences for numbers up to 70.

EXTRA FACILITIES
Orienteering route. Concerts, Open Air Theatre, Country Fairs, Art Exhibitions in the house.

ADVICE TO COURIERS & DRIVERS
Advance bookings necessary; discounts available. Minimum 10 people. No photography and no dogs in the house. Allow 1½ hours for house and Earl's Garden. Small tea-room in the house, main restaurant half mile down hill.

FACILITIES FOR THE DISABLED
Special parking near the house. Lavatories, wheelchairs, lift in house.

PARKING FOR COACHES & CARS
Signposted car and coach park near the House and near Cremyll.

CATERING
Cedar Tea-room admission through the house only, 20 seats. Orangery Restaurant and café in 18th century Italian garden, 120 seats. Bookings for groups and functions: Tel: 01752 822586.

GUIDED TOURS
Special tours of the house can be arranged; room stewards are also on duty.

GIFT SHOP
There are two gift shops, one in the house, the other at the Visitor Centre at Cremyll.

GUIDE BOOKS
A guide book and leaflets on trees, fortifications, gardens and walks are available.

SCHOOL VISITS/CHILDREN
Mown grass close to the gardens and beach offer informal spaces. School groups welcome; assistance with environmental subjects available from rangers. Book in advance.

CONTACT

Mrs. Cynthia Gaskell-Brown
Mt Edgcumbe House
Cremyll
Torpoint
Cornwall
PL10 1HZ

Tel: (01752) 822236
Fax: (01752) 822199

Owner:
Cornwall County
Council and Plymouth
City Council.

LOCATION

10 mls W of Plymouth, via Torpoint car ferry 1 hour.
Tourist signposts from Torpoint and in Cornwall.

Bus: From Royal Parade Plymouth to Cremyll foot ferry, 15 minutes

---

OPENING TIMES

HOUSE AND
EARL'S GARDEN
April - October
Wed - Sun and Bank
Holiday Mondays
11.00am - 5.00pm

Closed Mon and Tues.

LOWER GARDEN
AND PARK
Open all year.
Admission free.

ADMISSION

HOUSE AND
EARL'S GARDEN
  Adult £3.50
  Child* £1.70
  OAP £2.50
  Student £2.50
  Concession** . . .£2.50
  Family*** £8.00
  Season £6.50

*   Aged 5 - 16 yrs.
** NACF, Friends of Plymouth Museum, Unemployed, Disabled
*** 2 Adults and 2 Children.

TREBAH GARDEN
Mawnan Smith

The Enchanted Garden

Trebah is no pampered pristine, prissy garden with rows of clipped hedges, close-mown striped lawns and daily raked paths. Here is a magnificent old, wild, enchanted Cornish garden - the end product of 100 years of inspired and dedicated creation, followed by 40 years of mellowing neglect and 10 years of love and restoration.

"Like a corner of the Himalayas only better cared for", Trebah is the home of Major and Mrs Anthony Hibbert. The family have given the estate to the Trebah Garden Trust, an independent charity, to ensure the garden will remain open to the public forever.

The 26 acre sub-tropical ravine garden runs down to the private beach on the Helford River. A stream winding down though water gardens with waterfalls and Koi Carp is flanked with carpets of arums and primula candelabra and two acres of blue and white hydrangeas. 100 year old rhododendrons and magnolias over-hang glades of giant gunnera and tree ferns. The side curtains of magnificent beeches and copper beeches climbing the steep walls of the ravine, and the back-curtain of the Helford River and the distant Bosahan hills, form a theatrical set of extraordinary beauty.

❖

CONTACT

Sally Jones
Trebah Garden Trust
Mawnan Smith
Cornwall TR11 5JZ

Tel: (01326) 250448

Fax: (01326) 250781

LOCATION

4 miles SW of Falmouth

1 mile SW of Mawnan Smith

Follow brown and white tourism signs from Treliever Cross Roundabout on A39 on approach to Falmouth

ADVICE TO COURIERS & DRIVERS
Free car parking for 3 coaches and 140 cars. Free entrance and meal for couriers and drivers. Dogs on leads welcome.

CATERING
The new coffee shop seats 65 in a charming and exotic setting. The adjacent picnic area can seat a further 60. The kitchen offers excellent morning coffee, light lunches and cream teas.

GIFT SHOP
The Gift Shop holds an extensive range of books, maps, postcards and gifts for all ages, tastes and pockets.

GUIDE BOOKS
Illustrated garden guides with colour photographs and detailed map are on sale for 50p. Translations in French, Dutch, German and Japanese will be available.

GUIDED TOURS
Guided Tours of the garden available for parties of 12. Pre-booking required.

PLANT SALES
A unique collection of exotic plants suitable for English gardens is on sale in the sunken garden.

TREWITHEN
Probus

TREWITHEN means 'house of the trees', and the name truly describes this fine early Georgian House in its splendid setting of wood and parkland. Country Life described the house as "one of the outstanding West Country houses of the 18th century."

The origins of the house go back to the 17th century, but it was the architect Sir Robert Taylor, as well as Thomas Edwards of Greenwich who was responsible for the fine building we see today. The rebuilding was commissioned by Philip Hawkins, who bought the house in 1715, and was completed only some 40 years later. The house has been lived in by the same family for over 250 years.

Behind Trewithen's facade of quiet elegance hides a fascinating history. The Hawkins family were eminent landowners, they encouraged tin, copper and china clay mining in Cornwall and they built a railway and a harbour (Pentewan). The most notable member was Christopher Hawkins, created a baronet in 1799, who was MP for Grampound and, later, Father of the House of Commons. All Hawkins were great collectors and much of their contribution to both county and national life is reflected inside the house.

GARDENS

The gardens at Trewithen, (some 12 hectares) are outstanding and of international fame. Created since the beginning of the century by George Johnstone - a direct Hawkins descendant - they contain a wide and rare collection of flowering shrubs. Many of the plants here are unique to Trewithen: they were sent in seed form during the 1920s from Tibet, China and Nepal, and now flower spectacularly in the mild Cornish climate. Some of the Magnolias and Rhododendron species in the garden are known throughout the world. Plants and Shrubs are available for sale. The gardens, impressive throughout the year, are particularly attractive between March and the end of June, and again in the Autumn. They are one of the two attractions in this county to be awarded three stars by Michelin.

ADVICE TO COURIERS & DRIVERS
Please pre-book to visit the House. No dogs or photography in the house. Dogs on leads in the garden.

FACILITIES FOR THE DISABLED
There are toilet facilities for the disabled.

PARKING FOR COACHES & CARS
Parking for 150 cars & 7 coaches 50 yards from the house.

CATERING
Tea shop at Trewithen for light refreshments.

GUIDED TOURS
These are available for groups of up to 10 people for the House only. There is no additional cost for this. Average time taken to see the House $\frac{1}{2}$ hour. There is a new video room: a 25 minute video showing the history of the House and Garden is shown free of charge.

GARDEN SHOP
The Garden Shop is open for the same hours as the Gardens themselves. The shop sells guide books, postcards and a substantial range of plants and shrubs, many of which are rare, highly prized or famous Trewithen hybrids. There is a picnic area and exciting children's play corner.

GUIDE BOOKS
Colour guide books, 80p.

ANTHONY HOUSE & GARDEN
ANTHONY WOODLAND GARDEN

See Page 27 for full page entry.

BOSVIGO HOUSE GARDENS

Tel: 01872 75774   **Fax:** 01872 75774

Bosvigo Lane, Truro, Cornwall TR1 3NH
Owner: Michael & Wendy Perry   **Contact:** Mr Michael Perry
Series of walled and enclosed gardens surrounding Georgian House (not open).
Location: ³/₄ mile from city centre. Turn down Dobbs Lane near Sainsbury roundabout.
Opening Times: Mar - 30 Sept, Wed - Sat, 11am - 6pm.
Admission: Adult £2.00, Child 50p.

CAERHAYS CASTLE & GARDEN

Tel: 01872 501310   **Fax:** 01872 501870

Caerhays, Gorran, St Austell, Cornwall PL26 6LY
Owner: F J Williams Esq   **Contact:** Miss Alison Mayes
Location: South coast of Cornwall - between Mevagissey and Portloe.
One of the very few Nash built castles still left standing - situated within approximately 60 acres of informal woodland gardens created by J.C. Williams, who sponsored plant hunting expeditions to China at the turn of the century. Noted for its camellias, magnolias, rhododendrons and oaks. English Heritage listing - Grade One: Outstanding.
Opening Times: House; 25 Mar - 3 May: Mon - Fri (excluding Bank Hols) 2 - 4pm.
Gardens: 18 Mar - 3 May: Mon - Fri, 11am - 4pm.
Admission: House: £3.00. Gardens: £2.50, Child £1.50. House/Gardens £5.00.
Guided tours by Head Gardener, for groups, can be arranged outside normal opening times £3.50ea.

CHYSAUSTER ANCIENT VILLAGE

Tel: 01736 61889

Nr. Newmill, Penzance, Cornwall TR20 8XA
Owner: English Heritage   **Contact:** The Custodian
On a windy hillside, overlooking the wild and spectacular coast, is this deserted Romano-Cornish village with a 'street' of eight well preserved houses, each comprising a number of rooms around an open court. Guided tours available if booked in advance.
Location: 2¹/₂m NW of Gulval off B3311.
Opening Times: 1 Apr - 30 Sept: Daily 10am - 6pm. 1 - 31 Oct: Daily 10am - 6pm/dusk.
Admission: Adult £1.50, Child 80p, Conc. £1.10.

COTEHELE

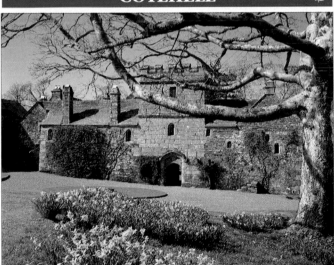

ST. DOMINICK, NR. SALTASH, CORNWALL PL12 6TA
Owner: The National Trust   Contact: The Property Manager

Tel: 01579 351346

Enchantingly remote, perched high above the wood banks of the Tamar, Cotehele was home to the Edgcumbe family for nearly six centuries. The house retains a remarkably medieval atmosphere and contains a wealth of contemporary furnishings and *objets d'art*. The large estate includes a working watermill, a river quay with restored sailing barge and miles of woodland walks, with formal and valley gardens by the house.
Location: On west bank of Tamar, 1 m west of Calstock by footpath (6 mls by road),8 mls south-west of Tavistock, 14 mls from Plymouth via Saltash Bridge.
Opening Times: 1 Apr - 31 Oct: House. Restaurant & Mill 11.00am - 5.30pm, daily except Fris, (open Good Fri). Last Adm. ¹/₂hr before closing
Garden, Shop & Tea room: daily, 11am to 5.30pm. All close 5pm in Oct.
Gallery: Daily 12 noon - 5pm. Garden: Nov - Mar, Daily.
Admission: House, Garden, Mill: £ 5.60. Garden & Mill: £2.80.
Parties (by prior written arrangement only): £4.50

GLENDURGAN

MAWNAN SMITH, FALMOUTH, CORNWALL TR11 5JZ
Owner: The National Trust
Contact: Reception

Tel: 01326 250906
(opening hours only)
or 01208 74281

A valley garden of great beauty with fine trees, shrubs and water gardens. The laurel maze, recently restored, is an unusual and popular feature. The garden runs down to the tiny village of Durgan and its beach on the Helford River.
Location: 4m SW of Falmouth, ¹/₂m SW of Mawnan Smith, on road to Helford Passage.
Admission: £2.90. Pre-arranged parties: £2.50.

OPEN

1 Mar - 31 Oct: Tues - Sat and Bank Holiday Mons (Closed Good Friday): 10.30am - 5.30pm.
Last admission 4.30pm

GODOLPHIN

OPEN
1 May - 30 Sept.
May & June
Thurs 2 - 5pm
July & September
Tues & Thurs: 2 - 5pm
August
Tues : 2 - 5pm
Thurs: 10am - 1pm
and 2 - 5pm
Open Bank Hol Mons
(not Christmas).
Groups by arrangement.

Tel: 01736 762409

BREAGE, HELSTON, CORNWALL TR13 9RE
Owner: Mrs. M. Schofield   Contact: Mrs. M. Schofield

Godolphin is a Tudor and Stuart house with original Elizabethan stables. The recently discovered gardens show the ancient raised walks and carp ponds and are at present undergoing clearance. The most eminent Godolphins were Sidney the poet, killed in the Civil War fighting for the King, and Sidney the 1st Earl, who was Queen Anne's Lord High Treasurer. His son, the 2nd Earl, owned the famous Godolphin Arabian and a painting of the horse by John Wootton hangs in the dining room.
Location: Breage, Helston.
Admission: Adult: £3. Child £1. Reductions for groups of 15+ by prior arrangement.

Lanhydrock.

LANHYDROCK

BODMIN, CORNWALL PL30 5AD

Owner: *The National Trust*   *Contact:* *The Property Manager*

Tel: 01208 73320

The grandest and most welcoming house in Cornwall, Lanhydrock is superbly set in 450 acres of woods and parkland and encircled by a garden of rare shrubs and trees, lovely in all seasons. Although dating from the 17th century, Lanhydrock was largely rebuilt after a fire in 1881 and now exemplifies the great Victorian country house. A total of 49 rooms are open to the public.

Location: 2½ miles SE of Bodmin, follow signposts from either A38 or B3268.

Opening Times: 1 Apr - 31 Oct: Daily except Mondays when the house only is closed (open Bank Holiday Mons) 11am - 5.30pm. Closes 5pm in October. Last admission ½ hr before closing. Garden: Nov - Mar: Daily.

Admission: House, Garden & Grounds: Adult £5.90. Garden & Grounds: £3.00. Pre-arranged parties £5.00. Family ticket £15.00.

LAUNCESTON CASTLE

Tel: 01566 772365

Castle Lodge, Launceston, Cornwall PL15 7DR

Owner: English Heritage   **Contact:** The Custodian

Set on the motte of the original Norman castle and commanding the town and surrounding countryside, the shell keep and tower survive of this medieval castle which controlled the main route into Cornwall.

Location: In Launceston.

Opening Times: 1 Apr - 30 Sept: 10am - 6pm. 1 - 31 Oct: 10am - 6pm or dusk if earlier.

Admission: Adult £1.50, Child 80p, Conc £1.10.

THE LOST GARDENS OF HELIGAN

OPEN
Every day except Christmas Day.
10.00 - 6.00pm
last admission 4.30pm.

Tel: 01726 844157
Fax: 01726 843023

PENTEWAN, ST. AUSTELL, CORNWALL PL26 6EN

Owner: *Mr. T Smit*   *Contact:* *Mr. C.A. Howlett*

The award winning Lost Gardens of Heligan are 57 acres of superb pleasure grounds together with a magnificent complex of four walled gardens and kitchen garden, all being restored to their former glory as a living museum of 19th century horticulture. An Italian Garden, Fern Ravine, Crystal Grotto, Summerhouses, Rides, Lawns and a 20 acre sub-tropical "Jungle Garden" are just some of the delights of this "Sleeping Beauty".

Location: From St. Austell take B3273 towards Mevagissey and follow tourist signs.

Admission: Adult: £2.90. Child (5-15) £1.70, OAP's £2.50. Family £8.20. Groups by prior arrangement.

MOUNT EDGCUMBE

See Page 28 for full page entry.

PENCARROW

OPEN
Easter - 15 Oct
1.30 - 5.00pm
Sun - Thurs.

1 June - 10 Sept
& Bank Holiday Mondays
opens 11.00am.

Tel: 01208 841369

BODMIN, CORNWALL PL30 3AG

Owner: *Molesworth-St Aubyn family*   *Contact:* *The Administrator*

Still owned and lived in by the family. Georgian house and grade II listed gardens. Superb collection of pictures, furniture and porcelain. Marked walks through 50 acres of beautiful formal and woodland gardens, Victorian rockery, Italian gardens, lake and ice house. Craft centre, tearooms, children's play area and plant shop. Facilities for the disabled. Dogs welcome in the grounds.

Location: 4 miles north west of Bodmin off A389 and B3266 at Washaway.

Admission: Adult £3.80. Child £1.80.

PENDENNIS CASTLE

Tel: 01326 316594

Falmouth, Cornwall TR11 4LP

Owner: English Heritage   **Contact:** The Custodian

This castle is a testament to the quality of the coastal defences erected by Henry VIII. The well preserved granite gun fort and outer ramparts with great angled bastions defended against invasion from the sea, but it was captured from the land after a long siege during the Civil War.

Location: On Pendennis Head 1m SE of Falmouth.

Opening Times: 1 Apr - 30 Sept: Daily 10am - 6pm. 1 Oct - 31 Mar: Daily 10am - 4pm. (10am - 6pm or dusk in October).

Admission: Adult £2.50, Child £1.30, Conc £1.70.

PENJERRIC GARDENS

Tel: 01872 870105

Budock, Falmouth, Cornwall TR11 5ED

Owner: Mrs Rachel Morin   **Contact:** Mrs Rachel Morin

Location: 3m from Falmouth between Budock and Mawnan Smith.

Opening Times: 1 Mar - 30 Sept, Wed, Fri and Sun, 1.30pm - 4.30pm.

Admission: Adult £1, Child 50p.

PRIDEAUX PLACE

OPEN
Easter - Mid Oct
Sun - Thurs
1.30 - 5.00pm
closed Fri & Sat
Easter, Late Spring and August Bank Hol
11am - 5pm
Mid Oct - Easter
Open by arrangement for groups 10+.

Tel: 01841 532945
or 01841 532411

PADSTOW, CORNWALL PL28 8RP

Owner: *Peter Prideaux-Brune*   *Contact:* *Peter Prideaux-Brune*

Tucked away in the busy port of Padstow, the family home of the Prideaux family for the past four hundred years, is surrounded by gardens and wooded grounds overlooking a deerpark and the Camel estuary to the moors beyond. The house still retains its 'E' shape Elizabethan front, contains family treasures and has a homely atmosphere. The impressive outbuildings have been restored in recent years and the 16th century plaster ceiling in the great chamber has been uncovered for the first time since 1760.

Location: 5m from A39 on A389 Newquay/Wadebridge link road. Signposted by Historic House Signs.

Admission: House & Garden: Adult/OAP £4.00. Child £1.00. Grounds only: £2.00 Groups: £3.50. School visits by arrangement.

PROBUS GARDENS

Tel: 01726 882597   **Fax:** 01726 883868

Probus, Nr. Truro, Cornwall TR2 4HQ

Owner: Cornwall County Council   **Contact:** Mr Alistair Rivers

This seven and a half acre garden with displays of annuals, herbaceous, perennials, shrubs, trees, conifers and hedges.

Location: East of Probus village on A390

Opening Times: 11 Mar - 11 Oct: Daily 10am - 5pm. 14 Oct - 14 Mar: Mon - Fri 10am - 4pm.

Admission: Adult £2.50, Child free, Groups 20+ £2.00. Guided tours Min. 15 persons £3.00ea, pre-booking is essential.

RESTORMEL CASTLE

Tel: 01726 882597

Lostwithiel, Cornwall PL22 0EE

Owner: English Heritage   **Contact:** The Custodian

Perched on a high mound, surrounded by a deep moat, the huge circular keep of this splendid Norman castle survives in remarkably good condition.

Location: 1¹/₂m N or Lostwithiel off A390.

Opening Times: 1 Apr - 30 Sept: 10am - 6pm. 1 - 31 Oct: 10am - 6pm or dusk if earlier.

Admission: Adult £1.50, Child 80p, Conc £1.10.

ST CATHERINE'S CASTLE

Tel: 01179 750700

Fowey, Cornwall.

Owner: English Heritage   **Contact:** The South West Regional Office

A small fort built by Henry VIII to defend Fowey harbour, with fine views of the coastline and river estuary.

Location: ³/₄m SW of Fowey along footpath off A3082.

Opening Times: Any reasonable time.

ST MAWES CASTLE

OPEN

1 April - 30 Sept

Daily: 10am - 6pm

1 Oct - 31 Oct

Daily: 10am - 6pm or dusk if earlier

1 Nov - 31 Mar

Weds - Suns only

10am - 4pm (closed luch 1-2 Nov - Mar)

Tel: 01326 270526

ST MAWES, CORNWALL TR2 3AA

Owner: English Heritage   *Contact: The Custodian*

The pretty fishing village of St Mawes is home to this castle. On the opposite headland to Pendennis Castle, St Mawes shares the task of watching over the mouth of the River Fal as it has done since Henry VIII built it as a defence against the French. The Castle offers views of St. Mawes little boat filled harbour, the passenger ferry tracking across the Fal and the splendid coastline which featured in the Poldark television series. This is also the start of some delightful walks along the coastal path.

Location: In St. Mawes on A3078.

Admission: Adult £2.00, Conc. £1.50, Child £1.00. Discount on parties of 11 or more.

Tintagel Old Post Office.

ST MICHAEL'S MOUNT

MARAZION, NR PENZANCE, CORNWALL TR17 0EF

Owner: The National Trust   *Contact: The Manor Office*

Tel: 01736 710507

This magical island is the jewel in Cornwall's crown. The great granite crag which rises from the waters of Mount's Bay is surmounted by an embattled 14th century castle, home of the St. Aubyn family for over 300 years. The Mount's flanks are softened by lush sub-tropical vegetation and on the water's edge there is a harbourside community which features shops and restaurants.

Location: At Marazion there is access on foot over causeway at low tide. In summer months there is a ferry at high tide.

Opening Times: 1 Apr - 31 Oct: Mon - Fri 10.30am - 5.30pm Last admission 4.45pm. 1 Nov - end Mar: It is essential to telephone before setting out in order to ascertain the opening arrangements for that day.

Admission: £3.70, Family Ticket £9.00, Pre-arranged parties £3.20

TINTAGEL CASTLE

Tel: 01840 770328

Tintagel, Cornwall PL34 0AA

Owner: English Heritage   **Contact:** The Custodian

The spectacular setting for the legendary castle of King Arthur is the wild and windswept Cornish coast. Clinging precariously to the edge of the cliff face are the extensive ruins of a medieval royal castle built by Richard, Earl of Cornwall, younger brother of Henry III. Despite extensive excavation since the 1930's and a mass of picturesque legend, Tintagel is still an enigma, its history full of gaps and the nature of its earlier occupation quite uncertain.

Location: On Tintagel Head, ¹/₂ m along uneven track from Tintagel. No vehicles.

Opening Times: 1 Apr - 30 Sept: Daily 10am - 6pm. 1 Oct - 31 Mar 10am - 4pm (10am - 6pm or dusk if earlier in October).

Admission: Adult £2.50, Child £1.30, Conc. £1.90.

TINTAGEL OLD POST OFFICE

Tel: 01840 770024 or 01208 74281

Tintagel, Cornwall PL34 0DB

Owner: The National Trust   **Contact:** The Custodian

One of the most characterful buildings in Cornwall, and a house of great antiquity, this small 14th century manor is full of charm and interest. Tumble-roofed and weathered by the centuries, it is restored in the fashion of the Post Office it was for nearly 50 years.

Location: In the centre of Tintagel.

Opening Times: 1 Apr - 31 Oct: Daily 11.00am - 5.30pm. Closes 5.00pm in October.

Admission: £2.00. Pre-arranged parties £1.50.

TREBAH GARDEN

See Page 29 for full page entry.

TREGREHAN

OPEN

Mid March - end June
(closed Easter
Sunday)

10.30am - 5.00pm

Tel: 01726 814389
Fax: 01726 812438

PAR, CORNWALL PL24 2SJ

Owner: Mr. T.C. Hudson   *Contact: Mr. T.C. Hudson*

Large woodland garden created since early 19th century by the Carlyon family, concentrating on species from warm-temperate regions. Fine glasshouses range in walled garden. Small nursery also open by appointment, specialising in wild source material, and the Tregrehan Camellias. Tea available. Parking for cars and coaches. Self catering accommodation available.

Location: 2 miles E of St. Austell. $^1/_2$ mile W of St. Blazey on A390.

Admission: Adult £2.50, Child Free.

TRENGWAINTON GARDEN

OPEN

1 Mar - 31 Oct

Wed - Sat & Bank
Holiday Mondays

10.30am - 5.30pm.

N.B.Closes 5pm
in March and
October.

Last admission
$^1/_2$ hour before
closing.

Tel: 01736 68410
during opening
hours
or   01736 63021

PENZANCE, CORNWALL TR20 8RZ

Owner: The National Trust   *Contact: The Agent*

This large shrub garden, with views over Mount's Bay, is a beautiful place throughout the year and a plantsman's delight. The walled gardens have many tender plants which cannot be grown in the open anywhere else in England.

Location: 2m NW of Penzance, $^1/_2$ mile W of Heamoor on Penzance-Morvah road (B3312) , $^1/_2$ mile off St. Just road (A3071).

Admission: Adult: £2.90.

TRELISSICK GARDEN

FEOCK, TRURO, CORNWALL TR3 6QL

Owner: The National Trust   *Contact: The Property Manager*

Tel: 01872 862090

The rare shrubs and plants make this large garden attractive in all seasons. There is also an extensive park, and woodland walks beside the river and farmland, with splendid, panoramic views over the Fal Estuary and Falmouth harbour. There is an Art and Craft Gallery by the Home Farm Courtyard.

Location: 4m S of Truro, on both sides of B3289 above King Harry Ferry

Opening Times: 1 Mar - 31 Oct, Mon - Sat 10.30am - 5.30pm (restaurant opens 11am), Sun 12.30 - 5.30pm (restaurant opens 12pm). Closes 5pm in Mar & Oct. Last admission $^1/_2$ hr before closing. Woodland walks open all year.

Admission: £3.80, Family £9.50, Pre-arranged party rate £3.00, £1 car park fee refundable on admission.

TRERICE

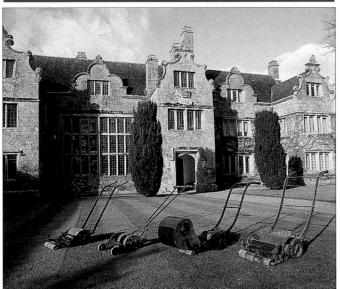

NEWQUAY, CORNWALL TR8 4PG

Owner: The National Trust   *Contact: The Property Manager*

Tel: 01637 875404

Trerice is an architectural gem and something of a rarity - a small Elizabeth manor house hidden away in a web of narrow lanes and still somehow caught in the spirit of its age. An old Arundell house, it escaped the common fate of material alteration over the centuries and has what is possibly the earliest Dutch-style gabled façade in the country. A small barn museum traces the development of the lawn mower.

Location: 3 mls SE of Newquay via the A392 & A3058 (turn right at Kestle Mill).

Opening Times: 1 Apr - 31 Oct: Daily except Tues, 11am - 5.30pm. Closes 5pm in October. Last admission $^1/_2$ hour before closing.

Admission: £3.80. Pre-arranged parties £3.00.

KEY TO SYMBOLS: THE NATIONAL TRUST   ENGLISH HERITAGE   HISTORIC HOUSES ASSOCIATION

TRESCO ABBEY GARDENS

OPEN

All year
10.00am - 4.00pm

Tel: 01720 422849

ISLES OF SCILLY, CORNWALL PL28 8RP

Owner: Mr. R A and Mrs L A Dorrien-Smith   *Contact: Mr. M.A Nelhams*

Tresco Abbey built by Augustus Smith has been the family home since 1834. The garden here flourishes on the small island. Nowhere else in the British Isles does such an exotic collection of plants grow in the open. Agaves, Aloes, Proteas and Acacias from such places as Australia, South Africa, Mexico and the Mediterranean grow within the secure embrace of massive Holm Oak hedges. Valhall Ships Figurehead Museum.

Location: Isles of Scilly. Isles of Scilly Steamship 01720 422849. B.I.H. Helicopters 01736 463871. Details of day trips on application.

Admission: Adult £4, Child under 14 Free. Weekly ticket £10. Guided group tours available.

TREWITHEN   See page 30 for full page entry.

TRURO CATHEDRAL

Tel: 01872 76782   **Fax:** 01872 77788

Truro, Cornwall, TR1 2AH

Contact: The Visitors Officer

Truro Cathedral was the first Anglican cathedral to be built on a new site since mediavel times. It is a perfect example of a Gothic Cathedral. The architect was J.L. Pearson. The Victorian stained glass is considered to be the finest in England. The famous Father Willis organ was installed during the building of the cathedral, and uniquely, has remained unchanged. The Cathedral has a licensed refectory and shop.

Location: Truro city centre.

Opening Times: 7.30am - 6.30pm. Sunday services: 8.00am, 9.00am, 10.00am and 6.00pm. Weekday services: 7.30am, 8.00am and 5.30pm.

Where to Stay

For Private Accommodation and Johansens recommended Hotels, see Accommodation Section.

St. Michael's Mount.

SPECIAL EVENTS

◇ **MOUNT EDGCUMBE**   **16 – 17 MARCH**
Camellia Show in conjunction with International Camellia Society. Competition classes; nursery stands; sales.

◇ **MOUNT EDGCUMBE**   **23 MARCH**
Garden archaeology conference: local and national speakers

◇ **MOUNT EDGCUMBE**   **21 – 23 JUNE**
Floral Celebration - Flowers in the House, Orangery, Temples, Grottoes, on the ferry !

◇ **TRURO CATHEDRAL**   **26 JUNE – 6 JULY**
3 Spires Music Festival

◇ **MOUNT EDGCUMBE**   **7 – 8 SEPTEMBER**
A Wood Fair: in conjunction with Sylvanus Trust. Woodland management, forestry demonstrations, craft, environmental, renewable resources.

For National Trust and English Heritage Events see separate section.

BRANTWOOD
Coniston

BRANTWOOD is the most beautifully situated house in the Lake District. It enjoys the finest lake and mountain views in England, and no other house in the district has such diverse literary and artistic associations.

The home of John Ruskin from 1872 until 1900, Brantwood became an intellectual powerhouse and one of the foremost cultural centres in Europe. Tolstoy, Mahatma Gandhi, Proust and William Morris can all be counted amongst Ruskin's disciples.

Ruskin was one of the greatest figures of the Victorian age. Poet, artist and critic, he was also a social revolutionary who challenged the moral foundations of 19th century Britain.

Ruskin's ideas came to shape much of our thinking today, and his words are as relevant now as ever they were in his own lifetime.

Brantwood today contains a glorious collection of Ruskin drawings and watercolours, and the house still retains that special feeling which has given inspiration to so many.

GARDENS
In the oakwoods and beside the lake-shore Ruskin created a garden which is under active and imaginative restoration. It is a special place, a true lakeland paradise. The woods in springtime are carpeted with bluebells and the heavy scent of the yellow "azalea luteum" fills the air.

❖

SUITABILITY FOR OTHER EVENTS
The house is spectacularly situated, with magnificent lake and mountain views and lends itself particularly to photographic or film use, but is suitable for a variety of events. Ruskin's wonderful Dining Room has potential for groups of up to 12.

EXTRA FACILITIES
3/4 mile Lakeshore with large pier. 250 acre estate, woodland and moorland. Grand Piano.

ADVICE TO COURIERS & DRIVERS
Coaches have access to Brantwood but the last 1 1/2 miles are a little slow. Parties can come by water from Coniston Pier a delightful approach with good access for coaches. New Ferry service from Coniston. Dogs not allowed in the House.

FACILITIES FOR THE DISABLED
Disabled visitors may alight at the entrance to the property. There are special toilet facilities available.

PARKING FOR COACHES & CARS
75 cars and 2 coaches within 100 yards of the property.

GIFT SHOP
Bookshop and high quality craft gallery.

SCHOOL VISITS/CHILDREN
School visits are welcomed but special facilities are not yet available. Nature and Woodland Walks are of special interest.

GUIDE BOOKS
Colour guide book, £2.50.

CATERING
'Jumping Jenny' Tearooms & Restaurant seating 60. Groups can book in advance but the total capacity cannot be booked during normal opening hours. Menus available on request and prices are very flexible according to requirements, special rates available for groups. Catering facilities available for special functions, conferences etc.

GUIDED TOURS
Visitors are usually free to tour the property at leisure but guided tours can be arranged. The Administrator will meet groups visiting the House. Lectures on the property can be arranged.

CONTACT

J B C Hanson Esq
Brantwood
Coniston
Cumbria
LA21 8AD

Tel: (015394) 41396

LOCATION

Road: M6 Junct. 36, 25 miles, London 5 hours, Edinburgh 3 hours, Chester 2 1/2 hours.

Rail: Windermere Station 14 miles.

Water: Steam Yacht "Gondola" sails regularly to Brantwood from Coniston Pier. New Ferry Service M.V. "Ruskin" sails hourly. (30 mins past the hour).

Taxi: Coniston Taxis (015394) 41683

CONFERENCE AND FUNCTION FACILITIES
Rooms are available but only during the evening in Summer or all day Monday or Tuesday in Winter. The Administrator will participate in Functions and meet groups if required. Full details available upon request.

OPENING TIMES

Summer
Mid March - Mid Nov
Daily: 11.00am - 5.30pm

Winter
Mid Nov - Mid March
Daily: 11.00am - 4.00pm

ADMISSION

All Year
Adult £3.50
Child* . . . . .FREE
*Under 18
Groups
Adult £2.75

DALEMAIN
Penrith

DALEMAIN is a fine mixture of Medieval, Tudor and Early Georgian architecture. The imposing Georgian facade strikes the visitor immediately but in the cobbled courtyard the atmosphere of the North Country Tudor Manor is secure. The present owners family have lived at Dalemain since 1679 and have collected china, furniture and family portraits. Visitors can see the grand Drawing Rooms with 18th century Chinese wallpaper and fine oak panelling, also the Nursery and House-keeper's Room. The Norman Pele Tower contains the regimental collection of the Westmoreland and Cumberland Yeomanry. The House is full of the paraphernalia of a well established family House which is still very much lived in by the family.

The 16th century Great Barn holds a collection of agricultural bygones and a Fell Pony Museum.

GARDENS
The Gardens have a long history stretching back to a medieval Herb Garden. Today a Knot Garden remains, with a fine early Roman fountain and box hedges enclosing herb beds. The imposing terrace wall supports a full and colourful herbaceous border during the summer months. The late Mrs McCosh revitalised the gardens, replanting many of the borders and introducing rare and exotic plants. Visitors can enjoy the fine views of the park and the woodland and riverside walks.

The gardens have been featured on television's 'Gardeners World' and also in 'Country Life'.

CONTACT
Bryan McDonald
Administrator
Dalemain Estate Office
Dalemain
Penrith
Cumbria
CA11 0HB

Tel: (01768) 486450
Fax: (01768) 486223

LOCATION
From London, M1, M6 exit 40: 4 hours.

From Edinburgh, A73, M74, M6 exit 40: 2$^{1}/_{2}$ hrs.

Rail: Penrith 3 miles.

Taxi: Walkers Taxis, Penrith (01768) 862349

OPENING TIMES
Summer
31 March - 6 October
Daily except Fris & Sats
11.15am - 5.00pm

NB. Parties of 15 or more should pre-book.

Winter
Mid October - Easter
Open by special arrangement.

ADMISSION
HOUSE & GARDEN
Adult £4.50
Child* £3.00
Family £12.00
Disabled** . . . . .FREE

Groups***
Adult £3.80
Child* £2.80

* Under 16 years.
** Disabled in wheelchair.
*** Min. 12 Adults

All Prices include VAT.

SUITABILITY FOR OTHER EVENTS
Fashion shows, archery, clay pigeon shooting, garden parties, rallies, filming, caravan rallies, antique fairs and children's camps. Business Meetings and Conferences with limited numbers during closed season.

EXTRA FACILITIES
Grand piano, parkland and Lake District National Park are available for use. Lectures on the House, contents, gardens and history can be arranged for up to 60 people. Cost for hire of room and lecture on request. Deer Park.

ADVICE TO COURIERS & DRIVERS
Parties of 20 or more must pre-book. Allow 2 hours to see Dalemain. No dogs. Parking for 100 cars and 30 coaches, 50 yards from the House. No photography in the House.

FACILITIES FOR THE DISABLED
Disabled or elderly visitors may alight at the entrance prior to parking in the allocated areas. There are toilet facilities for the disabled. Free admission for disabled visitors in wheelchairs.

GUIDED TOURS
German and French translations in every room. Tours take 1 hour approx. Garden Tour for parties extra.

CATERING (SELF SERVICE)
Licensed Restaurant/Tea Room seats 60. Prices and menus on request. Groups should pre-book for lunches and high teas. Catering available for special functions/conferences.

GIFT SHOP
Items include local crafts, house souvenirs, fine china, high quality gifts, postcards, stamps etc. Surplus plants on sale in the courtyard and collection of old-fashioned roses in conjunction with Stydd Nurseries are also available for sale.

GUIDE BOOK
Colour guide £2.00.

SCHOOL VISITS/CHILDREN
School groups are welcome and guides can be provided. The house has much to interest children of all ages. Military, Country Life, Agricultural and Fell Pony Museums. Pleasant country walk past Dacre Castle to St Andrews Church, Dacre, where there is a fine Laurence Whistler window.

CONFERENCE AND FUNCTION FACILITIES

ROOM	DIMENSIONS	CAPACITY	LAYOUT	POWER POINTS	SUITABLE FOR A/V
Dining Room		40	Theatre	3	✓
		15	Boardroom	3	✓
Old Hall		50	Buffet	4	✓
		50	Lunch/Dinner	4	✓

HOLKER HALL
Grange-over-Sands

HOLKER HALL, home of Lord and Lady Cavendish, shows the confidence, spaciousness and prosperity of Victorian style on its grandest scale. The New Wing, built by the 7th Duke of Devonshire (1871-4), replaced a previous wing totally destroyed by fire. Workmanship throughout is of the highest quality, particularly the detailed interior carving and linenfold panelling.

Despite this grand scale, Holker is very much a family home. Visitors can wander freely throughout the New Wing. Photographs, beautiful floral displays and bowls of scented pot pourri create the warm and friendly atmosphere so often remarked upon by visitors. Varying in period and style, Louis XV pieces happily mix with the Victorian. Pictures range from an early copy of the famous triple portrait of Charles I by Van Dyck to a modern painting by Douglas Anderson.

GARDENS

Christies/HHA Garden of the Year (1991), includes formal and woodland areas covering 24 acres. Designated "amongst the best in the world in terms of design and content" by the Good Gardens Guide. This wonderful Italianate-cum-English Garden includes a limestone cascade, a fountain, a rose garden and many rare and beautiful plants and shrubs. Holker is also home to the Great Garden and Countryside Festival held on the first weekend in June.

❖

CONTACT

Mrs Carolyn Johnson
Holker Hall & Gardens
Cark-in-Cartmel
Grange-over-Sands
Cumbria
LA11 7PL

Tel: (015395) 58328

Fax: (015395) 58776

LOCATION

From Kendal, A6, A590, B5277, B5278: 16 mls.

Motorway: M6 Junct. 36

Bus: From Grange-over-Sands

Rail: To Cark-in-Cartmel.

Taxi: Parkers Motors, Grange-over-Sands. Nelsons Garage, Cark-in-Cartmel.

SUITABILITY FOR OTHER EVENTS
Filming and still photography. Promotion venues include: limestone escarpments and quarries.

EXTRA FACILITIES
Deer Park and Discovery Walks. Lakeland Motor Museum, adventure playground and exhibitions.

ADVICE TO COURIERS & DRIVERS
No dogs in Gardens or Hall. No photography in Hall.

FACILITIES FOR THE DISABLED
Disabled and elderly visitors may be dropped at the entrance. There are unisex toilet facilities for the disabled. Ramps where necessary.

PARKING FOR COACHES & CARS
Capacity of the car park, 50+ cars and 12 coaches, 100-150 yards from Hall. Plus grass car parking.

CATERING
The Clocktower Cafeteria (capacity 120), is a self-service café, selling salads, hot and cold sandwiches, home made cakes and beverages (including wine by the glass and canned beer and lager).

GUIDED TOURS
Tours of Hall available at additional cost of 50p per person: must be pre-booked.

GIFT SHOP
Open 10.30am - 5.30pm, same days as the Hall, wide range of gifts from toys to fine china.

GUIDE BOOKS
Colour guide book, £2.00. Translations available in French, Spanish and German. Children's Guide 75p. Guide to the Woodland Gardens by Lord Cavendish.

SCHOOL VISITS/CHILDREN
Environmental study day for primary school children, cost per child from £2.00. Holker is the holder of two Sandford Awards for Heritage Education. Holker provides a wide range of educational opportunities for primary aged children to fit in with curriculum requirements i.e: Houses & Home; Technology & Design; Structures; Victorians.

OPENING TIMES

Summer
1 April - 31 October

Daily except Saturdays
10.00am - 6.00pm

NB Last admission 4.30pm

Winter
1 November - 31 March
Closed

ADMISSION

Summer   1995 prices
HOUSE & GARDEN
Adult £4.95
Child £2.95

Groups
Adult £3.35
OAP £3.10
Child £2.40

MUNCASTER CASTLE
Ravenglass

MUNCASTER CASTLE has been owned by the Pennington family since 1208. It has grown from the original pele tower built on Roman foundations to the impressive structure visible today. Outstanding features are the Great Hall and Salvin's octagonal library and the Drawing Room with its barrel ceiling.

The Castle contains many treasures including beautiful furniture, exquisite needlework panels, tapestries and oriental rugs. The family silver is very fine and is accompanied in the Dining Room by the Ongley Service, the most ornamental set of porcelain ever created by the Derby factory, Florentine 16th century bronzes and an alabaster lady by Giambologna can be seen. The Castle has 3 ghosts. All the rooms open to the public are lived in by the family who are actively involved in entertaining their many visitors.

The woodland gardens cover 77 acres and command spectacular views of the Lakeland Fells, with many delightful walks. From mid March to June the rhododendrons, azaleas, camellias and magnolias are at their best.

The Owl Centre boasts a fine collection of owls from all over the world. 'Meet the Birds' occurs daily at 2.30pm (24th March to 3rd November), when a talk is given on the work of the centre. Weather permitting the birds fly.

SUITABILITY FOR OTHER EVENTS
Muncaster provides a backdrop for fashion shoots, garden parties, filming, clay pigeon shooting and wedding receptions.

EXTRA FACILITIES
Lectures can be arranged on the property, its contents, gardens and history. By prior arrangement a grand piano can be hired.

ADVICE TO COURIERS & DRIVERS
For groups, please apply for information pack and book in advance to qualify for discounts. No photography or filming inside castle. Free parking for 500 cars 800 yds from the House. Coaches and disabled visitors may park closer.

FACILITIES FOR THE DISABLED
Toilets, wheelchair for loan. Special tapes available for Walkman tour for the partially sighted or those with learning difficulties. Disabled and elderly visitors may alight near to Castle.

OWL CENTRE
Home of the World Owl Trust run by TV naturalist Tony Warburton.

GIFT SHOPS & PLANT CENTRE
Open daily 24th March to 3rd November 11am to 5pm selling a wide variety of gifts and plants. Colour guide book available.

GUIDED TOURS
All castle visitors are offered a Sony Walkman individual tour narrated by the family that lasts 40 mins (included in the entry price). Private tours with a personal guide (option family member) can be organised for an additional fee.

CATERING
The Stables Buttery caters for up to 80 with a full menu. Groups may book meals in advance (01229) 717432. Catering in the Castle can also be arranged (01229) 717614.

SCHOOL VISITS/CHILDREN
School visits are welcome and guides are provided if required. Cost per child £2.20. Historical subjects from the Romans to W.W.II. Special work sheets available.

CONTACT

Peter Frost-Pennington
Muncaster Castle
Ravenglass
Cumbria
CA18 1RQ

Tel: (01229) 717614
Fax: (01229) 717010

LOCATION

From London 6 hrs,
Chester 2 $^{1}/_{2}$ hrs
Edinburgh 3 $^{1}/_{2}$ hrs
M6 exit 36, A590,
A595 (from south).
M6 exit 40, A66, A595
(from east). Carlisle,
A595 (from north).

Rail: Ravenglass
(on Barrow-in-Furness-
Carlisle Line) 1$^{1}/_{2}$ mls.

OPENING TIMES

Summer
24 March - 3 November

CASTLE
Daily except Mons
(but open Mon Bank Hols.)
1.00 - 4.00pm
Last entry: 4.00pm

GARDENS AND
OWL CENTRE
Daily: 11.00am - 5.00pm

Winter
CASTLE Closed.
Open by appointment
for groups.

GARDENS AND OWL
CENTRE
Daily: 11.00am - 5.00pm

ADMISSION

1996 provisional prices.

CASTLE, GARDENS &
OWL CENTRE
  Adult £5.00
  Child* £3.00
  Family (2+2) . .£14.00
Groups**
  Adult £4.00
  Child* £2.50
Season Tickets
  Adult £12.50
  Family (2+3) . . .£28.00

GARDENS & OWL
CENTRE
  Adult £3.50
  Child* £2.00
  Family (2+2) £9.00
Groups
  Adult £3.00
  Child* £1.50

* Aged 5 - 15 years;
  Under fives free.
**Min payment £40.

CONFERENCE AND FUNCTION FACILITIES

ROOM	DIMENSIONS	CAPACITY	LAYOUT	POWER POINTS	SUITABLE FOR A/V
Drawing Room	–	120	Theatre	6+	✓
Dining Room	–	30 / 70	Various	2+	✓
Family Dining Room	–	45	Boardroom/Dinner	4	
		45	Theatre		
Great Hall	–	110	Various	6	✓

NAWORTH CASTLE
Brampton

NAWORTH CASTLE is a historic Border fortress built by the Dacre family in 1335. Originally a strong-hold for the wardens of the West March and subsequently an impressive residence for the powerful Earls of Carlisle. Now owned by Philip Howard. Much pre-Raphaelite restoration by Philip Webb and Burne-Jones following the 1844 fire. Dungeons and 17th century walled garden.

Rooms include the Great Hall, 100ft in length with Gobelin Tapestries and four heraldic Beasts. The Philip Webb Library for conferences, lectures and corporate functions. The Drawing Room for dining parties up to 50. The Old Library with a Marriage Licence and corporate function use. The Long Gallery for art exhibitions and Lord Williams Tower with a Bridal Suite, Old Library and Chapel.

The Castle is in its second year of being a functions venue and takes pride in being able to offer an exceptional standard of service.

❖

CONTACT

Philip Howard (Owner)
Colleen Hall (Function
Co-ordinator)
Naworth Castle
Brampton
Cumbria CA8 2HE

Tel: (01697) 73229
Fax: (01697) 73679

LOCATION

$1/2$ mile off main A69 Carlisle - Newcastle road. Carlisle 12 m. Newcastle 46m. M6 is 9 miles.

Rail: Carlisle, Brampton Junction 2 miles.

Air: Carlisle Airport (private planes 6m). Newcastle 50 minutes. Manchester and Glasgow 2 hours.

SUITABILITY FOR OTHER EVENTS
WEDDINGS: The Great Hall seats up to 200. We are licenced for marriage ceremonies and have a drinks licence.

EXTRA FACILITIES
We hold conferences, fashion shoots, recitals & concerts, film shoots, charity events, antique sales & fairs, charity balls, dinners /dances, game and clay pigeon shooting, fishing and horse riding.

ACCOMMODATION
There are ten bedrooms available for overnight parties.

ADVICE TO COURIERS & DRIVERS
Contact Colleen Hall. 40 space car park and 10 acres of field.

CATERING
There is an excellent retained caterer available.

CONFERENCE AND FUNCTION FACILITIES

ROOM	DIMENSIONS	CAPACITY (seated)	LAYOUT	POWER POINTS	SUITABLE FOR A/V
The Great Hall		200	Various	✓	✓
Philip Webb Library		50	Various	✓	✓
The Drawing Room		50	Lunch/Dinner	✓	✓
The Old Library		75	Various	✓	✓
The Long Gallery			60/75 (standing)	✓	✓

ABBOT HALL ART GALLERY

Tel: 01539 722464   **Fax:** 01539 722494

Kirkland, Kendal, Cumbria LA9 5AL
Owner: Lake District Art Gallery & Museum Trust   **Contact:** Mr E King
Georgian house with good portraits and furniture displayed in restored rooms.
Location: Kirkland, Kendal, Cumbria, LA9 5AL
Opening Times: 1 Apr - 31 Oct: Daily 10.30am - 5pm. 1 Nov - 31 Mar: Daily 10.30am -
4pm. Closed mid December to mid February.
Admission: Adult £2.50, Child/Student £1.00, OAP £1.90, Family £6.00.

ACORN BANK GARDEN ✿

Tel: 017683 61893

Temple Sowerby, Penrith, Cumbria CA10 1SP
Owner: The National Trust   **Contact:** The Administrator
A 2½ acre garden protected by fine oaks under which grow a vast display of daffodils.
Inside the walls there are two orchards containing a variety of fruit trees. Surrounding the
orchards are mixed borders with shrubs, herbaceous plants and roses, while the
impressive herb garden has the largest collection of culinary and medicinal plants in the
north. A circular woodland walk runs beside the Crowdundle Beck; the mill is under
restoration, but not yet open to visitors. The house is let to the Sue Ryder Foundation and
is not open to the public.
Location: Just N of Temple Sowerby, 6m E of Penrith on A66.
Opening Times: 1 Apr - 31 Oct: 10.00am - 5.30pm, last admission 5.00pm.
Admission: Adult £1.70, Child 80p, pre-arranged party £1.10.

APPLEBY CASTLE

Tel: 017683 51402   **Fax:** 017683 51082

Appleby-in-Westmorland, Cumbria CA16 6XH
Owner: Ferguson International Holdings Plc   **Contact:** Tessa Edwards
27 acres of beautiful riverside grounds. Fine 11th century Norman keep and Great Hall of
the house. Large collection of birds; wildfowl, parakeets, owls and rare breeds of farm
animals in the grounds. Gift Shop, Café & Tea room; children's Tarzan Trail. Picnic areas.
Location: Situated on A66 Scotch Corner to Penrith trunk road. 11 miles SE of J38/40.
Opening Times: 30 Mar - 29 Sept: Daily 10am - 5pm and then daily 10am - 4pm to the
end of Oct. Winter months by appointment only.
Admission: Adult £4.00, Child (5-15) £2.00, OAP £2.00, Family (2+2) £10.00. Groups of
20+: Adult £3.00, Child £1.50, OAP £1.50, Driver free + free tea. School parties (excluding
Great Hall): Adults & Teachers £2.50, Children £1.25. One Teacher free per 15 pupils.
Season tickets: Adult £20.00, Child £10.00.

BEATRIX POTTER GALLERY ✿

Copyright © Frederick Warne & Co. 1904, 1987.

**MAIN STREET, HAWKSHEAD,
CUMBRIA LA22 0NS**
Owner: The National Trust
Contact: Miss F Clark
Tel: 01539 436355
An annually changing exhibition
of Beatrix Potter's original
illustrations from her children's
story books. One of the many
historic buildings in the picturesque village of Hawkshead,
the gallery was once the office of
her husband, the solicitor William
Heelis, and the interior remains
largely unaltered since his day.
Location: In the Square,
Hawkshead.
Admission: Adult £2.60, Child
£1.30. No reduction for parties.

OPEN

1 Apr - 3 November: Sun - Thur
(closed Fri and Sat except Good Fri)
10.30am - 4.30pm. Last admission
4.00pm. Admission is by timed ticket
including NT members.

BEATRIX POTTER'S LAKE DISTRICT ✿

A MULTI-MEDIA PRESENTATION
✿ The National Trust

**PACKHORSE COURT,
KESWICK,
CUMBRIA CA12 5JB**
Owner: The National Trust
Contact: Mrs A Evans

Tel: 01768 775173

Peter Rabbit is only part of the
Tale! 16 minute dramatic slide
and video presentations bring
to life Beatrix Potter's most
important achievement: her
'saving' of 2429.15 ha. of the
Lake District and her careful
and sensitive conservation of
this magnificent area on behalf
of the Nation, which is continued by the National Trust.
Location: In the centre of
Keswick, signposted within
Packhorse Court.
Admission: Adult £2.50, Child
£1.30. Discount for NT
Members. Family ticket £7.00.
Pre-arranged parties: Adult
£2.15, Child £1.00.

OPEN

April - June Sept and Oct: Daily 10.00am - 5.00pm.
July and August:: Daily 10.00am - 5.30pm.
November - March: Weekends 12 noon - 4.00pm

BRANTWOOD

See page 36 for full page entry.

BROUGH CASTLE ⊞

Tel: 01912 611585

Brough, Cumbria.
Owner: English Heritage   **Contact:** The North Regional Office
Perched on a superb vantage point overlooking an old trade route, now the A66, this
ancient site dates back to Roman times. The 12th century keep replaced an earlier strong-
hold destroyed by the Scots in 1174. The castle was restored by Lady Anne Clifford in the
17th century.
Location: 8m SE of Appleby S of A66.
Opening Times: Any reasonable time.

BROUGHAM CASTLE ⊞

Tel: 01768 862488

Penrith, Cumbria CA10 2AA
Owner: English Heritage   **Contact:** The Custodian
These impressive ruins on the banks of the River Eamont include an early 13th century
keep and later buildings. You can climb to the top of the keep and survey the domain of
its eccentric one time owner Lady Anne Clifford, who restored the castle in the 17th
century. There is a small exhibition of Roman tombstones from the nearby fort.
Location: 1½m SE of Penrith on minor road off A66.
Opening Times: 1 Apr - 30 Sept: 10am - 6pm. 1 - 31 Oct: 10am - 6pm or dusk if earlier.
Admission: Adult £1.50, Child 80p, Conc £1.10.

CARLISLE CASTLE ⊞

Tel: 01228 591922

Carlisle, Cumbria CA3 8UR
Owner: English Heritage   **Contact:** The Custodian
This impressive medieval castle, where Mary Queen of Scots was once imprisoned, has a
long and tortuous history of warfare and family feuds. A portcullis hangs menacingly over
the gatehouse passage, there is a maze of passages and chambers, endless staircases to
lofty towers and you can walk the high ramparts for stunning views. There is also a
medieval manor house in miniature: a suite of medieval rooms furnished as they might
have been when used by the castle's former constable. The castle is also the home of the
Museum of the King's Own Border Regiment (included in the admission price).
Location: N of Carlisle town centre.
Opening Times: 1 Apr - 30 Sept: Daily 9.30am - 6pm. 1 Oct - 31 Mar: Daily 10am - 4pm
(10am - 6pm or dusk if earlier in October). Closed 24-26 Dec, 1 Jan.
Admission: Adult £2.50, Child £1.30, Conc £1.90.

CARLISLE CATHEDRAL

Tel: 01228 48151

Carlisle, Cumbria CA3 8TZ

     Contact: Ms C Baines
Fine sandstone Cathedral, founded in 1122. Medieval stained glass. Carvings and painted
wall panels. Treasury with displays of silver, diocesan and cathedral treasures.
Location: Carlisle city centre, 2m from junction 43 of M6.
Opening Times: 7.45am - 6.15pm daily. Closes 4.00pm between Christmas Day and New
Year. Sunday services: 8.00am, 10.30am and 3.00pm. Weekday services: 8.00am, 12.30pm
and 5.30pm and a 12.30 service on Wednesdays, Fridays and Saints Days.
Admission: Donation.

CONISHEAD PRIORY

Tel: 01229 584029 **Fax:** 01229 580080

Ulverston, Cumbria LA12 9QQ
Owner: Manjushri Mahayana Buddhist Centre   **Contact:** Mr R Tyson
A Victorian Gothic mansion on site of a medieval Augustinian Priory. Now a major Buddhist Centre and under restoration. It has fine plaster ceilings, stained glass windows, a cantilever staircase, an Oak Room, vaulted hall and cloister. Private woodland walk to Morecambe Bay.
Location: 2 m S of Ulverston on Bardsea Coast Rd A5087.
Opening Times: Easter - Sept, w/e & Bank Hols, 2 - 5pm. Closed 25/27 May, 22/23 July, 29/30 Jul, 5/6 Aug, 12/13 Aug.
Admission: Free. House tours and audio visual: Adult £2.00, Conc. £1.00, Child 75p.

DALEMAIN

See Page 37 for full page entry.

DOVE COTTAGE & WORDSWORTH MUSEUM

Tel: 015394 35544/35547   **Fax:** 01539 435748
Grasmere, Cumbria LA22 9SH
Owner: Wordsworth Trust   **Contact:** Sylvia Wordsworth
Dove Cottage, Wordsworth's home 1799 - 1808. Guided Tours. Garden open weather permitting. Award-winning Wordsworth Museum houses permanent exhibition and a programme of special exhibitions. Book & Gift shop, Teashop. Reciprocal discount with Rydal Mount and Wordsworth House, Cockermouth.
Location: Main car park on A591 Kendal/Keswick road, next to Dove Cottage Teashop.
Opening Times: Daily 9.30am - 5.30pm. Last adm. 5pm. Closed: 8 Jan - 4 Feb & 24 - 26 Dec.
Admission: Adult £4.00, Child £2.00, Family ticket from £6.00. Adult group rate £3.20.

FURNESS ABBEY

Tel: 01229 823420

Barrow-in-Furness, Cumbria LH13 0TJ
Owner: English Heritage   **Contact:** The Custodian
Hidden in a peaceful green valley are the beautiful red sandstone remains of the wealthy abbey founded in 1123 by Stephen, later King of England. This abbey first belonged to the Order of Savigny and later to the Cistercians. There is a museum and exhibition.
Location: 1¹/₂m N of Barrow-in-Furness on minor road off A590.
Opening Times: 1 Apr - 30 Sept: Daily 10am - 6pm. 1 Oct - 31 Oct: Daily 10am - 6pm or dusk if earlier, 1 Nov - 31 Mar: Wed - Sun, 10am - 4pm (Closed lunch 1 - 2pm Nov - Mar).
Admission: Adult £2.30, Child £1.20, Conc £1.70.

HARDKNOTT ROMAN FORT

Tel: 01912 611585

Ravenglass, Cumbria.
Owner: English Heritage   **Contact:** The North Regional Office
One of the most dramatic sites in Britain, with stunning views across the Lakeland fells. This fort, built between AD120 and 138, controlled the road from Ravenglass to Ambleside. There are visible remains of granaries, the headquarters buildings and the commandant's house, with a bath house and parade ground outside the fort.
Location: 9m NE of Ravenglass, at W end of Hardknott Pass.
Opening Times: Any reasonable time. Access may be hazardous in winter.
Admission: Free

HERON CORN MILL & MUSEUM OF PAPERMAKING

Tel: 01539 563363

c/o Henry Cooke, Waterhouse Mills, Beetham, Milnthorpe, Cumbria LA7 7AR
Owner: Heron Corn Mill Beetham Trust   **Contact:** Mr Neil Stobbs
Location: 1m south of Milnthorpe on the A6.
Opening Times: Easter 1 Apr - 30 Sept: Tues - Sun & Bank Hol Mons. 11am - 5pm .
Admission: Adult £1.25, Child 80p, Family £4 (2+2), OAPs 80p, Coach parties/Groups 10% discount if pre-booked.

HILLTOP

Tel: 01539 436269

Near Sawrey, Ambleside, Cumbria LA22 0LF
Owner: The National Trust   **Contact:** The Administrator
Beatrix Potter wrote many Peter Rabbit books in this little 17th century house, which contains her furniture and china.
Location: 2m S of Hawkshead, in hamlet of Near Sawrey, behind the Tower Bank Arms.
Opening Times: 1 Apr - 3 Nov: Sat - Wed & Good Fri, 11am - 5pm. Last adm: 4.30pm.
Admission: Adult £3.40, Child £1.70, no reduction for parties.

HOLEHIRD

Tel: 01539 446008

Patterdale Road, Windermere, Cumbria LA23 1NP
Owner: Lakeland Horticultural Society   **Contact:** The Hon. Secretary
3¹/₂ acres of hillside gardens overlooking Troutbeck Valley, with magnificent views of Windermere lake and fells, including a walled garden and national collection of astilbes, hydrangeas and polystichum ferns. All of the work in the gardens is done by volunteers.
Location: On A592, ³/₄m N of junction with A591.
Opening Times: All year, dawn to dusk.
Admission: By donation, suggestion of £1.00 per adult.

HOLKER HALL

See Page 38 for full page entry.

HUTTON-IN-THE-FOREST

OPEN
House:
Easter 7 - 11 Apr
2 May - 29 Sept
Thurs, Fris, Suns
Bank Hols & Weds
in August.
1 - 4pm
Tearoom:
As house
12 noon - 4.30pm
Grounds:
Daily except Sats.
11am - 5pm
Tel: 01768 484449
Fax: 01768 484571

PENRITH, CUMBRIA CA11 9TH
Owner: **Lord Inglewood**   *Contact:* **Edward Thompson**

The home of Lord Inglewood's family since 1605. Built around a medieval pele tower with 17th, 18th and 19th century additions. Fine collections of furniture and paintings, ceramics and tapestries. Outstanding gardens and grounds with terraces, walled garden, dovecote, lake and woodland walk through magnificent specimen trees. Tearoom with giftstall. Picnic area. Dogs on leads are welcome in the grounds.
Location: 7 miles NW of Penrith and 2¹/₂ miles from exit 41/M6 on B5305.
Admission: House, Gardens & Grounds: Adult £3.50, Child £1.50, Family £9.00. Gardens & Grounds: Adult £2.00, Child Free.

LANERCOST PRIORY

Tel: 01697 73030

Brampton, Cumbria CA8 2HQ
Owner: English Heritage   **Contact:** The Custodian
This Augustinian priory was founded c.1166. The nave of the church, which is intact and in use as the local parish church, contrasts with the ruined chancel, transepts and priory buildings.
Location: Off minor road S of Lanercost, 2m NE of Brampton.
Opening Times: 1 Apr - 30 Sept: 10am - 6pm. 1 - 31 Oct 10am - 6pm or dusk if earlier.
Admission: Adult £1.00, Child 50p, Conc 80p.

LEVENS HALL

OPEN
Garden:
1 Apr - 30 Sept.
Sun - Thur
11am - 5pm
House:
12 noon - 5pm
Mon - Thur
Last admission
4.30pm
Steam Collection
2 - 5pm.
Tel: 01539 560321

KENDAL, CUMBRIA LA8 0PD
Owner: **C H Bagot Esq**   *Contact:* **P Milner**

This Elizabethan mansion contains a fine collection of Jacobean furniture, panelled interiors, plasterwork, Cordova leather wall coverings and the earliest English patchwork. The world famous topiary garden was laid out in 1694 by Monsieur Beaumont and has since remained largely unaltered. Garden lovers will appreciate the colourful spring and summer bedding together with many unusual herbaceous plants. In addition there is a working collection of model steam engines. Winner of the HHA/Christies Garden of the Year Award 1994.
Location: 5 miles south of Kendal on the A6 (M6 exit 36).
Admission: House & Garden: Adult £4.80, Child £2.50
Garden: Adult £3.50, Child £1.80

LINGHOLM GARDENS

Tel: 01768 772003

Lingholm, Keswick, Cumbria CA12 5UA
Owner: Viscount Rochdale   **Contact:** Owner
40 acres of formal terraces and woodland gardens. Renowned for spectacular rhododendrons, azaleas, blue poppies and specimen trees and shrubs. Spring bulbs, herbaceous borders and autumn colours in magnificent mountain setting. Excellent plant centre. Home cooking in tearoom with scenic verandah. Disabled facilities.
Location: Signposted 1m S of Portinscale village, off A66 West of Keswick.
Opening Times: 1 Apr - 31 Oct: Daily 10am - 5pm.
Admission: Adult £2.70, accompanied children free. Group rates on request.

MIREHOUSE

OPEN
Grounds:
Mar & Nov open
each weekend.
Apr - Oct: Daily
10.30am - 5.30pm
House:
Suns, Weds
(also Fris in Aug)
2pm - last entry
at 4.30pm. At other
times throughout the
year by appointment

Tel: 01768 772287
Fax: 01768 772287

KESWICK, CUMBRIA CA12 4QE
Owner: *John Spedding Esq.*　　**Contact:** *Clare Spedding*

Built in 1666, this family home has passed by descent since 1688. Interesting literary and artistic associations. Well illustrated by paintings, old photography, books and manuscripts. Live piano music. Grounds include the Walled Bee Garden, walks by Bassenthwaite Lake, four adventure playgrounds. Access to 10th century church of St Bega. French, German, Spanish spoken. Children particularly welcome. Full facilities for people with disabilities.
Location: Beside A591, 3½ miles north of Keswick.
Admission: House & Grounds: Adult £3.20, Child £1.60. Grounds: Adult £1.20, Child 80p (10% reduction for pre-booked groups of 20 plus).

SIZERGH CASTLE

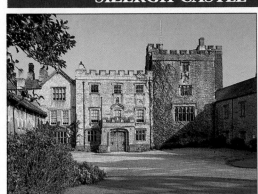

OPEN
1 Apr - 31 Oct
Sunday - Thursday

Castle:
1.30 - 5.30pm

Garden:
Dates as castle
12.30pm - 5.30pm

Last admission
5.00pm.

Tel: 01539 560070

SIZERGH, NR. KENDAL, CUMBRIA LA8 8AE
Owner: *The National Trust*　　**Contact:** *Mr Brian Doling*

The Strickland family have lived here for more than 750 years. The impressive 14th century pele tower was extended in Tudor times, with some of the finest Elizabethan carved overmantels in the country. Contents include good English and French furniture and family portraits. The castle is surrounded by gardens of beauty and interest.
Location: 3½ miles south of Kendal, north west of the A590/A591 interchange.
Admission: Adult £3.30, Child £1.70, Family ticket £9.00. Garden only: £1.70 Parties of 15+ £2.50, by arrangement.

MUNCASTER CASTLE 　　　　　　**See Page 39 for full page entry.**

MUNCASTER WATER MILL　　　　　　**Tel:** 01229 717232

Ravenglass, Cumbria CA18 1ST
Owner: R Park Esq　　　　　　**Contact:** R Park Esq
Old Manorial Mill with 13ft overshot wheel and all milling equipment.
Location: 1m N of Ravenglass on A595.
Opening Times: Jun - May: Daily 10.30am - 5.30pm. Apr - May & Sept - Oct 11am - 5.30pm.
Admission: Adult £1.20, Child 60p, Family £3.00.

NAWORTH CASTLE　　　　　　**See page 40 for full page entry.**

PENRITH CASTLE 　　　　　　**Tel:** 01912 611585

Penrith, Cumbria
Owner: English Heritage　　　　　　**Contact:** The North Regional Office
This 14th century castle, set in a park on the edge of the town, was built to defend Penrith against repeated attacks by Scottish raiders.
Location: Opposite Penrith railway station.
Opening Times: Park opening hours.

RYDAL MOUNT 　　**Tel:** 01539 433002　**Fax:** 01539 431738

Ambleside, Cumbria LA22 9LU
Owner: Rydal Mount Trustees　　　　　　**Contact:** Mr & Mrs P Elkington
The historic house of William Wordsworth from 1813 until his death in 1850, now the family home of his descendants. It contains family portraits and his personal possessions. The extensive garden, landscaped by the poet, includes terraces, rare shrubs, trees and the poet's summerhouse which overlooks beautiful Rydal Water.
Location: 1½ miles from Ambleside on A591 Grasmere Road.
Opening Times: Mar - Oct 9.30am - 5pm, Nov - Feb 10am - 4pm. Closed Tuesdays in winter months.
Admission: Adult £3.00, Child £1.00, OAPs/Students £2.50, Groups £2.50 (10+). Garden only: £1.50. Free parking. Reciprocal discount ticket with Dove Cottage and Wordsworth House.

STAGSHAW GARDEN 　　　　　　**Tel:** 015394 35599

Ambleside, Cumbria LA22 0HE
Owner: The National Trust　　　　　　**Contact:** The Administrator
This woodland garden was created by the late Cubby Acland, Regional Agent for the National Trust. It contains a fine collection of azaleas and rhododendrons, planted to give good blends of colour under the thinned oaks on the hillside; also many trees and shrubs, including magnolias, camellias and embothriums.
Location: ½m S of Ambleside on A591.
Opening Times: 1 Apr - end Jun: Daily 10am - 6.30pm. Jul - end Oct: by appointment.
Admission: £1.00, no reduction for parties.

STEAM YACHT GONDOLA 　　　　　　**Tel:** 01539 441288

Pier Cottage, Coniston, Cumbria LA21 8AJ
Owner: The National Trust　　　　　　**Contact:** The Manager
The Steam Yacht Gondola, first launched in 1859 and now completely renovated by the Trust, provides a steam-powered passenger service, carrying 86 passengers in opulently upholstered saloons. A superb way to see Coniston's scenery.
Location: Coniston village (½ mile to Coniston Pier).
Opening Times: 30 March - 3 November. Sails to a scheduled daily timetable, weather permitting, starting at 11am, except Saturdays when sailings start at 12.05 pm.
Admission: Ticket prices and timetable on application and published locally.

STOTT PARK BOBBIN MILL 　　　　　　**Tel:** 01539 531087

Finsthwaite, Cumbria LA12 8AX
Owner: English Heritage　　　　　　**Contact:** The Custodian
When this working mill was built in 1835 it was typical of the many mills in the Lake District which grew up to supply the spinning and weaving industry in Lancashire but have since disappeared. A remarkable opportunity to see a demonstration of the machinery and techniques of the Industrial Revolution. This is a working Static Steam Engine on Tuesdays to Thursdays.
Location: ½ m N of Finsthwaite near Newby Bridge.
Opening Times: 1 Apr - 30 Sept: Daily 10am - 6pm. 1 - 31 Oct 10am - 6pm or dusk if earlier. Tour only (book in advance) 45 mins, 12 - 15 people per tour. 10 min intervals.
Admission: Adult £2.50, Child £1.30, Conc £1.90.

KEY TO SYMBOLS:　　🌿 THE NATIONAL TRUST　　⌗ ENGLISH HERITAGE　　🏛 HISTORIC HOUSES ASSOCIATION

TOWNEND

OPEN

2 Apr - 1 Nov
Tuesday - Friday,
Sundays and Bank
Holiday Mondays

1 - 5pm or dusk
if earlier.

Last admission
4.30pm.

Tel: 01539 432628

TROUTBECK, WINDERMERE, CUMBRIA LA23 1LB
Owner: The National Trust   *Contact:* Mrs. M Gregg

An exceptional relic of Lake District life during past centuries. Originally a 'statesman' (wealthy yeoman) farmer's house, built about 1626. Townend contains carved woodwork, books, papers, furniture and fascinating implements of the past which were accumulated by the Browne family who lived here from 1626 until 1943.

Location: 3m SE of Ambleside at south end of Troutbeck village.

Admission: Adult £2.60, Child £1.30, Family ticket £7.00. No reduction for parties which must be pre-booked.

WORDSWORTH HOUSE

OPEN

1 Apr - 1 Nov
Weekdays
11am - 5pm.
Also Saturday
6 April, 4 & 5 May,
all Saturdays from
29 June to 7 Sept
and Saturday
26 October. Closed
remaining Sats and
all Sundays.

Last admission
4.30pm.

Tel: 01900 824805

MAIN STREET, COCKERMOUTH, CUMBRIA CA13 9RX
Owner: The National Trust   *Contact:* Mrs. J Durey

The house where William Wordsworth was born in 1770. This north-country Georgian town house was built in 1745. Seven rooms are furnished in 18th century style, with some personal effects of the poet; his childhood garden, with terraced walk, leads down to the Derwent. Video display.

Location: Main Street, Cockermouth.

Admission: Adult £2.50, Child £1.25, Family ticket £6.50. Pre-booked parties £1.80. Reciprocal discount scheme allows visitors to enjoy Dove Cottage, the Wordsworth Museum and Rydal Mount (not NT) at reduced prices.

Where to Stay

For Private Accommodation and Johansens recommended Hotels, see Accommodation Section.

SPECIAL EVENTS

❖ **HOLKER HALL AND GARDENS**   **31 MAY – 2 JUNE**
The Great Garden and Countryside Festival: Fabulous horticultural and floral art displays, countryside displays, advice centres, demonstrations, gardeners question time, traditional and modern crafts, trade stands, wine and champagne bar and much more. Telephone Show Office [015395 58838] for advance tickets/information.

❖ **NAWORTH CASTLE**   **17 JUNE**
Antique Car Rally. 250 Cars drive through 12noon - 2pm.

❖ **NAWORTH CASTLE**   **27 JUNE**
Thomson Roddick and Lawie Antiques Fair.

❖ **DALEMAIN**   **20 – 21 JULY**
Rainbow Craft Fairs.

❖ **NAWORTH CASTLE**   **23 – 26 AUGUST**
Antiques Fair with Galloway Fairs.

❖ **HOLKER HALL AND GARDENS**   **25 AUGUST**
MG Rally: Post and pre 1955 MGs in concours and driving trials.

For National Trust and English Heritage Events see separate section.

CHATSWORTH
Bakewell

The great treasure house of Chatsworth is everything a palace should be but still maintains the sympathetic proportions of a family home. The first house was built by Bess of Hardwick in 1552 and it has been lived in by the Cavendish family, Dukes of Devonshire ever since. The House today owes its appearance to the 1st Duke who remodelled the building at the end of the 17th century, while the 6th Duke added a North Wing by Sir Jeffry Wyatville 200 years later. Visitors see 24 rooms including the run of 5 virtually unaltered 17th century State Rooms and Chapel. There are painted ceilings by Verrio, Thornhill and Laguerre, furniture by William Kent and Boulle, tapestries from Mortlake and Brussels, a library of over 17,000 volumes, sculpture by Cibber and Canova, old master paintings by Rembrandt, Hals, Van Dyck, Tintoretto, Giordano, Lely as well as Landseer and Sargent; the collection of classical sculpture,

Oriental and European porcelain and the dazzling silver collection, including an early English silver chandelier. The present Duke is a collector like his ancestors and the sculptures by Angela Conner and paintings by Lucian Freud bring the treasures up to date.

GARDEN
The garden was the creation of the 6th Duke and his gardener Sir Joseph Paxton, who later built the Crystal Palace. Together they devised a system of cascades, fountains and pools culminating in the 290ft jet of the Emperor Fountain. They planted rare trees and specimen shrubs and placed naturalistic rocks, buildings and statuary to enhance the design. More recent additions include the Maze and the now famous serpentine beech hedge. From bulbs in Spring to rich colours in Autumn, Chatsworth's vast garden provides a worthy setting for the great House.

SPECIAL ATTRACTIONS
Maze in Garden; collection of paintings, drawings, sculpture, silver and porcelain; cascade; 'Capability' Brown landscape; farmyard; adventure playground.

ADVICE TO COURIERS & DRIVERS
Allow a minimum of 2 hours to see Chatsworth. There is a coach drivers' rest room. Unlimited parking for cars, 100 yards from the House, and coaches, 25 yards from the House.

FACILITIES FOR THE DISABLED
Unfortunately it is not possible for people in wheelchairs to tour the House due to the number of stairs. They are most welcome in the garden & 2 electric & 2 standard wheelchairs are available at the entrance. Toilet facilities & a leaflet specially designed for our disabled visitors, on arrival.

CATERING
The Restaurant serving home-made food can cater for up to 300 for afternoon tea and other meals. Menus on request.

GUIDED TOURS
Tours of the House and Behind The Scenes days are available by arrangement. Extra charges apply.

GUIDE BOOKS
Two full-colour guide books for sale: Chatsworth House, available in French, German and Japanese translations and Chatsworth Garden. Special guide for children.

GIFT SHOP
There are two shops open at the same time as the House. Items chosen for the shops by the Duchess of Devonshire.

AUDIO TOURS
A cassette with a tape recorded tour can be hired at the Entrance Hall. Group bookings must be made in advance.

SCHOOL VISITS/CHILDREN
Guided tours, packs, trails and schools room are available to support a school visit. Free preliminary visits can be arranged. Free Teacher's Day on 21 September 1996. For further details telephone Simon Seligman on Baslow (01246) 582204.

CONTACT

Mr John Oliver
Chatsworth
Bakewell
Derbyshire
DE45 1PP

Tel: (01246) 582204

Fax: (01246) 583536

LOCATION

From London 3 hours, M1 Junction 29, signposted via Chesterfield.

Rail: Chesterfield Station, 9 miles.

Bus: Chesterfield - Bakewell, 1½ miles.

OPENING TIMES

Summer
20 March - 3 November

Daily: 11.00am - 4.30pm

Winter
Closed

ADMISSION

HOUSE & GARDEN
Adult £5.75
Child £3.00
OAP/Student . . £5.25
Family £15.00
Pre-booked parties
Adult £5.25
Schools £2.75
OAP/Student . . £4.50
GARDEN ONLY
Adult £3.50
Child £1.75
OAP £3.00
Student £3.00
Family £9.00
SCOTS SUITE
Adult £1.00
Child £0.50
Car Park £1.00

HADDON HALL
Bakewell

THIS WONDERFULLY ROMANTIC house, the most complete surviving medieval manor house in the country, is situated in the heart of the Peak District. Built over a period of 400 years, its architecture progresses from Norman, through Medieval and Tudor, to Elizabethan, thereby displaying every aspect of domestic life from the past. Natural, rather than formal, Haddon is wrapped in an atmosphere of homeliness and is a truly 'understandable' house.

Since the 12th century, Haddon has been the home of the Vernon and Manners families. It was the Vernons, owners from 1170 to 1567, who were largely responsible for the construction of the house as we see it today. The House changed ownership in 1567,

through the marriage of Dorothy Vernon to John Manners, 2nd son of the 1st Earl of Rutland. In 1703, the Dukedom of Rutland was conferred upon the Manners family and Haddon was abandoned in favour of Belvoir Castle, the Ducal seat in Rutland for 200 years. Haddon was uninhabited, until the 9th Duke of Rutland returned early this century to make the house's restoration his life's work.

The terraced Rose Gardens, stepping down to the fast-flowing River Wye, are planned for year-round colour. Over 150 varieties of rose and clematis, many over 70 years old, provide colour and scent throughout the summer. Winner of the H.H.A./Christie's "Garden of the Year" Award.

SUITABILITY FOR OTHER EVENTS
Fashion shows archery, garden parties and filming. Haddon is able to provide the finest facilities for clay pigeon shooting in the North of England, with the shooting ground adjacent to the Hall which provides magnificent backdrops. A full clay pigeon shooting package, with tutoring by olympic coaches, is available, accompanied by excellent catering facilities. Please write for further details and dates.

CONFERENCE FACILITIES
This Medieval House is able to offer restricted facilities for conferences and functions in the Main Banqueting Hall and Long Gallery. Please contact the Estate Office with any enquiries, and we should be delighted to assist.

EXTRA FACILITIES
There is provision for helicopters if required. Lectures on the property, its contents, gardens and history can be arranged for up to 35 people. Projector and screen can be provided.

ADVICE TO COURIERS & DRIVERS
Owing to the age of the House, and its uneven, worn stone floors and staircases, Haddon is not entirely suitable for large groups of elderly people. No dogs are allowed in the House or Grounds, except guide dogs.

FACILITIES FOR THE DISABLED
Disabled and elderly people may alight at the entrance and vehicles then parked in the allocated area. A courtesy vehicle is available to help disabled visitors from the coach park to the Hall. Please advise us of your requirements.

PARKING FOR COACHES & CARS
Parking for 200 cars and coaches, 500 yards from the House. Charge for cars 50p.

CATERING
The Restaurant/Tea Room seats up to 75 people. Prices range from £2 - 3 for tea and other meals. For special functions, buffets lunches and dinners can be arranged.

GUIDED TOURS
£20.00 extra for groups of 20. 7 days notice required.

GUIDE BOOKS
Colour guide book, £2.20.

SCHOOL VISITS/ CHILDREN
School groups are welcome, price £2.40 per child. Schools' pack is available, enabling children to follow interesting project work. There is an in-school introductory talk by the guide who will take the children round the house on the day if their visit. Schoolroom available. Special guide books can be purchased and dressing up and talks with slides can be arranged.

CONTACT

The Comptroller
Estate Office
Haddon Hall
Bakewell
Derbyshire
DE45 1LA

Tel: (01629) 812855

Fax: (01629) 814379

LOCATION

From London 3 hours
Sheffield ½ hour
Derby ¾ hour
Haddon is on the A6
1½ miles south
of Bakewell.

M1 Junct. 29/30, M6
Junct. 17/18/19, 1 hour.

From Manchester
1 hour.

OPENING TIMES

Summer
1 April - 30 September

Daily: 11.00am - 5.45pm
Last entry 5.00pm.

NB Also closed on Sundays in July & August, except 25 Aug.

Winter
October - 30 March
Closed

ADMISSION

Summer
Adult £4.50
Child* £2.80
OAP £3.50
Family Ticket . .£12.50
(2 adults/2 children)

GROUPS*
Adult £3.50
Child* £2.40
OAP £3.25

* Aged 5-16
** Min 20 people

BAKEWELL OLD HOUSE MUSEUM

OPEN

Easter to 31 October
Daily
2.00 - 5.00pm

Parties by
arrangement.

Tel: 01629 813165

CUNNINGHAM PLACE, BAKEWELL, DE45 1DD

Owner: *Bakewell & District Historical Society*   **Contact:** *Dr J T Brighton*

A rare and curious Peakland house built by Ralf Gell in 1534. Period fire-places, garderobe and timber interior. Collections of costume, lace, samplers, toys etc. Old craft tools, workshops and a 19th century kitchen. Sir Richard Arkwright converted the house into mill workers' tenements in the late 18th century. It was saved and restored after 1954.
Location: 100 yards west of Bakewell Parish Church.
Admission: Adult £2.00, Child £1.00.

BOLSOVER CASTLE

Tel: 01246 823349

Castle Street, Bolsover, Derbyshire S44 6PR
Owner: English Heritage   **Contact:** The Custodian
An enchanting and romantic spectacle, situated high on a wooded hilltop dominating the surrounding landscape. Built on the site of a Norman castle, this is largely an early 17th century mansion. Most delightful is the 'Little Castle', a bewitching folly with intricate carvings, frescoes and wall painting. There is also an impressive 17th century Indoor Riding School which is still used on occasions.
Location: Off M1 at junction 29, 6m from Mansfield.
Opening Times: 1 Apr - 30 Sept: Daily 10am - 6pm. 1 - 31 Oct: Daily 10am - 6pm or dusk if earlier. 1 Nov - 31 Mar, Wed - Sun, 10am - 4pm (closed lunch 1-2pm)
Admission: Adult £2.60, Child £1.30, Conc £2.00.

CALKE ABBEY

Tel: 01332 863822   **Fax:** 01332 865272

Ticknall, Derby, Derbyshire DE73 1LE
Owner: The National Trust   **Contact:** The Property Manager
The house that time forgot, this Baroque mansion, built 1701 - 03 for Sir John Harpur, is virtually unaltered since the death of the last baronet in 1924. Within the house there is a Caricature Room, gold and white drawing room, Sir Vauncey's childhood bedroom, the Gardner Wilkinson Library and beer cellar. Fascinating natural history collections. Magnificent early 18th century state bed. A carriage display in the stable block, walled gardens and pleasure grounds, Portland sheep in the park, an early 19th century church.
Location: 10m S of Derby, on A514 at Ticknall between Swadlincote and Melbourne.
Opening Times: House, Garden & Church: 30 Mar to end Oct: Sat - Wed & BH Mon (closed Good Fri). House & Church: 1 - 5.30pm, Garden: 11am - 5.30pm. Ticket Office: 11am - 5pm. Last admission 5pm. Park: open during daylight hours all year: Apr - Oct closed 9pm (or dusk if earlier): Nov - Mar closes at dusk.
Admission: All sites: Adult £4.70, Child £2.30, Family £11.70. Garden only: £2.10. Discount for pre-booked parties.

CATTON HALL

CATTON, SWADLINCOTE, DERBYSHIRE DE12 8LN

Owners: *Robin & Katie Neilson*   **Contact:** *The owners*

Tel: 01283 716311   **Fax:** 01283 712876

Catton, built in 1745 is not open to the public. It has been in the hands of the same family since 1405 and is still lived in by the Neilsons as their private home. This gives the house a unique relaxed and friendly atmosphere making guests feel at home whether they are inside for a formal occasion, or outside enjoying activities from a marquee. The 100 acres of parkland are ideal for all types of outdoor events and we can arrange most types of activities from corporate multi-activity days to the more traditional country sports of shooting, fishing or falconry. Eight double bedrooms are available for groups who may require accommodation for conferences or perhaps events at the N.E.C in Birmingham. There is also a small private chapel which is ideal for special weddings.
Location: ½ hour N of Birmingham off A38 Nr Lichfield.
Opening Times: By arrangement only: Corporate entertainment, management training, meetings, multi-activity days, weddings, fairs, dinners, 4 x 4 course, etc.

CHATSWORTH

See Page 45 for full page entry.

ELVASTON CASTLE COUNTRY PARK   **Tel:** 01332 571342   **Fax:** 01332 758751

Borrowash Road, Elvaston, Derby, Derbyshire DE72 3EP
Owner: Derbyshire County Council   **Contact:** Mr M Marshall
200 acre park landscaped in 19th century. Walled kitchen garden. Estate museum with exhibitions of traditional crafts.
Location: 5m SE of Derby, A6 or A52.
Opening Times: Park: All year, dawn - dusk. Shop/Tea Room/Exhibitions: 30 Mar - 3 Nov, Daily 11am - 4.30pm. Museum: 30 Mar - 3 Nov: Wed - Sat, 1 - 4.30pm. Sun & BHs, 10am - 5pm.
Admission: Car park: Midweek 60p, weekends/Bank Hols £1.20, Coaches £6.00. Museum: Adult £1.20, Child £60p, Family (2+2) £3.00. Park and Gardens Free.

EYAM HALL

OPEN

31 Mar - 3 Nov
Weds, Thur, Suns,
Bank Hol Mons.
11 am - 5.30pm
last tour 4.30pm.

Schools: Tuesdays
and weekdays
11 - 29 Mar

Buttery & Gift Shop
open Tues to Sun,
Bank Hol Mons.

Tel: 01433 631976

EYAM, SHEFFIELD, DERBYSHIRE S30 1QW

Owner: *The Wright family*   **Contact:** *Miss Carolyn Fooks*

Built by the Wright family in 1671 and still their family home, Eyam Hall is a cosy and intimate house, only recently opened to the public. All visitors receive a guided tour at no extra cost, including the Jacobean staircase, tapestry room "wallpapered" with tapestries and impressive old kitchen. Family portraits, furniture, china, glass, silver, embroidery, costumes and clocks.
Location: 100 yards west of Church in centre of village. Eyam is off A623 between Baslow and Chapel-en-le-Frith.
Admission: Adult £3.25, Child £2.25, Concessions £2.75.
Family (2 adults + 4 children) £9.50. Party rates available, must pre-book.

HADDON HALL 🏛

See Page 46 for full page entry.

HARDWICK ESTATE - STAINSBY MILL 🌿   Tel: 01246 850430   Fax: 01246 854200

Stainsby, Chesterfield, Derbyshire S44 5QJ
Owner: The National Trust   **Contact:** The Property Manager
18th century water-powered corn mill in working order.
Location: From M1 junction 29 take A6175, signposted to Clay Cross then first left and left again to Stainsby Mill.
Opening Times: 30 Mar - end Oct: Wed, Thur, Sat, Sun & BH Mon 11.30am - 4.30pm. July - Sept: also open Fridays 11.30am - 4.30pm. Last admissions 4pm.
Admission: Adult £1.50, Child 70p, Family £3.70. Pre-booked parties (no reduction).

HARDWICK HALL 🌿   Tel: 01246 850430   Fax: 01246 854200

Doe Lea, Chesterfield, Derbyshire S44 5QJ
Owner: The National Trust   **Contact:** The Property Manager
A late 16th century 'prodigy house' designed by Robert Smythson for Bess of Hardwick. The house contains outstanding contemporary furniture, tapestries and needlework including pieces identified in an inventory of 1601; a needlework exhibition is on permanent display. Walled courtyards enclose fine gardens, orchards and a herb garden. The Country Park contains Whiteface Woodland sheep and Longhorn cattle.
Location: $6^{1}/_{2}$m W of Mansfield, $9^{1}/_{2}$m SE of Chesterfield: approach from M1 (exit 29) via A6175.
Opening Times: Hall: 30 Mar - end Oct: Wed, Thur, Sat, Sun & BH Mon, 12.30 - 5pm (closed Good Fri). Last admission to Hall 4.30pm. Garden: 30 Mar - end Oct: Daily 12 noon - 5.30pm.
Admission: Hall & Garden: Adult £5.50, Child £2.70, Family £13.70. Garden only: £2.50, Child £1.00, Family £6.00. No reduction for parties.

HARDWICK OLD HALL ✠   Tel: 01246 850430

Doe Lea, Nr. Chesterfield, Derbyshire S44 5QJ
Owner: English Heritage   **Contact:** The Custodian
This large ruined house, finished in 1591, still displays Bess of Hardwick's innovative planning and interesting decorative plasterwork. A joint ticket is available for the New Hall and Gardens and the Old Hall. A 30 minute guided tour is available if booked in advance.
Location: $9^{1}/_{2}$ m SE of Chesterfield, off A 6175.
Opening Times: 1 Apr - 31 Oct: Wed - Sun, 12 noon - 6pm or dusk.
Admission: Adult £1.50, Child 80p, Conc. £1.10.

KEDLESTON HALL 🌿   Tel: 01332 842191   Fax: 01332 841972

Quarndon, Derby, Derbyshire DE22 5JH
Owner: The National Trust   **Contact:** The Property Manager
Experience the age of elegance in this neo-classical house built between 1759 and 1765 for the Curzon family and little altered since. Set in 800 acres of parkland with an 18th century pleasure ground, garden and woodland walks - a day at Kedleston is truly an experience to remember. The influence of the architect Robert Adam is everywhere, from the Park buildings to the decoration of the magnificent state rooms. Parties are welcome and an introductory talk can be arranged if booked in advance.
Location: 5m NW of Derby, signposted from roundabout where A38 crosses A52.
Opening Times: House: 30 Mar - end of Oct: Sat - Wed. Park & Gardens: 11am - 6pm. Restaurant: 11am - 5pm. House: 1 - 5.30pm. Last admission 5pm. (Park only: Thursday & Friday 11am - 6pm - vehicle charge.)
Admission: Adult £4.50, Child £2.20, Family £11.20. Garden & Park only: Adult £2.00. Child £1.00. Discount for parties, please telephone the Property Manager.

MELBOURNE HALL 🏛   Tel: 01332 862502   Fax: 01332 862263

Melbourne, Derbyshire DE73 1EN
Owner: Lord & Lady Ralph Kerr   **Contact:** Mrs Gill Weston
This beautiful house of history, in its picturesque poolside setting, was once the home of victorian Prime Minister William Lamb. The fine gardens, in the French formal style, contain Robert Bakewell's intricate wrought iron arbour and a fascinating yew tunnel. Tearoom and craft centre.
Location: 8 miles South of Derby. M1 from London exit 24.
Opening Times: Hall: August only (not first 3 Mondays) 2 - 5pm. Gardens: 1 April - 30 Sept: Wed, Sat, Sun, Bank Hol Mons 2 - 6pm.
Admission: Hall: Adult £2.50, OAP £2.00, Child £1.00. Gardens: Adult £3, OAP & Child £2.00. Hall & Gardens Adult £4.50, OAP £3.50, Child £2.50.

PEVERIL CASTLE ✠   Tel: 01433 620613

Market Place, Castleton, Derbyshire S30 2WX
Owner: English Heritage   **Contact:** The Custodian
There are breathtaking views of the Peak District from this castle, perched high above the pretty village of Castleton. The great square tower stands almost to its original height.
Location: On S side of Castleton, 15m W of Sheffield on A625.
Opening Times: 1 Apr - 30 Sept: Daily 10am - 6pm. 1 - 31 Oct: Daily 10am - 6pm or dusk if earlier. 1 Nov - 31 Mar: Wed - Sun, 10am - 4pm.
Admission: Adult £1.30, Child 80p, Conc £1.10.

RENISHAW HALL 🏛

OPEN

Every Friday, Saturday, Sunday and Bank Holiday Monday

Good Friday to Sunday 15 Sept

10.30am - 4.30pm

Tel: 01246 432310

SHEFFIELD, DERBYSHIRE S31 9WB

Owner: *Sir Reresby Sitwell, Bt., DL*   **Contact:** *Sir Reresby Sitwell, Bt., DL*

George Sitwell built in 1625 a small H-shaped manor house to which his descendant Sitwell Sitwell later 1st baronet, added vast additions, also the Georgian Stables (now containing a small museum) and various follies in and around the Park. The beautiful Italianate garden, park and lake were the creation of the eccentric Sir George Sitwell, grandfather of the present owner.
Location: 6 miles equidistant from Sheffield & Chesterfield, 3 miles junct. 30 of M1.
Admission: House: by written application only.
Garden only: Adult £3.00, OAP £2.00, Small Child £1.00.
Museum only: Adult £1.50, OAP £1.00, Small Child 50p.
Garden & Museum: Adult £4.00, OAP £3.00, Small Child £1.25.

REVOLUTION HOUSE   Tel: 01246 453554/559727   Fax: 01246 206667

High Street, Old Whittington, Chesterfield, Derbyshire, S41 9LA.
                                           Contact: Ms A M Knowles
Originally the Cock and Pynot ale house, now furnished in 17th century style.
Location: 3m N of Chesterfield on B6052 off A61.
Opening Times: Good Fri - Oct: Daily 10am - 4pm. Special opening over Xmas period.
Admission: Free.

SIR RICHARD ARKWRIGHT'S CROMFORD MILL   Tel: 01629 824297

Cromford, Nr. Matlock, Derbyshire DE4 3RQ
                                           Contact: The Visitor Services Centre
Built in 1771, Cromford Mill is the world's first successful water powered cotton spinning mill. It is set in the beautiful Derwent Valley surrounded by limestone Tors and rolling hills. There is a wholefood restaurant on site with shops, free car parking and friendly staff. A tour guide will explain the story of this important historic site and describe the development plans for the future.
Location: 3 miles S of Matlock, 17 miles N of Derby just off A6.
Opening Times: All year except Christmas Day, 9am - 5pm.
Admission: Free entry. Guided tours: Adult £2.00, Concessions £1.50.

SUDBURY HALL 🌿   Tel: 01283 585305   Fax: 01283 585139

Ashbourne, Derbyshire DE6 5HT
Owner: The National Trust   **Contact:** The Administrator
One of the most individual of late 17th century houses, begun by George Vernon c.1660. The rich decoration includes wood carvings by Gibbons and Pierce, superb plasterwork, mythological decorative paintings by Laguerre. The great staircase is one of the finest of its kind in an English house.
Location: 6m E of Uttoxeter at the crossing point of A50 Derby - Stoke and A515 Lichfield - Ashbourne.
Opening Times: Hall: 30 Mar - end of Oct: Wed - Sun & BH Mon (Closed Good Fri) 1 - 5.30pm. Last admission 5pm. Grounds: 12.30pm - 6pm.
Admission: Hall: Adult £3.30, Child £1.30, Family £7.90. Parties by prior arrangement.

KEY TO SYMBOLS: 🌿 THE NATIONAL TRUST   ✠ ENGLISH HERITAGE   🏛 HISTORIC HOUSES ASSOCIATION

SUTTON SCARSDALE HALL ⛶   Tel: 01604 730320

Chesterfield, Derbyshire
Owner: English Heritage   **Contact:** Midlands Regional Office
The dramatic hilltop shell of a great early 18th century baroque mansion.
Location: Between Chesterfield and Bolsover.
Opening Times: Hall: 3 May - 29 Oct: Wed - Sun & BH Mon (Closed Good Fri) 1pm - 5.30pm or sunset if earlier. Last admission 5pm. Grounds: 12.30pm - 6pm.

WINSTER MARKET HOUSE 🦋   Tel: 01335 350245

Matlock, Derbyshire
Owner: The National Trust   **Contact:** The Property Manager
A market house of the late 17th or early 18th century. The ground floor is of stone with the original five open arches filled in, while the upper storey is of brick with stone dressings. The building was bought in 1906 and restored. It is now an NT Information Room.
Location: 4m W of Matlock on S side of B5057 in main street of Winster.
Opening Times: 1 Apr - end Oct: Daily.
Admission: Free.

Chatsworth.

SPECIAL EVENTS

❖ **CHATSWORTH**   **11 – 12 MAY**
Chatsworth Angling Fair - the only specialist Angling Fair in the Country, catering for game, coarse and sea-fishing enthusiasts with added family attractions.

❖ **HADDON HALL**   **29 – 30 JUNE**
Craft Show

❖ **EYAM HALL**   **5 – 6 JULY**
7.00pm - 'Macbeth', Box Hedge Theatre Company. Outdoor Shakespeare, produced in walled garden. Ticket includes glass of wine. High quality production by dynamic young professional troupe.

❖ **EYAM HALL**   **13 JULY**
7.30pm. Roman Rudnytsky: Piano Recital

❖ **CHATSWORTH**   **2 – 3 SEPTEMBER**
Chatsworth Country Fair: 2-Day Country Fair spectacular for all the Family, including massed pipe and military bands, hot-air balloons, free-fall parachuting and over 150 trade stands.

❖ **EYAM HALL**   **28 SEPTEMBER**
7.00pm - Steve Marsh & Elaine Thompson: Concert for guitar and flute.

For National Trust and English Heritage Events see separate section.

POWDERHAM CASTLE
Exeter

Historic family home of the Earl of Devon, Powderham Castle was built between 1390 and 1420 by Sir Philip Courtenay. The present Earl is his direct descendant. The Castle was extensively damaged during the Civil War and fell to the Parliamentary Forces after a protracted siege. When the family returned to the Castle 70 years later they embarked on a series of rebuilding and restoration which continued into the 19th Century.

The Castle contains a large collection of portraits by many famous artists, including Cosway, Reynolds, Kneller and Hudson as well as some charming paintings by gifted members of the family. The 14ft high Stumbels Clock and the magnificent rosewood and brass inlaid bookcases by John Channon are particularly fine. One of the most spectacular rooms on view is the Music Room, designed for the 3rd Viscount by James Wyatt. It contains an exceptional Axminster Carpet upon which sits recently commissioned carved gilt wood furniture.

GARDENS
The Castle is set within an ancient deer park beside the Estuary of the River Exe and the Gardens and grounds are informally laid out. The Rose Garden is planted mostly with older sweet scented varieties and enjoys fine views from its terraces across the Park. Timothy, a 150 year old tortoise, lives here and keeps the lawns weed free. The woodland garden is being restored and is open to visitors in the spring.

❖

CONTACT

Mr Tim Faulkner
The Estate Office
Powderham Castle
Kenton
Exeter
Devon
EX6 8JQ

Tel: (01626) 890243
Fax: (01626) 890729

LOCATION

6 miles south west of Exeter, 4 miles Junct 30, M5.
Air: Exeter Airport 9 miles.
Rail: Starcross Station 2 miles.
Bus: Devon General Nos 85, 85A, 85B to Castle Gate.

SUITABILITY FOR OTHER EVENTS
Antique and Craft Fairs, conferences, dinners, charity balls, filming and wedding receptions, car launches including 4WD, vehicle rallies, clay pigeon shoots etc.

EXTRA FACILITIES
Grand piano in Music Room, 3800 acre Estate, Tennis Court, Cricket Pitch Horse Trials Course.

ADVICE TO COURIERS & DRIVERS
Commission and complimentary drinks and meals for drivers in the Courtyard Tea Rooms . Advance warning of group bookings preferred but not essential. Unlimited parking.

FACILITIES FOR THE DISABLED
Limited. Toilet and some ramps.

CATERING
Home made lunches and proper Devon Cream Teas.

GIFT SHOP AND MUSEUM
A gift and souvenir shop with a variety of quality items.

GUIDE BOOKS
New guide books are available in English with French, Dutch and German translations.

GUIDED TOURS
All visits by guided tour which lasts about 1 hour.

SCHOOL VISITS/CHILDREN
Schools and children of all ages very welcome. Guided tour is a fascinating and useful insight into the life of one of England's Great Houses over the centuries. There is also a Victorian School Room and Teacher Pack.

OPENING TIMES

Summer
31 March - 27 October

Daily: 10.00am - 5.30pm
Except Saturdays closed to public, but available for private hire.

Winter
30 October - Easter

Available for hire for conferences, receptions and functions.

ADMISSION

1995 prices.
Adult £4.40
OAP £4.25
Child £2.95

Group Rates
Adult £3.75
OAP £3.55
Child £1.95
Family £11.75

(2 adults + 2 children or
1 adult + 3 children)

CONFERENCE AND FUNCTION FACILITIES

ROOM	DIMENSIONS	CAPACITY	LAYOUT	POWER POINTS	SUITABLE FOR A/V
Music Room	56' x 25'	150	Theatre		
		130	Seated		
		150	Buffet		
Dining Room	42' x 22'	65	Seated		
		90	Buffet		
		100	Theatre		
Ante Room	28' x 18'	25	Theatre		
Library 1	32' x 18'	50	Seated		
		75	Buffet		
		50	Theatre		
Library 2	31"x18'	As Library 1			

A LA RONDE

Tel: 01395 265514

Summer Lane, Exmouth, Devon EX8 5BD

Owner: The National Trust   **Contact:** The Administrator

A unique 16-sided house built in 1796 for two spinsters, Jane and Mary Parminter. The fascinating interior decoration includes a shell-encrusted room, a feather frieze, and many 18th century contents and collections brought back by the two women from a European Grand Tour.

Location: 2m N of Exmouth on A376.

Opening Times: 1 Apr - 31 Oct: Daily except Fri & Sat, 11am - 5.30pm. Last admission $^{1}/_{2}$ hour before closing.

Admission: Adult £3.10, Child £1.50, no reduction for parties.

BICKLEIGH CASTLE

OPEN
Easter Week
(Good Fri to Fri.)
then Weds, Suns &
Bank Hols to late
May Bank Hol, then
to early Oct, daily.
(closed Sats.)
2 - 5.30pm
Groups of 20+
welcome by prior
arrangement.

Tel: 01884 855363

BICKLEIGH, TIVERTON, DEVON EX16 8RP
Owner: O N Boxall Esq   *Contact: O N Boxall Esq*

Royalist stronghold: 900 years of history and architecture. 11th century detached Chapel; 14th century Gatehouse comprising Armoury (with Cromwellian arms and armour), Guard Room - Tudor furniture and fine oil paintings, Great Hall - 52' long and 'Tudor' Bedroom, massive fourposter. 17th century Farmhouse: inglenook fireplaces, bread ovens, oak beams. Museum: Maritime exhibitions: 'Mary Rose', 'Titanic' and model ships, World War II spy and escape gadgets. Spooky Tower, The Great Hall and picturesque moated garden make Bickleigh Castle and Garden a favoured venue for functions, particularly wedding receptions.

Location: Off the A396 Exeter-Tiverton road. Follow signs from Bickleigh Bridge.

Admission: Adult £3.50, Child (5 - 15) £1.80, Family Tickets £9.50

ARLINGTON COURT

OPEN

House, Victorian
Garden & Park:
1 Apr - 31 Oct
Daily except Sat
(but open Sats on
BH weekends)
11am - 5.30pm.

Park: Footpaths
across parkland
open during daylight
hours Nov - Mar.

Tel: 01271 850296

ARLINGTON, NR BARNSTAPLE, DEVON EX31 4LP
Owner: The National Trust   *Contact: The Administrator*

One of the country's finest collections of horse-drawn vehicles is displayed in the stables and visitors can enjoy rides in an open carriage drawn by Arlington's carriage horses. The house is set in 30 acres of park and garden and contains collections for every taste. Shetland ponies and Jacob sheep graze the park and there are walks through the woodland and beside the lake.

Location: 7m NE of Barnstaple on A39.

Admission: House & Garden: Adult £4.00, Child £2.40, Family £12. Garden only: Adult £2.50. Pre-arranged parties (15+) £1.00ea.

BICTON PARK & GARDENS

Tel: 01395 568465   **Fax:** 01395 568889

Budleigh Salterton, Devon EX9 7DP

Owner: Bicton Park Charitable Trust   **Contact:** Jennifer Stevens

Over 60 acres of Parkland and Gardens, including Italian, American and Hermitage Gardens: Palm House and specialist greenhouses: Countryside Museum housing nationwide collection of farm and country implements, machinery and vehicles. "Fabulous Forest" Large indoor play area for under teens plus acres of Adventure Playground. 25 minute woodland Railway Ride. Full catering facilities. Plant & Gift Shop.

Location: 2 m north of Budleigh Salterton on B3178

Opening Times: Apr - Oct: Daily 10am - 6pm (4pm in Oct). Nov - Mar: Daily 10am - 4pm (weekends only).

Admission: Adult £3.75, OAP £2.75, Child £3.00, Family Ticket £13. Group & school rates.

BAYARD'S COVE FORT

Tel: 01179 750700

Dartmouth, Devon

Owner: English Heritage   **Contact:** The South West Regional Office

Set among the picturesque gabled houses of Dartmouth, on the waterfront at the end of the quay, this is a small artillery fort built 1509 - 10 to defend the harbour entrance.

Location: In Dartmouth, on riverfront.

Opening Times: Any reasonable time.

Admission: Free.

BOWDEN HOUSE

Tel: 01803 863664

Totnes, Devon TQ9 7PW

Owner: Mrs Belinda Petersen   **Contact:** Mrs Belinda Petersen

Elizabethan mansion with Queen Anne facade.

Location: Follow brown signs on A381 from Totnes.

Opening Times: 25 Mar - 31 Oct: Mon - Thurs plus BH Suns. Museum opens at 12 noon, Tours start at 2pm, or 1.30pm in high season, with ghost stories.

Admission: Adult £4.50, 10 - 13 yrs £2.50, 6 - 9 years £1.50, under 6 free, Group £3.50 pp. Tickets include Photo Museum and old film shows.

BERRY POMEROY CASTLE

Tel: 01803 866618

Totnes, Devon TQ9 6NJ

Owner: English Heritage   **Contact:** The Custodian

A romantic late medieval castle, dramatically sited half-way up a wooded hillside, looking out over a deep ravine and stream. It is unusual in combining the remains of a large castle with a flamboyant courtier's mansion.

Location: 2$^{1}/_{2}$m E of Totnes off A385.

Opening Times: 1 Apr - 31 Oct: Daily 10am - 6pm. 1 - 31 Oct: 10am - 6pm or dusk.

Admission: Adult £2.00, Child £1.00, Conc £1.50.

BRADLEY MANOR

Tel: 01626 54513

Newton Abbot, Devon TQ12 6BN

Owner: The National Trust   **Contact:** Mrs A H Woolner

A small medieval manor house set in woodland and meadows.

Location: On Totnes road A381.

Opening Times: Apr - end Sept: Wed 2 - 5 pm: also Thur 4 & 11 Apr, 19 & 26 Sept. Last admission 4.30pm.

Admission: £2.60, no reduction for parties.

KEY TO SYMBOLS: THE NATIONAL TRUST   ENGLISH HERITAGE   HISTORIC HOUSES ASSOCIATION

BUCKFAST ABBEY

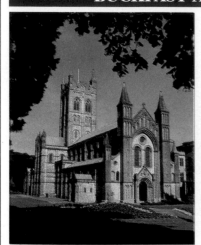

BUCKFASTLEIGH, DEVON TQ11 0EE

Owner: Buckfast Abbey Trust
Contact: Robin Clutterbuck

Tel: 01364 642519
Fax: 01364 643891

The Benedictine monks of Buckfast welcome visitors to their Abbey, which they rebuilt themselves on its medieval foundations. The Abbey is famous today for its pioneering work in beekeeping, its tonic wine and spectacular modern stained glass. Restaurant, video, exhibition and shops selling the products of Buckfast and other European monasteries. Facilities for conferences and accommodation for guests and retreats. Few visitors leave untouched by the peace and serenity of Buckfast.

OPEN

Church & Grounds: All year 5.30am - 7.00pm. Shops, Restaurant, Video, Exhibition: Easter - Oct: 9am - 5pm. Nov - Easter: 10am - 4pm. Shops closed Good Fri & Xmas Day. Restaurant closed Xmas Eve and Xmas Day.

Location: ¹/₂ m from A38 Plymouth - Exeter route at Buckfastleigh turn off.

Admission: Free. Car parking £1. Exhib: 75p / 30p.

BUCKLAND ABBEY

YELVERTON, DEVON PL20 6EY

Owner: The National Trust
Contact: The Property Manager

Tel: 01822 853607

The spirit of Sir Francis Drake is rekindled at his home with exhibitions of his courageous adventures and achievements throughout the world. One of the Trust's most interesting historical buildings and originally a 13th century monastery, the abbey was transformed into a family residence before Sir Francis bought it in 1581. Outside there are monastic farm buildings, herb garden, craft workshops and country walks. Introductory video presentation.

OPEN

1 April - 3 Nov: Daily except Thurs 10.30am - 5.30 pm.
9 Nov - March 1997: Sat and Sun. Wed pre-arranged parties 2 - 5.00pm. Closed 6 - 24 Jan 1997.
Last admissions ³/₄ hr before closing

Location: 6 m S of Tavistock; 11 m N of Plymouth off A386.

Admission: Adult £4.20, Child £2.10. Family £10.50. Grounds only: Adult £2.10; pre-arranged parties (15+) £3.40. Winter admission (Nov-March) £2 .10.

CADHAY

OPEN

July & Aug
Tues, Weds, Thurs

Also Sun & Mon in late spring and summer Bank Holidays.

2 - 5.30pm

Groups by appointment only.

Tel: 01404 812432

OTTERY ST. MARY, DEVON EX11 1QT

Owner: Mr O.N.W. William Powlett   *Contact: Lady William Powlett*

Cadhay is approached by an avenue of lime-trees, and stands in a pleasant listed garden, with herbaceous borders and yew hedges, with excellent views over the original medieval fish ponds. The main part of the house was built about 1550 by John Haydon who had married the de Cadhay heiress. He retained the Great Hall of an earlier house, of which the fine timber roof (about 1420) can be seen. An Elizabethan Long Gallery was added by John's successor at the end of the 16th century, thereby forming a unique and lovely courtyard.
Location: 1 mile north west of Ottery St. Mary on B3176.
Admission: Adult £3.00, Child £1.50.

CASTLE DROGO

DREWSTEIGNTON, NR. EXETER, DEVON EX6 6PB

Owner: The National Trust
Contact: The Property Manager

Tel: 01647 433306

The last Castle to be built in Britain, this 20th century home designed by Sir Edwin Lutyens incorporates modern conveniences with a medieval atmosphere enhanced by bare granite and timber and tapestry hung walls. It stands at over 900 ft. above sea level, overlooking the wooded gorge with beautiful views and spectacular walks through the surrounding estate.

Location: 4 miles S of A30 Exeter - Okehampton Road.

OPEN

Castle: 1 April - 31 Oct: Daily except Fris 11am - 5.30pm (open Good Friday)

Garden: 1 Apr - 31 Oct: Daily 10.30am - 5.30pm. Last admission 5pm.

Admission: Adult £4.80, Child £2.40. Family £12. Pre-arranged parties £4.00, Garden and Grounds only £2.20.

COLETON FISHACRE GARDEN
Tel: 01803 752466

Coleton, Kingswear, Dartmouth, Devon TQ6 0EQ
Owner: The National Trust   **Contact:** The Property Manager
20 acre garden in a stream-fed valley set within the spectacular scenery of this NT Coast. The garden was created by Lady Dorothy D'Oyly Carte between 1925 and 1940, and is planted with a wide variety of uncommon trees and rare and exotic shrubs. Coleton Fishacre House is a private family home and is of special interest to people studying 20th century architecture and design. View by written appointment to Mr. B Howe.
Location: 2m from Kingswear; take Lower Ferry road, turn off at toll house.
Opening Times: Mar: Sun only, 2 - 5pm. 1 Apr - 31 Oct: Wed, Thur, Fri, Sun & BH Mons 10.30am - 5.30pm or dusk if earlier. Last admission ¹/₂ hour before closing.
Admission: £3.10, pre-booked parties £2.50 ea.

COMPTON CASTLE
Tel: 01803 872112

Marldon, Paignton TQ3 1TA
Owner: The National Trust   **Contact:** The Administrator
A fortified manor house with curtain wall, built at three periods: 1340, 1450 and 1520 by the Gilbert family. It was the home of Sir Humphrey Gilbert (1539-1583), coloniser of Newfoundland and half-brother of Sir Walter Raleigh; the family still lives here.
Location: At Compton, 3m W of Torquay.
Opening Times: 1 Apr - 31 Oct: Mon, Wed & Thur 10am - 12.15pm & 2 - 5pm.
The courtyard, restored great hall, solar, chapel, rose garden and old kitchen are shown. Last admission ¹/₂ hour before closing.
Admission: £2.70, pre-arranged parties £2.10.

DARTINGTON HALL GARDENS
Tel: 01803 862367   **Tel:** 01803 862367

Dartington, Totnes, Devon TQ9 6EL
Owner: Dartington Hall Trust   **Contact:** Mr G Gammin
28 acre gardens surrounds 14th century Hall.
Location: 30 mins from M5 at Exeter (off A38 at Buckfastleigh).
Opening Times: All year.
Admission: Donations welcome.

DARTMOUTH CASTLE
Tel: 01803 833588

Castle Road, Dartmouth, Devon TQ6 0JN
Owner: English Heritage   **Contact:** The Custodian
This brilliantly positioned defensive castle juts out into the narrow entrance to the Dart estuary, with the sea lapping at its foot. It was one of the first castles constructed with artillery in mind and has seen 450 years of fortification and preparation for war.
Location: 1m SE of Dartmouth off B3205, narrow approach road.
Opening Times: 1 Apr - 30 Sept: Daily 10am - 6pm. 1 - 31 Oct: Daily 10am - 6pm or dusk if earlier. 1 Nov - 31 Mar: Wed - Sun 10am - 4pm (closed lunch 1 - 2pm Nov - Mar).
Admission: Adult £2.20, Child £1.10, Conc £1.70.

DOCTON MILL & GARDEN

Tel: 01237 441369   **Fax:** 01237 441369

Spekes Valley, Hartland, Devon EX39 6EA

Owner: Martin G Bourcier Esq   **Contact:** Martin G Bourcier Esq

Garden for all seasons in 8 acres of sheltered wooded valley.

Location: 3m Hartland Quay.

Opening Times: Mar - Oct: 10am - 5pm. No coaches.

Admission: Adult £2.50, Child 50p.

ESCOT

Tel: 01404 822188   **Fax:** 01404 822903

Parklands Farm, Escot, Ottery St Mary, Devon EX11 1LU

Owner: Mr J M Kennaway   **Contact:** Mr J M Kennaway

Otters, wild boar, 2 acre walled Victorian rose garden, 25 acres of shrubbery, rhododendrons and azaleas. 'Capability' Brown parkland, pet and aquatic centre, wetlands and waterfowl park, Coach House Restaurant (all home cooking), gift and craft shops. The Kennaway family estate for over 200 years.

Location: 9m E of Exeter on A30 at Fairmile.

Opening Times: Easter - 1 Oct, 10am - 6pm. 1 Oct - Easter: 11am - 4pm. Closed Christmas Day and Boxing Day.

Admission: Adult £2.25, Child £1.90 (under 5 free), Family of 5 £9, Senior Citizens £1.90, Groups £1.75.

EXETER CATHEDRAL

Tel: 01392 55573   **Fax:** 01392 498769

Exeter, Devon EX1 1HS

Contact: Mrs Juliet Dymoke-Marr

Cathedral shop, refectory. Facilities for the visually impaired and disabled. Parking within $1/2$ mile. The Exeter Rondels - 333 ft of Tapestry on the plinth around the walls of the Nave. This depicts national, local and Cathedral history from Roman times to the present day.

Location: Central to the City - between High Street and Southernhay. Groups may be put down in South Street.

Opening Times: All year: Mon - Fri 7.30am - 6.30pm, Sat 7.30am - 5pm, Sun 8am - 7.30pm.

Admission: No formal charge - donation requested of £2 per person.

FURSDON HOUSE

Tel: 01392 860860

Cadbury, Thorverton, Exeter, Devon EX5 5JS

Owner: E D Fursdon Esq   **Contact:** Mrs E.D Fursdon

The Fursdon family have lived here for over 700 years. The house is set in parkland with views stretching south to Dartmoor and the grounds include a walled and terraced garden. The house has a Regency library, Jacobean features in the dining room, and portraits. A small museum exhibits fine examples of family costumes, quilting and embroidery. Home made teas are served in The Coach Hall when the house is open.

Location: On A3072 between Tiverton and Crediton, 9m North of Exeter.

Opening Times: Easter - end Sept, Thurs & Bank Hol Mons. Tours at 2.30pm & 3.30pm.

Admission: Adult £3.00, Child under 16 £1.50, Child under 10 free. Groups of 20+ £2.80 each.

THE GARDEN HOUSE

Tel: 01822 854769

Buckland Monachorum, Yelverton, Devon PL20 7LQ

Owner: Fortescue Garden Trust   **Contact:** Mr K Wiley

An 8-acre garden of interest throughout the year including a romantic terraced, walled garden around the ruins of a 16th century vicarage. A quarry garden, acer glade, cottage garden, spring garden, rhododendron walk, herbaceous glade and lovely views. Plant centre selling interesting and unusual plants. Tea room in the house (open April - Sept).

Location: Signposted West off A386 near Yelverton, 10 m North of Plymouth.

Opening Times: 1 Mar - 31 Oct: Daily, 10.30am - 5pm. Last admission 4.40pm.

Admission: Adult £3, Child £1, OAP £2.50. Pre-booked parties 15+ £2.50 (if deposit paid).

HARTLAND ABBEY

Tel: 012374 41264

Leigh Farm, Hartland, Bideford, Devon

Owner: Sir Hugh Stucley Bt.   **Contact:** Mrs Mary Heard

Augustinian Abbey founded in 12th century. Victorian and Edwardian photographic exhibition. Shrub gardens and woodland walk to remote Atlantic cove.

Location: 15m W of Bideford, 4m off A39.

Opening Times: May - Sept: Wed, 2 - 5.30pm. Jun - Sept: Thurs & Sun. Easter - Aug: Bank Holiday Sundays and Mondays.

Admission: Adult £3.50, Child £1.50, Group £3.

HEMYOCK CASTLE

Tel: 01823 680745

Hemyock, Cullompton, Devon EX15 3RJ

Owner: Capt Sheppard   **Contact:** Mrs P M Sheppard

Former medieval moated castle, displays show site's history as fortified manor house, castle and farm. Medieval, civil war and Victorian tableaux, archeological finds, cider press and cow parlour.

Location: Exit Junction 26 M5, Blackdown Hills, Devon/Somerset border. Wellington 5m.

Opening Times: Bank Hol Mons 2 - 5pm. Other times by appointment. Groups and private parties welcome.

Admission: Adult £1.00, Child 50p, Group rate available.

HOUND TOR DESERTED MEDIEVAL VILLAGE

Tel: 01179 750700

Ashburton Road, Manaton, Dartmoor, Devon

Owner: English Heritage   **Contact:** The South West Regional Office

The remains of the dwelling.

Location: $1^1/2$ m S of Manaton off Ashburton road.

Opening Times: Any reasonable time.

Admission: Free.

KILLERTON HOUSE & GARDEN

OPEN

House:
16 March - 31 Oct
Daily except Tues
11am - 5.30 pm

Park & Garden:
open all year
Daily
10.30am - dusk

Last admission 5pm.

Tel: 01392 881345

BROADCLYST, EXETER EX5 3LE

Owner: The National Trust   *Contact:* The Administrator

The spectacular hillside garden is beautiful throughout the year with spring-flowering bulbs and shrubs, colourful herbaceous borders and fine trees. The garden is surrounded by parkland and woods offering lovely walks. The house is furnished as a family home and includes a costume collection dating from the 18th century in a series of period rooms and a Victorian laundry.

Location: off Exeter - Cullompton Rd. (B3181). M5 Northbound J29, South J28.

Admission: Adult £4.70, Child £2.30. Family £11.70. Garden & Park only: £3.10 (reduced Nov - Feb). Pre-booked parties £3.80ea.

KNIGHTSHAYES COURT

BOLHAM, TIVERTON, DEVON EX16 7RQ

Owner: The National Trust
Contact: The Property Manager

Tel: 01884 254665

One of the finest gardens in Devon, mainly woodland and shrubs with something of interest throughout the seasons. Drifts of spring bulbs, summer flowering shrubs, pool garden and amusing animal topiary. The striking Victorian Gothic house is a rare survival of the work of William Burges with ornate patterns in many rooms.

Location: 2 miles North of Tiverton (A396) at Bolham.

OPEN

House: 1 Apr - 31 Oct Daily: 11am - 5.30pm (except Fri, but open Good Fri). Last adm. 5pm.
Nov & Dec Suns: 2 - 4pm (pre-booked parties only).
Garden: 16 March - 31 Oct: Daily 11am - 5.30pm

Admission: Adult £4.80, Child £2.40. Family £12.00 Garden & Grounds only: £3.10 Pre-booked parties £4.00

LYDFORD CASTLES AND SAXTON TOWN

Tel: 01179 750700

Lydford, Okehampton, Devon
Owner: English Heritage   **Contact:** The South West Regional Office
Standing above the lovely gorge of the River Lyd, this 12th century tower was notorious as a prison. The earthworks of the original Norman fort are to the south. A Saxon town once stood nearby and its layout is still discernible.
Location: In Lydford off A386 8 m S of Okehampton.
Opening Times: Any reasonable time.

MARKERS COTTAGE

Tel: 01392 461546

Broadclyst, Exeter, Devon EX5 3HR
Owner: The National Trust   **Contact:** The Administrator
Fascinating medieval cob house which contains a cross-passage screen decorated with a painting of St Andrew and his attributes.
Location: Off B3181 in village of Broadclyst.
Opening Times: 1 Apr - 31 Oct: Sun, Mon and Tues, 2 - 5pm.
Admission: £1.00

MARWOOD HILL

Tel: 01271 42528

Barnstaple, Devon EX31 4ER
Owner: Dr J A Smart   **Contact:** Dr J A Smart
20 acre garden with 3 small lakes. Extensive collection of camellias, bog garden. National collection of astilbes.
Location: 4m North of Barnstaple.
Opening Times: Dawn to dusk throughout the year.
Admission: Adult £2.00, Child free under 12.

MORWELLHAM QUAY

Tel: 01822 832766   Fax: 01822 833808

Tavistock, Devon PL19 8JL
Owner: The Morwellham & Tamar Valley Trust   **Contact:** Gary Emerson
Mid 19th century river copper port which has been restored by the Trust for over 25 years. Docks, ships, quaysides, cottages. Assayers, coopers and blacksmiths workshops. Incline plane railways, copper mine tramway ride underground.. Farm shire stables, trails, shops and restaurants.
Location: M5 Okehampton junction then A30 Tavistock.
Opening Times: Summer 10am - 5.30pm, Winter (Nov - Easter) 10am - 4.30pm.
Last admissions 2 hours before closing. Closed Christmas week 23 Dec - 2 Jan.
Admission: Adult £7.50, Child £5.00, Senior Citizens £7.00. Groups: Adult £5.75, Child £4.00, Senior citizens £5.00.

MOUNT BATTEN TOWER

Tel: 01179 750700

Mount Batten Point, Plymstock, Devon
Owner: English Heritage   **Contact:** The South West Regional Office
A 17th century gun tower, 30 feet high and with original windows and vaulted roof. There are good views across Plymouth Sound from here.
Location: In Plymstock, on Mount Batten Point.
Opening Times: Summer 10am - 5.30pm. Winter (Nov-Easter) 10am - 4.30pm.
Last admissions 2 hours before closing.
Admission: Contact South West Regional Office.

OKEHAMPTON CASTLE

Tel: 01837 52844

Okehampton, Devon EX20 1JB
Owner: English Heritage   **Contact:** The Custodian
The ruins of the largest castle in Devon stand above a river surrounded by splendid woodland. There is still plenty to see, including the Norman motte and the jagged remains of the Keep. There is a picnic area and lovely woodland walks.
Location: 1m SW of Okehampton town centre.
Opening Times: 1 Apr - 30 Sept: 10am - 6pm. 1 - 31 Oct: 10am - 6pm or dusk if earlier.
Admission: Adult £2.20, Child £1.10, Conc £1.70.

THE OLD BAKERY

Tel: 01297 680333

Branscombe, Seaton, Devon EX12 3DB
Owner: The National Trust   **Contact:** The National Trust
A traditional stone built and partially rendered building beneath a thatch roof which was, until 1987, the last traditional bakery in use in Devon. The baking room has been preserved and houses traditional baking equipment. The remainder of the building is used as tea-rooms.
Location: In Branscombe off A3052.
Opening Times: Daily Easter to Oct and weekends in winter 11am - 5pm.

OVERBECKS MUSEUM & GARDEN

Tel: 01548 842893

Sharpitor, Salcombe, Devon TQ8 8LW
Owner: The National Trust   **Contact:** The Administrator
Spectacular views over Salcombe estuary can be enjoyed from the beautiful 6 acre garden, with its many rare plants, shrubs and trees. The elegant Edwardian house contains collections of local photographs taken at the end of the last century, local ship building tools, model boats, toys, shells, birds, animals and other collections, together with a secret room for children. Also of interest is an exhibition showing the natural history of the area.
Location: 1¹/₂m S of Salcombe, signposted from Malborough and Salcombe.
Opening Times: Museum: 1 Apr - 31 Oct: Daily except Sat 11am - 5.30pm. Last admission 5pm. Garden: Daily throughout year 10am - 8pm or sunset if earlier.
Admission: Museum & Garden: £3.50, Garden only: £2.30. No reductions for parties.

POWDERHAM CASTLE

See page 50 for full page entry.

RHS GARDEN ROSEMOOR

OPEN

Apr - Sept
10am - 6pm

Mar & Oct
10am - 5pm

Nov - Feb
10am - 4pm

Tel: 01805 624067
Fax: 01805 624717

GREAT TORRINGTON, DEVON

Owner: The Royal Horticultural Society   *Contact:* The Royal Horticultural Society

A stunning new National Garden often seen on TV, situated in the breathtaking setting of the Torridge Valley just south of Great Torrington. Rosemoor is designed to delight and inspire all gardeners from novice to professional. Its 40-acres contain a wide range of features; the mature planting in Lady Anne's magnificent garden and arboretum around Rosemoor House. A licenced restaurant, shop and plant centre.
Location: Great Torrington, North Devon.
Admission: Adult £3, Child £1. Groups of 10+ £2.50. Shop, Plant Centre Free.

ROYAL CITADEL

Tel: 01179 750700

Plymouth Hoe, Plymouth, Devon
Owner: English Heritage   **Contact:** The South West Regional Office
A large, dramatic 17th century fortress, with walls up to 70 feet high, built to defend the coastline from the Dutch and still in use today.
Location: At E end of Plymouth Hoe.
Opening Times: By guided tour only (1¹/₂ hrs) at 11.30am and 2pm. 1 May - 30 Sept. Assemble at Plymouth Dome below Smeaton's Tower on the Hoe.
Admission: Contact The South West Regional Office.

KEY TO SYMBOLS: THE NATIONAL TRUST   ENGLISH HERITAGE   HISTORIC HOUSES ASSOCIATION

SALTRAM HOUSE

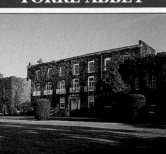

PLYMPTON, PLYMOUTH, DEVON PL7 3UH

Owner: The National Trust
Contact: The Property Manager

Tel: 01752 336546

The finest Georgian house west of Bath, with two important rooms designed by Robert Adam, with magnificent plasterwork and decoration. The house contains fine period furniture, china and pictures, including many portraits by Reynolds. The Old Kitchen is fitted out with the original copper utensils, obsolete culinary gadgets and turning spits. There is a gallery of West Country art in the chapel.

Location: 2 miles west of Plympton, 3½ miles east of Plymouth city centre.

Admission: Adult £5.20, Child £2.60, Family £13.00. Garden only: £2.40. Groups of 15+ £4.40.

OPEN

House. 1 Apr - 31 Oct: Daily 12.30 - 5.30pm except Fri & Sat but open Good Friday

Garden: 2 - 31 March Sat & Sun only 11 - 4pm and 1 Apr from 10.30am. Art Gallery & Great Kitchen open as house but from 10.30am. Last admission 5pm.

SAND

Sidbury, Sidmouth, Devon EX10 0QN
Owner: Lt.Col. P Huyshe   **Contact:** Lt.Col. P Huyshe
Lived in house, owned by Huyshe family from 1560, rebuilt 1592 - 94 in unspoilt valley. Screens passage, heraldry, family documents. Also Sand Lodge roof structure of late 15th century hall house.
Location: Grid Ref: SY 146925. ¼m off A375 Honiton to Sidmouth.
Opening Times: Sun, Mon: Apr 7, 8, May 5, 6, 26, 27, Jul 28, 29, Aug 25, 26, 2 - 5.30pm. Last tour 4.45pm.
Admission: Adult £3.00, Child/full time student 60p.

Tel: 01395 597230

SHOBROOKE PARK

Crediton, Devon EX17 1DG
Owner: Dr J R Shelley   **Contact:** Dr J R Shelley
A classical English 180-acre park. The lime avenue dates from about 1800 and the cascade of four lakes was completed in the 1840s. The southern third of the Park is open to the public under the Countryside Commission Access Scheme. The 17 acre garden created c.1845 has Portland stone terraces and the woodland is being restored.
Location: 1 mile East of Crediton on the Shobrooke Road off A3072.
Opening Times: Park: open at all times. Gardens: May Day Bank Hol Mon 2 - 5.30pm.
Admission: Park access is free. Gardens £2.00, accompanied children under 14 free.

SHUTE BARTON

Shute, Axminster, Devon EX13 7PT
Owner: The National Trust   **Contact:** The Administrator
One of the most important surviving non-fortified manor houses of the Middle Ages. Commenced in 1380 and completed in the last 16th century, then partly demolished in the late 18th century, the house has battlemented turrets, late Gothic windows and a Tudor gatehouse.
Location: 3m SW of Axminster, 2m N of Colyton on B3161.
Opening Times: 1 Apr - 31 Oct: Wed & Sat, 2 - 5.30pm. Last admission 5.00pm.
Admission: £1.60, No party reductions.

Tel: 01297 34692

TIVERTON CASTLE

Tel: 01884 253200   **Fax:** 01884 254200

Tiverton, Devon EX16 6RP
Owner: Mr A K Gordon   **Contact:** Mrs A K Gordon
Historic castle originally built in 1106 by order of Henry I, once home of the medieval Earls of Devon, one of whom married Princess Katherine Plantagenet. Besieged by Fairfax in 1645, a lucky shot hit the drawbridge chain. Magnificent medieval gateway, Norman tower, romantic ruins, impassable secret passages, important Civil War armoury, superb holiday apartments.
Location: Centre of Tiverton.
Opening Times: Easter - end of June. Sept: Sun & Thur only. Jul & Aug: Sun - Thur. Bank Hol Mons 2.30 - 5.30pm. Open to parties (12+) by prior arrangement at any time.
Admission: Adult £3.00, Child (7-16) £2.00, Children under 7 free.

TORRE ABBEY

OPEN

Apr - Oct

Daily

9.30am - 6pm

Last adm. 5pm

Tel: 01803 293593

THE KINGS DRIVE, TORQUAY, DEVON TQ2 5JX

Owner: Torbay Borough Council   *Contact:* L Retallick

Torre Abbey was founded as a monastery in 1196. Later adapted as a country house and in 1741-3 remodelled by the Cary family. Bought by the Council in 1930 for an art gallery. Visitors can see monastic remains, historic rooms, family chapel, mementoes of Agatha Christie, Victorian paintings including Holman Hunt & Burne-Jones & Torquay terracotta. Torre Abbey overlooks the sea and is surrounded by parkland and gardens. Teas served in Victorian kitchen.
Location: On Torquay sea front.
Admission: Adult £2.50, OAP/student £2.00, Child £1.50, Family £5.95. Pre-arranged parties (10+) £1.80. Guided tours by prior arrangement.

TOTNES CASTLE

Tel: 01803 864406

Castle Street, Totnes, Plymouth, Devon TQ9 5NU
Owner: English Heritage   **Contact:** The Custodian
By the North Gate of the hill town of Totnes you will find a superb motte and bailey castle, with splendid views across the roof tops and down to the River Dart. It is a symbol of lordly feudal life and a fine example of Norman fortification.
Location: In Totnes, on hill overlooking the town.
Opening Times: 1 Apr - 30 Sept: Daily 10am - 6pm. 1 - 31 Oct: Daily 10am - 6pm or dusk if earlier. 1 Nov - 31 Mar: Wed - Sun, 10am - 4 pm (closed lunch 1 - 2pm, Nov - Mar).
Admission: Adult £1.50, Child 80p, Conc £1.10.

YARDE MEDIEVAL FARMHOUSE

Tel: 01548 842367

Malborough, Kingsbridge, Devon TQ7 3BY
Owner: John R Ayres Esq   **Contact:** John R Ayres Esq
Location: 5m S of Kingsbridge off A381.
Opening Times: Easter - 30 Sept: Wed, Fri, Sun 2 - 5pm.
Admission: Adult £2, Child 50p, Child under 5 free, Groups by appointment only.

SPECIAL EVENTS

◆ **POWDERHAM CASTLE** The Strawberry Fayre	**1 – 2 JUNE**	
◆ **POWDERHAM CASTLE** Powderham Horse Trials	**29 – 30 JUNE**	
◆ **POWDERHAM CASTLE** Open Air Concert 'Summer Music in the Park'	**6 JULY**	
◆ **POWDERHAM CASTLE** Historic and Classic Vehicle gathering	**13 – 14 JULY**	
◆ **TORRE ABBEY** Annual Show: Torbay Flower Club	**13 – 14 JULY**	
◆ **POWDERHAM CASTLE** Outdoor Boat and Leisure Show	**21 – 22 JULY**	
◆ **TORRE ABBEY** Annual Show: South Devon Fuschia Society	**27 – 28 JULY**	
◆ **POWDERHAM CASTLE** Medieval Tournament	**28 – 29 JULY**	
◆ **TORRE ABBEY** Classic Car Rally - as one of a series of events to celebrate the 800th anniversary of the founding of Torre Abbey.	**8 SEPTEMBER**	
◆ **TORRE ABBEY** Annual Torre Abbey Flower Festival	**13 – 16 SEPTEMBER**	

For National Trust and English Heritage Events see separate section.

ATHELHAMPTON HOUSE & GARDENS

ATHELHAMPTON, DORCHESTER, DORSET DT2 7LG

Owner: *Patrick Cooke*　　***Contact:*** *Patrick Cooke*

Tel: 01305 848363　**Fax:** 01305 848135

Athelhampton is one of the finest 15th century manor houses and is surrounded by one of the great architectural gardens of England. Enjoy the Tudor Great Hall, Great Chamber, Wine Cellar and the East Wing restored after the fire in Nov 1992. Wander through 20 acres of beautiful grounds dating from 1891, including the Great Court with 12 giant yew pyramids. The walled gardens include collections of tulips, magnolias, roses, clematis and lilies in season. This glorious garden of vistas is full of surprises and gains much from the fountains and River Piddle flowing through. Restaurant serving lunches, cream teas & refreshments. Gift shop and free car park.

Location: On A35, 5 miles East of Dorchester.

Opening Times: 31 March - 27 October: Daily 11am - 5pm (except Saturdays).

Admission: House & Gardens: Adult £4.50, OAP £4.20, Child £1.50, Family £10. Grounds only: Adult/OAP £2.80, Child Free.

CHETTLE HOUSE
Tel: 01258 830209　**Fax:** 01258 830380

Chettle, Blandford Forum, Dorset DT11 8DB
Owner: Patrick Bourke Esq　　　　**Contact:** Patrick Bourke Esq
Fine Queen Anne house by Thomas Archer set in 5 acres of garden.
Location: 6m NE of Blandford off A354.
Opening Times: 5 Apr - 13 Oct: Daily (except Tue and Sat) 11am - 5pm.
Admission: Standard £2.00, Child free, Groups by arrangement.

CHRISTCHURCH CASTLE & NORMAN HOUSE 　　**Tel:** 01179 750700

Christchurch, Dorset
Owner: English Heritage　　　　**Contact:** The South West Regional Office
Early 12th century Norman keep and Constable's house, built c.1160.
Location: In Christchurch, near the Priory.
Opening Times: Any reasonable time.

CLOUDS HILL
Tel: 01929 405616

Wareham, Dorset BH20 7NQ
Owner: The National Trust　　　　**Contact:** The Administrator
T E Lawrence (Lawrence of Arabia) bought this cottage in 1925 as a retreat; it contains his furniture.
Location: 9m E of Dorchester, 1¹/₂m E of Waddock crossroads B3390.
Opening Times: 3 Apr - 31 Oct: Wed, Thur, Fri, Sun and BH Mon, 12 noon - 5pm or dusk if earlier.
Admission: £2.20, no reduction for children or parties.

COMPTON ACRES GARDENS
Tel: 01202 700778　**Fax:** 01202 707537

Canford Cliffs Road, Canford Cliffs , Poole, Dorset BH13 7ES
Owner: Compton Acres Ltd　　　　**Contact:** P Willsher Esq
Cliff top series of gardens overlooking Poole Harbour, very colourful planting.
Location: Canford Cliffs Road.
Opening Times: 7 days a week, 10.30am - 6.30pm (or dusk if earlier). Last entry 5.45pm.
Admission: Adult £4.20, Child £1, Family £9, Senior citizens/students £3.20. Groups: Adult £3.50, Senior Citizens £2.70.

BROWNSEA ISLAND

POOLE HARBOUR, DORSET BH15 1EE

Owner: *The National Trust*　　***Contact:*** *The Property Manager*

Tel: 01202 707744

A 202.42 ha island of heath and woodland, with wide views of Dorset coast, the island includes a 80.97ha nature reserve leased to the Dorset Trust for nature conservation. Boats run from Poole Quay and Sandbanks, Swanage & Bournemouth. Visitors may land from own boat at Pottery Pier at west end of island. Accessible at all stages of the tide.

Location: In Poole Harbour, Boats run from Poole Quay and Sandbanks. Visitors may land on the beach with a dinghy.

Opening Times: 1 Apr - 29 Sept: Daily 10am - 8pm (or dusk if earlier).

Admission: Landing fee: Adult £2.20, Child £1.10. Parties £1.90 (Child 90p), Family (2 adults & 2 children) £5.20 (Apr, May, Jun & Sept).

CORFE CASTLE

WAREHAM, DORSET BH20 5EZ

Owner: *The National Trust*　　***Contact:*** *The Property Manager*

Tel: 01929 481294

One of the most impressive medieval ruins in England, this former royal castle was besieged and sleighted by parliamentary forces in 1646. Visitor centre at castle view on A351 north of castle: opening spring 1996.

Location: On A351 Wareham - Swanage road.

Opening Times: 4 Mar - 24 Mar: Daily 10am - 4.30pm. 25 Mar - 27 Oct: Daily 10am - 5.30pm. 28 Oct - 3 Nov: Daily, 10 - 4.30pm. 4 Nov - 3 Mar 1997: Daily 11am - 3.30pm. Closed 25 & 26 Dec.

Admission: Adult £3.00, Child £1.50, Party £2.50 (Child £1.25).

DEANS COURT

WIMBORNE MINSTER, DORSET BH21 1EE

OPEN
Daffodil Weekends:
16/17 & 24/25 Mar
2 - 5pm,

Bank Hol Mons
10am - 6pm.

Organic Weekend
22/23 June
2 - 6pm

First and last
Sundays May - Sept
and last opening Sun
6 Oct
2 - 6pm.

Tel: 01202 886116

Owner: Sir Michael and Lady Hanham　*Contact:* Wimborne Tourist Centre

A partly wild garden with specimen trees, monastery fishpond, peacocks, herb garden (over 200 species), walled kitchen garden. Produce & herb plants for sale - all chemical free. The house, formerly the Deanery is open by prior written appointment. Wholefood teas and coffee on Bank Holiday mornings served in former housekeeper's room.
Location: 2 mins walk south from centre of Wimborne Minster.
Admission: Adult £1.50, Child 70p. Groups by arrangement. Guide dogs only, no unaccompanied children.

EDMONDSHAM HOUSE　　　　**Tel:** 01725 517207

Cranborne, Wimborne, Dorset BH21 5RE
Owner: Mrs. Julia E Smith　　　　　**Contact:** Mrs. Julia E Smith
Charming blend of Tudor and Georgian architecture with interesting contents. Old fashioned walled garden.
Location: Between Cranborne and Verwood, 9m from Ringwood.
Opening Times: Garden:Sun & Wed, 2 5pm. House & Gdn:Apr & Oct, BH Mons, Wed, 2-5pm.
Admission: Adult £2.50, Child £1.00. under fives free. Groups by arrangement.

FIDDLEFORD MANOR 　　**Tel:** 01179 750700

Sturminster Newton, Dorset
Owner: English Heritage　　　　**Contact:** The South West Regional Office
Part of a medieval manor house, with a remarkable interior. The splendid roof structures in the hall and upper living room are the best in Dorset.
Location: 1 m E of Sturminster Newton off A357.
Opening Times: 1 Apr-30 Sept & 1- 31 Oct: 10am - 6pm/dusk in Oct. 1 Nov-31 Mar 10am - 4pm.

FORDE ABBEY

NR. CHARD, SOMERSET TA20 4LU

OPEN
Gardens:
All year: Daily
10am - 4.30pm

House:
1 April - end Oct.
Suns, Weds &
Bank Holidays
1 - 4.30pm
Last admission.

Tel: 01460 220231
Fax: 01460 220296

Owner: Mark Roper Esq.　*Contact:* Mark Roper Esq.

"Winners of Christies/HHA Garden of Year Award 1993"

Founded by Cistercian monks almost 900 years ago. Today it remains a genuine family home, unchanged since the middle of the 17th century. Situated in some of the most beautiful countryside in west Dorset. 30 acres of gardens with herbaceous borders, arboretum, magnificent trees and shrubs, 5 lakes, Bog garden. Here you can enjoy the peace and beauty of a past age. There are no ropes or barriers in the house and no sideshows in the gardens. Conference facilities available.
Location: Just off the B3167 4 miles south of Chard.
Admission: House & Gardens: Adult £4.80, OAP £4.30, Groups £3.50, Child Free. Gardens only: Adult £3.50, OAP £3.25, Groups £3.00, Child Free.

HARDY'S COTTAGE 　　**Tel:** 01305 262366

Higher Bockhampton, Dorchester, Dorset DT2 8QJ
Owner: The National Trust　　　　**Contact:** The National Trust
A small thatched cottage where the novelist and poet Thomas Hardy was born in 1840. It was built by his great grandfather and little altered, furnished by the Trust.
Location: 3m NE of Dorchester, ¹/₂m S of A35.
Opening Times: 1 Apr - 30 Oct: Daily (not Thurs) 11am - 6pm/dusk if earlier. Open Good Fri.
Admission: £2.50.

HORN PARK　　**Tel:** 01308 862212　**Fax:** 01308 863778

Beaminster, Dorset DT8 3HB
Owner: John Kirkpatrick Esq　　　**Contact:** John Kirkpatrick Esq
Extensive garden with good views. Wildflower meadow. Plants for sale.
Location: Beaminster, Dorset.
Opening Times: 1 Apr - 31 Oct: Tues, Wed, Sun and BH Mon, 2 - 6pm.
Admission: Adult £2.50, Child under 14 free , Group £2.50 ea.

ILSINGTON HOUSE

PUDDLETOWN, DORCHESTER DT2 8TQ

OPEN
House tours:
1 May - 26 Sept
Wed and Thurs
2 - 6pm.
Last tour 5pm.
Also Suns and
Bank Hol Mons
in August.

Tel: 01305 848454
Fax: 01305 848909

Owner: P J Duff Esq　*Contact:* Mrs P Duff

A family home, set in the picturesque village of Puddletown (Thomas Hardy's Weatherbury). A classical William and Mary mansion built by the 7th Earl of Huntingdon. Home of George III's illegitimate grandson, born to HRH Princess Sophia in 1800, kept a secret until the Royal Scandal of 1829. Visited by many members of the Royal Family during George III's reign. Fine furniture and present owner's private collection of pictures and sculpture. A fully guided house tour given. Formal and landscape gardens with probably the longest haha in Dorset. Large collection of beautiful bearded irises and unusual peonies.
Location: Puddletown, Dorchester.
Admission: £4.00.

KINGSTON LACY

WIMBORNE MINSTER, DORSET BH21 4EA

Owner: The National Trust　*Contact:* The Administrator

Tel: 01202 883402

A 17th century house designed for Sir Ralph Bankes by Sir Roger Pratt and altered by Sir Charles Barry in the 19th century. The house contains an outstanding collection of paintings, including works by Rubens, Titian, Van Dyck and Lely. The Spanish room is in gilded leather with a gilded ceiling brought from the Contarni palace in Venice. A fine collection of Egyptian artifacts. The mansion is set in 250 acres of wooded park with a fine herd of Red Devon cattle.
Location: On B3082 - Blandford/Wimborne road, 1.5m W of Wimborne.
Opening Times: 1 Apr - 30 Oct: Daily except Thurs & Fri. House: 12 - 5.30pm. Last admission 4.30pm. Garden & Park: 11.30am - 6pm or dusk if earlier.
Admission: Adult £5.50, Child £2.70, Party £4.80 (child £2.50).

KNOLL GARDENS & NURSERY   **Tel:** 01202 873931   **Fax:** 01202 870842

Stapehill Road, Hampreston, Wimborne, Dorset BH21 7ND

Owner: J & J Flude and N.R. Lucas   **Contact:** Mr John Flude

Award winning 6 acre gardens, now with 4000+ named plants from the world over. Wide range of trees, shrubs and colourful hardy plants in an informal English setting. Beautiful water gardens, tumbling waterfalls, streams and ponds with exotic fish. Two national collections: Ceanothus and Phygelius. Spacious visitor centre with extensive plant sales, video presentations, licensed cafeteria, gift/bookshops. Ideal for less mobile visitors. A *true* garden experience.

Location: Off B3073 (Hampreston) Exit A31 Canford Bottom Roundabout (signed 1 ¹/₂m). Between Wimborne and Ferndown.

Opening Times: Mar: Wed - Sun 10am - 4.00pm. 1 Apr - 31 Oct: Daily 10am - 5.30pm. Nov - Christmas: Wed - Sat 10am - 4pm.

Admission: Adult £3.45, Child (4 - 16) £1.70, Senior citizens £2.90, Family £8.30, Student £2.40. Groups; Adult £2.95, Senior citizen £2.60.

LULWORTH CASTLE   **Tel:** 01929 41352

East Lulworth, Wareham, Dorset

Owner: English Heritage   **Contact:** The Custodian

Built in the early 16th century as a romantic hunting lodge, Lulworth Castle was changed into a fashionable country house set in beautiful parkland during the 18th century. Gutted by fire in 1929 the exterior of the castle is now being restored by English Heritage.

Location: In East Lulworth off the B3070, 3 m NE of Lulworth Cove.

Opening Times: 1 Apr - 30 Sept: Daily 10am - 6pm. 1 - 31 Oct: Daily 10am - 6pm or dusk. 1 Nov - 22 Dec: Daily, 10am - 4pm.

Admission: Adult £1.50, Child 75p, Conc £1.20.

THE MANOR HOUSE   **Tel:** 01963 250400

Purse Caundle, Sherborne, Dorset DT9 5DY

Owner: Michael de Pelet Esq   **Contact:** Michael de Pelet Esq

15th & 16th century manor house. Great Hall with minstrels gallery. Upstairs great chamber with barrel ceiling and oriel window. Family home.

Location: 4m E of Sherborne, just off A30.

Opening Times: Easter Mon and then 1 May - 29 Sept: Thur, Sun and BHs, 2 - 5pm.

Admission: Adult £2.50, Child free. Groups by appointment.
Tea by appointment for groups.

MAPPERTON

OPEN

Gardens.
1 March - 31 Oct.
Daily
2.00 - 6.00pm

House:
Open only to groups
by appointment
(times as above)

Tel: 01308 862645
Fax: 01308 863348

BEAMINSTER, DORSET DT8 3NR

Owner: Earl & Countess of Sandwich   *Contact:* Earl & Countess of Sandwich

Jacobean 1660's manor with Tudor features and classical north front. Italianate upper garden with orangery, topiary and formal borders descending to fish ponds and shrub gardens. All Saints Church forms south wing opening to courtyard and stables. Area of outstanding natural beauty with fine views of Dorset hills and woodlands.

Location: 1 mile off B3163, 2 miles off B3066, 2 miles Beaminster, 5 miles Bridport.

Admission: Gardens: £2.50, House (tour) £3.50. Under 18 £1.50, under 5 free.

MAX GATE   **Tel:** 01305 262538

Alington Avenue, Dorchester, Dorset DT1 2AA

Owner: The National Trust   **Contact:** The Tenant

Poet and Novelist Thomas Hardy designed and lived in the house from 1885 until his death in 1928. The house is leased to tenants and contains several pieces of Hardy's furniture.

Location: 1 mile E of Dorchester on A352 to Wareham. From Dorchester follow A352 signs for Wareham until the mini roundabout to A35 Dorchester bypass. Turn left and left again into cul-de-sac outside Max Gate.

Opening Times: Garden & Drawing Room : 1 Apr - 2 Oct: Mon, Wed, Sat & Sun. 2 - 5pm.

Admission: Adult £2.00, Child £1.00.

MILTON ABBEY CHURCH   **Tel:** 01258 880489

Milton Abbas, Blandford, Dorset DT11 0BP

Owner: Diocese of Salisbury   **Contact:** Mrs D Illingworth

A church has stood here for over 1,000 years. Present Abbey dates from 14/15th century. 18th century Gothic style house built to complement Abbey and Abbots Hall. Exterior by Sir William Chambers, interior in classic style by James Wyatt. Beautiful tranquil setting in heart of Dorset ¹/₂ mile from 200 yr old "New" village of Milton Abbas with its identical cottages. Abbey situated in grounds of Milton Abbey School.

Location: 3¹/₂ m from A354 Puddletown to Blandford Road. Mid Dorset.

Opening Times: Abbey Church: Daily. House & Grounds: (Council of Milton Abbey School) mid-July - end August: Daily 10am - 6pm. Groups by arrangement only please.

Admission: By donation except during Easter, mid-July to end August. Adult £1.75, accompanied children free.

MINTERNE GARDENS   **Tel:** 01300 341370   **Fax:** 01300 341747

Minterne Magna, Nr Cerne Abbas, Dorchester, Dorset DT2 7AU

Owner: The Lord Digby   **Contact:** The Lord Digby

Large wild woodland garden landscaped in 18th century with over a mile of walks. Many rare rhododendrons and magnolias tower over small lakes, cascades and streams.

Location: Sherborne/Dorchester road A352 2m North of Cerne Abbas.

Opening Times: Apr - 10 November: Daily.

Admission: £2.00, accompanied children free.

PARNHAM HOUSE

BEAMINSTER, DORSET DT8 3NA

Owner: John Makepeace   *Contact:* The House Manager - Cdr Bruce Hunter-Inglis

Tel: 01308 862204   **Fax:** 01308 863494

Inspiring 20th century craftsmanship. displayed in the home of John and Jennie Makepeace, who have restored and enlivened this fascinating tudor Manor House. Exhibitions of exciting contemporary work in glass, wood, textiles and ceramics. Licensed buttery, shop and furniture workshop, romantic terraces and topiary in 14 acres of fine gardens and woodland walks.

Location: On A3066 5 miles north of Bridport, ¹/₂ mile south of Beaminster.

Opening Times: 3 Apr - 30 Oct: Wed, Suns and Bank Holidays 10am - 5pm. Tuesdays & Thursdays groups only.

Admission: Adult £4.00, Child 10-15 yrs £2.00, Child under 10 Free.

PORTLAND CASTLE   **Tel:** 01305 820539

Castletown, Portland, Weymouth, Dorset DT5 1AZ

Owner: English Heritage   **Contact:** The Custodian

One of the best preserved of Henry VIII's coastal forts, built of white Portland stone. Now standing quietly overlooking the harbour, it was originally intended to thwart attack by the Spanish and French, and changed hands several times during the Civil War.

Location: Overlooking Portland harbour adjacent to RN helicopter base.

Opening Times: 1 Apr - 30 Sept: Daily 10am - 6pm. 1 - 31 Oct: Daily 10am - 6pm or dusk if earlier.

Admission: Adult £2.00, Child £1.00, Conc £1.50.

THE PRIEST'S HOUSE MUSEUM

Tel: 01202 882533   **Fax:** 01202 882533

23-27 High Street, Wimborne Minster, Dorset BH21 1HR
Owner: Priest's House Museum Trust   **Contact:** Ms K Osborne
Location: 8m N of Poole/Bournemouth off A31.
Opening Times: 1 Apr - 31 Oct: Mon - Sat 10.30am - 5pm. BH Suns and Suns
Jun - Sept, 2 - 5pm.
Admission: Adult £1.95, Child 75p, Family £4.75, Conc £1.50. 10% discount for 30+.

SANDFORD'S ORCAS MANOR HOUSE

Tel: 01963 220206

Sandford Orcas, Sherborne, Dorset DT9 4SB
Owner: Sir Mervyn Medlycott Bt   **Contact:** Sir Mervyn Medlycott Bt
Tudor Manor House with gatehouse, fine panelling, furniture, pictures. Terraced gardens
with topiary and herb garden. Personal conducted tour by owner.
Location: 2 1/2m N of Sherborne, Dorset. Entrance next to church.
Opening Times: Easter Mon, 10am - 6pm. May - Sept: Sun, 2 - 6pm, Mon 10am - 6pm.
Admission: Adult £2.00, Child £1.00. Group: Adult £1.70, Child 80p.

SHERBORNE CASTLE

OPEN

Easter Sat - Sept.
Thurs, Sats, Suns and
Bank Hol Mons.

Castle:
1.30 - 5.00pm

Grounds & Tea
Room
12.30 - 5.00pm

Tel: 01935 813182
Fax: 01935 816727

SHERBORNE, DORSET DT9 3PY

Owner: Mr Simon Wingfield Digby   *Contact: June Taylor*

A fully furnished Historic House built by Sir Walter Raleigh in 1594 and home of
the Digby family since 1617, reflecting various styles from the Elizabethan Hall to
the Victorian Solarium. Splendid collections of art, furniture and porcelain. Well
informed guides are happy to answer questions. Set in beautiful parkland with
lawns, wooded walks and a 50 acre lake.

Location: 3/4 mile south east of Sherborne town centre. Follow brown signs from
A30 or A352
Admission: Grounds & Castle: Adult £4.00, OAP £3.50, Child £2.00.
Grounds only Adult/OAP £2.00, Child £1.00.

SHERBORNE OLD CASTLE

Tel: 01935 812730

Castleton, Sherborne, Dorset D19 5NR
Owner: English Heritage   **Contact:** The Custodian
The ruins of this early 12th century castle are a testament to the 16 days it took Cromwell to
capture it during the Civil War, after which it was abandoned.
Location: 1/2 m E of Sherborne off B3145.
Opening Times: 1 Apr - 30 Sept: 10am - 6pm. 1 Oct - 31 Oct: 10am - 6pm/dusk if earlier.
1 Nov - 31 Mar: Wed - Sun 10am - 4pm. (Closed lunch 1 - 2pm Nov - Mar).
Admission: Adult £1.50, Child 80p, Conc £1.10.

SPECIAL EVENTS

◇ **ATHELHAMPTON HOUSE AND GARDENS**   **5 – 8 APRIL**
Arts and Craft Fair

◇ **ATHELHAMPTON HOUSE AND GARDENS**   **26 – 29 MAY**
Flower Show

◇ **ATHELHAMPTON HOUSE AND GARDENS**   **7 JULY**
MG Owners' Club Car Rally

◇ **ATHELHAMPTON HOUSE AND GARDENS**   **24 – 26 AUGUST**
Arts and Craft Fair

For National Trust and English Heritage Events see separate section.

SMEDMORE HOUSE

OPEN

House & Garden:
15 Sept. &
19 May

2.00 - 5.00pm
Groups by
arrangement.

Tel: 01929 480719

SMEDMORE, KIMMERIDGE, WAREHAM, DORSET BH20 5BG

Owner: Dr Philip Mansel   *Contact: Mr. T Gargett*

The home of the Mansel family for nearly 400 years nestles at the foot of the
Purbeck hills looking across Kimmeridge Bay to Portland Bill. Originally built in
1620 by the present owner's ancestor William Clavell, the imposing Georgian front
was added in 1760's. Beautiful walled garden with many special and interesting
plants. Popular for Holiday lets, weddings, business and private functions.

Location: 15 miles south west of Dorchester.
Admission: Full details from the Warden.

ST CATHERINE'S CHAPEL

Tel: 01179 750700

Abbotsbury, Dorset
Owner: English Heritage   **Contact:** The South West Regional Office
A small stone chapel, set on a hilltop, with an unusual roof and small turret used as a
lighthouse.
Location: 1/2 m S of Abbotsbury by pedestrian track.
Opening Times: Any reasonable time.

WHITE MILL

Tel: 01258 858051

Sturminster Marshall, Nr. Wimborne, Dorset
Owner: The National Trust   **Contact:** The Administrator
Rebuilt in 1776 on Domesday site this corn mill was extensively repaired in 1994 and con-
tains much of the original and rare timber 18th century machinery (now too fragile to be
operative). Peaceful setting by river Stour. Riverside picnic area nearby.
Location: On the River Stour North of Sturminster Marshall from B3082 Blandford -
Wareham road take right hand turn signposted Sturminster Marshall. Mill is 1 mile on right.
Car park nearby.
Opening Times: 30 Mar - 27 Oct: Weekends & Bank Holidays 11am - 5pm.
Admission: Adult £1.50, Child £1.

WOLFETON HOUSE

OPEN

May - Sept.
Tues, Thurs and
Bank Holiday
Mondays
2.00 - 6.00pm

At other times
throughout the
year parties by
appointment

Tel: 01305 263500
Fax: 01305 265090

NEAR DORCHESTER, DORSET DT2 9QN

Owner: Capt N.T.L.L. Thimbleby   *Contact: The Steward*

A fine mediaeval and Elizabethan Manor House lying in the water-meadows near
the confluence of the rivers Cerne and Frome. It was much embellished around
1580 and has splendid plaster ceilings, fireplaces and panelling of that date. To be
seen are the Great Hall, Stairs and Chamber, Parlour, Dining Room, Chapel and
Cyder House. The mediaeval Gatehouse has two unmatched and older towers.
There are good pictures and furniture.
Location: 1 1/2 miles from Dorchester on the A37 towards Yeovil. Indicated by
Historic House signs.
Admission: Adult £3.00, Child £1.50

RABY CASTLE
Darlington

RABY CASTLE, home of Lord Barnard's family for over 360 years, is set in a 200 acre Deer Park. The Castle was mainly built in the 14th century, on the site of an earlier Manor House, by the powerful Neville family, who owned it until the Rising of the North in 1569, when Raby was seized by the Crown. It remained Crown property until 1626, when it was bought from Charles I by the eminent statesman and politician Sir Henry Vane, Lord Barnard's ancestor.

Despite its appearance, Raby was intended to be a fortified home rather than a fortress, although it played an important part in the Wars of the Roses and the English Civil War.

In the 18th century, the Castle was transformed from a rugged stronghold to an elegant country residence, with further alterations in the mid 19th century. Despite this, much of the original exterior remains, with important medieval rooms, notably the Great Kitchen (used for over 600 years until 1952), with its vast ranges and collection of Victorian copper utensils, and the original Garrison of the Castle now the Servants' Hall.

Today, serene in its tranquil setting, Raby still conveys the sense of its historic past, enhanced by its elegant furnishings and renowned collection of Meissen porcelain. Raby is living history, not a dead museum.

❖

SUITABILITY FOR OTHER EVENTS
By arrangement, though Raby is unsuitable for meetings, conferences or corporate catering.

EXTRA FACILITIES
These include: Picnic tables, 200 acres of parkland and 3½ acres of gardens. Lectures can be provided on the Castle, its contents, gardens and history.

ADVICE TO COURIERS & DRIVERS
No photography or video filming is permitted in the Castle: slides are on sale. No dogs allowed in the Castle (except guide dogs). Dogs must be on leads in the park. Unaccompanied children are not admitted to the Castle or park. Unlimited parking on the grass car park and coaches will find hard standing nearby.

FACILITIES FOR THE DISABLED
Disabled or elderly visitors may alight at the entrance to the Castle. The vehicles should then return to the car park. There are two toilets specially adapted for the disabled, near the Car Park and Tearoom. Doors to Tearoom (1 step) are wide enough for wheelchairs.

CATERING
Stables converted to self-service Tearooms, offering light refreshments, seating 60. For other requirements, please contact Curator.

GUIDED TOURS
Tours with experienced guides available at no extra cost, guides posted in most rooms on general open days, when no guided tours are available. Tours last about 1½ hours. For special interest groups, in-depth tours with the Curator may be arranged, for an additional fee. Garden tours with the Head Gardener can also be organised.

GIFT SHOP
There are two gift shops, one in the Castle, the other in the gardens. Open from 1pm - 5pm. A wide variety of gifts are available. Venison, game and soft fruits available in season.

GUIDE BOOKS
Colour guide book currently reprinting. Full text available.

SCHOOL VISITS/CHILDREN
Raby welcomes school parties of up to 60 children, who must be accompanied in a ratio of 1:20. Experienced guides available for school visits. Raby is suitable for several educational purposes: Social history, architecture, art and natural history. Schools are welcome to use the picnic tables, space for supervised games nearby. Room available for picnics when weather inclement.

CONTACT

Mrs E A Steele
Curator
Raby Castle
Staindrop
Darlington
Co Durham
DL2 3AH

Tel: (01833) 660202
or (01833) 660888

LOCATION

From Edinburgh, 170 miles via A1 or A68. From London, 250 miles via M1 and A1.

Rail: Darlington Station, 12 miles.

Air: Teeside Airport, 20 miles.

OPENING TIMES

Castle
Easter and all Bank Holiday Weekends
Saturday - Wednesday

May - June
Weds & Suns only
1.00 - 5.00pm

July - September
Daily except Sats
1.00 - 5.00pm

Garden and Park
11.00am - 5.30pm on days shown above

Parties by arrangement
Easter - end June
Mondays - Fridays
10.00am - 4.30pm
and
July - end September
Mondays - Fridays
Mornings only.

Winter
October -Easter
Closed

ADMISSION

Summer
HOUSE & GARDEN
Adult £3.50
Child £1.50
OAP £3.20
Bulmer's Tower . .50p
(when open)
Family Ticket . . .£9.00
(2 Adults, 2-3 Children)
W/chair users . .£1.50
GARDEN ONLY
Adult £1.00
Child (5-15yrs) . .£0.75
OAP £0.75

Groups (min 25 people)
By arrangement.

AUCKLAND CASTLE

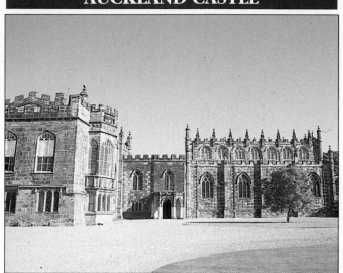

BISHOP AUCKLAND, COUNTY DURHAM DL14 7NP

Owner: *Church Commissioners*   **Contact:** *The Warden*

Tel: 01388 601627   **Fax:** 01388 605264

Principal country residence of the Bishops of Durham since Norman times and now the official residence of the present day Bishops. The Chapel, reputedly the largest private chapel in Europe, was originally the 12th C. banquet hall. Chapel and State Rooms, including the Throne Room, Long Dining Room and King Charles Dining Room are open to the public. Exhibition in the medieval kitchens dedicated to the life of St Cuthbert and the history of the Durham diocese. Access to the adjacent Bishop's park with its 18th C. Deer House.
Location: Bishop Auckland.
Opening Times: Castle: May - Sept., Suns, Tues, Weds & Thurs: 2 - 5pm Bank Hol Mons, & Sats in Aug: 2 - 5pm. Last adm 4.30pm. Group bookings & school visits available throughout the year. Bishop's Park: Daily, 7am to sunset.
Admission: Castle: Adult £2.50, Child and Over 60's £1.50. Concessions available for group bookings. Bishop's Park: Free.

AUCKLAND CASTLE DEER HOUSE
Tel: 01912 611585

Bishop Auckland, Durham
Owner: English Heritage   **Contact:** The North Regional Office
A charming building erected in 1760 in the Park of the Bishops of Durham so that the deer could shelter and find food.
Location: In Bishops Auckland Park, just N of town centre on A689.
Opening Times: Park opening times.

BARNARD CASTLE
Tel: 01833 638212

Barnard Castle, Castle House, Durham DL12 9AT
Owner: English Heritage   **Contact:** The Custodian
The substantial remains of this large Castle stand on a rugged escarpment overlooking the River Tees. You can still see parts of the 14th century Great Hall and the cylindrical 12th century tower, built by the Baliol family.
Location: In Barnard Castle.
Opening Times: 1 Apr - 30 Sept: Daily 10am - 6pm. 1 - 31 Oct: Daily 10am - 6pm or dusk if earlier. 1 Nov - 31 Mar: Wed - Sun, 10am - 4pm (closed lunch 1 - 2pm Nov - Mar).
Admission: Adult £2.00, Child £1.00, Conc £1.50.

THE BOWES MUSEUM
Tel: 01833 690606   **Fax:** 01833 637163

Barnard Castle, Durham DL12 8NP
Owner: Durham County Council   **Contact:** Mrs Elizabeth Conron
Imposing building standing above the River Tees, having an important collection of European art and antiques.
Location: 2m N of A66 (Bowes or Greta Bridge).
Opening Times: Mon - Sat, 10am - 5.30pm. Sun 2 - 5pm. Closes at 5pm in Apr and Oct and 4pm Nov - Feb (under review).
Admission: Adult £3.00, Child £2.00, Conc £2.00. Groups 10% discount.

DERWENTCOTE STEEL FURNACE
Tel: 01207 562573

Newcastle, Durham
Owner: English Heritage   **Contact:** The Custodian
Built in the 18th century it is the earliest and most complete authentic steel making furnace to have survived.
Location: 10 m SW of Newcastle on A694 between Rowland's Gill and Hamsterley.
Opening Times: 1 Apr - 30 Sept: 1 - 5pm, 1st & 3rd Sunday of every month.
Admission: Free.

DURHAM CATHEDRAL
Tel: 0191 3864266   **Fax:** 0191 3864267

Durham DH1 3EH
Contact: Ms W Nugent
A world heritage site. Norman architecture. Burial place of St Cuthbert and the Venerable Bede. Claustral buildings including Monk's Dormitory and Medieval kitchen.
Location: Durham city centre.
Opening Times: Summer: 7.15am - 8pm (29 May - 8 Sept), Winter: 7.15am - 6pm (9 Sept - 28 May). Sun services: 8am, 10am, 11.15am and 3.30pm. Weekday services: 7.30am, 9am and 5.15pm.
Admission: Tower: Adult £2.00, Child £1.00, Monk's Dormitory: Adult 80p, Child 20p, AV: Adult 50p, Child 20p, Treasury: Adult £1.00, Child 20p.

EGGLESTONE ABBEY
Tel: 01912 611585

Durham.
Owner: English Heritage   **Contact:** The North Regional Office
Picturesque remains of a 12th century abbey, located in a bend of the River Tees. Substantial parts of the church and abbey buildings remain.
Location: 1 m S of Barnard Castle on minor road off B6277.
Opening Times: Any reasonable time.

FINCHALE PRIORY
Tel: 01913 863828

Finchdale Priory, Brasside, Newton Hall, Co Durham DH1 5SH
Owner: English Heritage   **Contact:** The Custodian
These beautiful 13th century priory remains are located beside the curving River Wear.
Location: 3 m NE of Durham, on minor road off A167.
Opening Times: 1 Apr - 30 Sept: Daily 12 noon - 5pm.
Admission: Adult £1.00, Child 50p, Conc 80p.

RABY CASTLE
See Page 60 for full page entry.

Where to Stay
For Private Accommodation and Johansens recommended Hotels, see Accommodation Section.

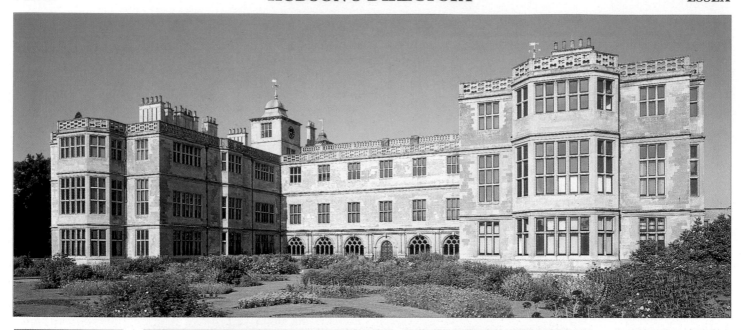

AUDLEY END HOUSE & PARK
Saffron Walden

Audley End was a palace in all but name. Built by Thomas Howard, Earl of Suffolk, to entertain King James I. The King may have had his suspicions, for he never stayed there; in 1619 Howard was imprisoned and fined for embezzlement. The house was gradually demolished, and by the 1750's it was about the size you see today. There are still over 30 rooms to see, each with period furnishings.

The house and its gardens, including a 19th century parterre and rose garden, are surrounded by an 18th century landscaped park.

CONTACT

The Custodian
Audley End House
Audley End
Saffron Walden
Essex
CB11 4FF

Tel: (01799) 522842

Fax: (01799) 521276

LOCATION

1 mile W of Saffron Walden on B1383, M11 exits 8 and 9 northbound exit 10 southbound.

Rail: Audley End 1 mile

OPENING TIMES

House
1 April - 30 September

Wednesday - Sunday and Bank Holidays

12 noon - 6.00pm

Last admission 5.00pm

Park & Gardens
1 April - 30 September

Wednesday - Sunday and Bank Holidays

10.00am - 6.00pm

Last admission 5pm.

ADMISSION

House and Grounds
   Adult £5.50
   Child* £2.80
   OAP/Students/
   UB40 holders . . £4.10

Grounds only
   Adult £3.30
   Child* £1.70
   Concessions . . . £2.50

* Child 5 - 15yrs.
   Under 5 free.

Groups
15% off groups of 11 or more.

SUITABILITY FOR OTHER EVENTS
Suitable for open air concerts and other events.

ADVICE TO COURIERS & DRIVERS
Dogs must be kept on a lead. Free entry for coach drivers & tour guides. One additional place for every extra 20 people.

FACILITIES FOR THE DISABLED
Ground floor suitable for disabled access.

PARKING FOR COACHES & CARS
Car parking is available. Coaches to book in advance, £5.00 per coach.

CATERING
Restaurant facilities available.

GUIDED TOURS
By arrangement for groups. Please telephone for details.

GIFT SHOP
Situated in old kitchens, wide range of souvenirs and gifts.

GUIDE BOOKS
Colour Guide available.

SCHOOL VISITS/CHILDREN
School visits free if booked in advance. Contact Administrator.

HEDINGHAM CASTLE
Nr Halstead

Hedingham Castle is one of the finest Norman keeps in England and is in an excellent state of preservation. It was built in 1140 by the famous medieval family the de Veres, Earls of Oxford, and is still owned by their descendants. For 500 years the kings and queens of England looked to this family to fill the highest positions in the land. In 1137 Aubrey de Vere was created Lord Great Chamberlain and this office was held by the de Veres until the death of the 18th Earl of Oxford in 1623. He died aged 32 from wounds received at the Battle of the Hague, a year after his marriage to Diana Cecil, a great beauty, daughter of the Earl of Exeter. The castle was besieged by King John and visited by King Henry VII, King Henry VIII and Queen Elizabeth I. A dry moat separates the Inner and Outer Baileys and is spanned by a lovely, brick Tudor bridge, built to replace the drawbridge by the 13th Earl in 1496. The four floors include the Garrison, a magnificent Banqueting Hall with fine Minstrels' Gallery, decorative stonework and a splendid Norman arch. On the Outer Bailey can be seen the Queen Anne house built in 1719 by Sir Thomas Ashhurst.

GROUNDS

The five spring-fed medieval fishponds were made into the formal Canal in the 18th century. The Valley Walk shows the huge scale of the original earthworks and the beautiful grounds and woodland contain much of natural interest. There is a peaceful lakeside meadow ideal for family picnics. Allow time to visit the medieval village and fine Norman church.

❖

SUITABILITY FOR OTHER EVENTS
The Castle, 18th century house (closed to the public), and grounds are available for filming and a variety of events by arrangement.

ADVICE TO COURIERS & DRIVERS
We are open to parties/groups all year by appointment. No smoking in the castle please. Dogs on leads only. Free refreshments for coach drivers.

FACILITIES FOR THE DISABLED
The disabled are very welcome and are given free entry. They can enjoy the grounds, but the steep steps up to the Castle make a visit to the interior unsuitable. Cars/coaches carrying disabled may disembark by the Tudor bridge at the top of the drive.

PARKING FOR COACHES AND CARS
Ample free parking in the Castle grounds.

CATERING
Tea, coffee, home-made cakes and light refreshments. Cream teas by arrangement.

GIFT SHOP
A wide range of gifts, books and historical items are always on sale in the Castle.

GUIDE BOOKS
Colour Guide Books on sale. Basic guide sheets are available in French, German and Dutch, also children's guide/colouring sheets.

SCHOOL VISITS / CHILDREN
School visits welcome all year by appointment and there is no charge for teachers/helpers. Teachers' Information Pack supplied on booking. Preliminary visits free. Children's work sheets available. In wet weather schools can work/have their packed lunches on the top floor of the Castle.

CONTACT

The Manager
Hedingham Castle
Castle Hedingham
Nr. Halstead
Essex
C09 3DJ

Tel: (01787) 460261

LOCATION

On B1058, 1 mile off A604 between Cambridge (30m) and Colchester (16m).

Close to Lavenham and Constable country, within easy reach of London (60m) via the M25, M11, A12.

OPENING TIMES

Castle and Grounds

30 Mar - 27 October
& Good Friday and
Bank Holiday Mondays.

10.00am - 5.00pm

For other opening times please telephone.

House
Closed

ADMISSION

CASTLE & GROUNDS

Adult £2.75
Child £1.75
OAP/Student . . .£2.50
Family Ticket . .£7.50
Groups (min 20 people)
Per person £2.50

MOYNS PARK
Birdbrook

CONTACT

Rosie Coutts
Moyns Park
Birdbrook
Essex
CO9 4BP

Tel: (01440) 730073
Fax: (01440) 730060

LOCATION

London - 1 hour
Cambridge - 30 minutes
Newmarket - 30 minutes

15 minutes from Junct. 9
off the M11, just 2 miles
south of Haverhill.

Please ring for details
and Colour Brochure.

MOYNS PARK is the home of Lord and Lady Ivar Mountbatten: Lord Ivar is the younger son of the late 3rd Marquess of Milford Haven. Set in 250 acres of classical rolling parkland, Moyns is one of the country's finest examples of an Elizabethan manor house.

Situated on the Essex/Suffolk border, within one hour's drive of London, and 30 minutes from Cambridge and Newmarket, the Estate takes its name from the Le Moign family, who owned the lands from the time of the Norman Conquest in 1066. During the reign of Henry VII the manor passed to the Gent family, who retained ownership until 1880, when Moyns was sold to General St Ives, Silver-Stick-in-Waiting to Queen Victoria and grandfather of the late Ivar Bryce, previous owner and uncle to Lord Ivar Mountbatten.

Moyns Park is not only steeped in its own fabulous history, but reflects the fascinating history of the Mountbatten and Milford Haven family and their relationship to every Royal household in Europe.

Ian Fleming based the exploits of James Bond on those of his great friend, the late Ivar Bryce, who was an OSS Agent during the Second World War.

Moyns Park is not open to the public, but available on an exclusive use basis for guests seeking complete privacy in relaxed, elegant and traditional surroundings.

❖

FACILITIES
The House is available for Conferences, Seminars, Incentive Programmes, Corporate Hospitality Events, Wedding Receptions, Private Parties and Banquets.
A full range of outdoor activities can be organised within the Estate and are located close to the House. Multi-Activity Events are particularly well suited.
There is plenty of space for Marquee or steel framed structures including utilisation of the Stables and Courtyards for additional Exhibitions and Product Launches.

CATERING
An exceptionally high standard of in-house catering is guaranteed, matched with professional and friendly service. Clients are treated as guests and leave as friends.

ACCOMMODATION
9 Principal Bedrooms, all with private or en-suite bathrooms, currently available. Further secondary bedrooms available if required. Lord and Lady Ivar Mountbatten believe in maintaining the Moyns Park tradition of style and service rarely offered nowadays, including Maid Service and breakfast in bed for the ladies.

OPENING TIMES

Available throughout the year.

ADMISSION

Day Delegate Rate
from £35 per person

24 hour Delegate Rate
from £137.50 per person

Private Dinner Party/ Banquet
from £27.50 per head

Venue Hire From
from £400

For full Tariff and Terms of Business, please contact Rosie Coutts.

CONFERENCE AND FUNCTION FACILITIES

ROOM	DIMENSIONS	CAPACITY	LAYOUT	POWER POINTS	SUITABLE FOR A/V
Great Hall	41' x 30'	60	Boardroom	6	✓
		80	Dining		
		130	Theatre		
Drawing Room	22' x 24'	24	Boardroom	6	✓
		18	U-Shaped		
		36	Theatre		
		30	Dining		
Library	22' x 16'	8	Boardroom/Dining	3	✓
Dining Room	22' x 19'	20	Boardroom	5	✓
		16	U-Shaped		
		34	Theatre		
		40	Dining		

AUDLEY END HOUSE & PARK ⊞

See Page 62 for full page entry.

BOURNE MILL

Tel: 01206 572422

Colchester, Essex
Owner: The National Trust   **Contact:** The Tenant
Originally a fishing lodge built in 1591. It was later converted into a mill with a 4 acre mill pond. Much of the machinery, including the waterwheel, is intact.
Location: 1 m S of Colchester centre, in Bourne Road, off the Mersea Road B1025.
Opening Times: Only BH Mon & Sun preceding BH Mon; also Sun & Tues in Jul and Aug, 2 - 5.30pm.
Admission: £1.30, children must be accompanied by an adult, no reduction for parties.

CHELMSFORD CATHEDRAL

Tel: 01245 263660

New Street, Chelmsford., Essex CM1 1AT
     Contact: Mrs Gillian Brandon
15th century building became a Cathedral in 1914. Extended in 1920s, major refurbishment in 1980s with contemporary works of distinction and a splendid new organ in 1994.
Location: In Chelmsford.
Opening Times: 8am - 5.30pm daily. Sun services: 8am, 9.30am, 11.15am and 6pm. Weekday services 8.15am and 5.15pm.

COGGESHALL GRANGE BARN

Tel: 01376 562226

Coggeshall, Colchester, Essex CO6 1RE
Owner: The National Trust   **Contact:** The Custodian
The oldest surviving timber framed barn in Europe, dating from around 1140, and originally part of the Cistercian Monastery of Coggeshall. It was restored in the 1980s by the Coggeshall Grange Barn Trust, Braintree District Council and Essex County Council. Features a small collection of farm carts and wagons.
Location: Signposted off A120 Coggeshall bypass.
Opening Times: 31 Mar - 13 Oct: Tues, Thurs, Sun and BH Mon, 1 - 5pm.
Admission: £1.50, parties £1.00, joint ticket with Paycocke's £3.00.

COLCHESTER CASTLE MUSEUM

Tel: 01206 282937

14 Ryegate Road, Colchester, Essex CO1 1YG
Owner: Colchester Borough Council   **Contact:** The Resource Centre
The largest Norman Castle Keep in Europe with fine archaeological collections on show.
Location: In Colchester town centre, off A12.
Opening Times: Mar - Nov: Mon - Sat, 10am - 5pm. Sun 2 - 5pm.
Admission: Adult £3.00, Child £2.00, Family £8, Conc £2.00, Groups of 20 or more booked in advance £2.50.

FLATFORD BRIDGE COTTAGE

Tel: 01206 298260

Flatford, East Bergholt, Colchester, Essex CO7 6OL
Owner: The National Trust   **Contact:** The Property Manager
Just upstream from Flatford Mill, the restored thatched cottage houses a display about John Constable, several of whose paintings depict this property. Facilities include a tea garden, shop, boat hire and an Information Centre.
Location: On N bank of Stour, 1m S of East Bergholt B1070.
Opening Times: 30 Mar - end May & Oct: Wed - Sun & BH Mon 11am - 5.30pm. Jun - end Sept: daily 10am - 5.30pm (closed Good Fri). Nov: Wed - Sun 11am - 3.30pm.
Admission: Guided tours £1.50, accompanied children free.

GOSFIELD HALL

Tel: 01787 472914

Gosfield, Halstead, Essex CO9 1SF
Owner: Country Houses Association   **Contact:** Mr G Brown
Very fine Tudor gallery.
Location: On the A1017 between Braintree and Sible Hedingham. 2 1/2 m SW of Halstead.
Opening Times: 1 May - 30 Sept: Wed & Thur, 2 - 5pm.
Guided tours of house 2.30pm & 3.15pm.
Admission: Adult £2.50, Child under 12 £1, Group driver and organiser free.

HARWICH REDOUBT

Tel: 01255 503429

The Harbour, Harwich, Essex
Owner: The Harwich Society   **Contact:** Mr Sheard
180ft diameter circular fort built in 1808 to defend the port against Napoleonic invasion. Being restored by Harwich Society and part is a museum. Eleven guns and battlements.
Opening Times: Every Sun throughout the year.
Admission: Adult £1.00, Accompanied child free.

HEDINGHAM CASTLE 🏛

See Page 63 for full page entry.

HYDE HALL RHS GARDEN

OPEN

24 March - 27 Oct

Wed - Sun and
Bank Holidays

11.00am - 5.00pm

Sept. - Oct
11am - 4pm

Gates close 5pm.

Tel: 01245 400256
Fax: 01245 401363

RETTENDON, NR. CHELMSFORD, ESSEX

Owner: The Royal Horticultural Society

A charming hilltop garden which extends to over 8 acres. Highlights include the gold garden, the modern tall and intermediate bearded irises in late May, and the rope walk of climbing roses and large beds ablaze with floribunda and hybrid tea roses in midsummer. There is also a small plant centre and delightful hot and cold meals are available when the garden is open.
Location: Rettendon, six miles South East of Chelmsford. Signed off the A130.
Admission: Adult £2.70, Child (under 6) Free, Child (6 - 16) 70p. Groups of 20+ £2.20. Visitors in wheelchairs and blind visitors: Free.

HYLANDS HOUSE

Tel: 01245 490490 ext. 2406   **Fax:** 01245 265848

Hylands Park, Writtle, Chelmsford CM1 3HW
Owner: Chelmsford Borough Council   **Contact:** Vicky Parr
Impressive Georgian mansion built in 1730 in red brick. Wings were added in the early 19th century, and the house clad in white stucco under Repton's guidance. The first phase of internal restoration is open to visitors which includes Entrance Hall, The Blue Room (formerly the Drawing Room) and the Staircase Hall. There are original plaster cast reliefs by Thorvaldsen of *Day and Night* and *Alexander the Great*. Visitors can also view the unrestored areas of the ground floor through glazed screens as well as an exhibition on the history of the house, the park and its owners. The grounds of Hylands Park (400 acres) include beautifully maintained woodland, open parkland and formal gardens.
Location: Hylands Park is signposted from A414 between Chelmsford and Writtle.
Opening Times: Easter - October, please tel. for details. Grounds: Dawn until dusk all year.
Admission: House: Adult £2.00, Family Groups - Child Free , unaccompanied child £1.00. Grounds: Free.

INGATESTONE HALL 🏛

OPEN

6 Apr - 29 Sept
Sat, Sun & Bank
Holiday Mondays

Also

10 July - 30 Aug
Wed, Thurs & Fri
1 - 6pm.

Tel: 01277 353010
Fax: 01245 248979

HALL LANE, INGATESTONE, ESSEX CM4 9NR

Owner: The Lord Petre   *Contact: Phillip Paterson*

16th century mansion, set in 11 acres of grounds (formal garden and wild walk), built by Sir William Petre, Secretary of State to four Tudor monarchs, which has remained in the hands of his family ever since. The 2 Priests' hiding places can be seen, as well as the furniture, portraits and family memorabilia accumulated over the centuries.
Location: Off A12 between Brentwood & Chelmsford. Take Station Lane at the London end of High Street, cross level crossing and continue for 1/2 mile.
Admission: Adult £3.50, OAP & Students £3, Child £2. Under 5's Free. 50p per head discount for parties of 20+. Family Ticket (admits 5, up to 3 adults) £10.50.

LAYER MARNEY TOWER

COLCHESTER, ESSEX CO5 9US

Owner: Mr Nicholas Charrington   *Contact:* Mr Nicholas Charrington

Tel: 01206 330784   **Fax:** 01206 330784

Built in the reign of Henry VIII, the tallest Tudor gatehouse in Great Britain. Lord Henry Marney clearly intended to rival Wolsey's building at Hampton Court, but he died before his masterpiece was finished. His son John died two years later, in 1525, and building work stopped. Layer Marney Tower has some of the finest terracotta work in the country, most probably executed by Flemish craftsmen trained by Italian masters. The terracotta is used on the battlements, windows, and most lavishly of all, on the tombs of Henry and John Marney. Visitors may climb The Tower, passing through the History Room, and enjoy the marvellous views of the Essex countryside. There are fine outbuildings, including the Long Gallery with its magnificent oak roof and the medieval barn which now houses some of the Home Farm's collection of Rare Breed farm animals.

Location: 5 miles SW of Colchester, signed off B1022 Colchester-Maldon.

Opening Times: 1 Apr - 30 Sept: Daily except Saturdays 2 - 6pm. July & August: Sundays only 12 noon - 6pm. Guided tours & school visits all year long.

Admission: Adult £3.25, Child £1.75, Family (2 adults & 2 children) £9.00. Groups 20+: Adult £3.00, Child £1.50. Guided tours: £4.50.

LOWER DAIRY HOUSE GARDEN

Tel: 01206 262220

Water Lane, Nayland, Colchester, Essex CO6 4JS

Owner: Mr. and Mrs D J Burnett   **Contact:** The Owners

Plantsman's garden, approx 1 1/2 acres.

Location: 7m N of Colchester off A134.

Opening Times: Apr; 6/7/8, 14/21/28. May; 4/5/6, 12, 19, 25/26/27. Jun; 1/2, 15/16, 23, 29/30. Jul; 6/7. 2 - 6pm.

Admission: Adult £2.00, Child 50p, Groups welcome by appointment.

MISTLEY TOWERS

Tel: 01206 393884

Colchester, Essex

Owner: English Heritage   **Contact:** Mrs G Owens

The remains of one of only two churches designed by the great architect Robert Adam. Built in 1776, it is unusual in having towers at both the east and west ends.

Location: On B1352, 1 1/2 m E of A137 at Lawford, 9m E of Colchester.

Opening Times: Telephone 01206 393884 for opening times.

Admission: Telephone 01206 393884 for prices.

MOYNS PARK

See Page 64 for full page entry.

PAYCOCKE'S

Tel: 01376 561305

West Street, Coggeshall, Colchester, Essex C06 1NS

Owner: The National Trust   **Contact:** The Tenant

A merchant's house, dating from about 1500, with unusually rich panelling and wood carving. A display of lace for which Coggeshall was famous is on show. Delightful garden leading down to small river.

Location: Signposted off A120.

Opening Times: 31 Mar - 13 Oct: Tues, Thurs, Sun & BH Mon, 2 - 5.30pm, last adm: 5pm.

Admission: £2.00, parties of 6+ by prior arrangement, no reduction for parties. Joint ticket with Coggeshall Grange Barn £3.00.

PRIORS HALL BARN

Tel: 01604 730320

Widdington, Newport, Essex

Owner: English Heritage   **Contact:** The Midlands Regional Office

One of the finest surviving medieval barns in south east England and representative of the group of aisled barns centred on north west Essex.

Location: In Widdington, on unclassified road 2m SE of Newport, of B1383.

Opening Times: Telephone 01604 730320 for opening times.

Admission: Telephone 01604 730320 for prices.

SALING HALL GARDEN

Tel: 01371 850 243   **Fax:** 01371 850 274

Great Saling, Braintree, Essex CM7 5DT

Owner: Hugh Johnson Esq   **Contact:** Hugh Johnson Esq

12 acres including a walled garden dated 1698. Extensive collection of unusual plants with emphasis on trees – some very big.

Location: 6m NW of Braintree, 2m N of A120.

Opening Times: May, Jun and Jul: Wed 2 - 5pm. Sun 30 Jun: 2 - 6pm.

Admission: Standard £2, Child free.

TILBURY FORT

Tel: 01375 858489

No. 2 Office Block, Tilbury Fort, Tilbury, Essex RM18 7NR

Owner: English Heritage   **Contact:** Mr Bernie Truss

The best and largest example of 17th century military engineering in England, commanding the Thames and showing the development of fortifications over the following 200 years. Exhibitions, the powder magazine and the bunker-like 'casemates' demonstrate how the fort protected London from seaborne attack.

Location: 1/2m E of Tilbury off A126.

Opening Times: 1 Apr - 30 Sept: Daily 10am - 6pm. 1 - 31 Oct: Daily 10am - 6pm or dusk if earlier. 1 Nov - 31 Mar: Wed - Sun 10am - 4pm. Lunchtime closure 1 - 2pm.

Admission: Adult £2.00, Child £1.00, Conc £1.50.

WALTHAM ABBEY GATEHOUSE AND BRIDGE

Tel: 01604 730320

Waltham Abbey, Essex.

Owner: English Heritage   **Contact:** The Midlands Regional Office

The late 14th century abbey gatehouse, part of the north range of the cloister and the medieval "Harold's Bridge" of one of the great monastic foundations of the Middle Ages.

Location: In Waltham Abbey off A112.

Opening Times: Any reasonable time.

SPECIAL EVENTS

◇ **LAYER MARNEY TOWER**   **7 – 8 APRIL**
Silver Cloud Craft Fair & Easter Egg Hunt

◇ **LAYER MARNEY TOWER**   **21 APRIL**
Wildlife & Countryside Day: Explore the countryside with FWAG.

◇ **LAYER MARNEY TOWER**   **5 – 6 MAY**
Sheep Shearing Show & Goat Show (Sunday only)

◇ **LAYER MARNEY TOWER**   **12 MAY**
Bicycle Day: £1 off entry for those who arrive on a bicycle

◇ **LAYER MARNEY TOWER**   **27 MAY**
Church Fete

◇ **LAYER MARNEY TOWER**   **2 JULY**
Castle Theatre Company, 'The Taming of the Shrew'

◇ **LAYER MARNEY TOWER**   **1 – 2 AUGUST**
Mad Dogs and Englishmen. A Midsummer Night's Dream.

◇ **LAYER MARNEY TOWER**   **25 – 26 AUGUST**
Fair

◇ **HYLANDS HOUSE   AUGUST BANK HOLIDAY WEEKEND, THURSDAY – MONDAY**
The Chelmsford Spectacular - evening concerts and daytime events
(telephone 01245 490490 Ext.2411 for further information)

◇ **LAYER MARNEY TOWER**   **6 OCTOBER**
Open Day for St John Ambulance Brigade and Cambridge Children's Hospice

For National Trust and English Heritage Properties see separate section.

BERKELEY CASTLE
Berkeley

Not many can boast of having their private house celebrated by Shakespeare nor of having held it in the possession of their family for nearly 850 years, nor having a King of England murdered within its walls, nor of having welcomed at their table the local vicar and Castle Chaplain, John Trevisa (1342-1402), reputed as one of the earliest translators of the Bible, nor of having a breach battered by Oliver Cromwell, which to this day it is forbidden by law to repair even if it was wished to do so. But such is the story of Berkeley.

This beautiful and historic Castle, begun in 1117, still remains the home of the famous family who gave their name to numerous locations all over the word, notably Berkeley Square in London, Berkeley Hundred in Virginia and Berkeley University in California. Scene of the brutal murder of Edward II in 1327 (visitors can see his cell and nearby the dungeon) and besieged by Cromwell's troops in 1645, the Castle is steeped in history but twenty-four generations of Berkeleys have gradually transformed a Norman fortress into the lovely home it is today.

The State Apartments contain magnificent collections of furniture, rare paintings by primarily English and Dutch masters, and tapestries. Part of the world-famous Berkeley silver is on display in the Dining Room. Many other rooms are equally interesting including the Great Hall upon which site the Barons of the West Country met in 1215 before going to Runnymede to force King John to put his seal to the Magna Carta.

The Castle is surrounded by lovely terraced Elizabethan Gardens with a lily pond, Elizabeth I's bowling green, and sweeping lawns.

CONTACT

The Custodian
Berkeley Castle
Gloucestershire
GL13 9BQ

Tel: (01453) 810332

LOCATION

Midway between Bristol and Gloucester, just off the A38.

From motorway M5 use exit 14 (5 miles) or exit 13 (9 miles).

Bus: No 308 from Bristol and Gloucester

SUITABILITY FOR OTHER EVENTS
Wedding receptions, fashion shows, corporate entertainment, receptions, filming.

EXTRA FACILITIES
Butterfly farm; hundreds of exotic butterflies in free flight.

ADVICE TO COURIERS & DRIVERS
No photography allowed inside the Castle. No dogs admitted beyond car park. Evening parties by arrangement. GROUP VISITS MUST BE BOOKED.

FACILITIES FOR THE DISABLED
In exceptional circumstances disabled/elderly visitors may alight in the Outer Bailey. No toilet facilities for the disabled.

PARKING FOR COACHES & CARS
Free Car Park: 150 yds from the Castle. Up to 15 coaches can be parked 250 yds from the Castle.

CATERING
Tea Rooms serving light lunches and home-made teas. Separate room for up to 60 people (pre-book groups).

GUIDED TOURS
At no extra charge. Max. size 120. Min. tour time 1 hour.

GIFT SHOP
Open at the same time as the Castle. It is well-stocked with quality gifts for adults and children.

GUIDE BOOKS
Colour guide book by Vita Sackville West £1.50. Special children's guide book.

SCHOOL VISITS/CHILDREN
School groups welcome. The Castle has much of interest for all age groups, in particular general history, social history and architecture. School groups visiting the Castle have free admission to Butterfly Farm.

CONFERENCE AND FUNCTION FACILITIES

ROOM	DIMENSIONS	CAPACITY	LAYOUT	POWER POINTS	SUITABLE FOR A/V
Great Hall		128	Dinner	2	✓
		160	Theatre style		
		200	Reception		
		100	School room style		
Long Drawing Room		100	Reception	2	✓
		40	Dinner		
		40	School room style		

CHAVENAGE
Tetbury

CHAVENAGE is a wonderful Elizabethan house of mellow grey Cotswold stone and tiles which contains much of interest for the discerning visitor.

The approach aspect of Chavenage is virtually as it was left by Edward Stephens in 1576. Only two families have owned Chavenage; the present owners since 1891 and the Stephens family before them. A Colonel Nathaniel Stephens, M.P. for Gloucestershire during the Civil War was cursed for supporting Cromwell giving rise to legends of weird happenings at Chavenage since that time.

Inside Chavenage there are many interesting rooms housing tapestries, fine furniture, pictures and many relics of the Cromwellian period. Of particular note are the Main Hall,

where a contemporary screen forms a minstrel's gallery and two tapestry rooms where it is said Cromwell was lodged.

Recently Chavenage has been used as a location for T.V. and film productions including a Hercule Poirot story 'The Mysterious Affair at Styles Manor', many episodes of the sequel to 'Are you Being Served' now called 'Grace & Favour' a "Gotcha" for 'The Noel Edmunds House Party' and an episode of "The House of Elliot".

Chavenage is especially suitable for those wishing an intimate, personal tour, usually conducted by the owner, or for small groups wanting a change from large establishments. It also provides a charming venue for small conferences and functions.

❖

CONTACT

D Lowsley - Williams
Chavenage
Tetbury
Gloucestershire
GL8 8XP
Tel: (01666) 502329
Fax: (01453) 836778

LOCATION

Less than 20 miles from M4 Junctions 16, 17 or 18. Signed from Tetbury ($1^3/4$ miles) on the B4104.
Less than 15 miles from M5 junction 13 or 14. Signed from the A46 (Stroud -Bath road)

Rail: Kemble Station, 7 miles.

Taxi: Tetbury Cars, Tetbury 503393

SUITABILITY FOR OTHER EVENTS
Corporate entertaining. Clay pigeon shooting, archery, cross-bows, pistol shooting, A.T.V. driving, weddings, dinners, lunches, small fashion shows, concerts, plays, seminars, filming, product launching, photography.

ADVICE TO COURIERS & DRIVERS
Coaches only by appointment. Stop at the front gates for instructions as to parking.

PARKING
Up to 100 cars and 2-3 coaches.

FACILITIES FOR THE DISABLED
Ground floor accessible to 'chairs'. There are toilet facilities for the disabled.

CATERING
In-house catering available for Weddings, functions, lunches, teas, dinners and picnics by arrangement.

GUIDED TOURS
Normally the owner gives a guided tour to all visitors. Larger groups are given a talk about the house prior to viewing on their own but with the owner present to answer questions. (No extra charge for the above services). Couriers and group leaders should arrange the format required prior to the visit.

GUIDE BOOKS
New colour guide book available.

SCHOOL VISITS/CHILDREN
School groups are welcome. Chairs can be arranged for lecturing. Tour of working farm, modern dairy and corn facilities can be arranged.

OPENING TIMES

Summer
May - September
Easter Sun & Mon
and Bank Holidays
2.00 - 5.00pm

Thurs and Suns
2.00 - 5.00pm

NB Will open at other times by prior arrangement for groups.

Winter
October - March
By appointment only
for groups.

ADMISSION

Summer
Adult £2.50
Child (0 - 16 yrs). . .£1.25
Friend of HHA . .Free

CONCESSIONS
By prior arrangement, concessions may be given to groups of 20+ and also to disabled and to exceptional cases.

Winter
Groups only: Rates by arrangement.

CONFERENCE AND FUNCTION FACILITIES

ROOM	DIMENSIONS	CAPACITY	LAYOUT	POWER POINTS	SUITABLE FOR A/V
Ballroom	70' x 30'	100	Theatre	8	
		120	Schoolroom		
		70	U-shape		
		26	Boardroom		
		100	Dinner/Dance		
		100	Lunch/Buffet		
Oak Room	25 'x 20'	30	Schoolroom	4	
		16	U-shape		
		12	Boardroom		

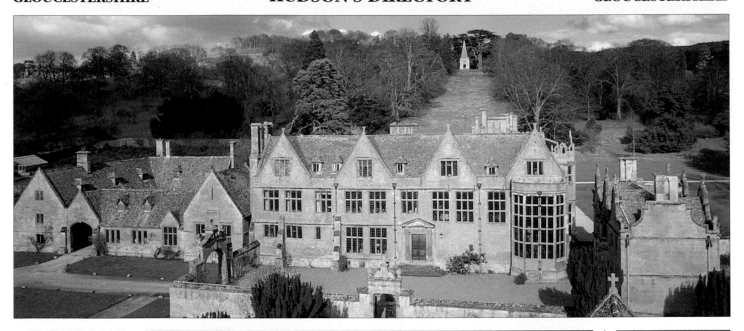

STANWAY HOUSE
Cheltenham

STANWAY, home of Lord Neidpath, is a jewel of Cotswold Manor houses, very much lived in rather than a museum.

All rooms visited are used daily and there is an atmosphere of stepping back in time. Most of the furniture has been in the house since it was built. The paintings, nearly all family portraits, give a vivid impression of Stanway's often colourful owners and their relatives over five centuries - for instance one was a gunpowder plotter, two died in a "drinking match", one was sentenced to death for rape and one sat in Parliament for a (record) 72 years.

Visit the Audit Room where Estate tenants still assemble every quarter day to pay their rent in person; the Great Hall with its funeral hatchments and 23ft shuffleboard table; the drawing room with its Chippendale Chinese Day Beds.

The evocative landscape includes a typical village cricket field (with a pavilion built by Sir James (Peter Pan) Barrie - a frequent guest). The mellow Jacobean architecture, the exquisite Gatehouse, the old Brewery, the Medieval Tithe Barn, the Pyramid and formal landscape contribute to the timeless charm of one of the most romantic and beautiful houses in England.

❖

SUITABILITY FOR OTHER EVENTS
Stanway House is suitable for fashion shows, archery, clay pigeon shooting, equestrian events, garden parties, rallies, shows, filming and wedding receptions.

EXTRA FACILITIES
These include: Piano, parkland, farm, fields, cricket pitch, arboretum and old mill.

ADVICE TO COURIERS & DRIVERS
No unaccompanied children. No dogs or photography. Morning coffee and biscuits or afternoon tea with sandwiches and cakes can be provided for pre-booked groups on days when the house is not open to the public.

FACILITIES FOR THE DISABLED
There are no toilet facilities for the disabled.

PARKING FOR COACHES & CARS
Capacity of the car park: 200 cars and 5 coaches, 20 yds from the House.

CATERING
For special functions/conferences, buffets, lunches and dinners can be arranged. Teas are available during opening hours, at the Old Bakehouse in the village from June - August.

GUIDED TOURS
Tours can be arranged for up to 70 people. During winter cost per tour £4.50 per head. Tea or coffee and tour £6.00 per head. Tours are available in French. If requested, the owner may meet groups visiting the House. Average time taken for tour 1¼ hours.

GUIDE BOOKS
A guide book can be purchased, price £1.00.

SCHOOL VISITS/CHILDREN
Groups of children are welcome. Cost per child £1.00. If requested a guide can be provided. There are nature walks.

CONTACT

Liz Foley
Stanway House
Stanway
Cheltenham
Gloucestershire
GL54 5PQ

Tel: (01386) 584469

LOCATION

From London M40, A40 to Burford, A424 to Stow, B4077 towards Tewkesbury. Stanway is 9 miles past Stow. London, 2 hours.

Motorway: M5 Exit 9, approx 8 miles. (Take A438 towards Stow).

OPENING TIMES

Summer
June - September
Mon, Wed
By appointment

Tues, Thur
2.00pm - 5.00pm

Fri, Sat, Sun
By appointment

Winter
Open by appointment for guided tours only.

ADMISSION

Summer

Adult	£3.50
Child*	£1.00
OAP	£3.00
Student	£3.00

Groups**

Adult	£3.00
Child*	£1.00
OAP	£3.00
Student	£3.00

** Min payment £50.00

Winter (Tours only)
HOUSE & GARDEN

Adult	£4.50
Child*	£3.50
OAP	£4.50
Student	£4.00

HOUSE & GARDEN WITH TEA

Adult	£6.00
Child*	£4.00
OAP	£6.00
Student	£6.00

* Under 16

CONFERENCE AND FUNCTION FACILITIES

ROOM	DIMENSIONS	CAPACITY	LAYOUT	POWER POINTS	SUITABLE FOR A/V
Great Hall	40' x 25'	100	Buffet	5	✓
		50	Boardroom		
		40	Lunch/Dinner		
Dining Room	25' x 20'	25	Boardroom	3	✓
		20	Lunch/Dinner		
Tithe Barn	90' x 30'	300	Various	4	✓

SUDELEY CASTLE
Winchcombe

Nestling among the rolling Cotswold Hills, Sudeley Castle, the home of Lord and Lady Ashcombe, is one of England's great historic houses.

Sudeley has royal connections stretching back 1000 years. Once the property of King Ethelred the Unready, Sudeley was later the magnificent palace of Queen Katherine Parr, Henry VIII's sixth wife, who is buried in the Castle Church.

Henry VIII, Anne Boleyn, Lady Jane Grey and Elizabeth I stayed at the Castle. Charles I resided here while Prince Rupert established his headquarters during the Civil War.

During the Victorian era, a sympathetic programme of reconstruction enhanced Sudeley's earlier magnificence. Among a wealth of history on show is an impressive collection of treasures including masterpieces by Turner, Van Dyck and Rubens.

GARDENS

Surrounding the Castle are seven enchanting gardens which have gained recognition for their floral displays and topiary. Famous for its fine collection of old-fashioned roses, the Queen's Garden is well worth a visit.

New for 1996 is a Tudor Knot Garden, with intricate patterns, mosaics and water features. The design has been inspired by the pattern of the cloth taken from a dress worn by Queen Elizabeth I in a painting by Lucas de Heere, "An Allegory of the Tudor Succession", which hangs in the Castle.

Visitors can wander at leisure through avenues of majestic trees, wide stretches of still water, grand yew hedges and fragrant roses.

1996 Special Events include Open Air Theatre, Concerts, Special Plant Fair and Falconry.

SUITABILITY FOR OTHER EVENTS
Photography shoots, filming, concerts, product launches, exclusive banquets, corporate entertainment. Various events during the season.

EXTRA FACILITIES
A wide range corporate events, such as conferences, private dining, training and a variety of organised activities all year. Special interest tours can be arranged, including lace and gardens.

ACCOMMODATION
14 holiday cottages, each accommodating 2 - 5 people.

ADVICE TO COURIERS & DRIVERS
Coach operators: meal vouchers & free access. No dogs, photography or video cameras in the Castle. Parking for 1,000 cars.

FACILITIES FOR THE DISABLED
Regretfully the Castle and Gardens are not suitable for the disabled.

CASTLE SHOP
Gift shop and specialist plant centre open 10.30 - 5.30pm.

CATERING
A fully licensed restaurant and tea rooms can cater for morning coffee, lunches and afternoon tea. Booking for groups are taken in advance. Receptions and medieval dinners can be booked all year. Menus are available on request.

GUIDED TOURS
By prior arrangement only. Guide Book £2.50.

SCHOOL VISITS/CHILDREN
Worksheets available on request. For a small fee a preliminary talk can be given in the Church. A guide can be provided on request. Areas of particular interest include: Adventure playground and wildfowl Sanctuary.

CONTACT

Sudeley Castle
Winchcombe
Nr Cheltenham
Gloucestershire
GL54 5JD

Tel: (01242) 603197
or (01242) 602308
Fax: (01242) 602959

LOCATION

8 miles E of Cheltenham on B4632. From Bristol or Birmingham M5, Exit 9. Take A438 towards Stow-on-the-Wold.

Bus: Castleways to Winchcombe.

Rail: Cheltenham Station 8 miles.

OPENING TIMES

Summer
March:
GARDENS, PLANT CENTRE & SHOP
Daily: 10.30am - 4.30pm

1 April - 31 October:
CASTLE APARTMENTS
Daily: 11.00am - 5.00pm

CHURCH
Daily: 10.30am - 5.00pm

ADMISSION

Summer
CASTLE & GARDEN
  Adult £5.40
  Child (5-15 yrs.) . .£3.00
  OAP £4.70
  Family £14.00
  (2 Adults & 2 children)
Groups (min 20 people)
  Adult £4.10
  Child (5-15 yrs.) . .£2.20
  OAP £3.80
GARDENS ONLY
  Adult £4.00
  Child (5-15 yrs.) . .£1.80
  OAP £3.20
FRIENDS OF SUDELEY
SEASON TICKET
Local & Founder Members
  Adult £12.00
  Family £25.00

Other Friends
  Adult £15.00
  Family £30.00

ADVENTURE PLAY-
GROUND ONLY . . .£0.75

CONFERENCE AND FUNCTION FACILITIES

ROOM	CAPACITY	LAYOUT	POWER POINTS	SUITABLE FOR A/V
Chandos Hall	20	Boardroom	✓	✓
	40	Theatre		
	80	Reception		
	40	Dining		
North Hall	20	Boardroom	✓	✓
	40	Reception		
	20	Dining		
Library	20	Boardroom	✓	✓
	60	Theatre		
	80	Reception		
	40	Dining		
Banqueting Hall	100	Reception	✓	
	80	Dining		

ASHLEWORTH TITHE BARN

Tel: 01684 850051

Ashleworth, Gloucestershire
Owner: The National Trust **Contact:** The Administrator
A 15th C tithe barn with two projecting porch bays and fine roof timbers with queenposts.
Location: 6m N of Gloucester, 1¼ E of Hartpury A417.
Opening Times: Apr - end Oct: Daily 9am - 6pm or sunset if earlier. Closed Good Fri, other times by prior appointment only.
Admission: 60p.

HAILES ABBEY

Tel: 01242 602398

Nr Winchcombe, Cheltenham, Gloucestershire GL54 5PB
Owner: English Heritage **Contact:** The Custodian
Seventeen cloister arches and extensive excavated remains in lovely surroundings of an abbey founded by Richard, Earl of Cornwall, in 1246. There is a small museum and covered display area.
Location: 2m E of Winchcombe off B4632.
Opening Times: 1 Apr - 30 Sept: Daily 10am - 6pm. 1 - 31 Oct: Daily 10am - 6pm or dusk if earlier. 1 Nov - 31 Mar: Wed - Sun, 10am - 4pm. (Closed lunch 1 -2pm Nov - Mar).
Admission: Adult £2.20, Child £1.10, Conc £1.70.

BATSFORD PARK GARDENS

OPEN

1 Mar - 5 Nov
Daily
10am - 5pm.

House not open.

Tel: 01608 650722
Fax: 01608 650290

MORETON-IN-MARSH, GLOS GL56 9QF

Owner: The Batsford Foundation **Contact:** Polly Blick

Designed and planted as a wild garden, the 50 acres of arboretum contain well over 1,500 different species of tree and shrubs. The spring is heralded by carpets of snowdrops and daffodils followed by the blossom of magnolias and flowering cherries. The large collection of maples and sorbus provide wonderful autumn colour.
Location: 1½m NW of Moreton-in-Marsh, off A44 to Broadway.
Admission: Adult £2.50, OAP £2.00, Child (5 -15yrs) £2.00.

BERKELEY CASTLE

See Page 67 for full page entry.

BLACKFRIARS

Tel: 01179 750700

Southgate Street, Gloucester.
Owner: English Heritage **Contact:** The South West Regional Office
A small Dominican priory church converted into a rich merchant's house at the Dissolution. Most of the original 13th century church remains, including a rare scissor-braced roof.
Location: In Ladybellegate St, off Southgate St and Blackfriars Walk.
Opening Times: Please contact the South West Regional Office.

CHAVENAGE

See Page 68 for full page entry.

CHEDWORTH ROMAN VILLA

YANWORTH, CHELTENHAM, GLOUCESTERSHIRE GL54 3LJ

Owner: The National Trust
Contact: The Administrator

Tel: 01242 890256

The remains of a Romano-British villa, excavated 1864. Set in beautiful wooded combe. Includes fine 4th century mosaics, two bath houses, spring with temple. A museum houses the smaller finds.
Location: 3m NW of Fossebridge on A429.
Admission: Adult £3.00, Child £1.50, Family £7.50.
Pre-booked parties by arrangement.

OPEN

6 Feb - 1 Mar: Tues - Fri 10am - 4pm.
Site open for pre-booked parties.
5 Mar - 3 Nov: Tues - Sun, Bank Hol Mons only & Good Fri: 10am - 5pm.
5 Nov - 1 Dec & 7 & 8 Dec:
Wed - Sun 10am - 4pm..

HIDCOTE MANOR GARDENS

CHIPPING CAMPDEN, GLOUCESTERSHIRE

Owner: *The National Trust*
Contact: *The National Trust*

Tel: 01386 438333

One of the most delightful gardens in England, created this century by the great horticulturist Major Lawrence Johnston; a series of small gardens within the whole separated by walls and hedges of different species; famous for rare shrubs, trees, herbaceous borders, 'old' roses and interesting plant species.

Location: 4 miles north east of Chipping Campden, 1 mile east of B4632 (originally A46) off B4081.

Admission: Adult £5.20, Child £2.60, Family Ticket £13.00.

National Trust / K. Statham

OPEN

April - 30 Sept: Daily except Tues & Fri 11am - 7pm
Also open Tues in June & Jul only.
Oct. Daily except Tues & Fri 11am - 6pm
Last admission 1hr before closing.

KELMSCOTT MANOR

KELMSCOTT, NR. LECHLADE, GLOUCESTERSHIRE GL7 3HJ

Owner: *Society of Antiquaries* **Contact:** *Mrs Helen Webb*

Tel: 01367 252486 **Fax:** 01367 253754

Kelmscott Manor was the country home of William Morris, poet, craftsman and socialist - from 1871 until his death in 1896. The house contains an interesting collection of the possessions and works of Morris and his associates including furniture, textiles, carpets and ceramics. A centenary exhibition of "William Morris at Kelmscott" is being held in one of the barns during normal opening times.
Location: 2 miles SE of Lechlade, off the Lechlade/Faringdon Road.
Opening Times: Apr - Sept:Every Wed, 11am - 1pm and 2 - 5pm & 3rd Saturday in each month 2 - 6pm. Thursdays and Fridays by appointment.
Admission: Adult £6.00, Child (7-16yrs) and full-time students £3.00.

KIFTSGATE COURT GARDENS

OPEN

Apr, May, Aug, Sept
Wed, Thur & Sun
2 - 6 pm

June & July
Wed, Thur, Sat & Sun
12 noon - 6pm
and Bank Hol Mons
2 - 6pm

Coaches by
appointment only.

Tel: 01386 438777
Fax: 01386 438777

CHIPPING CAMPDEN, GLOUCESTERSHIRE GL55 6LW

Owner: Mr and Mrs J.G Chambers   *Contact: J.G. Chambers*

Magnificently situated garden on the edge of the Cotswold escarpment with views towards the Malvern Hills. Many unusual shrubs and plants including trees peonies, abutilons, specie and old fashioned roses. Tea room with light refreshments from Spring Bank Holiday to August Bank Holiday. Unusual plants for sale on opening days.
Location: 3 miles North East of Chipping Campden.
Admission: Adult £3.00, Child £1.00.

OWLPEN MANOR

**ULEY, NR DURSLEY, GLOUCES-
TERSHIRE GL11 5BZ**

Owner: Mr and Mrs Nicholas Mander
Contact: Mrs M Keevil

Tel: 01453 860261
Fax: 01453 860819

Romantic Tudor manor house, 1450-1616, with some Cotswold Arts & Crafts restoration. Remote wooded valley setting, with 16th & 17th C. formal terraced gardens and magnificent yews. Contains unique painted cloth wall hangings, family & Cotswold arts & crafts collections. Mill (1726), Court House (1620); licensed restaurant in medieval Cyder House. Victorian estate church. 9 period holiday cottages. Corporate events. "Owlpen - ah, what a dream is there!" - Vita Sackville-West.

Location: 3 miles E of Dursley, 1 mile E of Uley, off B4066, by Old Crown pub.

Admission: Adult £3.50, Child £2. Grounds: £2. Group rates.

OPEN

2 April - 30 Sept: Tues, Thurs, Sun & Bank Hol. Mons 2 - 5pm
July and August: Wed 2 - 5pm
Restaurant and Grounds open 12 noon

LITTLEDEAN HALL

Tel: 01594 824 213

Littledean, Gloucestershire GL14 3NR
Owner: D M Macer Wright Esq   **Contact:** D M Macer Wright Esq
'Reputedly England's oldest inhabited house' Guinness Book of Records. Site of Roman temple.
Location: 2m S of Cinderford off A4151.
Opening Times: 1 Apr - 31 Oct: Daily, 10.30am - 6pm.
Admission: Adult £2.50, Child £1.25, Groups £2 pp (by appointment).

LYDNEY PARK GARDENS

Tel: 01594 842844

Lydney, Gloucestershire GL15 6BU
Owner: The Viscount Bledisloe   **Contact:** Mrs Beryl Butcher
8 acres of extensive valley gardens with trees and lakes. Roman temple site and museum.
Location: 2m S of Cinderford off A4151. On A48 between Lydney and Aylburton.
Opening Times: Easter - 9 Jun, Sun, BHs and Wed, 11am - 6pm.
Admission: Adult £2.00 (Wed £1), Child free, Car park free, Groups of 25 + (min) by appointment.

PAINSWICK ROCOCO GARDENS

**THE STABLES, PAINSWICK
HOUSE, PAINSWICK,
GLOUCESTERSHIRE GL6 6TH**

Owner:
Painswick Rococo Garden Trust
Contact: P.R Moir

Tel: 01452 813204

Unique 18th century garden restoration situated in a hidden 6 acre Cotswold combe. Charming contemporary buildings are juxtaposed with winding woodland walks and formal vistas. Famous for its early spring show of snowdrops. Coffee, light lunches and teas.

Location: $^{1}/_{2}$ mile outside village of Painswick on B4073.

Admission: Adult £2.75, Senior Citizens £2.35, Child £1.50.

OPEN

House: 2nd Wed in Jan - 30 Nov
Wed - Sun and Bank Hols.
Garden: Daily in Jul & Aug
11.00am - 5.00pm

MISARDEN PARK GARDENS

**STROUD,
GLOUCESTERSHIRE GL6 7JA**

Owner: Major M T N H Wills
Contact: Major M T N H Wills

Tel: 01285 821303
Fax: 01285 821530

Noted in the spring for its bulbs and flowering trees and in mid summer for the large double herbaceous borders. Fine topiary throughout and a traditional rose garden.
Outstanding position, standing high overlooking the "Golden Valley". Garden nurseries open daily (except Mondays). Garden featured in Country Life 1992.

Location: 6 miles north west Cirencester. Follow signs off A417 from Gloucester or Cirencester or B4070 from Stroud.

Admission: Adult £2.50 (guided tours extra), Child Free. 10% reduction for groups 20+ who book in advance.

OPEN

1 April - 26 Sept, Tues, Weds, & Thurs
9.30am - 4.30pm

RODMARTON MANOR

OPEN

House:
Groups only
throughout the year
by prior written
appointment.

Garden:
Saturdays only
11 May - 31 Aug
2 - 5pm
and by appointment
throughout the year.

Tel: 01285 841253

CIRENCESTER, GLOUCESTERSHIRE GL7 6PF

Owner: Mr & Mrs Simon Biddulph   *Contact: Simon Biddulph*

One of the last great country houses to be built in the traditional way & containing beautiful furniture, ironwork, china and needlework specially made for the house. The large garden complements the house & contains many areas of beauty & character including herbaceous borders, topiary, roses, rockery & kitchen garden.
Location: Off A433 between Cirencester and Tetbury.
Admission: Conducted tour of the house with unconducted tour of the Garden £4.50, Child £2.20. Min. Group Charge £31.50. Garden only : £2, (Sats 2 -5pm, £2.50 at any other time), accompanied children free.

SEZINCOTE

Moreton-in-Marsh, Gloucestershire GL56 9AW
Owner: Mr and Mrs D Peake   **Contact:** Mrs D Peake
Exotic oriental water garden by Repton and Daniell. Large semi-circular orangery. House by S P Cockerell in Indian style was the inspiration for Brighton Pavilion.
Location: 1$^{1}/_{2}$ m SW of Moreton-in-Marsh. Turn W along A44 to Evesham and left just before Bourton-on-the-Hill..
Opening Times: Garden: Thurs, Fri & Bank Hol Mons, 2 - 6pm. House: May - Jul & Sept, 2.30 - 6pm.

SNOWSHILL MANOR

OPEN
Apr & Oct:
Daily except Tues
1 - 5pm
May - end Sept: 1 - 6pm
Grounds & visitor
facilities open: 12 noon.
Closed Good Fri.
Last adm. to house &
restaurant $^{1}/_{2}$hr
before closing.
Timed tickets will be
issued for the house.
Liable to serious
overcrowding on
Sun & BH Mons.
Tel: 01386 852410

SNOWSHILL, NR. BROADWAY, WORCESTERSHIRE WR12 7JU

Owner: The National Trust   *Contact: The National Trust*

A Tudor house with a c.1700 facade; 21 rooms containing Charles Paget Wade's collection of craftsmanship, including musical instruments, clocks, toys, bicycles, weavers' and spinners' tools, Japanese armour; small formal garden and Charles Wade's cottage. The Manor is a 10 minute walk (500 yds) along an undulating countryside path.
Location: 3 miles SW of Broadway, turning off the A44. [150:SP096339].
Admission: Adult £5.70, Child £2.60, Family ticket £13.00.
Grounds restaurant and shop only £2.00.

STANWAY HOUSE

See Page 69 for full page entry.

ST MARY'S CHURCH

Tel: 01179 750700

Kempley, Gloucestershire
Owner: English Heritage   **Contact:** The South West Regional Office
A delightful Norman church with superb wall paintings from the 12th - 14th centuries which were only discovered beneath white-wash in 1871.
Location: On unclassified road W of A228.
Opening Times: 1 Apr - 30 Sept: 10am - 6pm, 1 - 31 Oct: 10am - 6pm/dusk if earlier.

SUDELEY CASTLE

See Page 70 for full page entry.

WESTBURY COURT GARDEN

OPEN
April - end Oct.
Wed - Sun and
Bank Hol. Mons
11.00am-6.00pm

Closed Good Friday.

Tel: 01452 760461

WESTBURY-ON-SEVERN, GLOUCESTERSHIRE

Owner: The National Trust   Contact: The National Trust

A formal water garden with canals and yew hedges, laid out between 1696 and 1705; the earliest of its kind remaining in England. Restored in 1971 and planted species dating from pre-1700 including apple, pear and plum trees.
Location: 9 miles south west of Gloucester on A48 [162: SO718138]
Admission: Adult £2.50, Child £1.25.

WESTONBIRT ARBORETUM

Tel: 01666 880220   **Fax:** 01666 880559

Tetbury, Gloucestershire GL8 8QS
Owner: The Forestry Commission   **Contact:** Mr A Russell
600 acres arboretum begun in 1829, now with 18,000 catalogued trees. Excellent visitor centre.
Location: 3 miles S of Tetbury on the A433.
Opening Times: 365 days a year, 10m - 8pm (or dusk if earlier).
Admission: Adult £2.80, Senior citizen £1.80, Child £1.00.

WHITTINGTON COURT

Tel: 01242 820556

Whittington, Cheltenham, Gloucestershire GL54 4HF
Owner: Mr and Mrs Jack Stringer   **Contact:** Mrs J Stringer
Elizabethan manor house. Family possessions.
Location: 4m E of Cheltenham on A40.
Opening Times: 6 - 21 Apr and 10 - 26 Aug: Daily 2 - 5pm.
Admission: Adult £2, Child £1, Senior citizen £1.50, Groups by arrangement at £3 per head, minimum charge £75.00.

WOODCHESTER PARK MANSION

Tel: 01453 750455

High Street, Stroud, Gloucestershire GL5 1AP
Owner: Woodchester Mansion Trust   **Contact:** Mr R Shipton
Gothic style mansion in secret wooded valley, started in 1856 but abandoned before completion.
Location: 5m S of Stroud on B4066. Near to village of Nympsfield.
Opening Times: Easter - Oct: First Sat & Sun each month & BH weekends (Sat/Sun/Mons) 11am - 4pm.
Admission: Adult £3.00, Child under 12 £1.00, Student £2,.00 Groups by arrangement.

▽ *Where to Stay*
For Private Accommodation and Johansens recommended Hotels, see Accommodation Section.

SPECIAL EVENTS

◈ **KELMSCOTT MANOR**   **APRIL – SEPTEMBER**
Centenary Exhibition, 'William Morris at Kelmscott', during normal house opening times.

◈ **SUDELEY CASTLE**   **21 APRIL**
National Gardens Scheme

◈ **SUDELEY CASTLE**   **17 – 18 AUGUST**
Festival Players, 'The Merchant of Venice' (evening performances)

◈ **SUDELEY CASTLE**   **15 SEPTEMBER**
National Gardens Scheme

For National Trust and English Heritage Events see separate section.

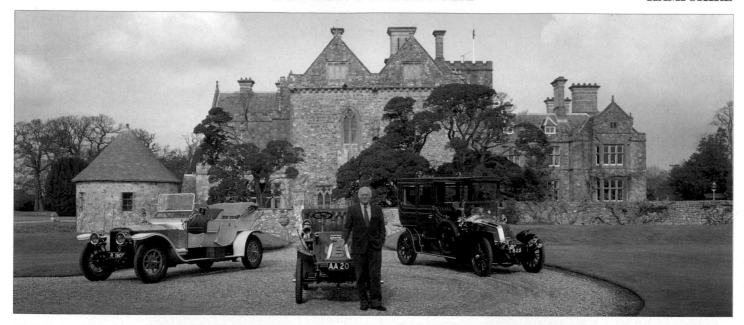

BEAULIEU
Beaulieu

BEAULIEU, in the beautiful New Forest between Bournemouth and Southampton, has been Lord Montagu's family home since 1538, when it was purchased by Lord Montagu's ancestor, Thomas Wriothesley, 1st Earl of Southampton. Palace House and gardens have been open to the public since 1952, when the present Lord Montagu inherited.

Beaulieu Abbey was founded in 1204 and, although most of the buildings were destroyed during the Dissolution, much of beauty and interest remains. The Domus, a fine remaining building, houses an exhibition which takes the visitor back to the ages of King John and medieval monastic life.

The inclusive admission to Beaulieu covers entry to the National Motor Museum, Palace House and Gardens, Beaulieu Abbey and Exhibition of Monastic Life.

❖

SUITABILITY FOR OTHER EVENTS
Rallies, product launches, promotions, banquets, filming, outdoor events, exhibitions. Most requests considered.

EXTRA FACILITIES
Helicopter landing point, audio-visual facilities, lectures, private dining room of Palace House available for receptions, dinners, lunches etc., hardstanding exhibition arena adjacent to Motor Museum, veteran and vintage cars and buses available to transport guests.

ADVICE TO COURIERS & DRIVERS
During the season the very busy period is from 11.30am to 1.30pm. It is advisable to allow 2 hours or more for visits. Last admission 40 minutes before closing. On arrival at the Information Centre, where hostesses are on hand to welcome and assist you. Coach drivers should sign in at the Information Desk. Free admission is given to coach drivers and they receive a voucher which can be exchanged for food, drink and souvenirs. No dogs in the buildings.

FACILITIES FOR THE DISABLED
Disabled and elderly visitors may be left at the entrance to the Palace House, before parking in the allocated areas. There are toilets for the disabled. There are some concessions for handicapped parties. Wheelchairs are available at the Information Centre for use within the grounds.

PARKING FOR COACHES & CARS
Parking for 1,500 cars and 30 coaches.

CATERING
The Brabazon seats 300 in a self-service Restaurant and Bar. Open daily. Prices from £4 for tea and £7 for lunch. Groups can book in advance. Further details and menus available from Catering Manager (01590) 612102.

GUIDED TOURS
Attendants on duty in Palace House and National Motor Museum. Guided tours by prior arrangement.

GIFT SHOP
Information Centre Shop, open as property. Palace House Shop, Kitchen Shop, Herb Shop, Abbey Shop open Summer only. Gifts include motoring items, books, comestibles and toiletries.

GUIDE BOOKS
Colour guide books available.

SCHOOL VISITS/CHILDREN
Beaulieu offers an extensive education service to student groups of all ages. Professionally qualified staff are available to assist in planning of visits to all attractions. Services include introductory talks, films, guided tours, role play and extended projects.

In general, educational services incur no additional charges, and publications are sold at cost. Starter sets of material are available free of charge to pre-booked parties. Full information pack available from Education at Beaulieu, John Montagu Building, Beaulieu, Hampshire SO42 7ZN.

Responsible behaviour is expected at all times.

CONTACT

Groups Organiser
John Montagu Building
Beaulieu
Brockenhurst
Hampshire
SO42 7ZN

Tel: (01590) 612345
Fax: (01590) 612624

LOCATION

From London, M3 West, M27, M1, A35 then B3056 from Lyndhurst.

Bus: Bus stops within complex.

Rail: Stations at Brockenhurst and Beaulieu Rd both 7 miles away.

OPENING TIMES

Summer

Easter - October
Daily 10.00am - 6.00pm

Winter

October - Easter
Daily 10.00am - 5.00pm

ADMISSION

All Year

Individual rates upon application.

Groups (min 15 people)
(1996 rates)

Adult £6.75
Child (4-16yrs) . .£4.50
OAP £5.75
Student £5.25

BEAULIEU CONTINUED...

CATERING/FUNCTIONS

New conference and function brochure available for those requesting it.

The Brabazon and Domus (pictured above) banqueting halls can be hired all year round. For a fee Lord Montagu may meet groups and participate in functions.

Groups can be booked in advance for buffets, lunches, dinners and Royal Feasts. Please contact the Catering Manager for further details and menus. Tel: (01590) 612102.

CONFERENCE AND FUNCTION FACILITIES

ROOM	DIMENSIONS	CAPACITY	LAYOUT	POWER POINTS	SUITABLE FOR A/V
Brabazon (3 sections)	40'x40'(x3)	120(each)	Theatre	3	✓
		70	Schoolroom		
		40	U-shape		
		40	Boardroom		
		100	Buffet		
		300	Dinner/Dance		
		80 (each)	Lunch/Dinner		
Domus	69'x27'	170	Theatre	3	✓
		60	Schoolroom		
		40	U-shape		
		40	Boardroom		
		120	Lunch/Dinner		
Classic Car Theatre		200	Tiered Theatre Style Seating	3	✓

THE NATIONAL MOTOR MUSEUM

When Lord Montagu inherited Beaulieu, he displayed a handful of early vehicles in the Front Hall as a memorial to his father, one of the leading pioneers of motoring in Britain. From this beginning the now famous National Motor Museum grew.

The Museum traces the story of motoring from 1894 to the present day, with many special displays and 250 cars, commercial vehicles and motorcycles. It is especially proud to have four World Land Speed Record Breaking Cars (see left).

'Wheels - The Legend of the Motor Car', is a major feature in the Museum. This spectacular ride-through display is a tribute to man's motoring achievements. 'Wheels' transports visitors in space-age 'pods' through 100 years of motoring, from the early pioneers and their problems, to fantasies of the future, and shows how the motor vehicle has revolutionised our lives.

A monorail transports visitors to the Motor Museum, entering the building at roof level. There are rides on a 1912 open-topped London Bus or in Miniature Veteran Cars; Remote Controlled Model Cars.

Entry to the museum is included in the inclusive admission price.

HIGHCLERE CASTLE
Newbury

Designed by Charles Barry in the 1830s at the same time as he was building the Houses of Parliament, this soaring pinnacled mansion provided a perfect setting for the 3rd Earl of Carnarvon one of the great hosts of Queen Victoria's reign. The extravagant interiors range from church Gothic through Moorish flamboyance and rococo revival to the solid masculinity in the long Library. Old master paintings mix with portraits by Van Dyck and 18th Century painters. Napoleon's desk and chair rescued from St. Helena sits with other 18th and 19th Century furniture.

The 5th Earl of Carnarvon, discovered the Tomb of Tutankhamun with Howard Carter. The castle houses a unique exhibition of some of his discoveries which were only rediscovered in the castle in 1988. The current Earl is the Queen's Horseracing Manager. In 1993 to celebrate his 50th year as a leading owner and breeder "The Lord Carnarvon Racing Exhibition" was opened to the public, and offers a fascinating insight into a racing history that dates back three generations.

GARDENS
The magnificent parkland with its massive cedars was designed by 'Capability' Brown. The walled gardens also date from an earlier house at Highclere but the dark yew walks are entirely Victorian in character. The glass Orangery and Fernery add an exotic flavour. The Secret Garden has a romance of its own with a beautiful curving lawn surrounded by densely planted herbaceous gardens. A place for poets and romantics.

SUITABILITY FOR OTHER EVENTS
Ideal for conferences, exhibitions, receptions, dinners, activity days, filming, concerts and corporate hospitality.

OUTDOOR EVENTS
Stunning backdrop for concerts, (cap. 8000) Fairs and displays.

ADVICE TO COURIERS & DRIVERS
Dogs are not permitted in the house or gardens except guide dogs. No photography in the house. Ample Parking.

FACILITIES FOR THE DISABLED
Disabled and elderly visitors may alight at the entrance to the house. There are toilet facilities for the disabled.

CATERING
Exceptional catering for corporate events. During public openings the tea rooms can accommodate 60. Lunches for parties of 24+ can be booked in advance.

GIFT SHOP
The Gift Shop is open throughout the Castle open season.

GUIDED TOURS
Guided tours are often provided, free of charge, to visitors.

GUIDE BOOKS
Colour guide book, £2.50.

SCHOOL VISITS/CHILDREN
Groups welcome by prior arrangement. Areas of interest: The Egyptian collection belonging to the 5th Earl of Carnarvon, discoverer of the Tomb of Tutankhamun, nature walks, beautiful old follies, Secret Garden.

CONTACT

A Wiley
Highclere Castle
Highclere Park
Newbury
RG20 9RN

Tel: (01635) 253210
Fax: (01635) 810193

LOCATION

Approx 4¹/₂ miles out of Newbury on A34 towards Winchester. From London: M4 Junct 13; A34, Newbury-Winchester 20 mins. M3 Junct. 5 approx 15 miles.
Air: Heathrow M4 45 mins.
Rail: Paddington-Newbury 45 mins.
Taxi: 4¹/₂ miles (01635) 40829.

CONFERENCE AND FUNCTION FACILITIES

ROOM	DIMENSIONS	CAPACITY	LAYOUT	POWER POINTS	SUITABLE FOR A/V
Library	43' x 21'	120	Theatre	✓	✓
Saloon		150	Reception	✓	✓
Dining Room		70	Lunch/Dinner Seated	✓	
Library, Saloon, Drawing Room Music Room, Smoking Room 400			Reception	✓	

SOMERLEY
Ringwood

To visit Somerley, even briefly, is to taste the elegant lifestyle. The architectural grandeur, the elegance of its interiors and its magnificent setting on the edge of the New Forest combine to make it one of Britain's finest houses. The house was designed by Samuel Wyatt in the mid 1700s and has been the residence of the Normanton family for almost 200 years. The sixth Earl and Countess live here today with their three children.

The house is not open to the public; the magnificently proportioned rooms with high gilded ceilings house a treasure trove of fine antique furniture, porcelain, paintings and objets d'art, and can be enjoyed by guests who visit to conduct business meetings, conferences, concerts, receptions, product launches and top level corporate hospitality. The house is 1½ miles from the nearest road and although easily accessible, provides privacy for meetings demanding security and complete confidentiality. The 7,000 acres of parkland can be used for incentive fun days, promotions and Golf events. The high standard of service and cuisine (much of the food comes from the Estate and gardens) and the warm friendly atmosphere are very rarely found in a house of this size. The peace and tranquillity of the grounds are a sheer delight.

OPENING TIMES

Privately Booked Functions only.

ADMISSION

Upon application for privately booked functions only.

CONTACT

Pamela Benton
Somerley
Ringwood
Hampshire
BH24 3PL

Tel: (01425) 480819
Fax: (01425) 478613

LOCATION

Off the M27 to Bournemouth, A31 1ml. London 1¾ hrs via M3, M27, A31.

Air: Bournemouth International Airport, 5miles.

Rail: Bournemouth Station 12 miles.

Taxi: A car can be arranged from the House if applicable.

SUITABILITY FOR OTHER EVENTS
Specialising in game and clay pigeon shooting, filming, archery, and golf. Large scale events, fashion shows, air displays, equestrian events, garden parties, shows, rallies, wedding receptions.

EXTRA FACILITIES
Also available for use: Grand Piano, organ, billiard room, parkland, formal gardens, croquet, tennis and golf driving range and 9-hole golf course, outdoor pool, salmon fishing, clay shoot. Picture Gallery includes work by Reynolds, Canaletto, Gainsborough, Murillo and Etty. Furniture mainly Louis XIV and XVI.

ACCOMMODATION
Somerley offers 1 single and 8 twin/doubles with bathrooms. All rooms to be taken by house party. Smaller numbers negotiable.

ADVICE TO COURIERS & DRIVERS
Liaise with Pamela Benton or the Earl of Normanton: 01425 480819. No individual visits. All uses of Somerley are on an exclusive basis, by application only.

FACILITIES FOR THE DISABLED
Disabled and elderly visitors may alight to the Front Entrance of the House.

PARKING FOR COACHES & CARS
There is parking for up to 200 cars and 20+ coaches adjacent to the house.

CATERING
The Dining Room is available for private parties (capacity 50 people). Parties must book in advance and menus are available on request. Meals from £23.00 per head. Outside caterers may be used in the Grounds if requested.

BROCHURES
A colour brochure is complimentary, given to conference/ function enquirers.

CONFERENCE AND FUNCTION FACILITIES

ROOM	DIMENSIONS	CAPACITY	LAYOUT	POWER POINTS	SUITABLE FOR A/V
Picture Gallery	80' x 30'	150	Reception	8	
Drawing Room	38' x 30'	50	Various	6	
Dining Room	39' x 19'	50	Various	4	
East Library	26' x 21'	20	Boardroom	4	
		20	Lunch/Dinner		
		30	Reception		

AVINGTON PARK

OPEN

May - Sept.
Suns & Bank Hols
2.30 - 5.30pm

Tea Bar open at
these times.
Last tour 5pm.

Pre-booked
coaches welcome.

Other times by
appointment only.

Tel: 01962 779260
Fax: 01962 779864

WINCHESTER, HAMPSHIRE SO21 1DD

Owner: Lt. Col and Mrs J B Hickson   *Contact:* Mrs S L Bullen

Avington Park, where Charles II and George IV both stayed at various times is an old house enlarged in 1670 by the addition of two wings and a classical Portico surmounted by three statues. The State rooms are magnificently painted and lead onto the unique pair of conservatories flanking the South Lawn. The Georgian St. Mary's Church, is in the grounds. Avington Park is available for Conferences, Filming and Receptions.

Location: 4 miles North East of Winchester off the B3047 in Itchen Abbas.
Admission: Adult £2.75, Child under 14 £1.50.

BASING HOUSE

Tel: 01256 467294

Redbridge Lane, Basing, Basingstoke, Hampshire RG24 7HB
Owner: Hampshire County Council   **Contact:** Alan Turton
Ruins, covering 10 acres, of huge Tudor palace. Recent recreation of Tudor formal garden.
Location: 2m from Basingstoke town centre.
Opening Times: 3 Apr - 29 Sept: Wed - Sun, 2 - 6pm.
Admission: Adult £1.50, Child 70p.

BEAULIEU

See Pages 74 & 75 for full page entry.

BISHOP'S WALTHAM PALACE

Tel: 01489 892460

Bishop's Waltham, Hampshire SO32 1DH
Owner: English Heritage   **Contact:** The Custodian
This medieval seat of the Bishops of Winchester once stood in an enormous park. There are still wooded grounds and the remains of Great Hall can still be seen and the three storey tower.
Location: In Bishop's Waltham, 5 miles from junction 8 of M27.
Opening Times: 1 Apr - 30 Sept: Daily 10am - 6pm. 1 - 31 Oct 10am - 6pm or dusk if earlier.
Admission: Adult £2.00, Child £1.00, Conc £1.50.

BOHUNT MANOR

Tel: 01428 7222080

Liphook, Hampshire GU30 7DL
Owner: Worldwide Fund for Nature   **Contact:** Lady Holman
Woodland gardens with lakeside walk, collection of ornamental waterfowl, herbaceous borders and unusual trees and shrubs.
Location: In Liphook village.
Opening Times: All year: Daily 10am - 6pm.
Admission: Adult £1.50, Child under 14 free, Conc £1.00, Group 10% off.

BRAMDEAN HOUSE

Tel: 01962 771 214   **Fax:** 01962 771 095

Bramdean, Alresford, Hampshire SO24 0JU
Owner: Mrs H Wakefield   **Contact:** Mrs H Wakefield
Walled garden with famous herbaceous borders.
Location: In Bramdean village on A272 midway between Winchester and Petersfield.
Opening Times: Garden only: 17 Mar, 7, 8, 21 Apr, 19 May, 16 Jun, 21 Jul, 13 Aug: 2 - 5pm. Also by prior appointment.

BREAMORE HOUSE

Tel: 01725 512233

Breamore, Fordingbridge, Hampshire SP6 2DF
Owner: Sir Westrow Hulse Bt   **Contact:** Edward Hulse Esq
Elizabethan Manor with fine collections of pictures and furniture. Countryside Museum takes visitors back to when a village was self sufficient. The Carriage Museum is in the Queen Anne stables.
Location: Off the A338, between Salisbury and Ringwood.
Opening Times: Countryside Museum: 1 - 5.30pm. House: 2 - 5.30pm April: Tues, Wed, Sun and Easter Holiday. May, Jun, Jul, Sept: Tues - Sun and all holidays. Aug: Daily.
Admission: Combined ticket for house and garden: Adult £4.50, Child £3.00.

CALSHOT CASTLE

Tel: 01703 892023

Calshot, Fawley, Hampshire SO45 1BR
Owner: English Heritage   **Contact:** The Custodian
Henry VIII built this coastal fort in an excellent position, commanding the sea passage to Southampton. The fort houses an exhibition and recreated pre-World War I barrack room.
Location: On spit 2m SE of Fawley off B3053.
Opening Times: 1 Apr - 30 Sept: Daily 10am - 6pm. 1 - 31 Oct: Daily 10am - 6pm or dusk if earlier.
Admission: Adult £1.80, Child 90p, Conc £1.40.

ELING TIDE MILL

Tel: 01703 869575

The Toll Bridge, Eling, Totton, Hampshire SO40 9HF
Owner: New Forest District Council   **Contact:** Mr. Martin Mears
Location: 4m W of Southampton.
Opening Times: Wed - Sun 10am - 4pm.
Admission: Adult £1.25, Child 65p, Family £3.50, Conc 95p, Groups 95p.

EXBURY GARDENS

Tel: 01703 891203

Exbury, Southampton, Hampshire SO45 1AZ.
Owner: Edmund de Rothschild Esq   **Contact:** Sheila Wise
Extensive landscaped woodland gardens overlooking the Beaulieu River. World famous Rothschild plant collection (rhododendrons, azaleas etc.) as well as many rare and wonderful trees: Rock Garden, Cascades, Ponds, River Walk, Rose Garden, Water Garden, Heather Gardens, seasonal trails and themed walks. Ample seating throughout. Lunches/cream teas in licensed restaurant. Ample free parking, interesting Plant Centre and Gift Shop. Gardens most spectacular in Spring and Autumn. Ask about Special Events.
Location: 20 minutes drive S off junction 2, M27.
Opening Times: Daily 17 Feb - 27 Oct: 10am - 5pm (dusk if earlier).

FORT BROCKHURST

Tel: 01590 642344

Gunner's Way, Gosport, Hampshire PO12 4DS
Owner: English Heritage   **Contact:** The Head Custodian
This was a new type of fort, built in the 19th century to protect Portsmouth with formidable fire-power. Largely unaltered, the parade ground, gun ramps and moated keep can all be viewed. An exhibition illustrates the history of Portsmouth's defences.
Location: Off A32, in Gunner's Way, Elson, on N side of Gosport.
Opening Times: 1 Apr - 30 Sept: Daily 10am - 6pm. 1 - 31 Oct: Daily 10am - 6pm or dusk if earlier.
Admission: Adult £2.00, Child £1.00, Conc £1.50.

FURZEY GARDENS

Tel: 01703 812464

Minstead, Lyndhurst, Hampshire SO43 7GL
Owner: Furzey Gardens Charitable Trust   **Contact:** M A Selwood
8 acres of informal garden surrounding a 16th century cottage with gallery of local Arts and Crafts.
Location: Signposted in Minstead. Off A31 or A337.
Opening Times: All year (except 25/26 Dec): 10am - 5pm (earlier in winter).
Admission: Nov - Feb: Adult £1.50, Child 75p, Conc £1.00, Family £3.50.
Mar - Oct: Adult £3.00, Child £1.50, Family £7.00. Groups 15% discount .

GILBERT WHITE'S HOUSE & GARDEN

OPEN

End Mar to
Christmas
Daily
11.00am - 5.00pm

Weekends only
during winter

Day and Evenings
also for groups by
appointment

Tel: 01420 511275

THE WAKES, HIGH STREET, SELBORNE, ALTON GU34 3JH

Owner: *Oates Memorial Trust* **Contact:** *Mrs. Anna Jackson*

Historic 18th c. House in heart of old Selborne, home of Rev Gilbert White, author of 'The Natural History of Selborne'. Lovely garden with many plants of the 18th c. Museum devoted to Captain Oates of Antarctic fame. Unusual plants fair, 22/23 June. Picnic to 'Jazz in June' 23 June, Mulled Wine Day 24 November.
Location: On B3006 in village of Selborne close to A3.
Admission: Adult £3.00, OAP £2.50, Child £1.00.

THE GRANGE ⛋   **Tel:** 01732 778000

Northington, Basingstoke, Hampshire
Owner: English Heritage **Contact:** The South East Regional Office
This magnificent neoclassical country house, built at the beginning of the 18th century could easily be mistaken for a Greek temple, with portico front and grand steps.
Location: 4m N of New Alresford off B3046.
Opening Times: Any reasonable time (exterior viewing only).

THE GREAT HALL   **Tel:** 01962 846476

Winchester Castle, Winchester, Hampshire SO23 8ZB
Owner: Hampshire County Council **Contact:** Miss K Mann
Remaining part of William the Conqueror's Castle built in 1235. Home of the famous King Arthur's round table.
Location: Central Winchester.
Opening Times: All year: 10am - 4pm. (Except 25 & 26 Dec).
Admission: Free.

GREATHAM MILL   **Tel:** 01420 538 245 **Fax:** 01420 538 21

Greatham, Liss, Hampshire GU33 6HH
Owner: Mr and Mrs E. Groves **Contact:** Mr E Groves
Interesting garden with large variety of plants surrounding a mill house.
Location: 2m from Liss; 7m from Alton.
Opening Times: Feb - Sept: Daily. Tearoom open Sats, Suns and Bank Hols.
Admission: Adult £1, Child Free. Organized tours by appointment.

GUILDHALL GALLERY **Tel:** 01962 848289 **Fax:** 01962 841365

The Broadway, Winchester, Hampshire SO23 9LJ
Owner: Winchester City Council **Contact:** Mr C Wardman Bradbury
19th century Guild Hall. Changing contemporary exhibitions.
Location: Winchester - 66 miles from London.
Opening Times: Tue - Sat: 10am - 5pm, Sun & Mon: 2 - 5pm. Closed Mondays Oct - Mar.
Admission: Free.

HIGHCLERE CASTLE 🏛 **See Page 76 for full page entry.**

HILLIER GARDENS   **Tel:** 01794 368787

Jermyns Lane, Ampfield, Romsey, Hampshire SO51 OQA
Owner: Hampshire County Council **Contact:** Mrs C Whitley
Gardens and arboretum extending over 160 acres with wide diversity of plants. Started by Sir Harold Hillier in the 1950s.
Location: 3m NE of Romsey, off A31.
Opening Times: Telephone for details.

HINTON AMPNER GARDEN ❦

OPEN

30 Mar - end Sept:
Garden:
Sat, Sun, Tues, Wed
& BH Mon
1.30 - 5.30pm.
House:
Tues & Wed only,
also Sat & Sun in
Aug, 1.30 -5.30pm
Last adm. 5.00pm.

Tel: 01962 771305

BRAMDEAN, NR. ALRESFORD, HAMPSHIRE SO24 0LA

Owner: *The National Trust* **Contact:** *The Administrator*

The garden, set in superb Hampshire countryside, combines formal design with informal planting, producing delightful walks with many unexpected vistas. After 5 years of restoration work the garden is now flourishing and highlights include the dell and sunken garden. The house was remodelled by the late Ralph Dutton in 1936, but was gutted by fire in 1960, destroying much of his collection. He rebuilt and refurnished the house with fine regency furniture, 17th century Italian pictures and porcelain.
Location: On A272, 1m W of Bramdean village, 8m E of Winchester.
Admission: House & Gdn: £3.90, Garden only: £2.50, Pre-booked parties £3.40.

HOUGHTON LODGE 🏛

OPEN

Garden:
March - Sept.
Sats. & Suns.
10am - 5pm
Mon, Tues, Fri
2 - 5pm
Other times by
appointment

House:
Groups only by
appointment.

Tel: 01264 810177
or 01264 810502

STOCKBRIDGE, HAMPSHIRE, SO20 6LQ

Owner: *Captain M W Busk* **Contact:** *Captain M W Busk*

Perhaps among the most 'picturesque' of 18th century Gothic "cottages ornees" with its architectural fantasy and perfect garden setting overlooking the tranquil beauty of the Test valley. The kitchen garden surrounded by rare chalkcob walls contains The Hydroponicum, a living exhibition of horticulture without soil, demonstrating its application worldwide and in space.
Location: 1^1/$_2$ mls south of Stockbridge (A30) on minor road to Houghton village.
Admission: £2.50. Discounts for parties. House prices on application.

HURST CASTLE ⛋   **Tel:** 01590 642344

Keyhaven, Lymington, Hampshire PO41 0PB
Owner: English Heritage **Contact:** The Custodian
This was one of the most sophisticated fortresses built by Henry VIII, and later strengthened in the 19th and 20th centuries, to command the narrow entrance to the Solent. There is an exhibition in the Castle, and two huge 38 ton guns form the fort's armaments.
Location: On Pebble Spit S of Keyhaven. Best approach by ferry from Keyhaven.
Opening Times: 1 Apr - 30 Jun: Daily 10am - 5.30pm. 1 Jul - 31 Aug: Daily 10am - 6pm. 1 Sept - 31 Oct: Daily 10am - 6pm/dusk in Oct. 1 Nov - 31 Mar: Daily 10am - 4pm.
Admission: Adult £2.00, Child £1.00, Conc £1.50.

JANE AUSTEN'S HOUSE

OPEN

April - Oct
Daily
11am - 4.30pm

Nov, Dec & Mar
Wed - Sun

Jan & Feb
Sats & Suns

Closed
25 & 26 Dec

Tel: 01420 83262
Fax: 01420 83262

CHAWTON, ALTON, HAMPSHIRE GU34 1SD.

Owner: Jane Austen Memorial Trust   *Contact:* The Curator

17th century house where Jane Austen wrote or revised her six great novels. Contains many items associated with her and her family, documents and letters, first editions of the novels, pictures, portraits and furniture. Pleasant garden, suitable for picnics, bakehouse with brick oven and wash tub, houses Jane's donkey carriage. Bookshop. Refreshments available in village.

Location: A31, 1 mile SW of Alton, signposted Chawton.
Admission: Adult £2.00, Groups (15+) £1.50, Child (8-18) 50p.

JENKYN PLACE

Tel: 01420 22561

Bentley, Hampshire GU10 5LU
Owner: Jenkyn Place Garden Trust
Well designed plantsman's garden with interesting shrubs and perennials.
Location: 1,000 metres N of A31 (Farnham to Alton).
Opening Times: Apr - Sep: Thur - Sun, 2 - 6pm.
Admission: Adult £2.00, Child 75p.

THE MANOR HOUSE

Tel: 01256 862827

Upton Grey, Basingstoke, Hampshire RG25 2RD
Owner: Mrs J Wallinger   **Contact:** Mrs J Wallinger
4 acre garden designed by Gertrude Jekyll in 1908, meticulously restored to original plans.
Location: 6m SE of Basingstoke.
Opening Times: By appointment for groups May - Jul.
Admission: Standard £3.00, Groups £3.00pp.

MEDIEVAL MERCHANT'S HOUSE ⌗

Tel: 01703 221503

58 French Street, Southampton, Hampshire SO1 0AT
Owner: English Heritage   **Contact:** The Custodian
The life of the prosperous merchant in the Middle Ages is vividly evoked in this recreated, faithfully restored 13th century townhouse.
Location: 58 French Street. 1/4 mile south of city centre just off Castle Way (between High St. & Bugle St).
Opening Times: 1 Apr - 30 Sept: Daily 10am - 6pm. 1 - 31 Oct: 10am - 6pm or dusk if earlier.
Admission: Adult £2.00, Child £1.00, Conc £1.50.

MOTTISFONT ABBEY GARDEN ❧

MOTTISFONT, NR. ROMSEY, HAMPSHIRE SO51 0LP

Owner: The National Trust   *Contact:* The Property Manager

Tel: 01794 340757

A country estate of timeless beauty. A tributary of the River Test flows through the garden forming a superb and tranquil setting for a 12th century Augustinian priory, which, after the Dissolution, became a house. It contains the spring or "font" from which the place name is derived. The magnificent trees, walled gardens and the national collection of old-fashioned roses combine to provide interest throughout the seasons.
Location: $4^1/2$m NW of Romsey, $3/4$m W of A3057.
Opening Times: Garden: 24 & 31 Mar, 1 Apr - 30 Oct: Sat - Wed 12 noon - 6pm or dusk if earlier. Jun: All week 12 noon - 8.30pm. Last adm. 1 hr before closing.
Admission: Garden: £3.00, £4.00 during June (rose season). No reduction for parties, coaches please book in advance.

NETLEY ABBEY ⌗

Tel: 01732 778000

Netley, Southampton, Hampshire
Owner: English Heritage   **Contact:** The South East Regional Office
There is a peaceful and beautiful setting for the extensive ruins of this 13th century Cistercian abbey converted in Tudor times for use as a house.
Location: In Netley, 4m SE of Southampton, facing Southampton Water.
Opening Times: Any reasonable time.

PORTCHESTER CASTLE ⌗

Tel: 01705 378291

Castle Street, Portchester, Hampshire PO16 9QW
Owner: English Heritage   **Contact:** The Custodian
A residence for Kings and a rallying point for troops, the history of this grand castle stretches back for nearly 2,000 years. There are Roman walls, the most complete in Europe, substantial remains of the Royal castle and an exhibition which tells the story of Portchester.
Location: On S side of Portchester off A27, junction 11 on M27.
Opening Times: 1 Apr - 30 Sept: Daily 10am - 6pm. 1 - 31 Oct: Daily 10am - 6pm or dusk if earlier. 1 Nov - 31 Mar: Wed - Sun 10am - 4pm.
Admission: Adult £2.50, Child £1.30, Conc £1.90.

PORTSMOUTH CATHEDRAL

Tel: 01705 823300   **Fax:** 01705 295480

Portsmouth, Hampshire PO1 2HH

Contact: Rosemary Fairfax

Maritime Cathedral founded in 12th century and finally completed in 1991. A member of the ship's crew of Henry VIII flagship Mary Rose is buried in Navy Aisle.
Location: $1^1/2$m from end of M275. Follow signs to Historic Ship and Old Portsmouth.
Opening Times: 7.45am - 6pm all year. Sun service: 8.00am, 9.30am, 11am, 6.30pm. Weekday: 7.20am, 7.45am, 6pm (Choral on Tue and Fri in term time).
Admission: Donation appreciated.

SANDHAM MEMORIAL CHAPEL ❧

BURGHCLERE, NR. NEWBURY, HAMPSHIRE RG15 9JT

Owner: The National Trust   *Contact:* The Property Manager

Tel: 01635 278394

Considered by many to be one of Stanley Spencer's greatest achievements, Sandham will intrigue anyone with an interest in 20th century art. The Chapel is a First World War memorial built in the 1920s and the paintings by Stanley Spencer of war scenes in Salonica cover the chapel walls.

Location: 4m S of Newbury, 1/2m E of A34.

Opening Times: 3 Apr - 31 Oct: Wed - Sun & Bank Hol Mon, 11.30am - 6pm. (Closed Wed following BH Mon). Mar & Nov, Sat & Sun, 11.30am - 4pm. Dec - Feb: by appointment only.

Admission: Adult £1.50, Child 75p. Groups, pre-booked, no reduction.

STRATFIELD SAYE HOUSE 🏛

STRATFIELD SAYE, READING, HAMPSHIRE RG7 2BT

Owner: The Duke of Wellington   *Contact:* The Comptroller

Tel: 01256 882882   **Fax:** 01256 882345

Stratfield Saye House was presented to the Great Duke of Wellington by a grateful nation after the battle of Waterloo in 1815, and is still the home of the present Duke and Duchess. The house retains, with many of his personal belongings, much of the atmosphere created by the Great Duke. The Wellington Exhibition houses his magnificent 18 ton funeral carriage, and within the grounds are the American Gardens and the grave of Copenhagen, the Great Duke's favourite charger.

Location: Equidistant from Reading (M4/J11) & Basingstoke (M3/J6) off the A33.

Opening Times: 1 May - last Sun in Sept: Daily except Fris. 11.30am - 4pm.

Admission: Adult £4.50, Child (5-15) £2.25. Group rates for 20 or more: Adult £4.00, Child £2.25, OAP £3.00.

SOMERLEY   **See Page 77 for full page entry.**

TITCHFIELD ABBEY ⊞   **Tel:** 01732 778000

Titchfield, Southampton, Hampshire

Owner: English Heritage   **Contact:** The South West Regional Office

Remains of a 13th century abbey overshadowed by the grand Tudor gatehouse. Reputedly some of Shakespeare's plays were performed here for the first time.

Location: 1/2 mile N of Titchfield off A27.

Opening Times: Telephone regional office 01732 778000 for details of times.

TUDOR HOUSE MUSEUM   **Tel:** 01703 635904   **Fax:** 01703 339601

Bugle Street, Southampton, Hampshire

Owner: Southampton City Council   **Contact:** Sian Jones

Late 15th century half timbered house. Unique Tudor knot garden.

Location: Follow signs to Old Town and waterfront from M27/M3.

Opening Times: Tues - Fri, 10am - 12 noon, 1 - 5pm. Sat 10am - 12 noon, 1- 4pm. Sun 2 - 5pm. Closed Mons.

Admission: Free.

THE VYNE ❧

SHERBORNE ST JOHN, BASINGSTOKE RG26 5DX

Owner: The National Trust   *Contact:* The Property Manager

Tel: 01256 881337   **Fax:** 01256 881720

Woodlands walks and lawns sloping to the lake provide a magnificent setting for this early Tudor house. The panelled gallery and chapel with renaissance glass are some of the finest examples in Britain. Outstanding collections of ceramics, textiles and furniture within a warm, historic atmosphere. The house will close earlier in the year to allow essential services and restoration to begin. The house will be closed throughout 1997 and will re-open mid 1998. The grounds are planned to remain open.

Location: 4m N of Basingstoke between Bramley and Sherborne St John.

Opening Times: House: 19 Mar - 1 Sept: Daily except Mon & Fri, 1.30 - 5.30pm. Grounds: 19 March - end Oct: Daily except Mon & Fri, 12.30 - 5.30pm. Also open Good Fri & BH Mons 11.00am - 5.30pm, but closed Tues following. Last admission 1/2 before closing.

Admission: House & Grounds: Adult £4.00, Child £2.00, Family £10.00. Pre-booked parties £3.00 each. Grounds only: Adults £2.00, Child £1.00.

WINCHESTER CATHEDRAL   **Tel:** 01962 853137   **Fax:** 01962 841519

Winchester, Hampshire SO23 9LS

       Contact: K Bamber

The Cathedral was founded in 1079 on a site where Christian worship had already been offered for over 400 years. Among its treasures are the 12th century illuminated Winchester Bible, the font, medieval wall paintings, six chantry chapels and much more.

Location: Winchester town centre.

Opening Times: 7.15am - 6.30pm. East end closes 5pm. Access may be restricted during services. Weekday services: 7.40am, 8am, 5.30pm. Sun services: 8am, 10.30am, 11.30am, 3.30pm.

Admission: Recommended donations: Adult £2.50, Child 50p, Conc £2.00, Family party £5.00, charges apply for Triforium gallery and Library - £1.00 and for Tower and Roof Tours £1.50. Group tours £3.00 should be booked through the Education centre. (Tel: 01962 866854 between 9am - 1pm).

The Vyne.

WINCHESTER COLLEGE

Tel: 01962 868778   **Fax:** 01962 840207

77 Kingsgate Street, Winchester, Hampshire SO23 9PE
Owner: Winchester College   **Contact:** Mr Maclure
One of the oldest public schools, founded by Bishop William of Wykeham in 1382.
Location: 77 Kingsgate Street.
Opening Times: Apr - Sept: Mon - Sat, 10am - 1pm and 2am - 5pm.
Oct - Mar:Mon - Sat, 10am - 1pm and 2pm - 4pm. Closed Sun mornings.
Admission: Adult £2.50, Child £2.00, Conc £2.00.
Guided tours may be booked for parties over 10.

WOLVESEY CASTLE

Tel: 01962 854766

College Street, Wolvesey, Winchester, Hampshire SO23 9NB
Owner: English Heritage   **Contact:** The Custodian
The fortified palace of Wolvesey was the chief residence of the Bishops of Winchester and one of the greatest of all medieval buildings in England. Its extensive ruins still reflect the importance and immense wealth of the Bishops of Winchester, occupants of the richest seat in medieval England. Wolvesey was frequently visited by medieval and Tudor monarchs and was the scene of the wedding feast of Philip of Spain and Mary Tudor in 1554.
Location: 1/4 m SE of Winchester Cathedral, next to the Bishop's Palace; access from College Street.
Opening Times: 1st Apr - 30 Sept: Daily 10am - 6pm. 1 - 31 Oct: 10am - 6pm or dusk if earlier.
Admission: Adult £1.50, Child 80p, Conc £1.10.

Where to Stay

For Private Accommodation and
Johansens
recommended Hotels,
see Accommodation
Section.

SPECIAL EVENTS

◇ **HIGHCLERE CASTLE**   26 – 28 APRIL
Home and Design Exhibition

◇ **HIGHCLERE CASTLE**   26 – 27 MAY
Festival of Transport

◇ **HIGHCLERE CASTLE**   1 – 2 JUNE
Southern Counties Country Fair

◇ **THE VYNE**   8 JUNE
Jazz at The Vyne - An evening of traditional jazz on the lawn.
Floodlights and flambeaux. Bring a picnic

◇ **AVINGTON PARK**   21 – 23 JUNE
Antiques Fair

◇ **AVINGTON PARK**   22 JUNE
Shakespeare's Play - out of doors

◇ **HIGHCLERE CASTLE**   22 JUNE
Summer Classical Fireworks Spectacular

◇ **GILBERT WHITE'S HOUSE AND GARDEN**   22 – 23 JUNE
Unusual Plants Fair (Plants from Specialist Nurseries and Garden Accessories)

◇ **GILBERT WHITE'S HOUSE AND GARDEN**   23 JUNE
Bring a picnic to 'Jazz in June'

◇ **HIGHCLERE CASTLE**   6 JULY
Castle Theatre Company, 'The Taming of the Shrew'

◇ **HIGHCLERE CASTLE**   7 JULY
Strawberries & Cream in the Secret Garden

◇ **HIGHCLERE CASTLE**   16 JULY
Cricket Match - Allan Lamb/Robin Smith's XI v Lord Carnarvon's XI

◇ **THE VYNE**   19 – 20 JULY
Music and Fireworks - Classical orchestral favourites by the Lake.
Fireworks, floodlights and flambeaux. Bring a picnic.

◇ **HIGHCLERE CASTLE**   21 JULY
Classic Car Show

◇ **HIGHCLERE CASTLE**   11 AUGUST
Teddy Bears' Picnic Jackdaws Castle

◇ **HIGHCLERE CASTLE**   25 – 26 AUGUST
Highclere Horse Trials

◇ **HIGHCLERE CASTLE**   31 AUGUST
Concert Spectacular

◇ **HIGHCLERE CASTLE**   7 – 8 SEPTEMBER
Craft Fair - David Read

◇ **GILBERT WHITE'S HOUSE AND GARDEN**   24 NOVEMBER
Mulled Wine Day - Sip a glass of mulled wine and enjoy Christmas shopping

◇ **HIGHCLERE CASTLE**   30 NOVEMBER – 1 DECEMBER
Christmas Fayre

For National Trust and English Heritage Events see separate section.

BERRINGTON HALL
Nr. Leominster

BERRINGTON HALL is the creation of Thomas Harley, the 3rd Earl of Oxford's remarkable son, who made a fortune from supplying pay and clothing to the British Army in America and became Lord Mayor of London in 1767 at the age of thirty-seven. The architect was the Fashionable Henry Holland. The house is beautifully set above the wide valley of a tributary of the River Lugg, with views west and south to the Black Mountains and Brecon Beacons. This was the site advised by 'Capability' Brown who created the lake with its artificial island. The rather plain neo-classical exterior with a central portico gives no clue to the lavishness of the interior. Plaster ceilings now decorated in muted pastel colours adorn the principal rooms. Holland's masterpiece is the staircase hall rising to a central dome. The rooms are set off with a collection of French furniture, including pieces which belonged to the Comte de Flahault, natural son of Talleyrand, and Napoleon's step daughter Hortense.

In the dining room, vast panoramic paintings of battles at sea, three of them by Thomas Luny, are a tribute to the distinguished Admiral Rodney.

CONTACT

The Administrator
Berrington Hall
Nr. Leominster
Herefordshire
HR6 0DW
Tel: (01568) 615721

LOCATION

3 miles north of Leominster, 7 miles south of Ludlow on west side of A49.

Rail: Leominster, 4 miles.

ADVICE TO COURIERS & DRIVERS
Tour time approx. 1 hr, no indoor photography for conservation reasons. Parties must pre-book.

FACILITIES FOR THE DISABLED
Special arrangements can be made if requested - access via steep flights of steps. Adapted WC.

PARKING FOR COACHES & CARS
Coaches: parking facilities; instructions given when booking is made.

GIFT SHOP
A good range of National Trust goods can be purchased. Open as house from 1pm.

GUIDE BOOKS
Can be purchased.

CATERING
Licensed restaurant open as house. Home made lunches 12.30 - 2pm, teas 2.30 - 5.30pm. Last orders 1/2 hour before closing. October 12.30 - 4.30pm.

SCHOOL VISITS/CHILDREN
Children's quizzes.

OPENING TIMES

HOUSE
29 Mar - 30 Apr
& October

Fri, Sat & Sun
(open Bank Hol Mon, closed Good Friday)
1.30 - 5.30pm
(4.30pm in October)

May - end June & Sept
Wed to Sun & Bank Holiday Mondays
1.30 - 5.30pm

July & August
Daily: 1.30 - 5.30pm

Last admission 1/2 hr before closing.

GARDENS
Open same days as House: 12.30 - 6pm
(5.30pm in October)

PARK WALK
July to Oct
same days as above.

ADMISSION

Adult	£3.80
Child	£1.90
Family	£9.50
Grounds only	£1.70

EASTNOR CASTLE
Ledbury

Encircled by the Malvern Hills and surrounded by a famous arboretum and lake, this fairytale castle is as dramatic inside as it is outside.

The atmosphere   Everyone is struck by it. The vitality of a young family brings the past to life and the sense of warmth and optimism is tangible. Eastnor, however grand, is a home.

"Sleeping" for the past fifty years, the Castle has recently undergone a triumphant renaissance - 'looking better than it probably ever has', Country Life 1993.

Hidden away in attics and cellars since 1939, many of the castle's treasures are now revealed for the first time – early Italian Fine Art, 17th century Venetian furniture and Flemish tapestries, Mediaeval armour and paintings by Van Dyck, Reynolds, Romney and Watts, photographs by Julia Margaret Cameron. Drawing Room by Pugin.

'The princely and imposing pile' as it was described in 1812 when it was being built to pitch the owner into the aristocracy, remains the home of his descendants. The Castle contains letters diaries, clothes and furnishings belonging to friends and relations who include: Horace Walpole, Elizabeth Barret Browning, Tennyson, Watts, Julia Margaret Cameron and Virginia Woolf.

Encircled by the Malvern Hills, the mediaeval beauty of the estate remains unchanging.

GARDENS
Castellated terraces descend to a 21 acre lake with a restored lakeside walk. An arboretum holds a famous collection of mature specimen trees. There are spectacular views of the Malvern hills across a 300 acre deer park, once part of a mediaeval chase and now designated a Site of Special Scientific Interest. The historic house that welcomes dogs.

CONTACT

Simon Foster
Portcullis Office
Eastnor Castle
Nr. Ledbury
Herefordshire
HR8 1RN
Tel: (01531) 633160
or (01531) 632302
Fax: (01531) 631776/
or (01531) 631030

LOCATION

2¹/₂ miles east of Ledbury on the A438 Tewkesbury road. Alternatively M50 junct. 2 and from Ledbury take the A449/A438.

Tewkesbury 20 mins, Malvern 20 mins, Gloucester 25 mins Hereford 25 mins, Worcester 30 mins, Cheltenham 35 mins Birmingham 1 hour, London 2¹/₂ hours

Taxi: Meredith Taxis
(01531) 632852
Clive Fletcher
(0589) 299283

SUITABILITY FOR OTHER EVENTS
The Castle is at the centre of an unspoilt 5,000 acre estate, used with great success for off-road driving, clay pigeon shooting, quad bikes, archery and falconry. The varied terrain ideal for team-building activity days and survival training for which accommodation is available. The impressive interior of the castle makes an original setting for product launches, corporate hospitality, fashion shows, concerts, weddings (Civil Wedding licence), charity events, craft fairs, television & feature films.

EXTRA FACILITIES
Exclusive off-road driving on the "Land Rover" test track with qualified instructors. Luxury Accommodation within the castle for small exclusive groups. Meeting Room/Dormitory for Survival/Team-building days with showers and kitchen. Chapel for small Weddings/Christenings.

ADVICE TO COURIERS & DRIVERS
Please telephone in advance to arrange parking space near the Castle and any catering requirements. Free meal for drivers. No smoking in the house

FACILITIES FOR THE DISABLED
Disabled and elderly visitors may alight at the Castle entrance. Priority for nearby parking.

PARKING FOR COACHES & CARS
70 cars and a few coaches. 10-100 yds from the Castle.

GIFT SHOP
Eastnor souvenirs, books, gifts and toys. All excellent value.

GUIDE BOOKS
Guide Book, £2.00. Additional room notes in every room.

CATERING
Excellent country house cooking within the Castle for booked events. Home-made light lunches, teas and ice-cream in the Tea Room. Menus on request. Groups please book in advance.

GUIDED TOURS
Throughout the year by appointment.

SCHOOL VISITS/CHILDREN
School parties welcome. Guides available if required. Day out combining Castle with new Countryside study Centre.

OPENING TIMES

Summer
Bank Holiday Mondays,
Easter - Sept: Sundays
July & August: Sun to Fri
11.00 - 4.30pm

Other times and dates throughout the year by appointment.

NB Parties must pre-book. Groups by appointment at any time, including evenings, when the Castle is closed to casual visitors.

ADMISSION

Summer
CASTLE & GROUNDS
Adult £4.00
Child (5-14yrs) . . .£2.00
Groups* (with guide)
Adult £4.75
Child £2.75
Groups* (without guide)
Adult £3.50
Child £1.50

GROUNDS ONLY
Adult £2.00
Child (5-14yrs) . . .£1.00
* Min. payment for 20 people.

Winter
By appointment only.

CONFERENCE AND FUNCTION FACILITIES

ROOM	DIMENSIONS	CAPACITY	LAYOUT	POWER POINTS	SUITABLE FOR A/V
Library		120	Various	✓	✓
Great Hall		160	Various	✓	✓
Dining Room		120	Various	✓	✓
Gothic Room		50	Various	✓	✓
Octagon Room		50	Various	✓	✓

ABBEYDORE COURT GARDENS
Tel: 01981 240419   **Fax:** 01981 240279

Abbey Dore, Hereford, Herefordshire HR2 0AD
Owner: Mrs C L Ward   **Contact:** Mrs C L Ward
5 acre rambling garden, intersected by the river Dore. Shrubs and herbaceous perennials, rock garden and ponds. Small nursery. Country gift gallery and Teddy Bear loft. Licensed restaurant, home made food.
Location: 3 m W of A465 midway Hereford - Abergavenny.
Opening Times: 2 Mar - 20 Oct: Daily except Weds. 11am - 6pm.
Christmas opening 1 Nov - 1 Jan: Daily from 10.00am for gift gallery.
Admission: Adult £1.75, Child 50p.

BERRINGTON HALL
See Page 83 for full page entry.

BROBURY HOUSE GARDENS
Tel: 01981 500229

Brobury, Hereford, Herefordshire HR3 6BS
Owner: E Okarma Esq   **Contact:** Mrs L Weaver
A Victorian Gentleman's Country House set in 8 acres of magnificent gardens with stunning views over the Wye Valley. Overnight accommodation available, art gallery with antique maps and prints on site.
Location: Off the A438 Hereford/Brecon Road at Brewardine Bridge.
Opening Times: All year, except Christmas and New Year: Mon to Sat, 10am - 4.30pm.

CROFT CASTLE

LEOMINSTER, HEREFORDSHIRE HR6 9PW

Owner: The National Trust
Contact: The Administrator

Tel: 01568 780246

Home of the Croft family since Domesday (with a break of 170 years from 1750). Walls and corner towers date from 14th and 15th centuries, interior mainly 18th century when fine Georgian Gothic staircase and plasterwork ceilings were added; splendid avenue of 350 year old Spanish chestnuts. Iron age Fort (Croft Ambrey) may be reached by footpath. The walk is uphill (approx. 40 minutes).
Location: 5 miles north-west of Leominster, 9 miles south-west of Ludlow; approach from B4362.
Admission: Adult £3.20, Child £1.60, Family £8.00.

Car park charge for estate only £1.50 per car; £10 per coach.

OPEN
Apr & Oct :1.30 - 4.30pm (Closed Good Fri)
Easter: Sat, Sun & Mon: 1.30 - 4.30pm
May - end Sept: Wed - Sun
& Bank Hol Mon: 1.30 - 5.30pm
Last admission to house ½ hr before closing

CWMMAU FARMHOUSE
Tel: 01497 831251

Brilley, Whitney on Wye, Herefordshire HR3 6JP
Owner: The National Trust   **Contact:** Mr D Joyce
Early 17th century timber-framed and stone-tiled farmhouse.
Location: 4m SW of Kington between A4111 & A438, approach by a narrow lane leading S from Kington - Brilley road at Brilley Mountain.
Opening Times: Easter, May Spring & Summer Bank Holiday weekends (Sat, Sun & Mon): 2 - 5.30pm. Also Weds in August: 7, 14, 21, 28: 2 - 5.30pm. Other times by prior appointment with the tenant, Mr. Joyce.
Admission: £2.00.

DINMORE MANOR
Tel: 01432 830322   **Fax:** 01432 830503

Hereford, Herefordshire HR4 8EE
Owner: Mr R G Murray   **Contact:** Mr P Smollett
A range of impressive architecture from 14th - 20th century, Chapel, Cloisters and Great Hall, stained glass from 1930s. Outstanding views.
Location: 6½m N of Hereford on A49.
Opening Times: All Year: 10am - 5.30pm.
Admission: Standard £2.50, Child accompanied by adult free.

EASTNOR CASTLE
See Page 84 for full page entry.

GOODRICH CASTLE
Tel: 01600 890538

Goodrich, Ross-on-Wye, Herefordshire HR9 6HY
Owner: English Heritage   **Contact:** Ms Gillian Duberley
This magnificent red sandstone castle is remarkably complete, with a 12th century keep and extensive remains from the 13th and 14th centuries. From the battlements there are fine views of the Wye valley.
Location: 5m S of Ross-on-Wye off A40.
Opening Times: 1 Apr - 30 Sept: Daily 10am - 6.pm. 1 - 31 Oct: Daily 10am - 6pm or dusk if earlier. 1 Nov - 31 Mar: Wed - Sun 10am - 4pm (Closed 1-2pm).
Admission: Adult £2.20, Child £1.10, Conc £1.70.

HEREFORD CATHEDRAL
Tel: 01432 359880

Hereford, Herefordshire HR1 2NG

     Contact: Mr D Harding

Location: Hereford city centre on A49.
Opening Times: 7.30am - 5pm. Sun services: 8am, 10am, 11.30am and 3.30pm. Weekday services: 8am and 5.30pm. 10.30am - 5pm from May 1996.
Admission: Admission only for Mappa Mundi and Chained Library £4.00.

HERGEST CROFT GARDENS

OPEN
Daily
5 April - 27 Oct
1.30 - 6.30pm
Gardens open
until 7pm.
Season tickets
and groups by
arrangement
throughout the year.

Winter by
appointment.

Tel: 01544 230160
Fax: 01544 230160

KINGTON, HEREFORDSHIRE HR5 3EG

Owner: W L Banks and R A Banks   *Contact:* Elizabeth Banks

From spring bulbs to autumn colour, this is a garden for all seasons. An old fashioned kitchen garden has spring & summer borders & roses. Over 59 champion trees & shrubs grow in one of the finest collections in the British Isles. Holds national collection of birches, maples & zelkovas. Park Wood is a hidden valley with Rhododendrons up to 30 ft tall. Events will be arranged to celebrate the 100th anniversary. Delicious homemade lunches and teas. Rare plants & gifts for sale.
Location: On west side of Kington. ½ mile off A44 turn left at Rhayader end of bypass. Turn right and gardens are ¼ mile on left. Signposted from bypass.
Admission: Adult £2.50, Child (under 15) Free, Groups 20+ £2, Season ticket £9.

HOW CAPLE COURT GARDENS
Tel: 01989 740626   **Fax:** 01989 740611

How Caple, Hereford HR1 4SX
Owner: P L Lee Esq   **Contact:** P L Lee Esq
Exciting 11-acre garden overlooking river Wye. Combining terraced Edwardian gardens with water features and sunken Florentine garden. Mature trees and shrubs. Nursery selling old fashioned roses and specialised herbaceous plants. Shop with interesting gifts and Fabrics range. Teas and light meals. Group visits and coach parties welcome also for evening visits.
Location: In How Caple - off B4224 Ross-on-Wye/Fownhope Road.
Opening Times: All year: Mon - Sat 9.30am - 5pm. Apr - Oct: Daily 10am - 5pm.
Admission: Adult £2.50, Child £1.25.

LONGTOWN CASTLE
Tel: 01604 730320

Abbey Dore, Herefordshire
Owner: English Heritage   **Contact:** The Midlands Regional Office
An unusual cylindrical keep built c.1200 with walls 15ft thick. There are excellent views of the nearby Black Mountains.
Location: 4m SW of Abbey Dore.
Opening Times: Any reasonable time.

 THE NATIONAL TRUST   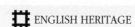 ENGLISH HERITAGE    HISTORIC HOUSES ASSOCIATION

ROTHERWAS CHAPEL

Tel: 01604 730320

Hereford, Herefordshire
Owner: English Heritage   **Contact:** Midlands Regional Office
This chapel, dating from the 14th and 16th centuries is testament to the past grandeur of
the Bodenham family and features an interesting mid-Victorian side chapel.
Location: 1¹⁄₂ m SE of Hereford on B4399.
Opening Times: Any reasonable time. Keykeeper at nearby filling station.

THE WEIR

Tel: 01684 850051

Swainshill, Hereford, Herefordshire
Owner: The National Trust   **Contact:** The Administrator
Delightful riverside garden particularly spectacular in early spring, with fine view over the
River Wye and Black Mountains.
Location: 5m W of Hereford on A438.
Opening Times: 14 Feb - end Oct: Wed to Sun (inc Good Fri) & BH Mon 11am - 6pm.
Admission: £1.50.

Where to Stay
For Private Accommodation and
Johansens
recommended Hotels,
see Accommodation
Section.

SPECIAL EVENTS

✧ **EASTNOR CASTLE** Spring Craft Fair	5 – 6 MAY	
✧ **HERGEST CROFT GARDENS** Centenary Flower Fair	6 MAY	
✧ **EASTNOR CASTLE** Steam Rally	18 – 19 MAY	
✧ **EASTNOR CASTLE** Estate Life Open Day	2 JUNE	
✧ **EASTNOR CASTLE** Children's Week	19 – 26 AUGUST	
✧ **EASTNOR CASTLE** Christmas Craft Fair	5 – 6 OCTOBER	

For National Trust and English Heritage Events see separate section.

Painting by Stanley Spencer on walls of Sandham Memorial Chapel, Hampshire, see page 81.

HATFIELD HOUSE
Hatfield

This celebrated Jacobean house, which stands in its own great park, was built between 1607 and 1611 by Robert Cecil, 1st Earl of Salisbury and Chief Minister to King James I. It has been the family home of the Cecils ever since.

The main designer was Robert Lyminge helped, it is thought, by the young Inigo Jones. The interior decoration was the work of English, Flemish and French craftsmen, notably Maximilian Colt. The State Rooms are rich in world-famous paintings including The Rainbow Portrait of Queen Elizabeth I, and The Ermine Portrait by Nicholas Hilliard. Other paintings include works by Hoefnagel, Mytens, John de Critz the Elder and Sir Joshua Reynolds. Fine furniture from the 16th, 17th and 18th centuries, rare tapestries and historic armour can be found in the State Rooms.

Within the delightful gardens stands the surviving wing of The Royal Palace of Hatfield (1497) where Elizabeth I spent much of her girlhood and held her first Council of State in November 1558. Some of her possessions can be seen in the House.

GARDENS

The West Gardens contain a formal garden, a scented garden with a herb garden at its centre, and a knot garden, planted with plants and bulbs which would have grown there in the 15th, 16th and 17th centuries.

❖

CONTACT

Col D McCord
Hatfield House
Hatfield
Hertfordshire
AL9 5NQ

Tel: (01707) 262823
Fax: (01707) 275719

LOCATION

21 miles North of London, A1(M), Junction 4.

Bus: Local bus services from St Albans, Hertford.

Rail: From Kings Cross every 30 mins. Hatfield Station is immediately opposite entrance to Park.

SUITABILITY FOR OTHER EVENTS
Archery, equestrian events, shows, filming, wedding receptions, lunches and dinners up to 250 people.

EXTRA FACILITIES
The National Collection of Model Soldiers, 3,000 models in panoramic display. William IV Kitchen Exhibition. Nature Trails with supporting handbook or leaflet. Small children's Venture Play Area. Indoor and outdoor picnic areas.

ADVICE TO COURIERS & DRIVERS
Hardstanding for coaches. No dogs in House or gardens, and only in Park on leads. No photography is allowed in the House.

FACILITIES FOR THE DISABLED
Disabled and elderly visitors may alight at the entrance to the House, before parking. Toilet and lift facilities for the disabled.

PARKING FOR COACHES & CARS
Unlimited free parking for cars and coaches.

CATERING
The Old Palace Yard Restaurant/Coffee Shop seats up to 120. Prices from £2.00 to £6.00. Pre-booked lunch and tea available for parties of 10 or more: (01707) 262030. Special rates offered for groups. Catering facilities for special functions can be arranged. Elizabethan Banquets held in the Old Palace throughout the year: (01707) 262055.

GUIDED TOURS
Groups of 40 or more are split into two, no extra charge for tour. Available in French, German, Italian or Spanish, by prior arrangement. Garden tours may be booked in advance: price £10.00 per tour. House Tours can be tailored to special interests.

GIFT AND GARDEN SHOPS
Open one hour before the House, selling items such as pot pourri made at Hatfield. Open six weekends prior to Christmas.

GUIDE BOOKS
House Guide Book £1.50, Garden Guide Book £1.70. Leaflets available in French, German, Spanish, Italian and Japanese.

SCHOOL VISITS/CHILDREN
Groups are welcome. 1 teacher free per 15 children. A guide is provided. Areas of interest include: kitchen exhibition, model soldier collection, adventure playground and picnic trails.

OPENING TIMES

Summer
25 March - 13 October

PARK
Daily 10.30am - 8.00pm

GARDENS
Daily 11.00am - 6.00pm

Last entry 5.00pm

HOUSE
Closed Mondays
Tues - Sat: Noon - 5pm
Last admission 4.00pm
Sun: 1.00 - 4.30pm

NB Open Easter, May Day, Spring and August Bank Hol Mondays. 11.00am - 5.00pm Closed Good Friday.

Winter
14 October - 24 March
Closed.

ADMISSION

HOUSE, GARDENS & EXHIBITIONS
Adult £5.20
Child* £3.30
OAP £4.40

Groups (Min 20m people)
Adult £4.40
Child* £2.80

PARK, GARDENS & EXHIBITIONS
Adult £2.90
Child* £2.20
OAP £2.70

Groups (Min 20 people)
Adult £2.70
Child* £2.00

* Aged 5-15

CONFERENCE AND FUNCTION FACILITIES

ROOM	DIMENSIONS	CAPACITY	LAYOUT	POWER POINTS	SUITABLE FOR A/V
The Old Palace	112' x 33'	300	Theatre	3	✓
		240	Schoolroom		
		100	U-shape		
		250	Buffet		
		250	Dinner/Dance		
		250	Lunch/Dinner		

KNEBWORTH HOUSE
Knebworth

Knebworth House has been the home of the Lytton family for over 500 years. Originally a Tudor Manor House, it was transformed 150 years ago with spectacular High Gothic decoration by Victorian romantic novelist Edward Bulwer-Lytton. There are many beautiful rooms, important portraits and furniture. The magnificent Jacobean Hall, where Charles Dickens acted in private theatricals and Winston Churchill painted at his easel, recently underwent restoration work which revealed an unknown early 17th century hand-painted archway under the original panelling, now on permanent display to the public. Knebworth was the home of Constance Lytton, the suffragette, and Robert Lytton, Viceroy of India. Lord Lytton's Viceroyalty and the Great Delhi Durbar of 1877 are commemorated in a fascinating exhibition and audio-visual display.

GARDENS

The elaborate formal gardens of the Victorian era were simplified by Sir Edwin Lutyens. The unique quincunx pattern Herb Garden was designed for Knebworth in 1907 by Gertrude Jekyll and contains a delightful mixture of many herbs. A new feature is the reinstated Maze. The House stands in 250 acres of parkland, with herds of Red and Sika Deer, Fort Knebworth, (a large Adventure Play-ground) Miniature Railway and is the setting for many Special Events.

CONTACT

John Hoy
The Estate Office
Knebworth House
Knebworth
Hertfordshire
SG3 6PY

Tel: (01438) 812661
Fax: (01438) 811908

LOCATION

Public entrance direct from A1(M) at Junct. 7, 30 miles North of Central London and 12 miles North of M25.

Rail: Stevenage Station 2 miles (from Kings Cross).

Air: Luton Airport 8mls.

Taxi: (01438) 811122.

Landing facilities

SUITABILITY FOR OTHER EVENTS
Fashion shows, air displays, archery, clay pigeon shooting, equestrian events, garden parties, shows, rallies and filming. Marquees and semi-permanent structures can be erected for a variety of requirements.

EXTRA FACILITIES
Evening House tours available by prior arrangement. Parkland, cricket pitch, helicopter landing facilities and Knebworth Barns (capacity 450) are all available for use. Speciality evenings, incorporating full use of all Knebworth facilities, can be arranged to suit your requirements. These include Indian Raj Evenings and Elizabethan Banquets with jousting.

ADVICE TO COURIERS & DRIVERS
All group visits must be booked in advance with Estate Office. In the House no dogs, pushchairs, photography, smoking or drinking are allowed. Dogs on leads are allowed in the Park.

FACILITIES FOR THE DISABLED
Disabled and elderly visitors may be driven to the entrance to the House, before parking in the allocated areas. The ground floor of the House is accessible to wheelchairs. Guide dogs are welcome in the House.

PARKING FOR CARS & COACHES
Parking for coaches and cars is unlimited.

CATERING BY LYTTON CATERING
Restaurant in 400 year old tithe barn. Special rates are available for groups who can book in advance. Menus available on request. Lytton Catering offers a full catering service in the Park as well as an extensive high quality outside catering service.

GUIDED TOURS
Guided tours operate Tuesdays - Fridays, at approx 30 minute intervals, or at specifically booked times up to 4.30pm. Tours at other times, including evenings, are available by prior arrangement. Average tour time 1 hour. Shorter tours by arrangement. Room Wardens on duty at weekends. A special 'Gothick Visions' tour is also available.

GIFT SHOPS
Open when the House is open to the public. Colour Guide Book £2.50 (1995 price).

SCHOOL VISITS/CHILDREN
National Curriculum based worksheets and children's guide available, covering a variety of topics ranging from the Tudors to the Victorians.

Summer
PARK, GARDENS, FORT KNEBWORTH
29 Mar - 15 Apr &
25 May - 3 Sept.
Daily: 11am - 5.30pm

Plus: Weekends & Bank Hols from 20 Apr - 19 May; and weekends only from 7 Sept - 29 Sept 11.00 am - 5.30pm

HOUSE
As above but closed Mondays, except Bank Holiday Mondays. Noon - 5.00pm.

Pre-booked Parties 29 Mar - 29 Sept
(Subject to special events)

Winter
Closed, except to pre-booked parties.

ADMISSION

Summer
HOUSE, GARDEN, PARK & PLAYGROUND
Adult £4.50
Child*/OAP £4.00
Groups (min. 20 people)
Adult £3.60
Child*/OAP £3.20
(subject to special events)

GARDENS, PARK & PLAYGROUND
All persons £3.50
Fam. Ticket . . .£12.00
(4 persons)
Groups (min. 20 people)
All persons £2.80

SUPPLEMENT TICKETS TO HOUSE (individuals)
Adult £1.00
Child*/OAP 50p

Season Tickets available on site.

* Age 3 - 16

CONFERENCE AND FUNCTION FACILITIES

ROOM	DIMENSIONS	CAPACITY	LAYOUT	POWER POINTS	SUITABLE FOR A/V
Banqueting Hall	26 'x 41'	45 - 80	Various	2	
Dining Parlour	21' x 38'	25 - 50	Various	3	
Library	32' x 21'	20 - 40	Various	2	
In Knebworth Barns Conference & Banqueting Centre, adjacent to Knebworth House:					
Manor Barn	70' x 25'	50 - 300	Various	8	✓
Lodge Barn	75' x 30'	30 - 250	Various	6	

WROTHAM PARK
Barnet

WROTHAM PARK, a privately owned Palladian Mansion, is located just 30 minutes from central London, surrounded by 300 acres of Parkland and set in the heart of a delightful Estate in excess of 2,000 acres.

A house of outstanding quality, Wrotham Park is an exciting new and unique venue ideally suited for private parties, corporate hospitality events, banquets, receptions, product launches and seminars.

The house is not open to the public and therefore offers clients exclusive and private use for their event. No overnight accommodation is available, but being located 17 miles from Hyde Park, there are excellent hotels within a short distance. Just 5 minutes from the junction of the A1(M) and M25 Wrotham is easily accessible from all major motorways, airports and train stations.

Commissioned by Admiral Byng in 1754, Wrotham Park was designed to allow guests to feel comfortable in glorious surroundings, whilst capable of entertaining on a grand scale. Wrotham Park is a beautiful home which proudly offers an ambience and style for which it was originally designed.

❖

CONTACT

Felicity L Buxton
Wrotham Park
Barnet
Hertfordshire
EN5 4SB

Tel: (0181) 441 0755

Fax: (0181) 449 9359

LOCATION

Central London: 17 miles
A1(M): 1.5 miles
M25: 1.5 miles
M1: 10 miles
Tube & Rail: 3 miles
Heathrow: 27 miles

OPENING TIMES

Available for business throughout the year.

CHARGES

A Location Fee granting exclusive use of the house is charged, from £1,500.

A detailed quotation will be provided subject to size of group and period required.

Wrotham Park does not offer in-house catering; a list of Preferred Caterers ranging from the elegantly simple to the flamboyant experience have been selected, all having the common denominator of excellence and good value.

CONFERENCE AND FUNCTION FACILITIES

ROOM	DIMENSIONS	CAPACITY	LAYOUT	POWER POINTS	SUITABLE FOR A/V
The Saloon		50	Banqueting	✓	✓
The Drawing Room		150	Banqueting	✓	✓
The Dining Room		80	Banqueting	✓	✓

Banqueting based on round tables of 10. Larger numbers can be accommodated within the house for receptions and theatre-style conferences or by providing marquees as an extension to the main house.

ASHRIDGE

Tel: 01442 851227

Ringshall, Berkhamsted, Hertfordshire HP4 1NS
Owner: The National Trust   **Contact:** Mr T Harvey
The Ashridge Estate comprises over 4,000 acres of woodlands, commons and downland. At the northerly end of the Estate the Ivinghoe Hills are an outstanding area of chalk downland which supports a rich variety of plants and insects. The Ivinghoe Beacon itself offers splendid views from some 700ft above sea level. This area may be reached from a car park at Steps Hill. The rest of Ashridge is an almost level plateau with many fine walks through woods and open commons.
Location: Between Northchurch & Ringshall, just off B4506.
Opening Times: Estate: All year. Monument, Shop & Visitor Centre: Apr - end Oct: Mon - Thur & Good Fri, 2 - 5pm. Sat, Sun & BH Mon 2 - 5.30pm. Last adm. 1/2 hr before closing.
Admission: Monument: £1.00.

BENINGTON LORDSHIP GARDENS

OPEN

Gardens only

April - August
Weds & Bank
Hol Mons
12 noon - 5pm

Suns 2 - 5pm

Sept : Weds only

Parties any time
by arrangement.

Tel: 01438 869668
Fax: 01438 869622

STEVENAGE, HERTFORDSHIRE SG2 7BS

Owner: Mr C H A Bott   *Contact: Mrs C H A Bott*

A hilltop garden which appeals to everyone with its intimate atmosphere, ruins, Queen Ann Manor, herbaceous borders, old roses, lakes, vegetable garden, nursery and verandah teas. For films, fashion shoots etc. the gardens & estate offer excellent facilities. Air strip, mediaeval barns & cottages and other unique countryside features.
Location: In village of Benington next to the church.
Admission: Adult £2.50, Accompanied Child under 18 Free. Wheelchairs Free.

BERKHAMSTED CASTLE

Tel: 01604 730320

Berkhamsted, St Albans, Hertfordshire.
Owner: English Heritage   **Contact:** The Midlands Regional Office
The extensive remains of a large 11th century motte and bailey castle which held a strategic position on the road to London.
Location: Adjacent to Berkhamsted station.
Opening Times: Any reasonable time.

CATHEDRAL & ABBEY CHURCH OF ST ALBAN

Tel: 01727 860780   **Fax:** 01727 850944

St Albans, Hertfordshire AL1 1BY

Contact: Mrs Susan Evans
Abbey church of Benedictine Monastery founded 793AD. Britain's first martyr. Rebuilt 1077 became Cathedral in 1877. Many 13th century wall paintings, ecumenical shrine of St Alban (1308). Spectacular audio visual show. Shop & restaurant.
Location: Centre of St Albans.
Opening Times: Summer 9am - 6.45pm. Winter 9am - 5.45pm. Telephone for details of services, concerts and special events Mon - Sat 11am - 4pm.
Admission: Free of charge. (AV show, Adult £1.50, Child £1.00).

CROMER WINDMILL

Tel: 01438 861662

Ardeley, Stevenage, Hertfordshire SG2 7QA
Owner: Hertfordshire Building Preservation Trust   **Contact:** Simon Bennett
17th century Post Windmill under restoration to working order.
Location: 4m NE of Stevenage on B1037.
Opening Times: 11 May - 8 Sept: Suns, 2nd & 4th Saturdays & Bank Hols 2.30 - 5pm.
Admission: Adult £1.00, Child 25p, Coach parties £10.00.

THE GARDENS OF THE ROSE

Tel: 01727 850461   **Fax:** 01727 850360

Chiswell Green, St Albans, Hertfordshire AL2 3NR
Owner: Royal National Rose Society   **Contact:** Lt Col Grapes
Showgrounds of the Royal National Rose Society with over 30,000 plants in 1,650 varieties.
Location: 2m S of St Albans.
Opening Times: Mon - Sat 9am - 5pm. Sun and Aug BH 10am - 6pm.
Admission: Adult £4.00, Senior citizens £3.50, Conc £3.50, Groups of 20 plus £3.50. Accompanied child under 16 free.

GORHAMBURY HOUSE

Tel: 01727 854051   **Fax:** 01727 843675

St Albans, Hertfordshire AL3 6AH
Owner: The Earl Of Verulam   **Contact:** The Administrator
Late 18th century house by Sir Robert Taylor. Extensive collection of 17th century portraits.
Location: 2 miles west of St Albans.
Opening Times: May - Sept: Thurs, 2 - 5pm.
Admission: Adult £4.00, Child £2.50, OAP £2.00, Guided tour £3.50. Other Days £5.00.

HATFIELD HOUSE

See Page 87 for full page entry.

KNEBWORTH HOUSE

See Page 88 for full page entry.

OLD GORHAMBURY HOUSE

Tel: 01604 730320

St Albans, Hertfordshire
Owner: English Heritage   **Contact:** The Midlands Regional Office
The remains of the Elizabethan mansion, particularly the porch of the Great Hall, illustrate the impact of the Renaissance on English architecture.
Location: 1/4 m W of Gorhambury House and accessible only through private drive from A4147 at St Albans (2m).
Opening Times: May - Sept: Thur only 2 - 5pm, or other times by appointment.

SCOTT'S GROTTO

Tel: 01920 464131

Ware, Hertfordshire
Owner: East Hertfordshire District Council   **Contact:** J Watson
One of the finest grottos in England built in the 1760s by Quaker Poet John Scott.
Location: Off A119 Hertford Road.
Opening Times: 1 Apr - 30 Sept: Sat and BH Mon, 2 - 4.30pm. Also by appointment.
Admission: Suggested donation of £1.00 for adults. Children free. Please bring a torch.

SHAW'S CORNER

Tel: 01438 820307

Ayot St. Lawrence, Welwyn, Hertfordshire AL6 9BX
Owner: The National Trust   **Contact:** The Administrator
An early 20th century house, and the home of George Bernard Shaw from 1906 until his death in 1950. Many literary and personal relics are shown in the downstairs rooms, which remain as in his lifetime. Shaw's bedroom and bathroom are also on view, and there is a display room upstairs.
Location: At SW end of village, 2m NE of Wheathampstead, approx. 2m from B653.
Opening Times: 30 Mar - end Oct: Wed - Sun & BH Mon, 2 - 6pm. Closed Good Fri. Parties by written appointment only, Mar to end Nov. Last admission 5.30pm.
Admission: £3.00, family £7.50, no reduction for parties.

WROTHAM PARK

See Page 89 for full page entry.

SPECIAL EVENTS

❖ **BENINGTON LORDSHIP GARDENS**   **FEBRUARY 1996**
Snowdrop Bonanza. Ring for details

❖ **BENINGTON LORDSHIP GARDENS**   **OCTOBER 1996**
Special opening for Autumn colour and sale of bare rooted herbaceous plants. Guided walks and verandah teas

❖ **HATFIELD HOUSE**   **9 – 12 MAY**
Living Crafts - 22nd year - Europe's largest craft fair. Over 500 craftsmen, many demonstrating a wide variety of skills

❖ **HATFIELD HOUSE**   **22 – 23 JUNE**
Festival of Gardening at Midsummer - staged in outstanding gardens. Leading nurseries, question time, lectures and demonstrations. Trade stands. Combines the atmosphere of Flower Show and Garden Party. Arena Events. Something for all the family.

For National Trust and English Heritage Events see separate section.

OSBORNE HOUSE
East Cowes

OSBORNE HOUSE was the peaceful, rural retreat of Queen Victoria, Prince Albert and their family , they spent some of their happiest times here.

The prince personally supervised the building, landscaping and alterations of this beautiful Italianate villa and its gardens which command a stunning view of the River Solent.

Many of the apartments have a very intimate association with the Queen who died here in 1901 and have been preserved almost unaltered ever since. The nursery bedroom remains just as it was in the 1870's when Queen Victoria's first grandchildren came to stay. Children were a constant feature of life at Osborne (Victoria and Albert had nine). The Swiss Cottage – a charming chalet in the grounds for the children can be reached by authentic Victorian carriage.

CONTACT

The House Administrator
Osborne House
Royal Apartments
East Cowes
Isle of Wight
PO32 6JY

Tel: (01983) 200022

LOCATION

1 mile south east
of East Cowes.

Isle of Wight ferry terminal: East Cowes.

OPENING TIMES

Summer

HOUSE
1 April - 30 September
Daily: 10.00am - 5.00pm

Last admission 4.30pm

GROUNDS
1 April 30 September
Daily: 10.00am - 6.00pm

Winter

HOUSE & GROUNDS

1 October - 31 October
Daily: 10.00am - 6.00pm
or dusk if earlier.
Last admission 4.00pm

ADMISSION

Adult £6.00
Child* £3.00
OAP/Students/ . . . . . .
UB40 Holders . .£4.50

GROUNDS ONLY
Adult £3.50
Child* £1.80
OAP/Students/ . . . . . .
UB40 Holders . .£2.60

* 5 - 15 yrs. Under 5's free.

SUITABILITY FOR OTHER EVENTS
Filming , Concerts, Drama.

ADVICE TO COURIERS & DRIVERS
No photography in the House. Coach drivers and tour leaders have free entry. One extra place for every additional 20 people.

FACILITIES FOR THE DISABLED
Wheelchairs available. Access to house via ramp. Ground floor access only. Adapted toilet in reception centre.

PARKING FOR COACHES & CARS
Plenty of car and coach spaces available.

CATERING
Teas, coffees and light snacks.

GUIDED TOURS
Personal stereos available.

GIFT SHOP
A wide selection of souvenirs available.

GUIDE BOOK
Souvenir Guides available for purchase.

SCHOOL VISITS/CHILDREN
School visits are free, please book in advance. An education room is available.

APPULDURCOMBE HOUSE

Tel: 01983 852484

Wroxhall, Shanklin, Isle Of Wight

Owner: English Heritage   **Contact:** The Custodian

The bleached shell of a fine 18th century baroque style house standing in grounds landscaped by 'Capability' Brown.

Location: 1/2 m W of Wroxall off B3327.

Opening Times: 1 Apr - 30 Sept: Daily, 10am - 6pm. 1 - 31 Oct: 10am - 6pm or dusk if earlier.

Admission: Adult £1.50, Child 80p, Conc £1.10.

MORTON MANOR

Tel: 01983 406186

Brading, Isle Of Wight

Owner: Mr J B Trzebski   **Contact:** Mr J B Trzebski

Morton was a hamlet on the edge of Brading Harbour, built in 1249 on the existing site for the de Aula family, of Norman descent. Since then it was structurally altered with the addition of a Tudor Longhouse, followed by major rebuilding in 1680. Refurbished in the Georgian period. Magnificent gardens.

Location: Off A3055 in Brading.

Opening Times: 2 Apr - 31 Oct: Daily except Sat, 10am - 5.30pm.

Admission: Adult £3.00, Conc £2.50, Group £2.

BEMBRIDGE WINDMILL

OPEN

1 April - 1 Nov
Sun - Fri

Easter Weekend

July & August
Daily

10.00am - 5.00pm

Tel: 01983 873945

MILL REACH, KINGS ROAD, BEMBRIDGE, ISLE OF WIGHT PO35 5NT

Owner: The National Trust   *Contact: The Custodian*

Dating from around 1700, this is the only windmill to survive on the Island. Much of its original wooden machinery is still intact and there are spectacular views from the top. There is a small shop and picnic field.

Location: 1/2m S of Bembridge on B3395.

Admission: Adult £1.20, Child 60p. Special charge for guided tours.

MOTTISTONE MANOR GARDEN

OPEN

27 March - 2 Oct
Wed & BH Mon

2.00 - 5.30pm

House:
Aug BH Mon only

Tel: 01983 740012

MOTTISTONE, ISLE OF WIGHT

Owner: The National Trust   *Contact: The Gardener*

A haven of peace and tranquillity with colourful herbaceous borders and a backdrop of the sea making a perfect setting for the historic Manor House. An annual open air Jazz Concert is held in the grounds during July/August. Dogs on leads.

Location: 2m W of Brighstone on B3399.

Admission: Adult £1.80, Child 90p. Special charge for guided tours.

CARISBROOKE CASTLE

OPEN

1 April - 30 Sept:
Daily: 10am - 6pm

1 Oct - 31 March:
Daily: 10am - 6pm or
dusk if earlier.

Tel: 01983 523660

NEWPORT, ISLE OF WIGHT PO30 1XY

Owner: English Heritage   *Contact: The Custodian*

Set in a superb position with spectacular views from the battlement and 7 acres of grounds to explore. Much of the Castle was built by the de Redvers family, in particular, the formidable Lady Isabella, who ruled castle and island for 30 years. Charles I was imprisoned here, and made several inept attempts to escape. The most popular site, particularly with younger visitors, is the well-house, where donkeys work a 16th century wheel to draw water from the 161ft (49m) well.

Location: 1 1/4 m SW of Newport.

Admission: Adult £3.80, Conc. £2.90, Child £1.90. 15% discount for parties 11+.

NEEDLES OLD BATTERY

OPEN

24 March - 31 Oct
Sun - Thurs

Easter Weekend

July & August
Daily

10.30am - 5.00pm

Tel: 01983 754772

ALUM BAY, ISLE OF WIGHT

Owner: The National Trust   *Contact: The Administrator*

High above the sea, the Old Battery was built in the 1860's against the threat of French invasion. Original gun barrels, cartoon information panels and a tea-room with one of the finest views in Britain. A 200ft tunnel leads to a restored searchlight position from which dramatic views of the Needles rocks can be seen.

Location: Needles Headland W of Freshwater Bay and Alum Bay (B3322).

Admission: Adult £2.40, Child £1.20, Family ticket £6.00. Special charge for guided tours.

HASELEY MANOR

Tel: 01983 865420   **Fax:** 01983 867547

Arreton, Isle of Wight PO30 3AN

Contact: Mr R J Young

The oldest and largest manor open to the public on the Island, recently restored with over 20 rooms on view. A walk through history from Medieval to Victorian times. Come and see why Haseley is such a success.

Location: Main Sandown to Newport Road.

Opening Times: Easter - 31 Oct: Daily, 10am - 5.30pm.

Admission: Adult £3.65, Child £2.75, Conc £3.10, Groups £3.10.

NUNWELL HOUSE & GARDENS

Tel: 01983 407240

Brading, Isle Of Wight PO36 0JQ

Owner: Mrs J A Aylmer   **Contact:** Mrs J A Aylmer

A lived in family home with fine furniture, attractive gardens and historic connections with Charles I.

Location: 3 m S of Ryde signed off A3055.

Opening Times: 7 Jul - 25 Sept (groups at other dates by arrangement). Sun 1 - 5pm. Mon, Tues, Wed, 10am - 5pm. Thurs, Fri and Sat, closed.

OLD TOWN HALL

OPEN

1 April - 30 Oct
Sun, Mon, Wed

Easter: Fri - Mon

July & August
Sun - Thurs

2.00 - 5.00pm

Tel: 01983 741052

NEWTOWN, ISLE OF WIGHT

Owner: *The National Trust*   ***Contact:*** *The Custodian*

A charming small 18th century building that was once the focal point of the '"rotten borough" of Newtown. There is also an exhibition depicting the history of the famous 'Ferguson's gang'.

Location: Between Newport and Yarmouth, 1m N of A3054.
Admission: Adult £1.10, Child 55p. Special charge for guided tours.

OSBORNE HOUSE   See Page 91 for full page entry.

YARMOUTH CASTLE   **Tel:** 01983 760678

Quay Street, Yarmouth, Isle of Wight   PO41 0PB
Owner: English Heritage   **Contact:** The Custodian
This last addition to Henry VIII's coastal defences was completed in 1547 and is, unusually for its kind, square with a fine example of an angle bastion. It was garrisoned well into the 19th century. It houses exhibitions of paintings of the Isle of Wight and photographs of old Yarmouth.
Location: In Yarmouth adjacent to car ferry terminal.
Opening Times: 1 Apr - 30 Sept: Daily, 10am - 6pm. 1 Oct - 31 Oct. Daily, 10 am - 6pm or dusk if earlier.
Admission: Adult £2.00, Child £1.00, Conc £1.50.

Where to Stay
For Private Accommodation and Johansens recommended Hotels, see Accommodation Section.

The Needles.

KEY TO SYMBOLS: THE NATIONAL TRUST   ENGLISH HERITAGE   HISTORIC HOUSES ASSOCIATION

BOUGHTON MONCHELSEA PLACE
Maidstone

A Battlemented manor house of Kentish Ragstone, situated above its own landscaped deer park. The house was built in 1576 by Robert Rudston. The home of the late Michael Winch, the house has been in the Winch family since 1903. Standing in a prominent position 310 feet above sea level with the 'reputed' finest view of the Weald of Kent.

The interior is still that of an inhabited home, and contains fine examples of period furniture and works of art to which successive generations have added. Nursery, schoolroom displays of dresses and agricultural bygones.

GARDENS AND GROUNDS
The 60 acre Deer Park has a herd of fallow deer - records of which go back as far as 1669. Two walled gardens: the lower contains a fine mixture of unusual herbaceous plants and shrubs, the top older varieties of fruit trees and unusual shrubs.

SUITABILITY FOR OTHER EVENTS
Licensed premises for Civil Marriage Ceremonies. Wedding receptions, corporate days, private dining, private parties, board meetings, conferences, seminars, fashion shows, garden parties, filming. Exquisite site for marquees and fireworks displays.

EXTRA FACILITIES
Deer Park.

ADVICE TO COURIERS & DRIVERS
Free refreshments for coach drivers and couriers. No photography or dogs in the House.

FACILITIES FOR THE DISABLED
Disabled toilets available. Disabled and elderly visitors may alight at the rear entrance to the House. Access for disabled into Tea Room and lower floor of the House.

PARKING FOR COACHES & CARS
Unlimited parking for cars & coaches 300 yards from House.

CATERING
Afternoon Teas in Tudor Tea Room, or Inner Courtyard (weather permitting). Lunches, Suppers, Dinners available, menus on request.

PRIVATE DINING
Luncheons, Suppers and Dinners in House (max. formal seating 45 in either Red Dining Room, Drawing Room or Courtyard Room; informal (buffets) 140 in House, 55 in Courtyard Room.

GIFT SHOP
The Gift Shop is open whenever house is open.

GUIDED TOURS
Visitors are always guided. Average time taken to see the House 55 minutes.

GUIDE BOOKS
Colour guide book available.

SCHOOL VISITS/CHILDREN
Educational Booklet available. Discounted admission. Any day during open season, by prior arrangement. Groups of 20 or more.

GROUP VISITS
By prior arrangement - on weekday mornings or afternoons, during open season. Discounted admission. Groups of 20 or more.

CONTACT
C W Gooch
Boughton Monchelsea Place
Boughton Monchelsea
Maidstone
Kent
ME17 4BU

Tel: (01622) 743120

LOCATION
Junction 8 off M20, take B2163 through Leeds to A274. Cross A274 on to B2163. Boughton Monchelsea Place is 3 miles on left.

4¹/₂ miles south of Maidstone. A229 from Maidstone at Linton on B2163.

London 1 hour, 10 mins.

Rail: Maidstone Station

OPENING TIMES
Summer

Easter - 20 October
Sundays: 2 - 6pm

June, July & August
Wednesdays: 2 - 6pm

Bank Holiday
Mondays: 2 - 6pm

Last Tour 5.15pm

Groups welcome any day, by appointment - NOT Saturdays

Winter
Closed for tours.

Open for marriage ceremonies, wedding receptions, private dining and parties, etc.

ADMISSION
HOUSE & GROUNDS
Family Ticket (2+2) £10
Adult £4.00
Child* £2.75
OAP/Disabled . . £3.75
Groups (min 20 people)
Adult £3.50
Child £2.50

GROUNDS ONLY
Adult £3.25
Child* £1.75
OAP/Disabled . . £2.75

* Child aged 0 - 5 Free.

CONFERENCE AND FUNCTION FACILITIES

ROOM	DIMENSIONS	CAPACITY	LAYOUT	POWER POINTS	SUITABLE FOR A/V
Red Dining Room	31' 3" x 19' 6"	25 - 60	Various	3	✓
Drawing Room	31' 3" x 19' 6"	25 - 60	Various	5	✓
Courtyard Room	36' 9" x 13' 5"	25 - 75	Various	8	✓
Entrance Hall	26' x 19'	50 - 60	Buffet	2	✓

COBHAM HALL
Cobham

'One of the largest, finest and most important houses in Kent', Cobham Hall is an outstandingly beautiful, red brick mansion in Elizabethan, Jacobean, Carolean and 18th Century styles.

It yields much of interest to the student of art, architecture and history. The Elizabethan wings were begun in 1584 whilst the central section contains the Gilt Hall, wonderfully decorated by John Webb, Inigo Jones' most celebrated pupil, 1654. Further rooms were decorated by James Wyatt in the 18th century.

Cobham Hall, now a girls' school, has been visited by several of the English monarchs from Elizabeth I to Edward VIII, later Duke of Windsor. Charles Dickens used to walk through the grounds from his house in Higham to the Leather Bottle Pub in Cobham Village. In 1883, the Hon Ivo Bligh, later the 8th Earl of Darnley, led the victorious English cricket team against Australia bringing home the "Ashes" to Cobham.

GARDENS

The gardens, landscaped for the 4th Earl by Humphry Repton, are gradually being restored by the Cobham Hall Heritage Trust. Extensive tree planting and clearing have taken place since the hurricanes of the 1980s. The Gothic Dairy and some of the classical garden buildings are being renovated. The gardens are particularly delightful in Spring, when they are resplendent with daffodils and a myriad of rare bulbs.

CONTACT

Mrs Sue Anderson
Cobham Hall
Cobham
Kent
DA12 3BL

Tel: (01474) 824319
or (01474) 8233/1
Fax: (01474) 822995

LOCATION

Situated adjacent to the A2/M2, 8 miles east of Junc. 2 on M25 between Gravesend and Rochester
London - 25 miles
Rochester - 5 miles
Canterbury - 30 miles

Rail: Meopham 3 miles.
Gravesend 5 miles.
Taxis at both stations.

Air: Gatwick 45 mins.
Heathrow 60 mins,
Stansted 50 mins.

OPENING TIMES

March: 24, 27, 28, 31
April: 5, 6, 7, 8, 10, 11, 14, 17, 18
May: 30, 31
June: 2
July: 10, 11, 14, 17, 18, 21, 24, 25, 31
August: 1, 4, 7, 8, 11, 14, 21, 25,26, 28, 29
September: 1
October: 19, 20
2 - 5pm (Last tour 4.45pm).

ADMISSION

Adult £2.50
Child (4 - 14yrs.) . . . £2.00
OAP £2.00

GARDENS & PARKLAND
• Self-guided tour
and booklet £1.00
• Historical/Conservation
tour of Grounds
(by arrangement)
Per person £2.50

SUITABILITY FOR OTHER EVENTS
Cobham Hall is a unique venue for any function, business or social. Providing for residential (250 beds) or non-residential courses. A wide choice of period or modern rooms, including the magnificent 1,200 sq.m .Gilt Hall, to suit every occasion. 150 acres of parkland ideal for sports events and open air concerts.

EXTRA FACILITIES
New multi-purpose sports centre and indoor 25m swimming pool. Use of Art Studios, Music Wing, Tennis Courts. Helicopter landing area, field study area, nature conservation. Lectures on the property, gardens and history can be arranged in the Gilt Hall for up to 180 people.

ADVICE TO COURIERS & DRIVERS
Pre-booked coach parties are welcome outside advertised opening times. Coffee, teas, lunch (cap. 200). Special events days. No smoking. Large free parking area.

FACILITIES FOR THE DISABLED
Disabled and elderly visitors should be aware that the house tour involves two staircases. Limited access for wheelchairs, ground floor only.

CATERING
Excellent in-house catering team for private and corporate events (cap. 200). Afternoon Teas served when open to public. Other meals by arrangement.

GUIDED TOURS
All tours guided: Historical guided tours of house, time taken 1½ hours. Special tours of garden arranged outside standard opening times.

GIFT SHOP
Open as House. Guide books of house and garden.

SCHOOL VISITS/ CHILDREN
Guide provided, £2.00 per child.

CIVIL WEDDINGS
In 1995 Cobham Hall was granted its Civil Marriage Licence. Couples can now get married in the magnificent Gilt Hall.

CONFERENCE AND FUNCTION FACILITIES

ROOM	DIMENSIONS	CAPACITY	LAYOUT	POWER POINTS	SUITABLE FOR A/V
Gilt Hall	41' x 34'	180	Theatre	4	✓
		90	Banquet		
Wyatt Dining Room	49' x 23'	135	Theatre	6	✓
		85	Banquet		
Clifton Dining Room	24' x 23'	75	Theatre	3	✓
		50	Banquet		
Activities Centre	119' x 106'	300	Theatre	10	✓
		250	Banquet		

FINCHCOCKS
Goudhurst

In 1970 Finchcocks was acquired by Richard Burnett, leading exponent of the early piano, and it now contains his magnificent collection of some eighty historical keyboard instruments: chamber organs, harpsichords, virginals, spinets and early pianos. About half of these are restored to full concert conditions and are played whenever the house is open to the public. The house, with its high ceilings and oak panelling provides the perfect setting for music performed on period instruments, and Finchcocks is now a music centre of international repute. Many musical events take place here.

There is also a fascinating collection of pictures and prints, mainly on musical themes, and there is a special exhibition on display on the theme of the 18th century Pleasure Gardens, such as Vauxhall and Ranelagh, which includes costumes and tableaux.

Finchcocks is a fine Georgian baroque manor noted for its outstanding brickwork, with a dramatic front elevation attributed to Thomas Archer. Named after the family who lived on the site in the 13th century, the present house was built in 1725 for barrister Edward Bathurst, kinsman to Earl Bathurst. Despite having changed hands many times, it has undergone remarkably little alteration and retains most of its original features.

The beautiful grounds, with their extensive views over parkland and hopgardens, include the newly restored walled garden, which provides a dramatic setting for special events.

CONTACT

Mrs Katrina Burnett
Finchcocks
Goudhurst
Kent
TN17 1HH

Tel: 01580 211702

Fax: 01580 211007

LOCATION

Off A262, 2 miles west of village of Goudhurst. 5 miles from Cranbrook, 10 miles from Tunbridge Wells, 45 miles from London (1 1/2 hours)

Rail: Marden 6 miles (no taxi), Paddock Wood 8 miles (taxi), Tunbridge Wells 10 miles (taxi).

Air: Gatwick, 1 hour.

SUITABILITY FOR OTHER EVENTS
Ideal for music events: chamber music concerts, demonstration recitals, lectures and courses. For the 1996 Special Events at Finchcocks, see page 109. Also very suitable for private functions, corporate entertaining, conferences, seminars and promotions. The gardens lend themselves to receptions and events such as archery and ballooning. Can be hired for films and television. Keyboard instruments and musical furniture also can be hired.

EXTRA FACILITIES
There is a brick terrace to the side of the house made for a marquee. Ideal for functions which would be too large for the house itself, such as larger weddings, opera, masked balls and fairs. Marquees can also be set up on the back lawn and the recently restored walled garden.

ADVICE TO COURIERS & DRIVERS
Groups welcome most days from start of April to the end of October. In some circumstances groups can be taken up to Christmas. Most private group visits include a personal tour of the house and collection by Richard and Katrina Burnett, and a demonstration by Richard Burnett (see Guided Tours) Min. no. usually 25, max. 100. All groups must pre-book. No videos in the house, and photography by permission only. No dogs in the garden but allowed in the parkland to the front of the house. Free meals for couriers and drivers.

FACILITIES FOR THE DISABLED
Limited. Good parking close to the house. Toilets on the level, but main indoor toilets involve stairs. Very suitable for visually handicapped visitors.

PARKING FOR COACHES & CARS
2 to 3 coaches and 100 cars on gravel forecourt in front of house. Additional parking available for special events.

CATERING
The vaulted cellar restaurant can accommodate up to 100. Full catering available by arrangement from formal waitress served dinners, buffets, teas and light refreshments. Wide range of prices from £2.90 to £25.00. Fully licensed. Picnics permitted in the grounds.

GUIDED TOURS
Demonstrations/recitals on instruments of the collection whenever required. These are usually given by Richard Burnett himself, and are extremely lively and entertaining, and suitable for those who have no interest in classical music as well as musical audiences. Average length of visit 2 1/2 - 4 hrs, to allow time for looking round house, instruments, exhibition and garden, the demonstration/ recital and a meal or refreshments.

GIFT SHOP
Well stocked shop with wide range of goods, and many musical items, including second-hand sheet music. Many compact discs and cassettes, over 50 of which were recorded at Finchcocks.

GUIDE BOOKS
A general guide book with coloured photographs at £2.50; catalogues of the collection also £2.50.

SCHOOL, STUDENT VISITS/ CHILDREN
Opportunity to play instruments. Can be linked to special projects and National Curriculum syllabus. Also special visits for children: 'A Window on the Eighteenth century' with costumes and talk.

CIVIL MARRIAGES AND WEDDINGS
Licenced for Civil Marriages. The Main Hall is the marriage room and can take up to 100 people. Also very suitable for small ceremonies. Music a speciality, and musicians can be provided. Receptions can be held in the vaulted cellar restaurant or in a marquee adjacent to the house. Full catering (our own).

OPENING TIMES

Summer

Easter Sun – end of Sept
Suns & Bank Hol Mons
Daily in August except
Mondays and Tuesdays
2.00 - 6.00pm

Pre-booked groups welcome most days: April to October and in some circumstances up to Christmas.

Winter

Closed January - March. Available for private functions October, November & December.

ADMISSION

OPEN DAYS
House, Garden & Music
  Adults/OAP £5.00
       (some concessions)
    Child £3.50
    Student £3.80

GARDEN ONLY:
  Adult £1.50
  Child 50p

PRIVATE DAYS
  Depending on numbers and
  programme . . . . .£5 - £7

(Minimum of 25 people to open house).

GROOMBRIDGE PLACE GARDENS 🏛
Tunbridge Wells

CONTACT

The Estate Office
Groombridge Place
Groombridge
Tunbridge Wells
Kent
TN3 9QG

Tel: (01892) 861444

Fax: (01892) 863996

LOCATION

Groombridge Place
Gardens is located on
the B2110 just off
the A264.
4 miles South West of
Tunbridge Wells and 9
miles East of
East Grinstead.

Rail: London Charing
Cross to Tunbridge
Wells 55minutes.

Surrounded by 164 acres of breathtaking parkland, this mystical site has an intriguing history stretching back to medieval times. The gardens, laid out in the 17th century by Philip Packer, a friend of Sir Christopher Wren and the famous diarist and horticulturist John Evelyn, have been described as a most remarkable and a very special survival.

- The stunning period setting for Peter Greenaway's acclaimed film "The Draughtsman's Contract"
- Medieval moat and stunning 17th century walled gardens.
- 17th century formal gardens with ancient topiary and fountain displays.
- The Enchanted Forest and designer water gardens - a major new garden in the making.
- Canal boat rides.
- One of England's largest Birds of Prey Sanctuaries.
- Award winning children's garden.

"Extreme and almost sylvan beauty"
W Oustram Tristram. Moated Houses - 1910.

"The beautiful moat, as still and luminous as quicksilver." Sir Arthur Conan Doyle.

"So satisfying", "A charm that enticed".
Vita Sackville-West. The Heir - 1922

"Enjoy a gem from the Restoration period"
The Times - 1994

"A mysterious beauty that feeds the imagination". Homes & Gardens - 1994.

❖

SUITABILITY FOR OTHER EVENTS
Ideal for weddings, concerts, filming, fairs & corporate events.

EXTRA FACILITIES
Is an approved registry for marriages.

ADVICE TO COURIERS & DRIVERS
Free parking and entry for coach drivers. No dogs permitted in the gardens.

FACILITIES FOR THE DISABLED
Toilets for the disabled, some access to the Formal Gardens

PARKING FOR COACHES AND CARS
Free parking for cars and coaches.

CATERING
Restaurant and special catering facilities for functions.

GUIDED TOURS
Must be pre-booked, 50p extra per person for 1 hour tour.

GIFT SHOP
The Country Store, stocked with an excellent range of gifts and souvenirs.

GUIDE BOOK
Available at £2.50.

SCHOOL VISITS/CHILDREN
School groups are welcome at £3.00 per student, 1 teacher free of charge per 10 students. Free teachers packs available.

OPENING TIMES

Summer
1 April - 31 October

Daily 10.00am - 6.00pm

Winter
1 November to 31 March.
Closed to the general public.

ADMISSION

Adult £5.00
 Child (under 17) . .£3.50
 OAP £4.50
Groups
 Per person £4.50
 Child £3.00
 OAP £4.00

CONFERENCE AND FUNCTION FACILITIES

ROOM	DIMENSIONS	CAPACITY	LAYOUT	POWER POINTS	SUITABLE FOR A/V
Baronial Hall	42' 6" x 17' 6"	80	Various	3	✓
Marquee	30' x 80'	150 - 200	Various	6	✓
Matrix Tent	100' x 100'	300 - 1,200	Various	-	✓

HEVER CASTLE
Edenbridge

HEVER CASTLE dates back to 1270, when the gatehouse, outer walls and the inner moat were first built. 200 years later the Bullen (or Boleyn) family added the comfortable Tudor Manor house constructed within the walls. This was the childhood home of Anne Boleyn, Henry VIII's second wife and mother of Elizabeth I. A costume exhibition in the Long Gallery includes all the familiar characters from this royal romance. The Castle was later given to Henry VIII's fourth wife, Anne of Cleves.

In 1903, the estate was bought by the American millionaire William Waldorf Astor, who became a British subject and the First Lord Astor of Hever. He invested an immense amount of time, money and imagination in restoring the castle and grounds. Master craftsmen were employed and the castle was filled with a magnificent collection of furniture, tapestries and other works of art.

The Miniature Model Houses exhibition, a collection of $1/12$ scale model houses, room views and gardens, depicts life in English Country Houses from Mediaeval to Victorian times.

GARDENS
Between 1904-8 over 30 acres of formal gardens were laid out and planted, these have now matured into one of the most beautiful gardens in England. The unique Italian garden is a 4 acre walled garden containing a superb collection of statuary and sculpture exhibited amongst the flowers and shrubs. Other areas include the rose garden, Anne Boleyn's Tudor style garden, a herb garden, a traditional yew maze and some unusual topiary. The grounds contain many water features. Along with a 35 acre lake there are fountains, cascades, grottoes, an inner and outer moat, and pools. The yew-hedge maze is open to the public.

SUITABILITY FOR OTHER EVENTS
Filming, product launches and wedding receptions. Dinner dances in Pavilion Restaurant.

EXTRA FACILITIES
Lectures on the property, its contents, gardens and history for up to 70 people in summer and 250 in winter. Prices on application. Projectors, and screen can be provided. Additional facilities for clients using the Tudor Village include outdoor heated pool, tennis court, billiard room, gardens/grounds.

ADVICE TO COURIERS & DRIVERS
Free coach parking. Free admission for driver and tour leader. Voucher for driver. Advisable to book in advance. Group rates for 15+. Allow 2 hours for visit.

FACILITIES FOR THE DISABLED
There are toilets for the disabled. Gardens mostly accessible, but ground floor only of Castle. No ramps into castle so can be difficult. Access to restaurants, gift shop and book shop. Some additional wheelchairs available.

PARKING FOR COACHES & CARS
Capacity of car park - approx 1000 cars, 100 yards from the Castle and 30 coaches, 200 yards from the Castle.

CATERING
Two self-service restaurants offer visitors lunch, tea and refreshments. Supper is provided during Open Air Theatre season. Special rates are offered to groups and menus/prices on request. Catering facilities for special functions/conferences include buffets, lunches and dinners.

SCHOOL VISITS/CHILDREN
School groups are welcome at a cost of £2.80 per child.

A guide can be provided for groups of 20 at £4.40 per person. Areas of particular interest: Kent and Sharpshooters Museum, torture instruments, exhibition on Anne Boleyn, adventure playground and maze. 1 teacher/adult free per 10/12 children. Free preparatory visits for teachers within normal opening hours.

GUIDED TOURS
Pre-booked guided tours can be arranged outside normal opening hours. Basic £8.40 per head, £10.40 with guide book, £13.40 Connoisseurs including coffee, sherry and guide book. Tours in French, German, Dutch, Italian and Spanish for a small additional premium. Garden tours with Head Gardener £6.50 per person (min 10 persons).

GIFT SHOP / GUIDE BOOKS
The Gift, Book and Garden shops are open at the same times as the Gardens, Castle Guide £2.00 Garden Guide £1.80.

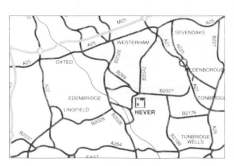

CONTACT

Janet Owens
Hever Castle
Hever
Edenbridge
Kent
TN8 7NG

Tel: (01732) 865224

Fax: (01732) 866796

LOCATION

Exit M25 Junct. 5 and 6
M23 Junct. 10,

A21 North Tonbridge
exit, follow signs.

Rail: Hever Station
1 mile (no taxis),
Edenbridge Town
3 miles (taxis).

Taxi: Relyon Car
Services,
Tel: (01732) 863800,
Beeline Taxis
Tel: (01732) 456214

OPENING TIMES

Summer
1 March - 30 November

DAILY
Gardens: 11.00am
Castle: 12 noon
Last admission: 5.00pm
Closes: 6.00pm

Winter
March & November
11am - 4pm

Pre-booked private guided tours only December, January and February.

ADMISSION

CASTLE & GARDEN
Adult £6.00
Child (5-16 yrs) . . £3.00
OAP £5.30
Family (2+2) . . . £15.00

GARDEN ONLY
Adult £4.40
Child (5-16 yrs) . . £2.60
OAP £3.90
Family (2+2) . . . £11.40

Group* prices on request. Groups must be 15 plus people. Total must be paid in one amount.

Private guided tours are available outside normal opening hours.

HEVER CASTLE CONTINUED...

The Tudor Village was built for William Waldorf Astor in the style of the Tudor period, but with every modern comfort and luxury.

All twenty, individually decorated rooms have private bathrooms, colour televisions, direct dial telephones, tea/coffee making facilities and hair dryers. Guests can enjoy a Billiard Room, outdoor heated swimming pool, tennis court and croquet lawn.

The Village is available year round for groups requiring high standards of accommodation and service, delicious foods and wines and top-level conference facilities. There are three interconnecting reception rooms which can be used for conferences, dining or meetings. There are also a number of smaller syndicate rooms.

The Hever Castle Estate includes Stables House, an imposing five bedroomed property overlooking the River Eden. This is an ideal venue for smaller groups, which can also make use of the Tudor Village amenities.

In addition the magnificent Dining Hall in the Castle is available for a truly memorable dinner. Guests can enjoy a private guided tour of the Castle and a Tudor Banquet with minstrels.

Laser Clay Pigeon Shooting, Archery, Fishing, Riding, Golf and other pursuits can be arranged on or near the estate.

In all, the Tudor Village provides a unique and unusual venue for private meetings, receptions, product launches or corporate hospitality.

Hever Castle/Tudor Village offers the following accommodation (see picture below):
- 4 singles with bath
- 10 twins with bath
- 6 doubles with bath
- 4 twins and 1 double (in the Stables House)

CONFERENCE AND FUNCTION FACILITIES

The Dining Hall, Breakfast Room and Sitting Room (which together form the Tudor Suite) are available throughout the year. Smaller seminar rooms are also available. The Pavilion can be hired between November and March. Overhead projector, flip charts and screen can be provided and specialist audio-visual equipment hired. There are a number of magnificent private dining rooms available for receptions, Tudor banquets, lunches and dinners.

ROOM	DIMENSIONS	CAPACITY	LAYOUT	POWER POINTS	SUITABLE FOR A/V
Dining Hall	35' x 20'	70	Theatre	5	✓
		32	Schoolroom		
		25	U-shape		
		25	Boardroom		
		70	Lunch/Dinner		
Breakfast Room	22' x 15'	20	Theatre	3	✓
		16	Schoolroom		
		16	Boardroom		
		16	Lunch/Dinner		
Sitting Room	24' x 20'	12	Boardroom	4	✓
		12	Lunch/Dinner		
Pavilion	96' x 40'	250	Theatre	24	✓
		200	Schoolroom		
		250	Buffet		
		250	Dinner/Dance		
Moat Restaurant	25' x 60'	75	Dinner/Dance	6	

Above: Tulip Bedroom in Tudor Village.

Above Right: Tudor Suite Dining Room in Tudor Village.

Right: The Music Room in Tudor Village.

KNOLE
Sevenoaks

CONTACT

John Coleman
Administrator
Knole
Sevenoaks
Kent TN15 0RP

Tel: (01732) 462100

Fax: (01732) 465528

LOCATION

25 miles south of London. Just off M25 and A225 at South end of High Street, Sevenoaks.

Rail: 1/2 hr from London Charing Cross to Sevenoaks, and bus to house. Special rail/bus and ticket admission available.

Set in an extensive deer park owned by Lord Sackville, Knole is one of the "Great" houses of England. It has been the home of the Sackville family since 1603, including four Dukes of Dorset, and houses an extensive collection of furnishings and paintings, many in the house since the 17th century.

The largest private house in England, Knole is a spectacular example of late medieval architecture overlaid with extensive Jacobean embellishments, including remarkable carving and plasterwork. The Sackville family crest of the leopard rampant recurs throughout.

An internationally renowned collection of Royal Stuart furnishings, including three state beds, celebrated silver furniture, and the prototype of the 'Knole' settee. Thirteen years were spent restoring the fabrics on the bed in the Kings' room.

The 6th Earl of Dorset played host to poets Pope and Dryden. Knole was the birthplace of the writer, Vita Sackville-West, and the setting for Virginia Woolf's novel 'Orlando'.

Important collection of paintings, including works by Van Dyck, Lely, Kneller, Gainsborough, Hoppner, Wootton, and a room devoted to the works of Sir Joshua Reynolds, commissioned for the house by the 3rd Duke of Dorset, including portraits of Dr Johnson, David Garrick, and Oliver Goldsmith.

The experience of visiting the house, which has been little altered since the 18th century, is like stepping back in time.

OPENING TIMES

30 Mar - 2 November

Wed and Fri to Sun and Bank Holiday Mondays 11am - 5pm

Thursdays: 2 - 5pm.

Last admission 4pm.

ADMISSION

Adult £4.50
Child £2.25
Family £11.25
(2 Adults & 2 Children)

Groups
Adult £3.50
Child £1.50

SUITABILITY FOR OTHER EVENTS
Concerts and other events in Great Hall and Stone Court.

FACILITIES FOR THE DISABLED
Wheelchair access to Green Court, Stone Court and Great Hall.

PARKING FOR COACHES AND CARS
Ample parking available.

CATERING
Brewhouse Restaurant serving morning coffee, lunches and teas. Also ice-creams and snacks in courtyard.

GUIDED TOURS
Only for pre-booked parties Thursday mornings.

GIFT SHOP
Full range of National Trust goods and souvenirs of Knole.

SCHOOL VISITS / CHILDREN
Always welcome. Special reduction for booked parties.

GARDENS
Only open 1st Wed, May - September.

LEEDS CASTLE
Maidstone

Surrounded by 500 acres of magnificent parkland and gardens, and built on two small islands in the middle of a natural lake, Lord Conway christened Leeds "the loveliest Castle in the world."

The site of a manor of the Saxon royal family in the 9th century, it was then re-built in stone by the Normans and later converted into a Royal Palace by Henry VIII.

For some 300 years, the Castle was home to the Kings and Queens of medieval England. Now lovingly restored and beautifully furnished, it contains a magnificent collection of medieval furnishings, tapestries and paintings.

The Castle was purchased in 1926 by the late the Hon Olive, Lady Baillie, whose American Whitney inheritance helped restore the Castle and cement strong Anglo-American links. The Leeds Castle Foundation now preserves the Castle for the Nation, hosts important medical conferences and supports the Arts.

A unique collection of Dog Collars can be viewed in the Castle Gate House.

Popular attractions within the Castle grounds include the colourful Culpeper Garden, Wood Garden, Duckery, Castle greenhouses and vineyard. An aviary houses rare and endangered species from around the world, beyond which can be found a traditional maze and underground grotto. A challenging nine hole golf course surrounds the Castle, whose moat occasionally comes into play!

SUITABILITY FOR OTHER EVENTS
Residential conferences and corporate hospitality (including large scale marquee events); exhibitions, wedding receptions, sporting days with clay shooting, falconry, field archery, hot air ballooning and golf.

EXTRA FACILITIES
Parkland, golf course, croquet lawn and heli-pad. Talks given by specialist staff can be arranged for horticultural, viticultural, historical and cultural groups.

ADVICE TO COURIERS & DRIVERS
Pre-booking advisable but not essential. Couriers/guides and coach drivers admitted free. Voucher for refreshments. Shuttle transport for elderly / disabled. No dogs, or radios.

FACILITIES FOR THE DISABLED
Accessible mini-bus, wheelchairs on loan, wheelchair lift in Castle, purpose-built toilets. Special rates - leaflet available.

PARKING FOR COACHES & CARS
5,000 cars and 20 coaches, 800 yds from the Castle. For special functions/tours parking nearer the Castle can be arranged.

CATERING
17th century tithe barn, self-service restaurant plus the Terrace Restaurant (table service) offer a full range of hot meals, salads & cream teas. Group lunch menus available. For special functions/conferences, buffets and dinners can arranged.

GUIDED TOURS
Guides in every room except winter mid-week when there are regular guided tours. French, Spanish, Dutch and German, Italian & Russian guides. Average tour time 1 hr.

GIFT SHOPS
Castle Shop, Book Shop, Park Shop and Special Christmas Shop (Nov - Dec).

GUIDE BOOKS
Illustrated Guide available in English, French, German Dutch, Spanish, Italian and Japanese, £3.00. Aviary Guide and Children's Activity Book 95p.

SCHOOL VISITS/CHILDREN
Educational groups welcome, outside normal opening hours private tours can be arranged. Teachers Resource Pack including Fact Sheets and Discovery Sheets on six different topics.

CONFERENCE AND FUNCTION FACILITIES

ROOM	DIMENSIONS	CAPACITY	LAYOUT	POWER POINTS	SUITABLE FOR A/V
Fairfax Hall	64' 6" x 36'	50 - 250	Various	✓	✓
Gate Tower	34' x 20'	16 - 120	Various	✓	✓
Culpeper	20' 8" x 25'	8 - 30	Various	✓	✓

CONTACT

Nick Day
Leeds Castle
Maidstone
Kent
ME17 1PL

Tel: (01622) 765400
Fax: (01622) 735616

LOCATION

From London, A20/M20, Exit 8, 40 miles, 1 hour.
Rail: BR combined train and admission, London Charing Cross and Victoria - Bearsted.
Coach: Nat Express/ Invictaway coach and admission from Victoria
Air: Gatwick 45 miles Heathrow 65 miles
Channel Tunnel: 25 miles
Channel ports: 38 miles

OPENING TIMES

Summer
1 March - 31 October
Daily: 10.00am - 5.00pm

Winter
Nov - End Feb
Daily: 10am - 3.00pm
(except Christmas Day)

Also special private tours for pre-booked groups at any other time by appointment

Castle & Grounds closed 29 June, 6 July & 2 November, prior to special events.

ADMISSION

Proposed rates from 1 March 1996.

CASTLE, PARK AND GARDENS
Adult £8.00
Child (5 -15yrs) . .£5.20
OAP/Student . . .£6.30
Family (2+3) . . .£22.00
Disabled Visitors
Adult £4.00
Child (5 -15yrs) . .£2.80
Groups (Min 20 people)
Adult £6.00
Child (5 -15yrs) . .£4.20
OAP/Student . . .£5.00

PARK & GARDENS
Adult £6.00
Child (5 -15yrs) . .£3.70
OAP/Student . . .£4.80
Disabled Visitors
Adult £3.00
Child (5 -15yrs) . .£1.80
Groups (Min 20 people)
Adult £5.00
Child (5 -15yrs) . .£3.20
OAP/Student . . .£3.80

PENSHURST PLACE
Nr. Tonbridge

CONTACT

Jane Wallis
Penshurst Place
Penshurst
Nr Tonbridge
Kent
TN11 8DG

Tel: (01892) 870307

Fax: (01892) 870866

LOCATION

From London M25 Junct. 5 then A21 to Tonbridge North, B2027 via Leigh; from Tunbridge Wells A26, B2176.

Bus: Maidstone & District 231, 232, 233 from Tunbridge Wells.

Rail: Charing Cross/ Waterloo- Hildenborough, Tonbridge or Tunbridge Wells; then taxi

PENSHURST PLACE is one of England's greatest family-owned stately homes with a history going back six and a half centuries.

In some ways time has stood still at Penshurst; the great House is still very much a medieval building with improvements and additions made over the centuries but without any substantial rebuilding. Its highlight is undoubtedly the mediaeval Baron's Hall, built in 1341, with its impressive 60ft-high chestnut beamed roof.

A marvellous mix of paintings, tapestries and furniture from the 15th, 16th and 17th centuries can be seen throughout the House, including the helm carried in the state funeral procession to St Paul's Cathedral for the Elizabethan courtier and poet, Sir Philip Sidney, in 1587. This is now the family crest.

GARDENS
The Gardens, first laid out in the 14th century, have been developed over successive years by the Sidney family who first came to Penshurst in 1552. A twenty-year restoration and re-planting programme undertaken by the late Viscount De L'Isle has ensured that they retain their historic splendour. He is commemorated with a new Arboretum, planted in 1991. The gardens are divided by a mile of yew hedges into "rooms", each planted to give a succession of colour as the seasons change. There is also a Venture Playground, Nature Trail and Toy Museum for children.

❖

SUITABILITY FOR OTHER EVENTS
Private Banqueting, product launches, wedding ceremonies and receptions, garden parties, photography, filming, fashion shows.

EXTRA FACILITIES
Archery, clay pigeon shooting, falconry. Parkland available for hire for public events, fairs, product launches. Lectures on the property, its contents and history can be arranged for up to 60. Specialist garden tours can be arranged.

ADVICE TO COURIERS & DRIVERS
No access to bus park by double decker buses; these to be parked in village. Entrance arrangements for morning booked parties notified in advance to organisers. No dogs. No photography in the House. Parking for unlimited cars and 10 coaches 250 yds from the house.

GUIDED TOURS
Tours available (mornings only) by arrangement. Adult £5.50, child £2.75. Lunch/Dinner can be arranged in Private Dining Room Out of season, tours by appointment: adult £5.50, minimum charge £150.00. Guided tours of the gardens also available at £6.50.

CATERING
Self-service Restaurant for light refreshments, lunches and teas. Restaurant and waitress service can be booked by groups of 20+.

FACILITIES FOR THE DISABLED
Wheelchair-bound visitors' access limited due to age/architecture of buildings. Disabled and elderly visitors may be left at entrance while vehicles are parked in allocated area.

GIFT SHOP
Open seven days a week, hours as House.

GUIDE BOOKS
Colour Guide Book, £3.00. Room Guides available in French, German, Dutch, Japanese, Italian and Spanish.

SCHOOL VISITS/ CHILDREN
Visits all year by appointment. Discount rates. Education room and packs available.

OPENING TIMES

Summer
1 April - 29 September

HOUSE
Daily Noon - 5.30pm
Last Entry 5.00pm

GROUNDS
Daily 11.00am - 6.00pm

Winter
30 September - 31 March

Open to Groups by appointment only (see Guided Tours).

House and Grounds only open weekends in March and October 1996.

ADMISSION

HOUSE & GARDEN
Adult £5.50
Child* £3.00
Concessions** . .£5.10
Fam. Ticket . . .£14.50
Groups***
Adult £5.10

GARDEN ONLY
Adult £4.00
Child* £2.75
Concessions** . .£3.50
Fam. Ticket . . .£10.50

Wheelchairs Welcome

* Aged 5-16; under 5s FREE.

** Concessions: OAP/Students/UB40

*** Min 20 people, afternoons only. Special rates for morning Guided Tours

CONFERENCE AND FUNCTION FACILITIES

ROOM	DIMENSIONS	CAPACITY	LAYOUT	POWER POINTS	SUITABLE FOR A/V
Sunderland Room	45' x 18'	100	Various	6	✓
Baron's Hall	64' x 39'	250	Theatre	4	✓
Buttery	20' x 23'	50	Various	4	✓

Photograph: Jeremy Whitaker

SQUERRYES COURT
Westerham

SQUERRYES COURT has been the home of the Wardes since 1731 and is still lived in by the family today . Although it was built in Charles II's reign in 1681 it is a typical William and Mary Manor House. Squerryes is 22 miles from London and easily accessible from the M25. Surrounded by parkland, there are fine views over the lake to the hills beyond.

The house has an important collection of Italian, 18th century English and 17th century Dutch paintings acquired and commissioned by the family in the 18th century. John Warde who inherited in 1746 purchased 93 paintings in the space of 25 years. He did not go on the Grand Tour but bought from auction houses, dealers and private sales in England. This gives an insight into the taste of a man of his time and also what was available on the art market in England in the mid 18th century.

The furniture and porcelain have been in the house since the 18th century and the Tapestry Room contains a fine set of Soho tapestries made c.1720. General Wolfe of Quebec was a friend of the family and there are items connected with him in the Wolfe Room.

GARDENS

These were laid out in the formal style but were re-landscaped in the mid 18th century. Some of the original features in the 1719 Badeslade print survive. The family have restored the formal garden using this print as a guide. The garden is lovely all year round with bulbs, wild flowers and woodland walks, azaleas, summer flowering herbaceous borders and roses.

SUITABILITY FOR OTHER EVENTS
Fashion shows, archery, clay pigeon shooting, garden parties, promotions, shows, wedding receptions (marquee in garden).

EXTRA FACILITIES
Grand Piano, Parkland, Lake for fly fishing.

ADVICE TO COURIERS & DRIVERS
Groups welcome any day. Please book in advance. No photography in the House. Dogs on leads in grounds. Free teas for drivers and couriers.

FACILITIES FOR THE DISABLED
Disabled and elderly visitors may alight at the entrance to the property. Toilets for the disabled.

PARKING FOR COACHES & CARS
Parking for up to 60 cars and 2 coaches on the gravel forecourt.

CATERING
Teas are served in the Old Library (capacity 53 people). Parties must book in advance for lunch/tea/supper. Menus are available upon request. Teas from £2.20. Lunch/Supper prices on request. Facilities for buffets, lunches and dinners.

GUIDED TOURS
Available for groups of up to 55 people, small additional charge payable. The owner will meet groups visiting the house, by prior arrangement. Average time to see the house ³/₄ hour.

GIFT SHOP
The small Gift Shop is open at the same time as the House.

GUIDE BOOKS
Colour guide book, £1.00.

SCHOOL VISITS/CHILDREN
Groups are welcome, cost £1.50 per child. A guide is provided. Areas of interest include: Nature Walk, ducks and geese.

CONTACT

Curator or Mrs Warde
Squerryes Court
Westerham
Kent
TN16 1SJ

Tel: (01959) 562345
or (01959) 563118

Fax: (01959) 565949

LOCATION

Off the M25, Junct. 6,
6 miles, ¹/₂ mile west of
Westerham.

London 1-1¹/₂ hours.

Rail: Oxted Station
4 miles.
Sevenoaks 6 miles.

Air: Gatwick,
30 minutes.

CONFERENCE AND FUNCTION FACILITIES

ROOM	DIMENSIONS	CAPACITY	LAYOUT	POWER POINTS	SUITABLE FOR A/V
Hall	32' x 32'	50 - 60	Buffet U-shape Boardroom Lunch/Dinner	4	✓
Old Library	20' x 25' 6"	40	Buffet Boardroom	5	✓

OPENING TIMES

Summer
March: Sundays only

1 April - 30 September
Mon Bank Hols only
2 .00 - 6.00pm

Closed: Tues, Thur, Fri.

Wed, Sat, Sun
2.00 - 6.00pm

NB Pre-booked groups welcome any day.

Winter
October - end February
Closed

ADMISSION

HOUSE & GARDEN
Adult £3.70
Child* £1.80
OAP/Student . . .£3.40
Groups**
Adult £3.20
Child* £1.60
OAP £3.20

HOUSE ONLY
Adult £3.70
Child* £1.80
OAP £3.40
Groups**
Adult £3.20
Child* £1.60
OAP £3.20

GARDEN ONLY
Adult £2.20
Child* £1.20
OAP £2.00
Groups**
Adult £2.00
Child* £1.00
OAP £2.00

* Aged 14 and under.
** Min 20 people.

THE ARCHBISHOP'S PALACE

Tel: 01622 663006   **Fax:** 01622 682451

Mill Street, Maidstone, Kent ME15 6YE

Owner: Maidstone Borough Council   **Contact:** The Heritage Services Manager

Recently refurbished 14th century Palace used as a resting place for Archbishops travelling from London to Canterbury.

Location: On the banks of the River Medway in the centre of Maidstone.

Opening Times: Daily: 10.00am - 4.30pm.

Admission: To 1st floor rooms entrance is free.

BEDGEBURY NATIONAL PINETUM

Tel: 01580 211044   **Fax:** 01580 212423

Goudhurst, Cranbrook, Kent TN17 2SL

Owner: Forestry Commission   **Contact:** Mr Colin Morgan

Britain and Europe's best and most comprehensive collection of conifers from all five continents set in a dramatic parkland with lakes, avenues and hills. Rhododendrons, maples, rare oaks and wild flowers appeal to all visitors for all seasons.

Location: 7m E of Tunbridge Wells on A21, turn N on to B2079 for 1 mile.

Opening Times: All year. Grounds only 10am to dusk or 7pm.
Shop and Info.Centre (Tel: 01580 211781) weekends March and daily 1 Apr - 22 Dec.

Admission: Adult £2.00, OAP £1.50, Child £1.20.

BELMONT

OPEN

7 Apr - 29 Sept
Sat, Sun and
Bank Hols.
2.00 - 5.00pm.

Last adm: 4.30pm

Groups of 20+ on
other days by
appointment.

Tel: 01795 890202

BELMONT PARK, THROWLEY, FAVERSHAM ME13 0HH

Owner: Harris (Belmont) Charity   *Contact: Lt. Col F.E. Grant*

Charming late 18th century country mansion by Samuel Wyatt set in fine parkland. Seat of the Harris family since 1801 when it was acquired by general George Harris, the victor of Seringapatnam. The mansion remains in its original state and contains interesting mementos of the family's connections with India and the colonies, plus the fifth Lord Harris' fine clock collection.

Location: 4¹/₂ miles SSW of Faversham, off A251.

Admission: House & Garden: Adult £4.50, Child £2.50.
Garden: Adult £2.50, Child £1.00.

BOUGHTON MONCHELSEA PLACE    **See Page 94 for full page entry.**

CANTERBURY CATHEDRAL

Tel: 01227 762862   **Fax:** 01227 762897

Canterbury, Kent CT1 2EH

Contact: Mr D Earlam

Founded in 597AD, Mother Church of the Anglican Communion, Norman Crypt, 14 - 15th century Nave. Site of Becket's martyrdom. Notable stained glass.

Location: Canterbury city centre.

Opening Times: Easter - 30 Sept: Mon - Sat 8.45am - 7pm.
1 Oct - Easter: Mon - Sat 8.45am - 5pm.

Admission: £2.00, Conc. £1.00.

Dover Castle.

CHARTWELL

WESTERHAM, KENT TN16 1PS

Owner: The National Trust   *Contact: The Property Manager*

Tel: 01732 866368

Home of Sir Winston Churchill from 1924 until the end of his life. The rooms left as they were in his lifetime, evoke his career and interests with memorabilia from his political career. Exhibition on his life at Chartwell & studio containing many of his paintings. Terraced gardens descend to the Lake. Shop and licensed restaurant, Mulberry Room can be booked for meetings, conferences, dinners. Please telephone for details.

Location: 2 miles S of Westerham, forking left off B2026.

Opening Times: Mar & Nov: House: Sat, Sun & Wed 11am - 4.30pm. last adm 4pm. 30 Mar - 3 Nov: House, Garden & Studio: Daily (except Mon & Fri) 11- 5.30pm. Bank Hol Mons: 11 - 5.30pm, last adm 4.30pm. Closed Mons, Fris & Tues following Bank Hol Mons. Restaurant & shop same as house. Tel. re: Xmas.

Admission: House & Garden only: Adult £4.50, Child £2.25, Family £11.25. Garden only: Adult £2, Child £1. House only: Mar - Nov, Adult £2.50, Child £1.25, Studio 50p.

CHIDDINGSTONE CASTLE

Tel: 01892 870347

Edenbridge, Kent TN8 7AD

Owner: Trustees of Denys Eyre Bower Bequest   **Contact:** The Custodian

17th century house remodelled into fantasy castle c1800. Contains Stuart and Jacobite paintings, Japanese lacquer and swords and Egyptian antiquities.

Location: Off B2027 (Edenbridge - Tonbridge Road). Turn at Bough Beech.

Opening Times: Apr - Oct: Apr, May, Oct; Easter Hol, Sun and Public Holidays. Jun - Sept; Tues - Sun. Weekdays 2 - 5.30pm. Sun & Public Hols, 11.30am - 5.30pm. Booked parties (min. 20) can be arranged at other times and out of season.

Admission: Adult £3.50; Parties of 20 plus £3.00, Child 5 - 15 years £1.50, Child under 5 free with an adult. Groups 20+ booked in advance £3.00 (Out of hours visits, special rates).

COBHAM HALL

See Page 95 for full page entry.

DEAL CASTLE

Tel: 01304 372762

Victoria Road, Deal, Kent CT14 7BA

Owner: English Heritage   **Contact:** The Custodian

Crouching low and menacing, the huge, rounded bastions of this austere fort, built by Henry III, once carried 119 guns. A fascinating castle to explore, with long, dark passages, battlements and a huge basement with an exhibition on England's coastal defences. Coach parking on main road. There is a gift shop and also a stereo tour included in the admission (French & German). Restricted disabled access.

Location: SW of Deal town centre.

Opening Times: 1 Apr - 30 Sept: Daily 10am - 6pm. 1 - 31 Oct: Daily 10am - 6pm or dusk if earlier, 1 Nov - 31 Mar: Wed - Sun, 10am - 4pm.

Admission: Adult £2.80, Child £1.40, Conc £2.10.

DODDINGTON PLACE GARDENS

Tel: 01795 886101

Doddington, Sittingbourne, Kent ME9 0BB

Owner: Mr Richard Oldfield   **Contact:** Mr Richard Oldfield

10 acres of landscaped gardens in an area of outstanding natural beauty. Woodland garden (spectacular May/Jun); Edwardian rock garden; formal terraces with mixed borders; impressive clipped yew hedges, fine trees and lawns. Gift shop and restaurant.

Location: 4m N from A20 at Lenham or S from A2 at Ospringe, W of Faversham. Signposted.

Opening Times: May - September: Sundays 2 - 6pm. Weds & Bank Holidays 11am - 6pm. Other times by appointment for groups.

Admission: Adult £2.00, Child 25p.

DOVER CASTLE

Tel: 01304 201628

Dover, Kent CT16 1HU

Owner: English Heritage   **Contact:** The Custodian

Dramatically sited above the famous White Cliffs, Dover Castle has the longest recorded history of any major fortress in England, beginning in the Iron Age and continuing beyond World War II. There is much to see, including the great keep, towering up to 95 feet, the Roman lighthouse, the restored Saxon church of St Mary Castro and ancient tunnels dating back to 1216. Special attractions include Hellfire Corner, the underground complex of tunnels from which the Dunkirk evacuation was masterminded. Guided tour available of Hellfire Corner only.

Location: On E side of Dover.

Opening Times: 1 Apr - 30 Sept: 10am - 6pm. 1 - 31 Oct 10am - 6pm or dusk if earlier. 1 Nov - 31 Mar: Wed - Sun 10am - 4pm.

Admission: Adult £6.00, Conc. £4.50, Child £3.00.

DYMCHURCH MARTELLO TOWER

Tel: 01424 63792

Dymchurch, Kent

Owner: English Heritage   **Contact:** The Custodian

One of many artillery towers which formed part of a chain of strongholds intended to resist an invasion by Napoleon. It is fully restored with an original 24 pounder gun on the roof.

Location: Access from High Street, not from seafront.

Opening Times: 5 - 8 April & August: Daily 12 noon - 4pm. May - July: Weekends only.

Admission: Adult £1.00, Child 50p, Conc 80p.

GOODNESTONE PARK GARDENS

OPEN

31 Mar - 20 Oct
Sundays
12 noon - 6pm

25 Mar - 25 Oct
Monday to Friday
(closed Tues & Sats)
11am - 5pm

Tel: 01304 840107

NR. WINGHAM, CANTERBURY, KENT CT3 1PL

Owner: The Lord & Lady FitzWalter

The garden is approximately 14 acres, set in 18th Century parkland. There are many fine trees, a woodland area and a large walled garden with a collection of old fashioned roses, clematis and herbaceous plants. Jane Austen was a frequent visitor, her brother Edward having married a daughter of the house.

Location: S of Canterbury, off the B2046 which runs from the A2 to Wingham signposted from this road.

Admission: Adult £2.30, Senior Citizen £2.00, Disabled in wheelchairs £1.00, Child(under 12) 20p. Parties of 20+ Adults £2.00. Guided Parties of 20+ £2.50. House open by appointment for parties of 20 people £1.50.

EMMETTS GARDEN

OPEN

Mar: Sats & Suns only
2 - 5pm.

30 Mar - 2 Nov,
Wed - Sun and
BH Mon 1 - 6pm.
Last admission 5pm.

Guided tours for
groups by prior
arrangement with
Head Gardener.

Tea room
30 Mar - 2 Nov,
days as garden
1 - 5pm.

Tel: 01732 750367
or 01732 750429

IDE HILL, SEVENOAKS, KENT TN14 6AY

Owner: The National Trust   **Contact:** *The Head Gardener*

This charming hill side garden boasts the highest tree top in Kent. Noted for its rare trees and shrubs, bluebells and rose and rock gardens. Wonderful views across The Weald and Bough Beech Reservoir. 18 acres open to the public.

Location: 1½ miles North of Ide Hill off B2042. Leave M25 at J5, then 4 miles.

Admission: Adult £3.00, Child £1.50, Family £7.50. Pre-booked parties £2.00.

GREAT COMP GARDEN

OPEN

1 March - 31 Oct
Daily

11.00am - 6.00pm

Tel: 01732 886154

COMP LANE, PLATT, BOROUGH GREEN, KENT TN15 8QS

Owner: R Cameron Esq.   **Contact:** *Mr W Dyson*

One of the finest gardens in the country, comprising ruins, terraces, tranquil woodland walks and sweeping lawns with a breathtaking collection of trees, shrubs, heathers and perennials, many rarely seen elsewhere. The truly unique atmosphere of Great Comp is further complemented by its Festival of Chamber Music held in July/September. Unusual plants for sale. Teas on Sundays, Bank Holidays and by prior arrangement.

Location: 2 miles east of Borough Green, B2016 off A20. First right at Comp crossroads. ½ mile on left.

Admission: Adult £2.50, Child £1. Parties 20+ Adult £2. Annual ticket £7.50. OAP £5.

FINCHCOCKS

See Page 96 for full page entry.

THE FRIARS

Tel: 01622 717272   **Fax:** 01622 715575

Aylesford Priory, Aylesford, Kent ME20 7BX

Owner: The Order of The Carmelites   **Contact:** Mrs M Dunk

Location: Aylesford village.

Opening Times: Summer: Daily, 10am - 5pm. Winter: Daily, 10am - 4pm.

Admission: Parking: Cars £1.00. Coaches £5.00.

GODINTON HOUSE

Tel: 01233 620773

Godinton Park, Ashford, Kent TN23 3BW

Owner: A Wyndham Green Esq   **Contact:** A Wyndham Green Esq

Location: 1½m from Ashford at Potter Corner on A20.

Opening Times: House open to visitors by permission of Mr Alan Wyndham Green on: Easter Sat, Sun & Mon, Sundays and Bank Hols; or by appointment from 1 Jun - 30 Sept from 2 - 5pm.

Admission: Adult £2, Child £1, Garden only £1, Parties of 20+ £1.50.

GROOMBRIDGE PLACE

See Page 97 for full page entry.

HEVER CASTLE

See Page 98 - 99 for full page entry.

HISTORIC DOCKYARD

Tel: 01634 812251

Chatham, Kent ME4 4TE

Contact: Ms F Leinster-Evans

Most complete Georgian/Early Victorian dockyard in the world. 80 acre working museum.

Location: Access from High Street, not from seafront.

Opening Times: Please telephone for details.

 THE NATIONAL TRUST    ENGLISH HERITAGE    HISTORIC HOUSES ASSOCIATION

IGHTHAM MOTE

IVY HATCH, SEVENOAKS, KENT TN15 0NT
Owner: The National Trust
Contact: The Property Manager

Tel: 01732 810378
Fax: 01732 811029

Beautiful moated manor house covering 650 years of history from the Medieval Great Hall to the Victorian housekeepers room. A major repair programme began last year. Visitors will not have access to the first floor but can now see the Robinson Library. Opportunities to follow work and traditional skills used. Lovely garden with lakes & woodland. Surrounding estate provides many country walks. Shop and tea pavilion. House is busy on Sun and BH Mon, 2 - 4pm, visitors may have to wait.

OPEN
31 Mar - 1 Nov: Daily (except Tues & Sats) Weekdays:12 noon - 5.30pm, Sun & BH Mon, 11am - 5.30pm. Last adm. 5pm. Tea Pavilion 11.30 - 5pm weekdays 10.30 - 5pm Suns Oct 12 noon - 3pm (weather permitting)

Location: 6 m E of Sevenoaks off A25. 2$^{1}/_{2}$ m S of Ightham off A227.
Admission: Adult £4, Child £2, Family £10.00. Pre-booked parties (20+) weekdays only £3 . No reduction Sundays and Bank Holidays.

KNOLE

See Page 100 for full page entry.

LADHAM HOUSE

Tel: 01580 211203

Ladham Lane, Goudhurst, Kent TM17 1DB
Owner: Lady Jessel   **Contact:** Lady Jessel
10 acre gardens with spectacular twin mixed borders and fine specimen and newly planted arboretum.
Location: NE of Goudhurst off A262.
Opening Times: Unconfirmed at time of going to press.

LEEDS CASTLE

See Page 101 for full page entry.

LULLINGSTONE CASTLE

Tel: 01322 862114

Lullingstone Castle, Eynsford, Kent DA4 0JA
Owner: Guy Hart Dyke Esq   **Contact:** Guy Hart Dyke Esq
Fine state rooms, family portraits and armour in beautiful grounds. The 15th century gatehouse was one of the first ever to be made of bricks.
Location: 1m S Eynsford on A225.
Opening Times: Apr - Sept: Sat, Sun, BHs, 2 - 6pm. Wed, Thur, Fri by arrangement.
Admission: Adult £3.50, Child £1.50, Conc £3.00, Groups over 25 midweek 10% discount.

LULLINGSTONE ROMAN VILLA

Tel: 01322 863467

Lullingstone Lane, Eynsford, Kent DA4 0JA
Owner: English Heritage   **Contact:** The Custodian
Some splendid mosaic tiled floors can be seen among the remains of this large country villa which has been extensively excavated in recent years. Four distinct periods of building have been identified as well as one of the earliest private Christian chapels.
Location: $^{1}/_{2}$m SW of Eynsford off A225, off Junction 3 of M25.
Opening Times: 1 Apr - 30 Sept: Daily 10am - 6pm. 1 - 31 Oct: Daily 10am - 6pm or dusk if earlier. 1 Nov - 31 Mar: Wed - Sun 10am - 4pm. (Closed 24 - 26 Dec, 1 Jan).
Admission: Adult £2.00, Child £1.00, Conc £1.50.

LYMPNE CASTLE

Tel: 01303 267571

Hythe, Kent CT21 4LQ
Owner: H H Margary Esq   **Contact:** H H Margary Esq
Ancient Castle, rebuilt 1360 and restored in 1905, situated on high ground with magnificent views.
Location: 4 m from Hythe. 9 miles from Folkstone.
Opening Times: Easter - 30 Sept: 10.30am - 6.00pm. Closed occasional Saturday.
Admission: Adult £2.00, Child 50p.

MAISON DIEU

Tel: 01732 778000

Ospringe, Faversham, Kent.
Owner: English Heritage   **Contact:** The South East Regional Office
This forerunner of today's hospitals remains largely as it was in the 16th century with exposed beams and an overhanging upper storey. It contains an exhibition about Ospringe in Roman times.
Location: In Ospringe on A2 $^{1}/_{2}$ m W of Faversham.
Opening Times: Easter - 31 Oct: Weekends and Bank Holidays only, 2 - 5pm.

MILTON CHANTRY

Tel: 01732 778000

New Tavern Fort Gardens, Gravesend, Kent
Owner: English Heritage   **Contact:** The South East Regional Office
A small 14th century building which housed the chapel of the leper hospital and the chantry of the de Valence and Montechais families and later became a tavern and in 1780 part of a fort.
Location: In New Tavern Fort Gardens E of central Gravesend off A226.
Opening Times: 1 Mar - 31 Dec: Weekends & Bank Holidays 10am - 5pm and Tues - Fris 1 - 5pm. Closed Mons (except Bank Hol Mons).
Admission: Free. Telephone the keykeeper 01732 778000 Mon - Fri, 9am - 5pm for details.

MOUNT EPHRAIM

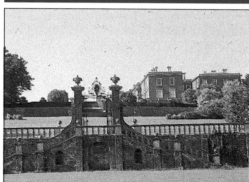

OPEN

Gardens
Mid Apr - 30 Sept.
1 - 6pm
Sundays in Oct.

Bank Hols
11am - 6pm

Groups other times by appointment.

House by appointment.

Tel: 01227 751496
Fax: 01227 750940

HERNHILL, NR FAVERSHAM, KENT ME13 9TX
Owner: Mr and Mrs Dawes   *Contact: Mrs L.E. Dawes*

In this enchanting Edwardian garden, terraces of fragrant roses lead to a small lake and woodland area. Mount Ephraim Gardens house an extensive collection of trees and shrubs including rhododendrons. There is also a herbaceous border, topiary and an extensive Japanese rock garden as well as a vineyard. Mount Ephraim house and grounds are available for private and corporate functions. Adequate parking. Tea room and gift shop.
Location: 1 mile from end of M2. Follow tourist signs from A2 & A299.
Admission: Adult £2.00, Child 50p, Groups £1.50.

NORTHBOURNE COURT GARDENS **Tel:** 01304 611281 **Fax:** 01304 614512

Northbourne, Deal, Kent CT14 0LW
Owner: The Hon Charles James   **Contact:** The Hon Charles James
Originally the site of a Saxon palace, given to St Augustine's Abbey and later to Sir Edwyn Sandys. A fine and beautifully preserved example of Tudor terraced gardens. There is a wide range of shrubs and plants on chalk soil, planted around the brick terraces of the earlier mansion.
Location: A256 and A258 nearby, follow signs to Northbourne village.
Opening Times: June, July and August 1996: Sundays only 2 - 5pm.
Groups any time by appointment.
Admission: Adult £2.50, Child/OAP £1.50.

OLD SOAR MANOR

Tel: 01892 890651

Plaxtol, Borough Green, Kent TN15 0QX
Owner: The National Trust   **Contact:** The Administrator
The solar block of a late 13th century knight's dwelling.
Location: 1 m E of Plaxtol.
Opening Times: Apr - end Sept: Daily, 10am - 6pm.

PATTYNDENNE MANOR

Tel: 01580 211361

Goudhurst, Kent TN17 2QU

Owner: Mr and Mrs DC Spearing   **Contact:** Mr DC Spearing

One of the great timber houses of England, built of oak trees felled from the surrounding forest twenty years before Columbus discovered America. Special architectural details include the jettying, dragon beams, king post and tie beam, corner posts of upturned oaks, and an amazing wealth of timbering only to be seen in a house built before the modern iron industry destroyed England's forests. 13th Century prison. Associated with Henry VIII as a hunting lodge.

Location: 10 miles E of Tunbridge Wells.

Opening Times: By prior appointment only. Parties of 20 - 55 people. Connoisseur Tours. Light refreshments.

Admission: Party Rate. Adult £4.00.

PENSHURST PLACE

See Page 102 for full page entry.

QUEBEC HOUSE

Tel: 01959 562206

Westerham, Kent TN16 1TD

Owner: The National Trust   **Contact:** The Custodian

General Wolfe spent his early years in this gabled, red-brick 17th century house. Four rooms containing portraits, prints and memorabilia relating to Wolfe's family and career are on view. In the Tudor stable block is an exhibition about the Battle of Quebec (1759) and the parts played by Wolfe and his adversary, the Marquis de Montcalm.

Location: At E end of village, on N side of A25, facing junction with B2026, Edenbridge Road.

Opening Times: Apr - end Oct: Tues & Suns only, 2 - 6pm. Last admission 5.30pm. Parties during weekday opening times only and by prior arrangement.

Admission: Adult £2.20, Child £1.10. Pre-booked parties £1.50,

RECULVER TOWERS AND ROMAN FORT

Tel: 01732 778000

Reculver, Herne Bay, Kent

Owner: English Heritage   **Contact:** The South East Regional Office

This 12th century landmark of twin towers has guided sailors into the Thames estuary for seven centuries, but you can also see the walls of a Roman fort, which were erected nearly 2,000 years ago.

Location: At Reculver 3 m E of Herne Bay.

Opening Times: Any reasonable time.

RICHBOROUGH CASTLE

Tel: 01304 612013

Richborough, Sandwich, Kent CT13 9JW

Owner: English Heritage   **Contact:** The Custodian

This fort and township date back to the Roman landing in AD43. The fortified walls and the massive foundations of a triumphal arch which stood 80 feet high still survive.

Location: 1½m N of Sandwich off A257.

Opening Times: 1 Apr - 30 Sept: Daily 10am - 6pm. 1 Oct - 31 Oct: Daily 10am - 6pm or dusk if earlier.

Admission: Adult £2.00, Child £1.00, Conc £1.50

ROCHESTER CASTLE

Tel: 01634 402276

The Lodge, Rochester-upon Medway, Medway, Kent ME1 1SX

Owner: English Heritage   **Contact:** Head Custodian

Built in the 11th century to guard the point where the Roman road of Watling Street crossed the River Medway, the size and position of this grand Norman Bishop's castle, founded on the Roman city wall, eventually made it an important royal stronghold for several hundred years. The keep is truly magnificent - over 100 feet high and with walls 12 feet thick. At the top you will be able to enjoy fine views over the river and surrounding city of Rochester.

Location: By Rochester Bridge (A2), Junc 1 of M2 and Junc 2 of M25.

Opening Times: 1 Apr - 30 Sept: Daily 10am - 6pm. 1 Oct - 31 Oct: Daily 10am - 6pm or dusk if earlier. 1 Nov - 31 Mar, 10am - 4pm. (Closed 24 - 26 Dec, 1 Jan).

Admission: Please ring for 1996 admission prices.

ROCHESTER CATHEDRAL

Tel: 01634 401301   **Fax:** 01634 401410

Rochester, Kent ME1 1JY

Contact: Ms M Hawes

Founded in 604AD, Rochester Cathedral has been a place of Christian worship for nearly 1,400 years. The present building is a blend of Norman and Gothic architecture. In the cloister are the remains of the 12th century Chapter House and priory. A focal point is the Doubleday statue of Christ and the Blessed Virgin.

Location: Signposted from Junction 6 on the M20 and Junction 3 on the A2/M2.

Opening Times: 8.30am - 5.00pm. Visiting may be restricted during services.

Admission: Donation.

ROMAN PAINTED HOUSE

Tel: 01304 225922   **Fax:** 01304 203279

New Street, Dover, Kent CT17 9AJ

Owner: Dover Roman Painted House Trust   **Contact:** Mr B Philip

Discovered in 1970. Built around 200AD as a hotel for official travellers. Well preserved impressive wall paintings, central-heating systems and the Roman fort wall built through the house.

Location: Dover town centre.

Opening Times: 10am - 5pm except Mons. (Times are unconfirmed for 1996).

Admission: Adult £1.50, Child 50p, Senior citizens 50p, Conc 50p. (1995 prices).

ROYDON HALL

ROYDON LANE, EAST PECKHAM, NR TONBRIDGE TN12 5NH

Owner: Maharishi Foundation   *Contact:* The Events Manager

Tel: 01622 812121   **Fax:** 01622 813959

A splendid Tudor manor retaining many of its original features. Roydon Hall has a wonderfully peaceful ambience and is set in 10 acres of woodlands, lawns, terraces and courtyard, commanding a magnificent view of the Weald of Kent. The red brick exterior has weathered with the centuries mellowing to a warm rose colour. The interior contains fine examples of rich walnut, Elizabethan and oak panelling, in several large and small rooms.

Location: One hour's drive from London off the M20. 50 minutes by train from Charing Cross.

Opening Times: The building and grounds are open to the public and interested parties to view by prior appointment.

Admission: Free

RIVERHILL HOUSE

OPEN

April, May & June every Sun & Bank Holiday weekends 12 noon - 6pm.

Group bookings include tour of house any day in above period.

Tel: 01732 458802 or 01732 452557

SEVENOAKS, KENT TN15 0RR

Owner: The Rogers Family   *Contact:* Mrs Rogers

A lived in family home. Panelled rooms, portraits and interesting memorabilia. Historic hillside garden with sheltered terraces. Rhododendrons, azaleas and bluebells in woodland setting. Picnics allowed. Tearoom. No dogs. House available all year for board meetings and small conferences, maximum 20 people. Catering to country house standard.

Location: 2 miles South of Sevenoaks on A225.

Admission: House & Garden: (adults only) £3.50. Garden: Adult £2.50, Child 50p.

SCOTNEY CASTLE GARDEN

OPEN

GARDENS
30 Mar - 2 Nov
Wed - Fri: 11 - 6pm. Sat
& Sun: 2 - 6pm /dusk

BH Suns & Mons
12 - 6pm
(closed Good Fri)

OLD CASTLE
May - 15 Sept
times as for Gardens.
Last adm. 1 hr
before closing.

Tel: 01892 891081
Fax: 01892 890110

LAMBERHURST, TUNBRIDGE WELLS, KENT TN3 8JN

Owner: The National Trust *Contact:* Administration Assistant

One of England's most romantic gardens, surrounding the ruins of a 14th century moated castle. Rhododendrons, azaleas, water lilies & wisteria flower in profusion. Renowned for its autumn colour. The ruined old castle with its priest hole is open for the summer. The surrounding estate has many country walks. Shop open as garden. Tea rooms in Lamberhurst village.
Location: Signed off A21 1 mile S of Lamberhurst village.
Admission: Adult £3.50, Child £1.70, Family £8.70. Pre-booked parties £2.20 (no reduction Sat, Sun or BH Mon). NT members free.

SISSINGHURST CASTLE GARDEN **Tel:** 01580 712850 **Fax:** 01580 713911

Sissinghurst, Cranbrook, Kent TN17 2AB
Owner: The National Trust **Contact:** The Visitor Services Manager
The 5½ acre famous connoisseurs' garden created by Vita Sackville-West and her husband, Sir Harold Nicolson. Exhibition, woodland and lake walks.
Location: 1m East of Sissinghurst village off A262, 2 m NE of Cranbrook.
Opening Times: 2 Apr- 15 Oct: Tues - Fri, 1 - 6.30pm, Sat, Sun & Good Fri 10am - 5.30pm. Closed all Mons including BH Mon. Last admission ½ hr before close.
Ticket office & Exhibition: 12 noon weekdays. Restaurant: Tues - Fri, 12 noon - 5.30pm and Sat, Sun & Good Fri, 10am - 5.30pm. Shop as garden. Telephone for Xmas openings for shop and restaurant.
Admission: Adult £5.00, Child £2.50. Coaches & parties by appointment only. No reductions.

SMALLHYTHE PLACE **Tel:** 01580 762334

Smallhythe, Tenterden, Kent TN30 7NG
Owner: The National Trust **Contact:** The Custodian
Home of Shakespearean actress Dame Ellen Terry, containing personal and theatrical mementoes. Also garden and barn theatre.
Location: 2 miles S of Tenterden on E side of the Rye road B2082.
Opening Times: 30 Mar - end Oct: Sat to Wed (open Good Fri) 2 - 6pm or dusk if earlier. Last admission ½ hr before close. The Barn Theatre, open by courtesy of The Barn Theatre Society, may be closed some days at short notice.
Admission: Adult £2.70, Child £1.30, Family £6.70. Pre-booked parties (Tues am only) no reduction. Max 25 people in house at one time, garden has shelter for further 25.

SQUERRYES COURT   See Page 103 for full page entry.

ST AUGUSTINE'S ABBEY **Tel:** 01227 767345

Longport, Canterbury, Kent CT1 1TF
Owner: English Heritage **Contact:** The Custodian
Founded in 598, this was one of the earliest monastic sites in southern England. Here you will find remarkable remains of the foundations of the original 6th century churches, the Norman church and medieval monastery.
Location: In Longport ¼ m E of Cathedral Close.
Opening Times: 1 Apr - 30 Sept: Daily, 10am - 6pm. 1 - 31 Oct: Daily 10am - 6pm or dusk if earlier. (Closed 24 - 26 Dec, 1 Jan).
Admission: Adult £1.50, Child 80p, Conc £1.10.

ST JOHN'S COMMANDERY   **Tel:** 01732 778000

Densole, Swingfield, Kent
Owner: English Heritage **Contact:** The South East Regional Office
A medieval chapel built by the Knights Hospitallers, ancestors of the St John Ambulance Brigade. It has a moulded plaster ceiling and a remarkable timber roof which was converted into a farmhouse in 16C.
Location: 2 m NE of Densole off A260.
Opening Times: By appointment only.

STONEACRE **Tel:** 01622 862871

Otham, Maidstone, Kent ME15 8RS
Owner: The National Trust **Contact:** The Tenant
A half-timbered mainly late 15th century yeoman's house, with great hall and crownpost, and newly restored cottage style garden.
Location: At N end of Otham village, 3m SE of Maidstone, 1m S of A20.
Opening Times: Apr - end Oct: Wed & Sat, 2 - 6pm. Last admission 5pm.
Admission: £2.20. Child £1.10. No reduction for parties.

TEMPLE MANOR **Tel:** 01732 778000

Strood, Rochester, Kent
Owner: English Heritage **Contact:** The South East Regional Office
The 13th century manor house of the Knights Templar which mainly provided accommodation for members of the order travelling between London and the Continent.
Location: In Strood (Rochester) off A228.
Opening Times: By appointment only. Telephone keykeeper on 01634 842852 for details.

TONBRIDGE CASTLE **Tel:** 01732 844522 **Fax:** 01732 770449

Castle Street, Tonbridge, Kent TN9 1BG
Owner: Tonbridge & Malling Borough Council **Contact:** Mrs S Kostyrka
Remains of Norman motte and bailey castle with 13th century gatehouse set in gardens overlooking River Medway.
Location: Off Tonbridge High Street.
Opening Times: Mon - Fri, 8.30am - 5pm. Sat 9am - 5pm. Sun/BH 10.30am - 5pm. Oct - Mar, 4pm closure Sat/Sun.
Admission: Adult £3.00, Child/Conc. £1.50, Family £7.50. Groups of 10 or more entitled to 10% discount.

UPNOR CASTLE **Tel:** 01634 718742

Upnor, Kent
Owner: English Heritage **Contact:** The Custodian
This well preserved 16th century gun fort was built to protect Queen Elizabeth I's warships. However in 1667 it failed to prevent the Dutch navy which stormed up the Medway destroying half the English fleet.
Location: At Upnor, on unclassified road off A228.
Opening Times: 1 Apr - 30 Sept: Daily 10am - 6pm. 1 - 31 Oct: Daily 10am - 6pm or dusk if earlier.
Admission: Please telephone for admission prices.

WALMER CASTLE

OPEN

1 Apr - 30 Sept
Daily 10am - 6pm.

October:
Daily 10am - 6pm
or dusk if earlier.

1 Nov - 31 Mar:
Wed - Sun
10am - 4pm.

Tel: 01304 364288

KINGSDOWN ROAD, DEAL, KENT CT14 7LJ

Owner: English Heritage *Contact:* The Custodian

The great squat fortress at Walmer was built in 1540 by Henry VIII as part of his coastal defences, but for the past 300 years it has been used as a domestic residence by the Lords Warden of the Cinque Ports - among them the Duke of Wellington and HM Queen Elizabeth the Queen Mother. The Queen Mother's room can be seen when she is not in residence as well as those of the Duke of Wellington (and his 'Wellington boots'). The gardens with their herbaceous borders and huge yew hedges are well worth a visit in themselves.
Location: On coast S of Walmer on A258.
Admission: Adult £3.80, Child £1.90, Conc. £2.90.

WILLESBOROUGH WINDMILL **Tel:** 01233 625643

Mill Lane, Willesborough, Ashford, Kent
Location: Off A292 close to J10/M20.
Opening Times: April - Oct; Sat, Sun and Bank Holiday Mons, 2 - 5pm or dusk if earlier.
Admission: Adult £1.00, Child 50p, Conc 50p.Groups 10% reduction by arrangement only.

YALDING GARDENS

Tel: 01622 814650   **Fax:** 01622 814 650

Benover Road, Yalding, Maidstone, Kent ME18 6EX

Owner: Henry Doubleday Research Association   **Contact:** Peter Bateman

Fourteen newly created gardens reflecting mankind's experience of gardening over the centuries. A series of individual gardens from medieval times through to the present day illustrating themes such as stewardship of resources, respect for wildlife and the importance of genetic diversity. Tudor garden, Victorian garden, children's garden, wildlife gardens. Cafe and shop. Tours and party bookings welcome.

Location: 6m SW of Maidstone, ^{1}/2m south of the village at Yalding on B2162.

Opening Times: May - Sept: Wed - Sun and Bank Hol Mons, 10am - 5pm.
Oct: Sat and Sun only 10am - 5pm.

Admission: Adult £2.00, Child (5-16) £1.00, OAP £1.50, family £5.00.

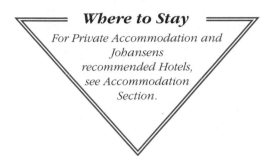

Where to Stay

For Private Accommodation and
Johansens
recommended Hotels,
see Accommodation
Section.

Chartwell.

SPECIAL EVENTS

❖ **HEVER CASTLE & GARDENS**		**THROUGHOUT THE SEASON**
Performances by Bands, & Jousting, Archery & Falconry events. Contact the Castle for details.		
❖ **GROOMBRIDGE PLACE & GARDENS**		**28 JANUARY**
South East of England Wedding Fair		
❖ **PENSHURST PLACE & GARDENS**		**23 – 25 FEBRUARY**
Home Design Exhibition		
❖ **BOUGHTON MONCHELSEA PLACE**		**9 – 10 MARCH**
Craft Show (Marqueed event)		
❖ **LEEDS CASTLE**		**23 – 31 MARCH**
Spring Gardens Week		
❖ **COBHAM HALL**		**24 MARCH**
National Garden Scheme Day		
❖ **COBHAM HALL**		**29 – 31 MARCH**
Antiques Fair		
❖ **COBHAM HALL**		**5 – 8 APRIL**
Medway Craft Fair		
❖ **LEEDS CASTLE**		**6 – 8 APRIL**
A Celebration of Easter		
❖ **BOUGHTON MONCHELSEA PLACE**		**7 – 8 APRIL**
Game Show		
❖ **THE FRIARS**		**14 APRIL**
Fun Run and Family Day		
❖ **GROOMBRIDGE PLACE & GARDENS**		**4 – 6 MAY**
Garden Fair		
❖ **HEVER CASTLE & GARDENS**		**4 – 6 MAY**
May Day Celebrations		
❖ **PENSHURST PLACE & GARDEN**		**4 – 6 MAY**
Weald of Kent Craft Show		
❖ **LEEDS CASTLE**		**18 – 19 MAY**
Food and Wine Festival		
❖ **HEVER CASTLE & GARDENS**		**25 – 27 MAY**
Merrie England Weekend		
❖ **FINCHCOCKS**		**26 – 27 MAY**
Garden Fair		
❖ **PENSHURST PLACE & GARDENS**		**26 – 27 MAY**
Classic Car Show		
❖ **THE FRIARS**		**27 MAY**
Spring Fayre and Flower Festival extravaganza (flower arrangements by NAFAS)		
❖ **PENSHURST PLACE & GARDENS**		**27 MAY**
Penshurst Wool Race		
❖ **LEEDS CASTLE**		**8 – 9 JUNE**
Balloon and Vintage Car Fiesta		
❖ **GROOMBRIDGE PLACE & GARDENS**		**15 – 16 JUNE**
The Battle of Groombridge - Civil War Excitement !		
❖ **LULLINGSTONE CASTLE**		**16 JUNE**
National Gardens Scheme		
❖ **GROOMBRIDGE PLACE & GARDENS**		**25 JUNE – 6 JULY**
Theatre in the Garden		
❖ **HEVER CASTLE & GARDENS**		**28 – 30 JUNE**
Gardeners' Weekend		

❖ **LEEDS CASTLE**		**29 JUNE**
Open Air Concert		
❖ **PENSHURST PLACE & GARDENS**		**30 JUNE**
Royal Scottish Country Dance Society		
❖ **BEDGEBURY PINETUM**		**JUNE**
Hastings Area Youth Symphony Orchestra performed by the Lake		
❖ **LEEDS CASTLE**		**6 JULY**
Open Air Concert		
❖ **BEDGEBURY PINETUM**		**7 JULY**
Craft Fair		
❖ **PENSHURST PLACE & GARDENS**		**7 JULY**
Territorial Army Display and Families' Day		
❖ **LULLINGSTONE CASTLE**		**11 – 14 JULY; 18 – 20 JULY**
Open Air Theatre - 'Wind in the Willows'		
❖ **COBHAM HALL**		**13 JULY**
Open Air Concert - British Red Cross		
❖ **PENSHURST PLACE & GARDENS**		**13 – 14 JULY**
Balloon Fiesta		
❖ **COBHAM HALL**		**26 – 28 JULY**
Antiques Fair		
❖ **PENSHURST PLACE & GARDENS**		**JULY WEEKENDS**
Elizabethan Entertainment		
❖ **FINCHCOCKS**		**24 – 26 AUGUST**
18th century Gala		
❖ **FINCHCOCKS**		**SEPTEMBER**
Festival of chamber music		
❖ **PENSHURST PLACE & GARDENS**		**1 SEPTEMBER**
Theatre Set-Up: 'Romeo & Juliet'		
❖ **PENSHURST PLACE & GARDENS**		**6 – 8 SEPTEMBER**
Weald of Kent Craft Show		
❖ **GROOMBRIDGE PLACE & GARDENS**		**8 SEPTEMBER**
South East of England Wedding Fair		
❖ **FINCHCOCKS**		**11 – 13 OCTOBER**
Craft Fair		
❖ **HEVER CASTLE & GARDENS**		**13 – 15 SEPTEMBER**
Patchwork and Quilting Exhibition		
❖ **LEEDS CASTLE**		**19 – 22 SEPTEMBER**
Flower Festival		
❖ **COBHAM HALL**		**19 – 20 OCTOBER**
Medway Craft Fair		
❖ **LEEDS CASTLE**		**2 NOVEMBER**
Grand Fireworks Spectacular		
❖ **BOUGHTON MONCHELSEA PLACE**		**23 – 24 NOVEMBER**
Craft Show (Marqueed event)		
❖ **PENSHURST PLACE & GARDENS**		**23 – 24 NOVEMBER**
Gift & Food Fair		
❖ **LEEDS CASTLE**		**2 – 24 DECEMBER**
Christmas at the Castle		
❖ **LEEDS CASTLE**		**1 JANUARY 1997**
Treasure Trail		

For National Trust and English Heritage Events see separate section.

HOGHTON TOWER
Nr. Preston

HOGHTON TOWER, home of the 14th Baronet Sir Bernard de Hoghton, is one of the most dramatic looking houses in Lancashire. The symmetrical fortified front, castellated gatehouse and flanking towers is reached by a steep straight avenue over half a mile long.

There have been three houses on the present site stretching back to 1100 AD whilst the estates have remained in unbroken succession since the Norman conquest. The present house was built almost entirely by Sir Thomas Hoghton in 1562-1565, though stylistically it could date from 100 years earlier. In 1617, King James I visited the house and knighted the Loin of Beef hence 'Sirloin'. During the Civil War, Sir Richard's son Gilbert held Lancashire for the Crown and the keep of Hoghton was blown up and never replaced.

In the late 17th century the 4th Baronet repaired and modernised the House.

In 1862, Sir Henry Hoghton Bt started restoration of the House. This was completed in 1901 under a London architect R D Oliver, who designed the Ballroom and grand chimney pieces. The King's Ante-chamber, the King's Bed-Chamber and the Buckingham Room all retain their 17th century interiors.

GARDENS
The grounds are sited on the hill commanding extensive views to the sea, the Lakes, and North Wales. Walled gardens.

CONTACT

The Administrator
Hoghton Tower
Hoghton
Lancashire
PR5 0SH

Tel: (01254) 852986
Fax: (01254) 852109

LOCATION

M6 Junct. 28 (10 mins)
3½ hrs to London
M61 (10 mins)
30 mins Manchester
Air: Manchester
Airport 45 mins.
Rail: Preston Station
15 mins: 3 hrs. London
Bus: Ribble Bus Co.
buses to the
bottom of drive.
Taxi: Preston Railway
Station and locals.

OPENING TIMES

Summer
Easter Sat - end October
Mondays: Closed
(Open some Bank Hol Mons)

July and Aug only
Tues, Wed, Thurs
11.00am - 4.00pm

Fris and Sats: Closed
Sundays: 1.00 - 5.00 pm
NB Group visits may be arranged all year round. Contact the Administrator.

Winter
31 Oct - Easter
Banqueting Hall open
for private events and
functions, capacity 120.

ADMISSION

Summer
GARDENS, SHOP & TEAROOM
    Adult £1.00
    Child . . . . .FREE

HOUSE TOURS
    Adult £2.50
    Child (under 5)   FREE
    Child (5-15) £1.25
    OAP/Student . . .£2.00
    Family (4) £6.00

PRIVATE TOURS
    Adult £3.50
    Child £1.75

Winter
Negotiable

SUITABILITY FOR OTHER EVENTS
Hoghton Tower provides a suitable setting for fashion shows, archery, clay pigeon shooting, equestrian events, garden parties, shows, rallies and filming, wedding receptions, corporate functions.

EXTRA FACILITIES
Lectures can be arranged, or video can be shown, in the Conference Room for up to 100 people. Facilities such as projectors and screens can be hired for clients. Hire or use of a grand piano, parkland, cricket pitch, golf course can be arranged. Cost negotiable.

ADVICE TO COURIERS & DRIVERS
Please telephone in advance to seek advice as to where to park prior to releasing the party or parties. Please ask visitors to treat the grassland with respect and advise the ground staff of any damage created. No interior photography, no dogs, no fires in the woods and no unaccompanied children.

PARKING FOR COACHES & CARS
Parking available for 300 cars or 200 cars and 20 coaches. Further parking by arrangement.

FACILITIES FOR THE DISABLED
Although disabled visitors are welcome to enjoy the extensive views from outside the House, there are no special facilities (toilets etc.) provided for them.

CATERING
A Tea Room is available for up to 80 people at any one time. Banqueting Hall available for max 120 persons. Groups can book in advance and menus are available upon request.

GUIDE BOOKS
Colour guide book is available giving a detailed history of the family and the estate. Short translations are available in French, German, Italian, Spanish and Swedish.

GUIDED TOURS
Tours are available and in some cases the owner may meet the group. Duration of the tour is approx 1 hour. Minimum 25 persons.

CONFERENCE AND FUNCTION FACILITIES

ROOM	DIMENSIONS	CAPACITY	LAYOUT	POWER POINTS	SUITABLE FOR A/V
Banqueting Hall	45' x 26'	120	Various	✓	✓
Smoking Room	41' x 20'	70	Various	✓	✓
Billiards	48' x 20' 6"	70	Various	✓	✓

The Banqueting Hall, Ballroom, Smoking Room and Billiards Room are all available throughout the year subject to availability. If requested the owner may meet the group visiting the House and when invited may participate in these functions. Slide and overhead projectors, screens and audio-visual equipment can be hired if required.

PLEASE TELEPHONE FOR FURTHER DETAILS AND RATES

LEIGHTON HALL
Carnforth

CONTACT

Mrs C. S. Reynolds
Leighton Hall
Carnforth
Lancashire
LA5 9ST

Tel: (01524) 734474

Fax: (01524) 720357

LOCATION

9 miles North of
Lancaster,
10 miles South of
Kendal,
3 miles from M6/A6,
Junct. 35, signed
from Junct. 35A.
Rail: Lancaster
Station, 9 miles.

Air: Manchester
Airport, 65 miles.

Taxi: Carnforth Radio
Taxis Carnforth 732763.

LEIGHTON HALL is one of the most beautifully sited houses in the British Isles, situated in a bowl of parkland, with the whole panorama of the Lakeland Fells rising behind. The Hall's neo-Gothic facade was superimposed on an 18th century house, which, in turn, had been built on the ruins of the original mediaeval house. The present owner is descended from Adam d'Avranches who built the first house in 1246.

The whole house is lived in by the Reynolds family and emphasis is put on making visitors feel welcome in a family home.

Connoisseurs of furniture will be particularly interested in the 18th Century pieces by Gillow of Lancaster. Mr Reynolds is directly descended from the founder of Gillow and Company, hence the strong Gillow connection with the house. Also on show are some fine pictures, clocks, silver and objets d'art.

GARDENS

The main garden has a continuous herbaceous border and rose covered walls, while the Walled Garden contains flowering shrubs, a herb garden, an ornamental vegetable garden and a maze. Beyond is the Woodland Walk, where wild flowers abound from early Spring.

A varied collection of Birds of Prey is on display in the Bird Garden, and flown each afternoon that the Hall is open - weather permitting.

❖

SUITABILITY FOR OTHER EVENTS
Product launches, small seminars, filming, garden parties, wedding receptions, rallies, overland driving, archery and clay pigeon shoots.

EXTRA FACILITIES
Lectures on the property, its contents, gardens and history can be arranged . Grand piano.

ADVICE TO COURIERS & DRIVERS
Photography is not allowed in the House. Please leave sufficient time (2hrs) for both tour of House and flying display. No dogs in the gardens. By appointment, parties of 25 and over may visit the Hall in the evening and out of season.

FACILITIES FOR THE DISABLED
Disabled and elderly visitors may alight at the entrance to the property, before parking in the allocated areas.

PARKING FOR COACHES & CARS
100 cars and 6 coaches, 150 yards from the Hall

CATERING
The Restaurant/Tea Room can cater for 55 people. Prices range form £3.25 for afternoon tea to £6.00 for other meals. Groups must book in advance and menus are available on request. For special functions/conferences buffets, lunches and dinners can be arranged.

GIFT SHOP
Open at the same time as the Hall. Items include small souvenirs. Colour guide book, £1.50.

GUIDED TOURS
Parties are taken round in groups. There is no additional cost for the facility. By prior arrangement the owner may meet the groups. Average time taken for a tour 45 minutes/1 hour.

SCHOOL VISITS/CHILDREN
Groups of children are welcome. School Programme from 10am-2pm daily May-Sept. except Mons and Sats. Birds of prey flown for schools at midday. Cost per child £1.80. The Schools Visit Programme won the Sandford Award for Heritage Education in 1983 and again in 1989.

During the afternoon when the house and grounds are open to the general public a large collection of birds of prey are on display, some of which fly at 3.30pm - weather permitting.

Where eagles fly

OPENING TIMES

Summer

1 May - 30 September

Daily
except Mons and Sats
2.00 - 5.00pm

Open Bank Holiday
Mondays.

August only
11.30-5.00pm

NB Pre-booked parties of
25 or more at any time by
appointment

Winter

1 October-30 April
Open to parties of 25 or
more which must be
pre-booked.

ADMISSION

Summer

HOUSE, GARDEN AND
BIRDS
   Adult £3.40
   Child* £2.20
   OAP £2.90
Groups**
   Adult £2.90
   Child* £1.80
   OAP £2.90
   Family Ticket . .£10.00
   (2 adults & up to 3 children)

*Age 0-16

**Minimum payment £65.00.

Winter

As above but groups by
appointment only.

CONFERENCE AND FUNCTION FACILITIES

ROOM	DIMENSIONS	CAPACITY	LAYOUT	POWER POINTS	SUITABLE FOR A/V
Music Room	24' x 21' 6"	80	Theatre	6	✓
		50	Dinner		
		60	Buffet		

ASTLEY HALL

Tel: (01257) 262166   **Fax:** (01257) 232441

Astley Park, Chorley, Lancashire PR7 1NP

Owner: Chorley Borough Council   **Contact:** The Curator

A charming house, dating back to 1580, with additions in the 1660's & 1820's. Interiors include sumptuous plaster ceilings, fine 17th century oak furniture and tapestries, plus displays of fine and decorative art. Set in parkland with café in a stable block.

Location: 2 miles west of Chorley, off A581.

Opening Times: Apr - Oct: Tues - Suns 12 noon - 5pm. Open Bank Holiday Mondays. November to March: Fris - Suns 12 noon - 4pm.

Admission: Adult £2.50, Conc. £1.50, Family £4.50. Discounts for pre-arranged groups.

BLACKBURN CATHEDRAL

Tel: 01254 51491   **Fax:** 01254 667309

Blackburn, Lancashire BB1 5AA

Contact: The Very Rev D Frayne

On a historic Saxon site in town centre. Built as the Parish Church in 1826, subsequent extensions give a uniqueness to both interior and exterior. Features including the lantern tower, central altar with corona above, fine Walker organ, stained glass from medieval period onwards. Recent restoration work gives a new magnificence.

Location: 9m E of exit 31 on M6, via A59 and A677.

Opening Times: Mon - Fri: 9am - 5.30pm, Sat: 9.30am - 4pm, Sun: 8am - 5pm.

Admission: Donation. Guided tours by prior arrangement.

BROWSHOLME HALL

Tel: 01254 826719

Clitheroe, Lancashire BB7 3DG

Owner: R R Parker Esq   **Contact:** R R Parker Esq

Tudor house with Elizabethan front, home of the Parker family since 1507.

Location: Clitheroe.

Opening Times: Easter W/e Fri - Mon; Spring Bank Hol; Every Sat and Sun In Aug: From 2am - 5pm. Booked parties may be arrraged by appointment at other times.

Admission: Historic House Association Members free; reduced rates for parties. Guided tour of house: Adult £3, Child £1.50.

GAWTHORPE HALL

OPEN

Hall
2 Apr - 31 Oct
Daily (not Mon & Fri,
but open Good Fri
& BH Mon)
1 - 5pm.

Last adm. 4.15pm.

Garden:
All year
Daily: 10am - 6pm.

Tel: 01282 778511

PADIHAM, NR BURNLEY, LANCASHIRE BB12 8UA

Owner: The National Trust   *Contact:* The Principal Keeper

The house was built in 1600-05, and restored by Sir Charles Barry in the 1850s. Barry's designs have been re-created in the principal rooms. Gawthorpe was the home of the Shuttleworth family, and the Rachel Kay-Shuttleworth textile collections are on display in the house. A restored 17th century estate building houses a broad programme of art, craft and also a collection of portraits on loan from the National Portrait Gallery.

Location: On E outskirts of Padiham, ³/₄m drive to house on N of A671.

Admission: Hall: Adult £2.30, OAP £1.15, Child £1.00, Family £6.00. Garden: free. Parties by prior arrangement.

HOGHTON TOWER

See Page 110 for full page entry.

LEIGHTON HALL

See Page 111 for full page entry.

MARTHOLME

Tel: 01254 872244   **Fax:** 01254 871253

Great Harwood, Blackburn, Lancashire BB6 7UJ

Owner: Tom H Codling Esq   **Contact:** Tom H Codling Esq

Part of medieval manor house with 17th century additions and Elizabethan gatehouse.

Location: 2m NE of Great Harwood off A680 to Whalley.

Opening Times: Daytime by appointment.

Admission: Exterior £1.00, Interior £2.00.

ROSSENDALE MUSEUM

Tel: (01706) 217777 or (01706) 226509

Whitaker Park, Rawtenstall, Rossendale, Lancashire BB4 6RE

Owner: Rossendale Borough Council   **Contact:** Mrs S Cruise

Former 19th century mill owner's house set in Whitaker Park. Displays include fine and decorative arts, furniture, a Victorian drawing room, plus local/social history, natural history and costume.

Location: Off A681, ¼ mile from rawtenstall Centre.

Opening Times: Apr - Oct: Mon - Fri 1 - 5pm, Sats 10am - 5pm, Suns 12 noon - 5pm. Nov - Mar: Mon - Fri 1 - 5pm, Sats 12 noon - 4pm, Suns 12 noon - 4pm. Bank Hols 1 - 5pm. Closed Christmas Day, Boxing Day and New Year's Day).

Admission: Free.

RUFFORD OLD HALL

OPEN

HOUSE
1 April - 30 October
Sat - Wed
1 - 5pm
Last admission:
4.30pm

GARDEN
Sat - Wed
12 noon - 5.30pm

Tel: 01704 821254

RUFFORD, NR. ORMSKIRK, LANCASHIRE L40 1SG

Owner: The National Trust   *Contact:* Mrs Maureen Dodsworth

There is a legend that William Shakespeare performed here for the owner Sir Thomas Hesketh in the Great Hall of this, one of the finest 16th century buildings in Lancashire. The playwright would have delighted in the magnificent Hall with its intricately carved movable wooden screen. Fine collections of 16th and 17th century oak furniture, arms, armour and tapestries.

Location: 7 miles north of Ormskirk.

Admission: Hall & Garden: Adult £3.00, Child £1.50. Family ticket £8.00. Garden only: £1.60. During school holidays children free.

WARTON OLD RECTORY

Tel: 01912 611585

Warton, Carnforth, Lancashire.

Owner: English Heritage   **Contact:** The North Regional Office

A rare medieval stone house with remains of the hall, chambers and domestic offices.

Location: At Warton, 1 m N of Carnforth on minor road off A6.

Opening Times: 1 Apr - 31 Oct: Daily 10am - 6pm. 1 Nov - 31 Mar: Daily 10am - 4pm. Closed 24 - 26 Dec, 1 Jan.

Where to Stay

For Private Accommodation and Johansens recommended Hotels, see Accommodation Section.

SPECIAL EVENTS

❖ **LEIGHTON HALL** Music & Fireworks		**6 – 7 JULY**
❖ **LEIGHTON HALL** Shakespeare in the Garden		**9 – 10 AUGUST**
❖ **LEIGHTON HALL** Teddy Bears' Extravaganza		**17 – 18 AUGUST**
❖ **LEIGHTON HALL** Craft Fair		**14 – 15 SEPTEMBER**
❖ **LEIGHTON HALL** Antiques Fair		**4 – 6 OCTOBER**
❖ **LEIGHTON HALL** Dolls' House and Miniaturist Fair		**13 OCTOBER**

For National Trust and English Heritage Events see separate section.

NOSELEY HALL
Billesdon

NOSELEY HALL, is one of the most friendly and successful locations in the East Midlands for all types of function. The house is not open to the public, but is available for private and corporate hire. It is especially suitable for outdoor activities, country pursuits, house parties and residential seminars.

The tranquillity of the setting, and the marvellous views, just 15 minutes from Leicester, make Noseley one of the nicest and most central locations for film and photographic work, board meetings, business seminars, conferences, product launches and private parties. Noseley's extensive parkland is ideal for outside events such as Multi-Activity Days. The five acres of lawn, immediately in front of the house, provide the perfect fully-serviced marquee site. All functions are personally overseen by the owner and his wife.

The present house, which dates from 1728, enjoys panoramic views over unspoilt parkland and has a very beautiful 13th century chapel on the lawn. The well preserved interior includes an exceptionally fine two storey Hall, in which guests are greeted on arrival, a panelled Dining Room and an elegant Drawing Room. The house has been the seat of the Hazlerigg family since 1419. The most famous Hazlerigg was one of the five members of parliament who led the rebellion against King Charles I in 1642. He was later Cromwell's general in the North East.

❖

EXTRA FACILITIES
All activities can be arranged. The chapel has excellent acoustics for concerts. Challenging 4 wheel drive course. Lawn for marquees. Noseley regularly holds multi-activity and other corporate days.

ACCOMMODATION
Can be arranged within the House in connection with functions held therein.

FACILITIES FOR THE DISABLED
Disabled and elderly visitors may alight at the entrance to the property, before parking in the allocated areas. There are no special toilets for the disabled.

PARKING FOR COACHES & CARS
100 cars within 50 yards. 10 more acres can be made available.

CATERING
The House is available for Corporate Entertainment functions only. Delicious country house food.

RATES
Noseley Hall is not open to the public. As a guide to rates for conferences and corporate entertainment, the following are given, but please contact the owners for full details and a quotation.

Conferences: Daily delegate rate to include morning coffee, lunch, afternoon tea: From £37.50 + VAT.

Activity Days: Average £60 + VAT per head fully catered (includes facility fee).

Lunches & Dinners: please apply for prices.

Facility Fee: (For other types of events). Exclusive use of grounds and facilities will be based on £800 + VAT per day but each event will be quoted for individually.

CONTACT

The Hon Arthur or
Mrs Hazlerigg
Noseley Hall
Billesdon
Leicestershire
LE7 9EH
Tel: (01162) 596606
(01162) 596322
Fax: (01162) 596774

LOCATION

From London M1 Junct. 15, A508 through N'hampton to Market Harborough, A6, B6047. 12 mls east of Leicester. A1 via A14 (A1-M1 link)
Rail: Mkt. Harborough or Leicester.
Air: Leicester (private). Helicopters: may land on lawn.

OPENING TIMES

Not open to the public. Available for corporate events, conferences, filming, etc. throughout the year.

ACTIVITIES

Off Road Driving (4 x 4)
Clay Pigeon Shooting
Archery
Pistols
Fly Casting
Quad Bikes
Pilot Buggies
Trials Cars
Argocat
Hovercraft
Land Rovers
Reverse Steer Car
Blind Driving
4 x 4 Troop Transporter
Grass Karts
Radio Controlled Minitrux
Autotest Driving Game
Tractor Driving Test
Laser Clay Shooting
Video Activities
Falconry
Scalextric
Golf Swing Analyser
Croquet
Virtual Reality
Management Training

CONFERENCE AND FUNCTION FACILITIES

ROOM	DIMENSIONS	CAPACITY	LAYOUT	POWER POINTS	SUITABLE FOR A/V
Stone Hall	28' x 21'	60	Buffet	5	
Drawing Room	42' x 22'	70	Theatre	4	✓
		40	Schoolroom		
		30	U-shape/Boardroom		
Dining Room	45' x 22'	70	Theatre	4	✓
		70	Schoolroom		
		100	Buffet		
		40 - 80	Lunch/Dinner		
Library	34' x 18'	50	Theatre	8	✓
		30	Schoolroom/Boardroom		
		25	U-shape		
Marquee on Lawn			Dinner/Dance		

STANFORD HALL
Nr Rugby

STANFORD has been the home of the Cave family, ancestors of the present owner, Lady Braye, since 1430. In the 1690s, Sir Roger Cave commissioned the Smiths of Warwick to pull down the old Manor House and build the present Hall, which is an excellent example of their work and of the William and Mary period.

As well as over 5000 books, the handsome Library contains many interesting manuscripts, the oldest dating from 1150. The splendid pink and gold Ballroom has a fine coved ceiling with four trompe l'oeil shell corners. Throughout the house are portraits of the family and examples of furniture and objects which they collected over the centuries. There is also a collection of Royal Stuart portraits, previously belonging to the Cardinal Duke of York, the last of the male Royal Stuarts. An unusual collection of family costumes is displayed in the Old Dining Room, which also houses some early Tudor portraits and a fine Empire chandelier.

The Hall and Stables are set in an attractive Park on the banks of Shakespeare's Avon. There is a walled Rose Garden behind the Stables. An early ha-ha separates the North Lawn from the mile-long North Avenue.

❖

SUITABILITY FOR EVENTS
Clay pigeon shoots, corporate incentive days, lunches, dinners, wedding receptions, filming and photography, fashion shows, car launches. Motor Car and Motorcycle Club Rallies held in the Park most Sundays from early May to end September. Further details on application.

EXTRA FACILITIES
These include parkland, Bluthner piano, helicopter landing area, river for fishing, raft races. Lecture Room available for up to 60 people. Cost for hire of the room £70.

ADVICE TO COURIERS & DRIVERS
Free meals for coach drivers. Coach parking on gravel in front of house. Dogs on leads in the park. No dogs or photography inside the house. Parking for 1,000 cars, 100 yds from the house and 6 to 8 coaches 25yds from the house.

CATERING
Groups of up to 70 can book in advance for homemade afternoon tea, lunches, high teas and suppers. Outside catering facilities are available for special functions/conferences.

FACILITIES FOR THE DISABLED
Disabled and elderly visitors may alight at the entrance to the house. There is a toilet for the disabled.

GUIDED TOURS
Tours last approx ¾ hr. in groups of about 25 people.

GIFT SHOP
Souvenir Shop opens 2.30pm (12 noon on Bank Holidays and Event Days). Craft Centre (most Suns) from 11.00am.

SCHOOL VISITS/CHILDREN
Groups are welcome, price per child £1.50. By prior arrangement a guide can be provided. There is a nature trail with special guide book and map. The Motorcycle Museum is of particular interest.

CONTACT

Lt Col E H L Aubrey-Fletcher
Stanford Hall
Lutterworth
Leicestershire LE17 6DH
Tel: (01788) 860250
Fax: (01788) 860870

LOCATION

M1 Junct. 18 , 6 miles,
M1 Junct. 19 (from/to the North only) 2 miles
M6 Exit/access at A14 /M1(N) junct. 2 miles,
A14, 2 miles.
Follow Historic House signs.
Rail: Rugby Station 7½ miles.
Air: Birmingham Airport 27 miles.
Taxi: Fone-A-Car. (01788) 543333

OPENING TIMES

Summer
Easter - end September
Mon Bank Hols & Tues following 2.30 - 5.30pm
Closed Wed, Thur, Fri.
Sat & Sun 2.30 - 5.30pm
Last admission 5.00pm

NB. On Bank Holidays and Events Days, open at 12 noon (House at 2.30pm). Open any day or evening for pre-booked parties.

Winter
October - Easter
Closed to public.
Open during October for Corporate Events.

ADMISSION

HOUSE & GROUNDS
Adult £3.50
Child* £1.70
Groups**
Adult £3.20
Child* £1.50
OAP £3.00

GROUNDS ONLY
Adult £1.90
Child* £0.80

MOTORCYCLE MUSEUM
Adult £1.00
Child* £0.30
School Group
Adult . . . . FREE
Child* £0.20

* Aged 4 - 15
** Min payment £64.00.

CONFERENCE AND FUNCTION FACILITIES

ROOM	DIMENSIONS	CAPACITY	LAYOUT	POWER POINTS	SUITABLE FOR A/V
Ballroom	39' x 26'	70	Theatre	4	✓
		60	Schoolroom		
		40	U-shape		
		100	Buffet		
		64 - 80	Lunch/Dinner		
Old Dining Room	30' x 20'	50	Theatre	4	✓
		30	Schoolroom		
		25	U-shape/Boardroom		
		70	Buffet		
		30	Lunch/Dinner		
Crocodile Room	39' x 20'	60	Theatre	1	✓

ASHBY DE LA ZOUCH CASTLE   Tel: 01530 413343

South Street, Ashby de la Zouch, Leicestershire LE65 1PR

Owner: English Heritage   **Contact:** The Custodian

The impressive ruins of this late medieval castle are dominated by a magnificent tower, over 80 feet high, which was split in two during the Civil War, when the castle defended the Royalist cause.

Location: In Ashby de la Zouch, 12 m S of Derby on A50.

Opening Times: 1 Apr - 30 Sept: Daily 10am - 6pm. 1 - 31 Oct: Daily 10am - 6pm or dusk if earlier. 1 Nov - 31 Mar, Wed - Sun 10am - 4pm, (Closed for lunch 1 - 2pm).

Admission: Adult £1.50, Child 80p, Conc £1.10.

BELGRAVE HALL   Tel: 0116 2666590

Church Road, Thurcaston Road, Leicester LE4 5PE

Owner: Leicestershire Museums, Arts & Records Service   **Contact:** Mr Bill Garrett

Queen Anne House. Period room settings from late 17- 19th century. Interesting gardens.

Location: Church Road, Leicester.

Opening Times: All Year: Mon - Sat; 10am - 5.30pm Sun: 2 - 5.30pm
Closed Christmas Day/Boxing Day and Bank Hols.

Admission: Free.

KIRKBY MUXLOE CASTLE   Tel: 0116 2386886

Kirkby Muxloe, Leicestershire.

Owner: English Heritage   **Contact:** The Custodian

Picturesque, moated, brick built castle begun in 1480 by William Lord Hastings. It was left unfinished after Hastings was executed in 1483.

Location: 4 m W of Leicester off B5380.

Opening Times: Telephone keykeeper 01604 730320 for opening details.

LYDDINGTON BEDE HOUSE   Tel: 01572 822438

Blue Coat Lane, Lyddington, Uppingham, Leicestershire LE15 9LZ

Owner: English Heritage   **Contact:** The Custodian

The Bede House was originally a medieval palace of the Bishops of Lincoln. It was later converted to an alms house.

Location: In Lyddington, 6m N of Corby, 1 m E of A6003.

Opening Times: 1 Apr - 30 Sept. Daily 10am - 6pm. 1 - 31 Oct 10am - 6pm or dusk if earlier. Lunchtime closure 1 - 2pm.

Admission: Adult £1.50, Child 80p, Conc £1.10.

NOSELEY HALL   See Page 113 for full page entry.

Stanford Hall.

PRESTWOLD HALL

LOUGHBOROUGH, LEICESTERSHIRE LE12 5SQ

Owner: S.J. Packe-Drury-Lowe   *Contact:* Mrs. Weldon

Tel: 01509 880236   **Fax:** 01636 812187

A magnificent private house, largely remodelled in 1843 by William Burn. For the past 350 years it has been the home of the Packe family and contains fine Italian plaster work, 18th century English and European furniture and a collection of family portraits. The house is not open to the general public but offers excellent facilities as a conference and corporate entertainment venue. Up to 170 guests can be seated and the 20 acres of gardens provide a perfect setting for larger meetings using marquees. Also available are excellent chefs providing a varied menu, a fully stocked wine cellar as well as clay pigeon shooting, motor sports and archery. Activity days on request.

Location: At the heart of the Midlands, 3 miles east of Loughborough on B675.

Admission: Corporate entertaining venues and conference centre by arrangement only. A licence to hold Civil Weddings has recently been obtained.

STANFORD HALL   See Page 114 for full page entry.

WHATTON HOUSE GARDEN   **Tel:** 01509 842268   **Fax:** 01509 842268

Long Whatton, Loughborough, Leicestershire, LE12 5BG.

15 acre garden including a unique Chinese/Japanese garden.

Location: On A6 4m N of Loughborough, 2m S of Kegworth. 3m from exit 24/M1.

Opening Times: Every Sun & BH Mon Easter - 31 Aug. Also 9 Apr, 7 May, 28 May. Also by appointment.

Admission: Adult £2.00, Child £1.00, Conc £1.00 (prices correct at time of going to press). Groups by arrangement.

Where to Stay

For Private Accommodation and Johansens recommended Hotels, see Accommodation Section.

BELVOIR CASTLE
Grantham

BELVOIR CASTLE, home of the Duke and Duchess of Rutland, commands a magnificent view over the Vale of Belvoir. The name, Belvoir, meaning beautiful view, dates back to Norman times, when Robert de Todeni, Standard Bearer to William the Conqueror, built the first Castle on this superb site. Destruction caused by two Civil Wars and by a catastrophic fire in 1816 have breached the continuity of Belvoir's history. The present building owes much to the inspiration and taste of Elizabeth, 5th Duchess of Rutland and was built after the fire.

Inside the Castle are notable art treasures including works by Poussin, Holbein, Rubens, and Reynolds, Gobelin and Mortlake tapestries, Chinese silks, furniture, fine porcelain and sculpture.

The Queens Royal Lancers Museum at Belvoir has a fascinating exhibition of the history of the Regiment, as well as a fine collection of weapons, uniforms and medals.

GARDENS
The Statue Gardens are built into the hillside below the Castle and take their name from the collection of 17th century sculptures on view. The garden is planted so that there is nearly always something in flower.

The Duchess' private Spring Gardens are available for viewing throughout the year by pre-booked groups of 10 persons or more. Details from the Estate Office.

❖

CONTACT

Richard Fenn
Castle Estate Office
Belvoir Castle
Grantham
Lincolnshire
NG32 1PD

Tel: (01476) 870262
Fax: (01476) 870443

LOCATION

A1 from London (110mls), York (100mls) & Grantham (7mls). A607 Grantham-Melton Mowbray.
Air: East Midlands Int'l.
Rail: Grantham Stn 7mls
Bus: Melton Mowbray - Vale of Belvoir via Castle Car Park.
Taxi: Grantham Taxis 63944/63988.

Summer
2 April - 29 September

Mon Bank Hols only
11.00am - 6.00pm

Tues, Wed, Thur, Sat
11.00am - 5.00pm

Fridays Closed
(Open Good Friday)
11.00am - 6.00pm

Sundays
11.00am - 6.00pm

Winter
Groups welcome by appointment.

ADMISSION

Adult £4.25
Child £2.75
OAP £3.00
Groups*
   Adult £3.25
   Child** £2.20

* 20 or more adults.
** School or Youth groups.

SUITABILITY FOR OTHER EVENTS
Ideal location for banquets, exhibitions, product launches and conferences. Filming welcomed.

EXTRA FACILITIES
Any activity or event is a possibility and we would be delighted to discuss requirements, regardless of size.

ADVICE TO COURIERS & DRIVERS
Coaches should report to the Main Car Park and Ticket Office on arrival. Photography welcomed (permit £1.00).

FACILITIES FOR THE DISABLED
Ground floor of Castle is easily accessible for disabled people, including the Restaurant and Toilet Facilities. Further access to Castle is restricted for wheelchairs. Please telephone for advice.

GUIDED TOURS (BY APPOINTMENT)
Guided tours available by prior arrangement. £7.50 per group (up to 20 persons). Duration approx 1¼ hours.

PARKING FOR COACHES & CARS
150 cars, next to the Castle and a further 500 spaces, 500 yds from the Castle. Up to 40 coaches can be parked. Coaches can take passengers to entrance by arrangement.

CATERING
Extensive choice of hot and cold home-made food available throughout the day in the 100-seat licensed restaurant. Groups and parties catered for, from afternoon tea to a set three-course meal. Private room available.

GIFT SHOP
Open when Castle is open to the public, offering many quality gifts and souvenirs. There is also an unusual plant stall open at the Castle on Sundays in Season.

GUIDE BOOKS
Pictorial guide with details of the Castle and contents. Translations in French, German, Italian and Spanish. Braille guide book available.

SCHOOL VISITS/ CHILDREN
Guided tours available to all schools parties, along with a private room for education or packed lunch purposes, subject to availability. Picnic area and Adventure Playground.

CONFERENCE AND FUNCTION FACILITIES

ROOM	DIMENSIONS	CAPACITY	LAYOUT	POWER POINTS	SUITABLE FOR A/V
State Dining Room	52' x 31'	100	Schoolroom	8	✓
		60	U-shape		
		80	Boardroom		
		150	Buffet		
		130	Theatre		
		100	Lunch/Dinner		
Regents Gallery	131' x 16' 6"	300	Reception		✓
Old Kitchen	45' x 22' 6"	120	Buffet	4	✓
		80	Lunch/Dinner		

BURGHLEY HOUSE
Stamford

BURGHLEY HOUSE, home of the Cecil family for over 400 years, was built as a country seat during the latter part of the 16th century by Sir William Cecil, later Lord Burghley, principal adviser and Lord Treasurer to Queen Elizabeth.

The House was completed in 1587 and there have been few alterations to the architecture since that date thus making Burghley one of the finest examples of late Elizabethan design in England.

The interior was remodelled in the late 17th century by John, 5th Earl of Exeter who was a collector of fine art on a huge scale, establishing the immense collection of art treasures at Burghley.

Burghley is truly a 'Treasure House', containing one of the largest private collections of Italian art, unique examples of Chinese and Japanese porcelain and superb items of 18th century furniture. The remodelling work of the 17th century mean that examples of the work of the principal artists and craftsmen of the period are to be found here at Burghley: Antonio Verrio, Grinling Gibbons and Louis Laguerre all made major contributions to the beautiful interiors.

GARDENS
The House is set in a 300-acre Deer Park landscaped by 'Capability' Brown under the direction of the 9th Earl. As was usual with Brown's designs, a lake was created and delightful avenues of mature trees feature largely. The park is home to a herd of fallow deer and is open to the public at all times of the year. The gardens surrounding the House are only open on certain weekends in the Spring. Please telephone for details.

❖

SUITABILITY FOR OTHER EVENTS
Burghley is suitable for a wide variety of events.

EXTRA FACILITIES
Large park, golf course, helicopter landing area, cricket pitch.

ADVICE TO COURIERS & DRIVERS
Parking and refreshments free for drivers. No dogs within the House. Please advise clients that there is no photography inside.

FACILITIES FOR THE DISABLED
Disabled and elderly visitors may alight at the entrance, before parking in the allocated areas. Toilets for the disabled. Chair lift to the Orangery Coffee Shop. Disabled visitors should be aware that the house tour involves two staircases.

PARKING FOR COACHES & CARS
Capacity of the Car Park, 500 cars, 100 yards from the House, and 20 coaches, 120 yards from the House.

GUIDE BOOKS
Colour guide book, £2.50.

CATERING
Restaurant/Tea Room seating up to 100/120 people. Groups can book in advance for lunch and afternoon tea. Prices from £2.80 for afternoon tea to £8.00 for lunch (three course).

GUIDED TOURS
Tours lasting approximately 1½ hours start at 15 minute intervals. Maximum size of each party taken round is 25.

SCHOOL VISITS/CHILDREN
School visits are welcome, a guide will be provided. Cost per child, £2.50. A children's guide book can be obtained.

CONTACT

J Culverhouse
Burghley House
Stamford
Lincolnshire
PE9 3JY

Tel: (01780) 52451

Fax: (01780) 480125

LOCATION

Burghley House
is 1 mile north
of Stamford.
From London
A1, 2 hours.

Rail: Stamford Station
1½ miles.

Taxi: Merritt
(01780) 66155.

OPENING TIMES

Summer
5 April - 6 October

Daily 11.00am - 5.00pm
NB Closed 7 September

Winter
7 October - 1 April
Closed to the general public.

ADMISSION

Adult* £5.50
Child** £2.50
OAP £5.20
Groups (min 20 people)
Adult £4.40
Child* £2.50

* One child (under 14) admitted FREE per paying adult.
** Aged up to 14yrs.

CONFERENCE AND FUNCTION FACILITIES

ROOM	DIMENSIONS	CAPACITY	LAYOUT	POWER POINTS	SUITABLE FOR A/V
Great Hall	70' x 30'	180	Theatre	2	
		90	Schoolroom		
		60	U-shape		
		42	Boardroom		
		100	Dinner		
Orangery	100' x 20'	120	Buffet	6	✓

AUBOURN HALL

Tel: 01522 788270   **Fax:** 01522 788199

Lincoln, Lincolnshire LN5 9DZ

Owner: Sir Henry Nevile   **Contact:** Sir Henry Nevile

Late 16th century house with important staircase and panelled rooms.

Location: 6m SW of Lincoln.

Opening Times: Weds in Jul and Aug, 2 - 6pm. Sun 19 May. Sun 2 Jun, 30 Jun.

Admission: Adult £2.50, Senior citizen £2.00.

BELTON HOUSE PARK & GARDENS   **Tel:** 01476 566116 **Fax:** 01476 79071

Grantham, Lincolnshire NG32 2LS

Owner: The National Trust   **Contact:** The Property Manager

The crowning achievement of Restoration country house architecture, built 1685 - 88 for Sir John Brownlow, and altered by James Wyatt in the 1770s. Plasterwork ceilings by Edward Goudge and fine wood carvings of the Grinling Gibbons school. The rooms contain portraits, furniture, tapestries, oriental porcelain, silver and silver gilt. Gardens with orangery, landscaped park with lakeside walk and woodland adventure playground, and Bellmount Tower. Fine church with family monuments.

Location: 3m NE of Grantham on A607. Signed off the A1.

Opening Times: House: 30 Mar - end Oct. Wed - Sun & BH Mon (closed Good Fri), 1 - 5.30pm. Garden & Park: 11am - 5.30pm. Last adm. to house, garden and park 5pm.

Admission: House & Garden: Adult £4.50, Child £2.20, Family £11.20. Reduced rates for parties.

BELVOIR CASTLE   See Page 116 for full page entry.

BISHOPS' OLD PALACE, LINCOLN   **Tel:** 01522 527468 / 532424

Minster Yard, Lincoln, Lincolnshire LN2 1PU

Owner: English Heritage   **Contact:** The Custodian

In the shadow of Lincoln Cathedral are the remains of this medieval palace of the Bishop of Lincoln.

Location: S side of Lincoln Cathedral.

Opening Times: 1 Apr - 30 Sept: Daily 12 noon - 5pm.

Admission: Adult £1.00, Child 50p, Conc 80p.

BURGHLEY HOUSE   See Page 117 for full page entry.

FULBECK HALL

OPEN

7, 8 April, 6, 27 May, 26 Aug & daily from 30 Jun - 28 July 2 - 5pm.

Arnhem Museum at any time by prior tel or written appointment. House, Garden & Museum open for groups (20+) at any time by written appointment.

Tel: 01400 272205
Fax: 01400 272205

GRANTHAM, LINCOLNSHIRE NG32 3JW

Owner: Mrs M Fry   Contact: Mrs M Fry

Home of the Fane family since 1632 with alterations and additions by nearly every generation. Mainly 18th century house. Arnhem Museum commemorates 1st Airborne Division for whom Fulbeck Hall was HQ during the War. 11 acres of garden with much interesting new planting within the Edwardian design. Conference facilities for up to 80 people, private dining room and corporate hospitality. Georgian evenings with 18th century six course dinner a speciality. All details on request.

Location: On A607 14 m S of Lincoln. 11m N of Grantham.

Admission: House & Garden: Adult £3.50, OAPs £3.00, Child £1.50, Family £9.50. Garden: Adult £1.50, Child £1.00, Arnhem Museum: Adult £1.50, Child £1.00.

GAINSBOROUGH OLD HALL ⊞   **Tel:** 01427 612669

Parnell Street, Gainsborough, Lincolnshire DN21 2NB

Owner: English Heritage   **Contact:** The Custodian

A large medieval house with a magnificent Great Hall and suites of rooms. A collection of historic furniture and a re-created medieval kitchen are on display.

Location: In centre of Gainsborough.

Opening Times: Mon - Sat:10am - 5pm. Sun 2 - 5.30pm. Closed Suns Nov - Easter.

Admission: Adult £1.75, Child 95p, Senior Citizens 95p.

DODDINGTON HALL

OPEN

March & April Spring Garden Days (garden only) Suns 2 - 6pm

May - Sept House & Garden: Weds, Suns, & BH Mons : 2 - 6pm.

Restaurant: 12 noon on Open Days. Parties at other times by arrangement.

Tel: 01522 694308
Fax: 01522 682584

LINCOLN LN6 4RU

Owner: Mr and Mrs A Jarvis   Contact: Mr and Mrs A Jarvis

Magnificent Smythson mansion completed in 1600 and standing complete with contemporary walled gardens and Gatehouse. The Hall has an elegant Georgian interior with fine collections of porcelain, furniture, paintings and textiles representing 400 years of unbroken family occupation. Wild garden, nature trail and gift shop. Fully licensed restaurant open from 12.00 noon. Sandford Award winning schools project.

Location: 5 m W of Lincoln on the B1190, signposted off the A46 Lincoln Bypass.

Admission: House & Garden: Adult £3.70, Child £1.85. Gardens: Adult £1.85, Child 90p, Family Ticket £10.50.

GRIMSTHORPE CASTLE, PARK & GDNS

GRIMSTHORPE, BOURNE, LINCOLNSHIRE PE10 0NB

Owner: Grimsthorpe and Drummond Castle Trust Ltd   Contact: Michael Tebbutt

Tel: 01778 591205 **Fax:** 01778 591259

Home of the Willoughby de Eresby family since 1576. Examples of 13th century architecture, Tudor period & Sir John Vanbrugh's last major work. State Rooms & picture galleries contain magnificent contents and paintings. 3,000-acre 'Capability' Brown landscaped Park, with lakes, ancient woods, nature trails, shop, woodland adventure playground, red deer herd, formal & woodland gardens, unusual ornamental vegetable gardens, family cycle trail, special events programme. The Grimsthorpe Conference Centre is available for meetings of up to 70, including catering, also private parties and weddings.

Location: 4m NW of Bourne on A151, 8m E of Colsterworth roundabout off A1.

Admission: Park & Garden: Adult £2.00, Conc £1.00. Additional charge for Castle: Adult £3.00, Conc £1.50. Combined ticket or Party Rate: (20+) Adult £4.00, Conc £2.00. Special charges will operate for the CLA Game Fair 26 - 28 July and for other major special events.

Opening Times: 7 Apr - 30 Sept: Sun, Thur & Bank Hols from Easter Sun. August: Daily except Fri & Sat. Park & Gardens: 11am - 6pm. Castle: 2 - 6pm. Last admission 5pm. Guided tours for parties & schools by arrangement. Coach House and licensed Tea Room open 11am - 6pm (last orders 5pm).

GUNBY HALL

Tel: 01909 486411   **Fax:** 01909 486377

Gunby, Spilsby, Lincolnshire PE23 5SS

Owner: The National Trust   **Contact:** J D Wrisdale

A red brick house with stone dressings, built in 1700 and extended in 1870s. Within the house, there is good early 18th century wainscoting and a fine oak staircase, also English furniture and portraits by Reynolds. Also of interest is the contemporary stable block, a walled kitchen and flower garden, sweeping lawns and borders and an exhibition of Field Marshall Sir Archibald Montgomery-Massingberd's memorabilia. Gunby was reputedly Tennyson's "haunt of ancient peace". Basement now open.

Location: 2m W of Burgh Le Marsh, 8m W of Skegness, from Gunby Lane off A158.

Opening Times: Ground floor of house & garden: 30 Mar - end Sept:Wed 2 - 6pm. Last admission 5.30pm. Closed public holidays. Garden also open Thur 2 - 6pm. House and garden also open Tues, Thurs and Fri by written appointment only with J D Wrisdale at above address.

Admission: House and garden: Adult £3.20, Child £1.60, Family £8.00.
Garden only: Adult £2.00, Child £1.00, Family £5.00. No reduction for parties.
Access roads unsuitable for coaches which must park in layby at gates ¹/₂m from Hall.

HARLAXTON MANOR

Tel: 01476 64541   **Fax:** 01476 70730

Harlaxton, Grantham, Lincolnshire NG32 1AG

Owner: University of Evansville   **Contact:** Mrs F Watkins

Neo-Elizabethan house. Grandiose and imposing exterior by Anthony Salvin. Internally an architectural tour de force with a mixture of various styles and an unparalleled Cedar Staircase.

Location: 3 m W of Grantham (10 mins from A1) A607.

Opening Times: Garden: April - Sept: 11am - 5pm. House: 26 May & 7 July: 11am - 5pm. House open at other times for group tours only by appointment.

LINCOLN CATHEDRAL

Tel: 01522 544544

Lincoln, Lincolnshire LN2 1PZ

Contact: Communications Office

Medieval Gothic Cathedral of outstanding historical and architectural merit. Shop, Coffee Shop, Disabled facilities, Toilets, Schools centre. Parking nearby.

Location: At the centre of Uphill, Lincoln.

Opening Times: All year: May - Aug, 7.15am - 8pm, Sun 7.15am - 6pm. Sept - May, 7.15am - 6pm, Sun 7.15am - 5pm. Tours daily: Oct, Nov, Dec, April 11am and 2pm. May - Sept 11am, 1pm, 3pm, Jan, Feb & Mar Sats only at 11am & 2pm. Roof and Tower Tours also available. Booked tours throughout the year.

Admission: Suggested donation of Adult £2.50, Child £1, Conc £1, Annual passes £10.

TATTERSHALL CASTLE

Tel: 01526 342543

Tattershall, Lincoln, Lincolnshire LN4 4LR

Owner: The National Trust   **Contact:** The Custodian

A vast fortified tower built c.1440 for Ralph Bromwell, Lord Treasurer of England. The Castle is an important example of an early brick building, with a tower containing state apartments, rescued from dereliction and restored by Lord Curzon 1911-14. Four great chambers, with ancillary rooms, contain late Gothic fireplaces and brick vaulting. There are tapestries and information displays in turret rooms.

Location: On S side of A153, 15m NE of Sleaford; 10m SW of Horncastle.

Opening Times: 30 Mar - end Oct: Sat - Wed & BH Mon (closed Good Fri), 10.30am - 5.30pm. Nov - 22 Dec: Sat & Sun only 10.30am - 4pm. Last adm. ¹/₂ hour before closing.

Admission: Adult £2.20, Child £1.10, Family £5.50. Discount for parties.

WOOLSTHORPE MANOR

Tel: 01476 860338

23 Newton Way, Woolsthorpe-by-Colsterworth, Grantham NG33 5NR

Owner: The National Trust   **Contact:** The Custodian

This small 17th century farmhouse was the birthplace and family home of Sir Isaac Newton. Some of his major work was formulated here, during the Plague years (1665 - 66); an early edition of his Principia Mathematica, pub. 1687, is on display. The orchard includes a descendant of the famous apple tree.

Location: 7m S of Grantham, ¹/₂m NW of Colsterworth, 1m W of A1.

Opening Times: 30 Mar - end Oct: Wed to Sun & BH Mon (closed Good Fri), 1 - 5.30pm. Last admission 5pm.

Admission: Adult £2.30, Child £1.10, Family £5.70, no reduction for parties which must book in advance.

Where to Stay

For Private Accommodation and Johansens recommended Hotels, see Accommodation Section.

NORMANBY HALL

OPEN

April - Sept
Daily
1.00 - 5.00pm

Park is open all year
9am - 5pm
(later in summer)

Tel: 01724 720588
Fax: 01724 721248

SCUNTHORPE, LINCOLNSHIRE DN15 9HU

Contact: The Park Manager

Regency mansion, once the home of the Sheffield family, former owners of Buckingham Palace. Rooms decorated in period style, costume galleries, ice house, servants' trail, sculpture trail, farming museum, 350 acres of gardens and parkland, deer herds, ducks and peacocks. Special events held on Sundays throughout the season.

Location: 4 miles N of Scunthorpe off B1430.

Admission: (1995 prices) April - Sept: Mon - Fri per car £1.00, Sat £1.70, Sun and BH Mon £2.30. Oct - Mar £1.00. Coach parties £12 per coach.

SIBSEY TRADER WINDMILL

Tel: 01522 553135

Sibsey, Boston, Lincolnshire.

Owner: English Heritage   **Contact:** The Custodian

An impressive old mill built in 1877, with its machinery and six sails still intact. It can still be seen in action on occasions.

Location: ¹/₂ m W of village of Sibsey, off A16 5 m N of Boston.

Opening Times: Please telephone for further information.

Admission: (1995 prices) Adult £1.30, Child 70p, Conc £1.00.

SPECIAL EVENTS

❖	**FULBECK HALL,** Plant Fair (Primrose Plant Fairs)	**7 APRIL,**
❖	**FULBECK HALL** Antiques Fair (Galloway Antiques Fairs)	**17 – 19 MAY**
❖	**DODDINGTON HALL** Concert "Visions of Italy" – The Dante Quartet	**25 MAY**
❖	**BELVOIR CASTLE** The Siege Group (Re-enactment of Civil War Siege)	**26 – 27 MAY**
❖	**BELVOIR CASTLE** Medieval Jousting Tournament	**30 JUNE**
❖	**FULBECK HALL** Christopher Macy Concert	**6 JULY**
❖	**FULBECK HALL** Lincoln Shakespeare Company 'The Taming of the Shrew'	**12 JULY**
❖	**FULBECK HALL** Food and Fiddle Festival	**13 – 14 JULY**
❖	**BELVOIR CASTLE** Craft Fair	**13 – 14 JULY**
❖	**GRIMSTHORPE CASTLE** Antiques Fair	**13 – 14 JULY**
❖	**FULBECK HALL** Concert, 'Under the Greenwood Trio'	**20 JULY**
❖	**FULBECK HALL** Box Hedge Theatre Co 'Macbeth'	**26 JULY**
❖	**GRIMSTHORPE CASTLE** CLA Game Fair	**26 – 28 JULY**
❖	**BELVOIR CASTLE** Medieval Jousting Tournament	**28 JULY**
❖	**GRIMSTHORPE CASTLE** Craft Fair	**10 – 11 AUGUST**
❖	**DODDINGTON HALL** Concert: Georgian music for soprano and harp - Musica Fabula	**24 AUGUST**
❖	**BELVOIR CASTLE** Medieval Jousting Tournament	**25 – 26 AUGUST**

For National Trust and English Heritage Events see separate section.

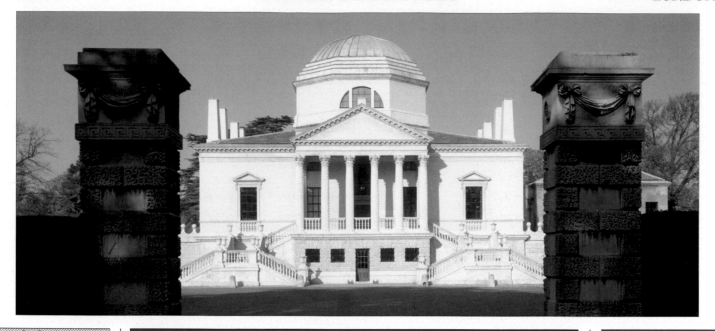

CHISWICK HOUSE
Chiswick

CHISWICK HOUSE is internationally renowned as one of the finest English buildings inspired by the architecture of Ancient Rome. Lord Burlington, who built the villa from 1725 - 1729, was inspired by similar attempts at neoclassical imitation by 16th century Italian architects. His aim was to create a fit setting for his fine collection of art and his library.

During the 19th century it was thought that Lord Burlington was just an interested owner of the House. In 1927, an American scholar proved that Burlington had actually been the architect of Chiswick.

The remarkable grounds surrounding Chiswick House have, at every turn, something to surprise and delight the visitor from the magnificent trees to the beautiful Italianate gardens with their statues, temples, urns and obelisks.

CONTACT

The Custodian
Chiswick House
Burlington Lane
Chiswick
London
W4 2RP

Tel: 0181 995 0508

LOCATION

Burlington Lane,
London W4

Rail: ¼ mile north east of Chiswick Station.

Bus: LT190,290 (Hammersmith to Richmond)

OPENING TIMES

Summer

1 April - 30 September
Daily
10.00am - 6.00pm

1 October - 31 October
Daily
10.00am - 6.00pm or dusk if earlier.

Winter

1 November - 31 March
Wed - Sun
10.00am - 4.00pm

closed for lunch 1 -2 pm

ADMISSION

Adult £2.50
Child* £1.30
OAP/Student/UB40
holder £1.90

15% discount on groups of 11 or more

* 5 - 15 years.
Under 5's free

SUITABILITY FOR OTHER EVENTS
Filming, plays, photographic shoots.

ADVICE TO COURIERS & DRIVERS
Tour leader and coach driver have free entry. 1 extra place for every 20 additional people.

FACILITIES FOR THE DISABLED
Restricted access/toilets. Wheelchair access to ground floor.

CATERING
Homemade refreshments available in the summer season.

GUIDED TOURS
Guided tours for pre-booked parties take approximately 1 hour. Free audio tours in English, French and German.

GIFT SHOP
Situated at the entrance to the house.

GUIDE BOOKS
Colour guide book £2.25.

SCHOOL VISIT/CHILDREN
Free if booked in advance. Tel: 0181 348 1268/7

KENWOOD HOUSE
Hampstead

KENWOOD, one of the treasures of London, is an idyllic country retreat on the fringes of the capital.

The house was remodelled in the 1760's by Robert Adam, the fashionable neoclassical architect. The breathtaking library or 'Great Room' is one of his finest achievements.

Kenwood is famous for the collection of paintings bequeathed to the nation by Edward Guinness, first Earl of Iveagh. Some of the world's finest artists are represented by works such as a Rembrandt *Self Portrait*. Vermeer's *Guitar Player, Mary, Countess Howe* by Gainsborough and paintings by Turner, Reynolds and many others.

As if the house and its contents were not riches enough, Kenwood stands in 112 acres of landscaped grounds on a ridge linking Hampstead and Highgate, commanding a fine prospect towards central London. The meadow walks and ornamental lake of the park designed by Humphry Repton contrast with the wilder Heath below. The open air concerts held in the summer at Kenwood have become part of London life, combining the charms of music with the serenity of the lakeside setting.

❖

CONTACT

The Custodian
The Iveagh Bequest
Kenwood
Hampstead Lane
London
NW3 7JR

Tel: 0181 348 1286

LOCATION

Hampstead Lane, NW3

Bus: London Transport 210

Rail: Finsbury Park, Golders Green

Underground: Highgate station 1 mile

OPENING TIMES

1 April - 30 September
Daily
10.00am - 6.00pm

1 - 31 October
Daily
10.00am - 6.00pm or dusk if earlier.

1 Nov - 31 March
Daily
10.00am - 4.00pm

ADMISSION

Free.

The 45 minute tour must be booked in advance. These can be given in French as well as English.

SUITABILITY FOR OTHER EVENTS
Concerts, exhibitions, filming.

EXTRA FACILITIES
The Old Kitchen is available for corporate entertainment and weddings.

ADVICE TO COURIERS & DRIVERS
No photography in the house.

FACILITIES FOR THE DISABLED
Ground floor access for wheelchairs, disabled parking in West Lodge car park.

PARKING FOR COACHES & CARS
West Lodge car park on Hampstead Lane.

CATERING
Refreshment facilities available.

GUIDED TOURS
Tours including some foreign languages available by prior arrangement. Personal stereo tours available.

GIFT SHOP
A wide selection of souvenirs are available.

GUIDE BOOKS
Souvenir guide book £3.50. Foreign language leaflets available.

SCHOOL VISIT/CHILDREN
Free when booked in advance on (0181) 348 1286/7.

THE QUEEN'S HOUSE
Greenwich

At the centre of a group of splendid historical buildings lies The Queen's House, a royal palace designed by Inigo Jones. The house has been sumptuously restored to show the vibrant colours of the decoration when occupied by the dowager queen Henrietta Maria, wife of Charles I. Built in the classical style of Palladio, the house in 1635 marked a major change for English architecture, and demonstrated new rules of proportion. The Great Hall is a 40' cube, and its ceiling is a reproduction of the original by the Gentileschis.

The vaults now house a Treasury of trophies, swords and plate marking great occasions in history. The elegant Tulip Staircase leads to rooms used for audiences which are now decorated with beautifully woven silk damask and brocatelle. A quiet loggia overlooks the royal park with a view of Wren's Observatory building with its unusual red time ball that marks Greenwich time at 1 o'clock daily.

The 3-site ticket includes admission to The Old Royal Observatory and the adjacent National Maritime Museum which is filled with stories of Britain's great naval heroes and explorers, impressive oil paintings and many fascinating exhibits. A new exhibition celebrates the life of Nelson.

A visit to all three buildings will occupy a full day or a visit can be combined with a river cruise on the Thames. The park, the oldest of the Royal Parks, is ideal for picnics and has an outstanding herbaceous border.

CONTACT

Bookings Unit
National Maritime
Museum
Romney Road
Greenwich
London
SE10 9NF

Tel: (0181) 858 4422
Fax: (0181) 312 6632

LOCATION

On the South Bank of the Thames at Greenwich. A2/A206 from London, elsewhere M25, Junct. 2 then A2.

Rail: From Charing Cross, Waterloo East or London Bridge to Maze Hill or Greenwich.

River: Cruises from Central London to Greenwich.

Air: London City Airport 4 miles.

SUITABILITY FOR OTHER EVENTS
Corporate hospitality, prestigious functions, fashion photography, filming, small balls.

EXTRA FACILITIES
Parkland and grounds. Lecture theatre in adjacent museum.

ADVICE TO COURIERS & DRIVERS
Set down only at property. Free coach parking on Blackheath. Pay and display at the Cutty Sark. Guides and drivers admitted free. Childrens groups must be pre-booked for admission to the Queen's House.

FACILITIES FOR THE DISABLED
Queens House accessible for wheelchairs (upper floor by "Stairmate"). Signed and Touch tours for groups by prior arrangement. Advisory leaflet available. Disabled groups welcome.

PARKING FOR COACHES & CARS
There is car parking for 115 cars within 100 yards and for 25 coaches within 600 yards. Coaches can set down nearby prior to parking.

CATERING
Restaurant seating for 150 in adjoining museum. Function catering from approved and recommended caterers.

GIFT SHOP
Open as the House. Located in an adjoining building.

GUIDED TOURS
Pre-book, Tel. 0181 312 6608. Cost approx £36 per group.

GUIDE BOOK
Colour guide book, £2.50. Handouts are also available in French, German, Italian, Spanish and Japanese.

SCHOOL VISITS/CHILDREN
Special educational services linked to National Curriculum available with gallery talks from experienced teaching staff. Education enquiries 0181 312 6608.

OPENING TIMES

Summer
April - September

Daily
10.00am -5.00pm

Winter
October - March

Daily
10.00am -5.00pm

Closed 24, 25, 26 December.

ADMISSION

3 SITE TICKET
  Adult £5.50
  Concessions* . . .£4.50
  Child (5 - 16yrs) . .£3.00

GROUPS
A discount of 20% for groups of 10 or more.

* Concessions for OAPs, Students, UB40, Disabled.

CONFERENCE AND FUNCTION FACILITIES

ROOM	DIMENSIONS	CAPACITY	LAYOUT	POWER POINTS	SUITABLE FOR A/V
Great Hall	40' x 40'	200*	Buffet	3	
		150*	Dinner		
Orangery		150*	Buffet	3	✓
		125*	Dinner		
* Incl. ante-rooms.					

ROYAL SOCIETY OF ARTS
John Adam Street

CONTACT

Ms Christine Bond
Conference Manager
Royal Society of Arts
8 John Adam Street
London
WC2N 6EZ

Tel: (0171) 930 5115
Fax: (0171) 321 0271

LOCATION

Rail: Near to two
mainline stations.
Charing Cross,
Waterloo.

Nearest underground:
Embankment,
Charing Cross,
Covent Garden

The House of the RSA (Royal Society for the encouragement of Arts, Manufactures and Commerce) was designed specially for the Society by Robert Adam in the early 1770's. Today the RSA's terrace of five 18th Century houses is the finest and historically most interesting remaining section of the Adam brothers' development known as the Adelphi. A complex £4,500,000 building and refurbishment programme has brought the RSA's magnificent vaults into full use for receptions and private dining.

The Great Room. The jewel in the RSA's crown is the Great Room, one of the most spectacular and delightful Lecture Halls in the country. Its walls are decorated by the celebrated sequence of allegorical paintings - *The Progress of Human Knowledge* by James Barry, together with portraits by Gainsborough and Reynolds.

A perfect setting for any gathering from Annual General Meeting to concert recital, the Great Room's unique atmosphere allows an audience from 50 to 200 to feel at ease and involved.

Benjamin Franklin Room: The classic Benjamin Franklin Room is a spacious assembly room with its chandelier and Adam fireplaces yet with a controlled ventilation system, ideal for meetings, receptions and banquets for 30-150 persons.

The Vaults: Beneath the Society's house lies the largest remaining part of the Adelphi arches. Originally built for storage and more recently used as wine cellars, the vaults have now been restored and converted to provide a unique venue for all forms of event. They feature the original 18th Century brickwork, and can be dressed to enhance product launches, parties, themed events and private exhibitions.

OPENING TIMES

Summer
Closed during the last
2 weeks of August.

9.00am - 8.00pm

Winter
Closed
24 Dec - 2 Jan 1997

9.00am - 8.00pm

ADMISSION

For Room Hire prices, please contact the RSA Conference Office direct for a brochure.

SUITABILITY FOR OTHER EVENTS
Product launches, themed parties, corporate announcements, film previews, dinner dances, private concerts, exhibitions.

EXTRA FACILITIES
Lectures can be arranged on the history of the house in the Great Room. There is a Steinway Baby Grand piano, which is available for private recitals in the Great Room.

ADVICE TO COURIERS AND DRIVERS
All visits are by prior arrangement. Coaches may only set down and pick up on John Adam Street or the Strand.

FACILITIES FOR THE DISABLED
There is wheel chair access to all the main rooms of the house via a lift. A disabled cloakroom is located on the 1st floor. Unfortunately Westminster Council does not permit disabled parking in restricted parking zones.

PARKING FOR COACHES AND CARS
The closest Coach parking area is at Vauxhall. Meters in John Adam Street. Car parks in Savoy Place and St Martin's Lane.

CATERING
Catering can be arranged for groups in a private room. Rooms may be hired for lunches, dinners, receptions. We regret we do not have facilities for individuals.

GUIDED TOURS
Tours of the house for groups of up to 25 people may be arranged in advance. All visitors to the house must pre-book.

CONFERENCE AND FUNCTION FACILITIES

ROOM	DIMENSIONS	CAPACITY	LAYOUT	POWER POINTS	SUITABLE FOR A/V
Great Room	42' x 36'	200	Theatre	✓	✓
Durham St Auditorium	36' x 30'	60	Theatre	✓	✓
B. Franklin Room	42' x 36'	150	Reception	✓	✓
Tavern Room	40' x 17'	70	Reception	✓	✓
Folkestone Room	20' x 20'	30	Reception	✓	✓
Gallery	40' x 20'		Reception	✓	✓
THE VAULTS					
Vault 1	55' x 28'	100	Reception	✓	✓
Vault 2	36' x 18'	50	Reception	✓	✓
Vault 3	20' x 18'	30	Reception	✓	✓
Vault 4	37' x 11'	75	Reception	✓	✓

SPENCER HOUSE
St. James's Place

SPENCER HOUSE, built 1756-66 for the 1st Earl Spencer, an ancestor of Her Royal Highness The Princess of Wales, is London's finest surviving 18th century town house. The magnificent private palace has regained the full splendour of its late 18th century appearance, after a painstaking ten-year restoration programme.

Designed by John Vardy and James 'Athenian' Stuart, the nine state rooms are amongst the first neo-classical interiors in Europe. Vardy's Palm Room, with its spectacular screen of gilded palm trees and arched fronds, is a unique Palladian setpiece, while the elegant mural decorations of Stuart's Painted Room reflect the 18th century passion for classical Greece and Rome. Stuart's superb gilded furniture has been returned to its original location in the Painted Room by courtesy of the V&A and English Heritage. Visitors can also see a fine collection of 18th century paintings and furniture, specially assembled for the house, including five major Benjamin West paintings, graciously lent by Her Majesty The Queen.

The state rooms are open to the public for viewing on Sundays. They are also available on a limited number of occasions each year for private and corporate entertaining during the rest of the week.

❖

CONTACT

Stephen Jones
Director
Spencer House
27 St James's Place
London
SW1A 1NR

Tel: 0171 409 0526

Fax: 0171 493 5765

LOCATION

Central London:
off St James's Street,
overlooking Green Park.

Nearest underground:
Green Park.

SUITABILITY FOR OTHER EVENTS
Cocktail receptions, lunches, dinners, board meetings, theatre style meetings, contract signings, wedding receptions, private parties.

ADVICE TO COURIERS & DRIVERS
No children under 10. No dogs admitted. No photography inside House.

FACILITIES FOR THE DISABLED
Ramps, lifts and accessible toilets available.

PARKING FOR COACHES & CARS
No parking facilities. Coaches can drop off at door.

CATERING
Excellent in-house catering team for private and corporate events. However, no catering for Sunday visitors.

GUIDE BOOKS
Comprehensive colour guide book £2.95.

GUIDED TOURS
All visits are by guided tour.

OPENING TIMES

All Year
Except Jan and Aug
Sundays
11.30am - 5.30pm.

Last tour 4.45pm.

Tours begin approx every 15 minutes and last 1 hour. Maximum number on each tour is 15.

Information:
0171 499 8620
Tues - Fri
10am - 1pm only.

Open for corporate hospitality except during January and August.

ADMISSION

To end March 1996

Adult £6.00
Concessions* . . . £5.00

* Students, Friends of V&A, Tate Gallery and Royal Academy (all with cards), children under 16 (no under 10's admitted).

Prices include guided tour.

CONFERENCE AND FUNCTION FACILITIES

Cocktail receptions for up to 400 (500 if using the Terrace). Lunches and dinners (from 2 - 130). Board meetings (max 40), theatre style meetings (max 100).

THE BANQUETING HOUSE
Tel: 0171 930 4179   **Fax:** 0171 930 8268

Whitehall, London SW1A 2ER
Owner: Historic Royal Palaces   **Contact:** Ms L Kennedy
Once part of the Great Palace of Whitehall, designed by Inigo Jones for James I.
Location: Whitehall.
Opening Times: Mon - Sat: 10am - 5pm. Closed on public hols.
Admission: Adult £3.00, Child £2.00, Conc £2.25, Groups 10% discount.

BLEWCOAT SCHOOL
Tel: 0171 222 2877

23 Caxton Street, Westminster, London SW1H 0PY
Owner: The National Trust   **Contact:** The Administrator
Built in 1709 at the expense of William Green, a local brewer, to provide an education for poor children. The building was used as a school until 1926, and is now a National Trust Shop.
Location: Near the junction with Buckingham Gate.
Opening Times: All year: Mon - Fri, 10am - 5.30pm; late-night shopping Thurs until 7pm; also 30 Nov, 7 & 14 Dec: 11am - 4.30pm. Closed BH Mon, Good Fri, 25 Dec - 1 Jan.

BRITISH ARCHITECTURAL LIBRARY
Tel: 0171 580 5533   **Fax:** 0171 486 3797

RIBA Drawings Collections and Heinz Gallery ~ 21 Portman Square, London W1H 9HF
Owner: Royal Institute of British Architects   **Contact:** The Curator
Changing architectural exhibitions throughout the year. Collection of 500,000 architectural drawings from c.1500 onwards.
Location: 21 Portman Square, London.
Opening Times: Exhibitions: Weekdays 11am - 5pm, Saturdays 10am - 1pm. The Study Collection seen by appointment.
Admission: Exhibitions free. Fee charged to consult drawings.

BUCKINGHAM PALACE
Tel: 0171 930 4832

Buckingham Palace Road, London SW1A 1AA
Owner: H M The Queen
Official London residence of H M The Queen. Bought for George III in 1762 and extensively remodelled by John Nash in the 1820s for George IV. The east wing, seen from The Mall was built to the designs of Edward Blore in 1846 and the whole facade was refaced by Sir Aston Webb in 1912. The state apartments shown are used mainly for official events.
Location: Central London
Opening Times: 8 Aug - 30 Sept: 9.30am - 5.30pm. Ticket office: 9am, last adm: 4.30pm.
Admission: State Apartments: Adult £8.50, Age 60+ £6.00, Child under 17 £4.50.

BURGH HOUSE
Tel: 0171 431 0144 / Buttery: 0171 431 2516

New End Square, Hampstead, London NW3 1LT
Owner: London Borough of Camden   **Contact:** Ms Pauline Pleasance
A Grade I listed building of 1703 in the heart of old Hampstead with original panelled rooms, "barley sugar" staircase banisters and a Music Room. Home of the Hampstead Museum, permanent and changing exhibitions. Terraced garden and licensed Basement Buttery. Regular programme of concerts, art exhibitions, and meetings.
Receptions, seminars and conferences. Licensed for weddings. Rooms for hire.
Location: New End Square, East of Hampstead underground station.
Opening Times: All year: Wed - Sun 12 noon - 5pm. Good Friday & Bank Holiday Mondays 2 - 5pm. Closed Christmas week and New Year. (Groups by Arrangement). Buttery: Wed - Sun 11am - 5.30pm. Bank Holidays 2 - 5.30pm. Closed Christmas fortnight.
Admission: Free.

CARLYLE'S HOUSE
Tel: 0171 352 7087

24 Cheyne Row, Chelsea, London SW3 5HL
Owner: The National Trust   **Contact:** The Custodian
This 18th century town house was the home of Thomas and Jane Carlyle from 1834 until their deaths. It contains furniture, books, personal relics and portraits.
Location: Off Cheyne Walk, between Battersea and Albert Bridges on Chelsea Embankment, or off Oakley Street.
Opening Times: 30 Mar - end Oct: Wed to Sun & BH Mon, 11am - 5pm. Closed Good Fri. Last admission 4.30pm.
Admission: £3.00, no reduction for students or parties, which must book in advance.

THE CHELSEA PHYSIC GARDEN
Tel: 0171 352 5646   **Fax:** 0171 376 3910

66 Royal Hospital Road, London SW3 4HS
Contact: Ms S Minter
The second oldest botanic garden in Britain, founded in 1673. For many years these 4 acres of peace and quiet with many rare and unusual plants was known only to a few. Specialists in medicinal plants, tender species and the history of plant introductions.
Location: Off embankment between Chelsea & Albert Bridges. Entrance - Swan Walk.
Opening Times: Snowdrop opening & Winter Festival: Suns 4 & 11 Feb, 11am - 3.00pm. 7 Apr - 27 Oct; Wed 2 - 5pm. Sun 2 - 6pm. 20 - 24 May (Chelsea Flower Show) and 3 - 7 Jun (Chelsea Festival Weeks), 12 noon - 5pm.
Admission: Adult £3.50, Child under 16, unemployed & students £1.80. School parties needing education office and groups (20+) need to pre-book.

CHISWICK HOUSE
See Page 120 for full page entry.

COLLEGE OF ARMS
Tel: 0171 248 2762

Queen Victoria Street, London EC4V 4BT
Owner: Corp. of the Kings, Heralds & Pursuivants of Arms   **Contact:** The Officer in Waiting
Mansion built in 1670s to house the English Officers of Arms and their records, and the panelled Earl Marshal's Court. Shop - books, souvenirs.
Location: On N side of Queen Victoria Street, S of St Paul's Cathedral.
Opening Times: Earl Marshal's Court only; open all the year (except Public holidays & on State & special occasions) Mon - Fri 10.00am - 4.00pm. Group visits (up to 10) by arrangement only. Record Room: open for tours (groups of up to 20) by special arrangement in advance with the Office in Waiting.
Admission: Free (parties by negotiation). No coaches, parking, indoor photography or dogs.

THE DICKENS HOUSE MUSEUM

48 Doughty Street, London SW1W 9TR
Contact: Price Haslan & Associates Ltd
Charles Dickens lived here as a young man, and his drawing room has been reconstructed. Numerous personal mementoes are on view.
Location: Doughty Street, London.
Opening Times: Sat, 10am - 5pm (last admission 4.30pm). Closed Sun and BH.
Admission: Adult £3.00, Student £2.00, Senior citizen £1.00, Child £1.00, Families £6.00.

DR JOHNSON'S HOUSE
Tel: 0171 353 3745

17 Gough Square, London EC4A 3DE
Owner: The Trustees   **Contact:** Mrs B Gathergood
Fine 18th century house, once home to Dr Samuel Johnson, the celebrated literary figure, famous for his English dictionary.
Location: Gough Square, London.
Opening Times: Oct - Apr: Mon - Sat, 11am - 5pm. May - Sept: Mon - Sat, 11am - 5.30pm.
Admission: Adult £3.00, Child over 10 £1.00, Child under 10 free, Conc £2.00.

ELTHAM PALACE
Tel: 0181 348 1286

London.
Owner: English Heritage   **Contact:** The London Regional Office
The most delightful feature of this 13th century Royal Palace is the Great Hall with its splendid roof.
Location: 3/4 m N of A20 off Court Yard, SE9. Train Stations: Eltham or Mottingham
Opening Times: Telephone for details.

FENTON HOUSE

OPEN

March
Sat & Sun only
2.00 - 5.00pm

Apr - end Oct
Sat, Sun &
Bank Holiday Mons
11.00am - 5.30pm

Wed - Fri : 2 - 5.30pm

Last admissions
half an hour
before closing.

Tel: 0171 435 3471

WINDMILL HILL, HAMPSTEAD, LONDON NW3 6RT
Owner: The National Trust   Contact: The Custodian
A late 17th century house with an outstanding collection of porcelain and early keyboard instruments. The large walled garden is sometimes used for open air plays.
Location: Visitors' entrance on west side of Hampstead Grove. Hampstead underground station 300 yds.
Admission: Adult £3.60, Child £1.80, Family Ticket £9.00.

FREUD MUSEUM

Tel: 0171 435 2002 **Fax:** 0171 431 5452

20 Maresfield Gardens, London NW3 5SX

Contact: Ms E Davies

The Freud Museum was the home of Sigmund Freud after he escaped the Nazi annexation of Austria. The house retains its domestic atmosphere and has the character of turn of the century Vienna. The centrepiece is Freud's study which has been preserved intact, containing his remarkable collection of antiquities: Egyptian, Greek, Roman, Oriental and his large library. The Freuds brought all their furniture and household effects to London; fine Biedermeier, and 19th century Austrian painted furniture. The most famous item is Freud's psychoanalytic couch, where his patients reclined. Fine oriental rugs cover the floor and tables. Videos are shown of the Freud family in Vienna, Paris and London.
Location: Maresfield Gardens, London.
Opening Times: Wed - Sun (inc) 12 noon - 5pm.
Admission: Adult £3.00, Under 12 free, Conc £1.50, Coach parties by appointment.

THE GEFFRYE MUSEUM

Tel: 0171 739 9893 **Fax:** 0171 729 5647

Kingsland Road, London E2 8EA

Owner: Independent Charitable Trust   **Contact:** Ms Christine Lalumia

The Geffrye is one of London's most friendly and enjoyable museums, set in elegant grade I listed 18th century almshouses with delightful gardens, just north of the city. It presents the changing style of the the English domestic interior from 1600 to 1950 through a series of period rooms. Walled herb garden open April to October. Innovative programme of lectures and activities. Shop and coffee bar.
Location: Buses: 22A, 22B, 149, 243, 67. Underground: Liverpool St. or Old St. Parking: available in neighbouring streets.
Opening Times: Tues - Saturday 10am - 5pm. Sundays and Bank Holiday Mondays 2 - 5pm. Closed Mondays (except Bank Hols) Good Friday, Christmas Eve, Christmas Day Boxing Day, New Years Day.
Admission: Free.

GEORGE INN

Tel: 0171 407 2056

77 Borough High Street, Southwark, London SE1

Owner: The National Trust

The only remaining galleried inn in London, famous as a coaching inn in the 18th and 19th centuries, and mentioned by Dickens in Little Dorrit. The George Inn is leased to and run by Whitbread Plc as a public house.
Location: On E side of Borough High Street, near London Bridge station.
Opening Times: During licensing hours.

GUNNERSBURY PARK MUSEUM

OPEN

Apr - Oct:
Daily: 1 - 5pm.
(6pm weekends
and BH's)

Nov - Mar:
Daily : 1 - 4pm.
Victorian Kitchens
summer weekends
only. Closed
Christmas Eve,
Christmas Day and
Boxing Day.
Park:
open dawn - dusk.

Tel: 0181 992 1612
Fax: 0181 752 0686

GUNNERSBURY PARK, LONDON W3 8LQ

Owner: London Boroughs of Ealing & Hounslow   *Contact: Ms S Levitt*

Built in 1802 and refurbished by Sydney Smirke for the Rothschild family. Their attractive park, splendid interiors and original kitchens survive. Now a social history museum with regularly changing displays.
Location: Acton Town underground station. Junction of A4, M4 North Circular.
Admission: Free, but small charge for guided tours and some types of school group visits.

HOGARTH'S HOUSE

**HOGARTH LANE,
GREAT WEST ROAD,
CHISWICK, LONDON W4 2QN**
Owner: London Borough of Hounslow
Contact: Allan Downend

Tel: 0181 994 6757

This late 17th century house was the country home of William Hogarth, the famous painter, engraver, satirist and social reformer between 1749 and his death in 1764. It contains a collection of his engravings and prints and the house is surrounded by an extensive garden which is in the process of restoration. The gallery of prints shows the development of Hogarth's genius.

Location: 100 yds. west of Hogarth roundabout on the Great West Road - junction of Burlington Lane. Car park in named spaces in Axis Business Centre behind house.
Admission: Free.

OPEN
April - September: Mon - Sat 11am - 6pm
Sundays 2 - 6pm
October - March: Mon - Sat 11am - 4pm
Sundays 2 - 4pm
Closed Tuesdays

JEWEL TOWER

Tel: 0171 222 2219

Abingdon Street, Westminster, London SW1P 3JY
Owner: English Heritage   **Contact:** The Custodian
Built c. 1365 to house the personal treasure of Edward III and formerly part of the Palace of Westminster. It was used to house valuables which formed part of the King's 'wardrobe', and subsequently used as a storehouse and government office. There is a new exhibition, 'Parliament Past and Present'.
Location: Opposite S end of Houses of Parliament (Victoria Tower).
Opening Times: 1 Apr - 30 Sept: Daily 10am - 6pm. 1 Oct - 31 Oct: Daily 10am - 6pm or dusk if earlier. 1 Nov - 31 Mar: Daily 10am - 4pm. Closed 1 - 2pm for lunch.
Admission: Adult £1.50, Child 80p, Conc £1.10.

KEATS HOUSE

Tel: 0171 435 2062 **Fax:** 0171 431 9293

Keats Grove, Hampstead, London NW3 2RR
Owner: London Borough of Camden   **Contact:** Mrs C M Gee
Regency home of the poet John Keats (1795 - 1821).
Location: Hampstead, NW3. Nearest underground: Belsize Park.
Opening Times: Apr - Oct: Mon - Fri, 10am - 1pm & 2 - 6pm. Sat, 10am - 1pm & 2 - 5pm. Sun & Bank Hols 2 - 5pm. Nov - Mar: Mon - Fri, 1 - 5pm, Sat, 10am - 1pm & 2 - 5pm. Sun, 2 - 5pm. Closed Xmas Eve, Xmas Day, Boxing Day, New Year's Day, Good Fri, Easter Sat and May Day.
Admission: Free.

KENWOOD HOUSE

See Page 121 for full page entry.

LEIGHTON HOUSE MUSEUM

Tel: 0171 602 3316 **Fax:** 0171 371 2467

12 Holland Park Road, Kensington, London W14 8LZ
Owner: Royal Borough of Kensington and Chelsea   **Contact:** Miss J Findlater
Opulent and exotic example of High Victorian taste, built for Frederic, Lord Leighton, President of the Royal Academy. The astounding Arab Hall is the centrepiece of the House, evoking the world of the Arabian Nights. Paintings by Leighton and other Victorian artists. In 1996, we will celebrate the centenary of the death of Lord Leighton; you are invited to look behind the canvas and discover the man. As you move through the house, the pieces of the jigsaw that was Leighton's life will gradually fall into place, conjured by an extraordinary theatrical interpretation.
Location: Kensington, W14 8LZ (off Kensington High Street).
Opening Times: Mon - Sat: 11am - 5.30pm. Closed Sundays and Bank Holidays.
Admission: Free. During the centenary celebrations 16th Feb - 21 Apr. an entrance fee of £3.50 will be charged. Pre-booking is essential, 0171 603 9115.

LINDSEY HOUSE

Tel: 01494 528051

99 -100 Cheyne Walk, London SW10
Owner: The National Trust   **Contact:** Mrs A Morgan
Part of Lindsey House was built in 1674 on the site of Sir Thomas More's garden, overlooking the River Thames. It has one of the finest 17th century exteriors in London.
Location: On Cheyne Walk, W of Battersea Bridge near junction with Milman's Street on Chelsea Embankment.
Opening Times: By written appointment only. Please telephone for details.

MARBLE HILL HOUSE

OPEN

1 Apr - 30 Sept.
10am - 6pm

1 - 31 Oct
10am - 6pm
or dusk if earlier.

1 Nov - 31 Mar
Wed - Sun
10am - 4pm
(closed for
lunch 1 - 2pm)

Tel: 0181 892 5115

RICHMOND ROAD, TWICKENHAM, MIDDLESEX TW1 2NL

Owner: *English Heritage*   **Contact:** *Mr Des Whittle*

This beautiful villa beside the Thames was built in 1724-29 for Henrietta Howard, mistress of George II. Here she entertained many of the poets and wits of the Augustan age including Alexander Pope and Horace Walpole. The perfect proportions of the Villa were inspired by the work of the 16th century Italian architect Palladio. Today, the house contains an important collection of paintings and furniture, including some pieces commissioned for the villa when it was built.

Location: Richmond Road, Twickenham.

Admission: Adult £2.50, Child £1.30, Conc. £1.90.

MUSEUM OF GARDEN HISTORY

Tel: 0171 261 1891   **Fax:** 0171 401 8869

Lambeth Palace Road, Lambeth, London SE1 7LB

Owner: The Tradescant Trust   **Contact:** Mrs R Nicholson

Replica 17th century garden. Exhibits on all aspects of gardening history.

Location: Next to Lambeth Palace.

Opening Times: Mon - Fri, 10.30am - 4pm. Sat closed. Sun 10.30am - 5pm.

Admission: Free. Groups by appointment.

THE MUSEUM OF THE ORDER OF ST. JOHN

**ST. JOHN'S GATE,
LONDON EC1M 4DA**

Owner: *The Order of St. John*
Contact: *Pamela Willis*

Tel: 0171 253 6644
Fax: 0171 336 0587

Headquarters of the Order of St John in England, the 16th century Gatehouse contains the most comprehensive collection of items relating to the Knights Hospitaller. Together with the nearby Priory Church and 12th century Crypt it now forms the headquarters of the modern Order whose charitable foundations include St John Ambulance and the Ophthalmic Hospital in Jerusalem. The collection includes Maltese silver, furniture, paintings and pharmacy jars.

Location: St. John's Lane, Clerkenwell. Nearest underground: Farringdon, Barbican

Admission: Free but donations are welcome.

OPEN

Mon - Fri: 10am - 5pm. Sats: 10am - 4pm
Closed Bank Holidays
Tours: Tues, Fri & Sats at 11am, 2.30pm
Ref. Library: Open by appointment.

PITSHANGER MANOR MUSEUM

Tel: 0181 567 1227   **Fax:** 0181 567 0595

Mattock Lane, Ealing, London W5 5EQ

Owner: London Borough of Ealing   **Contact:** Ms N Sohal

Built by the architect Sir John Soane as his family home.

Location: Mattock Lane, London.

Opening Times: Tues - Sat: 10am - 5pm. Times may vary, please ring for details. Closed Christmas, New Year and Easter.

Admission: Free. Groups by arrangement only.

THE QUEEN'S GALLERY

Tel: 0171 839 1377

Buckingham Palace, London SW1A 1AA

Owner: HM The Queen   **Contact:** The Visitor Office

Leonardo da Vinci: One hundred drawings from the Collection of Her Majesty The Queen.

Location: Buckingham Palace

Opening Times: 1 Mar 1996 - 12 Jan 1997: Daily, 9.30am - 4.30pm. Last admission 4pm. Closed 5 Apr, 25 & 26 Dec.

Admission: Adult £3.50, OAP £2.50, Child (under 17) £2.00.

THE QUEEN'S HOUSE

See Page 122 for full page entry.

THE RANGER'S HOUSE

OPEN

1 Apr - 30 Sept: 10am - 6pm
1 - 31 Oct: 10am - 6pm or dusk if earlier.
1 Nov - 31 Mar: Wed - Sun 10am - 4pm
(closed for lunch 1 - 2pm)

**CHESTERFIELD WALK,
BLACKHEATH, LONDON
SE10 8QX**

Tel: 0181 853 0035

Owner: *English Heritage*
Contact: *The Custodian*

A handsome, red-brick villa which lies between two of London's great open spaces, Greenwich Park and Blackheath. The house was built for a successful seafarer, Admiral Francis Hosier around 1700 who sited the house within view of the Thames estuary and used to boast that the grand bow-windowed gallery commanded the three finest views in the world. Today the Ranger's House is home to the Suffolk collection of paintings and the Dolmetsch Collection of musical instruments.

Location: Chesterfield Walk, Blackheath, London SE10

Admission: Adult £2.50, Child £1.30, Conc. £1.90.

THE ROYAL MEWS

Tel: 0171 839 1377

Buckingham Palace, London SW1A 1AA

Owner: HM The Queen   **Contact:** The Visitor Officer

Location: Buckingham Palace

Opening Times: 1 Jan - 25 Mar: Wed. 26 Mar - 4 Aug: Tue - Thur. 5 Aug - 3 Oct: Mon - Thurs. 4 Oct - 31 Dec: Wed. All days 12 noon - 4pm except 5 Aug - 3 Oct when 10.30am - 4.30pm. Closed 25 Dec.

Admission: Adult £3.50, OAP £2.50, Child (under 17) £2.00.

ROYAL SOCIETY OF ARTS

See Page 123 for full page entry.

SIR JOHN SOANE'S MUSEUM

Tel: 0171 4052107   **Fax:** 0171 8313957

13 Lincoln's Inn Fields, London WC2A 3BP

Owner: Trustees of Sir John Soane's Museum   **Contact:** Ms S Palmer

The celebrated architect Sir John Soane built this in 1812 as his own house. It now contains his collection of antiquities, sculpture and paintings. included among which are the Rake's Progress paintings by William Hogarth.

Location: Central London.

Opening Times: Tues - Sat, 10am - 5pm. 6pm - 9.pm on first Tues of the month. Closed BHs And Christmas Eve.

Admission: Free. Groups must book.

SOUTHSIDE HOUSE

Tel: 0181 947 2491

Wimbledon Common, London SW19 4RJ

Owner: The Pennington-Mellor-Munthe Charity Trust   **Contact:** The Administrator

One of the few houses open only during the winter. Late 17th and 18th century house with intriguing contents and collections.

Location: Opposite 'Crooked Billet' Inn on Wimbledon Common.

Opening Times: 1 Oct - 31 May (closed Xmas), BH Mons, Tues, Thurs, Sat. 2 - 4pm. Guided tours at 2pm, 3pm & 4pm lasting approx 1½hrs. Groups upon written application.

Admission: Adult £5.00, Child (11 - 18 years) £3.00.

SOUTHWARK CATHEDRAL

Tel: 0171 407 3708   **Fax:** 0171 357 7389

Southwark, London SE1 9DA

Contact: Ms K Johnson

Location: South side of London Bridge.
Opening Times: Daily 8.30am - 6pm. Sunday services: 9am, 11am and 3pm.
Weekday services: 8am, 12.30pm, 12.45pm and 5.30pm.
Admission: Donation.

SPENCER HOUSE

See Page 124 for full page entry.

ST GEORGE'S CATHEDRAL

Tel: 0171 928 5256

London SE1 7HY

Contact: Rev J P Pannett

Neo-Gothic rebuilt Pugin Cathedral bombed during the last war and rebuilt by Romily Craze in 1958.
Location: Opposite Imperial War Museum.
Opening Times: 8am - 8pm every day, except Bank Hols.

ST PAUL'S CATHEDRAL

Tel: 0171 236 4128   **Fax:** 0171 248 3104

St Paul's Chapter House, St Paul's Churchyard, London EC4M 8AD

Contact: The Registrar

This is Christopher Wren's masterpiece, begun in 1675 completed in 1710. Attractions include the Crypt where Wren & Nelson are buried and the galleries.
Location: City of London. Nearest underground: St Paul's.
Opening Times: Open for Matins 7.30am, Holy Communion 8am & 12.30pm. Thereafter 8.30am onwards. Open until 4pm. Evensong 5pm. Open on Suns 9am - 5pm. No touring during services.
Admission: Mon - Sat Adult £3.50, Child £2.00, Conc £3.00, Family (2+2) £9.00, Groups (10+) £3.00. Galleries extra.

SUTTON HOUSE 🍂

Tel: 0181 9862264

2 - 4 Homerton High Street, Hackney, London E9 6JQ
Owner: The National Trust   **Contact:** The Administrator
A rare example of a Tudor red-brick house, built in 1535 by Sir Rafe Sadleir, Principal Secretary of State for Henry VIII, with 18th century alterations and later additions. Recent restoration has revealed many 16th century details, even in rooms of later periods. Notable features include original linenfold panelling and 17th century wall paintings.
Location: At the corner of Isabella Road and Homerton High Street.
Opening Times: 4 Feb - 27 Nov & 5 Feb (1997): Wed, Sun & BH Mon 11.30am - 5.30pm (closed Good Fri). Last adm. 5pm. Cafe Bar: 16 Jan - 21 Dec: Wed - Fri 11am - 11pm, Sat & Sun 11am - 5pm.
Admission: £1.60. Group visits by prior arrangement.

TOWER BRIDGE

Tel: 0171 378 1928 (24hr)   **Fax:** 0171 357 7935

London SE1 2UP
Owner: Corporation of London   **Contact:** Amanda Moring
Explore the interior of this unique working bridge. New exhibition explains the bridge's history and how it operates, using modern audio visual techniques and animatronic characters from the bridge's past. Panoramic high walkways give spectacular views over London. The bridge may be hired for private receptions and other events.
Location: Adjacent to Tower of London, nearest Underground Tower Hill, London Bridge.
Opening Times: Nov - Mar: 9.30am - 6pm. Apr - Oct: 10am - 6.30pm.
Last entry 1¼ hours before closing. Closed Good Friday, 24 - 26 Dec, 1 Jan.
Admission: Adult £5.00, Student/Child (5-15) £3.50, OAP (60+) £3.50, Family (2+2) £14.00.

THE WALLACE COLLECTION

Tel: 0171 935 0687   **Fax:** 0171 224 2155

Hertford House, Manchester Square, London W1M 6BN
Owner: National Museum   **Contact:** Ms B King
Permanent collection of European paintings, miniatures and sculpture. French 18th century furniture and Sèvres porcelain. Home of Frans Hals, "Laughing Cavalier" - in elegant 18th century town house. Plus a magnificent collection of arms and armour.
Location: Behind Selfridges, Oxford Street.
Opening Times: Mon - Sat: 10am - 5pm. Sun 2 - 5.pm. Closed 24 - 26 Dec, New Year's Day, Good Friday, May Day.
Admission: Free.

WESTMINSTER ABBEY

Tel: 0171 222 5152   **Fax:** 0171 233 2072

London SW1P 3PA

Contact: Miss E St John Smith

Location: Westminster.
Opening Times: Royal Chapels: Mon - Fri, 9am - 4.45pm (last adm. 3.45pm),
Sat, 9am - 2.45pm (last adm.1.45pm) and 3.45 - 5.45pm.
Admission: Royal Chapels: Adult £4.00, Child (under 16) £1.00, Student & OAP £2.00.

WESTMINSTER ABBEY Chapter House, Pyx Chamber & Abbey Museum 🏛

East Cloisters, Westminster Abbey, London SW1P 3PE   **Tel:** 0171 222 5897
Owner: English Heritage   **Contact:** The Custodian
The Chapter House, built by the royal masons in 1250 and faithfully restored in the 19th century, contains some of the finest examples of medieval English sculpture to be seen. The building is octagonal, with a central column, and still has its original floor of glazed tiles. Its uses have varied, but in the 14th century it was used as a meeting place for the Benedictine monks of the abbey, and for Members of Parliament. The 11th century Pyx Chamber now houses the Abbey treasures, reflecting its use as the strongroom of the exchequer from the 14th to 19th centuries. The Abbey museum contains medieval Royal effigies.
Location: Approach either through the Abbey or through Dean's Yard and the cloister.
Opening Times: 1 Apr - 30 Sept. 10am - 6pm. 1 - 31 Oct 10am - 6pm or dusk if earlier. 1 Nov - 31 Mar 10am - 4pm
Admission: Adult £2.50, Child £1.30, Conc £1.90.

WESTMINSTER CATHEDRAL

Tel: 0171 798 9055   **Fax:** 0171 798 9090

Victoria, London SW1P 1QW

Contact: Monsignor G Stack

The Roman Catholic Cathedral of the Archbishop of Westminster. Spectacular building in the Byzantine style, designed by J F Bentley, opened in 1903, famous for its mosaics, marble and music. Westminster Cathedral celebrated the centenary of its foundation in 1995.
Location: On Victoria Street, between Victoria Station and Westminster Abbey.
Opening Times: Summer: 7am - 8pm. Winter: 7am - 7pm, Sunday Mass: 7am, 8am, 9am, 10.30am, 12 noon, 5pm and 7pm. Vespers 3.30pm. Weekday Mass: 7am, 8am, 8.30am, 9am, 10.30am, 12.30pm, 1.05pm & 5.30pm.
Confession: weekday, 11.30am - 6pm. Weekends: 9am - 6.30pm.

WILLIAM MORRIS GALLERY

Tel: 0181 527 3782

Forest Road, Walthamstow, London E17 4PP
Owner: London Borough of Waltham Forest   **Contact:** Ms Nora Gillow
Location: 15 mins walk from Walthamstow tube (Victoria line). 5 - 10 mins from M11/A406.
Opening Times: Tues - Sat and first Sun each month, 10am - 1pm and 2 - 5pm.
Admission: Admission is free for all visitors but a charge is made for guided tours which must be booked in advance.

Spencer House, Dining Room.

SPECIAL EVENTS

❖ **SPENCER HOUSE**   **AUTUMN 1996**
Craftsman Day. For one Sunday only 11.00am - 5.30 pm (precise date to be announced - telephone 0171 499 8620 from July 1996). The people behind the ten year restoration of Spencer House will be at the house to discuss and demonstrate their skills to members of the public. Over 100 people have been involved in the restoration over the last 10 years and those present on the Craftsman Day will include the wood and marble carvers, the decorators, painters and gilders, carpet designers, upholsterers and silk weavers. Admission: Adults £6.00, all concessions £5.00.

For National Trust and English Heritage Events see separate section.

LIVERPOOL CATHEDRAL

Tel: 0151 709 6271   **Fax:** 0151 709 1112

Liverpool, Merseyside L1 7AZ
Owner: The Dean and Chapter   **Contact:** Canon Noel Vincent
Sir Giles Gilbert Scott's greatest creation. Built this century from local sandstone with superb glass and stonework, it is the largest Cathedral in Britain with a fine musical tradition, a tower offering panoramic views and award-winning refectory.
Location: Central Liverpool, 1/2m from Lime Street Station.
Opening Times: 8am - 6pm. Sunday services: 8am, 10.30am, 3pm, 4pm. Weekdays: 8am and 5.30pm. Saturdays: 8am and 3pm.
Admission: Donation.

LIVERPOOL CATHEDRAL CHURCH OF CHRIST THE KING

Tel: 0151 709 9222   **Fax:** 0151 708 7274

Liverpool, Merseyside L3 5TQ
Owner: Roman Catholic Archdiocese of Liverpool   **Contact:** Rt Rev P Cookson
Modern circular cathedral with spectacular glass by John Piper and numerous modern works of art. Extensive earlier crypt by Lutyens. Grade II* listed.
Location: Central Liverpool, 1/4m E of Lime Street Station.
Opening Times: 8am - 6pm (closes 5.00pm Sun in Winter). Sun services: 8.30am, 10am, 11am, 3pm and 7pm. Weekday services: 8am, 12.15pm, 5.15pm and 5.45pm. Sat 9.00pm and 6.30pm.
Admission: Donation.

MEOLS HALL

Tel: 01704 28326   **Fax:** 01704 507185

Churchtown, Southport, Merseyside PR9 7LZ
Owner: Robert Hesketh Esq   **Contact:** Pamela Whelan
17th century house with subsequent additions. Interesting collection of pictures and furniture. Newly refurbished Tithe Barn for hire complete with fully fitted kitchen and amenities to entertain in the region of 120 people.
Location: 3m N of Southport town centre.
Opening Times: August: Daily 2 - 5pm.
Admission: Adult £3.00, Child £1.00.

PORT SUNLIGHT HERITAGE CENTRE

Tel: 0151 6446466   **Fax:** 0151 6458973

95 Greendale Road, Port Sunlight, Merseyside L62 4XE
Contact: Information Officer
Port Sunlight is a picturesque 19th century garden village on the Wirral, built by William Hesketh Lever for the Workers in his soap factory.
Location: Follow signs from junction 4 or 5/M53 or follow signs on A41.
Opening Times: 1 Apr - 30 Oct: Daily, 10am - 4pm. Nov - Mar: Mon - Fri, 10am - 4pm.
Admission: Adult 40p, Child 20p, Conc 40p, Groups under 13 people 40p ea. Groups 12+ £5. Guided tours available for coach party bookings by prior arrangement.

SPEKE HALL

Tel: 0151 427 7231   **Fax:** 0151 427 9860

The Walk, Liverpool L24 1XD
Owner: The National Trust   **Contact:** The Property Manager
An intricately decorated half-timbered house dating back to Tudor times. Victorian interiors, William Morris wallpapers, and life above and below the stairs reveal the rich diversity of this wonderful house.
Location: North bank of the Mersey, 6 miles east of city centre. Follow signs for Liverpool airport.
Opening Times: 30 Mar - 27 Oct: Daily except Mons (open BH Mons) 1 - 5.30pm. 2 Nov - 15 Dec: Sats & Suns only, 1 - 4.30pm. Last admission 30 mins before closing. Garden: 30 Mar - 27 Oct as house. 1 Nov - Mar 1997: Daily except Mon 12 noon - 4pm Hall and Garden closed Good Friday, 24 - 26 & 31 Dec, 1 Jan.
Admission: House & Garden: £3.80. Garden only: £1.20, half price for children. Family ticket (2 adults/2 children) £9.50.

◆ ◆ ◆ ◆ ◆ ◆ ◆ ◆ ◆ Periods and Styles of Furniture ◆ ◆ ◆ ◆ ◆ ◆ ◆ ◆ ◆

English furniture styles take their name from either the reigning monarch – Charles II, Queen Anne, George II etc., or from the great designers from the latter half of the 18th century - Thomas Chippendale, the brothers Adam, George Hepplewhite and Thomas Sheraton, whose names are immortalised in their furniture designs. These styles were taken up, sometimes promptly, sometimes with a time lag, by American craftsmen. Partly this was due to transport delays and partly to a hesitation to switch to "new models" before the public taste was ready to accept them.

As far as England was concerned, the 18th century was characteristically "Georgian" and the successive periods closely matched the reigns of the four Georges. In America, the dominant styles were (in modern terminology): 'William and Mary', 'Queen Anne', 'Chippendale', 'Hepplewhite', 'Sheraton' and 'Federal'. The chart below shows the reigning periods of the monarchs and the approximate dates when a given style enjoyed its peak of popularity, both in England and in the 'colonies'.

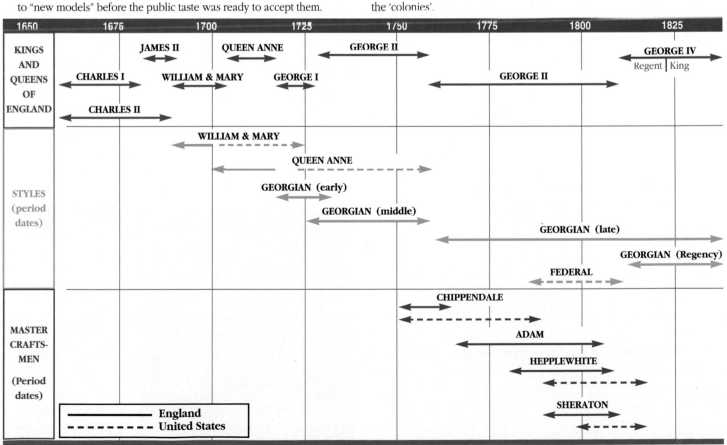

SYON PARK
Brentford

SYON takes its name from a monastery founded in 1415 by Henry V. After the dissolution it was given to the Protector Somerset who re-built it much as it is seen today. On his death Syon reverted to the Crown until granted by James I to the Percy family, now Dukes of Northumberland, who own and live in it to this day. In 1762 the First Duke of Northumberland retained Robert Adam to remodel the house, resulting in a set of state rooms, probably his finest work. From the classic Great Hall, the unique scagliola floor, Cipriani ceiling and spectacular Long Gallery, the visitor sees a collection of great paintings and 17th century furniture, some of which was designed by Adam for the House. Syon Park is available for hire for exclusive events.

GARDENS
The Gardens were transformed in the 1760s by 'Capability' Brown. Syon is thought to be the first garden where trees were used purely for ornament and there is a fine and rare collection. In the gardens stands The Great Conservatory, a beautiful glass and steel structure, designed in 1820 by Charles Fowler. The Great Conservatory is available for hire and is ideal for weddings and parties between May and October.

The gardens contain the steam-hauled Syon Park Miniature Railway.

The newly replanted Rose Garden will be open at the same times as Syon House.

❖

SUITABILITY FOR OTHER EVENTS
Fashion shows, archery, garden parties, shows, rallies, filming, photography functions and and weddings.

CONFERENCE FACILITIES
The Conference and Banqueting Centre offers 5 individual suites capable of seating between 10 and 200 people. Each Suite has its own patio area which overlooks the Gardens of Syon House. Syon Park is ideal for wedding receptions, dinner dances, conferences and exhibitions. Further information can be obtained by phoning (0181) 568 0778.

ADVICE TO COURIERS & DRIVERS
No dogs in Syon House or Park and no photography permitted in the House.

FACILITIES FOR THE DISABLED
There are toilet facilities for the disabled. Induction loop for the hard of hearing in House.

CATERING
PATIO RESTAURANT A self-service restaurant with ample seating is situated adjacent to the Gardens. A selection of hot food, sandwiches, cakes and pastries are offered daily. Coach parties are welcome and may book in advance. Phone (0181) 568 0778 for further information..

GUIDED TOURS
Tours are given at no additional cost. Average time taken 1 1/4 hours (not Suns). Free Sound Alive tours for all visitors.

NATIONAL TRUST GIFT SHOP
Open all year.

GUIDE BOOKS
Colour guide books available. House: £1.50 Garden:£1.50

SCHOOL VISITS/CHILDREN
Groups are welcome. Areas to visit include the butterfly house. Cost per child for guided tour varies according to venue. The formal Gardens provide a safe and enjoyable environment for school picnics.

CONTACT

R. Pailthorpe
Syon Park Ltd
Brentford
Middlesex
TW8 8JF

Tel: 0181 560 0881
Fax: 0181 568 0936

LOCATION

In London, off A310 and A315.

Rail: Southern Region: Waterloo to Kew Bridge, then bus. Nearest Station Syon Lane.
Underground: District or North London Line to Gunnersbury Station, then bus.
Bus: Gunnersbury or Kew Bridge to Brent Lea Gate, 237 or 267.

OPENING TIMES

Summer
1 April - 30 September
HOUSE (& ROSE GARDEN)
Wed - Sun, Bank Hols
11.00am - 5.00pm

Other days by prior arrangement.

Winter
HOUSE (& ROSE GARDEN)
October - 15 Dec
Sun   11.00am - 5.00pm

Rest of year special openings arranged by prior appointment only.

GARDENS & GREAT CONSERVATORY
10.00am - 6.00pm/dusk
Every day except the 25th, 26 Dec.
Season Ticket available.

STEAM RAILWAY
April - October
Weekends & Bank Holidays. Other times by prior arrangement. Runs during Garden opening hours.

ADMISSION

HOUSE & GARDEN
Adult £5.50
Concession £4.00
Family £13.00
GARDEN ONLY
Adult £2.50
Concession £2.00
Family £5.00
MINIATURE RAILWAY
(additional to Garden Admission)
Adult £1.00
Concession £0.50
SCHOOL PARTIES
House & Gdns . . .£2.00
Gardens only . . .£1.00

CONFERENCE AND FUNCTION FACILITIES

ROOM	DIMENSIONS	CAPACITY	LAYOUT	POWER POINTS	SUITABLE FOR A/V
Garden	14.95 x 11.47m	200	Various	4	
Lakeside	18.50 x 10.75m	150	Various	6	
Gunters	10.74 x 12.34m	110	Various	4	
Terrace	11.94 x 9.40m	80	Various	4	
Conservatory	12.34 x 6.1m	40	Various	2	

BOSTON MANOR HOUSE

OPEN

6 April - 27 Oct

Saturdays, Sundays
and Bank Hol Mons

2.30pm - 5.00pm

Park open daily

The ground floor
due to be open
during 1996

Tel: 0181 570 0622
Fax: 0181 862 7602

BOSTON MANOR ROAD, BRENTFORD, MIDDLESEX TW8 9JX

Owner: London Borough of Hounslow   *Contact: Allan Downend*

A fine Jacobean House built in 1623. The rooms that can be viewed include the State Drawing Room with a magnificent ceiling and fireplace designed in 1623. The ceiling is divided into panels representing the senses and the elements. A rare example of a Jacobean House in the London area.

Location: 10 minutes walk south of Boston Manor Station (Piccadilly Line) and 250 yds N of Boston Manor Rd junction with A4 - Great West Road, Brentford.

Admission: Free.

CAPEL MANOR GARDENS

OPEN

Daily in Summer
10.00am - 5.00pm

Last ticket at 4.30pm

Check for winter
opening times

Tel: 0181 366 4442
Fax: 01992 717544

BULLSMOOR LANE, ENFIELD, MIDDLESEX EN1 4RQ

Owner: Capel Manor Charitable Organisation   *Contact: Miss Julie Ryan*

These extensive, richly planted gardens are delightful throughout the year offering inspiration, information and relaxation. The gardens include various themes - historical, modern, walled, rock, water, sensory and disabled and an Italianate Maze, Japanese Garden and "Gardening Which?" demonstration and model gardens. Capel Manor is a college of Horticulture and runs a training scheme for professional gardeners devised in conjunction with the Historic Houses Association. New Visitors Centre and Garden Gift Shop.

Location: Minutes from exit 25 of M25. Tourist Board sign posted (yellow signs in summer)

Admission: Adult £3.00, Concessions £2.00, Child £1.50, Family Ticket £7.50. Charges alter for special show weekends and winter months.

CARSHALTON HOUSE

Tel: 0181 770 4781   **Fax:** 0181 770 4777

St Philomena's School, Pound Street, Carshalton, Surrey SM5 3PS

Owner: St Philomena's School   **Contact:** Ms Murphy

Early 18th century house around core of older house, with grounds first laid out by Charles Bridgeman. Main rooms with 18th century decoration. Guided tours.

Location: Off A232 by junction with B278.

Opening Times: Easter BH Mon and Aug BH Mon: 10am - 5pm.

Admission: Adult £2.50, Child £1.50, Groups by prior arrangement for visits outside normal opening times. Admission charge includes optional guided tour and lecture.

Where to Stay

For Private Accommodation and Johansens recommended Hotels, see Accommodation Section.

THE OCTAGON, ORLEANS HOUSE GALLERY

Tel: 0181 892 0221   **Fax:** 0181 744 0501

Riverside, Twickenham, Middlesex TW1 3DJ

Owner: London Borough of Richmond upon Thames   **Contact:** Stephen Nicholls

Outstanding example of baroque architecture built by James Gibbs c.1720. Adjacent art gallery holds varied exhibition programme.

Location: ¹/₄m S of A305 (Richmond Rd/Richmond Bridge).

Opening Times: Tues - Sat, 1 - 5.30pm (Oct - Mar, 1 - 4.30pm). Suns & BHs, 2 - 5.30pm (Oct - Mar 2 - 4.30pm). Garden open every day 9am - sunset.

Admission: Free. Donations to Octagon appeal gratefully received.

OSTERLEY PARK

OPEN

30 Mar - end Oct
Wed - Sun
1.00 - 5.00pm
Bank Hol Mon
11.00 - 5.00pm.

Closed Good Fri.
Last Adm. 4.30pm

Park and
Pleasure Grounds
All year:
9.00am - 7.30pm

Tel: 0181 560 3918

ISLEWORTH, MIDDLESEX TW7 4RB

Owner: The National Trust   *Contact: The Property Manager*

Set in 140 acres of landscaped park with ornamental lakes, Osterley is one of the last great houses with an intact estate in Greater London.

Location: Access via Thornbury Road on north side of A4 between Gillette Corner and Osterley Underground Station.

Admission: Adult £3.70, Child £1.80, Family Ticket £9.00.

SYON PARK

See Page 130 for full page entry.

Syon Park.

KEY TO SYMBOLS: 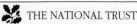 THE NATIONAL TRUST   ⊞ ENGLISH HERITAGE   ⊞ HISTORIC HOUSES ASSOCIATION

HOLKHAM HALL
Wells-next-the-Sea

CONTACT

The Administrator
Holkham Hall
Estate Office
Wells-next-the-Sea
Norfolk
NR23 1AB

Tel: (01328) 710227

Fax: (01328) 711707

LOCATION

From London 120mls
Norwich 35mls
Kings Lynn 30mls

Rail: Norwich Stn
35mls,
Kings Lynn Stn 30mls

Air: Norwich Airport
32mls.

Taxi: Lavender Taxi
Services, Fakenham.
(01328) 862906.

HOLKHAM HALL has been the home of the Coke family and the Earls of Leicester for almost 250 years. Built by William Kent between 1734 and 1762 it is a fine example of 18th century Palladian style. Constructed mainly of local yellow brick with a magnificent Entrance Hall of English alabaster, the House reflects Thomas Coke's natural appreciation of classical art developed during the Grand Tour.

The State Rooms occupy the first floor and contain Greek and Roman statuary, paintings by Rubens, Van Dyck, Claude, Poussin and Gainsborough and original furniture.

On leaving the House visitors pass Holkham Pottery and its adjacent shop, both under the supervision of the Countess of Leicester. Fine examples of local craftsmanship are for sale including the famous Holkham Florist Ware.

Beyond are the 19th century stables now housing the Holkham Bygones Collection; some 4,000 items range from working steam engines, vintage cars and tractors to craft tools and kitchenware. A History of Farming exhibition is in the former Porter's Lodge.

The House is set in a 3,000-acre park with 600 head of fallow deer. On the lake, 1 mile long, are many species of wildfowl. Two walks encircle either the lake or agricultural buildings.

The Holkham Garden Centre occupies the 18th century walled Kitchen Garden and a large range of stock is on sale to the public.

❖

SUITABILITY FOR OTHER EVENTS
Fashion shows, air displays, archery, clay pigeon shooting, equestrian events, shows, rallies and filming.

ADVICE TO COURIERS & DRIVERS
No smoking, dogs or flash photography in the Hall.

FACILITIES FOR THE DISABLED
Disabled and elderly visitors may be left at the entrance before parking in the allocated areas but there are stairs in the Hall. There are toilets for the disabled.

PARKING FOR COACHES & CARS
Capacity of the car park: over 1,000 cars and 20 coaches, 75 yards from the Hall.

CATERING
The Tea Room can cater for up to 100 people. Menus are available on request.

GUIDED TOURS
When the Hall is open to the public, guides are posted in each room. At other times guided tours can be arranged. Average time taken for a tour 1 hour.

GIFT SHOP
Open 10.00am-5.30pm Sun - Fri. Items include pottery, gifts and souvenirs.

GUIDE BOOKS
Colour guide book £2.00.

SCHOOL VISITS/CHILDREN
Groups of children are welcome. Price per child £1.50. Areas of interest: Bygones Collection, History of Farming Exhibition, 2 nature walks, deer park, lake and wildfowl.

OPENING TIMES

Summer
26 May - 30 September
Suns - Thurs (inc)
1.30 - 5.00pm

Easter, May, Spring &
Summer Bank Hols:
Sun & Mon
11.30am - 5.00pm

Last admission 4.40pm

Winter
October - May
Open by appointment.

ADMISSION

Summer

HALL
    Adult £3.00
    Child* £1.50

BYGONES
    Adult £3.00
    Child* £1.50

ALL INCLUSIVE
    Adult £5.00
    Child* £2.50

* Ages 5-15
Discounts on Parties of 20+

Winter
By arrangement

SANDRINGHAM
King's Lynn

The private country retreat of Her Majesty The Queen, Sandringham House is at the heart of the beautiful estate which has been owned by four generations of Monarchs. King George V described his home in the picturesque West Norfolk countryside as "dear old Sandringham, the place I love better than anywhere else in the world".

The neo-Jacobean house was built in 1870 for Albert Edward, Prince of Wales and his wife, Princess Alexandra, later King Edward VII and Queen Alexandra. A grand and imposing building, where all the main rooms used by the Royal Family when in residence are open to the public, Sandringham House has the warmth and charm of a well-loved family home. Visitors see portraits of the Royal Family, collections of porcelain, jade, quartz, enamelled Russian silver, gold and bronze set amongst fine furniture.

GROUNDS
Sixty acres of glorious grounds surround the House and offer beauty and colour throughout the seasons with a rich variety of flowers, shrubs and magnificent trees, informally planted round lawns and lakes to provide a multitude of tranquil views.

MUSEUM
Enlarged and improved in 1995, the Museum is full of Royal memorabilia imaginatively displayed, including vintage Daimlers, exhibitions of the Sandringham Fire Brigade and Carving School and an exciting new Safari Room.

CONTACT

Mrs Gill Pattinson
The Estate Office
Sandringham
King's Lynn
Norfolk
PE35 6EN

Tel: (01553) 772675
Fax: (01485) 541571

LOCATION

8 miles north east of Kings Lynn off A148.
3 hours from London
1½ hours from Stansted Airport via M11 and A10.

Rail: King's Lynn 8 miles.

SUITABILITY FOR OTHER EVENTS
Grounds for open-air concerts/theatre. 140-acre private park for rallies, fairs etc.

EXTRA FACILITIES
600 acre Country Park with Tractor and Trailer tour. Transport to the house by Land Train.

ADVICE TO COURIERS & DRIVERS
Parking, admission and refreshments free to drivers. No dogs inside grounds. No photography inside House.

FACILITIES FOR THE DISABLED
Wheelchair access throughout. Parking and lavatories for disabled persons.

PARKING FOR COACHES & CARS
Parking area for 600 cars/150 coaches close to Visitor Centre, 300 yards from Grounds entrance.

CATERING
A major re-development of the Sandringham Visitor Centre opened at Easter 1994 with air-conditioned restaurant seating up to 200 visitors. Traditional waitress-service tea room seating 60 also available and may be booked by groups. Open Easter to end of October.

GUIDED TOURS
Guided tours may be arranged for groups at certain times of the season.

GIFT SHOP
Large gift shop at Visitor Centre stocking a large range of quality gifts, books, foods and souvenirs open Easter to end of October.

GUIDE BOOKS
A guide book with colour photographs is available.

SCHOOL VISITS/CHILDREN
School visits are welcome. Educational sheets/question-naires available for House and Museum.

OPENING TIMES

Summer
4 April - 6 October

HOUSE:
11.00am - 4.45pm.
Closed 23 Jul - 7 Aug

GROUNDS open
10.30am - 5.00pm.

MUSEUM open
11.00am - 5.00pm

GROUNDS & MUSEUM
Closed 28 July - 6 Aug.

Winter
7 October - Spring 1996
House closed. Phone for grounds and museum opening details.

ADMISSION

HOUSE, GROUNDS & MUSEUM
Adult £4.00
Child* £2.00
Student £3.00
Sen. Citizen . . . £3.00
Family £10.00

GROUNDS & MUSEUM
Adult £3.00
Child* £1.50
Student £2.50
Sen. Citizen . . . £2.50
Family Ticket . . £7.50

Groups
Discount of 10% for pre-booked, pre-paid parties of 20 or more.
* Aged 5-15.

CONFERENCE AND FUNCTION FACILITIES

ROOM	DIMENSIONS	CAPACITY	LAYOUT	POWER POINTS	SUITABLE FOR A/V
Restaurant	35' x 50'	300 Buffet 150 200 50	Reception/ Dinner Theatre Boardroom	8	✓

BERNEY ARMS WINDMILL ⌗

Tel: 01493 700605

c/o 8 Manor Road, Southtown, Gt Yarmouth, Norfolk NR31 0QA
Owner: English Heritage　　　　　　　　**Contact:** The Custodian
A wonderfully situated marsh mill, one of the best and largest remaining in Norfolk, with seven floors, making it a landmark for miles around. It was in use until 1951.
Location: 3¹/2m NE of Reedham on N bank of River Yare, 5 miles from Gt Yarmouth
Opening Times: 1 Apr - 30 Sept: Daily 9.00am - 5.00pm. Closed 1 -2 pm.
Admission: Adult £1.00, Child 50p, Conc 80p.

BINHAM PRIORY ⌗

Tel: 01604 730320

Binham-on-Wells, Norfolk.
Owner: English Heritage　　　　　　　**Contact:** The Midlands Regional Office
Extensive remains of a Benedictine priory, of which the original nave of the church is still in use as a parish church.
Location: ¹/4 m NW of village of Binham-on-Wells road off B1388.
Opening Times: Any reasonable time.

BIRCHAM WINDMILL

Tel: 01485 578393

Snettisham Road, Great Bircham, Norfolk PE31 6SJ
Owner: Mr & Mrs G Wagg　　　　　　　**Contact:** Mr & Mrs G Wagg
One of the last remaining complete windmills.
Location: ¹/2m W of Snettisham.
Opening Times: 1 Apr - 31 Sept 10am - 6pm
Admission: Adult £2.20, Child £1.20, Conc £1.00.

BLICKLING HALL ❧

OPEN

23 March - 3 Nov
Tues, Wed, Fri,
Sat, Sun & Bank
Holiday Mondays.
(Closed Good Fri)
House opens
12.30pm - 4.30pm.

Garden: Daily
July & August.
10.30am - 5pm.

Shop, Restaurant
& plant sales
from 10.30am.

Tel: 01263 733084
Fax: 01263 734924

BLICKLING, NORWICH, NORFOLK NR11 6NF

Owner: The National Trust　　　*Contact: The Property Manager*

A spectacular 17th century red brick house, with extensive colourful garden. Fine Jacobean plaster ceilings, furniture and collections: including the Ellys library, Peter the Great tapestry. Garden contains extensive parterre, temple, orangery and secret garden. Parkland offers good lakeside and woodland walks. Free parking.
Location: B1354 off A140 Norwich/ Cromer road.
Admission: House & Garden: £5.50 (£6.50 Sunday & Bank Holiday Mondays). Garden: £3.20 (£3.50). Children half price. Group discount available.

BURGH CASTLE ⌗

Tel: 01604 730320

Breydon Water, Great Yarmouth, Norfolk.
Owner: English Heritage　　　　　　　**Contact:** The Midlands Regional Office
Impressive walls, with projecting bastions, of a Roman fort built in the late 3rd century as one of a chain to defend the coast against Saxon raiders.
Location: At far W end of Breydon Water, on unclassified road 3m W of Great Yarmouth.
Opening Times: Any reasonable time.

CASTLE ACRE PRIORY ⌗

Tel: 01760 755394

Stocks Green, Castle Acre, King's Lynn, Norfolk PE32 2XD
Owner: English Heritage　　　　　　　**Contact:** The Custodian
The great west front of the 12th century church of this Cluniac priory still rises to its full height and is elaborately decorated. Other substantial remains include the splendid prior's lodgings and chapel and the delightful walled herb garden should not be missed.
Location: ¹/4m W of village of Castle Acre, 5m N of Swaffham.
Opening Times: 1 Apr - 30 Sept: Daily 10am - 6pm. 1 - 31 Oct: Daily 10am - 6pm or dusk if earlier. 1 Nov - 31 Mar: Wed - Sun 10am - 4pm (Closed for lunch 1 - 2pm).
Admission: Adult £2.50, Child £1.30, Conc £1.90.

CASTLE RISING CASTLE ⌗

Tel: 01553 631330

Castle Rising, Kings Lynn, Norfolk PE31 6AH
Owner: English Heritage　　　　　　　**Contact:** The Custodian
A fine mid 12th century domestic keep, set in the centre of massive defensive earthworks. The keep walls stand to their original height and many of the fortifications are still intact.
Location: 4m NE of King's Lynn off A149.
Opening Times: 1 Apr - 30 Sept: Daily 10am - 6pm. 1 - 31 Oct: Daily 10am - 6pm or dusk if earlier. 1 Nov - 31 Mar: Wed - Sun, 10am - 4pm (closed for lunch 1- 2pm).
Admission: Adult £2.00, Child £1.00, Conc £1.50.

DRAGON HALL

Tel: 01603 663922

115 - 123 King Street, Norwich, Norfolk NR1 1QE
Owner: Norfolk & Norwich Heritage Trust Ltd　　　**Contact:** Ms Sarah Knights
Magnificent medieval merchant's hall described as "one of the most exciting 15th century buildings in England". A wealth of outstanding features include living hall, screens passage, vaulted undercroft, superb timber framed Great Hall, crown-post roof and intricately carved & painted dragon. Built by Robert Toppes, a wealthy and influential merchant. Dragon Hall is a unique legacy of medieval life, craftsmanship and trade.
Location: Norwich city centre.
Opening Times: April - Oct, Mon - Sat, 10.00am - 4.00pm. Nov - Mar, Mon - Fri, 10.00am - 4.00pm. Closed 23 Dec - 2 Jan and Bank Holidays.
Admission: Adult £1.00, Child 25p, Conc 50p.

THE FAIRHAVEN GARDENS

Tel: 01603 270449　**Fax:** 01603 270449

2 The Woodlands, Wymers Lane, South Walsham, Norwich NR13 6EA
Owner: The Trustees of Fairhaven Garden Trust　　　**Contact:** Mr G E Debbage
Woodland and water garden with private broad. Primroses, bluebells, primulas, rhododendrons in spring, wild flowers and much to interest naturalists and horticulturists in summer and autumn. Situated in a lovely peaceful part of the Norfolk Broads.
Location: 9m NE of Norwich on B1140 at South Walsham.
Opening Times: Good Fri - 1 Oct: Tues - Sun, 11am - 5.30pm (Sat 2 - 5.30pm). Closed Mons except Bank holidays.
Admission: Adult £3.00, Child £1.00 (under 5s free), OAPs £2.00, Group reductions.

FELBRIGG HALL ❧

OPEN

Hall:
23 Mar - 3 Nov
Mon, Wed, Thur,
Sat & Sun, 1 - 5pm.
Gardens: 11am - 5pm.

Shop: 11am - 5.30pm.
Catering:
11am - 5.15pm.
Groups /Guided tours
by arrangement.

Tel: 01263 837444
Fax: 01263 837032

ROUGHTON, NORWICH, NORFOLK NR11 8PR

Owner: The National Trust　　　*Contact: Elizabeth Carrington-Porter*

Felbrigg Hall is a 17th century house built on the site of a medieval Hall. It houses a superb collection of 18th century furniture, pictures and an outstanding library. There are 27 rooms to visit including the Domestic Wing, which offers the visitor a greater understanding of how a country house "worked". Close to the Hall is a beautiful Walled Garden with Dovehouse, and hundreds of acres of historic parkland and mature woods may be explored via a variety of waymarked walks.
Location: 2m SW of Cromer.
Admission: Hall & Gardens: Adult £5.00, Child £2.50. Gardens only: Adult £2.00, Child £1.00. Free to National Trust members.

GRIME'S GRAVES ⌗

Tel: 01842 810656

Thetford, Norfolk IP26 5DE
Owner: English Heritage　　　　　　　**Contact:** The Custodian
These remarkable Neolithic flint mines, unique in England, comprise over 300 pits and shafts. The visitor can descend some 30 feet by ladder into one excavated shaft, and look along the radiating galleries from where the flint used for making axes and knives was extracted.
Location: 7m N of Thetford off A134.
Opening Times: 1 Apr - 30 Sept: Daily 10am - 6pm. 1 - 31 Oct: Daily 10am - 6pm or dusk if earlier. 1 Nov - 31 Mar: Wed - Sun 10am - 4pm (closed for lunch 1 - 2pm).
Admission: Adult £1.50, Child 80p, Conc £1.10.

HOLKHAM HALL

See Page 132 for full page entry.

HOUGHTON HALL

HOUGHTON, KING'S LYNN, NORFOLK PE31 6UE

Owner: The Marquess of Cholmondeley   *Contact: Susan Cleaver*

Tel: 01485 528569   **Fax:** 01485 528167

Houghton Hall was built in the 18th century by Sir Robert Walpole. Original designs were by Colen Campbell and revised by Thomas Ripley with interior decoration by William Kent. It is regarded as one of the finest examples of Palladian architecture in England. Houghton was later inherited by the 1st Marquess of Cholmondeley through his grandmother, Sir Robert's daughter. Situated in beautiful parkland, the house contains magnificent furniture, pictures and china. A private collection of 20,000 model soldiers and militaria. Newly restored walled garden will be open for the first time.

Location: 13m E of King's Lynn, 10m W of Fakenham off A148.

Opening Times: Easter Sunday (7 Apr) - 29 Sept on Suns, Thurs and Bank Hol Mons from 2 - 5.30pm. Last admission 5pm

Admission: Adult £5.50, Child (5-16) £3, Party rate (20+): Adult £5, Child £2.50. Excluding house: Adult £3, Child £2, Party Rate: (20+) Adult £2.50, Child £1.50.

HOVETON HALL GARDENS

Tel: 01603 782798   **Fax:** 01603 784564

Wroxham, Norwich, Norfolk NR12 8RJ

Owner: Andrew Buxton Esq   **Contact:** Mrs Buxton

Hoveton Hall was built 1809 - 1812 in gault brick with slate roofs. Design of grounds attributed to Humphry Repton. (House not open).

Location: On A1151 8m N of Norwich.

Opening Times: Easter - mid September: Wed, Fri, Sun and BH Mon, 11am - 5.30pm.

Admission: Adult £2.50, Child £1.00, Groups £2.00 (if booked in advance).

MANNINGTON GARDENS & COUNTRYSIDE

Tel: 01263 584175   **Fax:** 01263 761214

Mannington Hall, Norwich, Norfolk NR11 7BB

Owner: The Lord and Lady Walpole   **Contact:** Lady Walpole

Gardens with lake, moat and woodland. Outstanding rose collection, heritage rose gardens.

Location: Signposted from Saxthorpe crossroads on the Norwich - Holt road B1149.

Opening Times: Gardens: Easter - Oct: Suns, 12 noon - 5pm. Jun - Aug, Wed, Thurs & Fri, 11am - 5pm. Walks: Daily from 9am. Medieval Hall open by appointment.

Admission: Adult £3.00, Child under 16 free, Conc £2.50, Groups by application.

NORWICH CASTLE MUSEUM

Tel: 01603 223624   **Fax:** 01603 765651

Norwich, Norfolk NR1 3JU

Owner: Norfolk Museums Service   **Contact:** Ms B Yates

Norman Castle keep, housing displays of art, archaeology and natural history especially Norwich School of Art. Also the world's largest collection of teapots.

Location: City centre.

Opening Times: Apr - Sept: Mon - Sun 10am - 5pm. Mar - Oct: Mon - Sat 10am - 5pm, Sun 2 - 5pm.

Admission: Adult £2.20, Child £1.00, Conc £1.50.

OLD MERCHANT'S HOUSE ROW 111 & GREYFRIARS CLOISTERS

South Quay, Great Yarmouth Norfolk NR30 2RQ   **Tel:** 01493 857900

Owner: English Heritage   **Contact:** The Custodian

Two 17th century Row Houses, a type of building unique to Great Yarmouth. Nearby are the remains of a Franciscan friary.

Location: Great Yarmouth on South Quay, 1/2 m inland from beach.

Opening Times: 1 Apr - 30 Sept: Suns 2 - 6pm, Mon - Wed 10am - 6pm. Closed 1 - 2pm.

Admission: Adult £1.50, Child 80p, Conc £1.10.

OXBURGH HALL

OXBOROUGH, KING'S LYNN, NORFOLK PE33 9PS

Owner: The National Trust   *Contact: The Administrator*

Tel: 01366 328258   **Fax:** 01366 328066

Moated house built in 1482 by the Bedingfeld family, who still live here. The rooms show the development from Medieval austerity to Victorian comfort. Embroidery worked by Mary Queen of Scots, during her captivity, is on display. There are delightful woodland walks and a French parterre in the garden.

Location: At Oxborough, 7m SW of Swaffham on S side of Stoke.

Opening Times: House: 23 Mar - 3 Nov: Sat - Wed 1 - 5pm, Bank Hol Mon 11am - 5pm. Garden: same days as house 12 noon - 5.30pm.

Admission: House, Garden & Estate: £4.50. Pre-arranged parties: £3.50 Garden and Estate only (pre-booked) £2.20.

RAVENINGHAM HALL GARDENS

Tel: 01508 548206   **Fax:** 01508 548958

Raveningham, Norwich, Norfolk NR14 6NS

Owner: Sir Nicholas Bacon Bt   **Contact:** Mrs J Woodard

Gardens laid out approximately 100 years ago around a red brick Georgian house – not open to the public.

Location: Between Beccles and Loddon off B1136/B1140.

Opening Times: Mid Mar - mid Sept: Wed 1 - 4pm & Sun and Bank Hol Mon 2 - 5pm.

Admission: Adult £2.00, Child free, Groups by prior arrangement.

SANDRINGHAM

See Page 133 for full page entry.

ST GEORGE'S GUILDHALL

Tel: 01553 774725

27 Kings Street, Kings Lynn, Norfolk PE30 1HA
Owner: The National Trust   **Contact:** The Administrator
The largest surviving English medieval guildhall, with adjoining medieval warehouse, now in use as an Arts Centre.
Location: On W side of King Street close to the Tuesday Market Place.
Opening Times: All year: Mon - Fri (closed Good Fri & Aug BH Mon) 10am - 5pm; Sat 10am - 12.30pm & 2 - 3.30pm (10 Jun - 8 Jul: 10am - 12.30pm): Sun 2 - 4pm (28 May - 24 Sept but closed 16, 23, 30 Jul). Closed 25, 26 Dec & 1 Jan.
Admission: Adult 50p, Child 25p.

STRANGER'S HALL

Tel: 01603 667229   **Fax:** 01603 765651

Charing Cross, Norwich Norfolk NR1 3JU
Owner: Norfolk Museums Service   **Contact:** Fiona Strodder / Cathy Terry
Once a splendid medieval merchant's house, now containing period rooms from early Tudor to Victorian times.
Location: Charing Cross, Norwich.
Opening Times: All Year: Tues - Sat 10am - 5pm. Suns May - September 2 - 5pm. Closed Good Friday, Christmas Day, 1 January.
Admission: Adult £1.40, Child 70p, Conc £1.20. Admission price includes entry to Bridewell Museum and the Regimental Museum.

WALSINGHAM ABBEY GROUNDS

Tel: 01328 820259   **Fax:** 01328 820098

Little Walsingham, Norfolk NR22 6BP
Owner: Walsingham Estate Company   **Contact:** The Agent
Priory ruins in peaceful surroundings, woodland walks.
Location: B1105 from Fakenham - 5 miles.
Opening Times: Apr - Jul and Sept: Wed, Sat and Sun, 2 - 5pm. Aug: Mon, Wed, Fri, Sat, Sun and all Bank Hols from Easter - Sept, or through Estate Office during office hours.
Admission: Adult £1.50, Child 75p, Senior citizens 75p. School parties and parties over 100 by arrangement.

WOLTERTON PARK

Tel: 01263 584175   **Fax:** 01263 761214

Norwich, Norfolk NR11 7BB
Owner: The Lord and Lady Walpole   **Contact:** The Lady Walpole
18th century Hall. Historic park with lake. Hawk and Owl Trust exhibition.
Location: Situated near Erpingham village; signposted from Norwich - Cromer Rd A140.
Opening Times: Park: Daily from 9am.
Admission: £2.00 car park fee only. Groups by application. Hall tours by prior arrangement from £3.50.

Sandringham.

SPECIAL EVENTS

◇ **WOLTERTON ESTATE** Hausmusik Concert	**11 FEBRUARY**	
◇ **SANDRINGHAM** Craft Fair	**20 – 22 APRIL**	
◇ **WOLTERTON ESTATE** Early Music Concert	**18 MAY**	
◇ **MANNINGTON GARDENS** Countryside Day	**26 MAY**	
◇ **SANDRINGHAM** Street Organ Festival	**27 – 29 MAY**	
◇ **SANDRINGHAM** Spring Spectacular	**28 – 29 MAY**	
◇ **SANDRINGHAM** Fireworks and Classical Concert	**7 JUNE**	

◇ **MANNINGTON GARDENS** Rose Festival	**29 – 30 JUNE**
◇ **SANDRINGHAM** Country Weekend	**6 – 7 JULY**
◇ **MANNINGTON GARDENS** Sheringham Little Theatre Day	**21 JULY**
◇ **SANDRINGHAM** Flower Show	**31 JULY**
◇ **SANDRINGHAM** Craft Fair	**23 – 26 AUGUST**
◇ **MANNINGTON GARDENS** Charities Day	**1 SEPTEMBER**

For National Trust and English Heritage Events see separate section.

ALTHORP HOUSE
Althorp

CONTACT

Althorp House
Althorp
Northampton
NN7 4HG

Tel: (01604) 770107
Fax: (01604) 770042

LOCATION

From the M1:
Exit 15A, 6 miles
Exit 16, 7 miles
Exit 18, 10 miles
Situated on A428
Northampton-Rugby.
London on average 85
minutes away.

ALTHORP, home of the Spencer family and the ancestral home of the Princess of Wales, was built in its original, red brick form by Sir John Spencer in 1508. Remodelled in 1660 by Anthony Ellis, the house's present appearance dates from 1790 when Henry Holland 'improved' both the interior and exterior, entirely facing the main house with fashionable grey brick tiles.

Inside, the main rooms show the complexity of the building's history: the Wootton Hall - a marvellous Palladian room by Morris, the Grand Staircase dating from 1650, and the breathtaking Picture Gallery - 115 feet of panelling, covered with masterpieces, culminating in Van Dyck's celebrated double portrait , 'War and Peace'. The present Earl has recently completed an extensive programme of redecoration. The House is maintained in immaculate condition.

Althorp houses one of the finest art collections in England, begun in the 17th century by Robert, 2nd Earl of Sunderland, and enlarged by nearly every successive Spencer generation. Rubens, Reynolds, Gainsborough, Salvatore Rosa, Guercino, Lely and Stubbs are all represented. The collection's quality is almost matched by that of the 18th century furniture, and the porcelain is also outstanding, with an extensive collection from Sèvres and Meissen.

GARDENS

Set in 550 acres of walled Parkland, the gardens were improved in 1790 by Samuel Lapidge, Capability Brown's chief assistant. The gardens seen today date from 1860 and were designed by the architect W M Teulon. It was here in 1904 that Silas Cole, the then Head Gardener, identified the Spencer Sweet Pea from which nearly all modern varieties are derived. The gardens are currently being developed and returning visitors can admire the extensive new beds and borders that have been added in the past two years.

EXHIBITION

Housed in the Stable Block, a grand rectangle of dark glowing ironstone, built in 1732, is an informal collection of historical items and memorabilia collected by the nine Earls. Admission to the Exhibition is included in the ticket price.

OPENING TIMES

1 - 30 August

The House and Park will be open between 2.00 - 5.00pm

ADMISSION

HOUSE & GARDEN
Adult £5.00
Child* £2.50
OAP £3.50

GARDEN ONLY
Adult £2.00
Child* £1.00

*Children under 14 free.
Groups rates available.

CORPORATE FACILITIES

The House and Park are available throughout the year for private lunches and dinners.
British Telecom have recently installed an extensive fibre optic telecommunications network which enables the House to offer the most technologically advanced conference facilities presently available

Theatre style seating for 200 can be accommodated, as well as lunches and dinners for up to 150. The secluded Parkland is an idyllic setting for open air activities. An area adjacent to the House has recently been levelled to accommodate marquees.

A cricket pitch is also available for hire.

EXTRA FACILITIES
Helicopters can land in front of the house.

ADVICE TO COURIERS & DRIVERS
Please book in advance. Group discounts are available. Rest and recreation facilities now available for drivers.

FACILITIES FOR THE DISABLED
Wheelchair access is available to the ground floor of the House and tea room. Toilet facilities are available.

PARKING FOR COACHES & CARS
Extensive facilities for coaches and cars are available within 100 yards of the House.

CATERING
A tea room is located in the Stable Block. Parties can be booked in advance. All foods are freshly prepared in the House, using local produce.

GUIDED TOURS
A free flow system will operate. Guided tours may be booked in advance.

GIFT SHOP/GUIDE BOOKS
Open when the House is open. Many Althorp souvenirs available. A guide book with colour photographs is available. There are also guide books in Japanese.

BOUGHTON HOUSE
Kettering

BOUGHTON HOUSE is the Northamptonshire home of the Duke of Buccleuch and Queensberry K.T., and his Montagu ancestors since 1528. A 500 year old Tudor monastic building gradually enlarged around seven courtyards until the French style addition of 1695, which has lead to Boughton House being described as 'England's Versailles'.

The house contains an outstanding collection of 17th and 18th century French and English furniture, tapestries, 16th century carpets, porcelain, painted ceilings and notable works by El Greco, Murillo, Caracci and 40 Van Dyck sketches. There is an incomparable Armoury and Ceremonial Coach.

Beautiful parkland with historic avenues, lakes, picnic area, gift shop, adventure woodland play area, garden centre and tearoom.
Boughton House is administered by The Living Landscape Trust, which was created by the present Duke of Buccleuch to show the relationship between the historic Boughton House and its surrounding, traditional, working estate.

There are exhibition and lecture rooms in the Stable Block with audio/visual facilities. For details of our specialist one, three and five day Fine Art Courses run in conjunction with Sotheby's and for our schools Education Facilities (Sandford Award Winner 1988 and 1993), telephone The Living Landscape Trust.

Silver award winner of the first Historic House Awards, given by AA and NPI, in co-operation with the Historic Houses Association, for the privately-owned historic house open to the public which has best preserved its integrity and the character of its architecture and furniture while remaining a lived in family home.

CONTACT

Gareth Fitzpatrick
The Living Landscape Trust
Boughton House
Kettering
Northamptonshire
NN14 1BJ

Tel: (01536) 515731

Fax: (01536) 417255

LOCATION

3 miles north of Kettering on A43 - spur road from A14.

SUITABILITY FOR OTHER EVENTS
Boughton House parkland is available for film location and other events by individual negotiation.

EXTRA FACILITIES
Stables Block adjacent to House contains 120 seats. Lecture Theatre and Catering facilities.

ADVICE TO COURIERS & DRIVERS
No unaccompanied children and dogs in House and Gardens. No internal photography.

FACILITIES FOR THE DISABLED
Full disabled access and facilities - no charge for wheelchair visitors.

PARKING FOR COACHES & CARS
There is unlimited parking adjacent to the House.

CATERING
Stables Restaurant seats 100. Parties must book in advance. Varied menus of home made fayre available.

GIFT SHOP
Gift and Garden shops are open daily 2.00 - 5.00pm.

GUIDE BOOKS
New edition recently published. Also specialist book "Boughton House - The English Versailles" available - contact for further details.

GUIDED TOURS
Group visits are all guided - please contact for rates etc.

SCHOOL VISITS/CHILDREN
Heritage Education Trust Sandford Award winner 1988 and 1993. School groups admitted free, teachers pack available to cover all aspects of Estate work to show the 'living landscape' of farming, forestry and conservation.

CONFERENCE AND FUNCTION FACILITIES

ROOM	DIMENSIONS	CAPACITY	LAYOUT	POWER POINTS	SUITABLE FOR A/V	Stables
Lecture		80	Buffet	10		✓
		120+	Theatre			
		80	Lunch/Dinner			
Seminar Room		30	Schoolroom	8		✓
		20	U-Shape			
		20	Boardroom			
		20	Buffet			
		30	Theatre			

Conference facilities available in stable block adjacent to House available for Countryside and Fine Art associated themes.

CASTLE ASHBY
Northampton

The lands at Castle Ashby were given to the Compton family in 1512 by Henry VIII and in 1574 Queen Elizabeth I gave William, 1st Earl of Northampton, permission to demolish the derelict 13th century Castle and rebuild on the site. The original plan of the building was in the shape of an 'E' in honour of Queen Elizabeth, and about sixty years later the courtyard was enclosed by a screen designed by Inigo Jones.

One of the features of Castle Ashby is the lettering around the House and terraces. The inscriptions when translated read "The Lord guard your coming in" and "The Lord guard your going out".

Castle Ashby belongs to the 7th Marquess of Northampton, Spencer Compton, and has been in the hands of the Compton family since it was built. The family trace their history back to the 11th century and came to Castle Ashby from Compton Wynyates in Warwickshire. The lands and titles have descended through the male line

since the 11th century. The Comptons were created Earl of Northampton in 1618 and Marquess of Northampton in 1812.

The Compton family have played host to members of the Royal Family, at Castle Ashby, on many occasions starting with Queen Elizabeth I. James I was a regular visitor, as well as Princess Anne (later Queen Anne) and William of Orange, King George V and Queen Mary visited Castle Ashby in 1907.

GARDENS
The Extensive gardens at Castle Ashby are a combination of several styles, with a mile long avenue dating back to 1695, Victorian Terrace Gardens, the more private and romantic Italian Gardens, an elegant Conservatory, Triumphal Arch, Gloriette and Camellia House standing in a garden of its own. The carriageway continues through 'Capability' Brown landscape parkland, past the Temple, round the lakes and back to the House, affording classic views on the way.

❖

CONTACT

The General Manager
Castle Ashby House
Castle Ashby
Nr Northampton
NN7 1LQ

Tel: (01604) 696696
Fax: (01604) 696516

LOCATION

From London via M1,
90 minutes.
From Birmingham,
50 minutes.
From Chester via M6,
2^1/$_2$ hours.

Rail: Northampton
7 miles; Wellingborough
8 miles.

OPENING TIMES

GARDENS
All year round.

HOUSE
Available throughout the year for Corporate /Private Functions.

ADMISSION

GARDENS
Adult £2.50
OAP £1.00
Child £1.00

Groups
Prices on application

ADVICE TO COURIERS & DRIVERS
25 acres of Gardens open to view. Dogs on leads in gardens. Parking available in Castle Ashby village which can be approached via A428 to Chadstone and Castle Ashby.

GUIDED TOURS
Guided group tours of the Gardens are available - bookings required.

SUITABILITY FOR OTHER EVENTS
26 bedrooms, all with en suite bathroom and a luxury private suite available incorporating the State Apartments. Castle Ashby is available on an exclusive basis for residential conferences, company weekends and social occasions.

7 Private Function Suites available for events, for meetings for 120 people to dinners for 12. 24 hr rate: £185 plus VAT, Day Delegate £42 plus VAT, (rates valid until Sept. 1996). Additional facilities include heated swimming pool, outdoor tennis court, gymnasium, trail bikes, parkland, cricket pitch, clay shooting, archery, fishing and horse and carriage.

CATERING
All catering provided by our team of award winning chefs. Our aim is to provide discreet service with a touch of informality, allowing guests to experience the complete enjoyment of using the house as if it were their own.

CONFERENCE AND FUNCTION FACILITIES

ROOM	DIMENSIONS	CAPACITY	LAYOUT	POWER POINTS	SUITABLE FOR A/V
Great Hall	48' x 26' x 33'	40 - 150	Various	10	✓
Reynolds Room	47' x 22' x 11'	40 - 120	Various	12	✓
China Drawing Room	18' x 20' x 11'	15 - 40	Various	5	✓
Long Gallery	80' x 14' x 12'	30 - 60	Various	3	
Armoury	18' x 30' x 11'	16	Various	4	✓
Study	19' x 20' x 11'	12	Various	4	
There are several smaller rooms available for Syndicate Meetings					

DEENE PARK
Corby

DEENE PARK has been transformed by successive generations of the Brudenell family over the last four centuries into one of Northamptonshire's finest country houses and is of considerable architectural interest.

Today Deene is still a family home containing fine examples of period furniture, family portraits and beautiful paintings; the House having been carefully restored after falling into a dilapidated state during the last war.

The oldest visible part of Deene is an arch c1300, which is to the right of a chimney in the east of the House which comprises the Hall of 1450. The Great Hall was completed by the end of the 16th century and has a magnificent sweet chestnut hammer-beam roof.

The stained glass is 17th century and depicts the arms of the Brudenells and related families.

A famous member of the family was James Brudenell, 7th Earl of Cardigan, who led the Charge of the Light Brigade at Balaklava and interesting records and historic relics about Lord Cardigan and the Charge have survived and are on show.

GARDENS
The gardens are mainly to the south of the House, with a parterre and terraced lawns to water, providing various walks with herbaceous borders, old fashioned roses, spring flowers, fine trees and shrubs.

❖

SUITABILITY FOR OTHER EVENTS
Suitable for a variety of indoor and outdoor events. Consideration given to all requests. Filming welcomed.

EXTRA FACILITIES
Specialist lectures about the house, its contents, gardens and history, can be provided by arrangement.

ADVICE TO COURIERS & DRIVERS
Access via north drive from Deene Village. No photography inside the house. Dogs allowed in car park only.

FACILITIES FOR THE DISABLED
Disabled and elderly visitors may alight at the entrance before parking in the allocated areas. Access to ground floor and garden. Toilets.

ACCOMMODATION
Residential conference facilities by arrangement.

PARKING FOR COACHES AND CARS
Unlimited parking for cars, 250 yards from the House, and space for three coaches, 10 yards from the House.

CATERING
The Restaurant/Tea Room caters for up to 60 people at any one time. Special rates are offered to groups. Bookings can be made in advance and menus are available on request.

Catering facilities are available for special functions and conferences, and include buffets, lunches and dinners.

GUIDED TOURS
Tours at no additional cost are conducted for up to 70 people at any one time. Average time taken for a tour is 90 minutes. The owner will meet the groups if requested.

GIFT SHOP
Open at the same time as the House.

GUIDE BOOKS
A colour guide book is available, £1.80.

CONTACT

The House Keeper
Deene Park
Corby
Northamptonshire
NN17 3EW

Tel: (01780) 450278
or (01780) 450223

Fax: (01780) 450282

LOCATION

6 miles NE of Corby off A43. From London via M1 to Junc. 15 then A43. or via A1, A14, A43 - 2 hours.

From Birmingham via M6, A14, A43 - 90 minutes

Rail: Kettering Station - 20 minutes.

OPENING TIMES

Summer
June - August

Sundays　2.00 - 5.00pm
Bank hol Mons only
2.00 - 5.00pm

Open Sunday and Monday for Easter, early and late Spring Bank Holiday and August Bank Holiday 2.00 - 5.00pm

Open at all other times by arrangement, including pre-booked parties.

Winter
(Out of season)
House and Gardens closed to casual visitors. Open by appointment for booked parties.

ADMISSION

Summer

HOUSE AND GARDENS
　Adult £4.00
　Child (10-14) £2.00
　Child (under 10) . . Free*
GARDENS ONLY
　Adult £2.50
　Child (10-14) £1.25
　Child (under 10) . . Free*
Groups (min 20 people)
　Weekdays £3.50
　(Min £70.00)
　Weekends and public
　open days £4.00
　(Min £80.00)

* Aged 10 and under free with an accompanying adult.

Winter
Groups visits only by prior arrangement.

CONFERENCE AND FUNCTION FACILITIES

ROOM	DIMENSIONS	CAPACITY	LAYOUT	POWER POINTS	SUITABLE FOR A/V
Great Hall	–	150	Theatre	✓	✓
		150	Buffet		
Tapestry Room	–	75	Theatre	✓	✓
East Room	–	18	U shape	✓	✓
		12	Boardroom		

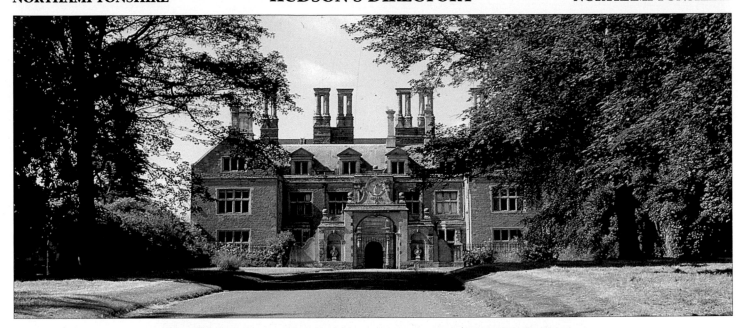

HOLDENBY HOUSE
Holdenby

"One of the most pleasing sites that ever I saw" (John Evelyn 1673).

Holdenby was built in 1583 by Sir Christopher Hatton, Lord Chancellor to Queen Elizabeth I. Once the largest house in England, it was sold to the crown by Sir Christopher's heirs to repay his debts. James I paid several happy visits here but King Charles I's memories were less happy. He was imprisoned here for five months in 1647 following his defeat in the Civil War. After his execution the house was largely demolished with the remains later adapted into the existing house by the present owner's Great-Great Grandmother.

Today, Holdenby House comprises both the original Elizabethan remains and a sympathetic Victorian restoration. It also provides a splendid backdrop to Holdenby's historic garden with its fragrant border and reconstructed Elizabethan garden planted by Rosemary Verey. At the Falconry Centre visitors can see, or try flying, birds of prey.

In the grounds an authentic armoury, a reconstructed 17th century homestead and a collection of rare farm animals - some dating back to Charles I's time - all enhance the sense of history at Holdenby. And for children there is the cuddle farm and play area.

❖

SUITABILITY FOR OTHER EVENTS
Conferences, Seminars, large Corporate Days, Weddings. Archery, Air Displays, Clay Pigeon Shoots, Equestrian Events, Garden Parties, Rallies, Filming etc.

EXTRA FACILITIES
Piano Museum, Falconry Displays, Croquet. A Lecture Room, Screen and Projector can all be provided.

FACILITIES FOR THE DISABLED
Disabled or elderly visitors can be left at the house prior to parking. There are toilet facilities for the disabled.

PARKING FOR COACHES & CARS
There is parking for 100 cars and 5 coaches.

CATERING
Exquisite menus from finger buffets to silver service in the Dining Room or Ball Room for our conference guests. For tours our Victorian Tearoom/Restaurant seats 45 serving teas from £2.50, light meals from £4.50. Menus upon request.

GUIDED TOURS
Tours for groups of up to 80 at no additional cost. Average time for a tour is 45 minutes.

GIFT SHOP
The Gift Shop is open when the house and grounds are open or by prior arrangement. Local Gifts, Crafts and Souvenirs.

GUIDE BOOKS
Colour guide book, £1.50.

EDUCATIONAL VISITS/CHILDREN
Winner of The Sandford Award 1985, 1990 and 1995. Groups are welcome, a guide is provided and a school room is available.

CONTACT

Barbara Brooker
Holdenby House
Holdenby
Northamptonshire
NN6 8DJ

Tel: (01604) 770074

Fax: (01604) 770962

LOCATION

From London via M1, 90 mins. Leave at Junction 15, 15a or 16. Entrance 6 miles N/W of Northampton off the A428, or A50.

Rail: Northampton Station (London - Euston) 1 hour.

Taxi: Favell Cars (01604) 28177 / 20209.

CONFERENCE AND FUNCTION FACILITIES

ROOM	DIMENSIONS	CAPACITY	LAYOUT	POWER POINTS	SUITABLE FOR A/V
Ballroom	44' x 26'	100	Theatre	3	✓
		50	Schoolroom	3	✓
		40	Boardroom	3	✓
Pytchley	24 'x 20'	30	Theatre	3	✓
		16	Boardroom	3	✓
Dining Room		48	Dinner	3	✓

OPENING TIMES

Summer
Easter Sunday - 30 Sept.

HOUSE
Bank Holiday Mondays. except May Day.
1.00 - 6.00pm
Other days by appointment.

GARDEN
Sundays 2.00 - 6.00pm
Bank Hol. Sundays and Bank Hol.Mondays
1.00 - 6.00pm
Thurs. in July and Aug.
1.00 - 5.00pm

Daily by appointment to pre-booked parties.

Winter
By prior arrangement.

Open all year for conferences and corporate days.

ADMISSION

HOUSE & GARDEN
Adult £3.75
Child* £2.00
OAP £3.75
Groups (min 25 people)
Per Person £3.75

GARDEN ONLY
Adult £2.75
Child* £1.75
OAP £2.25
Groups (min 25 people)
Per person £2.25

*Aged 3 - 15yrs.

LAMPORT HALL & GARDENS 🏛
Northampton

Home of the Isham family from 1560 to 1976. The 17th and 18th century façade is by John Webb and the Smiths of Warwick and the North Wing of 1861 by William Burn.

The Hall contains a wealth of outstanding furniture, books and paintings including portraits by Van Dyck, Kneller, Lely and others. The fine rooms include the High Room of 1655 with magnificent plasterwork, the 18th century library with books from the 16th century, the early 19th century Cabinet Room containing rare Venetian cabinets with mythological paintings on glass and the Victorian Dining Room where refreshments are served.

The first floor has undergone lengthy restoration allowing further paintings and furniture to be displayed as well as a photographic record of Sir Gyles Isham, a Hollywood actor, who initiated the restoration.

The tranquil gardens were laid out in 1655 although they owe much to Sir Charles Isham the eccentric 10th Baronet who, in the mid 19th century, created the Italian Garden and the Rockery where he introduced the first garden gnomes to England. There are also box bowers, a rose garden and lily pond and extensive walks, borders and lawns all surrounded by a spacious park.

❖

SUITABILITY FOR OTHER EVENTS
Wedding receptions and ceremonies, conferences, meetings, garden parties, company activity days, clay pigeon shoots, equestrian events, fashion shows, air displays, archery, rallies, filming, shows.

EXTRA FACILITIES
Parkland, Grand Piano, 2 exhibition rooms. Lectures can be arranged on the history of the property and gardens. Lecture/meeting rooms are available, seating a maximum of 50, with audio-visual equipment. Full details of costs on application. Free admission to the agricultural museum on Sundays from Easter to 6th October.

ADVICE TO COURIERS & DRIVERS
Use main entrance only (on A508). No unaccompanied children. No photography inside the house.

FACILITIES FOR THE DISABLED
Disabled or elderly visitors may alight at the entrance door. Access to ground floor and gardens. Toilets.

PARKING FOR COACHES & CARS
Free for 100 cars & 3 coaches, within 20 yds of the property.

GIFT SHOP
Open as house with a range of quality gifts and souvenirs.

CATERING
The Dining/Tea Room seats 50 maximum and groups can book meals in advance. Catering available for special functions, buffets, lunches & dinners. Guided Tours with refreshments.

GUIDED TOURS
Tours are available at no additional cost, by prior arrangement. Maximum size of party is 70, average time taken is $1^1/2$ hours.

GUIDE BOOKS
Colour guide book.

SCHOOL VISITS/CHILDREN
School groups welcome. A work room is available in the Study Centre. Groups are conducted round the house, gardens, church and village by specialist advisory teachers, who provide study packs. Further information contact the Education Officer or the Trust Office (01604) 686272. Special guide book available for children visiting individually or with families.

CONTACT

George Drye
Executive Director
Lamport Hall
Northampton
NN6 9HD

Tel: (01604) 686272
Fax: (01604) 686224

LOCATION

From London via M1, $1^1/4$ hours. Leave at Junction 15. Entrance on A508, 8 miles north of Northampton at junction with B576. 5 mins from A14 (A1/M1 link)

Rail: Kettering Station 15 miles; Northampton 8 miles.

Bus: From Northampton & Market Harborough.

OPENING TIMES

Summer
Easter - 6 October
Sundays and
Bank Hol Mons
2.15 - 5.15pm

August: Mon - Sat
1 tour at 4.30pm

26, 27 Oct 2.15 - 5.15pm

Tours on other days by prior arrangement.

Winter
Group visits only by arrangement.

ADMISSION

Summer
HOUSE & GARDEN
Adult £3.50
Child* £2.00
OAP £3.00
Group** . . . . . . £POA

* Aged 5 - 16yrs.
*Min. payment £125.00 including refreshments

Winter
Group visits only by prior arrangement.

CONFERENCE AND FUNCTION FACILITIES

ROOM	DIMENSIONS	CAPACITY	LAYOUT	POWER POINTS	SUITABLE FOR A/V
Dining Room	31' x 24' 6"	80	Theatre	4	✓
		48	Schoolroom		✓
		27	U-shape		✓
		34	Boardroom		✓
		60	Lunch/Dinner		✓
		60	Buffet		✓

ROCKINGHAM CASTLE
Nr. Corby

A Royal castle until 1530, since then home of the Watson family. Rockingham Castle was built by William the Conqueror on the site of an earlier fortification and was regularly used by the early Kings of England until the 16th century when it was granted by Henry VIII to Edward Watson whose family still live there today.

The house itself is memorable not so much as representing any particular period, but rather a procession of periods. The dominant influence in the building is Tudor within the Norman walls, but practically every century since the 11th has left its mark in the form of architecture, furniture or works of art. The Castle has a particularly fine collection of English 18th, 19th and 20th century paintings, and Charles Dickens, who was a frequent visitor, was so captivated by Rockingham that he used it as a model for Chesney Wold in Bleak House.

The Castle stands in 12 acres of formal and wild garden and commands a splendid view of five counties. Particular features are the 400 year old elephant hedge and the rose garden marking the foundations of the old keep. See Special Exhibition: 450 years a royal castle, 450 years a family home.

CONTACT

Miss K Barton
Rockingham Castle
Market Harborough
Leicestershire
LE16 8TH

Tel: (01536) 770240

LOCATION

2 miles north of Corby;
9 miles from Market Harborough;
14 miles from Stamford on A427;
8 miles from Kettering on A6003

SUITABILITY FOR OTHER EVENTS
Buffets, concerts, conferences, fashion shows, product launches, receptions and seminars. Air displays, clay pigeon shoots, archery, equestrian events, fairs, garden parties. Filming. Special exhibition celebrating 900 years of life in the castle from the Great Council of Rockingham in 1095 to the present day – 450 years a Royal Castle, 450 years a family home.

EXTRA FACILITIES
Grand Piano in the Long Gallery. 250 acres of parkland, grass tennis court, cricket pitch and eventing course. Strip for light aircraft 4 miles.

ADVICE TO COURIERS & DRIVERS
No photography is allowed in the Castle.

FACILITIES FOR THE DISABLED
Disabled toilets available. Elderly or disabled visitors may alight at the Castle entrance. Ramps provided.

PARKING FOR COACHES & CARS
Unlimited parking for cars up to 100 yards from the Castle. Up to 6 coaches can be parked 100 yards from the Castle.

CATERING
Home-made afternoon teas. Light lunches on Sundays and Bank Holidays. Meals on other days by arrangement. Maximum seating 86. Waitress service.

GUIDED TOURS
All pre-booked parties are given a guided tour, except on open-days, at no additional cost. By prior arrangement, the owner may meet the groups. Duration of the tour is 45 minutes.

GIFT SHOP
Open when the castle is open to the public.

GUIDE BOOK
Colour guide £1.95. Special children's guide.

SCHOOL VISITS/ CHILDREN
Rockingham has received 3 Sandford Awards for Heritage Education. There is much of interest for schools. A special pack has been designed with the National Curriculum in mind containing 27 booklets relating to different aspects of the Castle's history, including trails for the grounds, the village and the church. This can be obtained by post, price £7.50. Special tours for schools can be arranged and covered spaces are available for work and picnics when wet.

OPENING TIMES

Summer

Easter Sunday - 20 Oct

Thurs, Sun, BH Mon & Tues following and all Tues in August
1.00 - 5.00pm

Daily by appointment for parties and schools.

Grounds open 11.30 on Bank Hol. Suns & Mons and Suns May to August. Light refreshments available from 12.00 noon.

Winter

Daily by appointment for booked parties and schools. Closed to casual visitors.

ADMISSION

HOUSE & GARDEN
Adult £3.80
Child (to 16 yrs.) . .£2.40
OAP £3.30
Groups
Adult* £3.30
OAP £3.30
Student** £1.50
Family Ticket
2 + 2 . . . .£10.50

*Min. £66.00   **Min. £37.50

GROUNDS ONLY
Adult £2.40
Child (to 16 yrs.) . .£2.40
OAP £2.40

Prices may vary for special events in grounds.

CONFERENCE AND FUNCTION FACILITIES

ROOM	DIMENSIONS	CAPACITY	LAYOUT	POWER POINTS	SUITABLE FOR A/V
Great Hall	37'6" x 22'	100	Theatre	1	3
Panel Room	36' x 23'	100	Theatre	1	3
Long Gallery	87' x 16'6"	100	Theatre	2	
Walkers House 1	31' x 17'6"	60	Buffet	2	
Walkers House 2	24' x 18'	50	Buffet	2	

SULGRAVE MANOR
Sulgrave

SULGRAVE MANOR is the early English home of the ancestors of George Washington, first mentioned in the Domesday Book in 1086. The House was the birthplace of Reverend Lawrence Washington, whose son, Colonel John Washington, left England in 1656 to take up the land which later became Mount Vernon.

In 1914 Sulgrave Manor was presented by a body of British subscribers to the peoples of Great Britain and the United States of America in celebration of the Hundred Years Peace between the two countries. Restored and refurnished, it now presents a perfect example of a small manor house and garden during the time of Shakespeare.

Of special interest is the Washington Coat of Arms (three mullets and two bars) still clearly to be seen in a spandrel of the main doorway. This is said to have inspired the Stars and Stripes of the American National Flag.

Each room in the house is furnished in the style of its period. The Great Hall and Great Chamber above have fine collections of Tudor and Early Jacobean furniture. The Queen Anne wing, added in the year 1700, displays superb examples of 18th century craftsmanship. However it is perhaps the magnificent Kitchen with its unique collection of utensils, its perfect range and typical furniture, that is justifiably one of the great features of the house.

GARDENS
One of the attractive features of the Manor is its garden, designed in 1921 by Sir Reginald Blomfield.

❖

SUITABILITY FOR OTHER EVENTS
Craft fairs, Garden Parties, Receptions, Open Performances, Concerts.

EXTRA FACILITIES
Lectures can be arranged on the property and its history for up to 30 people.

ADVICE TO COURIERS & DRIVERS
Please book in advance as numbers and parking limited. No photography in house; dogs on leads in gardens only. No smoking in the House.

PARKING FOR COACHES & CARS
Parking for 40 cars and 4 coaches, 30 yards from House.

CATERING
'The Brew House' tea room (capacity 25/50 people). Parties can be booked in advance for tea and other meals.

GUIDED TOURS
Available for groups of up to 30 people at no additional cost. Average time taken to see the House 1-1¼ hours. There is a video of the 'Washington Trail', tracing the family links in this country.

GIFT SHOP
Gift Shop open at the same time as House.

GUIDE BOOKS
Colour guide book, £1.50.

SCHOOL VISITS/CHILDREN
Groups are welcome, cost £2.50 per child. A guide is provided. It is especially worthwhile for the young student as it is comparatively small. There is a special children's guide book and a paddock to play in. A teachers pack is available and preliminary visits are free.

CONTACT
Martin Sirot-Smith
Sulgrave Manor
Manor Road
Sulgrave
Banbury
Oxfordshire
OX17 2SD

Tel: (01295) 760205

LOCATION
M40 5mls, M1 15mls.
10 mins from Banbury, Brackley, Towcester.
20 mins to Buckingham.
30 mins to N'hampton.
45 mins to Oxford, Warwick, Stratford.
2hrs from London.

Rail: Banbury Stn 6mls.

Bus: From Banbury/ Brackley.

Taxi: Fisher's Taxis (01295) 760797.

CONFERENCE AND FUNCTION FACILITIES

ROOM	DIMENSIONS	CAPACITY	LAYOUT	POWER POINTS	SUITABLE FOR A/V
Great Hall	24' x 18'	50	Theatre	3	
		50	Buffet	3	
		30	Schoolroom	3	
		24	Dinner	3	

OPENING TIMES
All groups and individuals are taken around the Manor House in regularly conducted tours.

Weekdays:
1 April - 31 October
Daily except Weds
2.00 - 5.30pm

Closed 16 June.
Mornings by appointment only.

Bank Hols and Aug.
10.30 - 1.00pm and
2.00 - 5.30pm.

27 - 31 Dec
10.30am - 1.00pm and
2.00 - 4.30pm.

Weekends:
Apr - Oct
10.30am - 1.00pm and
2.00 - 5.30pm

Mar, Nov and Dec
10.30am - 1.00pm and
2.00 - 4.30pm

NB Last admissions 1 hour before closing times.

Special Event Days:
10.30am - 5.30pm.

Weekdays in Feb, Mar, Nov and Dec open by appointment only. Morning & evening pre-booked parties available throughout the year.

Closed Christmas Day, Boxing Day, the whole of January and Sunday 16 June.

ADMISSION

Adult	£3.50
Child*	£1.75
OAP	£3.50
Student	£1.75
Family**	£10.00

Groups (min 12 people)
Adult	£3.00
Child*	£1.50
OAP	£3.00
Student	£1.50

* Aged 5 - 16yrs.

** 2 adults and 2+ children.

ALTHORP HOUSE

See Page 137 for full page entry.

BOUGHTON HOUSE

See Page 138 for full page entry.

CANONS ASHBY

Tel: 01327 860044

Canons Ashby, Daventry, Northamptonshire NN11 6SD
Owner: National Trust   **Contact:** The Property Manager
Home of the Dryden family since the 16th century, this manor house was built c. 1550, added to in the 1590's, and altered in the 1630's and c. 1710; largely unaltered since. Within the house, Elizabethan wall paintings and outstanding Jacobean plasterwork are of particular interest. A formal garden includes terraces, walls and gate piers of 1710. There is also a medieval priory church and a 70 acre park.
Location: Access from M40, junct. 11 or M1 junct 16. Signposted from A5 2 miles S of Weedon crossroads.
Opening Times: House: 1 Apr - 30 Oct: Sat - Wed & BH Mons (closed Good Friday) 1 - 5.30pm/dusk. Last admissions 5pm. Park open as house, access through garden. Shop open as house.
Admission: Adult £3.40, Child £1.70. Discount for parties, contact Property Manager.

CASTLE ASHBY

See Page 139 for full page entry.

COTON MANOR GARDEN

OPEN

Easter - end Sept, Wed - Sun and Bank Holidays 12 noon - 6.00pm

Lunch: 12 - 2.30pm

Cream Teas: 3 - 6.00pm

Tel: 01604 740219
Fax: 01604 740838

GUILSBOROUGH, NORTHAMPTONSHIRE NN6 8RQ

Owner: Ian Pasley-Tyler Esq   Contact: Ian Pasley-Tyler Esq

17th century stone manor house with old English garden laid out on different levels. Water gardens, herbaceous borders, rose garden, old holly and yew hedges. Collection of ornamental waterfowl, cranes and flamingoes. The Groom's Cottage Restaurant offers delicious home made food at very reasonable prices.
Location: 9 m N of Northampton, off A50 or A428.
Admission: Adult £2.70, Child £1.00, Conc £2.20, Family £7.00. Groups: Standard £2.20, Conc £2.00.

COTTESBROOKE HALL

OPEN

Easter - end Sept
House & Garden: Thurs & Bk Hol Mon afternoons plus Sun afternoons in Sept 2.00 - 5.00pm

Gardens: Wed, Thur, Fri & Bk Hol Mon afternoons plus Sun afternoons in Sept 2.00 - 5.30pm.
Tel: 01604 505808
Fax: 01604 505619

COTTESBROOKE, NORTHAMPTONSHIRE NN6 8PF

Owner: Capt & Mrs Macdonald-Buchanan   Contact: The Administrator
Architecturally magnificent Queen Anne house commenced in 1702. Renowned picture collection, particularly of sporting and equestrian subjects. Fine English and Continental furniture and porcelain. Main vista aligned on celebrated 7th century Saxon church at Brixworth. House reputed to be the pattern for Jane Austen's "Mansfield Park". Notable gardens of great variety including fine old cedars, specimen trees and herbaceous borders.
Location: 10 miles north of Northampton near Creaton on A50, near Brixworth on A508 or Kelmarsh on A14.
Admission: House & Gdns: Adult £4. Gardens only: Adult £2.50, Child half price. Private parties welcome (except Weekends) by prior arrangement.

DEENE PARK

See Page 140 for full page entry.

ELEANOR CROSS

Tel: 01604 780320

Geddington, Kettering, Northamptonshire
Owner: English Heritage   **Contact:** The Midlands Regional Office
One of a series of famous crosses, of elegant sculpted design, erected by Edward I to mark the resting places of the body of his wife, Eleanor, when brought for burial from Harby in Nottinghamshire to Westminster Abbey.
Location: In Geddington, off A43 between Kettering and Corby.
Opening Times: Write for details.

HOLDENBY HOUSE

See Page 141 for full page entry.

KIRBY HALL

Tel: 01536 203230

Deene, Corby, Northamptonshire NN17 3EN
Owner: English Heritage   **Contact:** The Custodian
Outstanding example of a large, stone built Elizabethan mansion, begun in 1570 with 17th century alterations. There are fine gardens, currently being restored.
Location: On unclassified road off A43 NE of Corby.
Opening Times: 1 Apr - 30 Sept: Daily 10am - 6pm. 1 - 31 Oct: 10am - 6pm or dusk if earlier. 1 Nov - 31 Mar: Wed - Sun, 10am - 4pm. (closed lunch 1 - 2pm).
Admission: Adult £2.00, Child £1.00, Conc, £1.50.

LAMPORT HALL & GARDENS

See Page 142 for full page entry.

THE MENAGERIE

Tel: 01536 418205

Horton, Northampton, Northamptonshire NN7 2BX
Owner: The Executors of the late Gervase Jackson Stops   **Contact:** Mark Jackson-Stops
Folly built in the 1750s by Thomas Wright of Durham. The outstanding Rococo plasterwork in the main room includes signs of the zodiac. The gardens where Lord Halifax's animals were once kept, have been created by Ian Kirby and include formal ponds, wetland and bog area, herbaceous borders, two thatched arbours, one circular and classical, and the other triangular and Gothic, and a grotto featuring Orpheus playing to the animals covered in shells and minerals.
Location: 5m SE of Northampton.
Opening Times: House, Grotto and Gardens open to parties of 20 or more by prior appointment £5.00 pp. Gardens: only Thurs from Apr - Sept: 10am - 4pm.
Admission: Adult £2.50, Child £1.00.

NORTHAMPTON CATHEDRAL

Tel: 01604 714556   **Fax:** 01604 712066

Northampton, Northamptonshire NN2 6AG

Contact: Rev K Payne

Partly 19th century Pugin.
Location: ¹/₂m from town centre on A508.
Opening Times: Daily 8am - 7.30pm. Sun services: 8.30am, 10.30am, 5.15pm and 7pm. Weekday services: 9.30am and 7pm.
Admission: Guided visit by prior application.

PREBENDAL MANOR HOUSE

Tel: 01780 782575

Nassington, Nr Peterborough, Northamptonshire PE8 6QG
Owner: Mrs J Baile   **Contact:** Mrs J Baile
The oldest manor in Northamptonshire, dating from the early 13th century overlays a Late Saxon royal manor. Notable buildings included in the visit are the dovecote, tithe barn Museum and Lodgings from which teas and lunches are served. The property is surrounded by an extensive garden which includes two medieval fish ponds and a Herb garden.
Location: 6m N of Oundle, 9 m E of Peterborough, 7 m S of Stamford.
Opening Times: 1 May - 30 Sept: Suns & Weds 2 - 5.30pm. All Bank Holiday Mondays except Christmas. Parties welcome by prior booking outside these dates.
Admission: Adult £3.00, Child £1.50.

ROCKINGHAM CASTLE

See Page 143 for full page entry.

RUSHTON TRIANGULAR LODGE

Tel: 01536 710761

Rushton, Kettering, Northamptonshire NN14 1RP
Owner: English Heritage   **Contact:** The Custodian
This extraordinary building symbolises the Holy Trinity, it has three sides, three floors, trefoil windows and three triangular gables on each side.
Location: 1m W of Rushton, on unclassified road 3m from Desborough on A6.
Opening Times: 1st Apr - 30 Sept: Daily 12 noon - 5pm.
Admission: Adult £1.00, Child 50p, Conc 80p.

SOUTHWICK HALL

Tel: 01832 274064

Southwick, Peterborough, Northamptonshire, PE8 5BL
Owner: Christopher Capron Esq   **Contact:** Mr W.J Richardson
Medieval building with Tudor rebuilding and 18th century additions.
Location: 3 m N of Oundle (A605). 4m W of Bulwick (A43).
Opening Times: Easter - Aug: Bank Hols (Sun and Mon). May - Aug: Wed, 2 - 5pm.
Admission: Adult £3.00, Child £1.50, Conc £2.50.

STOKE PARK PAVILIONS

Tel: 01604 862172

Stoke Bruerne, Towcester, Northamptonshire, NN12 7RZ.
Owner: R D Chancellor Esq   **Contact:** Mrs C Cook
Two 17th century pavilions and colonnade by Inigo Jones.
Location: 7m S of Northampton.
Opening Times: Jun - Aug: Sat, Sun and BHs, 2 - 6pm.
Admission: Adult £1.00, Child 50p.

SULGRAVE MANOR

See Page 144 for full page entry.

Deene Park.

SPECIAL EVENTS

◇ **COTON MANOR GARDEN** Plant Sales	24 – 31 MARCH	
◇ **SULGRAVE MANOR** Festival of Easter Customs	5 - 8 APRIL	
◇ **LAMPORT HALL** Antiques Fair	7 – 8 APRIL	
◇ **SULGRAVE MANOR** Tudor Living History: Sulgrave 1593	20 – 28 APRIL	
◇ **COTON MANOR GARDEN** Outstandingly beautiful bluebell wood	LATE APRIL/EARLY MAY	
◇ **SULGRAVE MANOR** Plants & Gardens Festival	4 – 6 MAY	
◇ **LAMPORT HALL** Craft Festival	5 – 6 MAY	
◇ **DEENE PARK** National Gardens Scheme 2.00 - 5.00 pm (Home made teas)	19 MAY	
◇ **SULGRAVE MANOR** Stars, Stripes & Stitches. Needlework Festival	25 MAY – 2 JUNE	
◇ **LAMPORT HALL** Country Festival	26 – 27 MAY	
◇ **SULGRAVE MANOR** Re-enactment: American War of Independence	8 – 9 JUNE	
◇ **LAMPORT HALL** East Midlands Doll Fair	16 JUNE	
◇ **SULGRAVE MANOR** Stuart Living History: Sulgrave 1646	29 JUNE – 7 JULY	
◇ **SULGRAVE MANOR** Period re-enactment: Medieval Sulgrave	20 – 21 JULY	

◇ **SULGRAVE MANOR** Outdoor Play Production	3 – 4 AUGUST
◇ **SULGRAVE MANOR** Georgian Living History: Sulgrave 1780	23 – 26 AUGUST
◇ **LAMPORT HALL** Antiques Fair	25 – 26 AUGUST
◇ **SULGRAVE MANOR** Period Re-enactment: The Viking Raids	7 – 8 SEPTEMBER
◇ **LAMPORT HALL** Craft Festival	14 – 15 SEPTEMBER
◇ **SULGRAVE MANOR** Tudor Workshops	28 SEPTEMBER – 6 OCTOBER
◇ **COTON MANOR GARDEN** Plant Sales	29 SEPTEMBER – 6 OCTOBER
◇ **LAMPORT HALL** East Midlands Doll Fair	6 OCTOBER
◇ **SULGRAVE MANOR** Chamber Music Concert	12 OCTOBER
◇ **SULGRAVE MANOR** Apple Day Festival	19 – 20 OCTOBER
◇ **LAMPORT HALL** Crafts & Gifts Fair	26 – 27 OCTOBER
◇ **SULGRAVE MANOR** Chamber Music Concert	2 NOVEMBER
◇ **SULGRAVE MANOR** Chamber Music Concert	7 DECEMBER
◇ **SULGRAVE MANOR** A Tudor Christmas	DECEMBER WEEKENDS AND 27 – 31 DECEMBER

For National Trust and English Heritage Events see separate section.

ALNWICK CASTLE
Alnwick

ALNWICK CASTLE, home of the Duke of Northumberland, is the second largest inhabited Castle in England after Windsor and has been in the possession of the Percys, Earls and Dukes of Northumberland, since 1309. The earliest parts of the present Castle were erected by Yvo de Vescy, the first Norman Baron of Alnwick who became the owner of the town soon after 1096.

The rugged medieval exterior belies the richness of the interior, refurbished in the classical style of the Italian Renaissance. This replaces the Gothic decoration carried out by Robert Adam in the 18th century.

The Castle houses an exquisite collection of art treasures, including the finest examples of Italian paintings in the north of England with works by other great artists including Van Dyck and Turner. In addition to fine English and French furniture and ornately carved wooden ceilings, the Castle also houses one of the country's most important collections of early Meissen porcelain.

Other attractions include the Percy State Coach, the dungeon, the gun terrace and the gardens, which offer peaceful walks and superb views over the surrounding countryside.

❖

CONTACT

A Fricker
Alnwick Castle
Estate Office
Alnwick
Northumberland
NE66 1NQ

Tel: (01665) 510777
or (01665) 603942
weekends only

Fax: (01665) 510876

LOCATION

From London 6 hours,
Edinburgh 2 hours,
Chester 4 hours,
Newcastle under 1 hour.

Bus: from bus station in Alnwick.

Rail: Alnmouth Station 5 miles.

OPENING TIMES

Summer
4 April - 13 October
Daily   11.00am - 5.00pm
(except Fridays but open on Good Friday).

Last admission 4.30pm.

Winter
October - Easter
Pre-booked parties only

ADMISSION

Summer
HOUSE & GARDEN
   Adult £4.70
   Child* £2.50
   OAP £4.20
   Family (2+2) . £11.00

Groups (min 12 people)
   Adult £4.20
   Child* £2.20
   OAP £4.00
GROUNDS
   Adult £2.50

Winter
By arrangement only.

*Age 5 - 16

SUITABILITY FOR OTHER EVENTS
Fashion Shows, fairs and filming. The parkland is also available for hire. Please contact the head agent.

ADVICE TO COURIERS & DRIVERS
No unaccompanied children and animals. No photography inside the castle.

FACILITIES FOR THE DISABLED
These are being improved all the time, but please enquire first.

PARKING FOR COACHES & CARS
Parking for 70 cars and 4 coaches adjacent to the Castle. Coach and car parking facilities are also available close by in town.

CATERING
Excellent tearoom for morning coffee, light lunches and afternoon tea. Seats up to 80.

GIFT SHOP
Open at the same time as the Castle. Items include locally made pottery, small gifts and items for children.

GUIDE BOOKS
Colour guide book, published in English, French, Spanish and German.

GUIDED TOURS
Available for pre-booked parties only at £7.00 per head. Average time taken for a tour is 1 hour.

SCHOOL VISITS/CHILDREN
A special guidebook and worksheet are available for children. Parts of particular interest include the Barbican and Gun Terrace. Special rates for children and teachers.

CONFERENCE AND FUNCTION FACILITIES

ROOM	DIMENSIONS	CAPACITY	LAYOUT	POWER POINTS	SUITABLE FOR A/V
The Great Guest Hall	100' x 30'	300	Silver Service/ Buffet	✓	✓

BAMBURGH CASTLE
Bamburgh

BAMBURGH CASTLE is the home of Lady Armstrong and her family. The earliest reference to Bamburgh shows the craggy citadel to have been a royal centre by AD 547. Recent archaeological excavation has revealed that the site has been occupied since prehistoric times. The Norman Keep has been the stronghold for nearly nine centuries, but the remainder has twice been extensively restored, initially by Lord Crewe in the 1750s and subsequently by the first Lord Armstrong at the end of the 19th century. This Castle was the first to succumb to artillery fire - that of Edward IV.

The public rooms contain many exhibits, including the loan collections of armour from HM Tower of London, the John George Joicey Museum, Newcastle-upon-Tyne and other private sources, which complement the Castle's armour. Porcelain, china, jade, furniture from many periods, oils, water-colours and a host of interesting items are all contained within one of the most important buildings of Britain's national heritage.

VIEWS

The views from the ramparts are unsurpassed and take in Holy Island, The Farne Islands, one of Northumberland's finest beaches and, landwards, the Cheviot Hills.

❖

CONTACT

P Bolam
R G Bolam & Son
Townfoot
Rothbury
Northumberland
NE65 7SP

Tel: (01669) 620314
Fax: (01669) 621236

LOCATION

42 miles north of Newcastle upon Tyne.
20 miles south of Berwick upon Tweed.
6 miles east of Belford
B1342 from A1
at Belford.

Bus: Bus service 200 yards.

Taxi: J Swanston (01289) 306124.

OPENING TIMES

April - Sept
Daily 11.00am - 5.00pm

October
Daily 11.00am - 4.30pm

Tours by arrangement at any time.

ADMISSION

Summer
Adult £3.00
Child* £1.50
OAP £2.50
Groups**
Adult £2.00
Child* £0.90
OAP £1.60
* Up to 16
** Min payment £30

Winter
Group rates only quoted.

SUITABILITY FOR OTHER EVENTS
Bamburgh has been used as a location for films both interior and exterior.

ADVICE TO COURIERS & DRIVERS
No pets admitted. No cameras to be used in the interior of the building.

FACILITIES FOR THE DISABLED
Facilities for the disabled are restricted to one toilet and limited access dependant upon disability.

PARKING FOR COACHES & CARS
Capacity of the car park: approx. 100 cars adjacent to the Castle. Coaches park free on tarmac drive at entrance.

CATERING
Tea Rooms for light refreshments during viewing times. Meals for organised groups can be booked in advance.

GUIDED TOURS
By arrangement at any time. Minimum charge out of hours £30.00.

GIFT SHOP
Within the Castle, offering quality merchandise. Open during public viewing hours and also for booked parties.

GUIDE BOOKS
Colour guide book, £1.50.

SCHOOL VISITS/CHILDREN
Groups of children welcome; guide will be provided if requested. Of particular interest, displays of arms and armour and the Armstrong naval gun. No special facilities but guides pitch tours to suit age group. Educational pack available.

BELSAY HALL, CASTLE & GDNS. ⊞
Nr. Ponteland

BELSAY is one of the most remarkable estates in the Scottish border country. The buildings, set amidst 30 acres of magnificent landscaped gardens, have been occupied by the same family for nearly 600 years. The gardens, created largely in the 19th century, are a fascinating mix of the formal and the informal with terraced gardens, a rhododendron garden, magnolia garden, mature woodland and even a winter garden. The buildings comprise of a 14th century castle, a manor house and Belsay Hall, an internationally famous mansion designed by Sir Charles Monck in the 19th century in the style of classical buildings he had encountered during a tour of Greece.

❖

CONTACT

The Custodian
Belsay Hall
Belsay
Nr Ponteland
Northumberland
NE20 0DX

Tel: (01661) 881033

LOCATION

In Belsay
14 miles (22.4 km)
north west of
Newcastle on A696

SUITABILITY FOR OTHER EVENTS
Suitable for small concerts and craft fairs.

EXTRA FACILITIES
Education Centre. An exhibition of Belsay's architectural and landscape history in stable block.

ADVICE TO COURIERS & DRIVERS
Tour leader and Coach driver have free entry. 1 extra place for every 20 additional people.

FACILITIES FOR THE DISABLED
Disabled route through garden, converted W.C.

PARKING FOR COACHES & CARS
Free coach parking available - 200 yards.

CATERING
Catering facilities are available summer season and weekends in March and October. Need to pre-book.

GUIDED TOURS
Introductory talk provided on request.

GIFT SHOP
A wide selection of souvenirs and gifts are available.

GUIDE BOOKS
Souvenir guide book available in the shop.

SCHOOL VISIT/CHILDREN
School visits are free if booked in advance. Contact the Administrator.

OPENING TIMES

Summer
1 April - 30 September
Daily: 9.30am - 6.00pm

Winter
1 - 31 October
Daily: 10.00am - 6.00pm or dusk if earlier.

1 Nov - 31 Mar
Daily 10am - 4pm.

ADMISSION

Adult £3.00
Child* £1.50
Conc £2.30

15% discount on groups of 11 or more.

*5 - 15 years.
Under 5s free

CHILLINGHAM CASTLE
Near Alnwick

This remarkable Castle, the home of Sir Humphry Wakefield Bt, with its alarming dungeons is, and has been, since the 1200's, continuously owned by the family of the Earls Grey and their relations. You will see active restoration of complex masonry, metalwork and ornamental plaster as the great halls and state rooms are gradually brought back to life with antique furniture, tapestries, arms and armour as of old and even a torture chamber.

At first a 12th century stronghold, Chillingham became a fully fortified Castle in the 14th century. Wrapped in the nation's history it occupied a strategic position as fortress during Northumberland's bloody border feuds, often besieged and at many times enjoying the patronage of royal visitors. In Tudor days there were additions but the underlying medieval character has always been retained. The 18th and 19th Centuries saw decorative refinements and extravagances including the lake, garden and grounds laid out by Sir Jeffrey Wyatville, fresh from his triumphs at Windsor Castle.

GARDENS
With romantic grounds the Castle commands breathtaking views of the surrounding countryside. As you walk to the lake you will see according to the season, drifts of snowdrops, daffodils or bluebells and an astonishing display of rhododendrons. This emphasizes the restrained formality of the Elizabethan topiary garden, with its intricately clipped hedges of box and yew. Lawns, the formal gardens and woodland walks are all fully open to the public.

❖

SUITABILITY FOR OTHER EVENTS
Any form of corporate entertainment undertaken, we will also consider any other requests. Weddings welcome.

EXTRA FACILITIES
Chillingham is suitable for the use of light aircraft and helicopters. There is a pistol and rifle range. Salmon, sea trout and trout fishing available, also tuition from qualified shooting instructors, accommodation for up to 30 guests in the Castle. Must be arranged well in advance. Lunches, drinks and dinner for up to 150 people can be arranged at any time.

ADVICE TO COURIERS & DRIVERS
Avoid Lilburn route, gates wide enough to admit any coach. Coach parties welcome by prior arrangement.
Tel: (01668) 215 359 or (0171) 937 7829.
Fax: (01668) 21 5463. Sorry no dogs.

GUIDE BOOKS
There is a history of the Castle available, and a guide to the many ghosts resident at Chillingham. There will soon be a full colour guide to the Castle and its contents.

GUIDED TOURS
These can be arranged, and the owner is frequently available to take parties around personally.

GIFT SHOP
Gift/souvenir shop, also antique and curio shop.

CATERING
Tearoom for use of public, cap. 70. Booked meals for up to 100.

OPENING TIMES

Summer
May - 1 October
12 noon - 5.00pm
closed Tues.

July - August and Bank Holidays, every day
12 noon - 5.30pm

Winter
January - December
Any time by appointment only.

ADMISSION

Summer
Adult £3.50
OAP £2.80
Child* . . . . .Free

Groups (min 10 people)
Per person £2.50
Pre-booking is essential.

* up to 5 accompanied children

CONFERENCE AND FUNCTION FACILITIES

ROOM	DIMENSIONS	CAPACITY	LAYOUT	POWER POINTS	SUITABLE FOR A/V
King James I Room		120			
Great Hall		100			
Minstrels' Hall		50			
2 x Drawing Room		60 each			
Museum		150			
Tea Room		100			
Lower Gallery		30			
Upper Gallery		40			

ALNWICK CASTLE

See Page 147 for full page entry.

AYDON CASTLE

Tel: 01434 632450

Corbridge, Northumberland NE45 5PJ
Owner: English Heritage   **Contact:** The Custodian
One of the finest fortified manor houses in England, dating from the late 13th century. Its survival, intact, can be attributed to its conversion to a farmhouse in the 17th century.
Location: 1m NE of Corbridge, on minor road off B6321 or A68.
Opening Times: 1 Apr - 30 Sept: Daily: 10am - 6pm. 1 - 31 Oct, 10am - 6pm or dusk if earlier. Lunchtime closure 1 - 2pm.
Admission: Adult £1.80, Child 90p, Conc £1.40.

BAMBURGH CASTLE

See Page 148 for full page entry.

BELSAY HALL, CASTLE & GARDENS

See Page 149 for full page entry.

BERWICK BARRACKS

Tel: 01289 304493

The Parade, Berwick-upon-Tweed, Northumberland TD15 1DF
Owner: English Heritage   **Contact:** The Custodian
Among the earliest purpose built barracks, these have changed very little since 1717. They house an exhibition 'By Beat of Drum', which recreates scenes such as the barrack room from the life of the British infantryman, the Museum of the King's Own Scottish Borderers and the Borough Museum with fine art, local history exhibition and other collections. Guided tours available.
Location: On the Parade, off Church Street, Berwick town centre.
Opening Times: 1 Apr - 30 Sept: Daily 10am - 6pm, 1 - 31 Oct: Daily 10am - 6pm or dusk if earlier. 1 Nov - 31 Mar: Wed - Sun 10am - 4pm (closed for lunch 1 - 2pm).
Admission: Adult £2.30, Child £1.20, Conc £1.70.

BERWICK RAMPARTS

Tel: 0191 261 1585

Berwick upon Tweed, Northumberland.
Owner: English Heritage   **Contact:** The North Regional Office
A remarkably complete system of town fortifications consisting of gateways, ramparts and projecting bastions built in the 16th century.
Location: Surrounding Berwick town centre on N bank of River Tweed.
Opening Times: Any reasonable time.

BRINKBURN PRIORY

Tel: 01665 570628

Long Framlington, Morpeth, Northumberland NE65 8AF
Owner: English Heritage   **Contact:** The Custodian
This late 12th century church is a fine example of early Gothic architecture, almost perfectly preserved, and is set in a lovely spot beside the River Coquet.
Location: 4¹/₂m SE of Rothbury off B6334.
Opening Times: 1 Apr - 30 Sept: Daily 12 noon - 5pm.
Admission: Adult £1.40, Child 70p, Conc £1.10.

CHERRYBURN

Tel: 01661 843276

Station Bank, Mickley, Stocksfield, Northumberland NE43 7DB
Owner: The National Trust   **Contact:** The Administrator
Birthplace of Northumbria's greatest artist, wood engraver and naturalist, Thomas Bewick, b.1753. The Museum explores his famous works and life in the occasional demonstrations of hand printing from wood blocks in the printing house. Farmyard animals, picnic area, garden.
Location: 11m W of Newcastle on A695 (200yds signed from Mickley Square).
Opening Times: 1 Apr - end Oct: Daily except Tues & Wed, 1 - 5.30pm. Last adm. 5pm.
Admission: Adult £2.60. No party rate.

CHESTERS ROMAN FORT & MUSEUM

Tel: 01434 681379

Chollerford, Humshaugh, Hexham-on-Tyne, Northumberland NE46 4EP
Owner: English Heritage   **Contact:** The Custodian
The best preserved example of a Roman cavalry fort in Britain, including remains of the bath house on the banks of the River North Tyne. The museum houses a fascinating collection of Roman sculpture and inscriptions. Free coach parking. Catering in Summer.
Location: ¹/₂m W of Chollerford on B6318.
Opening Times: 1 Apr - 30 Sept: Daily 9.30am - 6pm. 1 Oct - 31 Oct: Daily 10am - 6pm or dusk if earlier. 1 Nov - 31 Mar 10am - 4pm.
Admission: Adult £2.50, Child £1.30, Conc £1.90.

CHILLINGHAM CASTLE

See Page 150 for full page entry.

CHIPCHASE CASTLE

Tel: 01434 230203 **Fax:** 01434 230740

Wark, Hexham, Northumberland NE48 3NT
Owner: Mrs P J Torday   **Contact:** Mrs P J Torday
The Castle overlooks the river North Tyne and is set in formal and informal gardens. One walled garden is used as a nursery specialising in unusual perennial plants.
Location: 2 m South of Wark on the Barrasford Road.
Opening Times: Castle: 1 - 28 June: Daily 2 - 5pm. Tours by arrangement at other times. Castle Gardens and Nursery: Easter - 31 July, Thur - Sun and Bk Hol Mon, 10am - 5pm.
Admission: Castle £3.00, Garden £1.50, concessions available, nursery free.

CORBRIDGE ROMAN SITE

Tel: 01434 632349

Corbridge on Tyne, Northumberland NE45 5NT
Owner: English Heritage   **Contact:** The Custodian
A fascinating series of excavated remains, including foundations of granaries with a grain ventilation system. From artifacts found, which can be seen in the site museum, we know a large settlement developed around this supply depot.
Location: ¹/₂m NW of Corbridge on minor road, signposted for Corbridge Roman Site.
Opening Times: 1 Apr - 30 Sept: Daily 10am - 6pm. 1 - 31 Oct: Daily 10am - 6pm or dusk if earlier. 1 Nov - 31 Mar: Wed - Sun 10am - 4pm (closed for lunch 1 - 2pm, Nov - Mar).
Admission: Adult £2.50, Child £1.30, Conc £1.90.

CRAGSIDE HOUSE, GARDEN AND GROUNDS

Tel: 01669 620333

Rothbury, Morpeth, Northumberland
Owner: The National Trust   **Contact:** The Property Manager
Designed by Richard Norman Shaw for the first Lord Armstrong and built between 1864 - 95, the house contains much of its original furniture and pre-Raphaelite paintings. It was the first house in the world to be lit by electricity generated by water power. The grounds are famous for their rhododendrons, magnificent trees and the beauty of the lakes.
Location: 5m E of Rothbury, 30m N of Newcastle-Upon-Tyne. Entrance off Rothbury/Alnwick road B6341, 1m N of Rothbury at Debdon Burn Gate.
Opening Times: 1 Apr - end Oct: Daily except Mon (open BH Mons) House: 1 - 5.30pm, last adm. 4.45pm. Grounds: 10.30am - 7pm, last adm. 5pm. 2 Nov - 15 Dec: Tues, Sat & Sun, 10.30am - 4pm. Visitor Centre: 1 Apr - end Oct: Daily except Mon (open BH Mons) 10.30am - 5.30pm. 2 Nov - 15 Dec: Tues, Sat & Sun 12 noon - 4pm.
Admission: House, Garden, Grounds, Museum & Power Circuit: Adult £5.60. Parties £5.30. Garden and Grounds: Adult £3.60. Parties £3.30. Family ticket £14.00.

DUNSTANBURGH CASTLE

Tel: 01665 576231

c/o 14 Queen Street, Alnwick, Northumberland NE66 1RD
Owner: English Heritage   **Contact:** The Custodian
An easy, but bracing, coastal walk leads to the eerie skeleton of this wonderful 14th century castle sited on a basalt crag, rearing up more than 100 feet from the waves crashing on the rocks below. The surviving ruins include the large gatehouse, which later became the keep, and curtain walls.
Location: 8m NE of Alnwick, on footpaths from Craster or Embleton.
Opening Times: 1 Apr - 30 Sept: Daily 10am - 6pm. 1 - 31 Oct: Daily 10am - 6pm or dusk if earlier. 1 Nov - 31 Mar: Wed - Sun 10am - 4pm (closed for lunch 1 - 2pm).
Admission: Adult £1.50, Child 80p, Conc £1.10.

EDLINGHAM CASTLE

Tel: 0191 261 1585

Edlingham, Alnwick, Northumberland.
Owner: English Heritage   **Contact:** The North Regional Office
Set beside a splendid railway viaduct this complex ruin has defensive features spanning the 13th and 15th centuries.
Location: At E end of Edlingham village, on minor road off B6341 6 m SW of Alnwick.
Opening Times: Any reasonable time.

HERTERTON HOUSE

Tel: 01670 774278

Cambo, Morpeth, Northumberland NE61 4BN
Owner: F Lawley Esq   **Contact:** F Lawley Esq
1 acre of formal garden in stone walls around a 16th century farmhouse, including a small topiary garden, physic garden and flower garden.
Location: 2m N of Cambo, just off B6342.
Opening Times: Garden only: 1 Apr - 30 Sept: Mon, Wed, Fri, Sat, Sun 1.30 - 5.30pm.
Admission: £1.60.

HOUSESTEADS FORT & MUSEUM (ROMAN WALL)

Tel: 01434 344363

Housesteads, Haydon Bridge, Hexham, Northumberland NE47 6NN
Owner: English Heritage   **Contact:** The Custodian
Perched high on a ridge overlooking open moorland, this is the best known part of the Wall. The fort covers five acres and there are remains of many buildings, such as granaries, barrack blocks and gateways. A small exhibition displays altars, inscriptions and models.
Location: 2³/₄m NE of Bardon Mill on B6318.
Opening Times: 1 Apr - 30 Sept: 10am - 6pm. 1 - 31 Oct: 10am - 6pm or dusk if earlier. 1 Nov - 31 Mar 10am - 4pm.
Admission: Adult £2.50, Child £1.30, Conc £1.90.

HOWICK HALL GARDENS

Tel: 01665 577285   **Fax:** 01665 577285

Howick, Alnwick, Northumberland NE66 3LB

Owner: Howick Trustees Ltd   **Contact:** Mrs D Spark

Romantically landscaped grounds surrounding the house in a little valley, with rare rhododendrons and flowering shrubs and trees.

Location: 6m NE of Alnwick

Opening Times: Apr - Oct: Daily 1 - 6pm.

Admission: Adult £2.00, Child £1.00, Senior Citizen £1.00.

KIRKLEY HALL GARDENS

Tel: 01661 860808   **Fax:** 01661 860047

Ponteland, Northumberland NE20 OAQ

Contact: Dr R McParlin

Herbaceous perennials, Victorian walled garden, ornamental borders, trees and shrubs, sunken garden, woodland garden, greenhouses, wildlife pond.

Location: 2 1/2 m NW of Ponteland on C151 to Morpeth.

Opening Times: Throughout the year: Daily 10am - 5pm

Admission: Adult £1.50, Child 70p, Child under 8 free, Family £3.00, Conc 70p, Group £1.20 per person, Guided group £2.50 per person.

THE LADY WATERFORD HALL & MURALS

Tel: 01890 820524

Ford, Berwick-upon-Tweed, Northumberland TD15 2QG

Contact: The Caretaker

Formerly the village school, built in 1862 by Louisa, Marchioness of Waterford, a friend of John Ruskin. She painted a series of murals using local children and their parents as models for Biblical scenes.

Location: 2³/₄m NE of Bardon Mill on B6318.

Opening Times: 30 Mar - 27 Oct: Daily 10.30am - 12.30pm, 1.30 - 5.30pm.

LINDISFARNE CASTLE

Tel: 01289 389244

Holy Island, Berwick-upon-Tweed, Northumberland TD15 2SH

Owner: The National Trust   **Contact:** The Administrator

Built in 1550 to protect Holy Island harbour from attack, the castle was restored and converted into a private house for Edward Hudson by Sir Edwin Lutyens in 1903. Small walled garden was designed by Gertrude Jekyll. 19th century lime kilns in field by the castle.

Location: On Holy Island, 6m E of A1 across causeway.

Opening Times: 1 Apr - end Oct: Daily except Fri (but open Good Fri) 1 - 5.30pm. Last admission 5pm. Admission to garden only when gardener in attendance.

Admission: £3.60, Family £9.00. No party rate. Parties of 15+ must pre-book.

LINDISFARNE PRIORY

Tel: 01289 389200

Holy Island, Berwick-upon-Tweed, Northumberland TD15 2RX

Owner: English Heritage   **Contact:** The Custodian

The site of one of the most important early centres of Christianity in Anglo-Saxon England. St Cuthbert converted pagan Northumbria, and miracles occurring at his shrine established this 11th century priory as a major pilgrimage centre. The evocative ruins, with the decorated 'rainbow' arch curving dramatically across the nave of the church, are still the destination of pilgrims today. The story of Lindisfarne is told in an exhibition which gives an impression of life for the monks, including a reconstruction of a monk's cell.

Location: On Holy Island, which can be reached at low tide across a causeway.

Opening Times: 1 Apr - 30 Sept: Daily 9.30am - 6pm. 1 - 31 Oct: Daily 10am - 6pm or dusk if earlier. 1 Nov - 31 Mar 10am - 4pm. Closed 24 - 26 Dec, 1 Jan.

Admission: Adult £2.50, Child, £1.30, Conc £1.90.

MELDON PARK

Tel: 01670 772661

Morpeth, Northumberland NE61 3SW

Owner: M J B Cookson Esq   **Contact:** M J B Cookson Esq

Early 19th century house by the renowned Newcastle architect, John Dobson. Fine plasterwork in Main Hall added by Lutyens in the 1920s. Rhododendron Garden in early June graces the house with many different colours.

Location: 7m W of Morpeth on B6343 15m N of Newcastle.

Opening Times: Last week in May and first 3 weeks of Jun, 2 - 5pm.

Admission: Adult £3.00, Child 50p, Conc 50%.

NORHAM CASTLE

Tel: 0191 261 1585

Norham, Northumberland.

Owner: English Heritage   **Contact:** The North Regional Office

Set on a promontory in a curve of the River Tweed, this was one of the strongest of the border castles, built c.1160.

Location: Norham village, 6¹/₂ m SW of Berwick-upon-Tweed on minor road off B6470 (from A698).

Opening Times: 1 Apr - 31 Sept: Daily 10am - 6pm. 1 - 31 Oct 10am - 6pm or dusk if earlier. 1 Nov - 31 Mar: Daily 10am - 4pm. Closed 24 - 26 Dec, 1 Jan.

PRESTON TOWER

Tel: 01665 589227

Chathill, Northumberland NE67 5DH

Owner: Major T Baker Cresswell   **Contact:** Major T Baker Cresswell

The Tower was built by Sir Robert Harbottle in 1392 and is one of the few survivors of 78 Pele Towers listed in 1415. The tunnel vaulted rooms remain unaltered and provide a realistic picture of the grim way of life under the constant threat of "Border Reivers".

Location: Follow Historic Property signs on A1 7m N of Alnwick.

Opening Times: Daylight hours all year.

Admission: Adult £1.00, Child 50p, Conc 50p, Groups 50p.

PRUDHOE CASTLE

Tel: 01661 33459

Prudhoe, Northumberland NE42 6NA

Owner: English Heritage   **Contact:** The Custodian

Set on a wooded hillside overlooking the River Tyne are the extensive remains of this 12th century castle including a gatehouse, curtain wall and keep.

Location: In Prudhoe, on minor road off A695.

Opening Times: 1 Apr - 30 Sept: Daily 12 noon - 5pm.

Admission: Adult £1.60, Child 80p, Conc £1.20.

SEATON DELAVAL HALL

SEATON SLUICE, WHITLEY BAY, NORTHUMBERLAND NE26 4QR

Owner: The Lord Hastings   *Contact:* F. Hetherington

Tel: 0191 237 3040 / 0191 237 1493

A splendid English baroque house, regarded by many as Sir John Vanbrugh's masterpiece. The playwright who turned so successfully to Architecture began the great house in 1718 for Admiral George Delaval. Building on the central block (Vanbrugh's Palladian Villa) ceased about 1728. The wings which are arcaded and pedimented include the East Wing containing the magnificent stables. In the grounds are extensive gardens. There is also a coach house and an ice house. For refreshment there is a tea room.

Location: 1/2 from coast at Seaton Sluice between Blyth and Whitley Bay. 10 miles from Newcastle upon Tyne.

Opening Times: 1 May - 30 Sept: Weds, Suns and Bank Holidays, 2 - 6pm.

Admission: Adult £2.50, Child (with adult) 50p. Free parking.

VINDOLANDA

Tel: 01434 344277   **Fax:** 01434 344060

Bardon Mill, Hadrian's Wall, Hexham, Northumberland NE47 7JN

Contact: Mrs P Birley

Recent excavations have uncovered some of the most unusual and well preserved objects to come from the Roman world.

Location: 8m W of Hexham off A69.

Opening Times: Feb - Nov: Daily from 10am. Closes: 4pm in winter & 6.30pm in summer.

Admission: Adult £3.25, Child £2.00, Conc £2.50, 10% discount for groups of 15 plus.

WALLINGTON

Tel: 01670 774283

Cambo, Morpeth, Northumberland NE61 4AR

Owner: The National Trust   **Contact:** The Visitor Manager

Built 1688, altered in 18th century. Central Hall added in 19th century, decorated by William Bell Scott, Ruskin and others. Fine porcelain, furniture and pictures in series of rooms including a late Victorian nursery and dolls' houses. Coach display in West Coach House. Woodlands, lakes, walled terraced garden and conservatory with magnificent fuchsias.

Location: Access from N 12m W of Morpeth on B6343, access from S, A696 from Newcastle. 6m NW of Belsay, B6342 to Cambo.

Opening Times: House: 1 Apr - end Oct: Daily except Tues 1 - 5.30pm. last adm. 5pm. Walled Garden: Daily 1 Apr - end Oct 10.30am - 7pm or dusk. Nov - Mar 10.30am - 4pm or dusk if earlier. Grounds: all year during daylight hours.

Admission: House, Walled Garden and Grounds: Adult £4.60. Parties £4.10. Walled Garden and Grounds only: Adult £2.30. Parties £1.80.

WARKWORTH CASTLE

Tel: 01665 711423

Warkworth, Morpeth, Northumberland NE66 0UJ

Owner: English Heritage   **Contact:** The Custodian

The great towering keep of this 15th century castle, once the home of the mighty Percy family, dominates the town and River Coquet.

Location: 7^1/$_2$m S of Alnwick on A1068.

Opening Times: 1 Apr - 30 Sept: 9.30am - 6pm. 1 - 31 Oct: 10am - 6pm or dusk if earlier.

Admission: Adult £2.00, Child £1.00, Conc £1.50.

WARKWORTH HERMITAGE

Tel: 01665 711423

Warkworth, Northumberland.

Owner: English Heritage   **Contact:** The Custodian

Upstream by boat from the castle this curious hermitage cuts into the rock of the river cliff.

Location: 7^1/$_2$ m S of Alnwick on A1068.

Opening Times: Telephone Warkworth Castle 01665 711423, for opening arrangements.

Where to Stay

For Private Accommodation and Johansens recommended Hotels, see Accommodation Section.

Alnwick Castle.

 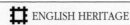

CARLTON HALL

Tel: 01636 821421

Carlton-on-Trent, Nottinghamshire NG23 6NW

Owner: Lt. Col & Mrs Vere-Laurie   **Contact:** Lt. Col & Mrs Vere-Laurie

Mid 18th century house by Joseph Pocklington of Newark. Stables attributed to Carr of York.

Location: 7 m N of Newark off A1.

Opening Times: By appointment only.

Admission: Hall and Garden £3.00, Minimum charge for a party £30.00.

CASTLE MUSEUM & ART GALLERY

Tel: 01159 483504 **Fax:** 01159 350988

Nottingham, Nottinghamshire NG1 6EL

Contact: The Curator

17th century with 13th century gateway, now a museum and art gallery.

Location: Centre of Nottingham.

Opening Times: Daily: 10am - 5pm. Closed Christmas Day and Boxing Day.

Admission: Weekdays free. Weekends: Adult £1.00, Child 50p, Conc for Passport to Leisure Holders. Nov - Feb, Museum opens at 12 noon on Fridays.

CLUMBER PARK

Tel: 01909 476592

Clumber Park, Worksop, Nottinghamshire S80 3AZ

Owner: The National Trust   **Contact:** Visitor Liaison Officer

3,800 acres of parkland, farmland, lake and woodlands. The mansion was demolished in 1938, but the fine Gothic Revival Chapel, built 1886 - 89 for the 7th Duke of Newcastle, survives. Park includes the longest double lime avenue in Europe and a superb 80 acre lake. Also, classical bridge, temples, lawned Lincoln Terrace, pleasure grounds and stable block. Walled Garden including Victorian Apiary. Vineries and Tools exhibition.

Location: 4½m SE of Worksop, 6½m SW of Retford, 1m from A1/A57, 11m from M1 Junction 30.

Opening Times: Park: All year during daylight hours. Walled Garden, Victorian Apiary, Fig House, Vineries & Garden Tools Exhib: 1 Apr - end Sept: Sat, Sun & BH Mon 10am - 5pm, last adm. 4.30pm. Conservation Centre: 1 Apr - 24 Sept: Sat, Sun & BH Mon 1 - 5pm. Chapel: Mar '96 - 12 Jan '97: Daily 10am - 4pm (closed Christmas Day).

Admission: Walled Garden, Victorian Apiary, Vineries & Garden Tools 70p.

HODSOCK PRIORY GARDENS

OPEN

February: Daily
Mon - Fri,
12 noon- 4pm.
Sat & Sun,
10am - 4pm.

April - end August:
2 - 5pm,
Tue, Wed, Thur.

Also 2nd Sun in
April, May & June.

Tel: 01909 591204
Fax: 01909 591578

BLYTH, NR. WORKSOP, NOTTINGHAMSHIRE S81 0TY

Owner: Sir Andrew & Lady Buchanan   *Contact: Lady Buchanan*

5 acre private garden on Domesday site. Sensational snowdrops, daffodils, bluebells, summer borders, roses, lilies, fine trees and woodland walk. Grade I listed gatehouse c.1500. Italianate terrace, Victorian house (not open).

Location: Off B6045 Worksop to Blyth road.

Admission: Adult £2.00, Child free.

HOLME PIERREPONT HALL

OPEN

7 May Bank Hol
June: Sun
July: Thurs & Sun
August: Tue, Thur,
Fris & Suns
Easter, spring &
summer holidays
Suns - Tues:
2.00 - 6.00pm

Groups by appoint-
ment throughout the
year including
evening visits.

Tel: 0115 933 2371

Photo: Richard Prescott

HOLME PIERREPONT, NOTTINGHAM NG12 2LD

Owner: Mr and Mrs Robin Brackenbury   *Contact: Mr Robin Brackenbury*

Visited by Henry VII in 1487, the house is peaceful and welcoming with splendid mediaeval rooms, a Charles II staircase and fine 17th to 20th century English country furniture and family portraits. The courtyard garden, 1875 is planted with roses, herbaceous beds and an elaborate box parterre. The Long Gallery seats 100 for business or charity functions or the Lodgings 30. Filming Welcome.

Location: Five miles from central Nottingham. Follow signs to the National Water Sports Centre and continue on for 1½ miles.

Admission: Adult £3.00, Child £1.00. Gardens only £1.50.

NEWSTEAD ABBEY

Tel: 01623 793557 **Fax:** 01623 797136

Newstead Abbey Park, Nottinghamshire NG15 8GE

Contact: Mr Brian Ayers

Historic home of the poet, Lord Byron, set in grounds of over 300 acres. Mementoes of Byron and decorated rooms from medieval to Victorian times.

Location: 12m N of Nottingham along A60 Mansfield Rd.

Opening Times: 1 Apr - 30 Sept: 12 noon - 6pm, last adm. 5pm. Grounds: All year except last Fri in Nov. Apr - Sept: 9am - 7.30pm. Oct - Mar: 9am - 5pm.

Admission: House & Grounds: Adult £3.50, Child £1.00, Conc £2.00. Grounds Only: Adult £1.70, Child £1.00, Conc £1.00.

NORWOOD PARK

Tel: 01636 815649 **Fax:** 01636 815649

Southwell, Nottinghamshire NG25 0PF

Owner: Sir John Starkey   **Contact:** Mrs Dodd

18th century hunting lodge set gloriously in a medieval park. Terracing, avenue, temple, cricket ground, orchards.

Location: W of Southwell off Halam Rd.

Opening Times: By appointment all year round.

Admission: Grounds, Stable Gallery and House available for all kinds of entertaining. Public Events in the press.

RUFFORD ABBEY

Tel: 01604 730320

Ollerton, Nottinghamshire

Owner: English Heritage   **Contact:** The Midlands Regional Office

A 12th century Cistercian abbey once largely concealed by a 17th century country house. Its demolition revealed the remains of the lay brothers' quarters.

Location: 2 m S of Ollerton off A614.

Opening Times: 1 Apr - 31 Oct: Daily, 10am - 5pm. 1 Nov - 31 Mar: Daily, 10am - 4pm. Closed 24 - 26 Dec, 1 Jan.

KEY TO SYMBOLS: THE NATIONAL TRUST    ENGLISH HERITAGE   HISTORIC HOUSES ASSOCIATION

THRUMPTON HALL

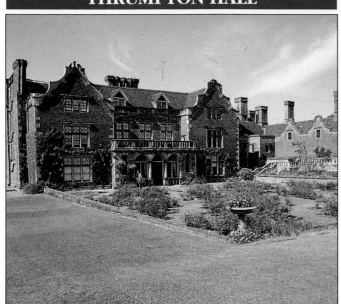

THRUMPTON, NOTTINGHAM NG11 0AX

Owner: *The Hon Mrs G Seymour*　　***Contact:*** *The Hon Mrs G Seymour*

Tel: 0115 9830333　**Fax:** 0171 916 2942

Fine Jacobean house, built in 1607 incorporating an earlier Manor House. Priest's hiding hole, magnificent carved Charles II staircase, carved and panelled saloon. Other fine rooms containing beautiful 17th and 18th century furniture and many fine portraits. Large lawns separated from landscaped park by ha-ha and by lake in front of the house. The house is still lived in as a home and the owner will show parties round when possible. Conferences & business lunches, dining room with capacity for 52 with silver service or buffet. Free access and meal for drivers, free parking near house. Disabled facilities. Gift shop.

Location: 7m S of Northampton, 3m E M1 at junction 24, 1m from A453.

Opening Times: By appointment. Parties of 20 or more 10.30am - 7.30pm.

Admission: Adult £4.00, Child £2.00.

WINKBURN HALL　　　　　　**Tel:** 01636 636465　**Fax:** 01636 636717

Winkburn, Newark, Nottinghamshire NG22 8PQ

Owner: Richard Craven-Smith-Milnes Esq　　**Contact:** Richard Craven-Smith-Milnes Esq

A fine William & Mary house recently restored, nestles besides a charming church.

Location: 8m W of Newark off A617.

Opening Times: Throughout the year by appointment only.

Admission: Standard £3.50.

WOLLATON HALL NATURAL HISTORY MUSEUM　　　**Tel:** 0115 928 1333

Wollaton Park, Nottingham, Nottinghamshire NG8 2AE

Owner: Nottingham City Council　　　　**Contact:** The Administrator

Flamboyant Elizabethan house built by Robert Smythson in a park, which despite being surrounded by Nottingham suburbs, remains attractively wild. Now used as a museum.

Location: Wollaton Park, Nottingham.

Opening Times: Throughout the year by appointment only.

Admission: Weekdays free. Weekends & Bank hols, Adult £1.00, Child 50p. Joint ticket for Wollaton Hall & Industrial Museum. Grounds 50p/car (free orange badge holders.

Where to Stay
For Private Accommodation and
Johansens
recommended Hotels,
see Accommodation
Section.

Kings and Queens from 1485 to 1996

DYNASTIES / Periods / Reigns	DATES	DYNASTIES / Periods / Reigns	DATES
TUDOR		**HANOVER**	
Tudor	1485 - 1558	Georgian	1714 - 1811
Henry VII	1485 - 1509	George I	1714 - 1727
Henry VIII	1509 - 1547	George II	1727 - 1760
Edward VI	1547 - 1553	George III	1760 - 1820
Mary I (Bloody Mary)	1553 - 1558	Regency	1811 - 1837
Elizabethan	1558 - 1603	George IV	1820 - 1830
Elizabeth I	1558 - 1603	William IV	1830 - 1837
STUART		Victorian	1837 - 1901
Jacobean	1603 - 1625	Victoria	1837 - 1901
James I	1603 - 1625	Edwardian	1901 - 1910
(James VI of Scotland)		Edward VII	1901 - 1910
Carolean	1625 - 1685	**WINDSOR**	
Charles I	1625 - 1649	George V	1910 - 1936
The Commonwealth	1649 - 1660	Edward VIII	1936
Charles II	1660 - 1685	George VI	1936 - 1952
Jacobean	1685 - 1688	Elizabeth II	1952 - Present
James II	1685 - 1688		
William and Mary	1688 - 1702		
William III (of Orange)	1688 - 1702		
and Mary II (died 1694)			
Queen Anne	1702 - 1714		
Anne	1702 - 1714		

BLENHEIM PALACE
Woodstock

BLENHEIM PALACE, home of the 11th Duke of Marlborough and birthplace of Sir Winston Churchill, was built between 1705-1722 for John Churchill, 1st Duke of Marlborough, in grateful recognition of his magnificent victory at the Battle of Blenheim in 1704. One of England's largest private houses, Blenheim was built in the Baroque style by Sir John Vanbrugh and is considered his masterpiece. The land and £240,000 were given by Queen Anne and a grateful nation.

Blenheim's wonderful interior reveals striking contrasts - from the lofty Great Hall to gilded State rooms and the majestic Long Library. The superb collection includes fine paintings, furniture, bronzes and the famous Marlborough Victories tapestries. The five room Churchill Exhibition includes his birth room.

GARDENS

The Palace grounds reflect the evolution of grand garden design. Of the original work by Queen Anne's gardener, Henry Wise, only the Walled Garden remains; but dominating all is the superb landscaping of 'Capability' Brown. Dating from 1764, his work includes the lake, Park and Gardens. Achille Duchêne, employed by the 9th Duke, subsequently recreated the Great Court and built the Italian Garden on the east and the Water Terraces on the west of the Palace. Recently the Pleasure Gardens complex has been developed. This includes the Marlborough Maze, Herb Garden, Adventure Playground, Butterfly House and Putting Greens.

CONTACT

Paul F D Duffie FTS
Blenheim Palace
Woodstock
Oxon
OX20 1PX

Tel: (01993) 811091
Fax: (01993) 813527

LOCATION

From London, M40, A44
(1¹/₂ hrs), 8 mls N of
Oxford. London 63mls
Birmingham 54mls

Air: Heathrow Airport
60mls (1hr)

Coach: From London
(Victoria) to Oxford

Rail: Oxford Station

Bus: Oxford
(Cornmarket) -
Woodstock

OPENING TIMES

Summer
Mid March - 31 October

Daily: 10.30am-5.30pm
Last admission 4.45pm

Winter
1 Nov - Mid March
Park only

The Duke of Marlborough reserves the right to close the Palace or Park or to amend admission prices without notice.

ADMISSION

- Palace Tour and Churchill Exhibition
- Park
- Garden
- Butterfly House
- Adventure Play Area
- Motor Launch
- Train
- Car or Coach Parking, but not entry to the maze or rowing boat hire.

Adult	£7.30
Child (5 - 15 yrs.)	£3.70
Child (16 & 17 yrs.)	£5.30
OAP	£5.30
Groups	
Adult	£6.00
OAP	£5.00
Child (5 - 15 yrs.)	£3.00
Child (16 & 17 yrs.)	£5.00

- Blenheim Park, Butterfly House, Adventure Play Area, Train, Parking, but not entry to the Marlborough Maze or Rowing Boat Hire.

Coaches*	£17.50
Cars*	£4.00
Adult**	£1.00
Child**	£0.50

* Including occupants.
** Pedestrians.

- Private visits† £15.00

† By appointment only.
Min. charge of £300 (mornings and £450 (evenings)

BLENHEIM PALACE CONT ...

The Mermaid Fountain in the Italian Garden.

CATERING
2 Restaurants, 2 Cafeterias. Group capacity 150. Groups can book for afternoon tea, buffets and luncheon. Menus available on request. Further information/bookings: Catering Manager, (01993) 811274.

FACILITIES FOR THE DISABLED
Disabled or elderly visitors may alight at the Palace entrance and vehicles are then parked in allocated area. Toilet facilities in both the Palace and Park.

GUIDED TOURS
Tours included in the cost of entry. Guide Book £3.00.

GIFT SHOPS
Open 10.30am - 5.30pm also a Bookshop, Souvenir Stall and Garden Shop.

EDUCATION SERVICE
Blenheim has held the Sandford Award for an outstanding contribution to Heritage Education since 1982. Operated by a very experienced Head Master, Education Groups may study virtually all subjects at all four stages of the National Curriculum as well as have general interest or leisure visits. Tourism Studies (all levels) available.

SUITABILITY FOR OTHER EVENTS
Corporate hospitality, including dinners and receptions, filming, equestrian events, craft fairs. Will consider any proposals. (Contact Admin Office). The Orangery, a new banqueting suite seats 150 for luncheon or dinner, available throughout the year together with the Spencer Churchill Conference Room.

For details contact Town and Country Catering tel: 01993 813874/5.

EXTRA FACILITIES
Lake (rowing boats for hire), motor launch trips, train rides. Private and language tours may be prebooked.

ADVICE TO COURIERS & DRIVERS
Advise Administrator of special requirements for groups over 100. Coaches/groups welcome without pre-booking. 'Notes for Party Organisers' available by post. Dogs on leash in Park. (Guide dogs only in House and Garden). Photography inside (no flash). Unlimited parking for cars and coaches.

CONFERENCE AND FUNCTION FACILITIES

ROOM	DIMENSIONS	CAPACITY	LAYOUT	POWER POINTS	SUITABLE FOR A/V
Orangery		150	Dinner	✓	✓
Spencer Churchill		80	Theatre	✓	✓
		60	Schoolroom		
		40	U-shape		
		40	Boardroom		
Great Hall	70' x 40'	150	Dinner	✓	✓
Saloon	50' x 30'	72	Dinner	✓	✓
with Great Hall		450	Reception		
with Great Hall & Library		750	Reception		
Library	180' x 40'	300	Dinner	✓	✓

The second State Room.

BROUGHTON CASTLE
Banbury

BROUGHTON CASTLE is essentially a family home lived in by Lord and Lady Saye and Sele and their family.

The original medieval Manor House, of which much remains today, was built in about 1300 by Sir John de Broughton. It stands on an island site surrounded by a 3 acre moat. The Castle was greatly enlarged between 1550 and 1600, at which time it was embellished with magnificent plaster ceilings, splendid panelling and fine fireplaces.

In the 17th century William 8th Lord Saye and Sele, played a leading role in national affairs. He opposed Charles I's efforts to rule without Parliament and Broughton became a secret meeting place for the King's opponents.

During the Civil War William raised a regiment and he and his 4 sons all fought at the nearby Battle of Edgehill. After the battle the Castle was besieged and captured.

Arms and armour for the Civil War and from other periods are displayed in the Great Hall. Visitors may also see the Gatehouse, Gardens and Park together with the nearby 14th century Church of St Mary, in which there are many family tombs, memorials and hatchments.

GARDENS
The garden areas consists of mixed herbaceous and shrub borders containing many old roses. In addition, there is a formal walled garden with beds of roses surrounded by box hedging and lined by more mixed borders.

❖

CONTACT

Mrs C M Cozens
Broughton Castle
Banbury
Oxfordshire
OX15 5EB

Tel: (01295) 262624
(01869) 337126

LOCATION

Broughton Castle is 2 miles west of Banbury Cross on the B4035, Shipston on Stour - Banbury Road. Easily accessible from Stratford-on-Avon, Warwick, Oxford, Burford and the Cotswolds. M40 exit 11.

Rail: From London/ Birmingham to Banbury.

OPENING TIMES

Summer

18 May - 14 September Wednesdays & Sundays: Also Thursdays in July and August and Bank Holiday Sundays and Bank Holiday Mondays (including Easter)

2.00 - 5.00pm

Groups welcome on any day and at any time throughout the year by appointment.

ADMISSION

Adult £3.50
Child (0-16) £2.00
OAP £3.00
Groups*
  Adult £3.00
  Child (0-16) £2.00
  OAP £3.00

* Min payment: adults £60.00 children £35.00

SUITABILITY FOR OTHER EVENTS
Broughton offers a most unusual setting for filming, product launches, advertising features, corporate events in Park.

ADVICE TO COURIERS & DRIVERS
Photography permitted for personal use. No dogs inside House.

FACILITIES FOR THE DISABLED
Disabled visitors allowed vehicle access to main entrance.

PARKING FOR COACHES & CARS
Capacity of the car park: 60 cars with unlimited overflow and 6 coaches with ample overflow. Both areas are 300 yards from the Castle.

CATERING
Tea Room available on open days. Tea/Coffee available for guided groups if pre-booked. Other meals by arrangement.

GUIDED TOURS
Available to pre-booked groups at no extra charge. Guided tours not available on open days.

GIFT SHOP
Open on public open days and also for pre-booked guided groups.

GUIDE BOOKS
Colour guide book, £1.50. Children's guide book, 50p. Brief notes are available in French, Spanish, Dutch, Italian, Japanese, German, Polish and Greek.

SCHOOL VISITS/CHILDREN
School visits welcomed. Children's guide books available. Children may try on armour.

KINGSTONE LISLE PARK
Wantage

KINGSTONE LISLE is a sensational Palladian House, home of the Lonsdale Family. The house is set in 140 acres of parkland. Superb views are enjoyed up to the Lambourn Downs where the Roman Ridgeway marks the southern boundary. Three spring-fed lakes beside the house complete this very attractive landscape.

The House built in 1677, is on the site of a fortified Castle which burnt down in 1620 (the original 12th century church is all that remains). The nearby Blowing Stone which according to legend was blown by King Alfred to muster his armies on the Downs is still in the village and can be blown by visitors during daylight hours.

The hall is in the style of Sir John Soane and there is a strong impression of entering an Italian Palazzo with beautiful ornate plaster ceilings, columns and figurines. By complete contrast the inner hall becomes the classical English country house, the most exciting feature being the Flying Staircase winding its way up, totally unsupported.

A fine collection of art, furniture, clocks, glass and needlework together with the architecture inspire visitors with admiration for the craftsmanship that has existed in Britain over the centuries.

GARDENS
Twelve acres of gardens include a shrubbery, pleached limes, an avenue leading up to an ornamental pond and a replica of Queen Mary's rose garden in Regent's Park.

CONTACT

The Secretary
Kingstone Lisle Park
Wantage
Oxfordshire
OX12 9QL

Tel: (01367) 820599

Fax: (01367) 820749

LOCATION

From London 76 miles,
M4 Junct. 14.
From Oxford A420,
20 miles

Air: Heathrow Airport approx 1 hour via M4.

Rail: To Didcot where taxis are available.

OPENING TIMES

Monday 6 May
1.30 - 5.00pm

Family Fun Day in aid of FSID on Monday 27 May

11.00am - 5.00pm

ADMISSION

Adult £6.00
Child (Under 16) . . .Free

Coach parties are welcome throughout the year by prior appointment only.

SUITABILITY FOR OTHER EVENTS
Filming and photography; shooting parties; exclusive house parties; dinner, bed and breakfast by arrangement.

EXTRA FACILITIES
Holiday accommodation. Trout fishing all year round. Coarse fishing (seasonal). Private 9 hole golf practice course.

ADVICE TO COURIERS & DRIVERS
Alternative accommodation available at the Blowing Stone Inn in the village.

FACILITIES FOR THE DISABLED
Disabled and elderly visitors may alight at the entrance to the property. There are no toilets for the disabled.

PARKING FOR COACHES & CARS
Capacity of the car park: 25 cars, 30 yards from the House, and 3 coaches, 10 yards from the House.

CATERING
Lunch and dinner parties available strictly by arrangement for up to 50 people in the superb formal dining room.

GUIDED TOURS
On the hour at 2, 3 and 4.00pm on Monday, 6 May.

GUIDE BOOKS
Colour guide book, £2.00.

CONFERENCE AND FUNCTION FACILITIES

ROOM	DIMENSIONS	CAPACITY	LAYOUT	POWER POINTS	SUITABLE FOR A/V
Dining Room	22' x 35'	22	Boardroom	✓	✓
		100	Buffet		
		50	Lunch/Dinner		
Hall	22' x 38'	100	Theatre	✓	✓
Drawing Room	35' x 21'	100	Theatre	✓	✓

STONOR
Henley-on-Thames

Stonor, family home of Lord and Lady Camoys and the Stonor family for over 800 years, is set in a valley in the beautiful woods of the Chiltern Hills and surrounded by an extensive deer park.

The earliest part of the house dates from the 12th century, whilst most of the house was built in the 14th century. Early use of brick in Tudor times resulted in a more uniform façade concealing the earlier buildings, and changes to the windows and the roof in the 18th century reflect the Georgian appearance still apparent today.

Inside, the house shows strong Gothic decoration, also from the 18th century, and contains many items of rare furniture, sculptures,

bronzes, tapestries, paintings and portraits of the family from Britain, Europe and America.

The Catholic Chapel used continuously through the Reformation is sited close by a pagan stone circle. In 1581, Stonor served as a sanctuary for St Edmund Campion, and an exhibition at the house features his life and work.

GARDENS

Extensive gardens enclosed at the rear of the house face south and have fine views over the park. The springtime display of daffodils is particularly outstanding.

For 1996 the garden will feature a display of stone sculpture from Zimbabwe.

CONTACT

D Boddy
Stonor Park
Henley-on-Thames
Oxfordshire
RG9 6HF

Tel: (01491) 638587

Fax: (01491) 638587

LOCATION

1 hour from London, M4 to Junct. 8/9. A4130 to Henley-on-Thames, then A4130/B480 to Stonor.

Bus: 3 miles along the Oxford - London route.

Rail: Henley-on-Thames Station 5 miles.

OPENING TIMES

Summer
April - September
Sunday: 2.00 - 5.30pm
Mons: 2.00 - 5.30pm
Bank Hols only
Tues: Groups by appointment
Weds: not April: 2.00 - 5.30pm
Thurs: Jul & Aug only 2.00 - 5.30pm
Fris: Closed
Sat: Aug only: 2.00 - 5.30pm

Groups by appointment on Weds & Thurs on the occasions the house is not open to the public.

Winter
Oct - Mar Closed

ADMISSION

HOUSE & GARDEN
Adult £4.00
Child (under 14) . . .Free
Groups** £3.50

GARDENS ONLY
Adult £2.00

** Min 12 persons, in a single payment. Visits outside normal hours at full rate and subject to a minimum of 20 persons.
School groups £2.50 per head, 1 teacher for every 10 children admitted free.
HHA Free.

SUITABILITY FOR OTHER EVENTS
Grounds available for filming, craft fairs, car displays, product promotion, clay pigeon shooting.

EXTRA FACILITIES
Coffee for morning tours, by arrangement. There are also a limited number of evening tours and buffet suppers, also by prior arrangement. Lectures can be given on the property, its contents and history.

ADVICE TO COURIERS & DRIVERS
Admissions from groups must be by single payment on arrival unless prior arrangements are made for payment with vouchers. No dogs except on leads and not allowed within the House, tearoom or shop. No smoking in House, tearoom or shop. No photography in House.

FACILITIES FOR THE DISABLED
Disabled and elderly visitors may be left at the entrance to the house before parking. There are no toilets for the disabled, although access to the toilets is level. Ramp access to gardens, tearoom and shop.

PARKING FOR COACHES & CARS
Capacity of the Car Park: unlimited area for cars and space for 30 coaches, 100 yards from the House.

CATERING
Groups can book lunch or supper. Afternoon Teas are available during all open times without prior booking. Menus available upon request.

GUIDED TOURS
Guided tours are available outside normal public hours. From 20 to 60 people can be taken round at any one time. Tour takes $1\frac{1}{4}$-$1\frac{1}{2}$ hours.

GIFT SHOP
Open for same hours as the House. Selection of Stonor and general souvenirs.

GUIDE BOOKS
Colour guide book, with separate handlist of contents, price £2.00

SCHOOL VISITS/CHILDREN
School groups are welcome, cost £2.50 per head. Lectures and guided tours by arrangement.

ARDINGTON HOUSE

Tel: 01235 833244

Wantage, Oxfordshire OX12 8QA

Owner: Mrs D C N Baring **Contact:** Mrs D C N Baring

Early 18th century exceptionally fine brickwork hall with imperial staircase, panelled dining room with plasterwork ceiling. Attractive garden and stable yard. Guided tours by members of the family.

Location: 12m S of Oxford, 12m N of Newbury, 2$^1/_2$m E of Wantage.

Opening Times: May - Sept: Mons & all Bank Hols 2.30 - 4.30pm. Parties welcomed by appointment.

Admission: House and Gardens £2.50. Small supper parties, coffee & tea by arrangement.

BLENHEIM PALACE

See Pages 156 & 157 for full page entry.

BROOK COTTAGE

Tel: 01295 670303 / 670590

Well Lane, Alkerton, Nr. Banbury OX15 6NL

Owner: Mr & Mrs David Hodges **Contact:** Mr & Mrs David Hodges

4 acre hillside garden. Wide variety of trees, shrubs and herbaceous plants in areas of differing character, water garden, alpine scree, one-colour borders, over 200 shrub and climbing roses, many clematis. Unusual plants for sale. Refreshments for parties by prior arrangement, otherwise DIY coffee/tea.

Location: 6m NW of Banbury, $^1/_2$ m from A422 Banbury to Stratford-upon-Avon road.

Opening Times: 1 April - 31 Oct: Mon - Fri, 9.00am - 6.00pm. Evenings, weekends and all group visits by appointment.

Admission: Adult £2.00, OAP £1.50, Child Free. In aid of National Garden Scheme.

BROUGHTON CASTLE

See Page 158 for full page entry.

BUSCOT OLD PARSONAGE

Tel: 01494 528051

Buscot, Faringdon, Oxfordshire SN7 8DQ

Owner: The National Trust **Contact:** The Tenant

An early 18th century house of Cotswold stone on the bank of the Thames with a small garden.

Location: 2m from Lechlade, 4m from Faringdon on A417.

Opening Times: Apr - end Oct, Wed only 2 - 6pm by appointment.

Admission: £1.00. Not suitable for parties.

BUSCOT PARK

Tel: 01367 242094

Buscot, Faringdon, Oxfordshire SN7 8DQ

Owner: The National Trust **Contact:** Lord Faringdon

A late 18th century house with pleasure gardens, set within a park.

Location: Between Lechlade and Faringdon on A417.

Opening Times: House & Grounds: Apr - end Sept (including Good Fri, Easter Sat & Sun): Wed to Fri 2 - 6pm. Also open every 2nd and 4th weekend 2 - 6pm. Grounds only in April to end Sept: Mon (not BH's) and Tues 2 - 6pm.

Admission: House & Grounds £4.00, Grounds only £3.00. No reduction for parties, which must book in advance.

CHRIST CHURCH CATHEDRAL

Tel: 01865 276154

The Sacristy, The Cathedral, Oxford OX1 1DP

Contact: Mr Jim Godfrey

12th century Norman Church, formerly an Augustinian monastery, given Cathedral status in 16th century by Henry VIII. Also the college chapel for Christ Church, the largest of the Oxford Colleges.

Location: City centre, off St Aldates. Entry via Meadow Gate visitors entrance on south side of college.

Opening Times: Mon - Sat: 9am - 5pm. Sun: 1pm - 5pm, closed Christmas Day. Services: weekdays 7.20am, 6pm. Sun 8am, 10am, 11.15am, 6pm.

Admission: Adult £3.00, Conc. £2.00, Family Ticket £6.00, Child under 5 Free.

COGGES MANOR FARM MUSEUM

Tel: 01993 772602 **Fax:** 01993 703056

Church Lane, Witney, Oxfordshire OX8 6LA

Owner: Oxfordshire County Council **Contact:** Ms Catherine Mason

The Manor House dates from the 13th century, rooms are furnished to show life at the end of the 19th century. Daily demonstrations of cooking on the Victorian range. On the first floor, samples of original wallpapers and finds from under the floorboards accompany the story of the history of the house. In one of the rooms, rare 17th century painted panelling survives. Farm buildings including two 18th century barns, stables and a thatched ox byre, display farm implements. Traditional breeds of farm animals, hand milking demonstration each day. Seasonal produce from the walled kitchen garden sold in the museum shop. Cafeteria selling light lunches, snacks and teas.

Location: Just off A40 Oxford - Burford Road.

Opening Times: April - end October: Tues - Fri 10.30am - 5.30pm. Sat & Sun, 12 noon - 5.30pm. Open BH Mons. Closed Good Fri. Early closing in Oct. Closed Mondays.

Admission: Adult £3.00, Child £1.50, Family £8.00, Conc £1.75.

DEDDINGTON CASTLE

Tel: 01179 750700

Deddington, Oxfordshire

Owner: English Heritage **Contact:** The South West Regional Office

Extensive earthworks concealing the remains of a 12th century castle which was ruined as early as the 14th century.

Location: S of B4031 on E side of Deddington, 17m N of Oxford on A423.

Opening Times: Any reasonable time.

DITCHLEY PARK

Tel: 01608 677346

Enstone, Oxfordshire OX7 4ER

Owner: Ditchley Foundation **Contact:** Brigadier Michael Willis

The most important house by James Gibbs with most distinguished interiors by Henry Flitcroft and William Kent. Ditchley was a regular weekend retreat for Churchill during the Second World War.

Location: 2m from Charlbury.

Opening Times: Visits only by prior arrangement with the Bursar.

FAWLEY COURT

HISTORIC HOUSE & MUSEUM, HENLEY-ON-THAMES RG9 3AE

Owner: *Marian Fathers* ***Contact:*** *The Secretary*

Tel: 01491 574917 **Fax:** 01491 411587

Designed by Christopher Wren, built in 1684 for Col W Freeman, decorated by Grinling Gibbons and by James Wyatt. The Museum consists of a library, various documents of the Polish Kings, a very well preserved collection of historical sabres and many memorable military objects of the Polish army. Paintings, early books, numismatic collections, arms and armour are also housed in a part of 12th century manor house.

Location: 1m N of Henley-on-Thames via A4155 to Marlow.

Opening Times: Mar - Oct: Wed, Thur & Sun, 2 - 5pm. Closed Easter and Whitsuntide weeks.

Admission: House, Museum & Gardens: Adult £3.00, OAP £2.00, Child £1.00. Groups over 15 £2 per person.

GREAT COXWELL BARN

Tel: 01494 528051

Great Coxwell, Faringdon, Oxfordshire

Owner: The National Trust **Contact:** The Administrator

A 13th century monastic barn, stone built with stone tiled roof, which has an interesting timber construction.

Location: 2m SW of Faringdon between A420 and B4019.

Opening Times: All year: Daily at reasonable hours.

Admission: 50p.

GREYS COURT

Tel: 01491 628529

Rotherfield Greys, Henley-on-Thames, Oxfordshire RG9 4PG

Owner: The National Trust   **Contact:** The Custodian

Rebuilt in the 16th century and added to in the 17th, 18th and 19th centuries, the house is set amid the remains of the courtyard walls and towers of a 14th century fortified house. A Tudor donkey wheel well-house and an ice house are still intact, and the garden contains Archbishop's Maze, inspired by Archbishop Runcie's enthronement speech in 1980.

Location: 3m W of Henley-on-Thames, E of B481.

Opening Times: Apr - end Sept: House: Mon, Wed & Fri 2 - 6pm (closed Good Fri). Garden: Daily except Thur & Sun 2 - 6pm (closed Good Fri) Last admission 5.30pm.

Admission: House & Garden: £4.00, Family £10.00. Garden only: £3.00, Family £7.50. No reduction for coach parties who must book.

KINGSTON BAGPUIZE HOUSE

ABINGDON, OXFORDSHIRE OX13 5AX

Owner: Mr & Mrs Francis Grant   *Contact: Mrs Francis Grant*

Tel: 01865 820259

Beautiful Charles II manor house. A family home, it has a fine cantilevered staircase and panelled rooms with some good furniture and pictures. Set in mature parkland, the gardens including shrub border and woodland garden contain many unusual trees, shrubs, perennials and bulbs. Available for functions and other events.

Location: In Kingston Bagpuize village, off A415 Abingdon to Witney road south of A415/A420 intersection. Abingdon 5 miles, Oxford 9 miles.

Opening Times: Easter - 22 Sept: Bk Hol weekends (Sat, Sun & Mon), Wed, Sat & Sun. Apr: 6, 7, 8, 17, 20, 21. May: 4, 5, 6, 25, 26, 27. Jun: 12, 15, 16 Jul: 17, 20, 21.Aug: 7, 10, 11, 24, 25, 26. Sept: 4, 7, 8, 18, 21, 22. 2.30 - 5.30pm. Last entry 5pm.

Admission: House & Garden: Adult £3.00, OAP £2.50, Child £2.00, (children under 5 not admitted to house). Gardens: £1.00 (child under 5 Free).
Groups by arrangement Feb - Nov only. No dogs.

KINGSTONE LISLE PARK

See Page 159 for full page entry.

MAPLEDURHAM HOUSE & WATERMILL

OPEN

Easter - end Sept:
Sat, Sun & Bank Hols.

Country Park:
12.30 - 6pm

Watermill: 1 - 5pm

House: 2.30 - 5pm

Midweek parties by arrangement only
(Tue, Wed, Thur).

Tel: 01734 723350
Fax: 01734 724016

MAPLEDURHAM, READING, BERKSHIRE RG4 7TR

Owner: JJ and Lady Anne Eyston   *Contact: Ms. Lucy Boon*

Late 16th century Elizabethan home of the Blount family. Original plaster ceilings, great oak staircase, fine collection of paintings and a private chapel in Strawberry Hill Gothic added in 1797. Interesting literary connections with Alexander Pope, Galsworthy's Forsyte saga and Kenneth Graham's "Wind in the Willows". 15th century watermill fully restored producing flour and bran which is sold in the giftshop.

Location: 4 miles north west of Reading off A4074, North of River Thames.

Admission: House and Mill £4.00. House only £3.00. Mill only £2.50. Children under 14 half price. Weekends group visits £3.80.

MILTON MANOR HOUSE

OPEN

August
Daily: 11am - 5pm
Guided tours of the House:11am, 12 noon, 2pm, 3pm, 4pm.
Also
Bank Holiday
Sats, Suns, Mons
(i.e. Easter, May BH's)
Same times.
Tel: 01235 831287
Fax: As phone

MILTON, ABINGDON, OXFORDSHIRE OX14 4EN

Owner: Anthony Mockler-Barrett   *Contact: Anthony Mockler-Barrett*

Extraordinarily beautiful family house traditionally designed by Inigo Jones, with a celebrated Gothick library and a beautiful Catholic chapel. Pleasant and relaxed atmosphere. Park with fine old trees; attractive walled garden; two lakes; stables (pony rides often available), dovecotes, rare-breed pigs, two llamas, other animals. Woodland Wigwam walk. Plenty to see and enjoy for all ages. Refreshments in the Old Kitchen.

Location: Just off A34, village and house signposted; 9 miles S of Oxford, 15 miles N of Newbury. 3 miles from Abingdon and Didcot.

Admission: House & Gdns: Adult £3.50, Child £2.00. House: Guided tours only. Grounds only: Adult £2.00, Child £1.00. Free parking. Groups by arrangement throughout the year. Also weddings, films, select conferences. etc.

MINSTER LOVELL & DOVECOTE

Tel: 01179 750700

Witney, Oxfordshire

Owner: English Heritage   **Contact:** The South West Regional Office

The ruins of Lord Lovell's 15th century manor house stand in a lovely setting on the banks of the River Windrush.

Location: Adjacent to Minster Lovell Church, 3m W of Witney off A40.

Opening Times: Any reasonable time.

Admission: Free. (Keykeeper).

PRIORY COTTAGES

Tel: 01494 528051

1 Mill Street, Steventon, Abingdon, Oxfordshire OX13 6SP

Owner: The National Trust   **Contact:** The Tenant

Former monastic buildings, converted into two houses. South Cottage contains the Great Hall of the original priory.

Location: 4m S of Abingdon, on B4017 off A34 at Abingdon West or Milton interchange on corner of The Causeway and Mill Street, entrance in Mill Street.

Opening Times: The Great Hall in South Cottage only: Apr - end Sept: Wed, 2 - 6pm by written appointment.

Admission: £1.00, no reduction for parties.

KEY TO SYMBOLS: THE NATIONAL TRUST   ENGLISH HERITAGE   HISTORIC HOUSES ASSOCIATION

ROUSHAM HOUSE

Tel: 01869 347110 / 0860 360407

Nr. Steeple Aston, Bicester, Oxfordshire OX6 3QX

Owner: Charles Cotterell-Dormer Esq   **Contact:** Charles Cotterell-Dormer Esq

Rousham represents the first stage of English landscape design and remains almost as William Kent (1685 - 1748) left it. One of the few gardens of this date to have escaped alteration. Includes Venus' Vale, Townesend's Building, seven arched Praeneste, the Temple of the Mill and a sham ruin known as the 'Eyecatcher'. The house was built in 1635 by Sir Robert Dormer.

Location: E of A4260 S of B4030.

Opening Times: House: Apr - Sept: Wed, Sun and Bk Hol Mondays 2 - 4.30pm. Garden: All year: Daily, 10am - 4.30pm, last entry.

Admission: House: £2.50. Garden: Adult £2.50. No children under 15.

RYCOTE CHAPEL ✠

Tel: 01869 347110 / 360407

Rycote, Oxfordshire.

Owner: English Heritage   **Contact:** The Custodian

A 15th century chapel with exquisitely carved and painted woodwork.

Location: 3 m SW of Thame, off A329.

Opening Times: 1 Apr - 30 Sept: 12 noon - 5pm.

Admission: Adult £1.50, Child 80p, Conc £1.10.

STONOR 🏛

See Page 159 for full page entry.

UNIVERSITY OF OXFORD BOTANIC GARDENS

Tel: 01865 276920

Rose Lane, Oxford, Oxfordshire OX1 4AX

Contact: Timothy Walker Esq

Location: E end of High St, on the banks of River Cherwell.

Opening Times: 9am - 5pm (4.30pm in winter). Greenhouses 2 - 4pm.

Admission: £1.00 during summer months per person, otherwise free. Guided tours by appointment only at £2.35 per person. (1995 prices).

WATERPERRY GARDENS

Tel: 01844 339254/226   **Fax:** 01844 339883

Wheatley, Oxford, Oxfordshire OX33 1JL

Contact: The Administrator

Location: Junction 8 on M40, 3m from Wheatley.

Opening Times: Mar - Oct: Mon - Fri 10am - 5.30pm. Sat & Sun 10am - 6pm. Nov - Feb: 10am - 5pm. 18 - 21 Jul open only for visitors to Art in Action.

Admission: Adult £2.30, Child 10 - 16 £1.00 (under 16 free), Senior citizens £1.80. Groups of 20+ £1.70.

STANTON HARCOURT MANOR 🏛

OPEN

Thurs, Sun and Bank Hol Mon.

April: 7, 8, 18, 21.

May: 2, 5, 6, 16, 19, 26, 27.

June: 6, 9, 20, 23.

July: 4, 7, 18, 21.

Aug: 1, 4, 15, 18, 25, 26.

Sept: 5, 8, 19, 22

2.00 - 6.00pm

Tel: 01865 881928

STANTON HARCOURT, NR. WITNEY, OXFORDSHIRE OX8 1RJ

Owner: The Hon Mrs Gascoigne   *Contact:* The Hon Mrs Gascoigne

12 acres of garden with Great Fish Pond and Stew Ponds provide tranquil surroundings for the unique mediaeval buildings - Old Kitchen (Alexander) Pope's Tower and Domestic Chapel. The House, a fine example of a very early unfortified house built to house the Harcourt family and its retainers, is still maintained as the family home.

Location: 9 miles west of Oxford, 5 miles south east of Witney off B4449 between Eynsham and Standlake.

Admission: House & Gardens: Adult £4.00, Child (under 12) /OAP £2.00. Gardens: Adult £2.50, Child (under 12) /OAP £1.50. Group visits by prior arrangement. Disabled visitors welcome at all opening times.

▽ *Where to Stay* ▽

For Private Accommodation and Johansens recommended Hotels, see Accommodation Section.

Broughton Castle.

SPECIAL EVENTS

◇ **BLENHEIM PALACE** Churchill Memorial Concert	**2 MARCH**	
◇ **BLENHEIM PALACE** Craft Fair	**4 – 6 MAY**	
◇ **BLENHEIM PALACE** Charity Cricket Match	**26 MAY**	
◇ **KINGSTONE LISLE PARK** Family Fun Day	**27 MAY**	
◇ **BLENHEIM PALACE** Rolls Royce Rally	**2 JUNE**	
◇ **BLENHEIM PALACE** Open Air Classic Concerts	**27 – 28 JULY**	
◇ **BLENHEIM PALACE** Craft Fair	**24 – 26 AUGUST**	
◇ **BLENHEIM PALACE** Blenheim Horse Trials	**19 – 22 SEPTEMBER**	

For National Trust and English Heritage Events see separate section.

ATTINGHAM PARK
Shrewsbury

ATTINGHAM PARK, home of the Hill family and more recently their descendants, the Berwicks, dates from 1785 when the present house, designed by George Steuart, largely replaced the earlier Tern Hall. The Nash Picture Gallery and new staircase in 1805 were the only major alterations to the house. After a period of inactivity in the 19th century the present house owes much to the late Lord and Lady Berwick who lived at Attingham from 1920. The house and 3,000-acre estate were given to the National Trust in 1953.

The elegant neoclassical house is a fine setting for French and Italian furniture, an extensive picture collection and the Ambassadorial silver used by members of the family serving in Italy. The delicate circular boudoir and the impressive red Dining Room are among the memorable rooms in this, the great country house of Shropshire.

GROUNDS

The house is set in a 250-acre deer park landscaped by Repton; features include the Mile Walk along the River Tern, a circular park walk (2 miles) through mixed woodland, specimen trees and parkland which is home to a herd of Fallow Deer.

CONTACT

The Property Manager
Attingham Park
Shrewsbury
SY4 4TP

Tel: (01743) 709203
Fax: (01743) 709352

LOCATION

Attingham Park is 4 miles S.E. of Shrewsbury on B4380 in village of Atcham.

From London M40/M42/M6/M54, 3 hours

Rail: Shrewsbury.

OPENING TIMES

HOUSE:
30 March - 30 September

Daily* except
Thurs & Fris.
1.30 - 5.00pm
*Bank Hol Mons
11.00am - 5.00pm.

October: Weekends only
1.30 - 5pm

GROUNDS:
Mar - Oct
8.00am - 8.00pm

Nov - Feb
8.00am - 5.00pm
(closed Christmas Day)

ADMISSION

National Trust members free.

HOUSE & GROUNDS

Adult £3.50
Child* £1.75
Family £8.70

Groups** £2.50

GROUNDS ONLY
Adult £1.40
Child* 70p

Evenings Tours+ ..£7.00

* Aged up to 17 (under 5 free)
** Minimum 20 people
\+ (min. 20 or £100)

SUITABILITY FOR OTHER EVENTS
Meetings in Servants Hall or Upper Tea-room. Park and Exterior for film locations. Lectures on the property can be arranged by request for up to 80 people.

ADVICE TO COURIERS & DRIVERS
Parking free. No dogs in house and deer park. Refreshments: £5 voucher for drivers. No indoor photography.

FACILITIES FOR THE DISABLED
Disabled visitors may be driven to the rear of the house. 4-wheel electric vehicle for use in park. Braille and large print guides to house. Adapted lavatories. Access to tea garden but difficult access to tea-room.

PARKING FOR COACHES & CARS
Extensive free parking for coaches & cars 120 yds from house.

CATERING
Licensed tea-room seats 50. Upper tea-room seats 50. Group bookings welcomed for lunch and tea.

GUIDED TOURS
Group tours to be arranged in advance. Tour times: 12 noon or 4.30pm. Min. 20 people (£5 ea; NT members £3.00 ea.).

GIFT SHOP
Open as tea-room selling quality National Trust gifts.

GUIDE BOOK
Cost £2.00. Family activity guide to Park £1.50. Children's house quiz 25p.

SCHOOL VISITS/CHILDREN
Environmental education facilities available all year, including exhibition and rooms for school use. Contact Education Assistant Tel: (01743) 709203.

HAWKSTONE PARK
Nr Shrewsbury

HAWKSTONE PARK, with its well hidden pathways, concealed grottos, secret tunnels and magical collection of follies is truly unique. It is a forgotten masterpiece; originally one of the most visited landscapes in Britain and now the only Grade 1 landscape in Shropshire.

Sir Roland Hill started it all in the 18th century with his son Richard 'The Great Hill', arranging for some 15 miles of paths and some of the best collections of follies in the world to be constructed in the grounds of their ancestral home. At the turn of the 19th century the Hills could no longer accommodate the growing number of sightseers to the Hall. As a result an Inn, which is now Hawkstone Park Hotel, was opened and guided tours were organised. Little has changed since then. The Park is full of attractions, surprises and features. You can see dramatic cliffs and rocks, towers, monuments, tunnels. passageways, precipice rocks, paths, rustic sofas, romantic secret valleys. It takes around three hours to complete the whole tour of the Park. From the Green House you embark upon a unique experience. Paths, steps, walls, even the Greek Urn, were put in place during the busy period at Hawkstone Park. Caves and seats, handy resting places for the weary visitor, were hewn into the rock face.

At the top of the Terrace sits a folly, the White Tower. Close by is the Monument, a 112 foot column, at the top of which stands the new statue of Sir Roland Hill, the first Protestant Lord Mayor of London. The seemingly endless numbers of tracks leading from the Terrace will tempt visitors off the straight and narrow perhaps to the Swiss Bridge or to St. Francis' Cave or the Fox's Nob.

The tour then continues from the bottom of the Terrace to Grotto Hill via Gingerbread Hall and the magnificent Serpentine Tunnel and cleft which leads to the longest grotto passageway in Europe.

After admiring the breathtaking view from the top of Grotto Hill you slowly make your way back towards the entrance but not before passing the Hermits Cave. One admission price covers entrance to the entire Park.

❖

CONTACT

K Darville-Smith
Hawkstone Park
Weston-under-Redcastle
Nr Shrewsbury
Shropshire
SY4 5UY

Tel: (01939) 200300

Fax: (01939) 200311

LOCATION

12 miles north of
Shrewsbury off A49
3 miles from Hodnet off
A53/A442
M6 to M54 either
A49, A41, A442

Rail: Shrewsbury
Station, 12 miles

Wem Station, 7 miles

OPENING TIMES

Summer

1 April - 31 October
PARK: Daily from 10am
Last admission July and
August 5pm.

Winter

Park Closed. Except for
Halloween Ghost Hunt
and December
weekends for Father
Christmas visits
in the caves.

Hotel open all year.
Tel: (01939) 200611

ADMISSION

Adult £4.50
Child £2.50
OAP/Student . . .£3.50
Family £12.00
(2 adults + 3 children)

Groups discounts
(min 12 people) book
and pay in advance;
50p off normal
admission prices.

SUITABILITY FOR OTHER EVENTS
Suitable for a wide variety of events including golf tournaments, film/TV location work, festivals, musical events and craft fairs.

EXTRA FACILITIES
Golf courses (2 x 18 hole) and academy course and practice ground, driving range, residential golf school, video analysis room, clay pigeon shooting, archery.

ADVICE TO COURIERS & DRIVERS
Parking/ refreshments free for drivers. Dogs on a lead and cameras permitted. Bring sensible shoes.

FACILITIES FOR THE DISABLED
Disabled toilets. The walk is not suitable for frail or disabled.

CATERING
Tea Room open all day tea/coffee sandwiches, snacks, salads, cakes. Restaurant available at Hotel (adjacent) serving snacks, grills and a full à la carte menu.

GUIDED TOURS
By arrangement. Maps provided.

GIFT SHOP
Open daily. Excellent range of souvenirs, traditional Gifts/Toys.

GUIDE BOOKS
Maps Free. Guide Books £3.50.

SCHOOL VISITS / CHILDREN
Very welcome. £2.50 per child, teacher free in 1:10 ratio **OR** £3.00 per child, with free use of classroom and picnic area and free monument cut out. Teachers free in 1:10 ratio.

CONFERENCE AND FUNCTION FACILITIES

ROOM	DIMENSIONS	CAPACITY	LAYOUT	POWER POINTS	SUITABLE FOR A/V
Waterloo	15.45m x 10m	200	Theatre/ reception	10	✓
Wellington	6.1m x 7.62m	50	Theatre/ reception	4	✓
Redcastle	12.2m x 8.8m	100	Theatre/ reception	16	✓
Hill	8.5m x 7m	50	Theatre/ reception	8	✓

OAKLEY HALL
Market Drayton

OAKLEY HALL is situated in magnificent countryside on the boundary of Shropshire and Staffordshire. The present Hall is a fine example of a Queen Anne mansion house and was built on the site of an older dwelling mentioned in the Domesday Survey of 1085. Oakley Hall was the home of the Chetwode family until it was finally sold in 1919.

GARDENS

Set in 100 acres of rolling parkland, the Hall commands superb views over the surrounding countryside and the gardens include wild areas in addition to the more formal parts.

Oakley Hall is a privately owned family house and since it is not open to the general public it provides a perfect location for exclusive private or corporate functions. The main hall can accommodate 120 people comfortably and has excellent acoustics for concerts. The secluded location and unspoilt landscape make Oakley an ideal setting for filming and photography.

The surrounding countryside is rich in historical associations. St. Mary's Church at Mucklestone, in which parish the Hall stands, was erected in the 13th century and it was from the tower of this Church that Queen Margaret of Anjou observed the Battle of Blore Heath in 1459. This was a brilliant victory for the Yorkist faction in the Wars of the Roses and the blacksmith at Mucklestone was reputed to have shod the Queen's horse back to front in order to disguise her escape.

SUITABILITY FOR OTHER EVENTS
Concerts, conferences, wedding receptions, fashion shows, product launches, seminars, clay pigeon shooting, garden parties and filming.

EXTRA FACILITIES
Grand piano, hard tennis court, croquet lawn, horse riding.

CONFERENCE FACILITIES
See below for rooms available. Slide projector, word processor, fax and secretarial assistance are all available by prior arrangement.

ACCOMMODATION
3 double and one twin bedroom with baths.

ADVICE TO COURIERS & DRIVERS
No stiletto heels. No dogs.

FACILITIES FOR THE DISABLED
Disabled and elderly visitors may alight at the entrance to the Hall, before parking in the allocated areas. There are toilet facilities for the disabled at the newly-refurbished stable block.

PARKING FOR COACHES & CARS
Parking for 100 cars, 100/200 yds from the Hall.

CATERING
Buffets, lunches and dinners can all be arranged for large or small groups, using high quality local caterers.

GROUP VISITS
By prior arrangement groups will be met and entertained by members of the Fisher family.

CONTACT

Mrs Ann E Fisher
Oakley Hall
Market Drayton
Shropshire
TF9 4AG

Tel: (01630) 653472
Fax: (01630) 653282

LOCATION

From London 3hrs: M1, M6 to exit 14, then A5013 to Eccleshall, turn right at T-junction, 200 yards, then left onto B5026. Mucklestone is 1³/₄ mls from Logger-heads on B5026. Turn left before Church, to end of lane then right. 200 yards turn left into small lane opposite telephone kiosk. Bear left between two lodges.

OPENING TIMES

All Year

Not open to the public. The house is available all year round for private or corporate events.

ADMISSION

Please telephone for details.

CONFERENCE AND FUNCTION FACILITIES

ROOM	DIMENSIONS	CAPACITY	LAYOUT	POWER POINTS	SUITABLE FOR A/V
Hall	50' x 30'	130	Theatre	10	✓
		130	Buffet		
		150	Lunch/Dinner		
Dining Room	40' x 27'	80	Theatre	6	✓
		30	U-shape		
		20	Boardroom		
		60	Buffet		
		80	Lunch/Dinner		
Ballroom	40' x 27'	80	Theatre	6	✓
		30	U-shape		
		20	Boardroom		
		60	Buffet		

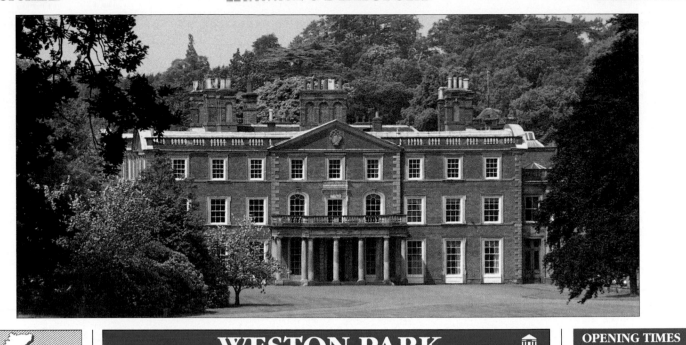

WESTON PARK
Near Shifnal

WESTON PARK has been the home of successive generations of the Earls of Bradford since the 12th Century and is today owned by a charity, 'The Weston Park Foundation'.

The present House was built on the site of the original medieval Manor House in 1671 and was designed by Lady Elizabeth Wilbraham. It boasts a fine collection of paintings with works by Stubbs, Van Dyck, Holbein, Gainsborough and Lely. The contents of the House, brought together by the family over the centuries, include some fine examples of 18th century English and European furniture, rare Parisian tapestries from the Gobelin factory and porcelain collections.

The House stands in 1,000 acres of formal gardens, arboretum and parkland designed by 'Capability' Brown. Particular features are the Italian Broderie and the Rose Garden of the South Terrace.

The Park now houses numerous visitor attractions, including a Woodland Adventure Playground, Miniature Railway and Pets Corner.

An extensive programme of events is held each season, and includes Classical Concerts, Horse Trials and the Midland Game & Country Sports Fair. Further details available from Weston Park.

❖

SUITABILITY FOR OTHER EVENTS
Residential parties, special dinners, wedding receptions, conferences, product launches, outdoor concerts and events, filming location.
Weston Park offers a full event organisation service.

EXTRA FACILITIES
Helipad and airstrip. Wide variety of sporting activities organised for private groups eg Clay Pigeon Shooting, Archery, Hovercrafts, Rally Driving.

ACCOMMODATION
Weston Park offers 28 delightful bedrooms with bathrooms, 18 doubles 7 twins, 3 singles.

ADVICE TO COURIERS & DRIVERS
Dogs must always be kept on leads. Interior photography by prior arrangement only.

PARKING FOR COACHES & CARS
There is unlimited parking at the front door for cars and coaches containing private parties. There is a public car and coach park 100 yards from the property.

FACILITIES FOR THE DISABLED
House and part of the grounds accessible by wheelchair. There are toilets for the disabled.

CATERING
The Old Stables Restaurant & Tea Room provides meals and snacks on public open days.
Dine and Stay arrangements in the House on selected dates.

GIFT EMPORIUM
Open at the same time as the Park.

GUIDE BOOKS
Colour guide book, £1.00.

SCHOOL VISITS/CHILDREN
Open on Tuesdays, Wednesdays and Thursdays in the latter half of June and all July. Advance booking is essential. Cost per child £1.50. Teachers' guidance notes and National Curriculum related Workpacks available.

CONTACT

Park: Helen Howat
House: Andy Sinclair
Weston Park
Weston-under-Lizard
Nr Shifnal
Shropshire
TF11 8LE

Tel: (01952) 850207
Fax: (01952) 850430

LOCATION

Birmingham 30 minutes.
Manchester 1 hour.
Motorway access -
Junct. 12 M6 or Junct. 3
M54. House situated
on A5.

Rail: Nearest
Railway Stations -
Wolverhampton
or Stafford.

Air: Birmingham

OPENING TIMES

Summer
Easter: 6, 7, 8, 9 April
4 May - 9 June : W/ends,
Bank Hols & Whit week
(25 May - 2 June)
10 June - 28 July
Daily except Mons & Fris
29 Jul - 1 Sept: Daily
2 - 15 Sept: W/ends only
House: 1.00 - 5.00pm
Park: 11.00am - 7.00pm

Winter
16 Sept - Easter: Closed

NB. Visitors are advised to telephone first to check this information.

ADMISSION

HOUSE & GARDEN
Adult £5.00
Child (3 - 16yrs.) . .£3.00
OAP £3.75

GARDEN ONLY
Adult £3.50
Child (3 - 16yrs.) . .£2.00
OAP £2.50

CONFERENCE AND FUNCTION FACILITIES

ROOM	DIMENSIONS	CAPACITY	LAYOUT	POWER POINTS	SUITABLE FOR A/V
Dining Room	52' x 23'	40 - 150	Various	15	✓
Orangery	51' x 20'	40 - 150	Various	12	
Music Room	50' x 20'	30 - 100	Various	24	✓
The Old Stables	58' x 20'	30 - 95	Various	4	✓
Conference Room	40' x 7'6"	20 - 60	Various	14	✓

ACTON BURNELL CASTLE ⛤

Tel: 01604 730320

Acton Burnell, Shrewsbury, Shropshire
Owner: English Heritage   **Contact:** The Midlands Regional Office
The warm red sandstone shell of a fortified 13th century manor house.
Location: In Acton Burnell, on unclassified road 8m S of Shrewsbury.
Opening Times: Any reasonable time.

ADCOTE SCHOOL

Tel: 01939 260202   **Fax:** 01939 261300

Little Ness, Shrewsbury, Shropshire SY4 2JY
Owner: Adcote School Educational Trust Ltd   **Contact:** Mrs S Cecchet
Adcote is a Grade I listed building designed by Norman Shaw, and built to a Tudor design in 1879. Its features include a Great Hall, Minstrel's Gallery, William De Morgan tiled fireplaces and stained glass windows. Landscaped gardens include many fine trees.
Location: 7m NW of Shrewsbury.
Opening Times: 23 Apr - 12 Jul (except 24 May - 28 May): 2 - 5pm. 9 Sept - 15 Oct.
Admission: Free, but the Governors reserve the right to make a charge.

ATTINGHAM PARK 🌠

See Page 164 for full page entry.

BENTHALL HALL 🌠

Tel: 01952 882159

Benthall, Nr. Broseley, Shropshire TF12 5RX
Owner: The National Trust   **Contact:** Mr & Mrs J Benthall
A 16th century stone house with mullioned windows and moulded brick chimneys. The interior includes an intricately carved oak staircase, decorated plaster ceilings and oak panelling, also family collections of furniture, ceramics and paintings. Carefully restored plantsman's garden. Restoration church.
Location: 1m NW of Broseley (B4375), 4m NE of Much Wenlock, 1m SW of Ironbridge.
Opening Times: 3 Apr - 29 Sept: Wed, Sun & BH Mon 1.30 - 5.30pm. Last adm. 5pm. Parties at other times by prior arrangement.
Admission: Adult: £3.00, Child: £1.00. Garden: £2.00. Reduced rates for booked parties.

BOSCOBEL HOUSE ⛤

OPEN

1 April - 30 Sept:
Daily : 10am - 6pm

1 - 31 Oct:
Daily:10am - 6pm
or dusk if earlier.

1 Nov - 31 Mar:
Wed - Sun
10am - 4pm

Closed in January

Tel: 01902 850244

BREWOOD, BISHOPS WOOD, SALOP ST19 9AR

Owner: English Heritage   *Contact: The Custodian*

This 17th century hunting lodge was destined to play a part in Charles II's escape from the Roundheads. A descendant of the Royal Oak which sheltered the fugitive Prince from Cromwell's troops after the Battle of Worcester still stands in the fields around Boscobel House. The timber-framed house where the King slept in a tiny 'sacred hole' has been fully restored and furnished and there are panelled rooms, secret hiding places and pretty gardens to explore.
Location: On unclassified road between A41 & A5. 8 mls NW of Wolverhampton.
Admission: Adult £3.50, OAP/Student/UB40 £2.60, Child £1.80
15% discount on parties of 11 or more.

BUILDWAS ABBEY ⛤

Tel: 01952 433274

Shropshire
Owner: English Heritage   **Contact:** The Custodian
Extensive remains of a Cistercian abbey built in 1135. The remains include the church which is almost complete except for the roof.
Location: On S bank of River Severn on B4378, 2 m W of Iron Bridge.
Opening Times: 1 Apr - 30 Sept: Daily 10am - 6pm. 1 - 31 Oct: Daily 10am - 6pm or dusk if earlier. 1 Nov - 31 Mar: Daily 10am - 4pm. Closed 1 - 2pm.
Admission: Adult £1.50, Child 80p, Conc £1.10.

BURFORD HOUSE GARDENS

Tel: 01584 810777   **Fax:** 01584 810673

Burford House, Tenbury Wells, Worcestershire WR15 8HQ
Owner: Treasures Of Tenbury Ltd   **Contact:** Mrs Patricia Cox
The beauty of Burford House Gardens is a tribute to the late John Treasure who, since the early 1950s, transformed the setting for this early Georgian House into a garden of quiet serenity and fascination. Harmonising combinations of colour have been achieved and especial use has been made of clematis - the garden, now boasting over 150 varieties, is home to the National Collection. The garden is famous for its range of unusual plants, many of which are sold in Treasure Plant Centre adjacent, which specialises in clematis, herbaceous, shrubs, trees and climbers. Also on site is the Burford House Gallery, Burford Buttery, Craft Shop and Craft Workshops.
Location: 8m from Ludlow, 1m W of Tenbury Wells on A456.
Opening Times: All year: Daily 10am - 5pm.
Admission: Adult £2.50, Child £1.00, Groups of 10+ £2.00 per person.

CLIVE HOUSE MUSEUM

Tel: 01743 354811

College Hill, Shrewsbury, Shropshire SY1 1LT
Owner: Shrewsbury and Atcham Borough Council   **Contact:** Mrs M White
Period room settings, fine and decorative arts, social history, temporary exhibitions and walled garden.
Location: Town centre, close to TIC.
Opening Times: Tues - Sat: 10am - 4pm, Summer Suns & Bank Hol Mons: 10am - 4pm.
Admission: Adult £1.00, Child 50p. Parties 10% discount.

CLUN CASTLE ⛤

Tel: 01604 730320

Clun, Ludlow, Shropshire.
Owner: English Heritage   **Contact:** The Midlands Regional Office
Remains of a four storey keep and other buildings of this border Castle are set in outstanding countryside. Built in the 11th century.
Location: In Clun, off A488, 18m W of Ludlow.
Opening Times: Any reasonable time.

COMBERMERE ABBEY

Tel: 01948 871637   **Fax:** 01948 871293

Whitchurch, Shropshire SY13 4AJ
Owner: Mrs S Callander Beckett   **Contact:** Mrs S Callander Beckett
Location: 5m E of Whitchurch, off A530.
Opening Times: By arrangement for groups.
Admission: Groups: £5.00 per person inclusive of refreshments.

DUDMASTON HALL 🌠

OPEN

31 Mar - 29 Sept
Weds & Suns
2.00 - 5.30pm
Thursdays booked
parties by
arrangement
2.00 - 5.30pm

Tea-room
1.00 - 2.00pm
Light lunches
2.00 - 5.30pm teas

Last admission to
house: 5pm

Tel: 01746 780866

QUATT, BRIDGNORTH, SHROPSHIRE WV15 6QN

Owner: National Trust   *Contact: The Administrator*

Late 17th century manor house, home of Sir George & Lady Labouchere. Contains furniture and china, Dutch flower paintings, watercolours, botanical art and modern pictures and sculpture, family and natural history. 9 acres of lakeside gardens and Dingle walk. Two estate walks $5^{1}/_{2}$ and $3^{1}/_{2}$ miles starting from Hampton Loade car park. Dogs in Dingle Park & Estate only on leads. Shop.
Location: 4 miles south-east of Bridgnorth on A442.
Admission: House & Garden: Adult £3.50, Child £2.00, Party £2.90.
Garden only: £2.50. Family £8.00.

HAUGHMOND ABBEY ⛤

Tel: 01743 709661

Upton Magna, Uffington, Shrewsbury, Shropshire SY4 4RW
Owner: English Heritage   **Contact:** The Custodian
Extensive remains of a 12th century Augustinian abbey, including the Chapter House which retains its late medieval timber ceiling.
Location: 3m NE of Shrewsbury off B5062.
Opening Times: 1 Apr - 30 Sept: 12 noon - 5pm.
Admission: Adult £1.50, Child 80p, Conc £1.10.

HAWKSTONE PARK

See Page 165 for full page entry.

HODNET HALL GARDENS

OPEN

2 April - 30 Sept
Tues - Sat
(closed Mons)
2.00 - 5.00pm

Sundays & Bank
Holiday Mondays
12 noon - 5.30pm

Tel: 01630 685202
Fax: 01630 685853

HODNET, MARKET DRAYTON, SHROPSHIRE TF9 3NN

Owner: Mr and the Hon Mrs A Heber-Percy   *Contact:* Mrs M. A Taylor

Beautiful woodland walks through trees and shrubs in 60 acres of flowering lakeside gardens. Tea Rooms (with animal trophy display). Gift Shop. Kitchen Garden sales. Free car and coach parking. Dogs allowed (on leash). Parties catered for. Contact the Secretary.

Location: 12 miles NE of Shrewsbury on A53; M6 Junction 15; M54 junction 3.

Admission: Adult £2.80, Child £1.00, OAP £2.30.

IRON BRIDGE

Tel: 01604 730320

Ironbridge, Shropshire

Owner: English Heritage   **Contact:** The Midlands Regional Office

The world's first iron bridge and Britain's best known industrial monument. Cast in Coalbrookdale by local ironmaster, Abraham Darby, it was erected across the River Severn in 1779.

Location: In Ironbridge, adjacent to A4169.

Opening Times: Any reasonable time.

IRONBRIDGE GORGE MUSEUM

OPEN

Daily
10.00am - 5.00pm
except Jul and Aug
10.00am - 6.00pm.

Please phone for
winter details.

Tel: 01952 433522
or 432166 (w/ends)
Fax: 01952 432204

IRONBRIDGE, TELFORD, SHROPSHIRE TF8 7AW

Owner: Independent Museum   *Contact:* Visitor Information

Scene of pioneering events which led to the Industrial Revolution. The Ironbridge Gorge is host to the many unique museums which tell the story of those momentous times. Stunning scenery, a recreated Victorian town, Coalport china and much more. You'll need 2 days here.

Location: Telford, Shropshire via M6/M54.

Admission: Passport ticket which allows admission to all museums; Adult £8.95, Child/Student £5.30, Family £27.00, Senior Citizens £7.95.

LANGLEY CHAPEL

Tel: 01064 730320

Acton Burnell, Shrewsbury, Shropshire

Owner: English Heritage   **Contact:** The Midlands Regional Office

A delightful medieval chapel, standing alone in a field, with a complete set of early 17th century wooden fittings and furniture.

Location: 1¹/₂m S of Acton Burnell, on unclassified road off A49 9¹/₂m S of Shrewsbury.

Opening Times: 1 Apr - 30 Sept: Daily 10.am - 6pm. 1 - 31 Oct: Daily 10am - 6pm or dusk if earlier. 1 Nov - 31 Mar: Daily, 10am - 4pm. Closed 24 - 26 Dec, 1 Jan.

LILLESHALL ABBEY

Tel: 01064 730320

Oakengates, Shropshire

Owner: English Heritage   **Contact:** The Midlands Regional Office

Extensive ruins of an abbey of Augustinian canons including remains of the 12th and 13th century church and the cloister buildings..

Location: On unclassified road off A518, 4 m N of Oakengates.

Opening Times: Any reasonable time.

LUDLOW CASTLE

Tel: 01584 873355

Castle Square, Shropshire SY8 1EG

Owner: Trustees of Powis Castle Estate   **Contact:** Jean Nicholas

Dating from about 1086. Circular nave in Norman chapel. 16th century Judges lodgings. Contemporary performances of Shakespeare in the Castle during the Ludlow Festival.

Location: 30m S Shrewsbury. Centre of Ludlow.

Opening Times: 1 Feb - 30 April: 10.30am - 4pm. 1 May - 30 Sept 10.30am - 5pm. 1 Oct - Christmas, 10.30am - 4pm.

Admission: Adult £2.50, Child £1.50, Family £7.50, Conc £2.00, Groups 10% discount.

MORETON CORBET CASTLE

Tel: 01604 730320

Moreton Corbet, Shrewsbury, Shropshire

Owner: English Heritage   **Contact:** The Midlands Regional Office

A ruined medieval castle with the substantial remains of a splendid Elizabethan mansion, captured in 1644 from Charles I's supporters by Parliamentary forces.

Location: In Moreton Corbet off B5063, 7 m NE of Shrewsbury.

Opening Times: Any reasonable time.

MORVILLE HALL

Bridgnorth, Shropshire WV16 5BN

Owner: The National Trust   **Contact:** Mrs J K Norbury

An Elizabethan house of mellow stone, converted in the 18th century. The Hall is in a fine setting, with three attractive gardens.

Location: Morville, nr. Bridgnorth.

Opening Times: By written appointment only.

OAKLEY HALL

See Page 166 for full page entry.

PREEN MANOR GARDENS

Tel: 01694 771207

Church Preen, Church Stretton, Shropshire SY6 7LQ

Owner: Mr & Mrs P Trevor Jones   **Contact:** Mrs P Trevor Jones

6 acre garden on site of Cluniac monastery, with walled, terraced, wild, water, kitchen and chess gardens. 12th century monastic church with a yew tree reputedly the oldest in Europe.

Location: 10m S of Shrewsbury.

Opening Times: Refer National Gardens Scheme Yellow Book. Coach parties June & July by appointment only.

ROWLEY'S HOUSE MUSEUM

Tel: 01743 361196

Barker Street, Shrewsbury, Shropshire SY1 1QH

Owner: Shrewsbury and Atcham Borough Council   **Contact:** Mrs M White

Impressive timber framed building and attached 17th century brick mansion with costume, archaeology and natural history, geology, local history and temporary exhibitions.

Location: Barker Street.

Opening Times: Tues - Sat: 10am - 5pm. Summer Suns and Bank Hol Mons: 10am - 4pm.

Admission: Adult £2.00, Child 50p, Conc £1.00, parties 10% discount.

SHIPTON HALL

Tel: 01746 785225

Much Wenlock, Shropshire TF13 6JZ

Owner: Mr J.N.R Bishop   **Contact:** Mrs M J Bishop

Elizabethan stone house with Georgian additions by T.F. Pritchard. Tudor and Jacobean panelling. Plasterwork on ceiling and chimney pieces is noteworthy. Family home.

Location: 6m SW of Much Wenlock on B4378.

Opening Times: Easter - 30 Sept: Thurs 2.30 - 5.30pm. BH Sun and Mon 2.30 - 5.30pm. Groups of 20 or more at any time of day or year.

Admission: Adult £2.50, Child £1.50, Groups less 10% for 20+.

SHREWSBURY ABBEY

Tel: 01743 232723

Shrewsbury, Shropshire SY2 6BS

Contact: T C Bumford

Benedictine Abbey founded in 1083, tomb of Roger de Montgomerie and remains of tomb of St Winefride, 7th century Welsh Saint. The Abbey was part of the monastery and has also been a parish church since the 12th century. Now made popular by Ellis Peters author of Brother Cadfael novels. Historical exhibition from Saxon times to present.
Location: Signposted from Shrewsbury bypass (A5 and A49).
Opening Times: Easter - 31 Oct: 9.30am - 5.30pm. Nov - Easter: 10am - 4pm.
Admission: Donation. Guided Tours £10.00 per pe-arranged party.

SHREWSBURY CASTLE & SHROPSHIRE REGIMENTAL MUSEUM

Tel: 01743 358516

Castle Street, Shrewsbury, Shropshire SY1 2AT
Owner: Shrewsbury & Atcham Borough Council   **Contact:** Mrs M White
Norman Castle with 18th century work by Thomas Telford. Free admission to attractive floral grounds. The main hall houses the Shropshire Regimental Museum and displays on the history of the castle.
Location: Town centre, adjacent BR and Bus stations.
Opening Times: Tues - Sat: 10am - 5pm. Summer Suns & Bank Hol Mons: 10am - 4pm.
Admission: Adult £2.00, Child 50p, OAP/Student £1.00, parties 10% discount.

WALCOT HALL

OPEN
House & Garden
May - Sept.
Bank Hol Suns
& Mons
(except Xmas &
New Year)
May: Sun, Wed, & Fri
June: Wed & Fri
July & Aug: Suns
Sept: Wed.
2.15 - 4.30pm.

Tel: 0171 581 2782
Fax: 0171 589 0195

LYDBURY NORTH, NR BISHOP'S CASTLE, SHROPSHIRE SY7 8AZ
Owner: C.R.W. Parish   *Contact:* C.R.W. Parish

Georgian home of Lord Clive of India who commissioned Sir William Chambers to re-design it and the Stable Block, in 1763. His son added the free-standing Ballroom and developed 30 acres of Arboretum and Pools to the rear, with mile-long Lakes in the front. Suitable for Film Locations; Balls, Corporate Events; Holiday Accommodation, Receptions, Parties and Shows.
Location: On the edge of the Clun Forest. 3 miles E of Bishop's Castle on B4385; 1/2 mile outside Lydbury North. The drive is adjacent to the Powis Arms Pub.
Admission: Adult £2.50, Child under 15 free. Groups of 10+ by arrangement. Teas by arrangement.

STOKESAY CASTLE

**NEAR CRAVEN ARMS,
SHROPSHIRE SY7 9AH**

Owner: English Heritage
Contact: The Custodian
Tel: 01588 672544

This perfectly preserved example of a fortified manor house gives us a glimpse of the life and ambitions of a rich medieval merchant. Lawrence of Ludlow built this country house to impress the landed gentry. Lawrence built a magnificent Great Hall where servants and guests gathered on feast days, but the family's private quarters were in the bright, comfortable solar on the first floor. From the outside the castle forms a picturesque grouping of castle, parish church and gatehouse set in the rolling Shropshire countryside.

Location: 1 ml from Craven Arms off A49.

Admission: Adult £2.50, Conc. £1.90, Child £1.30. Parties of 11+ 15% discount .

OPEN
1 April - 30 Sept: Daily 10am - 6pm
1 - 31 Oct: Daily 10am - 6pm or dusk if earlier
1 Nov - 31 Mar: Wed - Sun 10am - 4pm
Closed 1 - 2pm.

WENLOCK PRIORY

OPEN
1 April - 30 Sept:
Daily: 10am - 6pm

1 - 31 Oct:
Daily: 10am - 6pm
or dusk if earlier.

1 Nov - 31 Mar:
Wed - Sun
10am - 4pm
(closed lunch
1 - 2pm)

Tel: 01952 727466

MUCH WENLOCK, SHROPSHIRE TF13 6HS
Owner: English Heritage   *Contact:* The Custodian

A prosperous, powerful priory at its peak in the Middle Ages. A great deal of the structure still survives in the form of high, romantic ruined walls and there is still an atmosphere of strength and serenity. A monastery was first founded at Wenlock in the 7th century, and little more is known of the site until the time of the Norman Conquest when it became a Cluniac monastery. Visitors to the majestic ruins of the priory church set in green lawns may feel a sense of wonder at its departed glories.
Location: In Much Wenlock.
Admission: Adult £2.00, Conc. £1.50, Child £1.00. Discount for parties of 11+.

UPTON CRESSETT HALL

Tel: 01746 714307   **Fax:** 01746 714506

Bridgnorth, Shropshire WV16 6UH
Owner: William Cash Esq   **Contact:** William Cash
The Gatehouse is available for accommodation / renting. Medieval manor house in red brick, magnificent gatehouse in beautiful countryside, 14th century Great Hall.
Location: 4 m from Bridgnorth off A458.
Opening Times: May - Sept: Thursdays 2.30 - 5.30pm. Parties welcome throughout the year by appointment only.
Admission: Adult £2.50, Child £1.00, Parties over 12 £2.00.

WESTON PARK

See Page 167 for full page entry.

WILDERHOPE MANOR

Tel: 01694 771363

Longville, Much Wenlock, Shropshire TF13 6EG
Owner: The National Trust   **Contact:** The Warden
This limestone house stands on southern slope of Wenlock Edge in remote country with views down to Corvedale. Dating from 1586, it is unaltered but unfurnished. Features include remarkable wooden spiral stairs, unique bow rack and fine plaster ceilings. Circular walk through farmland and woods. Let to the Youth Hostels Association.
Location: 7m SW of Much Wenlock. 7m E of Church Stretton, 1/2m S of B4371.
Opening Times: Apr - Sept: Wed & Sat 2 - 4.30pm. Oct - Mar: Sat only 2 - 4.30pm.
Admission: £1.00, no reduction for parties.

WROXETER ROMAN CITY

Tel: 01743 761330

Wroxeter, Shrewsbury, Shropshire SY5 6PH
Owner: English Heritage   **Contact:** The Custodian
The excavated centre of the fourth largest city in Roman Britain. Impressive remains of the 2nd century municipal baths. The museum has finds from the town and earlier legionary fortress.
Location: At Wroxeter, 5m E of Shrewsbury, 1m S of A5.
Opening Times: 1 Apr - 30 Sept: Daily 10am - 6pm. 1 - 31 Oct: Daily 10am - 6pm or dusk if earlier. 1 Nov - 31 Mar: Wed - Sun 10am - 4pm (Closed for lunch 1 - 2pm).
Admission: Adult £2.50, Child £1.30, Conc £1.90.

Stokesay Castle.

SPECIAL EVENTS

❖ **HAWKSTONE PARK** Easter Egg Hunt	**6 – 8 APRIL**	
❖ **WESTON PARK** Festival of Transport	**7 – 8 APRIL**	
❖ **WESTON PARK** Craft Fair	**4 – 6 MAY**	
❖ **WESTON PARK** Spring Horse Trials	**10 – 12 MAY**	
❖ **WESTON PARK** National Hovercraft Championship	**29 – 30 JUNE**	
❖ **HAWKSTONE PARK** North Shropshire Country Fayre	**27 – 28 JULY**	
❖ **WESTON PARK** Napoleonic Battle	**3 – 4 AUGUST**	

❖ **WESTON PARK** Heart of England Music Festival	**14 – 18 AUGUST**
❖ **WESTON PARK** Town & Country Fayre	**25 – 26 AUGUST**
❖ **SHREWSBURY ABBEY** Flower Festival	**13 – 17 SEPTEMBER**
❖ **WESTON PARK** Game Fair	**14 – 15 SEPTEMBER**
❖ **HAWKSTONE PARK** Torchlight Ghost Hunts	**28 – 31 OCTOBER**
❖ **HAWKSTONE PARK** 23 – 24 November, then every Saturday and Sunday until 15 December and every day 16 – 23 December. Father Christmas Grotto Trips	**23 NOVEMBER – 23 DECEMBER**

For National Trust and English Heritage Events see separate section.

THE BISHOPS PALACE
Wells

The fortified and moated medieval Palace unites the early 13th century first floor hall, the late 13th century Chapel and the ruined Great Hall, as well as the 15th century wing which is today the private residence of the Bishop of Bath and Wells. The extensive grounds, where rise the springs that give Wells its name, are a beautiful setting for borders of herbaceous plants, roses, shrubs, mature trees and the Arboretum. The Moat is home to a collection of waterfowl and swans.

CONTACT

Mr C. Edwards
Managing Director
The Bishop's Palace
Wells
Somerset
BA5 2PD

Tel: (01749) 678691
Fax: (01749) 678691

LOCATION

20 miles south of Bristol and Bath on the A39

Rail: Castle Cary station situated 20 minutes from Wells on main London-Plymouth route.

PARKING FOR COACHES AND CARS
Coach parking is available in Princes Road. There are various car parks close to the Palace.

FACILITIES FOR THE DISABLED
Limited parking available within the grounds - free use of Motorised wheelchair for use in the garden.

CATERING
The Bishop's Buttery situated in the Undercroft offers coffee/tea and light snacks on open days.

GIFT SHOP
Limited gifts available. Colour guide book £1.00.

GUIDED TOURS
By prior arrangement.

SCHOOL VISITS / CHILDREN
Educational visits welcome. £15 plus 50p per pupil.

OPENING TIMES

Easter Sat - 31 October
Tuesday, Wednesday, Thursday and Bank Holiday Mondays and every day in August.
10.00am - 6.00pm

Sundays: 2.00 - 6.00pm

Last admission 1 hr before closing time.

ADMISSION

Adult £2.50
Child (under 12) . .Free
OAP £2.00
UB40/Student . .£1.00

Groups (min 10)
Adult £1.50

Guided tour: £30.00 plus £2.00 per person.

SUITABILITY FOR OTHER EVENTS
Wedding receptions, conferences, banquets, business seminars, open-air theatre events and product launches.

EXTRA FACILITIES
Ideal photo location.

ADVICE TO COURIERS & DRIVERS
Set down and pick up point available 100 metres away in Wells market place.

CONFERENCE AND FUNCTION FACILITIES

ROOM	DIMENSIONS	CAPACITY	LAYOUT	POWER POINTS	SUITABLE FOR A/V
Conference	36' x 21'	130	Theatre	6	Yes
Drawing	27' x 24'	20	Boardroom	3	–
Long Gallery	78' x 12'	80	Seminars	5	–
Restaurant	66' x 30'	130	Dining	10	–
Panelled	24' x 24'	30	Boardroom	3	–
Undercroft	78' x 12'	40	Reception	5	–

BARRINGTON COURT

BARRINGTON, ILMINSTER, SOMERSET TA19 0NQ

Owner: *The National Trust*   **Contact:** *The Administrator*

Tel: 01460 241938

A beautiful garden influenced by Gertrude Jekyll and laid out in a series of rooms, including the white garden, the rose and iris garden and the lily garden. The working kitchen garden has apple, pear and plum trees trained along high stone walls. The Tudor Manor House was restored in the 1920's by the Lyle family. It is let to Stuart Interiors and is also open to NT visitors (restoration continues throughout 1996).

Location: In Barrington village, 5m NE of Ilminster, on B3168.

Opening Times: Garden & Court House: 30 Mar - 1 Oct: Daily except Friday 11am - 5.30pm. Last admission: 5pm.

Admission: Adult £4.00, Child (12-17) £2.00. Groups: Adult £3.50, Child £1.80

DUNSTER CASTLE

DUNSTER, NR. MINEHEAD, SOMERSET TA24 6SL

Owner: *The National Trust*   **Contact:** *The Property Manager*

Tel: 01643 821314

The fortified home of the Luttrell family for 600 years, with a 13th century castle building below a Norman motte. The 17th century mansion was remodelled by Salvin in 1870 but retains its fine staircase and plasterwork. There is a terraced garden of rare shrubs and a 28 acre park.

Location: In Dunster, 3m SE of Minehead. NT car park.

Opening Times: Castle: 1 Apr - 30 Sept: Daily except Thur & Fri, 11am - 5pm. 1 - 31 Oct: Daily except Thur & Fri, 11am - 4pm. Garden & Park: Jan - Mar & Oct - Dec: Daily (open Good Fri) 11am - 4pm (closed 25 Dec). Apr - Sept:10am - 5pm . Last adm. $^1/_2$ hour before closing.

Admission: Castle, garden & park: Adult £5.00, Child (under 16) £2.60, Pre-booked parties £4.50, Family (2 adults & 2 children) £6.50.

THE BISHOP'S PALACE   **See Page 172 for full page entry.**

CLEEVE ABBEY   **Tel:** 01984 40377

Washford, Watchet, Somerset TA23 0PS

Owner: English Heritage   **Contact:** The Custodian

There are few monastic sites where you will see such a complete set of cloister buildings, including the refectory with its magnificent timber roof. Built in the 13th century, this Cistercian abbey was saved from destruction at the Dissolution by being turned into a house and then a farm.

Location: In Washford, $^1/_4$ m S of A39.

Opening Times: 1 Apr - 30 Sept: Daily 10am - 6pm. 1 - 31 Oct: Daily 10am - 6pm or dusk if earlier. 1 Nov - 31 Mar: Wed - Sun 10am - 4pm (closed lunch 1 - 2pm).

Admission: Adult £2.20, Child £1.10, Conc £1.70.

COLERIDGE COTTAGE   **Tel:** 01278 732662

35 Lime Street, Nether Stowey, Bridgwater, Somerset TA5 1NQ

Owner: The National Trust   **Contact:** The Custodian

Coleridge's home for three years from 1797. It was here that he wrote the Rhyme of the Ancient Mariner, part of Christabel and Frost at Midnight.

Location: At W end of Nether Stowey, on S side of A39, 8m W of Bridgwater.

Opening Times: Parlour & Reading room: 31 Mar - 1 Oct: Tues - Thur & Sun, 2 - 5pm. In winter by written application.

Admission: Adult £1.60, Child 80p, no reduction for parties which must book.

CROWE HALL   **Tel:** 01225 310322

Widcombe Hill, Bath, Somerset BA2 6AR

Owner: John Barratt Esq   **Contact:** John Barratt Esq

10 acres of romantic hillside gardens. Victorian grotto, classical Bath villa with good 18th century furniture and paintings.

Location: 1m SE of Bath.

Opening Times: Gardens only open 24 Mar, 21 Apr, 12 & 26 May, 16 Jun, 14 Jul. House and Gardens by appointment.

Admission: House & Gdns: Adult £3.00. Gardens only: Adult £1.50, Child 50p.

DUNSTER WORKING WATERMILL   **Tel:** 01643 821759

Mill Lane, Dunster, Minehead, Somerset TA24 6SW

Owner: The National Trust   **Contact:** The Administrator

Built on the site of a mill mentioned in the Domesday Survey of 1086, the present mill dates from the 18th century and was restored to working order in 1979.

Location: On River Avill, beneath Castle Tor, approach via Mill Lane or Castle gardens on foot.

Opening Times: Apr - end Jun: Daily, except Sat (open Easter) 11am - 5pm. Jul & Aug: Daily 11am - 5pm. Sept & Oct: Daily, except Sat 11am - 5pm.

Admission: £1.60. Family tickets available. Party rates by prior arrangement.

EAST LAMBROOK MANOR GARDEN   **Tel:** 01460 240763 **Fax:** 01460 242344

South Petherton, Somerset TA13 5HL

Owner: Mr & Mrs A Norton   **Contact:** The Secretary

Cottage style garden created post 1937 by Margery Fish and described in her well known book "We Made a Garden". Now restored by the present owners with the help of one of the original gardeners. House is not open to visitors.

Location: 7m E of Ilminster, signed off A303 at South Petherton.

Opening Times: Gardens only: 1 Mar - 30 Oct: Mon - Sat 10am - 5pm.

Admission: Adult £2.00, Child 50p, Conc £1.80, Groups by prior arrangement £1.80 pp.

FARLEIGH HUNGERFORD CASTLE   **Tel:** 01225 754026

Farleigh Hungerford, Nr. Bath, Somerset BA3 6RS

Owner: English Heritage   **Contact:** The Custodian

Extensive ruins of a 14th century castle with a splendid chapel containing wall paintings, stained glass and the fine tomb of Sir Thomas Hungerford, builder of the castle.

Location: In Farleigh Hungerford $3^1/_2$m W of Trowbridge on A366.

Opening Times: 1 Apr - 30 Sept: Daily 10am - 6pm. 1 - 31 Oct: Daily 10am - 6pm or dusk if earlier. 1 Nov - 31 Mar: Wed - Sun 10am - 4pm (closed lunch 1 - 2pm).

Admission: Adult £1.50, Child 80p, Conc £1.10.

 THE NATIONAL TRUST   ENGLISH HERITAGE   HISTORIC HOUSES ASSOCIATION

GAULDEN MANOR

OPEN

Easter Sunday &
Monday plus
5 May - 1 Sept:
Sundays and
Thursdays and all
summer Bank
Holidays.

2.00 - 5.30pm

Parties on other days,
morning or afternoon
or evening by prior
appointment.

Tel: 01984 667213

TOLLAND, LYDEARD ST. LAWRENCE, NR. TAUNTON, SOMERSET TA4 3PN

Owner: Mr James Le Gendre Starkie   *Contact: Mr James Le Gendre Starkie*

Small historic manor of great charm. A real lived in family home, guided tours by owner. Past seat of the Turberville family immortalised by Thomas Hardy. Magnificent early plasterwork, fine furniture, many examples of embroidery by owner's wife. Interesting gardens include herb garden, old fashioned roses, bog garden and secret garden beyond monks fish pond. Teas in garden tea room.

Location: 9 miles NW of Taunton off A358 and B3224.

Admission: House & Garden: Adult £3.50, Child £1.75. Garden only: £1.75.

GLASTONBURY TRIBUNAL   **Tel:** 01458 832954

Glastonbury High Street, Glastonbury, Somerset

Owner: English Heritage   **Contact:** The Custodian

A well preserved medieval town house, reputedly once used as the courthouse of Glastonbury Abbey.

Location: In Glastonbury High Street.

Opening Times: Easter - 30 Sept: Sun - Thurs 10am - 5pm (Fris & Sats to 5.30pm).
1 Oct - Easter: Sun - Thurs 10am - 4pm (Fris & Sats 4.30pm).

HATCH COURT

OPEN

House:
13 June - 12 Sept
Thursdays: 2 - 5pm
(homemade teas)

Garden:
15 Apr - 30 Sept
Mon - Thur
10am - 5pm

Plant and
produce sales.

Groups throughout
year by appointment.

Tel: 01823 480120
Fax: 01823 480058

HATCH BEAUCHAMP, TAUNTON, SOMERSET TA3 6AA

Owner: Dr & Mrs Robin Odgers   *Contact: Dr & Mrs Robin Odgers*

Hatch Court is an attractive and unusual Palladian Bath stone mansion, surrounded by beautiful parkland with a herd of fallow deer. Still very much a family home it has a good collection of pictures and furniture, a china room and military museum. The extensively restored gardens feature a spectacular working walled kitchen garden. Recently granted a 1995 Historic Garden Restoration Award. The house is fully equipped for both private and corporate functions.

Location: Off A358 5 miles SE of Taunton. M5 junction 25. Ample free parking.

Admission: House & Gdn: £3.00. Garden only: £1.50. Groups of 25+ £2.50ea.

HESTERCOMBE HOUSE GARDENS   **Tel:** 01823 413030 **Fax:** 01823 337222

Hestercombe Gardens, Cheddon Fitzpaine, Taunton, Somerset TA2 8LQ

Owner: Somerset County Council   **Contact:** D M Usher Esq

Designed in 1904, the garden has been restored in recent years by Somerset County Council using Miss Jekyll's original planting plans as a guide.

Location: 4m from Taunton, close to the village Cheddon Fitzpaine.

Opening Times: All year: Mon - Fri, 9am - 5pm. 1 May - 30 Sept: Sat & Sun 12 noon - 5pm.

Admission: Adult £2.50. Child under 16 free. Coach parties by arrangement.

KING JOHN'S HUNTING LODGE   **Tel:** 01934 732012

The Square, Axbridge, Somerset BS26 2AP

Owner: The National Trust   **Contact:** The Administrator

An early Tudor merchant's house, extensively restored in 1971.

Location: In the Square, on corner of High Street.

Opening Times: Easter - end Sept: Daily 2 - 5pm.

Admission: Free. School parties by arrangement.

LYTES CARY MANOR   **Tel:** 01985 843600

Charlton Mackrell, Somerset TA11 7HU

Owner: The National Trust   **Contact:** The Administrator

A manor house with a 14th century chapel, 15th century hall and 16th century great chamber. The home of Henry Lyte, translator of Niewe Herball (1578). Hedged gardens with long herbaceous border.

Location: 1m N of Ilchester bypass A303, signposted from roundabout at junction of A303. A37 take A372.

Opening Times: 1 Apr - 30 Oct: Mon, Wed & Sat, 2 - 6pm or dusk if earlier.
Last admission 5.30pm.

Admission: £3.70, no reduction for parties.

MAUNSEL HOUSE

OPEN

Weddings, Private
Parties,
Conferences,
Functions,
Filming, Fashion
Shows, Archery,
Clay Pigeon
Shooting,
Equestrian Events,
Garden Parties.
Coach & Group
Parties welcome
by appointment.

Tel: 01278 663413
Fax: 01278 661074

NORTH NEWTON, NR. BRIDGWATER, SOMERSET TA7 0BU

Owner: Sir Benjamin Slade   *Contact: Sir Benjamin Slade*

Imposing 13th century manor house, partly built before the Norman Conquest but mostly built around a Great Hall erected in 1420. Geoffrey Chaucer wrote part of "The Canterbury Tales" whilst staying at the house. Maunsel House is the ancestral seat of the Slade family and is now the home of the 7th baronet, Sir Benjamin Slade.

Location: Bridgwater 4 miles, Bristol 20 miles, Taunton 7 miles, junct. 24 M5, turn left North Petherton 1½ mls North Newton, ½ mile south St. Michael Church.

Admission: For further info tel: 01895 272929 during office hours or 01278 661076.

MIDELNEY MANOR

OPEN

1 May - 28 Sept
Every Thursday
and all Bank
Holiday Mondays

2.30 - 5.30pm

Last tour 4.30pm

Tel: 01458 251229

LANGPORT, SOMERSET TA10 0LW

Owner: J. M. R. Cely Trevilian Esq.   *Contact: J. M. R. Cely Trevilian Esq.*

Originally the Island Manor of the Abbots of Muchelney, the Grade I listed 16th-18th century Manor House situated in the middle of the Somerset Levels and Moors was built by and has been the property of the Trevilian family since the 16th century. 17th century falcons mews, gardens, woodland walks, Heronry.

Location: Signposted from A378 at Bell Hotel, Curry Rivel or from B3168 Hambridge/Curry Rivel road.

Admission: Adult £2.50, Child £1.00. Parties, Weddings & Private functions by appointment.

MILTON LODGE GARDENS

Tel: 01749 672168

Wells, Somerset BA5 3AQ

Owner: D. Tudway Quilter Esq.   **Contact:** D. Tudway Quilter Esq.

'The great glory of the gardens of Milton Lodge is their position high up on the slopes of the Mendip Hills to the north of Wells ... with broad panoramas of Wells Cathedral and the Vale of Avalon.' *Lanning Roper*. Charming, mature alkaline terraced garden dating from 1909. Replanned 1962 with mixed shrubs, herbaceous plants, old fashioned roses and ground cover; numerous climbers; old established yew hedges. Fine trees in garden and in 7 acre arboretum.

Location: ½ m N of Wells from A39. N up Old Bristol Road. Free car park first gate on left.

Opening Times: Garden & Arboretum: Good Friday - 31 Oct: Daily (except Sat) 2 - 6pm. Parties & coaches by prior arrangement.

Admission: Adult £2, Child (0-13) free. Open certain Suns in aid of National Gardens Scheme.

MONTACUTE HOUSE

MONTACUTE, SOMERSET TA15 6XP

Owner: *The National Trust*   **Contact:** *The Property Manager*

Tel: 01935 823289

A magnificent Elizabethan house, with an H-shaped ground plan and many Renaissance features, including contemporary plasterwork, chimneypieces and heraldic glass. The house contains fine 17th and 18th century furniture, an exhibition of samplers dating from the 17th century and Elizabethan and Jacobean portraits from the National Portrait Gallery displayed in the Long Gallery and adjoining rooms. The formal garden includes mixed borders and old roses, also a landscaped park.

Location: In Montacute village, 4m W of Yeovil, on S side of A3088, 3m E of A303.

Opening Times: House: 30 Mar - 3 Nov: Daily except Tues 12 noon - 5.30pm last admission 5pm. Garden & Park: 30 Mar - 3 Nov: Daily except Tues, 11.30am - 5.30pm/dusk. 6 Nov - 28 Mar: Wed - Sun 11.30am - 4pm.

Admission: Adult: £5.00, Child £2.50, Party £4.60 (child £2.20). Family (2 adults & 2 children) £12.50.

MUCHELNEY ABBEY

Tel: 01458 250664

Muchelney, Langport, Somerset TA10 0DQ

Owner: English Heritage   **Contact:** The Custodian

Well preserved ruins of the cloisters, with windows carved in golden stone, and abbot's lodging of the Benedictine abbey, which survived by being used as a farmhouse after the Dissolution.

Location: In Muchelney 2 m S of Langport.

Opening Times: 1 Apr - 30 Sept: Daily 10am - 6pm. Lunchtime closure 1 - 2pm.

Admission: Adult £1.50, Child 80p, Conc £1.10.

NUNNEY CASTLE

Tel: 01179 750700

Nunney, Somerset

Owner: English Heritage   **Contact:** The South West Regional Office

A small 14th century moated castle with a distinctly French style. Its unusual design consists of a central block with large towers at the angles.

Location: In Nunney 3½ m SW of Frome, off A361.

Opening Times: Any reasonable time.

ORCHARD WYNDHAM

Tel: 01984 632309   **Fax:** 01984 633526

Williton, Taunton, Somerset TA4 4HH

Owner: Mrs. Wyndham   **Contact:** Mrs. Wyndham

English manor house. Family home for 700 years encapsulating continuous building and alteration from the 14th to the 20th century. Guided tours only. Limited showing space within the house: **to avoid disappointment please book in advance.** Unsuitable for wheelchairs. Narrow access road suitable for light vehicles only.

Location: 1 mile from A39 at Williton.

Opening Times: House and garden – August: Thursdays and Fridays 2 - 5pm.

Admission: Adult £3.00, Child (under 12) £1.00.

PRIEST'S HOUSE

Tel: 01458 252621

Muchelney, Langport, Somerset TA10 0DQ

Owner: The National Trust   **Contact:** The Administrator

A late medieval hall house with large Gothic windows, originally the residence of priests serving the parish church across the road. Lived in and recently repaired.

Location: 1m S of Langport.

Opening Times: 1 Apr - 30 Sept: Sun & Mon 2 - 5pm.

Admission: £1.50, no reductions.

STEMBRIDGE TOWER MILL

Tel: 01458 250818

High Ham, Somerset TA10 9DJ

Owner: The National Trust   **Contact:** The Tenant

The last thatched windmill in England, dating from 1822 and in use until 1910.

Location: 2m N of Langport, ½m E of High Ham.

Opening Times: 31 Mar - 29 Sept: Sun, Mon & Wed, 2 - 5pm.

Admission: Adult £1.50, Child 80p, parties by prior arrangement.

STOKE-SUB-HAMDON PRIORY

Tel: 01985 843600

North Street, Stoke-sub-Hamdon Somerset TA4 6QP

Owner: The National Trust   **Contact:** The Administrator

A complex of buildings, begun in the 14th century for the priests of the chantry chapel of St Nicholas, which is now destroyed.

Location: Between A303 and A3000. 2m W of Montacute between Yeovil and Ilminster.

Opening Times: All year: Daily 10am - 6pm or dusk if earlier.

TINTINHULL HOUSE GARDEN

Tel: 01935 822545

Farm Street, Tintinhull, Somerset BA22 9PZ

Owner: The National Trust   **Contact:** The Gardener

A 20th century formal garden surrounding a 17th century house. The garden layout, divided into areas by walls and hedges, has border colour and plant themes, including shrub roses and clematis, there is also a kitchen garden.

Location: 5m NW of Yeovil, ½m S of A303, on E outskirts of Tintinhull.

Opening Times: 31 Mar - 29 Sept: Wed - Sun & BH Mon 12 noon - 6pm.

Admission: Adult £3.50, Child £1.60, no reduction for parties.

WELLS CATHEDRAL

Tel: 01749 674483   **Fax:** 01749 677360

Wells, Somerset, BA5 2PA.

Owner: Dean & Chapter of Wells   **Contact:** Mr John Roberts

Fine medieval Cathedral. The West front with its splendid array of statuary, the Quire with colourful tapestries and stained glass, Chapter House and astronomical clock should not be missed.

Location: In Wells, 20m from both Bath & Bristol.

Opening Times: Daily: 7.15am - 8.30pm /dusk (summer), or 7.15am - 6pm (winter).

Admission: No entry charge. Donations welcomed. Guided tours £1.00 per adult. Photo permit £1.00.

SPECIAL EVENTS

✧	**THE BISHOPS PALACE, WELLS** 7.00pm: Abervalley Male Voice Choir	**4 MAY**
✧	**THE BISHOPS PALACE, WELLS** 12.00 – 6.00pm: Mendip Vintage & Classic Car Run	**19 MAY**
✧	**THE BISHOPS PALACE, WELLS** 7.00pm: Classics West Open Air Concert	**21 JUNE**
✧	**THE BISHOPS PALACE, WELLS** 10.00am – 6.00pm: Sealed Knot Display	**13 JULY**
✧	**THE BISHOPS PALACE, WELLS** 2.00 – 6.00pm: Sealed Knot Display	**14 JULY**
✧	**THE BISHOPS PALACE, WELLS** 7.30pm: Medieval Banquet	**18 JULY**
✧	**THE BISHOPS PALACE, WELLS** 7.00pm: Classics West Open Air Concert	**19 JULY**

For National Trust and English Heritage Events see separate section.

SANDON HALL
Sandon

SANDON HALL, the home of the Earl and Countess of Harrowby, is in the heart of Staffordshire. The Estate has been in the family since 1776 when an earlier house designed by Joseph Pickford of Derby was bought by Nathaniel Ryder, 1st Baron Harrowby, son of Sir Dudley Ryder, Lord Chief Justice of England. After damage by fire in 1848 the imposing neo-Jacobean house was re-built by William Burn, the most proven Country House architect of the day.

The family has been prominent in legal and parliamentary affairs for 250 years, with seven generations in parliament, three successive ones in the Cabinet.

Visitors are struck by the atmosphere and by the elegant ambience. Sandon however, for all its grandeur, is first and foremost a home. The grounds and park are equally impressive, while the hall itself provides a wonderful backdrop for marquees.

Special events include Antiques Fairs, Veteran Car Rally, Craft Show, Home Decor Exhibition, Masked Ball, Country Sports Fair.

MUSEUM

The new museum comprises the State Drawing Room and Dining Room, and upstairs many items of unusual and varying interest including early costumes, childhood toys and photographs of early 20th century house parties. Also manuscript letters, albums and prints. There are political objets d'art, and the famous duelling pistols of Pitt the Younger. There is a complete room decorated with very rare hand-painted Chinese wallpaper of the 18th century and a probably unique collection of First World War Recruitment Posters.

GARDENS AND GROUNDS

The 47 acre garden is landscaped and especially beautiful at azalea/rhododendron time and in the autumn. There is a notable arboretum with many magnificent trees, and a network of paths for enjoyable walks. Pre-booking normally essential.

❖

SUITABILITY FOR EVENTS
The State Rooms are ideally suited for a variety of functions with the fine Conservatory, a perfect spot for light catering. The Saloon with excellent acoustics, a grand piano and an organ, is suitable for musical events, balls, cocktail parties, literary evenings etc. trade exhibitions, promotional events & fashion shows are easily accommodated. A large dining room provides an ideal setting for prestige dinner parties, while the elegant Library offers the tranquillity required for important business meetings/lectures. Excellent possibilities for filming.

EXTRA FACILITIES
400 acres of exceptionally attractive rolling parkland laid out in the mid-18th C. and can be booked for many types of outdoor events, including product launches and caravan rallies.

ADVICE TO COURIERS AND DRIVERS
No smoking indoors. No photography inside the House without advance permission. Dogs only in Park on lead.

PARKING FOR COACHES & CARS
Unlimited free parking available on grass, adjacent to the Hall. No parking on the forecourt.

CATERING
Organised by approved and recommended outside caterers. Internally several rooms can be hired out for lunch and dinner.

GUIDED TOURS
All visits to the museum are guided and last on approx. 1¼ hrs. Pre-booking essential. Refreshments may be available if requested in advance.

SCHOOL VISITS/ CHILDREN
Accompanied groups welcome. The museum has great historical interest while the parkland is particularly suitable for rural studies, including forestry and agriculture.

CONTACT

Michael Bosson
Sandon Hall
Stafford ST18 0BZ
Tel: (01889) 508004
Fax: (01889) 508586

LOCATION

A51. 10 miles north of Rugeley and 4 miles south of Stone. Entrance through double lodges opposite Sandon village War Memorial. From south (incl. Birmingham Airport): M42, exit 9, Lichfield, Rugeley. London 2¾ hrs, 151 miles. From north (incl. Manchester Airport) 1 hr: M6, exit 14. Stafford ring road B5066
Rail: Stafford station
Taxi: (01785) 48548

CONFERENCE AND FUNCTION FACILITIES

Subject to prior arrangement most state rooms can be made available for functions/meetings; by the way of example the saloon measures 84' x 23' and the main library is 820 sq. ft. Please telephone for further details.

OPENING TIMES

Daily throughout the year, with some exceptions, for events/functions and for pre-booked group visits to the museum / gardens.
Evening tours by special arrangement.

ADMISSION

MUSEUM
(inc. guided tour)
   Adult £3.00
   Child £2.00
   OAP £2.50

Guided group (max 20) tours by appointment only. Groups of 40 may be accommodated by combining museum and garden tours.

GARDENS & GROUNDS
Self-guided tour (guide booklet at extra cost) by appointment only - except during some public events.
   Adult £1.50
   Child £1.00
   OAP £1.00
Guided tours may be arranged at certain times. Please enquire.

SHUGBOROUGH ESTATE
Stafford

SHUGBOROUGH is the ancestral home of the fifth Earl of Lichfield, who as Patrick Lichfield is known worldwide as a leading photographer.

The 18th century Mansion House contains a fine collection of ceramics, silver, paintings and French furniture. Part of the House continues to be lived in by the Earl and his family. Nothing could be more English!

Visitors can enjoy the 18 acre Grade I Historic Garden and a unique collection of neo-classical monuments by James Stuart.

Other attractions include the original servants' quarters. The working laundry, kitchens, brewhouse and coach houses have all been lovingly restored. Costumed guides can show how the servants lived and worked over 100 years ago.

Shugborough Park Farm is a Georgian farmstead that features an agricultural museum, working corn mill and rare breeds centre. The livestock are all historic breeds and in the farmhouse visitors can see brick bread ovens in operation and butter and cheese making in the dairy.

The Estate is set in 900 acres of park and woodland with many walks and trails.

CONTACT

Anne Wood
Promotions and
Events Manager
Shugborough
Milford
Stafford
ST17 0XB

Tel: (01889) 881388

Fax: (01889) 881323

LOCATION

From London M1, M6
from junct. 19, leave M6
junct. 13, follow signs.

Rail: BR Intercity
trains at Stafford.

Taxi: Anthony's Stafford
(01785) 252255

SUITABILITY FOR OTHER EVENTS
Private and corporate entertainment, conferences, product launches and dinner parties. Catering can be arranged. Filming and event location.

EXTRA FACILITIES
Over 900 acres of parkland and gardens available for hire. Themed activities, tours and demonstrations.

FACILITIES FOR THE DISABLED
Disabled and elderly visitors may alight at the entrance to the property before parking in the allocated areas. Toilets for the disabled. Stair climber to House. Batricars available. Disabled friendly picnic tables available. Taped tours.

ADVICE TO COURIERS & DRIVERS
Discounted vouchers for drivers' meals available. Please advise clients that there is no photography allowed within the property.

PARKING FOR COACHES & CARS
Capacity of car park - 200 cars and 28 coaches, 150 yards from the House. Additional parking on the grass.

CATERING
Licensed Tea Room/Cafe seating 95 also tearoom at Farm seats 30. Prior notice for large groups. Catering for special functions/conferences.

GUIDED TOURS
Pre-booked tours of approx. 1 hour duration. Themed tours as required. Groups of 15 min. Please telephone for full adult group and educational package details.

GIFT SHOP/GUIDE BOOKS
National Trust Shop at main site open at the same time as the property. Selection of colour guide books available.

SCHOOL VISITS/CHILDREN
Variety of award winning educational packages and demonstrations available all year in all areas. Curriculum related. Pre-visits for teachers. Please contact education officer.

OPENING TIMES

23 March - 29 September
Daily: 11.00am - 5.00pm
Booked parties from
10.30am all year.

Pre-booked parties only
throughout the year.
28 October - 22 Dec
& 2 January - 22 March
Daily   10.30am - 4.00pm

ADMISSION

ALL ATTRACTIONS
Adults £8.00
Concessions* . . .£6.00
Family (3 Sites) . .£18.00

GARDENS & PARK
Cars £1.50
Coaches . . . . . . .Free

SINGLE SITES
(House, Museum or Farm)
Per site
Adult £3.50
Concessions* . . .£2.50

* Concessions for children
(under 5's FREE), OAPs,
Students, unemployed &
groups.

** NT Members free
to Mansion House,
reduced rate to Museum
and Farm.

CONFERENCE AND FUNCTION FACILITIES

ROOM	DIMENSIONS	CAPACITY	LAYOUT	POWER POINTS	SUITABLE FOR A/V
Saloon	60' x 24'	80	Theatre	✓	✓
			Lunch/Dinner		
Conference	35' x 24'	35	Theatre	✓	✓
Suite		30	U-shape		
		32	Boardroom		
		35	Buffet		

ANCIENT HIGH HOUSE

Tel: 01785 240204

Greengate Street, Stafford, Staffordshire ST16 2HS
Owner: Stafford Borough Council   **Contact:** R Halliwell
The largest timber framed townhouse in England. Built in 1595 by the Dorrington family. Permanent collection displayed in period room settings which relate to the house's history. Staffordshire Yeomanry museum on top floor. Souvenir shop and Video room.
Location: Stafford.
Opening Times: Apr - Oct: Mon - Fris 9am - 5pm & Sats 10am - 4pm.
Nov - Mar: Mon - Fris 9am - 5pm and Sats 10am - 3pm. Closed Suns.
Admission: Adult £1.50, Child £1.00.

BIDDULPH GRANGE GARDEN

OPEN

30 Mar - 30 October
Weds - Fri
12 noon - 6.00pm
Sat, Suns & Bank
Holiday Mondays
11.00am - 6.00pm
(Closed Good
Friday)
Also open
2 Nov - 22 Dec
Sat, Sun
12 noon - 4.00pm

Tel: 01782 517999

GRANGE ROAD, BIDDULPH, STOKE-ON-TRENT ST8 7SD
Owner: The National Trust   *Contact:* The Garden Office
A rare and exciting survival of a high Victorian garden - recently restored by the National Trust. The Garden is divided into a series of themed gardens within a garden, with a Chinese temple, Egyptian Court, Pinetum, Dahlia Walk, Glen and many other settings.
Location: Off A527, 3¹/₂ mls south of Congleton, 8 mls north of Stoke-on-Trent.
Admission: Adult £4.00, Child £2.00, Family (2 adults & 2 children) £10.00. Half price Nov & Dec. Joint ticket with Little Moreton Hall available during main season. Adult £6.00, Child £3.00, Family £15.00

CHILLINGTON HALL

Tel: 01902 850236

Codsall Wood, Wolverhampton, Staffordshire WV8 1RE
Owner: Mr & Mrs P Giffard   **Contact:** Mr & Mrs P Giffard
Georgian red brick house with fine saloon set in 'Capability' Brown park having the largest lake created by Brown.
Location: 2 m S of Brewood off A449.
Opening Times: Jun - 14 Sept, Thurs, Easter Sun, Suns prior to May Bank Hol & Suns in Aug.
Admission: Adult £2.50, Child £1.25.

ECCLESHALL CASTLE

Tel: 01785 850151

Stafford, Staffordshire ST21 6LS
Owner: T M Carter Esq   **Contact:** The Curator
William and Mary Mansion House among castle ruins.
Location: ¹/₄m N of Eccleshall on A519.
Opening Times: Gardens only, 2 - 5.30pm Easter Sun. Sun & Wed from 19 May - 18 Aug: House available for functions open to pre-booked parties.
Admission: Donations to local charities.

FORD GREEN HALL

Tel: 01782 534771

Smallthorne, Stoke-on-Trent, Staffordshire ST6 1NG
Owner: Stoke-on-Trent City Council   **Contact:** The Manager
Ford Green Hall is a timber framed Yeoman farmer's house built for the Ford family in 1624, with brick wings added in the 18th century. A rare survival from the pre-industrial Potteries, the rooms are furnished with original and reproduction pieces according to inventories of the 17th and 18th century. A period garden is being developed around the Hall.
Location: On B5051 Burslem - Endon road in Stoke-on-Trent (the route to Leek in the Staffordshire Moorlands).
Opening Times: All Year: Sun - Thur 1- 5pm all year except Christmas - New Year.
Admission: Free. Guided tours available.

IZAAK WALTON'S COTTAGE

Tel: 01785 760278

Worston Lane, Shallowford, Stafford, Staffordshire ST15 0PA
Owner: Stafford Borough Council   **Contact:** R Halliwell
Timber-framed cottage in the heart of the mid-Staffordshire countryside. Bequeathed by Izaak Walton, it has displays on the history of angling. Ground floor rooms are set out in 17th century style. Events programme during the summer. Souvenir shop.
Location: Stafford.
Opening Times: Apr - Oct: Tues - Sun 11am - 4.30pm. Closed Mons except Bank Hols.
Admission: Adult £1.50, Child/Conc. £1.00.

LICHFIELD CATHEDRAL

Tel: 01543 250300

Lichfield, Staffordshire WS13 7LD

Contact: Canon A Barnard

800 year old Gothic Cathedral with three spires on a 1300 year old Christian site. 8th century gospel manuscript, 16th century Flemish glass, silver collection - a worshipping community.
Location: Approach from A38 and A51, N from M42 and M6.
Opening Times: All year: Daily.
Admission: Donation.

MOSELEY OLD HALL

Photo: David Lee, Property Manager

FORDHOUSES, WOLVERHAMPTON WV10 7HY
Owner: The National Trust   *Contact:* The Property Manager
Tel: 01902 782808

An Elizabethan House with later alterations. Charles II hid here after the Battle of Worcester and the bed in which he slept is on view, as well as the hiding place he used. The small garden has been reconstructed in 17th century style with formal box parterre; 17th century plants only are grown. The property is a Sandford Education Award Winner. Tea-room in 18th century Barn, light lunches available in high season. Gift shop and Charles II exhibition in the Barn.
Location: 4 miles north of Wolverhampton between A449 and A460.
Opening Times: 16 March - 22 December. Mar - Apr: Sat & Sun, BH Mon and following Tues 1.30 - 5.30pm (BH Mon 11am - 5pm). May - Oct: Wed, Sat, Sun, BH Mon and following Tues, also Tues in July & Aug 1.30 - 5.30pm. (BH Mon 11am - 5pm). Nov & Dec: Sun only 1.30 - 4.30pm Guided tours only – last tour at 4pm).
Admission: Adult £3.30, Child £1.65, Family ticket (2 adults/2 children) £8.25.

SAMUEL JOHNSON BIRTHPLACE MUSEUM

Tel: 01543 264972   **Fax:** 01543 254562

Breadmarket Street, Lichfield, Staffordshire WS13 6LG
Owner: Lichfield City Council   **Contact:** Dr G Nicholls
The house where Samuel's father had a bookshop is now a museum with many of Johnson's personal relics.
Location: Breadmarket Street, Lichfield.
Opening Times: Daily: 10am - 5pm.
Admission: Adult £1.20, Child 70p, Family £3.20, Conc 70p, Groups 70p.

SANDON HALL

See Page 176 for full page entry.

SHUGBOROUGH HALL

See Page 177 for full page entry.

STAFFORD CASTLE

Tel: 01785 257698

Newport Road, Stafford, Staffordshire ST16 1BG
Owner: Stafford Borough Council   **Contact:** R Halliwell
The site of a Norman motte and bailey castle. The remains of the 19th century neo-gothic castle can be visited. The Visitor Centre is set out as a Norman guard room. An imaginative audio-visual presentation describes the castle's mixed fortunes. Souvenir shop.
Location: Stafford.
Opening Times: All Year: Tue - Sun, Closed Mons except Bank Hols. Apr - Oct 10am - 5.00pm, Nov - Mar 10am - 4pm.
Admission: Adult £1.50, Child/Conc. £1.00.

TAMWORTH CASTLE

Tel: 01827 63563 **Fax:** 01827 52769

The Holloway, Tamworth, Staffordshire B79 7LR
Owner: Tamworth Borough Council   **Contact:** Mrs Esme Ballard
Norman motte and bailey castle with fifteen period rooms spanning 800 years of history.
Location: Town centre off A453.
Opening Times: All year: Mon - Sat, 10am - 5.30pm. Sun 2 - 5.30pm. Last admission 4.30pm.
Admission: Adult £3.20, Child £1.60, Family £8.00, Conc £1.60. Groups of 10 plus: Adult £2.50, Children £1.10, School children 60p.

WOLSELEY GARDEN PARK

Tel: 01889 574888

Wolseley Bridge, Stafford, Staffordshire ST17 0YT
45 acres of gardens on a variety of themes, recently created by Sir Charles and Lady Wolseley. Scented garden for the blind.
Location: At junction of A51 and A513 (2m N of Rugeley in Staffordshire).
Opening Times: Apr - Oct: Daily 10am - 6pm. Nov - Mar: Daily except prices 10am - 4pm. Open every day except Christmas. Please telephone to check opening times.
Admission: Adult £2.00, Child £1.00, Conc £1.50, Group of 20 plus 50p discount.

Where to Stay
For Private Accommodation and Johansens recommended Hotels, see Accommodation Section.

Hudson's Choice

Where to stay

The 'Where to Stay' section towards the back of the book includes more than fifty private houses across the country offering B & B accommodation (by prior arrangement).
Each has been carefully selected by independent inspectors on the basis of ambience, a warm welcome and overall standard of accommodation.
Some of the houses in this section are shown below.

St. Mary's Hall, Suffolk, England.

The Old Rectory, Gwynedd, Wales.

Hartlip Place, Kent, England.

Llanwenarth House, Gwent, Wales.

Balgersho House, Tayside, Scotland.

Cleish Castle, Tayside, Scotland.

KENTWELL HALL
Long Melford

KENTWELL HALL is a beautiful redbrick Tudor Manor House surrounded by a broad moat.

Built by the Clopton Family, from wealth made in the wool trade, Kentwell has an air of timeless tranquillity. The exterior is little altered in 450 years. The interior was remodelled by Hopper in 1825 and his work has been embellished and enhanced in restoration by the present owners. Hopper's interiors, notably the Great Hall and Dining Room, emphasise their Tudor provenance, but the Drawing Room and Library are simply and restrainedly classical; all are eminently habitable.

Kentwell, as well as being a family home, conveys a deep feeling of the Tudor period with the service areas: Great Kitchen, Bakery, Dairy and Forge always fully equipped in 16th century style. Kentwell's unique 16th century atmosphere and large collection of 16th century artifacts make it an ideal location for films and videos.

The gardens are part of Kentwell's delight. Intimate yet spacious, you are seldom far from a moat, clipped yews (some 30ft high) or mellow brick wall. There is a fine walled garden with original 17th century layout and a well established large Herb Garden and Potager.

The farm is run organically and is set around timber framed buildings and stocked with rare breed farm animals.

Home to the **Award -Winning Re-Creations of Tudor Domestic Life** when visitors meet numerous 'Tudors' with dress, speech, activities and locations appropriate for the 16th century. These take place on selected weekends between April and September.

❖

SUITABILITY FOR OTHER EVENTS
We specialise in: Genuine Tudor Style Banquets, Wedding Receptions, formal but friendly luncheons and dinners and particularly 'Company Days' when the whole company, or a division, come to Kentwell for a specially devised one-day programme of fun, stimulation and challenge.

EXTRA FACILITIES
A wide variety of 'Tudor-style' activities can be arranged for visitors, including longbow shooting, working bakery, dairy and stillroom, spinning etc. Clay pigeon shooting in Park. Airstrip suitable for light aircraft and microlites.

ADVICE TO COURIERS & DRIVERS
No dogs or unaccompanied children. No photos in House.

FACILITIES FOR THE DISABLED
Disabled or elderly visitors may alight at house, with prior notice. New toilet for the disabled.

PARKING FOR COACHES & CARS
There is parking for several hundred cars and coaches.

CATERING
Kentwell provides its own catering, often from produce home grown or raised on Kentwell's own organic farm. Home-made teas and lunches on open days up to full catering for grander functions. The undercroft can comfortably seat 96. Overcroft can accommodate up to 300.

GIFT SHOP
Open at the same time as the House and selling a variety of local and 'Tudor-style' items.

SCHOOL VISITS/CHILDREN
We have a highly developed schools' programme dealing with 700 parties per year. Schools can visit a re-creation of Tudor Life, re-create Tudor life themselves for the day or take one of our tours conducted by a qualified teacher on the House, Garden, Farm or aspects of each.

CONTACT

Mrs J G Phillips
Kentwell Hall
Long Melford
Suffolk
CO10 9BA

Tel: (01787) 310207
Fax: (01787) 379318

LOCATION

Off the A134. 4 mls N of Sudbury, 14 mls S of Bury St. Edmunds.

Rail: Sudbury Stn 4 mls
Colchester Stn 20 mls

Air: Stansted 30 mls

Taxi: Sudbury Town Taxis (01787) 377366.

CONFERENCE AND FUNCTION FACILITIES

ROOM	DIMENSIONS	CAPACITY	LAYOUT	POWER POINTS	SUITABLE FOR A/V
Great Hall	40' x 24'	100	Buffet	✓	✓
		120	Theatre		
		30	Boardroom		
		60	Lunch/Dinner		
Main Dining Room	24' x 24'	75	Buffet	✓	
		40	Lunch/Dinner		
Drawing Room	35' x 24'	75	Buffet	✓	
		50	Lunch/Dinner		
Library	36' x 20'	20	Boardroom	✓	
Octagon Room	24' x 24'	20	Boardroom	✓	
Overcroft	120' x 22'	300	Buffet	✓	✓
		250	Theatre	✓	✓

OPENING TIMES

Spring:
10 Mar - 15 Jun: Suns only
5 - 13 Apr, 4 - 6 May and
25 - 31 May:
Daily: 12 noon - 5pm
Bank Hol weekends:
11am - 6pm

Summer
16 June - 7 July
Re-Creation of Tudor Life.
(See Below)

10 July - 22 Sept
Daily: 12 noon - 5pm

23 Sept. - end of Oct
Suns only: 12 noon - 5pm

Bank Hol weekends:
11am - 6pm

•Tudor Life re-created
• 5 Apr - 8 Apr
• 4 May - 6 May
• 25 May - 27 May
• 3 Aug & 4 Aug
• 23 Aug - 26 Aug
• 21 Sept & 22 Sept
Daily: 11am - 6pm.
Selected other days call Info line:
0891 517475. Calls cost 39p/min
cheap rate, 49/min other times.

•Great annual Re-Creation
•16 June - 7 July
 (Sats, Suns & Fri 5 July only)
11am - 5pm

ADMISSION

(Subject to variation in VAT) but not during Re-Creations when special prices apply.

FULL TICKET
Adult £4.75
Child (5-15) £2.75
OAP £4.00
GARDEN & FARM
Adult £2.75
Child (5-15) £1.75
OAP £2.50
Groups
20% discount for groups of
20 or more if pre-booked.

OWNERS TOURS
Standard £5.50
Extended £6.50
(min 20 people per tour)

SOMERLEYTON HALL
Lowestoft

SOMERLEYTON HALL is a perfect example of a House built to show off the wealth of the new Victorian aristocracy. The house was remodelled from a modest 17th century Manor House by the prolific builder Sir Morton Peto. When he was declared bankrupt in 1863, his extravagant concoction of red brick, white stone and lavish interiors was sold to another hugely successful businessman, carpet manufacturer Sir Francis Crossley. The present owner Lord Somerleyton, is his great-grandson.

No expense was spared in the building or the fittings. Stone was brought from Caen and Aubigny and the magnificent carved stonework created by John Thomas (who worked on the Houses of Parliament) is gradually being restored.

In the state rooms there are paintings by Landseer, Wright of Derby and Stanfield, together with fine wood carvings by Willcox of Warwick and from the earlier house, Grinling Gibbons.

The Oak Room retains its carved oak panelling and Stuart atmosphere: the rest is lavishly Victorian. Grandest of all is the Ballroom with its crimson damask walls reflected in rows of long white and gilt mirrors.

GARDENS
Somerleyton's 12 acre gardens are justly renowned. The 1846 yew hedge maze is one of the few surviving Victorian mazes in Britain. The stable tower clock by Vuilliamy made in 1847 is the original model for a great clock to serve as the Tower Clock in the new Houses of Parliament, now world famous as Big Ben. Colour is added to the gardens by rhododendrons, azaleas and a long pergola trailing mauve, pink and white wisteria. Special features include: a sunken garden; the Loggia Tea Room; glasshouses by Sir Joseph Paxton; an aviary; fine statuary; miniature railway.

CONTACT

Lord Somerleyton
Estate Office
Somerleyton Hall
Nr Lowestoft
Suffolk
NR32 5QQ

Tel: (01502) 730224
Fax: (01502) 732143

LOCATION

5 miles north-west Lowestoft off B1074: 7 miles Yarmouth (A143)

Rail: Somerleyton Station 1¹/₂ miles.
Taxi: Great Yarmouth and Lowestoft.

OPENING TIMES

Summer
Easter Sunday - end Sept inclusive

HOUSE, MAZE & GARDENS
Thurs, Suns and Bank holidays with the addition of Tues, and Weds in July and August

House.   1.30 - 5.00pm
Garden: 12.30 - 5.30pm

Winter
Closed except by appointment.

ADMISSION

Adult £3.95
OAP £3.50
Child (5-16yrs) . .£1.75
Family (2+2) . .£10.75

Groups
Adult £2.95
Child/Schools . .£1.50

SUITABILITY FOR OTHER EVENTS
Somerleyton Hall is suitable for conferences, business meetings, receptions, fashion shows, archery, clay pigeon shooting, equestrian events, garden parties, shows, rallies, filming, wedding receptions, fund raising events.

EXTRA FACILITIES
The Winter Garden, Loggia and Conference Room can be hired throughout the year.

ADVICE TO COURIERS & DRIVERS
No dogs. No photography in the House.

FACILITIES FOR THE DISABLED
If visitors are badly disabled they may alight at the entrance to the house, before parking in the allocated areas. Wheelchair and ramps are available. There are toilets for the disabled.

PARKING FOR COACHES & CARS
Capacity of the Car Park: 100 cars and 10 coaches, 20 yards from Garden entrance.

CATERING
Loggia Tea Room, fresh home baked cooking light lunches and the ever popular cream teas and cakes.

GUIDED TOURS
By prior arrangement. If requested owner may meet groups. Tours of Gardens, or Hall and Gardens, with ploughmans lunch/supper a speciality. Please contact the Administrator for details.

GIFT SHOP
Open at same time as the Hall and Gardens.

GROUP VISITS
Groups are most welcome, suggested length of visit 3-4 hours. Advisable to phone in advance.

GUIDE BOOKS
Colour guide book, £2.00.

SCHOOL VISITS/CHILDREN
Groups of children welcome by prior arrangement. A guide is provided. Areas of particular interest include: Maze and garden trail, aviary, dolls house, project study of Victorian history.

CONFERENCE AND FUNCTION FACILITIES

ROOM	DIMENSIONS	CAPACITY	LAYOUT	POWER POINTS	SUITABLE FOR A/V
Conference Suite	34' x 22'	65	Theatre	4	✓
The Loggia	48' x 24"	80	Various	3	✓
Winter Garden	99' x 16'	80	Various	1	✓

ABBEY VISITOR CENTRE

Tel: 01284 763110   **Fax:** 01284 757079

Samson Tower, Abbey Precinct, Bury St Edmunds, Suffolk IP33 1RS

Owner: St Edmundsbury Borough Council   **Contact:** T Meakin

Location: Town centre off A14.

Opening Times: Apr and Oct: Daily, 10am - 5pm. May and Sept: Daily, 10am - 6pm. Jun - Aug: Daily, 10am - 8pm. Nov - Mar: Wed, Sat, 10am - 4pm, Sun 12 noon - 4pm.

Admission: Adult 80p, Child 60p, Conc 60p, Groups 20% discount, Free for locals.

BELCHAMP HALL

Tel: 01787 372744

Belchamp Walter, Sudbury, Suffolk CO10 7AT

Owner: M M J Raymond Esq   **Contact:** Mr and Mrs Raymond

Exceptional red brick Queen Anne style house belonging to the Raymond family since 1611. Contemporary pictures and period furniture. Suitable for exhibitions, receptions and an ideal film location; often seen as Lady Jane's house in *Lovejoy*. Gardens including a cherry avenue, follies, a sunken garden, a walled garden, a lake and park wood. There are also elegant converted stables with a kitchen, and toilets. The Medieval Church opposite houses important 15th century wall paintings.

Location: 5 m SW of Sudbury. Opposite Belchamp Walter Church.

Opening Times: By appointment: May - Sept: Tues & Thurs & Bank Hol Mons 2.30 - 6pm.

Admission: Adult £3, Child £1.50. Discounts for parties. Refreshments by arrangement.

EUSTON HALL

Tel: 01842 766366

Suffolk. Postal address: Estate Office, Euston, Thetford, Norfolk IP24 2QP

Owner: The Duke of Grafton   **Contact:** Mrs L Campbell

18th century house contains a famous collection of paintings including works by Stubbs, Van Dyck, Lely and Kneller. The Pleasure Grounds were were laid out by John Evelyn and William Kent. 17th century parish church in Wren style. River walk and watermill. Teas and craft shop in old kitchens. Picnic area.

Location: 12 miles north of Bury St. Edmunds, on the A1088.

Opening Times: 6 Jun - 26 Sept: Thurs 2.30 - 5pm. Also Suns 30 June & 1 Sept: 2.30 - 5pm.

Admission: Adult £2.50, OAP's £2.00. Group rate (min 12): Adult £2.00 ea., Child 50p.

FRAMLINGHAM CASTLE ⛶

Tel: 01728 724189

Framlingham, Suffolk IP8 9BT

Owner: English Heritage   **Contact:** The Custodian

A superb 12th century castle which, from the outside, looks almost the same as when it was built. From the continuous curtain wall, linking 13 towers, there are excellent views of Framlingham and the charming reed fringed mere. At different times, the castle has been a fortress, an Elizabethan prison, a poor house and a school. The many alterations over the years have led to a pleasing mixture of historical styles.

Location: In Framlingham on B1116.

Opening Times: 1 Apr - 30 Sept: Daily 10am - 6pm. 1 - 31 Oct: Daily 10am - 6pm or dusk if earlier. 1 Nov - 31 Mar 10am - 4pm.

Admission: Adult £2.50, Child £1.30, Conc £1.90.

GAINSBOROUGH'S HOUSE

OPEN

All year
Tues - Sat
10.00am - 5.00pm.

Sun & Bank Hol
Mons 2 - 5.00pm
Closes at 4.00pm
Nov - March

Closed: Mondays,
Good Friday and
Christmas to
New Year.

Tel: 01787 372958

46 GAINSBOROUGH ST, SUDBURY, SUFFOLK CO10 6EU

Owner: *Gainsborough's House Society*   **Contact:** *Hugh Belsey*

Birthplace of Thomas Gainsborough RA (1727-88). Georgian fronted town house, with attractive walled garden, displays more of the artist's work than any other Gallery. The collection is shown together with 18th century furniture and memorabilia. Varied programme of contemporary exhibitions organised throughout the year includes; fine art, craft, photography, printmaking, sculpture and highlights the work of East Anglian artists.

Location: 46 Gainsborough Street, Sudbury town centre.

Admission: Adult £2.50, OAP £2.00. Children and students £1.25.

HELMINGHAM HALL

OPEN

Gardens only
28 Apr - 8 Sept
Sundays only
2.00 - 6.00pm

Wednesdays
between the
above dates
for pre arranged
groups of 30+ and
individuals.

Tel: 01473 890363
Fax: 01473 890776

STOWMARKET, SUFFOLK IP14 6EF

Owner: *The Lord and Lady Tollemache*   **Contact:** *Ms. J Tressider*

The Tudor Hall surrounded by its wide moat is set in a 400 acre deer park. Two superb gardens, one surrounded by its own moat and walls extends to several acres and has wide herbaceous borders and an immaculate kitchen garden. The second enclosed within yew hedges has a special rose garden with a Herb and Knot garden containing plants grown in England before 1750.

Location: B1077 9 miles north of Ipswich, 5 miles south of Debenham.

Admission: Adult £3.00, Concessions £2.50, Child (5 - 15) £1.50. Groups 30+ £2.50. Safari rides: Adult £2.00 Child £1.50

ICKWORTH HOUSE AND PARK ❀

OPEN

HOUSE
23 Mar - 3 Nov
Tues, Wed, Fri, Sat,
Sun and Bank Hol
Mondays: 1 - 5pm

PARK: All year:
Daily: 7am - 7pm

GARDEN
23 Mar - 3 Nov
Daily: 10am - 5pm

All closed on
Good Friday.

Tel: 01284 735270

HORRINGER, BURY ST. EDMUNDS, SUFFOLK IP33 2DH

Owner: *The National Trust*   **Contact:** *The Property Manager*

The eccentric Earl of Bristol (also Bishop of Derry) created this equally eccentric house, started in 1795 to display his collections. The paintings include works by Titian, Gainsborough and Velasquez and the magnificent Georgian Silver Collection is displayed in the oval Rotunda which is linked by curved corridors to flanking wings. The house is surrounded by an Italianate garden and is set in a 'Capability' Brown park with several waymarked woodland walks and a deer enclosure with hide.

Location: At Horringer 3 miles SW of Bury St. Edmunds on W side of A143.

Admission: House, Park & Gdns: Adult £4.75, Child £2.00. Park & Garden: Adult £1.75, Child £50p.

KENTWELL HALL

See Page 180 for full page entry.

LANDGUARD FORT ⛶

Tel: 01394 286403

Felixstowe, Suffolk

Owner: English Heritage   **Contact:** The Custodian

Impressive 18th century fort with later additions built on a site originally fortified by Henry VIII and in use until after World War II.

Location: 1 m S of Felixstowe near docks.

Opening Times: Museum - 29 May - 25 Sept: Wed & Sun only, 2.30 - 5pm. Guided tours of fort Wed & Sun 2.45pm & 4pm.

Admission: Adult £1.00, Child 60p, EH members 80p.

LAVENHAM GUILDHALL

Tel: 01787 247646

Lavenham, Suffolk

Owner: The National Trust   **Contact:** The Administrator

This early 16th century timber framed Tudor building, originally the hall of the Guild of Corpus Christi, overlooks and dominates the market place. Within the nine rooms of the Guildhall are displays of local history, farming, industry and the development of the railway, and a unique exhibition of 700 years of the medieval woollen cloth trade. There is a delightful walled garden with a 19th century lock up and mortuary.

Location: A1141 and B1071.

Opening Times: 23 Mar - 3 Nov: Daily, 11am - 5pm (closed Good Fri).

Admission: Adult £2.60, Child first 2 free then 60p (free during summer hols), Parties £2.20, School parties 50p by prior arrangement.

LEISTON ABBEY

Tel: 01604 730320

Leiston, Suffolk

Owner: English Heritage   **Contact:** The Midlands Regional Office

The remains of this abbey for Premonstratensian canons, including a restored chapel, are amongst the most extensive in Suffolk.

Location: 1 m N of Leiston off B1069.

Opening Times: Any reasonable time.

LITTLE HALL

Tel: 01787 247179   **Fax:** 01787 248341

Market Place, Lavenham, Suffolk CO10 9QZ

Owner: Suffolk Preservation Society   **Contact:** B W Forgham

Little Hall, a Grade II Listed Building with a Crown Post roof, reveals five centuries of change. Its history mirrors the rise and fall of Lavenham's cloth trade. Restored by the Gayer-Anderson twins in the 1930s.

Location: Market Place, Lavenham.

Opening Times: Easter - Oct: Wed,Thurs, Sat, Sun, 2.30 - 5.30pm. Bank Hols.

MANOR HOUSE MUSEUM

Tel: 01284 757076   **Fax:** 01284 757079

Honey Hill, Bury St Edmunds, Suffolk IP33 1HF

Owner: St Edmundsbury Borough Council   **Contact:** The Gallery Supervisor

Georgian mansion with displays specialising in horology from 17th to 20th century.

Location: Bury town centre off A14.

Opening Times: Mon - Sat: 10am - 5pm. Sun 2 - 5pm.

Admission: Adult £2.50, Child £1.50, Family £7.00, Conc £1.50, Groups 20% discount.

MELFORD HALL

Tel: 01787 880286

Long Melford, Sudbury, Suffolk CO10 9AH

Owner: The National Trust   **Contact:** The Administrator

A turreted brick Tudor mansion, little changed since 1578 with the original panelled banqueting hall, an 18th century drawing room, a Regency library and a Victorian bedroom, showing fine furniture and Chinese porcelain. There is also a special Beatrix Potter display and a garden.

Location: In Long Melford on E side of A134, 14m S of Bury St Edmunds, 3m N of Sudbury.

Opening Times: Apr: Sat, Sun & BH Mon 2 - 5.30pm. May - end Sept: Wed, Thur, Sat, Sun & BH Mon 2 - 5.30pm. Oct: Sat & Sun 2 - 5.30pm. Last admission 5pm.

Admission: Principal rooms & garden £4.00, pre-arranged parties £3.00 Wed & Thur only.

MOYSE'S HALL MUSEUM

Tel: 01284 757488   **Fax:** 01284 757079

Cornhill, Bury St Edmunds, Suffolk IP33 1DX

Owner: St Edmundsbury Borough Council   **Contact:** The Gallery Supervisor

Very early 12th century flint house, now a museum of Suffolk history.

Location: Town centre off A14.

Opening Times: Daily: 10am - 5pm, except Suns: 2 - 5pm.

Admission: Adult £1.25, Child 75p, Conc. 75p, Groups 20% discount, Free for local residents.

ORFORD CASTLE

Tel: 01394 450472

Orford, Woodbridge, Suffolk IP12 2ND

Owner: English Heritage   **Contact:** The Custodian

A royal castle built for coastal defence in the 12th century. A magnificent keep survives almost intact with three towers reaching to 90 feet. Inside there are many rooms to explore.

Location: In Orford on B1084.

Opening Times: 1 Apr - 30 Sept: Daily 10am - 6pm. 1 - 31 Oct: Daily 10am - 6pm or dusk if earlier. 1 Nov - 31 Mar 10am - 4pm. (closed lunch 1 -2 pm)

Admission: Adult £2.00, Child £1.00, Conc £1.50.

OTLEY HALL

OTLEY, IPSWICH, SUFFOLK IP6 9PA

Owner: Mr J Mosesson   **Contact:** The Secretary

Tel: 01473 890264   **Fax:** 01473 890803

A stunning 15th century Moated Hall (Grade I), set in gardens and grounds of 10 acres, frequently described as "one of England's loveliest houses". Voted in October 1994 by AA as one of Britain's top 20 historic houses. Rich in history and architectural detail. Features of particular note are richly carved beams, linenfold, fresco-work, herringbone brickwork and pargetting. Built around 1450 it was the home of the Gosnold family for 250 years. Some of the famous names and events connected with both the Gosnolds and the Hall are the Royal households of Elizabeth I, James I and Charles I; the Civil War (Colonel Robert Gosnold - siege of Carlisle); the Virginia colonisation of 1607 - Bartholomew Gosnold, who settled and named Cape Cod and Martha's (Gosnold) Vineyard, and later founded Jamestown; Lady Jane Grey; Shakespeare.

The Gardens are formal and informal, including part of a fascinating and historically important design by Francis Inigo Thomas (1866 - 1950), with canal mount, nutteries, croquet lawn, rose garden and moat walk.

Location: From A14 take Norwich/Diss junction (A140), then follow B1078 to T-Junction and follow signs for Otley. Approx 7 miles from Ipswich.

Opening Times: 7, 8 Apr; 26, 27 May; 25, 26 August: 2 - 6pm.

Admission: Adult £4.00, Child £2.50. Group and coach parties welcome throughout the year, by appointment only, for private guided tours - lunches or afternoon cream teas are available.

THE PRIORY, LAVENHAM

OPEN

Easter: 5 - 8 Apr
May Day: 4 - 6 May
Spring BH: 25 27 May

and

20 July - 8 September

Daily

10.30am - 5.30pm

Tel: 01787 247003
Fax: 01787 247029

WATER STREET, LAVENHAM, SUFFOLK CO10 9RW

Owner: Mr and Mrs Alan Casey   **Contact:** Mr and Mrs Alan Casey

Beautiful medieval timber-frame house in the heart of Lavenham, yet backing on to rolling countryside. Once the home of Benedictine monks, rich cloth merchants and an Elizabethan Rector. Superbly restored and furnished with a blend of antique and modern furniture, paintings and stained glass by Ervin Bossanyi (1891-1975); aromatic herb garden with culinary, medicinal and dyers herbs; kitchen garden, orchard and pond.

Location: The Priory is in the centre of Lavenham in Water Street.

Admission: Adult £2.50, Child £1.00

SAXTEAD GREEN POST MILL

Tel: 01728 685789

The Mill House, Saxtead Green, Framlingham, Suffolk IP13 9QQ

Owner: English Heritage   **Contact:** The Custodian

The finest example of a Suffolk Post Mill. Still in working order, you can climb the wooden stairs to the various floors, full of fascinating mill machinery.

Location: 2½ m NW of Framlington on A1120.

Opening Times: 1 Apr - 30 Sept: Mon - Sat 10am - 6pm.

Admission: Adult £1.50, Child 80p, Conc £1.10.

SOMERLEYTON HALL

See Page 181 for full page entry.

ST EDMUNDSBURY CATHEDRAL

Tel: 01284 754933   **Fax:** 01284 768655

Angel Hill, Bury St Edmunds, Suffolk IP33 1LS

Owner: The Church of England   **Contact:** The Administrator

Set in the renowned gardens of the ruined abbey, ancient and modern combine in harmony in Suffolk's Cathedral. Visitors commend the tranquil atmosphere of prayer and worship combined with a real sense of welcome. The 16th century nave, by the same builder as Kings College Cambridge, was enhanced with the addition of Quire and Crossing in present times by architect, Stephen Dykes Bower. The Cloisters Gallery has regular exhibitions and the treasury houses church plate from the Diocese.

Location: Bury St Edmunds, Suffolk.

Opening Times: All year: Daily 8.30am - 5.30. BST 8.30am - 6pm, Jun - Aug 8.30am - 8pm.

Admission: Donation invited.

WINGFIELD OLD COLLEGE

Tel: 01379 384888   **Fax:** 01379 384034

Wingfield Eye, Suffolk IP21 5RA.

Owner: Ian Chance Esq   **Contact:** Hilary Smith

Delightful family home with walled gardens; this lovely old Suffolk house has been described by Sir John Betjeman as 'a history of England in miniature'. Founded in 1362 by Sir John de Wingfield, chief of staff of the Black Prince, the College was surrendered to Henry VIII in 1542 and seized by Cromwell's Parliament in 1649. Magnificent medieval Great Hall and mixed period interiors. Collections of traditional and contemporary art and crafts including prints, ceramics, sculpture and textiles. Homemade teas in the Old Kitchen. Celebrated Arts and Music Festival.

Location: Signposted off B1118, 7m SE of Diss.

Opening Times: Easter Sat - end Sept: Sat, Suns & Bank Hols 2 - 6pm.

Admission: Adult £2.50, Conc £1.00.

WYKEN HALL

OPEN
1 Feb - 24 Dec: Thurs, Fri, Sun & Bank Hol Mons 10am - 6pm. Book for lunch in The Leaping Hare Cafe at Wyken Vineyards.

STANTON, BURY ST. EDMUNDS, SUFFOLK IP31 2DW

Owner: *Sir Kenneth & Lady Carlisle*

Contact: *Mrs. Barbara Hurn*

Tel: 01359 250287
Fax: 01359 250240

The Elizabethan Manor House is surrounded by a romantic, plant-lovers garden with maze, knot and herb garden and rose garden featuring old roses. A walk through ancient woodlands leads to Wyken Vineyards, winner of 1995's EVA Wine of the Year. In the 16th century barn, the Vineyard Restaurant serves a range of Wyken wines along with a menu of fresh fish, game and vegetables from the kitchen garden.

Location: 9 miles NE of Bury St. Edmunds off A143. Follow brown tourist signs to Wyken Vineyards from Ixworth.

Admission: Gardens: Adult £2.00, Conc. £1.50, Child under 12 Free. Groups 30+ by appointment on Wednesdays .

Hatchlands Park, Surrey, page 186.

The Double Cube Room, Wilton House, Wiltshire. page 220.

Clandon Park

CLANDON PARK/ HATCHLANDS
Guildford

Clandon Park and Hatchlands Park were built during the 18th century and are set amid beautiful parklands. They are two of the most outstanding country houses "in the country and are only 5 minutes drive apart".

Clandon Park - Clandon is a Palladian house of dramatic contrasts; from the neo-classical marble hall to the Maori Meeting House in the garden; the opulent saloon to the old kitchen - complete with original range - below stairs. All this adds up to a fascinating insight into the different lifestyles of the ruling and serving classes in the 18th century. The house is rightly acclaimed for its remarkable collection of ceramics, textiles, furniture and its excellent restaurant.

Hatchlands Park - was built in 1757 for Admiral Boscawen, a great Naval Hero. The house has the earliest known decorative plasterwork by Robert Adam in an English country house. The Cobbe collection of early keyboard instruments, paintings and furniture was introduced in 1988 when the house was extensively re-decorated. In the keyboard collection is an Evard pianoforte, one of the most beautiful square pianos to survive the 18th century and almost certainly made for Queen Marie Antoinette.

❖

SUITABILITY FOR OTHER EVENTS
Clandon House available for non-residential private and commercial functions and wedding ceremonies / receptions.

EXTRA FACILITIES
National Trust concerts during the season at both properties.

FACILITIES FOR THE DISABLED
Clandon Park - Parking near front of house for disabled visitors only or less - able visitors may be set down in front of house. WC on ground floor, accessible by electric stair climber. Wheelchairs available. The first floor is completely level. Restaurant is accessible. Braille Guide.

Hatchlands Park - Access to ground floor, terrace and part of garden. WC, Wheelchair available.

PARKING FOR COACHES & CARS
Available 300 yards from the house.

CATERING
Clandon - Licensed Restaurant open same days as house 12.30 - 5.30pm. Also Nov, Sat to Wed 12.30 - 5pm. Dec (to 23) daily 12.30 - 5pm. Tel: 01483 222502.

Hatchlands - As house 12.30 - 5.30pm. Tel: 01483 211120

GUIDED TOURS
Clandon - Parties and morning tours by arrangement with the Property Manager. Connoisseur Tours - please ring for info.

GIFT SHOP
Both open as house. Clandon Park shop open for Christmas Shopping and weekends in March. Tel: 01483 211412.

GUIDE BOOKS
Available at both properties.

CHILDREN
Children's quizzes. Changing facilities. Sorry, no backpacks.

Hatchlands Park.

LOCATION

Clandon
At West Clandon on the A247, 3 miles east of Guildford.
Rail: Clandon BR 1 mile.

Hatchlands
East of East Clandon on the A246 Guildford - Leatherhead road.
Rail: Clandon BR 2 1/2 miles, Horsley 3 miles.

OPENING TIMES

Clandon

30 Mar - 30 October
Sat - Wed
(open Good Fri.)

1.30 - 5.30pm
(Sats 12 noon - 4pm)

Bank Hol. Mons.
11.00am - 5.30pm

Garden open weekends in March, November and December.

Hatchlands

31 Mar - 31 October

Tues, Weds, Thurs, Suns & Bank Hol. Mons.
Fridays in August only.
2.00 - 5.30pm

Park Walks
Daily (Apr - Oct)
12.30 - 6.00pm

ADMISSION

Clandon
Adult £4.00
Child £2.00
Fam. ticket £10.00
Groups (Mons - Weds. only)
Adult £3.50

Hatchlands
Adult £4.00
Grounds only . .£1.50
Child £2.00
Grounds only 75p
Fam. ticket £10.00
Groups
(Tues-Thurs only)
Adult £3.50

HAM HOUSE
Richmond

Ham House, on the banks of the River Thames between Richmond and Kingston, is perhaps the most remarkable Stuart house in the country. Apart from the fact that its architectural fabric has survived virtually unchanged since the 1670's (when the building was enlarged by the Duke and Duchess of Lauderdale), it still retains many of the furnishing from that period - an extraordinary survival. The gardens have been restored to their original guise using plans and images which were found in the house. Ham is presented today principally as the late 17th century Lauderdale residence with overlays of the 18th and 19th centuries. Visitors view the rooms in the sequence intended at the time, progressing through a hierarchy of apartments towards the Queen's Closet - the culmination of the sequence. The gardens were laid out in compartments, reflecting the ordered symmetry of the house and together they present the modern visitor with a complete picture of 17th century aristocratic life.

CONTACT

The Property Manager
Ham House
Ham
Richmond
Surrey
TW10 7RS

Tel: (0181) 940 1950

Fax: (0181) 332 6903

LOCATION

Ham is 1 1/2 miles from Richmond and 2 miles from Kingston. On the south bank of the River Thames, west of A307 at Petersham.

Rail: Richmond or Kingston BR and Underground.

Bus: LT65 Ealing Broadway - Kingston; 371 Richmond - Kingston. London and Country 415 Victoria - Guildford; London & Country 427 Richmond - Addlestone; all passing BR Richmond and Kingston Tel: (0171) 222 1234

OPENING TIMES

Summer

HOUSE:
24 & 30 Mar - 31 Oct
Mons - Weds
1.00 - 5.00pm

Sats & Suns
12 noon - 5.30pm
(Open Good Fri
1.00 - 5.00pm
but closed Tues
following)

GARDEN:
Daily except Fri.
(open Good Friday)
10.30am - 6.00pm
(or dusk if earlier)

Closed 25 - 26 Dec
and 1 January.

Winter
HOUSE & GARDEN

2 Nov - 15 Dec
Sats & Suns only
1.00 - 4.00pm

Last admission 1/2 hour before closing.

ADMISSION

Adult £4.00
Child £2.00
Fam. Ticket . . .£10.00
Gardens . . . . . . .free

Groups
Pre-booked 15 or more.
Rates on application

SUITABILITY FOR OTHER EVENTS
Orangery and Rose Garden available for functions. Tel: (0181) 940 0735

EXTRA FACILITIES
Picnics in Rose Garden. Summer Concerts in garden. Video presentation in house.

ADVICE TO COURIERS & DRIVERS
Please advise that there is no photography allowed inside.

FACILITIES FOR THE DISABLED
Parking near house for drivers or disabled/elderly visitors may be set down and collected near house. Access to house by ramps; lift access to 1st floor on request. NB The grounds do include some deep gravel paths. Staff trained in sympathetic hearing scheme. 2 wheelchairs available. WC. Braille Guide.

PARKING FOR COACHES & CARS
Free parking within 400 yards (not NT)

CATERING
Orangery Restaurant (licensed) open Sundays, waitress service, lunches from 12.30. Tea room open April - end October: Daily (except Fri) 11am - 5.30pm. Restaurant bookings 0181 940 0735.

GUIDED TOURS
These are available for parties by prior arrangement, weekday mornings only.

GIFT SHOP
April - end October. days and times as house. Also open for Christmas shopping Tel: (0181) 948 2035 for details.

GUIDE BOOKS
Available from the house and gift shop.

CHILDREN
Baby changing facilities, highchairs in restaurant. House unsuitable for backpacks or pushchairs. Children's quiz sheet.

LOSELEY PARK
Guildford

LOSELEY PARK, built in 1562 by Sir William More, is a fine example of Elizabethan architecture, its mellow stone brought from the ruins of Waverley Abbey now over 850 years old. The House is set amid magnificent parkland grazed by the Loseley Jersey herd. Many visitors comment on the very friendly atmosphere of the House - it is a country house, the family home of descendants of the builder.

Furniture has been acquired by the family and includes an early 16th century Wrangel-schrank beautifully inlaid with many different woods, a Queen Anne cabinet, Georgian arm chairs and settee, a Hepplewhite four-poster bed, King George IV's coronation chair. The King's bedroom has Oudenarde tapestry and a carpet commemorating James I's visit.

The Christian pictures include the Henri Met de Bles triptych of the Nativity and modern mystical pictures of the living Christ, St Francis and St Bernadette. The Christian Trust Centre is in the Oak Room and a small Chapel is available for use by visitors. A Christian Cancer Help Centre meets twice monthly.

GARDEN
A magnificent Cedar of Lebanon presides over the front lawn. Parkland adjoins the lawn and a small lake adds to the beauty of Front Park.

In the Walled Garden are mulberry trees, yew hedges, a grass terrace and the Moat Walk with herbaceous borders including a newly planted rose garden, herb, fruit and vegetable garden.

SUITABILITY FOR OTHER EVENTS
Ideal for wedding receptions. Business launches and promotions. A 10 - 12 acre field adjoining can also be hired for events in addition to the lawns. Fashion shows, air displays, archery, garden parties, shows, rallies, filming.

EXTRA FACILITIES
These include: Parkland, moat walk and terrace. Lectures can be arranged on the property, its contents, gardens and history. Loseley Christian Trust Exhibition.

ADVICE TO COURIERS & DRIVERS
Coaches approach Loseley from B3000 only, as other roads too narrow. No dogs, except on leads in the car park, no unaccompanied children, no photography in the House, no videos on Estate. All party visits to the House and Farm must be booked in advance. Children's play area. Picnic area.

FACILITIES FOR THE DISABLED
Disabled and elderly visitors may alight at the entrance to the property. Vehicles can then be parked in the allocated area. There are toilet facilities for the disabled. Wheelchair access to ground floor of the House.

PARKING FOR COACHES & CARS
Capacity of the car park - 150 cars, 100 yards from the House and 6 coaches. Summer overflow car park.

CATERING
Health and wholeness are in the forefront at Loseley. The Barn has a capacity of up to 150 people. For special functions, banquets and conferences catering can be arranged by Alexander Catering. Additional marquees can also be hired. There is the Courtyard Tearoom in the house and Loseley Shop.

GUIDED TOURS
Average time for a tour of the House ¾ hour.

GUIDE BOOKS
Colour guide book, £1.50.

SCHOOL VISITS/CHILDREN
New for 1996 – Loseley Park Farms Education Centre. Loseley Park, home to the Jersey Herd since 1916, invites you to come and see a traditional English dairy farm at work. A tractor and trailer ride takes you across the Estate down to the Education Centre and milking can be seen at the appropriate time.

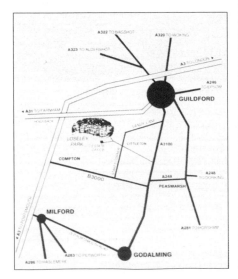

CONTACT
Miss Juliet Reeves
Loseley Park
Guildford
Surrey
GU3 1HS
Tel: (01483) 304440
Telex: 859972 LOSELG
Fax: (01483) 302036

LOCATION
From London (30 miles)
A3, leave at Compton,
South of Guildford, on
B3000 for 2 miles,
signposted.
Bus: 1¼ miles from
House.
Rail: Guildford
Stn 2 miles,
Godalming 3 miles.
Air: Heathrow 30 miles,
Gatwick 30 miles.

OPENING TIMES
Summer
27 May - 31 August
Wed - Sat & Bank Hol
Mons 11.00am - 5.00pm
Last entry 4.30pm

HOUSE TOURS &
FARM VISITS
2.00 - 5.00pm.

Winter
Tithe Barn available for
weddings and private/
business functions
all year.

ADMISSION
HOUSE & GARDENS
or
TRAILER RIDE AND
FARM VISIT
Adult £3.50
Child (3-16yrs) . . .£2.00
OAP/Disabled . .£3.00
Child (under 3) . . . .Free

ALL-IN-ONE
(House, gardens, trailer
ride and farm visit)
Adult £6.00
Child (3-16yrs) . . .£3.00
OAP/Disabled . .£5.00
Child (under 3) . . . .Free

Group rates are available
for parties of 20+.

The Great Hall.

THE TITHE BARN AT LOSELEY PARK

The Tithe Barn (originally 1635) is situated on the sweeping lawns of Loseley House and offers unrivalled views of the surrounding parkland and magnificent Cedar of Lebanon.

It is adaptable for a wide range of functions and will comfortably accommodate 50-150 people for a full sit-down meal, or up to 200 for a cocktail reception. Should a larger group be envisaged, our permanent marquee may be used and further marquees erected. The South Room of the Tithe Barn is ideal for small meetings and private lunches.

The location is ideal for business and corporate hospitality events and is in easy reach of the A3 and M25, an hour from London and some 40 minutes from Heathrow and Gatwick Airports. Ample car parking is available.

CONFERENCE AND FUNCTION FACILITIES

ROOM	DIMENSIONS	CAPACITY	LAYOUT	POWER POINTS	SUITABLE FOR A/V
C17th Tithe Barn	100' x 18'	150	Reception	3	3
		200	Theatre		
		140	U-shape		
		150	Buffet		
			Lunch/Dinner		
South Room	28' x 15'	20	Syndicate Room	3	3
Marquee	70' x 40'	250	Various		

The Tithe Barn.

The Tithe Barn.

CLANDON PARK/HATCHLANDS

See Page 186 for full page entry.

CLAREMONT LANDSCAPE GARDEN

Tel: 01372 469421

Portsmouth Road, Esher, Surrey KT10 9JG

Owner: The National Trust   **Contact:** The Administrator

One of the earliest surviving English landscape gardens, restored to its former glory. Begun by Sir John Vanbrugh and Charles Bridgeman before 1720, the gardens were extended and naturalised by William Kent. 'Capability' Brown also made improvements. Features include a lake, island with pavilion, grotto, turf amphitheatre, viewpoints and avenues.

Location: On S edge of Esher, on E side of A307 (no access from Esher bypass).

Opening Times: Jan - 31 Mar: Daily (except Mon) 10am - 5pm or sunset if earlier. Apr - 31 Oct: Mon - Fri, 10am - 6pm. Sat, Sun & BH Mon 10am - 7pm. Garden closed 10 July all day and at 2pm on 11 - 14 July. 4 Nov - end Mar: Daily (except Mon), 10am - 5pm or sunset if earlier. Last admission 1/2 an hour before closing. Closed 25 Dec. Open 1 Jan: 1 - 4pm.

Admission: Sun & BH Mon £3.00, Mon - Sat £2.00, no reduction for parties. Coach parties must book; no coach parties on Sun.

FARNHAM CASTLE KEEP ⚏

Tel: 01252 713393

Castle Hill, Farnham, Surrey GU6 0AG

Owner: English Heritage   **Contact:** The Head Custodian

Used as a fortified manor by the medieval Bishops of Winchester, this motte and bailey castle has been in continuous occupation since the 12th century. You can visit the large shell-keep enclosing a mound in which are massive foundations of a Norman tower.

Location: 1/2m N of Farnham town centre on A287.

Opening Times: 1 Apr - 30 Sept: 10am - 6pm. 1 - 31 Oct: 10am - 6pm or dusk if earlier.

Admission: Adult £2.00, Child, £1.00, Conc £1.50.

GODDARDS

Tel: 01306 730487

Abinger Lane, Abinger Common, Dorking, Surrey RH5 6JH

Owner: The Lutyens Trust   **Contact:** Capt Anthony Smith

Edwardian country house by Sir Edwin Lutyens with Gertrude Jekyll garden, in beautiful setting on slopes of Leith Hill.

Location: Half way between Guildford and Dorking. 2m South of A25.

Opening Times: Apr to Oct by telephoning the Administrator.

Admission: £3.50 for guided tour.

GREATHED MANOR

Tel: 01342 832577

Ford Manor Road, Dormansland, Lingfield, Surrey RH7 6PA

Owner: Country Houses Association   **Contact:** The Administrator

Victorian Manor House.

Location: 1 1/2 m SE of Lingfield off the B2028.

Opening Times: May - Sept: Wed and Thurs 2 - 5pm.

Admission: Adult £2.50, Child £1.00, Groups by arrangement.

GUILDFORD HOUSE GALLEY

Tel: 01483 444740   **Fax:** 01483 444742

155 High Street, Guildford, Surrey GU1 3AJ

Owner: Guildford Borough Council   **Contact:** Miss I.C. Rhodes - Curator

Fascinating Grade I listed town house dating from 1660. Finely decorated plaster ceilings, panelled rooms, wrought iron work and richly carved staircase. A wide range of changing exhibitions on display together with selections from Guildford Borough's collection which includes topographical pictures over 200 years, prints and contemporary craftwork. Pastel portraits by Guildford-born artist John Russell R.A. (1745-1806) are often on show. Workshops and free lunchtime talks. Tea room and gallery shop.

Location: Central Guildford.

Opening Times: All year: Tues - Saturday 10am - 4.45pm.

Admission: Free.

HAM HOUSE

See Page 187 for full page entry.

HAMPTON COURT PALACE

Tel: 0181 781 9500   **Fax:** 0181 781 9509

East Molesey, Surrey KT8 9AU

Owner: Historic Royal Palaces

Location: On the A309 which is just off A3 at Kingston.

Opening Times: April - Oct: Mon, 10.15am - 6pm, Tues - Sun, 9.30am - 6pm. Nov - Mar: Mon, 10.15am - 4.30pm. Tues - Sun, 9.30am - 4.30pm.

Admission: Adult £8.00, Child (5-16yrs) £4.90, Child under 5 free, Family £20.00, OAP/Students £5.75.

HERITAGE CENTRE

Tel: 0181 773 4555   **Fax:** 0181 770 4666

Honeywood Walk, Carshalton, Surrey SM5 3NX

Owner: London Borough of Sutton   **Contact:** Ms J Howard

17th century listed building with Victorian and Edwardian extensions. Contains permanent changing displays on local history and local life.

Location: Carshalton.

Opening Times: All Year: Wed - Fri, 10am - 5pm. Sat, Sun and BH Mons, 10am - 5.30pm.

Admission: Adult 90p. Child 40p. Groups call to verify rates.

LITTLE HOLLAND HOUSE

Tel: 0181 770 4781   **Fax:** 0181 770 4666

40 Beeches Avenue, Carshalton, Surrey SM5 3LW

Owner: London Borough of Sutton   **Contact:** Ms V Murphy

Home of Frank Dickinson (1874 - 1961) follower of Arts and Crafts movement, who built the house to his own design, and created all the furniture and fittings.

Location: On B278 1m S of junction with A232.

Opening Times: First Sun of each month and BH Sun & Mon 1.30 - 5.30pm. Closed Christmas and New Year.

Admission: Free. Groups outside normal opening hours £2.00 pp (includes guided tour).

LOSELEY PARK ⬛

See Pages 188 & 189 for full page entry.

OAKHURST COTTAGE

Tel: 01428 684733

Hambledon, Godalming, Surrey

Owner: The National Trust   **Contact:** Mrs E Hardy

A very small 16th century timber-framed cottage, restored and furnished as a simple cottager's dwelling. Delightful cottage garden with contemporary plant species.

Location: Hambledon, Surrey

Opening Times: 30 Mar - end Oct:Wed, Thur, Sat, Sun & BH Mon 2 - 5pm. *Strictly by appointment only.*

Admission: Adult £2.20, Child £1.10 (including guided tour). No reduction for parties.

PAINSHILL PARK

Tel: 01932 864674 or 01932 868113   **Fax:** 01932 868001

Portsmouth Road, Cobham, Surrey KT11 1JE

Owner: Painshill Park Trust   **Contact:** Mrs E Fox

This is one of the finest 18th century landscape gardens, created by the Hon Charles Hamilton (1704 - 86). Situated in 158 acres, visitors can take a circuit walk through a series of emerging scenes, each one more surprising than the last. A 14 acre lake fed by a massive water wheel gives a breathtaking setting for a variety of spectacular features including a Gothic temple, ruined abbey, Turkish tent, crystal grotto, magnificent cedars of Lebanon, replanted 18th century shrubberies and vineyard. Available for corporate and private hire, location filming, wedding receptions, etc.

Location: W of Cobham on A245, 2mls N of junc. 10 on M25. 100 metres E of A3/A245 junc.

Opening Times: 7 Apr - 13 Oct: 11am - 5pm (gates close 6pm) Suns only. Pre-booked groups of 10+ on other days all year. Please call for info on additional opening hours.

Admission: Adult £3.50, Child over 5 £1.00, under 5 free, Conc £3.00, Groups £2.80ea.

POLESDEN LACEY

OPEN

HOUSE:
Mar: Sat & Sun
1.30 - 4.30pm.

3 Apr - end Oct
Wed - Sun
(inc. Good Fri)
1.30 - 5.30pm
& BH Mon & preceding
Sun: 11am - 5.30pm.

Gardens: All year
Daily: 11am - 6pm/dusk

Last adm. to house
1/2 hour before closing.

Tel: 01327 458203

DORKING, SURREY RH5 6BD

Owner: The National Trust   *Contact:* The Property Manager

Originally an elegant 1820s Regency villa in magnificent landscape setting. The house was remodelled after 1906 by the Hon Mrs Ronald Greville, a well-known Edwardian hostess. Her collection of fine paintings, furniture, porcelain and silver are still displayed in the reception rooms, plus photographs from Mrs Greville's albums. Extensive grounds, walled rose garden, lawns and landscaped walks. King George VI and Queen Elizabeth spent part of their honeymoon here.

Location: 5m NW of Dorking, 2m S of Great Bookham, off A246.

Admission: Garden, grounds, restaurant, shop, plant sales and landscape walks: All year £3. House: £3, Pre-booked parties £5 (house, garden & walks).

RAMSTER GARDENS

Tel: 01428 644422

Ramster, Chiddingfold, Surrey GU8 4SN
Owner: Mrs M Gunn
Contact: Mrs M Gunn
20 acres of woodland and flowering shrub garden laid out in 1904. Well groomed but not over-disciplined appearance.
Location: 1 1/2m S of Chiddingfold on A283.
Opening Times: 20 Apr - 21 Jul: 11am - 5.30pm.
Admission: Adult £2.00, Child free, Conc £2.00, Group £2.00 pp.

ROYAL BOTANIC GARDENS

Tel: 0181 940 1171   **Fax:** 0181 332 5197

Kew, Richmond, Surrey TW9 3AB
Contact: The Administrator
Location: A307 / junction A305 and A205 (1m Chiswick roundabout M4).
Opening Times: 9.30am daily except Christmas Day and New Year's Day.
Admission: Adult £4.50, Child £2.50, Conc £3.00, Family £12.00, Groups 20% discount when pre-booked and paid.

WINKWORTH ARBORETUM

HASCOMBE ROAD, GODALMING, SURREY GU8 4AD

Owner: *The National Trust*
Contact: *The Head of Arboretum*

Tel: 01483 208477

Hillside woodland with two lakes, many rare trees and shrubs and fine views. The most impressive displays are in spring for bluebells and azaleas, autumn for colour and wildlife.

Location: Near Hascombe, 2m SE of Godalming on E side of B2130.

Admission: Adult £2.50, Child (5-17) £1.25, Family ticket £6.25 (2 adults & 2 children, additional family member £1.25)

OPEN
All year: Daily during daylight hours.

RHS GARDEN WISLEY

OPEN

All year

Mon through Sat

(except Christmas Day)

10.00am - sunset or 7.00pm during the summer

Tel: 01483 224234
Fax: 01483 211750

NR. WOKING, SURREY

Owner: *The Royal Horticultural Society*   **Contact:** *The Royal Horticultural Society*

A world famous garden which extends to 240 acres and provides the chance to glean new ideas and inspiration. Highlights include the azaleas and rhododendrons in spring, the glasshouses and the Model Gardens. The visitor centre offers the world's best selection of gardening books and over 8,500 varieties of plants for sale. Delightful restaurant facilities are open throughout the year.
Location: Off the A3 Nr. Woking, Surrey.
Admission: Adult £4.90, Child (up to 6) free, Child (6-16) £1.75. Groups 20+ £3.75

SHALFORD MILL

Shalford, Guildford, Surrey
Owner: The National Trust
Contact: The Administrator
18th century watermill on the Tillingbourne, given in 1932 by "Ferguson's Gang".
Location: 1 1/2m S of Guildford on A281, opposite Sea Horse Inn.
Opening Times: Apr - Sept: Tues - Fri
Admission: Free. No unaccompanied children.

WHITEHALL

Tel: 0181 643 1236   **Fax:** 0181 770 4777

1 Malden Road, Cheam, Surrey SM3 8QD
Owner: London Borough of Sutton
Contact: P Jackson & L Thornback
Early 16th century timber framed house with displays on Nonsuch Palace, medieval Cheam pottery, Cheam School, changing exhibitions.
Location: On A243 just N of junction with A232.
Opening Times: Apr - Sept: Tues - Fri & Sun 2 - 5.30pm. Sat 10am - 5.30pm. BH Mons Oct: Mar, Wed, Thurs & Sun 2 - 5.30pm; Sat 10am - 5.30pm. Also open Mons 2 - 5.30pm. Closed Christmas and New Year.
Admission: Adult 90p, Child 40p. Outside open hours: Groups £1.50ea inc guided tour. 35p per school child in organised groups. Teachers free.

The Privy Garden, Hampton Court Palace, in the final stages of restoration, 1995.

SPECIAL EVENTS

◇ **ROYAL BOTANIC GARDENS**
Orchid Festival
14 FEBRUARY – 31 MARCH

◇ **ROYAL BOTANIC GARDENS**
Summer Jazz Concerts. Telephone for details: 0181 940 1171
JULY

◇ **ROYAL BOTANIC GARDENS**
Christmas Events
DECEMBER

For National Trust and English Heritage Events see separate section.

ARUNDEL CASTLE
Arundel

This great castle, home of the Dukes of Norfolk, dates from the Norman Conquest, containing a very fine collection of furniture and paintings, Arundel Castle is still a family home, reflecting the changes of nearly a thousand years.

In 1643, during the Civil War, the original castle was very badly damaged and it was later restored by the 8th, 11th and 15th Dukes in the 18th and 19th centuries. Amongst its treasures are personal possessions of Mary Queen of Scots and a selection of historical, religious and heraldic items from the Duke of Norfolk's collection.

The Duke of Norfolk is the Premier Duke, the title having been conferred on Sir John Howard in 1483 by his friend King Richard III. The Dukedom also carries with it the hereditary office of Earl Marshal of England. Among the historically famous members of the Howard family are Lord Howard of Effingham who, with Drake, repelled the Spanish Armada; the Earl of Surrey, the Tudor poet and courtier and the 3rd Duke of Norfolk, uncle of Anne Boleyn and Catherine Howard, both of whom became wives of King Henry VIII.

❖

CONTACT

The Administrator
Arundel Castle
Arundel
West Sussex
BN18 9AB

Tel: (01903) 883136
or (01903) 882173
Fax: (01903) 884581

LOCATION

Brighton 40 minutes,
Worthing 15 minutes,
Chichester 15 minutes.
From London A3 or A24,
1½ hours.

Bus: Bus stop 100 yards.

Rail: Station 1/2 mile.

Air: Gatwick 25 miles.

Motorway: M25, 30 miles.

OPENING TIMES

Summer
1 April - 25 October.
Daily except Sats
12 noon - 5.00pm
Last admission 4.00pm
Good Fri. closed

Winter
26 October - 31 March
Pre-booked parties only

ADMISSION

Summer
Adult £5.20
Child (5-15) £3.70
OAP £4.70
Fam. Ticket . .£15.00
Groups (min 20 people)
Adult £4.70
Child (5-15) £3.20
OAP £4.20

Winter
PRE-BOOKED PARTIES
Mornings £7.00
Min Fee £350.00
Evenings, Sats &
Sundays £8.00
Min Fee £400.00
* Sats & Suns only

SUITABILITY FOR OTHER EVENTS
Fashion shows and filming.

ADVICE TO COURIERS & DRIVERS
No unaccompanied children, dogs or photography inside the Castle.

FACILITIES FOR THE DISABLED
Disabled and elderly visitors may alight at the entrance to the property, before parking in the allocated areas. There are toilets for the disabled.

PARKING FOR COACHES & CARS
Capacity of the car park: 200 cars within the grounds, 200 yards from the Castle with further space for cars elsewhere. Coaches can park opposite the Castle entrance.

CATERING
Groups need to book in advance for afternoon tea, lunch or dinner. The Restaurant seats 140 people and prices range from £1.95 for tea and £3.75 for lunch. Special rates are offered to pre-booked groups only. Self Service Restaurant within the Castle serves home-made food for lunch and afternoon tea.

GUIDED TOURS
These are available for pre-booked parties only at £7.00 per head. Tours are also available in French and German. Average time taken for a tour 1½ hours.

GIFT SHOP
The shop sells many items chosen by the Countess of Arundel and is always open at the same time as the Castle.

GUIDE BOOKS
Colour guide book, published in English, French, and German.

SCHOOL VISITS/CHILDREN
A special guide book can be purchased for children. Items of particular interest include a Norman Keep and Armoury. Special rates for schoolchildren (aged 5-15) and teachers.

CHARLESTON
Lewes

A mile or so from Firle village, near the end of a track leading to the foot of the Downs, lies Charleston. It was discovered in 1916 by Virginia and Leonard Woolf when Virginia's sister, the painter Vanessa Bell, was looking for a place in the country. Here Vanessa moved with fellow artist Duncan Grant, the writer David Garnett, her two young sons and an assortment of animals. It was an unconventional and creative household which became the focal point for artists and intellectuals later to be known as the Bloomsbury set - among them Roger Fry, Lytton Strachey and Maynard Keynes.

Over the years the artists decorated the walls, furniture and ceramics with their own designs, influenced by Italian fresco painting and post-impressionist art. Creativity extended to the garden too. Mosaics were made in the piazza, sculpture was cleverly positioned to intrigue and subtle masses of colour were used in the planting.

After Duncan Grant's death in 1978, the Charleston Trust was formed to save and restore the house to its former glory. The task has been described as "one of the most difficult and imaginative feats of restoration current in Britain".

CONTACT

Mrs Christina Jeffrey
Charleston
Firle
Lewes
East Sussex
BN8 6LL

Tel: (01323) 811265
(Visitor information)
(01323) 811626
(Admin.)
Fax: (01323) 811628

LOCATION

6mls east of Lewes on A27 between Firle and Selmeston. The lane to Charleston leads off the A27, 2 miles beyond the Firle turning.
London 60 miles, Brighton 15 miles, Monk's House, Rodmell (Leonard and Virginia Woolf's house) 11 miles.
Air: Gatwick 20 miles.
Rail: London (Victoria) hourly to Lewes (65 minutes). Occasional train to Berwick.
Bus: Route on A27.
Taxi: George and Graham, Lewes 473692.

SUITABILITY FOR OTHER EVENTS
Filming.

EXTRA FACILITIES
Small lecture room available by special arrangement.

ADVICE TO COURIERS & DRIVERS
No dogs, no photography. It is essential to arrange visits in advance and out of public hours. Please telephone the office. Details on restriction of coach size shown under 'parking'.

FACILITIES FOR THE DISABLED
Disabled and elderly visitors may alight at the entrance. Wheel-chair visitors by prior arrangement, outside public hours. There is no access beyond the ground floor for wheelchairs. Special toilets are available.

PARKING FOR COACHES & CARS
There is car parking for 30 cars, 50 yds from the property. Mini coaches only (up to 26 seats) may use the lane to the property. Large coaches may set down at the end of the lane - 10 minutes walk - or effect a Mini-Bus transfer. Details from office.

FUNCTION FACILITIES
The New Studio is available for hire by small groups. Full details available from the administrator.

CATERING
There is no restaurant at Charleston but refreshments are made available to groups by prior booking.

GUIDED TOURS
Tours available on Wednesdays, Thursdays, Fridays and Saturdays. The maximum size of each group is 12.

Groups up to 50 can be arranged with prior notification, out of public hours. Tours available in French if booked in advance.

There is no charge for the tour and the average time taken is 1 hr. (longer on connoisseur Fridays).

SHOP
The Shop is open whilst the house is open, and has a unique a range of ceramics, books and textiles.

GUIDE BOOKS
'Charleston Past and Present' contains photographs and reminiscences of family members and friends together with full details of the house and gardens, price £8.99. Guide notes are available at £2.00.

SCHOOL VISITS/CHILDREN
Particularly suitable for 6th Form and art groups. A guide is provided and at times a schoolroom is available for hire.

ADDITIONAL INFORMATION
Changing series of Exhibitions in Shop Gallery. The Charleston Festival is held in May every year. For Summer School details contact office. Special openings for Friends of Charleston.

OPENING TIMES

•April - October
Wed - Sun
2.00 - 5.00pm

Guided visits Wed - Sat.

House closed Mondays and Tuesdays except Bank Holiday Mons.

also

•Morning opening
July and August
Wed - Sat
11.30am - 5.00pm

•Connoisseur Fridays
April to June & September to October.
In-depth tour of house.

•Kitchen
Open Thur & Fri.

•Nov - 25 Dec
Saturday & Sunday only.
Admission 2.00 - 4.00pm
Short tours only plus Christmas Shopping.

ADMISSION

HOUSE/GROUNDS
Adult £4.50
Conc*. £3.00

CONNOISSEUR FRIDAYS
Adult £6.00

SHORT TOURS NOV/DEC
Adult £2.50

*Weds & Thurs throughout season.

GOODWOOD HOUSE
Chichester

GOODWOOD has been the country home of the Dukes of Richmond and Gordon for more than three centuries. The first Duke was the son of King Charles II and his French mistress, Louise de Keroualle. He was famous for his love of life and his brilliance at entertaining, a tradition which has continued at Goodwood to this day.

The third Duke not only built the great house but also collected many of its magnificent treasures. Paintings by Stubbs, Canaletto and Van Dyck, and a porcelain collection of exceptional excellence make this one of England's most important historic houses.

No other estate can offer the unique attraction of 19 days' racing on its own racecourse from May to October. Glorious Goodwood week in July is a renowned sporting and social event of international stature. Goodwood also offers the Festival Of Speed, held annually in June and now one of the most successful historic motor racing events in the world. The Festival attracts top cars and drivers for three days of classic motor sport.

Whether it is to reward the achievements of your sales team or to launch a new product, choosing Goodwood as the place to celebrate reflects the stature and style of your company. The estate is the essence of English life at its best with the famous racecourse, the historic motor circuit, the aerodrome and the secluded hotel, all within a mile of the house itself.

Simply, there is no better place to celebrate your success.

Goodwood House is used throughout the year for all kinds of corporate and social events. The State Apartments can be used for Product Promotions, Company Entertaining, One-Day Seminars, Conference Dinners, Luncheon and Dinner Parties including a private tour of the art collections, Wedding Receptions, Fashion Shows and as a location for filming. All catering is planned and prepared by Goodwood chefs. Lunches, dinners and receptions can be arranged all year round.

CONTACT

James Parker or
Julie Evans
Goodwood House
Goodwood
Chichester
West Sussex
PO18 0PX

Tel: (01243) 774107
Fax: (01243) 774313

LOCATION

Goodwood House is 4 miles north east of Chichester. M27/A27 from Southampton, Portsmouth, Worthing and Brighton. A3 from London, then A286 or A285 then signposted.

Rail: Chichester 5 miles
Arundel 9 Miles.

Taxi: Central
(01243) 789432

OPENING TIMES

Summer
Commencing Easter Sunday and Monday, 7 & 8 April, the House will be open on Sundays and Mondays until 30 September PLUS Tuesdays, Wednesdays and Thursdays in August 2 - 5.00pm

The House will be CLOSED on the following Event days:
21, 22 April
12, 13, 19, 20 & 26 May
23, 24 June
1 August

For more information contact The Events Office (01243) 774107

ADVICE TO COURIERS & DRIVERS
Free coach park; free tea for drivers.

PARKING FOR COACHES & CARS
Free car park with capacity for 300 cars and 20 coaches, 75 yards from the House.

FACILITIES FOR THE DISABLED
Disabled and elderly visitors may be dropped at door; State Apartments all on ground floor; 1 lavatory with wheelchair access.

PUBLIC OPEN DAY TEAS
Afternoon teas served most days: choice from buffet for individuals, pre-booked set menus for parties (min.15).

CONFERENCE AND FUNCTION FACILITIES

ROOM	DIMENSIONS	CAPACITY	LAYOUT	POWER POINTS	SUITABLE FOR A/V
Ball Room	79' x 23'	74 - 350	Various	✓	✓
Yellow Drawing Room	50' x 20'	40 -90	Various	✓	✓
Front Hall	38' x 35'	40 - 90	Various	✓	✓
NINE OTHER ROOMS ALSO AVAILABLE.					

LEONARDSLEE GARDENS
Horsham

LEONARDSLEE GARDENS represent one of the largest and most spectacular woodland gardens in England with one of the finest collections of mature rhododendrons, azaleas, choice trees and shrubs to be seen anywhere. It is doubly fortunate in having one of the most magnificent settings, within easy reach of London, only a few miles from the M23. Laid out by Sir Edmund Loder since 1889 the gardens are still maintained by the Loder family today. The 240 acre (100 hectare) valley is world-famous for its spring display of azaleas and rhododendrons around the 6 lakes, giving superb views and reflections.

The delightful Rock Garden - a photographer's paradise - is a kaleidoscope of colour in May. The superb exhibition of Bonsai in a walled courtyard shows the fascinating living art-form of Bonsai to perfection. The Alpine House has 400 different alpine plants growing in a natural rocky setting. Wallabies (used as mowing machines!) have lived wild in part of the garden for over 100 years, and deer (Sika, Fallow & Axis) may be seen in the parklands.

Many superb rhododendrons have been raised as Leonardslee. The most famous is Rhododendron loderi raised by Sir Edmund Loder in 1901. The original plants are still to be seen in the garden. In May the fragrance of their huge blooms pervades the air throughout the valley.

With many miles of paths to enjoy, visitors return frequently to savour a paradise in spring, serene in summer and mellow in autumn.

---❖---

SUITABILITY FOR OTHER EVENTS
Photography - Landscape and fashion, film location.

EXTRA FACILITIES
Clock Tower Restaurant available for private or corporate function in the evenings and out of season.

ADVICE TO COURIERS & DRIVERS
Parking and refreshments free to drivers. Average length of visit 2- 4 hours.

FACILITIES FOR THE DISABLED
Not suitable for the disabled.

PARKING FOR COACHES & CARS
Ample free parking.

CATERING
Clock Tower Restaurant and Garden Cafe. Morning coffee, lunches, teas.

GIFT SHOP
Large range of quality goods.

PLANTS FOR SALE
Good selection, especially Rhododendrons and Azaleas.

GUIDE BOOKS
Colour guide book £1.50.

SCHOOL VISITS/CHILDREN
So as to maintain the peace and tranquillity of the gardens, school visits are not encouraged.

CONTACT

R Loder
Leonardslee Gardens
Lower Beeding
Horsham
West Sussex
RH13 6PP

Tel: (01403) 891212
Fax: (01403) 891305

LOCATION

M23 to Handcross then A279 (signposted Cowfold) for 4 miles. From London: 1 hour 15 mins.

Rail: Horsham Station 4¹/₂ miles.

Bus: No. 107 from Horsham and Brighton

OPENING TIMES

Summer
1 April - 31 October
Daily 10.00am - 6.00pm
May 10.00am - 8.00pm

Winter
1 November - 31 March
Closed to the general public. Available for functions.

ADMISSION

May
  Adult £4.50
  Child £2.00
April, June - October
  Adult £3.50
  Child £2.00
Season Tickets . . £10.00

Groups
May Mon - Fri . . .£4.00
Sat, Sun &
Bank Hol Mons: . .£4.50

April, June - October
  Adult £3.00
  Child (any time) . .£2.00

CONFERENCE AND FUNCTION FACILITIES

ROOM	DIMENSIONS	CAPACITY	LAYOUT	POWER POINTS	SUITABLE FOR A/V
Clock Tower		80 100	Dinner Buffet	4	

PETWORTH HOUSE
Petworth

Petworth House is one of the finest houses in the care of the National Trust and is home to an art collection that rivals many London galleries. Assembled by one family over 350 years, it includes works by Turner, Van Dyck, Titian, Claude, Gainsborough, Bosch, Reynolds and William Blake. The state rooms contain sculpture, furniture and porcelain of the highest quality and are complemented by the opening of the old kitchens in the servants' block.

A continuing programme of repairs and restoration brings new interest for the Visitor each year. In 1996 visitors will find that the Somerset Room and the Beauty Room have been re-decorated and that the old kitchens have been extended with the opening of the Chef's Sitting Room, Larder and Still Room. Petworth House is also the home of Lord and Lady Egremont and extra family rooms are open on weekdays by kind permission.

Petworth Park is a 700 acre park landscaped by 'Capability' Brown and open to the public all year free of charge. Spring and autumn are particularly breathtaking and the summer sunsets over the lake are spectacular.

❖

CONTACT

The Administration Office
Petworth House
Petworth
West Sussex
GU28 0AE

Tel: (01798) 342207

Fax: (01798) 342963

LOCATION

In the centre of Petworth town (approach roads A292/A285); Car park signposted.

Rail: Pulborough BR 5 1/4 miles

EXTRA FACILITIES
Programme of events throughout the year. Large musical concerts in the park.

ADVICE TO COURIERS & DRIVERS
Coach parties alight at Church Lodge entrance, coaches then park in NT car park.

FACILITIES FOR THE DISABLED
As car park is 800 yards from house there is a vehicle available to take less able visitors to house.

PARKING FOR COACHES & CARS
Car park 800 yards from house.

CATERING
Light lunches and teas in licensed tea room from 12 noon - 5.00pm, open same days as house.

GUIDED TOURS
Available by arrangement with the administrator on variety of subjects - tailor-made to suit your group (additional charge).

GIFT SHOP
Open same days as house 12 noon - 5.00pm. Also open for Christmas shopping. Telephone for details.

GUIDE BOOKS
Available from the house and gift shop. Also Children's quiz and Children's guide book.

SCHOOL VISITS/CHILDREN
Pre-arranged school visits welcome. Baby feeding and changing facilities, highchairs. Pushchairs admitted in house but no prams please.

OPENING TIMES

House and Park:

1 April - 31 October
Daily except
Mons & Fri
1.00 - 5.30pm
(Open Good Fri and Bank Hol Mondays)

Last admissions 4.30pm

Extra rooms shown, Tues, Weds and Thurs.

Park Only: All year
Daily
8.00am - Sunset

Closed 28 - 30 June from 12.00 noon.

ADMISSION

HOUSE
Adult £4.20
Child £2.00
Fam. Ticket . . .£10.00

Park Only . . . . . Free

Groups
(pre-booked 15 or more)
Adult £3.70

GROUNDS
Free

THE ROYAL PAVILION
Brighton

Universally acclaimed as one of the most beautiful buildings in the British Isles, the Royal Pavilion is the famous seaside residence of King George IV.

Originally a simple farmhouse, in 1787 architect Henry Holland created a neo classical villa on the site. It was later transformed into its current Indian style by John Nash between 1815 and 1822. With interiors decorated in the Chinese taste and an astonishingly exotic exterior, this Regency Palace is quite breathtaking.

Magnificent decorations and fantastic furnishings have been re-created in the recent extensive restoration programme. From the opulence of the main state rooms to the charm of the first floor bedroom suites, the Royal Pavilion is filled with astonishing colours and superb craftsmanship.

Witness the magnificence of the Music Room with its domed ceiling of gilded scallop-shaped shells and hand-knotted carpet, and promenade through the Chinese bamboo grove of the Long Gallery.

Lavish menus were created in the Great Kitchen, with its cast iron palm trees and dazzling collection of copperware, and then served in the dramatic setting of the Banqueting Room, lit by a huge crystal chandelier held by a silvered dragon.

With the quiet grace of the galleries, the elegance of the King's private apartments and much more, the Royal Pavilion is quite an unforgettable experience.

Following the successful restoration of the exterior of the Royal Pavilion, the surrounding gardens have now also been returned to their original 1826 appearance. The picturesque Regency gardens, replanted to John Nash's elegant design, are a truly fitting setting for the magical Royal Pavilion.

CONTACT

Anne Burrill
Head of Public Services
The Royal Pavilion
Brighton
East Sussex
BN1 1UE
Tel: (01273) 603005
Fax: (01273) 779108

LOCATION

The Royal Pavilion is in the centre of Brighton easily reached by road and rail.

Road: From London M25, M23, A23 - 1 hr. 30 mins.

Rail: Victoria to Brighton station 55 mins.

15 mins. walk from Brighton station

Air: Gatwick 20 mins.

OPENING TIMES

Summer
June - September
Daily 10.00am - 6.00pm
Last entry at 6.00pm

Winter
October - May
Daily 10.00am - 5.00pm
Last entry at 5.00pm
Closed 25, 26 Dec. only.

ADMISSION

Adult £3.95
Child £2.35
OAP £2.95
Student/UB40 . . .£2.85

Groups (20+)
Adult £3.35
Prices valid until 31.3.97

SUITABILITY FOR OTHER EVENTS
Spectacular rooms available for prestigious corporate entertaining. Facilities for civil marriage ceremonies and wedding receptions. Ideal for filming and photography.

EXTRA FACILITIES
Surrounded by picturesque gardens replanted to their original Regency designs. Special events programme. Slide lecture presentations by prior arrangement.

ADVICE TO COURIERS & DRIVERS
Free entry and refreshments for drivers. Please advise clients that no photography is allowed inside the building.

FACILITIES FOR THE DISABLED
Toilet adapted for wheelchair users. Wheelchair access to ground floor. Free admission for disabled visitors. Guided tours, including tactile and signed tours, are free of charge to those with disabilities but must be booked in advance with Visitor Services Tel: (01273) 713232.

PARKING FOR COACHES & CARS
Close to NCP car parks, town centre voucher parking. Coach drop-off point in New Road, parking in Madeira Drive.

CATERING
The Queen Adelaide tearooms offer light lunches and teas, with a balcony providing sweeping views across the gardens.

GUIDED TOURS
In English, French, German and Spanish by prior arrangement Tel: Visitor Services (01273) 713232. Specialist tours on request.

GIFT SHOP
A wide range of books, prints, ceramics and gifts, from postcards to exquisite jewellery.

GUIDE BOOK
Colour guide £2.95. Available in English, French and German.

SCHOOL VISITS
Specialist tours relating to all levels of national curriculum, must be booked in advance with Visitor Services. Special winter student rates.

CONFERENCE AND FUNCTION FACILITIES

ROOM	DIMENSIONS	CAPACITY	LAYOUT	POWER POINTS	SUITABLE FOR A/V
Banqueting Room		90 - 200	Various	✓	
Great Kitchen		40 - 90	Various	✓	
Music Room		180	Various	✓	
Queen Adelaide Suite		50 - 100	Various	✓	
Small Adelaide		20 - 40	Various	✓	
William IV		40 - 80	Various	✓	✓

ST. MARY'S
Bramber

FAMOUS historic house in the downland village of Bramber. Built in 1470 by William Waynflete, Bishop of Winchester, founder of Magdalen College, Oxford. Classified (Grade I) as "the best example of late 15th century timber-framing in Sussex." Fine panelled rooms, including the unique trompe l'oeil 'Painted Room', decorated for the visit of Elizabeth I. The 'Kings Room' has connections with Charles II's escape to France in 1651. Rare 16th century painted wall leather. English furniture, ceramics, manuscripts and fine English costume-doll collection. The Library houses an important private collection of works by Victorian poet and artist Thomas Hood. Still a lived in family home, St. Mary's was awarded the 'Warmest Welcome' Commendation by the S.E. Tourist Board.

GARDENS
Charming gardens with amusing Topiary as seen on BBC TV. Features include an exceptional example of the Living Fossil Tree, Ginkgo Biloba, a magnificently tall Magnolia Grandiflora, and the mysterious ivy-clad Monk's Walk.

❖

CONTACT
Peter Thorogood or Roeger Linton (Curator)
St Mary's House
Bramber
West Sussex
BN44 3WE
Tel: (01903) 816205
Fax: (01273) 453143

LOCATION
Bramber village off A283 From London 56 miles, via M23/A23 or A24.

Bus: From Shoreham to Steyning, alight Bramber.

Taxi: Southern Taxis (01273) 461655, Access Cars (01273) 452424.

Train: To Shoreham-by-Sea with connecting bus 20 (4 miles).

SUITABILITY FOR OTHER EVENTS
Exclusive corporate or private functions, promotional product launches, wedding receptions. Atmospheric film-location.

EXTRA FACILITIES
Lecture/demonstration facilities for up to 70 people. Projector/screen available. Grand piano.

ADVICE TO COURIERS & DRIVERS
Parties must be booked in advance. Please allow 2½ hours for your visit. Free tour and tea for coach driver. Dogs on leads in car park only. No photography in House.

PARKING FOR COACHES & CARS
Pull-in gravel car park - 30 cars or 2 coaches, 20 yards from House. Also a village car park 50 yds.

CATERING
Superb Victorian Music Room seats up to 70. Groups can book in advance for morning coffee or afternoon teas. Quality catering for functions by in-house and top London caterers.

GIFT SHOP
Souvenirs of the House.

GUIDED TOURS
The owner and/or family usually meet groups visiting the House. Larger parties, maximum 60, divided into smaller groups. Average time taken for tour 1 hour. Allow extra time for refreshments.

SCHOOL VISIT/CHILDREN
Groups welcome by prior arrangement.

CONFERENCE AND FUNCTION FACILITIES

ROOM	DIMENSIONS	CAPACITY	LAYOUT	POWER POINTS	SUITABLE FOR A/V
Music Room	60' x 30'	80	Theatre	3	3
		30	U-shape		
		30	Boardroom		
		80	Buffet		
Monks' Parlour	26' x 22'	25	Buffet	3	3
Painted Room	26' x 15'	20		3	3

OPENING TIMES

Summer

General Public:
Easter - End September
Suns, Thurs. 2 - 6pm

Bank Holiday Mondays
2 - 6pm

Groups:
Easter - end October.
Daily by appointment
avoiding public opening
times.

Winter

November - March
By appointment only.

ADMISSION

HOUSE & GARDEN
Adult £3.80
Child £2.00
OAP £3.50
Student £3.00
Groups
Adult/OAP
25 or more £3.50
Less than 25 . . .£3.80
Child* £2.00
Student £3.00

GARDENS ONLY
Adult £1.00
Child 50p

Winter
Groups only
Per person £7.50

ALFRISTON CLERGY HOUSE

THE TYE, ALFRISTON, POLEGATE, EAST SUSSEX BN26 5TL

Owner: The National Trust
Contact: The Custodian
Tel: 01323 870001

This 14th century Wealden hall house was the first building to be acquired by the National Trust, in 1896. The house is half timbered and thatched and contains a medieval Hall, exhibition room and two other rooms open to the public. The charming garden is filled with traditional cottage favourites, some grown since roman times and now almost lost to cultivation. Small shop.

Location: 4m NE of Seaford, just E of B2108.

Admission: Adult £2.20, Child £1.10. Family ticket: £5.50 for 2 adults + up to 3 children. Pre-booked parties £1.60.

OPEN
30 Mar - 2 Nov: Daily 10.30am - 5pm/sunset if earlier. Last admission ½ hour before closing. N.B. Parking in village car parks only.

ANNE OF CLEVES HOUSE

Tel: 01273 474610   **Fax:** 01273 486990

52 Southover High Street, Lewes, Sussex BN7 1JA

Owner: Sussex Past   **Contact:** Mr Steven Watts

16th century timber-framed Wealden hall-house with wide ranging Sussex collections, furnished rooms and summer tours of adjacent Lewes Priory. The town house was given to Anne of Cleves by her ex-husband Henry VIII as part of her divorce settlement.

Location: South Lewes town centre, off A27/A26/ A275.

Opening Times: 25 March - 10 November: Daily 10am - 5.30pm (Suns 12 noon - 5.30pm). 11 November - 24 March: Tue & Thur 10am - 5.30pm. Closed Christmas.

Admission: Adult £1.90, Child £1.00, Family (2+2) £5. Combined ticket with Lewes Castle is also available.

ARUNDEL CASTLE

See Page 192 for full page entry.

ARUNDEL CATHEDRAL

Tel: 01903 882297

Parsons Hill, Arundel, Sussex BN18 9AY

Contact: Rev A Whale

French Gothic Cathedral, church of the RC Diocese of Arundel and Brighton built by Henry, 15th Duke of Norfolk and opened 1873. Carpet of Flowers and Floral Festival held annually on the Feast of Corpus Christi (60 days after Easter) and day preceding.

Location: Above junction of A27 and A284.

Opening Times: Summer: 9am - 6pm. Winter: 9am - dusk. Mass at 10am each day. Sunday Masses: 6.30pm Vigil Sat evening, 8am, 9.30am & 11am. Shop opened after services and on special occasions and otherwise at request.

BATEMAN'S

BURWASH, ETCHINGHAM, EAST SUSSEX TN19 7DS

Owner: The National Trust
Contact: The Administrator
Tel: 01435 882302

Home of author Rudyard Kipling 1902 - 36. The house was built by a local ironmonger in 1634. Today the rooms are left as they were when the Kiplings lived here and include Kipling's study. The exhibition rooms contain memorabilia and mementos of Kipling's work and life. The garden, laid out to complement the house and surrounding countryside includes a rose, herb and wild garden. Beautiful water mill, also see Kipling's Rolls Royce.

Location: ½ mile S of Burwash off A265.

Admission: Adult £4.00, Child £2.00. Family Ticket (2 adults & up to 3 children) £10.00. Pre-booked parties £3.00pp.

OPEN
30 Mar - end Oct: Sat - Wed 11am - 5.30pm (open Good Fri). Last admission: 4.30pm. The Mill Grinds corn most Sats at 2pm in open season. Shop & Restaurant as House (Xmas shop: tel for details)

BATTLE ABBEY

BATTLE, EAST SUSSEX TN33 0AD

Owner: English Heritage
Contact: The Custodian
Tel: 01424 773792

Battle Abbey marks the site of the Battle of Hastings, where in 1066 the English Army faced the troops of Duke William of Normandy. Harold fell mortally wounded on the field of Battle and William became King.

William built an abbey to atone for the terrible slaughter. The high altar was on the spot where Harold fell and is still marked by a stone. There is an exhibition in the C.14 gatehouse, and the mile-long Battlefield Walk takes you round the perimeter of the battlefield.

Location: At S end of Battle High Street.

Admission: Adult £3.50 OAP/Student/UB40 £2.60 Child £1.80. Discount on parties of 11+.

OPEN
1 April - 30 Sept: Daily 10am - 6pm
1 Oct - 31 Oct: Daily 10am - 6pm or dusk if earlier.
1 Nov - 31 Mar: Daily 10am - 4pm.

BAYHAM OLD ABBEY

Tel/Fax: 01892 890381

Lamberhurst, Sussex

Owner: English Heritage   **Contact:** The Custodian

These riverside ruins are of a house of 'white' canons, founded c.1208 and preserved in the 18th century, when its surroundings were landscaped to create the delightful setting in which you will find the ruins today.

Location: 1³/₄m W of Lamberhurst off B2169.

Opening Times: 1 Apr - 31 Oct: Daily 10am - 6pm. 1 - 31 Oct: Daily 10am - 6pm or dusk if earlier.

Admission: Adult £2.00, Child £1.00, Conc £1.50.

BENTLEY WILDFOWL & MOTOR MUSEUM

Tel: 01825 840573

Halland, Lewes, East Sussex BN8 5AF

Owner: East Sussex County Council   **Contact:** Mr Barry Sutherland - Manager

Brick Tudor farmhouse with a large reception room of Palladian proportions added on either end in the 1960s by the architect Raymond Erith, each lit by large Venetian windows. Furnished to form a grand 20th century evocation of a mid Georgian house.

Location: 7 miles NE from Lewes, signposted off A22, A26 & B2192. Please follow signs to Bentley Wildfowl & Motor Museum

Opening Times: 18 Mar - 31 Oct: Daily 10.30am - 4.30pm (last admissions). 5pm in Jul and Aug. House: 12 noon daily from 1 Apr. 1 Nov - 17 Mar weekends only 10.30am - 4pm (last admissions). Estate closed Dec & Jan, house closed all winter.

Admission: Adult £3.90 (£3.00 in winter), Child (4 - 15) £2.30, Child under 4 free, Senior Citizens /Students £3.00. Coach drivers free admission & refreshment ticket. 10% discount for parties of 11+. Special rates for the disabled. Call to verify prices.

Fireplace at Charleston.

BODIAM CASTLE

BODIAM, NR ROBERTSBRIDGE, EAST SUSSEX TN32 5UA

Owner: The National Trust   *Contact:* The Administrator

Tel: 01580 830436   **Fax:** 01580 830398

Built in 1385 against a French invasion that never came and as a comfortable dwelling for a rich nobleman, Bodiam Castle is one of the finest examples of medieval military architecture. The virtual completeness of its exterior makes it a popular filming location. Inside, although a ruin, floors have been replaced in some of the towers and visitors can climb the spiral staircase to enjoy superb views from the battlements. Audio-visual presentations of life in a castle, small museum, shop and restaurant.

Location: 3 miles south of Hawkhurst, 2 miles east of A21 Hurst Green.

Opening Times: 17 Feb - 3 Nov: Daily 10am - 6pm/dusk. 5 Nov - 5 Jan: Tues - Sun 10am - dusk (closed 24 - 26 Dec, open New Years Day). Last admission: $^{1}/_{2}$hr before close. Shop open as castle /restaurant (Xmas shop phone for details); Restaurant 17 Feb - end of Oct: Daily 10.30am - 5pm/dusk. Nov - Dec: Sat & Sun only 11am - 3pm.

Admission: Adult £2.70, Child £1.30, Family ticket (2 adults & up to 3 children) £6.70. Parties £2.00. Car Park 50p (1995 prices). NT members free.

BORDE HILL GARDEN

Tel: 01444 450326   **Fax:** 01444 440427

Balcombe Road, Haywards Heath, Sussex RH16 1XP

Owner: Borde Hill Garden Ltd   **Contact:** Mrs J Wilkinson

Large informal woodland garden, some formal areas with herbaceous borders. Woodland walk.

Location: 1 $^{1}/_{2}$m N of Haywards Heath.

Opening Times: 16 Mar - 29 Sept: Daily from 10am - 6pm.

Admission: Adult £2.00, Child £1.00, Family £5.00, Groups of 15 plus £2.00.

BOXGROVE PRIORY

Tel: 01732 778000

Boxgrove, Chichester, Sussex

Owner: English Heritage   **Contact:** The South East Regional Office

Remains of the Guest House, Chapter House and church of this 12th century priory, which was the cell of a French abbey until Richard II confirmed its independence in 1383.

Location: N of Boxgrove, 4 m E of Chichester on minor road off A27.

Opening Times: Any reasonable time.

BRAMBER CASTLE

Tel: 01732 778000

Bramber, Sussex

Owner: English Heritage   **Contact:** The South East Regional Office

The remains of a Norman castle gatehouse, walls and earthworks in a splendid setting overlooking the Adur valley.

Location: On W side of Bramber village off A283.

Opening Times: Any reasonable time.

BRICKWALL HOUSE

Tel: 01797 223329

Northiam, Rye, Sussex

Owner: Frewen Educational Trust   **Contact:** The Curator

Impressive timber framed house. 17th century drawing room with magnificent plaster ceilings and good portraits including by Lely, Kneller and Vereist. Topiary, chess garden.

Location: S side of Northiam village at junction of A28 and B2088.

Opening Times: Apr - 31 Sept: Sat and Bank Hol Mons, 2 - 5pm

Admission: £2.50.

CHARLESTON

See Page 193 for full page entry.

CHICHESTER CATHEDRAL

Tel: 01243 782595   **Fax:** 01243 536190

Chichester, Sussex, PO19 1PX.

        Contact: Mrs S E Papworth

The beauty of the 900 year old cathedral, site of the Shrine of St Richard, is enhanced by many art treasures, ancient and modern.

Location: West Street, Chichester.

Opening Times: Summer: 7.30am - 7pm, Winter: 7.30am - 5pm. Sun services: 8am, 10am, 11am and 3.30pm. Weekday services: 7.30am, 8am and 5.30pm.

Admission: Donation.

DANNY

Tel: 01273 833000

Hurstpierpoint, Sussex BN6 9BB

Owner: Country Houses Association   **Contact:** Mr J Grant

A late Elizabethan E shaped house in red brick, part modernised in 1728.

Location: Just outside Hurstpierpoint on the Hassocks road.

Opening Times: May - Sept: Wed and Thurs, 2 - 5pm

Admission: Adult £2.50, Child under 16 £1.00, Groups by arrangement.

FIRLE PLACE

NR. LEWES, EAST SUSSEX BN8 6LP

Owner: Viscount Gage   *Contact:* Showing Secretary

Tel: 01273 858335

Home of the Gage family since the 15th century, the original Tudor house was largely altered c1730. House contains a magnificent collection of European and British Old Masters. Also fine French and English furniture together with notable Sèvres porcelain. A House for connoisseurs. American connections.

Location: On A27 equidistant Brighton/Eastbourne, Lewes 5 miles.

Opening Times: May - Sept: Tours Wed, Thurs, Suns & Bank Hol Mons 2 - 5pm. Connoisseurs unguided tours with additional rooms shown 1st Wed in each month. Exclusive private viewing 25+ by arrangement.

Admission: Adult £3.85, Pre-booked Group 25+ £3.35. Connoisseurs Day £4.75 Private Viewing 25+ £5.85 by arrangement only.

FISHBOURNE ROMAN PALACE

Tel: 01243 785859   **Fax:** 01243 539266

Salthill Road, Fishbourne, Chichester, Sussex PO19 3QR

Owner: Sussex Past   **Contact:** Mr David Rudkin

Remains of largest known Roman residence north of Alps. Beautiful mosaics, museum and Roman Gardens. Audio-visual programme.

Location: Off A27/A259. 1.5 miles W of Chichester.

Opening Times: 12 Feb - 13 December: Feb, Nov, Dec: Daily 10am - 4pm. Mar - Jul, Sept - Oct: Daily 10am - 5pm. August 10am - 6pm. 14 December - 10 Feb: Sundays only 10am - 4pm. Closed Christmas.

Admission: Adult £3.60, Child £1.60, OAP £2.90, Student £2.90, Disabled £2.90, Family £ (2+2) £9.00, Partially sighted £1.60.

GLYNDE PLACE

GLYNDE, LEWES, SUSSEX BN8 6SX

Owners:
Viscount & Viscountess Hampden
Contact: Viscountess Hampden

Tel: 01723 858 224
Fax: 01723 858 224

Glynde Place is a magnificent example of Elizabethan architecture commanding exceptionally fine views of the South Downs. Amongst the collections of 400 years of family living can be seen a fine collection of 17th and 18th century portraits of the Trevors and a room dedicated to Sir Henry Brand, Speaker of the House of Commons 1872 - 1884 and an exhibition of 'Harbert Morley and the Great Rebellion 1638 - 1660' the story of the part played by the owner of Glynde Place in the Civil War.

Location: In Glynde village 4m SE of Lewes on A27.

Admission: Adult £3.25, Child £1.50. Free parking. Teas.

OPEN

Easter Sun & Mon. May: Suns & Bank Hols only.
June - September: Wed, Thur & Suns 2 - 5pm
(Last adm: 4.45pm)

GOODWOOD HOUSE

See Page 194 for full page entry.

GREAT DIXTER HOUSE & GARDENS

Tel: 01797 252878 **Fax:** 01797 252879

Northiam, Rye, East Sussex TN31 6PH
Owner: Mr C Lloyd   **Contact:** The Administrator

Built in the 15th century Great Dixter was restored and extended by Lutyens in 1910. It forms a splendid backdrop to Mr Christopher Lloyd's acclaimed gardens. Neither would seem complete in isolation.

Location: Signposted off the A28 in Northiam.

Opening Times: Daily except Mondays. 2- 5pm . Also open Bank Holidays.

Admission: House & Garden: Adult £3.80, Child 50p. Gardens: Adult £2.80, Child 25p.

HAMMERWOOD PARK

OPEN

Easter Monday - Sept

Weds, Sats &
Bank Holiday Mons
2 - 5.30pm

Guided tour
starts 2.05pm

Coaches strictly by appointment.

Small groups at any time throughout the year by appointment.

Tel: 01342 850594
Fax: 01342 850864

EAST GRINSTEAD, SUSSEX RH19 3QE

Owner: David Pinnegar   Contact: David Pinnegar

Built in in 1792 as an Apollo's hunting lodge by Benjamin Latrobe, architect of the Capitol and the White House, Washington D.C. Owned by Led Zepplin in the 1970's, rescued from dereliction in 1982. Cream Teas in the Organ Room, the work of French artists in the hall, whilst a derelict dining room still shocks the unwary. Guided tours by the family, said by many to be the most interesting in Sussex. Accommodation available.

Location: 3½ m E of East Grinstead on A264 to Tunbridge Wells; 1 m W of Holtye.

Admission: House & Park: Adult £3.50, Child £1.50. Private viewing by arrangement.

HIGH BEECHES GARDENS

Tel: 01444 400589

High Beeches, Handcross, Sussex RH17 6HQ
Owner: High Beeches Gardens Conservation Trust (non profit charity)   **Contact:** Sarah Bray
Help us to preserve these 20 acres of magically beautiful woodland and water gardens with glorious Spring & Autumn colour. Wildflower meadow.

Location: 1 m S of M23.

Opening Times: Apr - Jun, Sept - Oct: 6 afternoons a week. Closed Wednesdays.

Admission: Adult £3.00, Child free, Groups by appointment at any time.

HIGHDOWN GARDENS

Tel: 01903 501054

Littlehampton Road, Goring by Sea, Worthing, Sussex BN12 6PE
Owner: Worthing Borough Council   **Contact:** C Beardsley Esq
Unique gardens in disused chalk pit, begun in 1909.
Location: Littlehampton Road, Goring by Sea, Worthing.
Opening Times: 1 Apr - 30 Sept: Mon - Fri, 10am - 6pm. Sat and Sun including Bank Hols, 10am - 8pm. 1 Oct - 30 Nov: Mon - Fri, 10am - 4.30pm. 1 Dec - 31 Jan: 10am - 4pm. 1 Feb - 31 Mar: Mon - Fri, 10am - 4.30pm.
Admission: Free.

LAMB HOUSE

Tel: 01892 890651

West Street, Rye, Sussex TN31 7ES
Owner: The National Trust   **Contact:** The Administrator
The home of the writer Henry James from 1898 to 1916 where he wrote the best novels of his later period. The walled garden, staircase, hall and three rooms on the ground floor containing some of James's personal possessions are on view. Also once home to the author E F Benson.
Location: In West Street, facing W end of church.
Opening Times: Apr - end Oct: Wed & Sat only 2 - 6pm. Last admission 5.30pm.
Admission: £2.20, no reductions.

LEONARDSLEE GARDENS

See Page 195 for full page entry.

LEWES CASTLE

OPEN

All year
(except 25 & 26 Dec)

Daily
Mon - Sat:
10am - 5.30pm
Suns & Bank Hols
11am - 5.30pm
Castle closes at dusk
in winter.

Tel: 01273 486290
Fax: 01273 486990

BARBICAN HOUSE, 169 HIGH STREET, LEWES, SUSSEX BN7 1YE

Owner: Sussex Past   Contact: Mrs Helen Poole

Lewes's imposing Norman castle offers magnificent views across the town and surrounding downland. Across the road, spanned by the towering Barbican Gate is Barbican House, home of the Museum of Sussex Archaeology following the progress of Sussex people from their earliest beginnings to medieval times. A superb scale model of Victorian Lewes provides the centrepiece of a 25-minute audio visual presentation telling the story of the county town of Sussex.

Location: Lewes town centre off A27/A26/A275/A22.

Admission: Adult £3.00, Child £1.50, OAP/Student £2.50. Family (2 + 2) £8.00.

MICHELHAM PRIORY

OPEN

17 Mar - 31 Oct

Mar & Oct: Wed - Sun
11am - 4pm
Apr - July & Sept:
Wed - Sun 11am - 5pm
Aug: Daily
10.30am - 5.30pm

Open Bank Holiday Mon during season.

Tel: 01323 844224
Fax: 01323 844030

UPPER DICKER, HAILSHAM, SUSSEX BN27 3QS

Owner: Sussex Past   Contact: Ms. Allex Jenkinson

Set on a Medieval moated island in the Cuckmere Valley, Michelham Priory was colonised by Augustinian Canons in 1229. Following the Dissolution, the remains were incorporated into a splendid Tudor house. The imposing 14th century Gatehouse survives and the Elizabethan Great Barn forms the focal point of a courtyard containing a smithy and wheelwright's shop, a rope museum and a restaurant and tea room. Peaceful gardens with a watermill provide interest throughout the season. Events include music, opera and crafts.

Location: 8 miles NW of Eastbourne off A22/A27.

Admission: Adult £3.80, Child £2.00, OAP/Student £3.00, Disabled £1.80, Family (2+2) £9.60.

MOORLANDS

Tel: 01892 652474

Friar's Gate, Crowborough, East Sussex TN6 1XF

Owner: Dr Steven Smith   **Contact:** Dr Steven Smith

3 acres set in lush valley adjoining Ashdown forest; water garden with ponds and streams; herbaceous border, primulas, rhododendrons, azaleas, and many unusual trees and shrubs; good autumn colour. Featured in 'Weekend Today', 1995, 'VT Wochen' (Dutch) 1994 and 'Feeling' (Belgian) 1992.

Location: Friar's Gate, 2m N of Crowborough. Approach via B2188 at Friar's Gate - take L fork signposted 'Crowborough Narrow Road', entrance 100yds on left. From Crowborough crossroads take St Johns Road to Friar's Gate.

Opening Times: 1 Apr - 1 Oct: Weds 11am - 5pm. Sun 26 May, Suns 9 & 16 Jun, Sun 21 July 2 - 6pm. Also 1 Apr - 1 Oct at other times by appointment only.

Admission: Adult £2.00, Child free, OAP £1.50.

NYMANS GARDEN

OPEN

1 Mar - 31 Oct:

Daily except Mon & Tues but open Bank Holidays.

11am - 7pm or sunset if earlier.

Tel: 01444 400321
Fax: 01444 400253

HANDCROSS, HAYWARDS HEATH, SUSSEX RH17 6EB

Owners: *The National Trust*   **Contact:** *The Property Manager*

One of the great gardens of the Sussex Weald, with rare and beautiful plants, shrubs and trees from all over the world. Walled garden, hidden sunken garden, pinetum, laurel walk and romantic ruins. Woodland walks and Wild Garden.

Location: On B2114 at Handcross, 4½ m S of Crawley, just off London - Brighton M23 / A23.

Admission: Adult £4.20, Child £2.10, Family £10.00.

PALLANT HOUSE

Tel: 01243 774557   **Fax:** 01243 536038

9 North Pallant, Chichester, West Sussex PO19 1TJ

Owner: Pallant House Gallery Trust   **Contact:** David Coke

Lovingly restored Queen Anne townhouse with historic rooms in Georgian style, fine antique furniture and formal garden. Highly important collection of Bow porcelain and displays of modern British art (Nicholson, Nash, Moore, Sutherland, Piper etc). Georgian style walled garden.

Opening Times: All year: Tues - Sat 10.am - 5.15pm. Last admission 4.45pm. Closed Sun, Mon and Bank Hols.

PARHAM HOUSE & GARDENS

OPEN

3 April - 31 October
Weds, Thurs, Suns and Bank Holiday Monday afternoons.

Gardens*: 1 - 6pm
House: 2 - 6pm
Last entry 5pm

*Jul - Aug: Gardens open at 12 noon.

Tel: 01903 744888
Fax: 01903 746557

PARHAM PARK, PULBOROUGH, WEST SUSSEX RH20 4HS

Owners: *Parham Park Ltd Reg Charity*   **Contact:** *Patricia Kennedy*

Set in the heart of an ancient deer park this peaceful Elizabethan house with its light, panelled rooms contains a very important collection of paintings, furniture, needlework and carpets. Flowers for the beautiful arrangements in the house are grown in the award-winning gardens which are the setting for an annual garden weekend on 20/21 July.

Location: Mid-way between Pulborough & Storrington on A283.

Admission: House & Gardens: Adult £4.25, OAP £3.75, Child £1.00, Family ticket (2 + 2) £10. Garden only: Adult/OAP £3.00, Child 50p.

PASHLEY MANOR GARDENS

TICEHURST, WADHURST, EAST SUSSEX TN5 7HE

Owner: *Mr & Mrs James Sellick*   **Contact:** *Mr & Mrs James Sellick*

Tel: 01580 200692   **Fax:** 01580 200102

Pashley Manor Gardens, surrounding the Grade I Tudor timber-framed ironmaster's house dating from 1550 with a Georgian rear elevation of 1720, stands in a well timbered park with magnificent views across to Brightling Beacon. The 8 acres of formal garden, dating from the 18th century, were created in true English romantic style and are planted with many ancient trees and fine shrubs. New plantings over the past decade give additional interest and subtle colouring throughout the year. All is enhanced by waterfalls, ponds and a moat which encircled the original house built in 1262. The delightful view, peaceful environment and the sound of running water makes this garden very worthwhile visiting. Teas, coffees and light lunches. Coach and car park. No dogs. Plants for sale.

Location: Between Ticehurst and A21 on B2099. Wadhurst 5m.

Opening Times: Gardens only: 6 Apr - 28 Sept: Tues, Wed, Thur, Sat and all Bank Holiday Mondays, 11am - 5pm. Between 28 Apr & 18 Aug: Plant Fairs. 6 - 9 Jun: Rose Festival. 2 - 7 May: Tulip Festival.

Admission: Adult £3.00, OAPs £2.50. Coaches by appointment only.

PETWORTH HOUSE

See Page 196 for full page entry.

PEVENSEY CASTLE

Tel: 01323 762604

Pevensey, Sussex BN24 5LE

Owner: English Heritage   **Contact:** The Custodian

This medieval castle includes the remains of an unusual Keep enclosed within its walls which originally date back to the 4th century Roman fort Anderida. Restricted disabled access, pre-booking necessary, charged coach parking in village, 500yds.

Location: In Pevensey off A259.

Opening Times: 1 Apr - 30 Sept: 10am - 6pm. 1 - 31 Oct: 10am - 6pm or dusk if earlier. 1 Nov - 31 Mar: Wed - Sun 10am - 4pm (Closed lunch 1 - 2pm).

Admission: Adult £2.00, Child £1.00, Conc £1.50.

PRESTON MANOR

Tel: 01273 603005

Brighton, East Sussex BN1 1EE

Owner: Brighton Borough Council   **Contact:** Public Services

The beautifully preserved historic home of the Stanford family. Notable collections of fine furniture, portraits and antiquities show life upstairs and down. Over 20 charming rooms to explore, including the superbly renovated servants' quarters, day nursery and toy collection and Butler's Pantry. The beautiful lawns surrounding the Manor also contain a walled and scented garden, pets cemetery and the 13th century Parish Church of St Peter. The Manor is also available for hire, the perfect setting for select entertaining, combining elegance and tradition. Also used for filming and photographic work.

Location: Within easy reach of Brighton town centre in Preston Park.

Opening Times: Mon 1 - 5pm (10am - 5pm Bank Holidays), Tue - Sat 10am - 5pm, Sunday 2pm - 5pm. Closed Good Friday, 25 - 26 December.

Admission: Adults £2.85, Student/OAP £2.35. Groups: 20 Adults £2.45, Child £1.70.

THE ROYAL PAVILION

See Page 197 for full page entry.

ST MARY'S

See Page 198 for full page entry.

SHEFFIELD PARK GARDEN

DANE MILL, NR UCKFIELD, EAST SUSSEX TN22 3QX

Owner: The National Trust
Contact: The Property Manager

Tel: 01825 790231

A magnificent 100 acre landscape garden, with 5 lakes linked by cascades, laid out in the 18th century by 'Capability' Brown. Carpeted with daffodils and bluebells in spring, its rhododendrons, azaleas and spring garden are spectacular in early summer. Cool tree lined paths and lake reflections make it perfect for a stroll in high summer and the garden is ablaze with colour from its rare trees and shrubs in autumn.

Location: Midway between East Grinstead and Lewes, 5m NW of Uckfield on E side of A275.

Admission: Adult £4, Child £2, Family ticket (2 adults & up to 3 children) £10. Pre-booked parties. Adult £3, Child £1.50.

OPEN
March: Sat & Sun only 11am - 4pm.
30 Mar - 10 Nov: Tues - Sun & Bank Hol Mon 11am - 6pm or sunset if earlier.
13 Nov - 22 Dec: Wed - Sun 11 - 4pm.
Last adm. 1 hr before closing. Shop open as garden. Restaurant (privately owned, tel for opening times).

STANDEN

OPEN

1 Apr - end Oct
Wed - Sun and
Bank Holiday Mons

Gardens:
12.30 - 6.00pm

House:
1.30 - 5.00pm

Special weekend openings on 23/24 and 30/31 March 1.30 - 4.30pm

Tel: 01342 323029

EAST GRINSTEAD, WEST SUSSEX RH19 4NE

Owner: The National Trust   *Contact: The Property Manager*

Dating from the 1890's and containing original Morris & Co. furnishings and decorations, Standen survives today as a remarkable testimony to the ideals of the Arts and Crafts movement. The property was built as a family home by the influential architect Phillip Webb and retains a warm, welcoming atmosphere. Details of Webb's designs can be found everywhere from the fireplaces to the original electric light fittings.

Location: 2 miles south of East Grinstead, signposted from B2110.

Admission: House & Garden: £4.50. Garden only: £3.00, Children half price, Family Ticket £11.25.

STANSTED PARK

Tel: 01705 412265   **Fax:** 01705 413773

Rowlands Castle, Hampshire PO9 6DX

Owner: Trustees of Stansted Park Foundation   **Contact:** John Gowen

Built in 1903 on the site of its 17th century predecessor. Spectacular avenues through ancient Forests of Bere. 30 acre of grounds includes an arboretum.

Location: Follow brown heritage signs from A3 (Rowlands Castle) and A27 (Havant).

Opening Times: BH Sun & Mon. 7 Jul - 17 Sept: Sun - Tue, 2 - 5.30pm. June: Groups by arrangement only.

Admission: House & Gdns: Adult £3.50, Child £1.50, Groups £3. Grounds: Adult £1, Child 50p.

UPPARK

SOUTH HARTING, PETERSFIELD, SUSSEX GU31 5QR

Owner: The National Trust
Contact: The Property Manager

Tel: 01730 825415

Fine late 17th century house situated high on the South Downs with magnificent views towards the Solent. Important collection of paintings and decorative art. Interesting below-stairs servants' rooms. Harting Down, with one of the finest stretches of the South Downs Way, is within one mile of Uppark.

Location: 5m SE of Petersfield on B2146.

Admission: House, Garden & Exhibition: £5.00, Family £12.50. Parties (no reduction) must be pre-booked. Timed tickets in operation. Advance booking 01730 825317, 10am - 1pm, Mon - Fri.

OPEN
31 Mar - 31 Oct: House: 1 - 5pm
Last admission 4pm.
Car Park and Woodland Walk: Open at 11am.
Garden & Exhibition: 12 noon - 5.30pm.

WAKEHURST PLACE

Tel: 01444 892701

Ardingly, Haywards Heath, Sussex RH17 6TN

Owner: The National Trust   **Contact:** The Administrator

A superb collection of exotic trees, shrubs and other plants, many displayed in a geographic manner. Extensive water gardens, a Winter Garden, a Rock Walk and many other features. The Loder Valley Nature Reserve can be visited by prior arrangement.

Location: 1½m NW of Ardingly, on B2028.

Opening Times: Daily (not 25 Dec & 1 Jan) Nov - Jan: 10am - 4pm. Feb & Oct: 10am - 5pm. Mar: 10am - 6pm. Apr - Sept: 10am - 7pm. Mansion closes 1 hr before gardens.

Admission: Adult £4.00, Child (to 16) / Conc £2.00. Reductions for pre-paid booked parties.

WEALD & DOWNLAND OPEN AIR MUSEUM

Tel: 01243 811348

Singleton, Chichester, Sussex PO18 0EU

Collection of over 35 historic buildings rescued from destruction, including working watermill and various timber framed houses.

Location: 6m N of Chichester.

Opening Times: 1 Mar - 31 Oct: Daily & Nov - Feb: Weds & w/ends only. 10.30am - 4pm.

Admission: Adult £4.50, Child £2.20, Family £11.50, Senior Citizen £4.30.

SPECIAL EVENTS

◇ **PARHAM HOUSE**   **VARIOUS**
Needlework Conservation Days

◇ **HIGH BEECHES GARDENS**   **8 APRIL**
Daffodil Day. Covered Bazaar in aid of Marie Curie Cancer Care. Admission Gardens & Bazaar £3.00 pp

◇ **HIGH BEECHES GARDENS**   **6 MAY**
Bluebell Day. Sale of uncommon trees and shrubs. WI Market Stall Exhibition of Watercolour flower portraits by Helen Hilliard

◇ **CHARLESTON**   **23 – 27 MAY**
The Charleston Festival

◇ **HIGH BEECHES GARDENS**   **27 MAY**
Azalea Day. Sale of many varieties of Japanese and deciduous azaleas. WI Market Stall.

◇ **PARHAM HOUSE**   **LATE JUNE**
Open Air Opera on South Front lawn with house as a back-drop

◇ **CHARLESTON**   **7 – 14 JULY**
The Charleston Summer School

◇ **PARHAM HOUSE**   **20 – 21 JULY**
Garden Weekend: Specialist Nurseries, NAFAS Flower arranging Competition, Plant 'Doctor'. Food and drink.

◇ **HIGH BEECHES GARDENS**   **18 AUGUST**
Gentian Day. Gentians in the Gardens. Working Shire Horses on the Meadow. WI Market & Craft demonstrations.

◇ **HIGH BEECHES GARDENS**   **13 OCTOBER**
Autumn Splendour. Gorgeous Autumn colour. Covered Bazaar in aid of Aldingbourne Centre for Work for Persons with Learning Disabilities.

◇ **THE ROYAL PAVILION**   **11 – 17 NOVEMBER**
'Behind the Scenes' week: The award-winning week that gives a fascinating insight into the skills and techniques that have gone into restoring this extraordinary royal palace: Lectures, displays, tours and demonstrations. For all events/timetables and programmes telephone 01273 603005 for further information.

◇ **THE ROYAL PAVILION**   **19 JANUARY 1997**
FREEDAY: Annual event to celebrate the purchase of the Pavilion by the town in 1850. Free.

◇ **THE ROYAL PAVILION**   **FEBRUARY 1997**
Half-term fun at the Palace: Quizzes, puzzles, games and workshops.

For National Trust and English Heritage Events see separate section.

ARBEIA ROMAN FORT

Tel: 0191 456 1369 **Fax:** 0191 427 6862

Baring Street, South Shields, Tyne & Wear NE33 2BB
Owner: Tyne & Wear Museums Service **Contact:** The Curator
Extensive remains of 2nd century Roman fort, including fort defences, stone granaries, gateways, and latrines. Full scale simulation of Roman gateway and museum.
Location: Near town centre.
Opening Times: Easter - Oct: Tues - Sat: 10am - 5.30pm, Sun 2 - 5pm. Open Bank Hol Mons.
Admission: Free.

BEDE'S WORLD MUSEUM

Tel: 0191 489 2106 **Fax:** 0191 428 2361

Church Bank, Jarrow, Tyne & Wear NE32 3DY
Owner: Jarrow 700AD Ltd. **Contact:** Miss Susan Mills
Little remains of the original monastery where the Venerable Bede lived AD673 - 735 and which is now considered 'The Cradle of English Learning'.
Location: Just off A19 - S end of Tyne Tunnel.
Opening Times: Apr - Oct: Tues - Sat, 10am - 5.30pm, Sun 2.30 - 5.30pm. Nov - Mar: Tues - Sat, 11am - 4.30pm, Sun 2.30 - 5.30pm.
Admission: Adult £2.50, Child £1.25, Conc £1.25, Groups by arrangement.

BESSIE SURTEES HOUSE

Tel: 0191 261 1585

41 - 44 Sandhill, Newcastle, Tyne & Wear
Owner: English Heritage **Contact:** The Custodian
Two 16th and 17th century merchant's houses stand on the quayside near the Tyne Bridge. One is a rare example of Jacobean domestic architecture.
Location: 41- 44 Sandhill, Newcastle.
Opening Times: Weekdays only: 10am - 4pm. Closed Bank Hols, 24 - 26 Dec, 1 Jan.

CATHEDRAL CHURCH OF ST NICHOLAS

Newcastle upon Tyne, Tyne & Wear NE1 1GF **Tel:** 0191 232 1939 **Fax:** 0191 230 0735
Contact: Rev Canon Peter Strange
Mostly 14th century surmounted by 15th century lantern spire, one medieval window, two renaissance memorials, one large 15th century Flemish brass.
Location: City centre, $\frac{1}{2}$ m from A167 signposted from Swan House roundabout.
Opening Times: Sun: 7am - 12 noon, 4 - 7pm. Mon - Fri: 7am - 6pm. Sat: 8.30am - 4pm.

GIBSIDE

Tel: 01207 542255

Nr Rowlands Gill, Burnopfield, Newcastle upon Tyne NE16 6BG
Owner: The National Trust **Contact:** The Administrator
Gibside is one of the finest 18th century designed landscapes in the north of England. The Chapel was built to James Paine's design soon after 1760. Outstanding example of Georgian architecture approached along a terrace with an oak avenue. Walk along the River Derwent through woodland.
Location: 6m SW of Gateshead, 20m NW of Durham. Entrance on B6314 between Burnopfield and Rowlands Gill.
Opening Times: 1 Apr - end Oct: Daily except Mon (open BH Mons) 11am - 5pm. Last adm. 4.30pm.
Admission: Chapel and Grounds: Adult £2.90, Child half price. Pre-booked parties £2.60.

HYLTON CASTLE

Tel: 0191 261 1585

Sunderland, Tyne & Wear
Owner: English Heritage **Contact:** North Regional Office
This is a 15th century keep-gatehouse set in wooded parkland with a fine display of medieval heraldry adorning the facades.
Location: $3^3/_4$ m W of Sunderland.
Opening Times: Any reasonable time. (Access to grounds only).

SOUTER LIGHTHOUSE

Tel: 0191 529 3161

Coast Road, Whitburn, Tyne & Wear SR6 7NR
Owner: The National Trust **Contact:** The Property Manager
Shore based lighthouse and associated buildings, built in 1871, the first to be powered by an alternative electric current.
Location: $2^1/_2$m S of Southshields on A183. 5m N of Sunderland on A183.
Opening Times: 1 Apr - end Oct: Daily except Friday (open Good Friday) 11am - 5pm. Last admission 4.30pm.
Admission: Adult £2.40, Child half price. Pre-booked parties £1.80.

ST PAUL'S MONASTERY ⌗

Tel: 0191 489 2106

Jarrow, Tyne & Wear
Contact: The Custodian
The home of the Venerable Bede in the 7th and 8th centuries, partly surviving as the chancel of the parish church. It has become one of the best understood Anglo-Saxon monastic sites.
Location: In Jarrow, on minor road N of A185.
Opening Times: Monastery ruins - any reasonable time. Nearby museum open 1 Apr - 31 Oct, Tue - Sat & Bank Hols, 10.00am - 5.30pm. 1 Nov - 31 Mar, Tue - Sat, 11.00am - 4.30pm, Sun 2.30 - 5.30pm. Closed Christmas, New Year.
Admission: Museum: Adult 2.50, Child/Conc. £1.25. Family £6.00, UB40 Family £4.00.

TYNEMOUTH CASTLE AND PRIORY ⌗

Tel: 0191 257 1090

Jarrow, Tyne & Wear
Owner: English Heritage **Contact:** The Custodian
The castle walls and gatehouse enclose the substantial remains of a Benedictine priory founded c.1090 on a Saxon monastic site. Their strategic importance has made the castle and priory the target for attack for many centuries. In World War I, coastal batteries in the castle defended the mouth of the Tyne.
Location: In Tynemouth, near North Pier.
Opening Times: 1 Apr - 30 Sept: Daily 10am - 6pm. 1 Oct - 31 Oct: Daily 10am - 6pm or dusk if earlier. 1 Nov - 31 Mar: Wed - Sun 10am - 4pm (closed 1 - 2pm lunch).
Admission: Adult £1.50, Child 80p, Conc £1.10.

WASHINGTON OLD HALL ❧

Tel: 0191 416 6879

The Avenue, Washington Village, Tyne & Wear NE38 7LE
Owner: The National Trust **Contact:** The Property Manager
Jacobean Manor House incorporating portions of 12th century house of the Washington family.
Location: In Washington on E side of Avenue. 5m W of Sunderland (2m from A1); S of Tyne Tunnel, follow signs for Washington New Town District 4 and then village.
Opening Times: 1 Apr - end Oct: Daily except Fris & Sats (open Good Fri), 11am - 5pm. Last admission 4.30pm.
Admission: Adult £2.30, Child half-price, Parties (15 +) £1.80, by prior arrangement only.

Where to Stay
For Private Accommodation and Johansens recommended Hotels, see Accommodation Section.

Gibside.

KEY TO SYMBOLS: ❧ THE NATIONAL TRUST ⌗ ENGLISH HERITAGE ▥ HISTORIC HOUSES ASSOCIATION

ARBURY HALL
Nuneaton

Built on the site of the Augustinian Priory of Erdbury, Arbury Hall has been the seat of the Newdegate family for over 400 years. This Tudor/Elizabethan house was 'gothicised' by Sir Roger Newdigate, the 5th Baronet in the 18th century to become "The Gothick Gem of the Midlands".

The saloon and dining room ceilings are especially spectacular, the former modelled on the Henry VII Chapel in Westminster Abbey. Portraits include works by Lely, Romney, Reynolds and Devis, and furniture includes Hepplewhite and Gothick Chippendale. A collection of porcelain consists of oriental and Chelsea pieces amongst others, and there is a particularly splendid display of Jacobite Toasting Glasses.

The Hall stands in secluded parkland and the delightful landscaped garden of rolling lawns, winding paths and beautiful trees and lakes are mainly the result of the 2nd Baronet's influence. Spring flowers, especially daffodils and bluebells are profuse. Seen at their glorious best in June is the vista of rhododendrons, azalea and the giant wisteria. North of the house lies the haven of the rose garden.

The Stables portico was designed by Wren.

George Eliot, the novelist was born on the estate and Arbury and Sir Roger were immortalised by her in her book, 'Scenes of Clerical Life'.

SUITABILITY FOR OTHER EVENTS
Corporate hospitality, film location, small conferences. Product launches and promotion. Marquee functions.

EXTRA FACILITIES
Clay pigeon shooting, archery and other sporting activities. Grand piano in Saloon. Helicopter landing site.

ADVICE TO COURIERS & DRIVERS
Follow tourist signs. Approach map available for coach drivers. Dogs on leads only in gardens. No cameras or video recorders allowed.

FACILITIES FOR THE DISABLED
Ramp access to main hall. Disabled visitors may alight at the Hall main entrance before parking in allocated areas.

PARKING FOR COACHES AND CARS
Parking for 200 cars and 3 coaches 250 yards from house. Other parking available.

GIFT SHOP
Open during opening hours and for private parties.

CATERING
Stables Tearooms for teas and light meals. Menus available for pre-booked parties. Exclusive lunches and dinners for corporate parties in Dining Room, max. 50, buffets 120.

GUIDE BOOKS
Colour guide, £1.50.

GUIDED TOURS
All tours are guided. Duration of private tours, $1\frac{1}{2}$ hours.

SCHOOL VISITS
Pre-arranged school parties are welcome, school room available. Children's guide book 25p.

CONTACT

Maj. W D Morris-Barker
Arbury Hall
Nuneaton
Warwickshire
CV10 7PT

Tel: (01203) 382804
Fax: (01203) 641147

LOCATION

London, M1, M6 exit 3 (A444-Nuneaton), $1\frac{3}{4}$ hours.

Chester A51, A34, M6 (from exit 14 to exit 3), $2\frac{1}{2}$ hours.
Nuneaton 10mins.

Bus: Nuneaton 3 miles.

Rail: Nuneaton Station 3 miles.

Air: Birmingham Int'l 17 miles.

OPENING TIMES

Summer
7 April - 29 September

Hall: Suns and Bank Holiday Mons.
2.00 - 5.30pm

Gardens: Suns & Mons.
2.00 - 6.00pm.

Last admissions to Hall and Gardens 5.00pm.

Open for pre-booked parties on most dates. Minimum 25 persons.

Winter
October - Easter
Corporate functions only.

ADMISSION

Summer
Hall, Park & Gardens
Adult £3.50
Child (up to 14 yrs.) . £2.00

Gardens Only
Adult £2.00
Child (up to 14 yrs.) . £1.00

Groups
Adult £3.00

(Special rates for pre-booked parties of 25 or more persons).

CONFERENCE AND FUNCTION FACILITIES

ROOM	DIMENSIONS	CAPACITY	LAYOUT	POWER POINTS	SUITABLE FOR A/V
Dining Room	35' x 28'	50	Lunch/Dinner	2	✓
		120	Buffet		
Saloon	35' x 30'	70	Theatre	4	✓
		18	Schoolroom		
Drawing Room	38' x 21'	40	Theatre	3	✓
		24	Schoolroom		
Long Gallery	48' x 11'	40	Theatre	4	✓
Stables Tea Rooms	31' x 18'	60	Cafeteria	3	✓
		80	Theatre		

CHARLECOTE PARK
Wellesbourne

CHARLECOTE has been the home of the Lucy family for some 700 years. The present house, begun by Sir Thomas Lucy in the mid-16th century, lies at the centre of an extensive wooded deer park grazed by fallow and red deer and by a herd of rare Jacob sheep introduced by George Lucy in the 18th century.

The house is built of red brick to a pleasingly irregular E shape with great chimneys marching across the roofline and octagonal corner turrets crowned with gilded weathervanes. Charlecote seems to sum up the very essence of Elizabethan England, especially when the rose-coloured brickwork is turned to gold by the sun.

Queen Elizabeth I spent 2 nights here in 1572, celebrated in the proud display of her coat of arms over the two storeyed porch. George Lucy, a cultivated and much travelled bache-

lor, employed 'Capability' Brown to redesign the park, sweeping away the 17th century water gardens and altering the course of the River Hele so that it cascaded into the Avon within sight of the house. The balustraded formal garden, adorned with clipped yew is a 19th century addition. Steps lead to the cedar lawn with a Victorian orangery now a charming tea room.

Some of the earliest parts of the house are in the extensive outbuildings, where the stable block includes a brew-house which was in operation until the 1890s, a wash house and a coach house displaying a collection of vehicles used at Charlecote in the 19th century. But only the charming domestic gatehouse with its fretwork stone balustrade survives unaltered from the 16th century - a tantalising taste of what must have been lost.

CONTACT

Charlecote Park
Wellesbourne
Warwick
CV35 9ER

Tel: (01789) 470277

LOCATION

1m W of Wellesbourne,
5m E of Stratford-upon-Avon, 6m S of Warwick
on N side of B4086

OPENING TIMES

Summer
April - end October

Friday - Tuesday
(closed Good Friday)

11.00am - 6.00pm
Last admission 5pm.
House closed 1 - 2pm

Winter
Christmas Shop only
2 Nov - 15 Dec
Sat & Sun
1.30 - 4.30pm

ADMISSION

Adult £4.40
Child £2.20
Family £11.00

EXTRA FACILITIES
Baby changing and feeding room.

ADVICE TO COURIERS & DRIVERS
Coach parties must pre-book with the Property Administrator. For conservation reasons indoor photography is not permitted.

FACILITIES FOR THE DISABLED
Arrangements can be made to drop off disabled visitors or park near to the house. Access to all open rooms except Gatehouse Museum.

PARKING FOR COACHES AND CARS
Coaches need to pre-book.

CATERING
Morning coffees, lunches, afternoon teas in the Orangery licensed restaurant; open as property 11am - 5.30pm.

GIFT SHOP
For souvenirs and National Trust merchandise, opens as property, 11am - 5.30pm. Guide books available.

GUIDED TOURS
Evening guided tours for pre-booked parties May to September, Monday 7.30pm - 9.30pm, £4.40 including National Trust members.

SCHOOL VISITS / CHILDREN
School parties by prior arrangement with Administrator, schools base and resource book available.

CONTACT

Mr A McLaren
Coughton Court
Alcester
Warwickshire
B49 5JA

Tel: (01789) 400777
Fax: (01789) 765544

LOCATION

Located on A435,
2 miles north
of Alcester,
10 miles NW of
Stratford-on-Avon.
16 miles from
Birmingham
City Centre.

COUGHTON COURT
Alcester

COUGHTON COURT has been the home of the Thockmortons since the 15th century and the family still live here today. The magnificent Tudor gatehouse was built around 1530 with the north and south wings completed 10 or 20 years later. The gables and the first storey of these wings are of typical mid-16th century half timbered work.

Of particular interest to visitors is the Thockmorton family history from Tudor times to the present generation. On view are family portraits through the centuries, together with other family memorabilia and recent photographs. Also furniture, tapestries and porcelain.

A long standing Roman Catholic theme runs through the family history as the Thockmortons have maintained their Catholic religion until the present day. The house has a strong connection with the Gunpowder Plot and also suffered damage during the Civil War. Exhibitions on the Gunpowder Plot as well as Children's Clothes are open in 1996 (included in admission price).

Gardens

The house stands in 25 acres of gardens and grounds along with two churches and a lake. A formal garden was constructed in 1992 with designs based on an Elizabethan knot garden in the courtyard. A new garden in the old walled garden is open in 1996. Visitors can also enjoy a specially created walk beside the River Arrow, returning to the house alongside the lake.

SUITABILITY FOR OTHER EVENTS
Coughton is suitable for receptions, special dinners in the panelled dining room, filming, buffets, business meetings, fairs and garden parties. The excellent acoustics of the Saloon make it ideal for concerts, especially chamber music concerts. Weddings receptions are welcome.

EXTRA FACILITIES
Marquees can be erected on the large lawn area and there is a Grand Piano in the Saloon.

ADVICE TO COURIERS & DRIVERS
Coughton Court is located on the A435, 2 miles north of Alcester. Dogs allowed in car park only. No photography or stiletto heels in house. Unlimited parking for coaches and cars.

FACILITIES FOR THE DISABLED
Only the ground floor of the house is suitable for disabled visitors. Toilet for the disabled.

CATERING
There is a licensed restaurant open 11.00am - 5.30pm on days when the house is open. Capacity: 100 inside and 60 outside. Buffet or sit down meals can be provided, by arrangement, in the Dining Room and Saloon. Also in-house catering can be arranged for other events.

GUIDED TOURS
By arrangement.

GIFT SHOP AND PLANT CENTRE
Open when house is open.

GUIDE BOOKS
Guide book, £1.95.

OPENING TIMES

Summer
HOUSE
16 March - end April
& October
Sat & Sun
12 noon - 5.00pm

Easter
Sat - Wed (inclusive)
12 noon - 5.00pm

May - September
Daily except Thurs & Fri
12 noon - 5.00pm

House may close at 4pm some Saturdays.

GROUNDS
11.00am - 5.30pm

Winter
Closed

ADMISSION

HOUSE & GROUNDS
Adult £4.95
Child £2.50
Family* £13.50

GROUNDS ONLY
Adult £2.95
Child £1.50
Family* £7.50

* 2 adults and up to 4 children

CONFERENCE AND FUNCTION FACILITIES

ROOM	DIMENSIONS	CAPACITY	LAYOUT	POWER POINTS	SUITABLE FOR A/V
Dining Room	45' x 27'	40	Schoolroom	4	✓
		25	U-shape		
		20	Boardroom		
		55	Buffet		
		60	Theatre		
		46	Lunch/Dinner		
Saloon	60' x 36'	60	Schoolroom	6	✓
		35	U-shape		
		30	Boardroom		
		90	Buffet		
		100	Theatre		
		80	Lunch/Dinner		

THE SALOON, WHICH HAS PARTICULARLY GOOD ACOUSTICS, IS OFTEN USED FOR MUSIC RECORDING.

RAGLEY HALL
Alcester

RAGLEY HALL, home of the Earl & Countess of Yarmouth was designed by Robert Hooke in 1680 and is one of the earliest and loveliest of England's great Palladian country houses. The perfect symmetry of its architecture remains unchanged except for the massive portico added by Wyatt in 1780.

The present interior is almost entirely due to two widely separated generations: in 1750, when Francis Seymour owned Ragley, James Gibbs designed the magnificent baroque plasterwork of the Great Hall. On completion, Francis filled the Hall with French and English furniture and porcelain and had portraits of himself and his sons painted by Sir Joshua Reynolds.

The present owners are the Earl and Countess of Yarmouth who are continuing the ongoing task of restoration and renovation to maintain Ragley in its present glory. Notable also is the mural, by Graham Rust, in the South Staircase Hall which was completed in 1983.

GARDENS
The main formal garden descends in a series of wide rose covered terraces. The rest of the 27-acre garden consists of shrubs and trees interspersed with spacious lawns providing vistas across the 400-acre park.

Other features are the lake, created in 1625, the cricket pitch, still in regular use, the Adventure Playground, Maze and Sculpture Trail.

❖

CONTACT

Michael Barbour
Ragley Hall
Alcester
Warwickshire
B49 5NJ

Tel: (01789) 762090
Fax: (01789) 764791

LOCATION

From London 100 miles, M40 via Oxford and Stratford-on-Avon.

Bus: Birmingham - Evesham, from Lodge gates.

Rail: Evesham Station 9 miles.

Air: Birmingham Int'l 20 miles.

Taxi: 007 Taxi (01789) 414007

SUITABILITY FOR OTHER EVENTS
Private and corporate entertainment. Conferences and seminars, product launches, dinner parties and activity days can all be arranged. A comprehensive service is provided. Film and photographic location.

EXTRA FACILITIES
The park, lake and picnic area are also available for use.

ADVICE TO COURIERS & DRIVERS
Please advise in advance, especially if catering is required. Coach drivers admitted free and receive information pack and luncheon voucher. No dogs; no photography in house please. Guide book in French and German.

FACILITIES FOR THE DISABLED
Disabled and elderly visitors may alight at the entrance to the property, before parking in the allocated areas. Toilets for the disabled and lifts to the first floor for wheelchairs at the north side of the house.

CATERING
The licensed Terrace Tea Rooms are open 11.30am - 5pm for light lunches, snacks, afternoon teas and cakes. Groups must book. Supper and private tours can be arranged, as can Private Luncheons and Dinners in the State Dining Room or Great Hall for 2 - 150 people. Please contact the Business Manager for full details.

GIFT SHOP
Open same time as the Hall, with an excellent selection of

unusual and traditional gifts.

SCHOOL VISITS/CHILDREN
School groups are welcome, £2.00 per head. Teachers' packs and work modules available on request. Children can enjoy the Adventure Wood and Farm and Woodland Walk. Children's Guide Book.

GUIDED TOURS
Private tours by Lord Yarmouth are available outside opening hours. For a guided tour there is a cost of £9.00 per head, plus VAT. Duration of the tour is approx. 1 hour.

CONFERENCE AND FUNCTION FACILITIES

ROOM	DIMENSIONS	CAPACITY	LAYOUT	POWER POINTS	SUITABLE FOR A/V
Great Hall	70' x 40'	up to 150	Various	✓	✓
Red Saloon	30' x 40'	150	Reception	✓	
Green Drawing Rm	20' x 30'	150	Reception	✓	
Supper	45' x 22'	up to 100	Various	✓	✓

OPENING TIMES

Summer
2 April - 6 October

HOUSE
11.00am - 5.00 pm

GARDEN & PARK
10.00am - 6.00pm

Mon Bank Hols Only
(July & Aug: Park & Gardens open.)

OPEN Tues, Wed, Thur, Sat, & Sun

Fri Closed, except July & Aug, when Park & Gardens open.

Winter
6 October - 1 April
Open any time by prior arrangement.

ADMISSION

Summer
HOUSE & GARDEN
Adult £4.50
Child* £3.00
OAP £4.00
Groups**
Adult £4.00
Schoolchild* . . .£2.00
OAP £4.00

* Aged 5-16.
** Min. payment £80.00 for parties of 20 or more.

Winter
HOUSE & GARDEN
Private conducted tour by arrangement.

THE SHAKESPEARIAN PROPERTIES
Stratford-upon-Avon

Step back in time to enjoy these beautifully preserved Tudor homes connected with William Shakespeare and his family, architectural character, period furniture, special collections, attractive gardens, grounds and walks and craft displays.

In Town Houses: Shakespeare's Birthplace: This half timbered house where the dramatist was born was purchased as a national memorial in 1847. It has been a place of pilgrimage for nearly 300 yrs. Today it is approached through a Visitors' Centre, with a fine exhibition, *William Shakespeare: His Life and Background*, and the garden. **New Place/Nash's House:** The site and grounds of Shakespeare's home from 1597 until his death, with its Elizabethan style garden is approached through Nash's House adjoining, which contains exceptional furnishings and displays of the history of Stratford. **Hall's Croft:** A delightful Elizabethan town house,

once the home of Dr Hall, Shakespeare's physician son-in-law. Exceptional furniture and paintings. Exhibition on Tudor Medicine and fine walled garden. Meals and refreshments available which can also be served in the beautiful garden.

Out of Town Houses: Anne Hathaway's Cottage, Shottery: This famous, picturesque thatched cottage was Anne's home before her marriage to Shakespeare. Cottage garden and Shakespeare Tree Garden as well as a Garden Shop and attractive Shottery Brook and Jubilee Walks. Summer Tea Garden. **Mary Arden's House and The Shakespeare Countryside Museum, Wilmcote:** Tudor farmstead (home of Shakespeare's mother) with old outbuildings and nearby Glebe Farm containing exhibits illustrating country life over 400 yrs. Gypsy caravans, dovecote, duck pond, rare breeds, field walk, and all day displays of falconry. Refreshments & picnic area.

❖

SUITABILITY FOR OTHER EVENTS
Conference and function facilities, details upon request.

EXTRA FACILITIES
For those needing transport there is a regular guided bus tour service connecting the town properties with Anne Hathaway's Cottage and Mary Arden's House.

ADVICE TO COURIERS & DRIVERS
No photography inside the properties. Guide dogs only.

FACILITIES FOR THE DISABLED
Disabled toilets at all properties. Naturally difficult levels everywhere but much for disabled to enjoy at Mary Arden's House.

PARKING FOR COACHES & CARS
The Trust provides a free coach terminal for delivery and pick-up of groups, maximum stay 30 minutes at Shakespeare's Birthplace. Parking available at Anne Hathaway's Cottage and Mary Arden's House.

CATERING
Refreshments available on site or within close proximity.

GIFT SHOP
At Shakespeare's Birthplace, Hall's Croft, Anne Hathaway's Cottage and Mary Arden's House.

SCHOOL VISITS / CHILDREN
Educational group visits to all properties. Student/school groups, one member of staff to 10 pupils.

GUIDED TOURS
By special arrangement.

GUIDE BOOK
Available at various properties, The Shakespeare Bookshop offers a wide range of specialist books.

CONTACT

David J Atkinson
Administrator
The Shakespeare
Birthplace Trust
Henley Street
Stratford-upon-Avon
CV37 6QW

Tel: (01789) 204016

Fax: (01789) 296083

LOCATION

2 hours from London
1 hour from
Birmingham.
Direct rail services from
London (Paddington)
4m from M40
junction 15 and well
signed from all
approaches.

OPENING TIMES

Summer
20 Mar - 19 October
Mon - Sat: 9.30am - 5pm
Sun: 10.00am - 5pm
(Closed until 1.30pm
on 1 Jan & Good Fri)

Winter
1 Jan - 19 Mar
20 Oct - 31 Dec
Mon - Sat: 10am - 4pm
Sun: 10.30am - 4pm

Closed 24, 25, 26 Dec
and until 1.30pm on 1
Jan & Good Fri.

NB. Shakespeare's Birthplace & Anne Hathaway's Cottage open at 9am summer, 9.30am winter.

ADMISSION

*Shakespeare's
Birthplace
  Adult £3.30
  Child £1.50
  Family (2+2/3) .£8.50
*New Place / Nash's
House or Hall's Croft
  Adult £2.00
  Child £1.00
*Anne Hathaway's
Cottage
  Adult £2.40
  Child £1.20
*Mary Arden's House
  Adult £3.30
  Child £1.50
  Family (2+2/3) .£8.50
The Shakespeare
Heritage Trail options:
All 3 in-town properties
  Adult £6.00
  Child £2.75
  OAP/Student . . .£5.00
All five properties
  Adult £9.00
  Child £4.00
  OAP/Student . . .£7.50

Accompanied groups 20+, 10% discount, except at Birthplace.

UPTON HOUSE
Banbury

CONTACT

Upton House
Banbury
Oxfordshire
OX15 6HT

Tel: (01295) 670266

UPTON HOUSE stands less than a mile to the south of the battlefield of Edgehill and there has been a house on this site since the Middle Ages. The present house was built at the end of the 17th century and remodelled 1927 - 29 for the 2nd Viscount Bearsted.

He was a great collector of paintings, china and many other valuable works of art, and adapted the building to display them. The paintings include works by El Greco, Bruegel, Bosch, Memling, Guardi, Hogarth and Stubbs. The rooms provide an admirable setting for the china collection which includes Chelsea figures and superb examples of beautifully decorated Sèvres porcelain. The set of 17th century Brussels tapestries depict the Holy Roman Emperor Maximilian I's boar and stag hunts.

Recent extensive renovation work has resulted in the reinstatement of the 30ft high Sports Room which was originally created for the 2nd Viscount and allows the magnificent full length portraits to be hung and viewed at their best.

GARDEN

The outstanding garden is of interest throughout the season with terraces descending into a deep valley from the main lawn. There are herbaceous borders, the national collection of asters, over an acre of kitchen garden, a water garden laid out in the 1930s and pools stocked with ornamental fish.

Over a mile from the house, but just visible from the west end of the terrace on the garden front, is the lower lake which was formed in the mid-18th century after the fashion of 'Capability' Brown. A small temple with Doric columns and pediment sits in the centre of the one straight edge.

OPENING TIMES

Summer
1 April - 31 October
Sat - Wed inclusive of
Bank Holiday Mondays.
2.00 - 6.00pm
Last admission 5.30pm

Entry to House, tea-room & shop is by timed tickets at peak times on Sun & BH Mons, delays possible.

ADMISSION

Adult £4.80
Child £2.40
Family £12.00
GARDEN
Adult £2.40

LOCATION

On A422, 7m NW of Banbury
12m SE of Stratford-upon-Avon

Rail: Banbury Station 7 miles

SUITABILITY FOR OTHER EVENTS
For details of concerts and events please send a stamped, addressed envelope to the Administrator.

EXTRA FACILITIES
Parent and baby room.

ADVICE TO COURIERS & DRIVERS
Tour time approximately 1 hour. No indoor photography for conservation reasons. Parties must pre-book. Parking for coaches in the main car park.

FACILITIES FOR THE DISABLED
A wheelchair is available for use in the House. Access to all ground floor rooms and lavatory. Motorised buggy to/from lower garden.

CATERING
Tea room in the House.

GIFT SHOP
Selling a range of National Trust goods, including guide books.

GUIDED TOURS
Evening guided tours by written appointment (no reduction).

WARWICK CASTLE
Warwick

LOCATION

2m from M40 J15.
Birmingham 35mins
Leeds 2 hrs 5mins
London, 1 hr 30mins
Manchester, 1 hr 30mins
Rail: Intercity from Ldn
Euston to Coventry.
Direct service from
Marylebone &
Paddington,
direct to Warwick.

This dramatic fortress rises majestically from the banks of the River Avon, only a few miles from Shakespeare's Stratford on a site first fortified by William the Conqueror in 1068. From its soaring towers to the depths of the Dungeon, Warwick Castle epitomises the power and grandeur of the mediaeval fortress. For centuries it was home to the mighty Earls of Warwick, the most powerful noblemen in England.

The exciting new attraction *'Kingmaker, a preparation for battle 1471'* brings to life the mediaeval household making ready. As you wander through the stable, the smithy, the armoury, wardrobe and treasury, you can touch the armour and weapons and sense the tension mounting as Kingmaker's household help him prepare for battle.

The 14th century Great Hall lies at the heart of the Castle, the magnificent State Rooms contain an outstanding collection of furniture, paintings and tapestries.

"A Royal Weekend Party, 1898' recreates an actual weekend in 1898 with guests, including a young Winston Churchill and the future King Edward VII, when Victorian aristocracy met and dined in the elegant surroundings of the Castle.

Visit the 60 acres of Grounds and Gardens landscaped by Lancelot 'Capability' Brown including the Victorian Rose Garden and Peacock Garden where you can also see the roaming peacocks.

Special events from jousting to foot combat take place every weekend during the summer months and half term holidays.

SUITABILITY FOR OTHER EVENTS
Ideal location for corporate events, evening, receptions and Kingmaker's Feasts.

ADVICE TO COURIERS & DRIVERS
Free coach parking, free admission and luncheon voucher for coach driver.

FACILITIES FOR THE DISABLED
Car parking spaces in stables car park, free admission for registered blind and wheelchair bound visitors.

PARKING FOR COACHES & CARS
Limited free car parking in main car park.

CATERING
The catering outlets offer menus to suit all budgets, ranging from cream teas to three course hot meals. During the summer there is an open air barbecue and refreshment pavilions in the grounds.

GIFT SHOP
The four gift shops offer a superb range of interesting, quality gifts and souvenirs.

SCHOOL VISITS / CHILDREN
Warwick Castle makes an ideal school visit being a superb example of military architecture dating back to the Norman Conquest and with elegant interiors up to Victorian times. Group rates apply. Education packs are available.

GUIDE BOOK
A fascinating, beautifully photographed guide book for £3.00. In English, French, German, Japanese, Spanish and Italian.

GUIDED TOURS
Guided tours available for groups. Guides available in every room.

OPENING TIMES

Summer
April - October
10am - 6pm
Last Admission 5.30pm

Winter
November - March
10am - 5pm
Last admission 4.30pm

ADMISSION

Adult £8.75
Child* £5.25
OAP £6.25
Student £6.50
Family** £24.50

Groups
Adult £6.95
Child £4.50
OAP £5.50
Student £5.95

* 4 - 16 inclusive
** 2 adults & 2 children

CONFERENCE AND FUNCTION FACILITIES

ROOM	DIMENSIONS	CAPACITY	LAYOUT
Great Hall	61' x 34'	120	Dinner
		230	Reception
State Dining Room	40' x 25'	30	Dinner
Undercroft	46' x 26'	120	Kingmaker's Feast
		100	Dinner
Conservatory		30 - 70	Reception
		200	Recept with Awning
		40 - 60	Dinner
Stables Hayloft	44' x 19'	30 - 70	Conference
		100	Reception
Marquees		150 - 2000	Dinner/Reception

ARBURY HALL   🏛   See Page 205 for full page entry.

BADDESLEY CLINTON 🌿

OPEN

2 Mar - end Sept
Wed - Sun &
Bank Hol Mons
(Closed Good Fri)
2 - 6pm
Oct: Wed - Sun
2 - 5 pm
March '97
Wed - Sun
2 - 6 pm
Grounds open
from 12 noon

Last admission to
house, shop and
Restaurant ¹/₂ hr
before closing

Tel: 01564 783294

LAPWORTH, KNOWLE, SOLIHULL B93 0DQ

Owner: *The National Trust*   **Contact:** *The Administrator*

A romantically sited medieval moat manor house, dating from 14th century; little changed since 1634; family portraits, priest holes; garden; ponds and lake walk.
Location: ³/₄ miles west of A4141 Warwick/Birmingham road at Chadwick End.
Admission: Adult £4.50, Child £2.25, Family £11.25
Grounds, Restaurant & Shop: £2.25.

CHARLECOTE PARK   See Page 206 for full page entry.

COUGHTON COURT   See Page 207 for full page entry.

FARNBOROUGH HALL 🌿

OPEN

House, Grounds and
Terrace Walk

April - end Sept
Wed & Sat
also 5 & 6 May
2 - 6pm

Terrace Walk only
Thur & Fri
2 - 6pm
Last Adm. 5.30pm

Tel: 01295 690202

BANBURY, OXFORDSHIRE OX17 1DU

Owner: *The National Trust*   **Contact:** *The Administrator*

A classical mid-18th century stone house, home of the Holbech family for 300 years; notable plasterwork, the entrance hall, staircase and 2 principal rooms are shown; the grounds contain charming 18th century temples, a ²/₃ mile terrace walk and an obelisk.
Location: 6m N of Banbury, ¹/₂ m W of A423.
Admission: House, Grounds & Terrace Walk: £2.70. Garden & Terrace Walk: £1.50
Terrace walk only (Thur & Fri) £1.00. Children Half price.

HONINGTON HALL 🏛

OPEN

June - August
Wednesdays only

Bank Holiday
Mondays

2.30 - 5pm

Parties at other
times by
appointment.

Tel: 01608 661434
Fax: 01608 663717

SHIPSTON-ON-STOUR, WARWICKSHIRE CV36 5AA

Owner: *Benjamin Wiggin Esq*   **Contact:** *Benjamin Wiggin Esq*

This fine Caroline manor house was built in the early 1680's for Henry Parker in mellow brickwork and stone quoins and window dressings. Modified in 1751 when an octagonal saloon was inserted. The interior was also lavishly restored around this time and contains exceptional mid-Georgian plasterwork. Set in 15 acres of grounds.
Location: 10m S of Stratford-upon-Avon. 1¹/₂m N of Shipston-on-Stour. Take A3400 towards Stratford, then signed right to Honington.
Admission: Adult £2.75, Child £1.00.

KENILWORTH CASTLE ⊞

OPEN

1 Apr - 30 Sept
Daily
10am - 6pm
1 Oct - 31 Oct
10am - 6m or
dusk if earlier.
1 Nov - 31 Mar
10am - 4pm
Closed 24 - 26 Dec
& 1 Jan.

Tel: 01926 52078

KENILWORTH, WARWICKSHIRE CV8 1NE

Owner: *English Heritage*   **Contact:** *The Custodian*

Kenilworth is the largest castle ruin in England, the former stronghold of great Lords and Kings. Its massive walls of warm red sandstone tower over the peaceful Warwickshire landscape. The Earl of Leicester entertained Queen Elizabeth I with 'Princely Pleasures' during her 19 day visit. He built a new wing for the Queen to lodge in and organised all manner of lavish and costly festivities. The Great Hall where Gloriana dined with her courtiers still stands and John of Gaunt's hall is second only in width and grandeur to Westminster Hall. If you climb to the top of the tower beside the hall you will be rewarded by fine views over the rolling wooded countryside.
Location: On Western Edge of Kenilworth, off B4103.
Admission: Adult £2.50, Conc £1.90, Child £1.30. 15% discount for parties of 11+.

LORD LEYCESTER HOSPITAL   **Tel:** 01926 491422

High Street, Warwick, Warwickshire CV34 4BH
Owner: The Governors of Lord Leycester Hospital   **Contact:** Capt D I Rhodes
Location: 1m N of M40, J15 on A429.
Opening Times: Tues - Sun: 10am - 5pm (Oct - Mar 10am - 4pm).
Closed Good Fri and Christmas Day.
Admission: Adult £2.50, Child £1.25, Conc £1.75. Groups of 20+ adults 5% discount.

KEY TO SYMBOLS: 🌿 THE NATIONAL TRUST   ⊞ ENGLISH HERITAGE   🏛 HISTORIC HOUSES ASSOCIATION

PACKWOOD HOUSE

OPEN

Apr - end Sept.

Wed - Sun &
Bank Hol Mons
2 - 6pm

Gardens:
1.30 - 6pm

Closed Good Friday

Oct: Wed - Sun
12.30 - 4.30pm

Last adm. $^1/_2$hr
before closing.

Tel: 01564 782024

LAPWORTH, SOLIHULL B94 6AT

Owner: The National Trust   *Contact:* The Administrator

Originally a 16th century house, Packwood has been much altered over the years and today is the vision of Graham Baron Ash who recreated a Jacobean house in the 1920s and 30s. A fine collection of 16th century textiles and furniture. Important gardens with renowned herbaceous border and famous yew garden based on the Sermon on the Mount.

Location: 2m E of Hockley Heath (on A3400), 11m SE of Central Birmingham (139: SP174722).

Admission: Adult £3.80, Child £1.90, Family £9.50.

RAGLEY HALL 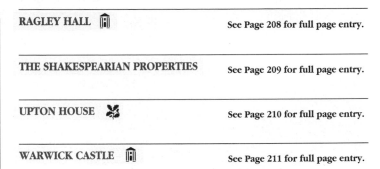   See Page 208 for full page entry.

THE SHAKESPEARIAN PROPERTIES   See Page 209 for full page entry.

UPTON HOUSE   See Page 210 for full page entry.

WARWICK CASTLE   See Page 211 for full page entry.

Where to Stay

For Private Accommodation and Johansens recommended Hotels, see Accommodation Section.

Warwick Castle.

SPECIAL EVENTS

◇ **RAGLEY HALL** Ragley Horse Trials	5 – 6 MAY	
◇ **ARBURY HALL** Arbury Motor Transport Spectacular	2 JUNE	
◇ **ARBURY HALL** Rainbow Craft Fair	15 – 16 JUNE	
◇ **RAGLEY HALL** Carmina Burana Concert (outdoors)	30 JUNE	
◇ **RAGLEY HALL** Transport Show	14 JULY	

◇ **RAGLEY HALL** Fireworks and Laser Symphony Concert (outdoors)	3 AUGUST
◇ **RAGLEY HALL** Warwickshire and West Midlands Game Fair	17 – 18 AUGUST
◇ **ARBURY HALL** Rainbow Craft Fair	31 AUGUST – 1 SEPTEMBER
◇ **ARBURY HALL** Warwickshire Country Show	DATE TO BE ANNOUNCED

For National Trust and English Heritage Events see separate section.

HAGLEY HALL
Stourbridge

HAGLEY HALL set in 350 acres of landscaped park where deer roam freely, offers conference facilities and corporate hospitality in historic surroundings. 20 - 300 guests can be catered for in the house and with the use of marquees numbers are virtually unlimited.

The house is offered on an exclusive basis and the stunning state apartments may be used in any combination giving great flexibility for conferences, product launches, exhibitions, lunches, country sporting days, dinner and wedding receptions.

The elegant Palladian house, completed in 1760, contains some of the finest examples of Italian plasterwork. Hagley's rich Rococo decoration is a remarkable tribute to the artistic achievement of the great 18th Century amateurs and still remains the much loved home of the 11th Viscount Cobham.

Our catering team offer a high standard of classic cuisine and excellent service. Events can be tailor made to suit your requirements and budget.

CONTACT

Mrs. Lesley Haynes
Hagley Hall
Stourbridge
West Midlands
DY9 9LG

Tel: (01562) 882408

Fax: (01562) 882632

LOCATION

Easily accessible from all areas of the country.

Close to the M42, M40, M6 and only 5 miles from junctions 3 and 4 of the M5.

Only 25 minutes from Birmingham International Airport, Railway Station and the NEC, only 12 miles from Birmingham City Centre.

OPENING TIMES

6 - 12 & 14 - 20 Apr
25 - 28 May
20 July - 31 August
2.00 - 5.00pm

ADMISSION

Adult £3.50
Child * £1.50
OAP £2.50

* Under 16 yrs.

SUITABILITY FOR OTHER EVENTS
Available for themed entertaining including murder mystery and casinos, as well as for filming.

EXTRA FACILITIES
Extensive parkland for sporting activity days including shooting, driving and team building events. Unlimited car parking.

ADVICE TO COURIERS & DRIVERS
Please treat the Hall and contents with care.

PARKING
Unlimited parking for coaches and cars.

FACILITIES FOR THE DISABLED
Disabled and elderly visitors may alight at the entrance. No toilet facilities for disabled.

CATERING
As well as our in-house catering service, we offer a unique outside catering service. Afternoon tea available during the summer.

GUIDED TOURS
Guides conduct visitors in groups. If requested the owner may meet groups. Average time for tour 50 minutes. Guided tours are available during the summer opening times and for function guests.

GUIDE BOOKS
Full-colour guide book available.

SCHOOL VISITS / CHILDREN
By arrangement.

CONFERENCE AND FUNCTION FACILITIES

ROOM	DIMENSIONS	CAPACITY	LAYOUT	POWER POINTS	SUITABLE FOR A/V
Gallery	85' x 17'	130 / 160	Dining / Theatre	8	✓
Crimson Room	23' x 31'	60	Dining / Theatre	6	✓
State Dining Room	34' x 27'	80 / 100	Dining / Theatre	10	✓
Westcote	31' x 20'	60	Dining / Theatre	6	✓

ASTON HALL

Tel: 0121 327 0062

Aston Park, Birmingham, West Midlands B6 6JD
Owner: Birmingham City Council   **Contact:** Ms L Flanaghan
Fine Jacobean mansion with panelled long gallery and outstanding plasterwork. Over 20 period rooms.
Location: 2 ¹/₂m N of Birmingham near Villa Park.
Opening Times: 1 April - 31 Oct: 2 - 5pm.
Admission: No charge at present.

THE BIRMINGHAM BOTANICAL GARDENS AND GLASSHOUSES

OPEN

Daily

9.00am - Dusk
(7.00pm latest
except pre-booked
parties)

Sundays opening
time 10.00 am.

Tel: 0121 454 1860

WESTBOURNE ROAD, EDGBASTON, BIRMINGHAM B15 3TR

Owner: Birmingham Botanical & Horticultural Society   **Contact:** *Mrs. N. Bate*

Tropical, Mediterranean and Desert Glasshouses contain a wide range of exotic and economic flora. 15 acres of beautiful gardens with the finest collection of plants in the Midlands. Home of the National Bonsai Collection. Children's adventure playground, Aviaries, Gallery, Gift Shop and Plant Centre. Refreshments.
Location: 2 mls W of city centre. Follow signs to Edgbaston then brown tourist signs.
Admission: Adult £3.50 (£3.80 on Suns & Bank Hols), Concessions £1.90
Children under 5 Free. Reduced rates for parties of 11+.

BLAKESLEY HALL

Tel: 0121 783 2193 **Fax:** 0121 236 1766

Blakesley Road, Yardley, Birmingham B25 8RN
Owner: Birmingham City Council   **Contact:** The Administrator
Late 16th century timber framed yeoman's house furnished according to an inventory of 1684.
Location: South East Birmingham.
Opening Times: April - October: 2 - 5pm.
Admission: Free. Groups by appointment.

COVENTRY CATHEDRAL

Tel: 01203 227597

Coventry, West Midlands.
Owner: Provost & Canons of Coventry Cathedral   **Contact:** The Visits Secretary
The remains of the blackened medieval Cathedral, bombed in 1940, stand beside the new Cathedral by Basil Spence, consecrated in 1962. Modern works of art include huge tapestry by Graham Sutherland, stained glass window by John Piper and bronze sculpture by Epstein. 'Reconciliation' statue by Josefina de Vasconcellos.
Location: City Centre.
Opening Times: Easter - Sept: from 9.30am. Oct - Easter: 9.30am - 5pm.
Admission: Donation £2.00 for Cathedral.

HAGLEY HALL

See Page 214 for full page entry.

HALESOWEN ABBEY

Tel: 01203 227597

Halesowen, Birmingham, West Midlands
Owner: English Heritage   **Contact:** The Custodian
Remains of an abbey founded by King John in the 13th century, now incorporated into a 19th century farm. Parts of the church and the monk's infirmary can still be made out.
Location: Off A456 Kidderminster road, 6 miles W of Birmingham City Centre.
Opening Times: Jul - Aug: Weekends only 10am - 6pm. Lunchtime closure 1 - 2pm.
Admission: Adult £1.00, Child 50p, Conc 80p.

RYTON ORGANIC GARDENS

Tel: 01203 303517 **Fax:** 01203 639229

Ryton-on-Dunsmore, Coventry, West Midlands CV8 3LG
Owner: Henry Doubleday Research Association   **Contact:** J Gear
The Midlands' most talked about gardens. 8 acres of beautiful and informative gardens including herbs, shrubs, flowers, rare and unusual vegetables, all organically grown. Enlarged award-winning restaurant and shop.
Location: 5m Southeast of Coventry off A45 on the road to Wolston.
Opening Times: Daily except during Christmas week: 10am - 5.30pm.
Admission: Adult £2.50, Child (5 - 16) £1.25, OAP £1.75, Family £6.50

WIGHTWICK MANOR

Tel: 01902 761108 **Fax:** 01902 764663

Wightwick Bank, Wolverhampton, West Midlands WV6 8EE
Owner: The National Trust   **Contact:** The Property Manager
Begun in 1887, the house is a notable example of the influence of William Morris, with many original Morris wallpapers and fabrics. Also of interest are Pre-Raphaelite pictures, Kempe glass and de Morgan ware. The 17 acre Victorian/Edwardian garden originally designed by Thomas Mawson has formal beds, Pergola, yew hedges, topiary and terraces, woodland and two pools.
Location: 3m W of Wolverhampton, up Wightwick Bank (A454), beside the Mermaid Inn.
Opening Times: 2 Mar - 31 Dec: Thur & Sat 2.30 - 5.30pm (Last entry 5pm) Admission by timed ticket. Guided groups through ground floor, freeflow upstairs. Minimum tour time approx. 1 hr. 30 min. Also open Bank Holiday Sat, Sun and Mon 2.30 - 5.30pm (last entry 5pm) - ground floor only, no guided tours. Pre-booked parties Wed and Thurs.
Admission: Adult £4.80, Child £2.40. Garden only: £2.20.

BOWOOD HOUSE
Calne

BOWOOD is the family home of the Earl and Countess of Shelburne, the Earl being the eldest son of the Marquess of Lansdowne. Begun c.1720 for the Bridgeman family, the House was purchased by the 2nd Earl of Shelburne in 1754 and completed soon afterwards. Part of the House was demolished in 1955, leaving a perfectly proportioned Georgian home, over half of which is open to visitors. Robert Adam's magnificent Diocletian wing contains a splendid library, the Laboratory where Joseph Priestly discovered oxygen gas in 1774, the Orangery - now a Picture Gallery, the Chapel and a Sculpture Gallery in which some of the famous Lansdowne Marbles are displayed. Among the family treasures shown in the numerous Exhibition Rooms are Georgian costumes, including Lord Byron's Albanian dress; Victoriana; Indiana (the 5th Marquess was Viceroy 1888-94); and superb collections of watercolours, miniatures and jewellery. The House is set in one of the most beautiful parks in England. Over 2,000 acres of gardens and grounds were landscaped by 'Capability' Brown between 1762 and 1768, and are embellished with a Doric Temple, a cascade, a pinetum and an arboretum. The Rhododendron Gardens are open for six weeks during May and June. All the walks have seats.

❖

CONTACT

The Administrator
Bowood House and
Gardens
Calne
Wiltshire
SN11 0LZ

Tel: (01249) 812102

LOCATION

From London M4,
Junct. 17, 2 hours.

Swindon 17 miles,
Bristol 26 miles and
Bath 16 miles.

Bus: to the gate,
1½ miles through
park to House.

Rail: Chippenham
Station 5 miles.

Taxi: AA Taxis,
Chippenham 657777.

SUITABILITY FOR OTHER EVENTS
Receptions, film location.

EXTRA FACILITIES
2,000 acre park, 40 acre lake, massive adventure playground, golf course and Country Club.

ADVICE TO COURIERS & DRIVERS
2-3 hours should be allowed to visit the house, gardens and grounds. We recommend parties who require lunch or tea to book in advance. No dogs allowed. Parking for over 1,000 cars and unlimited parking for coaches, 400 yards from the House.

FACILITIES FOR THE DISABLED
Disabled and elderly visitors may alight at the House before parking in the allocated area. There are toilet facilities for the disabled in the House and in the Gift Shop.

CATERING
Both The Bothy (self-service light snacks, capacity 50) and the Restaurant (waitress-service, capacity 85) are available. Pre-booked prices range from £3.95 to £6.75 for a two course lunch and coffee; £6.65 to £10.30 for the daily buffet, dessert and coffee; £2.80 for a cream tea. Catering facilities can be provided for functions, for 45 to 85 persons.

GUIDED TOURS
Groups can be met and given an introductory talk, and if requested can be given a guided tour, for which there is an additional charge. Average time for tour of House 1¼ hrs.

GIFT SHOP
Bowood souvenirs, china, toiletries etc. as well as a wide range of plants. Kitchen Shop open in the House.

GUIDE BOOKS
Colour guide book, £2.50. Translation sheets available in French, German, Japanese, Dutch and Spanish. Comprehensive guide to Bowood's trees and shrubs £1.50, Catalogue of the Collection of paintings £1.50.

SCHOOL VISITS/CHILDREN
School parties are welcome. Special guide books for children. Educational visit with teacher's notes for pre-, during and post-school visit, for both primary and secondary schools. Many picnic areas. Exciting and unique Adventure Playground.

GOLF COURSE & COUNTRY CLUB
In May 1992, the Bowood Golf and Country Club opened. The 18 hole course and practice area covers two hundred acres in the western corner of Capability Brown's park. Access to the course and club house is through Sir Charles Barry's famous 'golden gates' in Derry Hill. The course is open to all players holding a current handicap.

OPENING TIMES

HOUSE & GARDENS

30 March - 3 November
Daily
11.00am - 6.00pm
(or dusk if earlier)

RHODODENDRON WALKS

Daily for 6 weeks during
May & June
11.00am - 6.00pm

ADMISSION

HOUSE & GARDENS
Adult £4.80
Child* £2.60
OAP £4.10

Groups (min 20 people)
Adult £4.30
Child* £2.30
OAP £3.60

RHODODENDRON WALKS
Adult £2.50
Child* . . . . F.O.C.
OAP £2.50

* Aged 5-15.

CORSHAM COURT
Corsham

CORSHAM COURT is an Elizabethan house of 1582 and was bought by Paul Methuen in the mid-18th century, to house a collection of 16th and 17th century Italian and Flemish master paintings and statuary. In the middle of the 19th century, the House was enlarged to receive a second collection, purchased in Florence, principally of fashionable Italian masters and stone inlaid furniture.

Paul Methuen (1723-95) was a great-grandson of Paul Methuen of Bradford-on-Avon and cousin of John Methuen, ambassador and negotiator of the Methuen Treaty of 1703 with Portugal which permitted export of British woollens to Portugal and allowed a preferential 33$^1/_3$% duty discount on Portuguese wines - bringing about a major change in British drinking habits.

The architects involved in the alterations to the House and Park were Lancelot 'Capability' Brown in the 1760s, John Nash in 1800 and Thomas Bellamy in 1845-9. Brown set the style by retaining the Elizabethan Stables and Riding School, but rebuilding the Gateway, retaining the gabled Elizabethan stone front and doubling the gabled wings at either end and, inside, by designing the East Wing as Stateroom-Picture Galleries. Nash's work has now largely disappeared, but Bellamy's stands fast, notably in the Hall and Staircase.

The State Rooms, including the Music Room and Dining Room, provide the setting for the outstanding collection of over 150 paintings, statuary, bronzes and furniture. The collection includes work by such names as Chippendale, the Adams brothers, Van Dyck, Reni, Rosa, Rubens, Lippi, Reynolds, Romney and a pianoforte by Clementi.

GARDENS

'Capability' Brown planned to include a lake, avenues and specimen trees such as the Oriental Plane now with a 200 yard perimeter. The Gardens, designed not only by Brown but also by Repton, contain a Ha-ha, herbaceous borders, secluded gardens, lawns, a rose garden, a lily pool, a stone bath house and the Bradford Porch.

❖

SUITABILITY FOR OTHER EVENTS
Corsham is suitable for filming.

ADVICE TO COURIERS & DRIVERS
Bring coach parties up to the front door. PLEASE BOOK coach parties in advance. No photography, no umbrellas, dogs must be kept on leads in the garden.

FACILITIES FOR THE DISABLED
Disabled and elderly visitors may alight at the entrance to the property, before parking in the allocated areas.

PARKING FOR COACHES & CARS
Capacity of the Car Park: 400 cars, 120 yards from the House and coaches may park at the door to the House.

CATERING
No catering is provided. Audrey's Tea Rooms are recommended. Tel: Corsham (01249) 714931.

GUIDED TOURS
These are offered for up to 50-55 people on any one tour. If requested the owner may meet the group visiting the House. Approximate duration of the tour is 1$^1/_2$ hours.

GIFT SHOP
A sales area stocking postcards, slides and books. Colour guide book, for sale or hire.

SCHOOL VISITS/CHILDREN
School visits can be arranged: rate negotiable. A guide will be provided.

CONTACT

Corsham Court
Corsham
Wiltshire
SN13 0BZ

Tel: (01249) 701610
or (01249) 701611

LOCATION

Corsham is signposted from the M4.
From Edinburgh, A1, M62, M6, M5, M4, 8 hrs.
From London, M4, 2$^1/_4$ hrs.
From Chester, M6, M5, M4, 4 hours.

Motorway: M4 Junct. 17, 9 miles.

Rail: Chippenham Station 6 miles.

Taxi: (01249) 715959.

OPENING TIMES

Summer
Good Friday - 30 Sept

Daily except Mons
2.00 - 6.00pm
Last admission 5.30pm

Open Bank Hol Mons only.

Winter
1 Oct - Good Friday

Daily except
Mons and Fris
2.00 - 4.30pm
Last admission 4pm.

NB. Closed December

ADMISSION

All Year

HOUSE & GARDEN
Adult £3.50
Child* £2.00
OAP(U.K) £3.00

Groups**
Adult £3.00
Child*. £1.50

GARDEN ONLY
Adult £2.00
Child*. £1.00
OAP £1.50
Groups**
Per person. £1.50

* Aged 5 - 16yrs.
** Min payment £40.00

LONGLEAT HOUSE
Warminster

LONGLEAT HOUSE lies in a sheltered valley amidst rolling parkland, landscaped by 'Capability' Brown in the late 18th century. The magnificent Elizabethan property, built by Sir John Thynne with the help of the celebrated mason-architect Robert Smythson was completed in 1580 and has been the home of the same family ever since.

The house contains many treasures, including paintings by Titian, Tintoretto, Wootton, a fine Louis XVI desk and a fabulous silver table centrepiece weighing 1,000 ounces. Between 1801 and 1811 the architect Jeffrey Wyatville designed the magnificent stable block and also carried out many alterations to the House. However, the Great Hall was not altered and remains the same fine Elizabethan room as Sir John left it in 1580.

The formal gardens contain a beautiful Orangery and a delightful boathouse. In 1949 Longleat became the first Stately Home to open to the public thus starting a new industry in Britain. The first Safari Park outside Africa in 1966. *The Life and Times of Henry Lord Bath* – A Memorial Exhibition - shows the long and active life of the 6th Marquess and is told through this personal collection from early childhood memories on the Estate, through World War Two to his twilight years. Following his fascination for Churchill, he amassed one of the finest collections of Churchill memorabilia, which is housed in this moving and nostalgic exhibition. Lord Bath's Murals are a recent addition to the House continuing the tradition of each generation adding to and embellishing their family home.

❖

PASSPORT TICKETS
Apr - Sept. includes Safari Park, Longleat House, Dolls Houses, Boat Ride, Lord Bath's Bygones, VIP Vehicles, Doctor Who, Maze, Butterfly Garden, Postman Pat's Village, Railway, Pets Corner, Simulator, Adventure Castle, Memorial Exhibition, Grounds and Garden.

SUITABILITY FOR OTHER EVENTS
Fashion shows, concerts, archery, equestrian events, garden parties, shows, rallies, filming, promotions, product launches.

EXTRA FACILITIES
Available for use: Grand Piano, Parkland, Helicopter Pad. Specialist Lectures on the property and its history can be arranged by prior appointment for up to 50. Rooms can be hired.

ADVICE TO COURIERS & DRIVERS
Facilities available for coach drivers.

CATERING
There is a cellar Café (capacity 80). Parties can be booked in advance for tea and other meals. Menus are available on request. Cream Teas are available, as well as lunch from £5.00 and sandwiches and snacks from £1.20.

GUIDED TOURS
For groups of up to 20 people. Please pre-book tours when required in French, Spanish or German. Average time per tour is one hour.

GIFT SHOP
Open daily except 25 December from 10am - 6pm. in Summer and 10am - 4pm in winter. Wide range of souvenirs available.

GUIDE BOOKS
A full-colour guide book with photographs is available. French and German material on request.

SCHOOL VISITS / CHILDREN
Groups are welcome with 1 teacher given free entry per 8 children. Full group and education pack available on request.

CONTACT

Customer Services Dept.
The Estate Office
Longleat
Warminster
Wiltshire
BA12 7NW

Tel: (01985) 844400

Fax: (01985) 844885

LOCATION

London 2 hrs.
M3, A303, A36, A362.
Midway between
Warminster and Frome
or from North
West M4 exit 18.

Rail: mainline
Paddington to
Westbury 12 miles.

Air: Bristol airport
30 miles.

Taxi: Beeline Taxis
(01985) 212215

OPENING TIMES

Summer
16 March - 3 November
House, Grounds and
Safari Park
Daily 10.00am - 6.00pm
Last admission 5.30pm
or sunset if earlier.

Other attractions:
11.00am - 6.00pm.

Winter
November - March
(except Christmas Day)
House, Grounds only
Daily 10.00am - 4.00pm
by guided tour.
Times will vary.

ADMISSION

Summer
1996 prices -
phone for further info.

HOUSE ONLY
  Adult £4.80
  Child* £3.50
  OAP £4.00
Groups (min 15 people)
  Adult £3.25
  Child* £1.75
  OAP £2.75

GROUNDS ONLY
  Adult £2.00
  Child* £0.50
  OAP 1.50
Groups of over 15 Free.

PASSPORT TICKETS
(see left under photo)
  Adult £11.00
  Child* £9.00
  OAP £9.00
Groups (min 15 people)
  Adult £8.50
  Child* £7.00
  OAP £7.00
*Age 4 -14.

Winter
House only open.
Rates as summer.

CONFERENCE AND FUNCTION FACILITIES

ROOM	DIMENSIONS	CAPACITY	LAYOUT	POWER POINTS	SUITABLE FOR A/V
Green Library	42' x 22'	90	Various	✓	✓
		80	Dinner/Dance (with Great Hall)		
Great Hall	48' 9" x 27'	150	Various	✓	✓

SHELDON MANOR
Chippenham

CONTACT

Mrs M Gibbs
Sheldon Manor
Chippenham
Wiltshire
SN14 0RG

Tel: (01249) 653120

Fax: (01249) 461097

LOCATION

From London: M4 to
Exit 17, 4 miles. A429
towards Chippenham,
A420 towards Bristol.
Follow signposts.

Rail: Chippenham
Station 3 miles.

Bus: Chippenham Bus
Station 3 miles.

Taxi: Webbs,
(01249) 660022.

The surviving manor house of a long-gone medieval village has a great Porch described by Pevsner as 'astounding'. The parvise is late 13th century, the east wing dates from 1431 and the west wing was rebuilt in 1659. The oak staircase with carved open finials and dog-gate is contemporary with this. The Hall and Dining Room are oak-panelled and the main bedroom has William and Mary panelling.

The stone cistern in the thickness of the Plantagenet wall, fed by a wooden pipe from the roof, is unique. The Priest's Room has its original oak waggon roof and carved wallplates. The Chapel was built c.1450, and has three original windows and windbraces in the roof. The apple-house of half-timbered brick and thatch stands on staddle-stones. Visitors often remark on the welcoming 'feel' of the house, and its atmosphere, warm, serene and timeless.

Inside are collections of early oak furniture,

Nailsea glass, Persian rugs and saddle bags, porcelain and American Revolutionary War Memorabilia; a warm welcome, and no 'ropes'.

GARDENS
The forecourt probably comprises the medieval garden, with two exceptional yew trees. The terraces descending southwards to a long swimming pool in natural stone contain many old fashioned roses. A connoisseur collection of trees and flowering shrubs, some planted in old Dutch cheese vats. A newly-established maze of edible plants.

National Winner of the first Historic House Awards, given by the AA and the NPI, in co-operation with the Historic Houses Association, for the privately-owned historic house open to the public which has best preserved its integrity and the character of its architecture and furniture while remaining a lived-in family home.

EXTRA FACILITIES
Video, upright piano. Talks on the property, contents, garden and history can be arranged for up to 100 people. No extra charge for this Projector and screen can be hired.

ADVICE TO COURIERS & DRIVERS
No dogs or photography indoors. Facilities tailored to suit any function, always with a personal touch. Pre-booked coaches welcome. Parking for 200 cars, 100 yards from Manor. Area for coaches nearer house.

FACILITIES FOR THE DISABLED
Disabled and elderly visitors may alight at the entrance to the property, before parking in the allocated areas. Toilet facilities for the disabled on request.

CATERING
The Restaurant/Tea Room, which has won much praise from visitors, seats up to 84. The adjoining Cockloft (3 rooms) may be hired for private functions. Buffet lunches/dinners, cream teas, medieval/17th century meals, garden barbecues are all bookable for groups. Menus/prices on request.

GUIDED TOURS
Leisurely tours of the house can be arranged, usually with the owners (in French/Italian also). Average tour lasts 1 hour.

SCHOOL VISITS/CHILDREN
School groups welcome out of normal opening hours. Cost dependent on age and length of visit, guide and schoolroom available. Teachers welcome on familiarisation visit. Items of interest: dolls' house, Jacob sheep, parrot. Swimming is available for school visits provided there is a life saver in the party.

SUITABILITY FOR OTHER EVENTS
Wedding receptions, birthday celebrations, garden parties, clay-pigeon shooting, archery, shows, rallies and filming are a speciality

CONFERENCE AND FUNCTION FACILITIES

ROOM	DIMENSIONS	CAPACITY	LAYOUT	POWER POINTS	SUITABLE FOR A/V
Great Hall	21' x 30'	100	Various	1	✓
Stables	21' x 38'	150	Various	6	✓
	21'x24'	50			
Cockloft	3 rooms	50	Various	4	✓
Reception Room	21' x 21'		Various		
Library	18' x 15'		Various		

OPENING TIMES

Summer
Public Holidays, Suns, Thurs and Bank Hols from Easter Day - 6 Oct 12.30 - 6.00pm

House opens 2pm.

Private parties at any time by prior arrangement

Winter
Closed.
Private day groups any time by arrangement.

ADMISSION

Summer

HOUSE & GARDEN
Adult £3.25
Child* (11-16yrs) . £1.00
OAP £3.00
Student £3.00

GARDEN ONLY
Adult £2.00
Child* (11-16yrs) . £0.35
OAP £1.75
Student £1.75
Children free in family group.

Groups**
Adult
Private days £4.00
Open days £2.75
Child* . . . .Dependent on
. . . . . . .age/length of visit.
OAP . . . . .No private day
. . . . concessions.

* Children under 11yrs. . .Free

** Min. Payment 20 people. If no catering required, extra charge made.

Winter
Same as Summer.
Groups only.

WILTON HOUSE
Wiltshire

The 17th Earl of Pembroke and his family live in Wilton House which has been the ancestral home for 450 years. In 1544 Henry VIII gave the Abbey and lands of Wilton to Sir William Herbert who had married Anne Parr, sister of Catherine, sixth wife of King Henry.

The Tudor Tower, in the centre of the east front, is the only part of the original building to survive a fire in 1647. Inigo Jones and John Webb were responsible for the rebuilding of the House in the Palladian style, whilst further alterations were made by James Wyatt from 1801.

The chief architectural features are the magnificent 17th century state apartments (including the famous Single and Double Cube rooms) and the 19th century cloisters.

The House contains one of the finest art collections in Europe, with over 230 original paintings on display, including works by Van Dyck, Rubens, Joshua Reynolds and Breughel. Also on show - Greek and Italian statuary, a lock of Queen Elizabeth I's hair, Napoleon's despatch case, and Florence Nightingale's sash.

The visitor centre houses a dynamic introductory film (narrated by Anna Massey), the reconstructed Tudor Kitchen and Victorian Laundry. It also provides a new home for the 'Wareham Bears', a unique exhibition of some 200 miniature teddy bears with their own house, stables and other scenes.

21 acres of landscaped parkland and gardens. Palladian Bridge. Adventure playground.

SUITABILITY FOR OTHER EVENTS
Film location, Fashion Shows, Product Launches, Equestrian Events, Garden Parties, Antiques Fairs, Concerts, Vehicle Rallies, Exclusive Banquets.

ADVICE TO COURIERS & DRIVERS
Free coach parking. Group rates (Min 15 pax), meal vouchers, drivers' lounge. No photography/dogs in House.

FACILITIES FOR THE DISABLED
Toilets for the disabled. Excellent wheelchair access. Visitors may alight at the Entrance. Guide dogs admitted..

PARKING FOR COACHES & CARS
Car (200+) and coach (12) park adjacent to visitor entrance.

CATERING
Self-service restaurant open 11am - 5.30pm. Advance booking required for groups (waitress service available for coffee, lunch and tea).

GIFT SHOP
Open as House. Stocks a wide variety of quality souvenirs including 'The Wilton Collection', plus specialist teddy bear area.

GUIDE BOOKS
Full colour guide book. French, German, Spanish, Italian, Japanese and Dutch information sheets.

GUIDED TOURS
Pre-booking a necessity.

SCHOOL VISITS/CHILDREN
Teachers' handbook for National Curriculum and worksheets. EFL students welcome. Free preparatory visit for group leaders.

CONTACT

Mr Alun Williams
Wilton House
Wilton
Salisbury
SP2 0BJ

Tel: (01722) 743115
Fax: (01722) 744447

LOCATION

3 miles west of Salisbury on the A30.
Rail: Salisbury Station (3 miles)
Bus: Every 10 minutes from Salisbury.
Taxi: Sarum Taxi (01722) 334477

OPENING TIMES

Summer
3 April - 3 November

Daily 11.00am - 6.00pm
Last admission 5.00pm

Winter
Closed, except for private parties.

ADMISSION

Summer
HOUSE, GROUNDS & EXHIBITION
Adult £6.20
Child £3.80
OAP £5.20
Family (2+2) . .£16.20
Groups   (min 15 people)
Adult £5.00
OAP £5.00
Child £3.50

Winter
Prices on application.

CONFERENCE AND FUNCTION FACILITIES

ROOM	DIMENSIONS	CAPACITY	LAYOUT	POWER POINTS	SUITABLE FOR A/V
Double Cube	60' x 30'	120 150	Dinner U-Shape	12	
Exhibition Centre	50' x 40'	140	Dinner	6	
Film Theatre	34' x 20'	67	Theatre	2	✓

ALEXANDER KEILLER MUSEUM, AVEBURY   Tel: 01672 539250

Avebury, Nr. Marlborough, Wiltshire SN8 1RF
Owner: The National Trust   **Contact:** The Administrator
The investigation of Avebury Stone Circles was largely the work of Alexander Keiller in the 1930s. He put together one of the most important prehistoric archaeological collections in Britain which can be seen at the Alexander Keiller Museum.
Location: In Avebury 6 m W of Marlborough.
Opening Times: 1 Apr - 31 Oct: Daily 10am - 6pm. 1 Nov - 31 Mar: Daily 10am - 4pm. Closed 24 - 26 Dec, 1 Jan.
Admission: Adult £1.50, Child 80p. English Heritage members Free.

AVEBURY MANOR GARDEN   Tel: 01672 539388

Avebury, Nr. Marlborough, Wiltshire SN8 1RF
Owner: The National Trust   **Contact:** The Administrator
A regularly altered house of monastic origin, the present buildings date from the early 16th century, with notable Queen Anne alterations and Edwardian renovation by Col Jenner. The topiary and flower gardens contain medieval walls, ancient box and numerous compartments.
Location: 6m W of Marlborough, 1m N of the A4 on A4361 and B4003.
Opening Times: 2 Apr - 30 Oct: Manor: Tues, Wed, Sun & Bank Holiday Mon, 2 - 5.30pm Garden: Daily except Mon (open BH Mons) & Thur 11am - 5.30pm, last admission 5pm.
Admission: Adult £3.50, Child £1.75. Group £3.15 (Child £1.60).

AVEBURY STONE CIRCLES   Tel: 01672 539250

Avebury, Nr. Marlborough, Wiltshire SN8 1RF
Owner: The National Trust   **Contact:** The Property Manager
One of the most important Megalithic monuments in Europe, this 28½ acre site with stone circles enclosed by a ditch and external bank is approached by an avenue of stones. The site also includes the Alexander Keiller Museum and the Wiltshire Life Society's display of Wiltshire rural life in the Great Barn. The site is managed and owned by the National Trust.
Location: 6m W of Marlborough, 1m N of the A4 on A4361 and B4003.
Opening Times: Stone Circle: Daily. Great Barn: telephone for details.

BOWOOD HOUSE   See Page 216 for full page entry.

BRADFORD-ON-AVON TITHE BARN   Tel: 0117 975 0700

Bradford-on-Avon, Wiltshire
Owner: English Heritage   **Contact:** South West Regional Office
A magnificent medieval stone-built barn with a slate roof and wooden beamed interior.
Location: ¼ m S of town centre, off B3109.
Opening Times: Keykeeper (telephone 01272 750770 for details).

BROADLEAS GARDENS   Tel: 01380 722035

Devizes, Wiltshire SN10 5JQ
Owner: Broadleas Gardens Charitable Trust   **Contact:** Lady Anne Cowdray
10 acres full of interest, notably The Dell, where the combination of greensand and sheltered site allows plantings of magnolias, camellias, rhododendrons and azaleas with underplantings of spring bulbs and other woodland plants. Other areas include the secret garden and the grey border with many interesting perennials and roses. There is also the woodland walk where our Collection of Euonymus can be found.
Location: Signposted from town centre (coaches must use this entrance) or 1m S of Devizes on A360.
Opening Times: Apr - Oct: Sun, Wed & Thur 2 - 6pm or by arrangement for groups.
Admission: Adult £2.50, Child (under 12) £1.00, Groups over 10 £2.20.

CORSHAM COURT   See Page 217 for full page entry.

THE COURTS   Tel: 01225 782340

Holt, Trowbridge, Wiltshire BA14 6RR
Owner: The National Trust   **Contact:** Head Gardener
A 7 acre garden of mystery flanking an 18th century house (not open to the public), with an ornamental facade.
Location: 3m SW of Melksham, 3m N of Trowbridge, 2½m E of Bradford-on-Avon, on S side of B3107.
Opening Times: Garden: 1 Apr - 31 Oct: Daily (except Sats) 2 - 5pm. Other times by appointment.
Admission: £2.80, Child £1.40, parties by arrangement.

GREAT CHALFIELD MANOR   Tel: 01985 843600

Melksham, Wiltshire SN2 8NJ
Owner: The National Trust   **Contact:** The Tenant
Dating from 1480, the manor house is set across a moat between parish church and stables. Restored early this century by Major R Fuller, whose family still lives here.
Location: 3m SW of Melksham via Broughton Gifford Common.
Opening Times: 2 Apr - 31 Oct: Tues, Wed, Thur by guided tours only, starting 12.15pm, 2.15pm, 3pm, 3.45pm and 4.30pm. Guided tours of the manor take 45 minutes and numbers are limited to 25. It is suggested that visitors arriving when a tour is in progress visit the church and garden first. Closed on public holidays.
Admission: £3.50, no reductions.

HAMPTWORTH LODGE   Tel: 01794 390215   Fax: 01794 390700

Hamptworth, Landford, Salisbury, Wiltshire SP5 2EA
Owner: Mr N J M Anderson   **Contact:** Mr N J M Anderson
Rebuilt Jacobean Manor House standing in woodlands on the edge of the New Forest. Grade II* family house with period furniture including clocks. The Great Hall has an unusual roof construction. There is a collection of prentice pieces and the Moffatt collection of contemporary copies. Garden also open.
Location: 10 m SE of Salisbury on C44 road linking Downton on Salisbury - Bournemouth Road (A338) to Landford on A36, Salisbury - Southampton.
Opening Times: 29 Mar - 30 Apr: 2.15 - 5pm except Sundays. Coaches by appointment only 1 Apr - 30 Oct except Sundays.
Admission: £3.00, under 11 free.

HEALE GARDEN

OPEN

Garden, Shop & Plant Centre throughout the year

10.00am - 5.00pm

Tours of the house, lunches/teas for parties of over 20 by arrangement.

Tel: 01722 782504

WOODFORD, SALISBURY, WILTSHIRE SP4 6NT

Owner: Mr Guy Rasch   *Contact: Major David Rasch*

First winner of Christie's/HHA Garden of the Year award. Grade I Carolean Manor House where King Charles II hid during his escape in 1651. In January great drifts of snowdrops and aconites bring early colour and the promise of Spring. The garden provides a wonderfully varied collection of plants, shrub, musk and other roses, growing in the formal setting of clipped hedges and mellow stonework. Particularly lovely in Spring and Autumn is the water garden surrounding an authentic Japanese Tea House and Nikko Bridge which create an exciting focus in this part of the garden.
Location: 4m N of Salisbury on Woodford Valley road between A345 & A360.
Admission: Adult £2.50, accompanied child under 14 free.

IFORD MANOR GARDENS

OPEN

April & Oct. Suns only & Easter Mon. 2.00 - 5.00pm

May - Sept. Tue, Wed, Thurs, Sat, Suns & Bank Holiday Mons. 2.00 - 5.00pm

Coaches by appointment at other times

Tel: 01225 863146
Fax: 01225 862364

IFORD MANOR, BRADFORD-ON-AVON, WILTSHIRE BA15 2BA

Owner: Mrs. E. A. J. Cartwright-Hignett   *Contact: Mrs. E. A. J. Cartwright-Hignett*

An enchanted garden. Iford Manor, a Tudor house with a classical façade, was once a busy centre of the woollen industry. Set in a romantic river valley it is now surrounded by a peaceful terraced garden of unique character. Designed by the Edwardian architect Harold Peto, it has pools, statuary, a colonnade, terraces and a cloister. Featured in Landscape and Memory 1995, BBC.
Location: 7 miles SE from Bath via A36, signposted Iford.
Admission: Adult £2.20 , OAP/Student/Child (over 10yrs) £1.60. Free car parking. Picnic area by river.

THE KING'S HOUSE
Tel: 01722 332151

Salisbury & South Wiltshire Museum, 65 The Close, Salisbury, Wiltshire SP1 2EN
Owner: Salisbury & South Wiltshire Museum Trust Ltd   **Contact:** P R Saunders
Location: In Salisbury Cathedral Close, west side.
Opening Times: Mon - Sat: 10am - 5pm. Suns Jul, Aug and Salisbury Festival: 2 - 5pm.
Admission: Adult £3.00, Child 75p, Conc £2.00, Groups £2.00.

LUCKINGTON COURT
Tel: 01794 390215

Chippenham, Wiltshire SN14 6PQ
Owner: The Hon Mrs Trevor Horn   **Contact:** The Hon Mrs Trevor Horn
3 acre garden with walled flower gardens, shrubberies, young arboretum attached to Queen Anne manor house (not open).
Location: B4040 near Sherston.
Opening Times: Gardens: Weds 2 - 6pm (Sun 12 May, 1996 for NGS).
Admission: Adult £1.00, Child free.

LACOCK ABBEY

LACOCK, CHIPPENHAM, WILTSHIRE SN15 2LG
Owner: The National Trust   Contact: The Property Manager
Tel: 01249 730227
The Abbey was founded in 1232 and converted into a country house after 1539. There are Medieval Cloisters, Sacristy and Chapter House, a 16th century Stable Court, and an 18th century Gothic Hall. The 19th century home of William Henry Fox Talbot, inventor of photography. Interesting features in grounds: unusual trees, 18th century Summer House, 19th century Rose Garden. A museum of photography commemorating the achievements of William Henry Fox Talbot is located in the village of Lacock.
Location: In the village of Lacock, 3m N of Melksham, 3m S of Chippenham just E of A350.
Opening Times: Abbey: 1 Apr - 30 Oct: Daily except Tues, 1 - 5.30pm. Cloisters & Grounds: 1 Apr - 30 Oct: Daily 12 noon - 5.30pm, closed Good Friday. Fox Talbot Museum - 1 Mar - 3 Nov: Daily 11am - 5.30pm. All have last admission 5pm & all closed Good Fri. 9 Nov - Feb '97: Weekends 11am - 4pm.
Admission: Abbey, Cloisters & Grounds: Adult £4.20, Child £2.20, Group £3.70 (child £1.90). Fox Talbot Museum: Adult £2.30, Child £1.10, Group £2.00.

LYDIARD PARK

LYDIARD TREGOZE, SWINDON, WILTSHIRE SN5 9PA
Owner: Borough of Thamesdown   Contact: The Keeper
Tel: 01793 770401
Beautifully restored Georgian house set amid rolling lawns, woodland and lakes. Former ancestral home of Viscounts Bolingbroke rescued from dereliction in 1943. Fascinating 17th century painted window and Lady Diana Spencer room are just some of the delights in store in this friendly house. Adjacent church with glittering array of monuments. Cafe, gift shop, exciting adventure playgrounds, enjoyment for all the family.
Location: 4m W of Swindon, close to J16 of M4.
Opening Times: Mon - Sat 10am - 1pm, 2 - 5.30pm. Sun 2 - 5.30pm. Nov - Feb: Early closing at 4pm.
Admission: Adult 70p, Child 25p. Group guided tours by appointment.

LITTLE CLARENDON
Tel: 01985 843600

Dinton, Salisbury, Wiltshire SP3 5OZ
Owner: The National Trust   **Contact:** The Tenant
A Tudor house, but greatly altered in the 17th century.
Location: 1/4m E of Dinton Church.
Opening Times: By prior written appointment.
Admission: £1.50, no reductions.

LONG HALL GARDENS
Tel: 01985 850424

Stockton, Warminster, Wiltshire BA12 0SE
Owner: N H Yeatman-Biggs Esq   **Contact:** N H Yeatman-Biggs
4 acre mainly formal garden with herbaceous gardens, shrub rose gardens, spring bulbs and fine hellebore walk. Long Hall Nursery is adjacent to the gardens.
Location: Stockton 7m SE of Warminster, off A36, W of A303 Wylye interchange.
Opening Times: Gardens: 1 May - 3 Aug: first Sat in the month, 2 - 6pm. Nursery: 20 Mar - 29 Sept: Wed - Sat 9.30am - 5.30pm.
Admission: Adult £2.00, Child free, Groups by appointment at £5.00 including cream teas.

LONGLEAT HOUSE
See Page 218 for full page entry.

Stourhead.

MALMESBURY HOUSE

THE CLOSE, SALISBURY, WILTSHIRE SP1 2EB

Owner: *John Cordle Esq.*   **Contact:** *John Cordle Esq.*

Tel: 01722 327027   **Fax:** 01722 334414

Malmesbury House was originally a 13th century canonry. It was enlarged in the 14th century and was leased to the Harris family in 1660 whose descendants became the first Earl of Malmesbury. The west façade was added by Wren, to accommodate rooms displaying magnificent rococo plasterwork. Among the many illustrious visitors to the house were King Charles II and the composer Handel who used the Chapel above the St Ann Gate for recitals. Francis Webb, a direct ancestor of Queen Elizabeth II lived here in the 1770's. Self service cafeteria in garden orangery in summer season.

Location: Salisbury.

Opening Times: April - October: Tue - Sat 11am - 5.30pm.

Admission: Adult £3.00 (Tues - Fri) £4.00 (Sats), Child £1.50.

MOMPESSON HOUSE   **Tel:** 01722 335659

The Close, Salisbury, Wiltshire SP1 2EL

Owner: The National Trust   **Contact:** The Property Manager

Fine Queen Anne town house, furnished as the home of a Georgian gentleman, with a walled garden. Art exhibition throughout the season.

Location: On N side of Choristers' Green in Cathedral Close, near High Street Gate.

Opening Times: 1 Apr - 30 Oct: Daily except Thur & Fri, 12 noon - 5.30pm. Last adm. 5pm.

Admission: Adult £3.10, Child £1.55, Parties £2.75.

NEWHOUSE   **Tel:** 01725 510055

Redlynch, Salisbury, Wiltshire SP5 2NX

Owner: George and June Jeffreys   **Contact:** Mrs June Jeffreys

Brick Jacobean 'Trinity House', c. 1619, with two Georgian wings. Contents include costume collection, documents and the 'Hare' picture.

Location: 9m S of Salisbury, 3m from Downtow, off B3080.

Opening Times: 1 - 31 Aug: except Suns 2 - 5.30pm. May & Sept: Groups 25+ by arrangement.

Admission: Adult £2.00, Child under 15 £1.00.

OLD SARUM   **Tel:** 01722 335398

Castle Road, Salisbury, Wiltshire SP1 3SD

Owner: English Heritage   **Contact:** The Custodian

First an Iron Age fort, later inhabited by Romans, Saxons, Danes and Normans, there is much to disentangle from the 56 acres of ruins at this fascinating site. The Normans created a castle, the first Salisbury Cathedral and the Bishop's Palace. From the castle ramparts there are fine views of the surrounding countryside.

Location: 2m N of Salisbury off A345.

Opening Times: 1 Apr - 30 Sept: 10am - 6pm. 1 - 31 Oct: 10am - 6pm or dusk if earlier. 1 Nov - 31 Mar: 10am - 4pm.

Admission: Adult £1.70, Child 90p, Conc £1.30.

OLD WARDOUR CASTLE   **Tel:** 01747 870487

Tisbury, Wiltshire SP1 3DS

Owner: English Heritage   **Contact:** The Custodian

In a picture book setting, the unusual hexagonal ruins of this 14th century castle stand on the edge of a beautiful lake, surrounded by landscaped grounds which include an elaborate rockwork grotto.

Location: Off A30 2m SW of Tisbury.

Opening Times: 1 Apr - 30 Sept: 10am - 6pm. 1 - 31 Oct: 10am - 6pm or dusk if earlier. 1 Nov - 31 Mar: Wed - Sun 10am - 4pm. (Closed for lunch 1 - 2pm Nov - Mar).

Admission: Adult £1.50, Child 80p, Conc £1.10.

PHILLIPS HOUSE   **Tel:** 01722 716208

Dinton, Salisbury, Wiltshire SP3 5HJ

Owner: The National Trust   **Contact:** YWCA Warden

A neo-Grecian house by Jeffry Wyattville, completed in 1816.

Location: 9m W of Salisbury, on N side of B3089.

Opening Times: On Sat only, by prior written arrangement.

Admission: £1.50, no reductions.

SALISBURY CATHEDRAL   **Tel:** 01722 328726   **Fax:** 01722 323569

6 The Close, Salisbury, Wiltshire SP1 2EF

Owner: Dean & Chapter   **Contact:** Mrs P Hellewell

Surrounded by ancient stone walls and peaceful lawns, stands Salisbury Cathedral, a supreme masterpiece of Medieval architecture. Its 404 ft spire, the tallest in England, soars above the historic houses of The Close. Treasures include an original Magna Carta and Europe's oldest working clock. Regular tours of Cathedral and Tower available.

Location: Off M3 - London / West Country.

Opening Times: Cathedral: Mon - Sat 8am - 6.30pm (8.15pm Jun - Sept) Sun: 8 - 9am, 12.30 - 2.30pm and 4 - 6.30pm. Chapter House: Daily, except Dec.

Admission: Donation.Cathedral: Adult £2.50, Child 50p, Conc £1.50, Family £5.00. Chapter House: Adult 30p, Child free.

SHELDON MANOR   **See Page 219 for full page entry.**

STONEHENGE

OPEN

16 Mar - 31 May: 9.30am - 6.00pm.

1 Jun - 31 Aug: 9am - 7pm.

1 - 31 Sept 9.30am - 6pm.

1 - 31 Oct 9.30am - 6pm/dusk.

1 Nov - 15 Mar 9.30am - 4pm

Tel: 01980 624715

AMESBURY, WILTSHIRE SP4 7DE

Owner: *English Heritage*   **Contact:** *The Custodian*

Stonehenge is probably the most famous ruin in the world, a prehistoric monument of unique importance which has been designated a World Heritage site. The great stone circle aligned on the midsummer sunrise has been a focus for magic and mysticism over the centuries. Radiocarbon dating reveals that the monument was built over many years, beginning around 3050BC and ending over 1500 years later. Archaeology can only hint at how the work was organised and who directed the building but we will probably never solve the central mystery of why the monument was built. We can only look up at the ancient stones and wonder.

Location: 2m W of Amesbury on junction A303 and A344/A360.

Admission: Adult £3.50, Child £1.80, Conc £2.60.

Where to Stay

For Private Accommodation and Johansens recommended Hotels, see Accommodation Section.

STOURHEAD

STOURTON, WARMINSTER, WILTSHIRE BA12 6QD

Owner: The National Trust   *Contact:* The Property Manager

Tel: 01747 841152

Landscape garden laid out from 1741-80 with lakes and temples, rare trees and plants. The house, begun in 1721 by Colen Campbell, contains furniture by the younger Chippendale and fine paintings. King Alfred's Tower, a red-brick folly built in 1772 by Flitcroft at the edge of the estate, is 160ft high, giving fine views over the neighbouring counties of Somerset, Dorset and Wiltshire.

Location: At Stourton off B3092, 3m NW of Mere (A303).

Opening Times: Garden - Daily 9am - 7pm, or sunset if earlier (except 24 - 27 July when garden closes at 5pm, last entry is 4pm). House - 30 Mar - 30 Oct: Daily except Thur & Fri, 12 noon - 5.30pm or dusk if earlier. Last adm. 5pm.

Admission: Mar - Oct: Garden: Adult £4.20, Child £2.20, Party £3.60, Family (2 + 2) £10. Nov - 29 Feb: Garden: Adult £3.20, Child £1.50, Family £8.00. House: Adult £4.20, Child £2.20, Party £3.60, Family £10.00. House & Garden: Adult £7.50, Child £3.50, Party £7.20, Family £20.00. King Alfred's Tower: Adult £1.50, Child 70p.

STOURTON HOUSE FLOWER GARDEN   **Tel:** 01747 840417

Zeals, Warminster, Wiltshire BA12 6QF

Owner: Mrs E Bullivant   **Contact:** Mrs E Bullivant

4 acres of beautifully maintained gardens. Many unusual plants. Plants for sale. No dogs. Wheelchair friendly.

Location: 3m N of Mere next to Stourhead, A303.

Opening Times: Apr - 30 Nov: Wed, Thur, Sun, and BH Mons 11am - 6pm.

Admission: Adult £2.00, Child 50p. Group guided tours by appointment £2.00pp. Parking free.

WESTWOOD MANOR   **Tel:** 01225 863374

Bradford-on-Avon, Wiltshire BA15 2AF

Owner: The National Trust   **Contact:** The Tenant

A 15th century stone manor house, altered in the late 16th century, with late Gothic and Jacobean windows and Jacobean plasterwork. There is a modern topiary garden.

Location: 1½m SW of Bradford-on-Avon, in Westwood village, beside the church.

Opening Times: 2 Apr - 1 Oct: Sun, Tues & Wed 2 - 5pm.

Admission: £3.30, no reductions.

WILTON HOUSE   See Page 220 for full page entry.

Malmesbury House.

SPECIAL EVENTS

For National Trust and English Heritage Events see separate section.

AVONCROFT MUSEUM

Tel: 01527 831886 **Fax:** 01527 831363

Stoke Heath, Bromsgrove, Worcester B60 4JR

Owner: Council of Management   **Contact:** Dr Simon Penn

Historic Houses rescued and restored in 15 acres of Worcestershire countryside. Exhibits include the magnificent 14th century roof of the Guesten Hall of Worcester Cathedral, 1946 prefab. timber framed buildings, chainshop, nailshop, toll house, and a working windmill. New in 1994 - the National Telephone Kiosk Collection with examples from 1922 to today. Parking, refreshments, picnic site and gift shop.

Location: 2m S of Bromsgrove off A38 by-pass.

Opening Times: March - November: Most days.

Admission: Adult £3.60, OAP £2.90, Child £1.80, Family Ticket (2+3) £10.00. Booked parties at reduced rates.

ELGAR'S BIRTHPLACE MUSEUM

Tel: 01905 333224

Crown East Lane, Lower Broadheath, Worcester WR2 6RH

Owner: Elgar's Birthplace Trust   **Contact:** The Administrator

The cottage, where the composer Sir Edward Elgar was born in 1857, now houses a unique collection of priceless manuscripts and press cuttings.

Location: 3m W of Worcester off A44.

Opening Times: 1 May - 30 Sept: 10am - 6pm. 1 Oct - 15 Jan: 1.30 - 4.30pm. Closed 16 Jan - 15 Feb. 16 Feb - 30 Apr: 1.30 - 4.30pm. Closed on Weds throughout the year.

Admission: Adult £3.00, Child 50p, OAP's £2.00, Conc £1.00. Groups on application.

THE GREYFRIARS

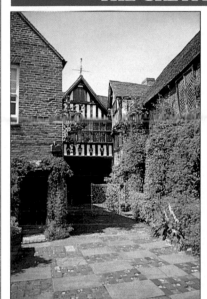

WORCESTER

Owner: The National Trust
Contact: The Property Manager

Tel: 01905 23571

Built in 1480, with early 17th and late 18th century additions, this timber-framed house was rescued from demolition at the time of the Second World War and has been restored and refurbished; interesting textiles and furnishings add character to the panelled rooms; an archway leads through to a delightful garden.

Location: Centre of Worcester.

Admission: Adult £2.20, Child £1.10, Family £5.50 (2 adults + up to 4 children).

OPEN
April - end Oct
Wed, Thu & Bank Hol Mons.
2.00 - 5.00pm

Where to Stay

For Private Accommodation and Johansens recommended Hotels, see Accommodation Section.

HANBURY HALL

DROITWICH, WORCESTERSHIRE WR9 7EA

Owner: The National Trust   *Contact: The Property Manager*

Tel: 01527 821214   **Fax:** 01527 821251

Set in 400 acres of parkland and gardens, this delightful William and Mary house was home to the Vernon family for three centuries. The permanent home of the Watney collection of fine porcelain and Dutch flower paintings, Hanbury Hall also boasts magnificent staircase and ceiling paintings by Sir James Thornhill. Restored 18th century garden, orangery and ice house. Available for corporate or private use for Civil Weddings, dinners or receptions outside opening hours.

Location: 4¹/₂m E of Droitwich, 10 minutes from Junction 5 of the M5.

Opening Times: Apr - Oct. Sun - Wed, 2- 6pm or dusk if earlier. Last adm. 5.30pm.

Admission: House & Garden: Adult £4.00, Child £2.00, Family £10.00. Garden only: Adult £2.50, Child £1.00. Special rates for parties by prior arrangement.

HARTLEBURY CASTLE

Tel: 01299 250416 (Museum) or 01299 250410 (State Rooms)

Kidderminster, Worcestershire

Owner: The Church Commissioners   **Contact:** The Secretary

Historic House of the Bishops of Worcester since 850AD. State Rooms include medieval Great Hall and 18th century Gothic interiors with fine plasterwork.

Location: 5m S of Kidderminster.

Opening Times: State Rooms - Easter Mon - 1 Sept, first Sun in every month (but tel. to check). Easter hols & Tues following BHs: 2 - 5pm. Also every Wed during this period, 2 - 4pm. County Museum - Mar - Nov: Mon - Thur 10am - 5pm, Fri & Sun 2 - 5pm. Closed Sat & Good Friday. Open BHs 10am - 5pm.

Admission: State Rooms: Adult 75p, Child 25p, Senior citizens 50p, Guided tours for parties of 30 or more on weekdays by arrangement. County Museum: Adult £1.90, Conc 90p, Family ticket £5.00. Call to verify.

HAWFORD DOVECOTE

Tel: 01684 850051

Hawford, Worcestershire

Owner: The National Trust   **Contact:** The Administrator

A 16th century half-timbered dovecote.

Location: 3m N of Worcester, ¹/₂m E of A449.

Opening Times: Apr - end Oct: Daily 9am - 6pm or sunset if earlier. Closed Good Fri, other times by prior appointment.

Admission: 60p.

LEIGH COURT BARN

Tel: 01604 730320

Worcester

Owner: English Heritage   **Contact:** The Midlands Regional Office

Magnificent 14th century timber framed barn built for the monks of Pershore. It is the largest of its kind in Britain.

Location: 5m W of Worcester on unclassified road off A4103.

Opening Times: 1 Apr - 30 Sept: Thur - Sun 10am - 6pm.

KEY TO SYMBOLS: THE NATIONAL TRUST   ENGLISH HERITAGE   HISTORIC HOUSES ASSOCIATION

LOWER BROCKHAMPTON 🌿

Tel: 01885 488099

Bringsty, Worcestershire WR6 5UH

Owner: The National Trust   **Contact:** The Administrator

A late 14th century moated manor house, with an attractive detached half timbered 15th century gatehouse, a rare example of this type of structure. Also, the ruins of a 12th century chapel.

Location: 2m E of Bromyard on A44, reached by a narrow road through 1^1/2m of woods and farmland.

Opening Times: Medieval Hall, parlour, gatehouse and chapel - Apr - end Sept: Wed - Sun & Bank Hol Mon, 10am - 5pm. Closed Good Fri. Oct: Wed - Sun, 10am - 4pm.

Admission: Adult £1.60, Child 80p, Family £4.00.

MADRESFIELD COURT

Tel: 01684 573614 **Fax:** 01684 569197

Madresfield, Malvern WR13 5AU

Owner: The Trustees of Madresfield Estate   **Contact:** Mr Peter Hughes

Elizabethan and Victorian house with medieval origins. Fine contents. Extensive gardens and arboretum.

Location: 6m SW of Worcester.

Opening Times: Limited, by appointment. Apr - Jul. Guided tours.

Admission: £6.00.

WICHENFORD DOVECOTE 🌿

Tel: 01684 850051

Wichenford, Worcestershire

Owner: The National Trust   **Contact:** The Administrator

A 17th century half timbered dovecote.

Location: 5^1/2m NW of Worcester, N of B4204.

Opening Times: Apr - end Oct: daily 9.00am - 6.00pm or sunset if earlier. Closed Good Fri, other times by appointment.

Admission: 60p.

WITLEY COURT ⌗

OPEN

1 Apr - 30 Sept
10.00am - 6.00pm

1 Oct - 31 Oct
10.00am - 6.00pm
or dusk if earlier.

1 Nov - 31 Mar
Wed - Sun
10.00am - 4.00pm
Closed lunch
1 - 2pm.

Tel: 01299 896636

GREAT WITLEY, WORCESTER WR6 6ST

Owner: English Heritage   *Contact: The Custodian*

The vast shell of Witley Court is one of the most spectacular country house ruins in England. The house was transformed, in the mid 19th century, into a breath-takingly luxurious palace in the Italian style with extensive gardens and immense fountains. It then fell into decay until it was rescued in 1972 and today it is being preserved as an amazing ruin.

Location: 10m NW of Worcester on the A443.

Admission: Adult £2.50, Conc £1.90, Child £1.30.

SPETCHLEY PARK GARDEN 🏛

OPEN

Apr - Sept:
Tues - Fri,
11am - 5pm

Sun: 2 - 5pm.

Bank Hol Mons:
11am - 5pm.

Closed Sat and
all other Mons.

Tel: 01905 345213
or 01905 345224

SPETCHLEY, WORCESTER WR5 1RS

Owner: Mr R J Berkeley   *Contact: Mr R J Berkeley*

30 acre private garden containing large collection of trees, shrubs and plants, many rare or unusual. Open for the first time in 1996 there is a new garden within the walled kitchen garden. This new garden is part formal, part sunk. Deer Park close by with herds of red and fallow deer. Teas.

Location: 2m E of Worcester on A422.

Admission: Adult £2.50, Child £1.20. Reduced rates for parties on application.

BRODSWORTH HALL
Doncaster

The mysterious Chevaliere Casentini designed the house for Charles Sabine Augustus Thellusson in an Italianate classical style which was unusual for its day. It was built between 1861 and 1863.

Brodsworth Hall and its contents have survived almost intact. An extraordinary time capsule which has been carefully conserved by English Heritage to preserve its faded grandeur. Brodsworth conveys a vivid picture of daily life in a country house. The decoration and furnishings reflect not only the function of the rooms but the class, sex and even the age of the people who used them. The elegance of the ladies' drawing rooms contrasts with the more masculine atmosphere of the billiard room, the luxury of the family rooms with the plainer quarters of the servants' wing and the practical equipment of the great kitchens.

The design of the gardens is also unchanged, with formal gardens, croquet lawns and a quarry garden, rich in wildlife and garden history.

CONTACT

The Custodian
Brodsworth Hall
Brodsworth
Doncaster
Yorkshire
DN5 7XJ

Tel: (01302) 722598

LOCATION

In Brodsworth, 6 miles north west of Doncaster on minor road. W of A1 between A635 or A638

EXTRA FACILITIES
Education Centre.

ADVICE TO COURIERS & DRIVERS
Groups must pre-book. Tour leader and Coach driver have free entry. 1 extra place for every 20 additional people.

FACILITIES FOR THE DISABLED
Most of the house accessible for wheelchairs, WC's for disabled available.

PARKING FOR COACHES & CARS
Spaces for 220 cars and 3 coaches.

CATERING
Tearoom on site, seating for 70 people.

GUIDED TOURS
The House will be open for pre-booked coach parties from 10.00am - 1.00pm.

GIFT SHOP
Located in the Servants' Hall.

GUIDE BOOKS
Colour guide book and children's guide.

SCHOOL VISITS/ CHILDREN
School visits are free if booked in advance.

OPENING TIMES

30 Mar - 27 Oct
Tues - Sun
Closed Mondays except
Bank Holidays

House: 1.00 - 6.00pm
Last admission 5.00pm

Grounds: 12 noon - 6pm

ADMISSION

Adult £4.20
Child* £2.10
Conc. £3.20

15% discount on groups of 11 or more

* 5 - 15 years.
Under 5's free

BROUGHTON HALL
Skipton

BROUGHTON HALL was built in 1597 by Henry Tempest and continues to be the home of the Tempest family, whose ancestry can be traced back 29 generations to Roger Tempest who was established in the area by 1120. This Grade I listed historic building has Elizabethan origins but was extensively added to during the 18th and 19th Centuries, hence its Palladian appearance.

Set in 3,000 acres of beautiful Yorkshire parkland and countryside, the Broughton Hall family home and Estate, is open to the public by prior arrangement and is also available as an exclusive venue for both business and pleasure.

The present design of the grounds owes much to the landscape architecture of Nesfield around 1855. To the east of the Hall is a fine Italianate garden with balustrades and a gazebo. To the rear there are sweeping lawns (ideal for marquee events) enhanced by extensive wooded views and fountains.

The owner likes to make every event unique and highly successful so he is always ready to discuss with clients how he can help them to achieve their objectives by placing his facilities and experience at their disposal. To arrange such a consultation it is only necessary to telephone the Estate Office on 01756 799608.

CONTACT

The Estate Office
Broughton Hall
Skipton
North Yorkshire
BD23 3AE

Tel: (01756) 799608
Fax: (01756) 700357
e-mail: tempest@
broton.demon.co.uk

LOCATION

Skipton A59, 3 miles.
From London M1 to
Leeds and Skipton, A59
to Broughton.

Air: Bradford/Leeds
Airport 40 minutes,
Manchester 1 hour.

Rail: Skipton Station
3 miles.

Bus: Regular service.

OPENING TIMES

Bank Holiday Mondays
11.00am - 4.00pm

Guided Tours can be
arranged by prior
appointment.
The duration of a tour is
approx. 1½ hours.

ADMISSION

HOUSE & GARDEN

Per person £5.00

Guided Tours
Groups*
Per person £5.00

* Minimum payment if
  by prior appointment £60.

SUITABILITY FOR EVENTS
Broughton Hall and its grounds are ideal for a wide range of activities; dinners, seminars, corporate entertainment, product launches, clay shoots, archery, fashion shows, equestrian events, firework and laser shows etc. The diversity of the Estate is ideal for filming and still photography. Being a private house your event will have exclusive use of the Hall and Grounds.

EXTRA FACILITIES
Ample parking and an area for light aircraft/helicopters. Lectures on property, contents, garden and history can be held in a lecture room seating 80. Musical evenings are very successful. A grand piano is available. Full size billiard table.

ADVICE TO COURIERS & DRIVERS
When travelling from Skipton on the A59 towards Clitheroe watch for the Bull Inn on left hand side 3 miles from Skipton. Take turning to left approx. 200 yards past Bull Inn. The Hall and entrance gates can then be seen.

FACILITIES FOR THE DISABLED
Disabled and elderly visitors may alight at the front door. The vehicle should then be parked in the allocated area.

PARKING FOR COACHES & CARS
Capacity of the car park - unlimited.

CATERING
This can be provided by prior arrangement. Wide range of options. Buffets and full sit down meals with accent on quality and value. Up to 150 people can be catered for.

GUIDED TOURS
At no additional cost guided tours are conducted for up to 200 people at any one time. Large groups are split up into smaller parties. If requested the owner will meet the group. Average time taken for a tour 1 hour 30 minutes.

LOCAL PLACES OF INTEREST
Broughton is only three miles from the historic market town of Skipton with its roofed castle. The Yorkshire Dales National Park with some of the finest countryside in England is on the doorstep. There are excellent local hotels for overnight accommodation.

CONFERENCE AND FUNCTION FACILITIES

SUBJECT TO PRIOR ARRANGEMENT ALL ROOMS CAN BE MADE AVAILABLE FOR FUNCTIONS.

CASTLE HOWARD
York

In a dramatic setting between two lakes with extensive gardens and impressive fountains, this 18th century Palace was designed by Sir John Vanbrugh in 1699. Undoubtedly the finest private residence in Yorkshire it was built for Charles Howard, 3rd Earl of Carlisle, whose descendants still live here.

With its painted and gilded dome reaching 80ft into the Yorkshire sky, this impressive house has collections of antique furniture, porcelain and sculpture, while its fabulous collection of paintings is dominated by the famous Holbein portraits of Henry VIII and the Duke of Norfolk.

GARDENS

Designed on a heroic scale covering 1,000 acres. The gardens include memorable sights like The Temple of the Four Winds and the Mausoleum, New River Bridge and the recently restored waterworks of the South Lake, Cascade, Waterfall and Prince of Wales Fountain.

The walled garden has collections of old and modern roses.

Ray Wood has a unique collection of rare trees, shrubs, rhododendrons, magnolias and azaleas.

CONTACT

Mrs. M E Carmichael
Castle Howard
York
North Yorkshire
YO6 7DA

Tel: (01653) 648444
Fax: (01653) 648462

LOCATION

York 15 miles (20 minutes), A64. From London: M1 exit 32, M18 to A1(M) to A64, York/Scarborough Road, 3½ hours.

Train: London Kings Cross to York 1 hr. 50 mins. York to Malton Station 30 mins.

Bus: Service and tour buses from York station to Castle Howard.

SUITABILITY FOR OTHER EVENTS
Concerts, craft fairs, fashion shows, clay pigeon shooting, equestrian events, garden parties, filming, product launches.

EXTRA FACILITIES
Helicopter Landing, Rose Garden Receptions, Firework Displays. Lectures (by arrangement) covering the House, History, Contents and Gardens.

ADVICE TO COURIERS & DRIVERS
Approaching from the south, A64 to Malton, on entering Malton, take the Castle Howard road via Coneysthorpe Village. Alternative route from A64 following signs to Castle Howard is via the Carrmire Gate 9' wide by 10' high.

FACILITIES FOR THE DISABLED
Toilets for the disabled. Transport equipped for wheelchairs. Chairlift in House to main floor.

PARKING FOR COACHES & CARS
Car park capacity - 400 cars and 20 coaches.

CATERING
Cafeterias at the House and Stable Courtyard. The Grecian

Hall available for pre-booked private parties - minimum 25. Prices and menus on request. Private dinner, lunches, buffets and functions by arrangement.

GIFT SHOP
Open 10.30am-5pm when House open. Large selection of gifts, souvenirs and books. Plant Centre Shop.

GUIDE BOOKS
Full colour guide book.

GUIDED TOURS
Guides are available throughout the House, no charge. Private tours and Garden Tours by arrangement.

SCHOOL VISITS/CHILDREN
School parties welcome, information pack available. Teacher/pupil ratio required is 1:10. Special interest: 18th century architecture, art, history, wildlife, horticulture.

OPENING TIMES

Summer
15 March - 3 November
Daily 11.00am - 4.30pm

Last admission 4.30pm

NB Grounds, Rose Gardens and Plant Centre open 10.00am

Winter
November - Mid March

Open by pre-booked appointment and availability.

Grounds open most days November, December and January - telephone for confirmation.

ADMISSION

Summer

HOUSE, GARDEN
Adult £6.50
Child* £3.50
OAP £5.50

Groups (min 12 people)
Adult £5.50
Child* £3.00
OAP £5.00

GARDEN ONLY
Adult £4.00
Child* £2.00

*Age 4-16

Winter
By arrangement.

CONFERENCE AND FUNCTION FACILITIES

ROOM	DIMENSIONS	CAPACITY	LAYOUT	POWER POINTS	SUITABLE FOR A/V
Long Gallery	197' x 24'	280	Theatre	20	✓
		280	Buffet/Lunch/Dinner		
Grecian Hall	40' x 40'	160	Various	20	✓
Chinese Room		60	Various	1	✓

DUNCOMBE PARK
Helmsley

The house dates from 1713 and was built for Thomas Duncombe by William Wakefield, a friend of Vanbrugh. A fine forecourt and two pavilions were added by Sir Charles Barry in 1843. Its interiors were remodelled by the First Earl of Feversham after a fire in 1879. The main showrooms are now a fine example of the type of grand interior popular at the turn of the century.

Following the death of the second Earl of Feversham at the Battle of the Somme in 1916, Duncombe Park was leased as a girls' school;. In 1985 the present Lord and Lady Feversham decided to restore the house to a family home. After the closure of the school, there was little more than an empty, echoing shell. Today the visitor will see a superb example of the best of British craftsmanship. The restoration is very much a family project and the interior finishes have been deliberately

chosen to show visitors a selection of the styles of decoration typical in the 18th and 19th centuries. There are fine family pictures and Lord Feversham's collection of English and Continental furniture.

The unique 30 acre early 18th century landscape garden, set in 300 acres of dramatic parkland, has been described as 'the supreme masterpiece of the art of the landscape gardener'. Its vast expanses of lawn, terraces, temples, woodland walks and fine views across the surrounding North York Moors are something to be explored at leisure.

Parkland Centre, Restaurant, Gift Shop, Picnic Area, Playground. Waymarked Country Walks.

Winner British Tourist Authority Come to Britain Special Award and Yorkshire & Humberside White Rose Awards. Duncombe Park is now a National Nature Reserve.

CONTACT

Estate Office
Helmsley
York
YO6 5EB

Tel: (01439) 770213

Fax: (01439) 771114

LOCATION

Entrance just off Helmsley Market Square, signed off A170 Thirsk - Scarborough road.

Taxi: (01439) 770817/771384/770512

SUITABILITY FOR OTHER EVENTS
Dinners, receptions, concerts, weddings, conferences, fashion shows, product launches, filming. Also suitable for wide range of outdoor events. Grand piano, tennis court, croquet lawn available.

SPECIAL EVENTS
Year round programme of events in house and park. Details from the Visitor Co-ordinator.

PARKING FOR COACHES & CARS
Free parking. Car park at Parkland Centre 400 yds from house. Coach park (Visitors may disembark at front gates).

ADVICE TO COURIERS & DRIVERS
No flash photography in house. Video permits available. Allow 3 hours for group visits.

FACILITIES FOR DISABLED
Disabled toilet. Portable ramps. Parking usually allowed in main forecourt. The House is not particularly suited to those with walking difficulties.

GUIDE BOOK
Full colour guide book available £2.00. Guided tours every day except Sundays and Bank Holiday Mondays.

CATERING
Home made lunches and teas. Maximum 60. Pre-booking recommended for groups.

SCHOOL VISITS/CHILDREN
School parties welcome. Information pack available. Teacher/Pupil ratio required is 1:10.

OPENING TIMES

HOUSE AND GARDEN
11.00am - 5.00pm
Last admittance 4.30pm

Easter Weekend
and all Bank Holidays

April, May and October
Saturday - Wednesday

June, July, August & Sept
Daily

Days and times may be changed for special events. Please check by phoning (01439) 770213

PARKLAND CENTRE
RESTAURANT & SHOP,
COUNTRY WALKS
Country Walks
10.30am - 5.30pm
Dates as house.

ADMISSION

HOUSE, GARDEN & PARK
Adult £4.95
Child (10-16) £2.50
O.A.P. £3.95
Student £3.95
Family (2+2) . . .£11.00
Group £3.95

GARDEN ONLY
Adult £2.95
Child £1.50

NATIONAL NATURE
RESERVE ONLY . .£1.50

SEASON TICKET £25.00
Includes events in
any 12 months.

NOTE: Joint visiting arrangements for groups in conjunction with Hovingham Hall (£5.75pp).

FAIRFAX HOUSE
York

FAIRFAX HOUSE was acquired and fully restored by the York Civic Trust in 1983/84. The House, described as a classic architectural masterpiece of its age and certainly one of the finest townhouses in England was saved from near collapse after considerable abuse and misuse this century, being converted into a Cinema and Dance Hall.

The richly decorated interior with its plasterwork, wood and wrought iron, is now the home for a unique collection of Georgian furniture, clocks, paintings and porcelain.

The Noel Terry Collection, gift of a former treasurer of the York Civic Trust, has been described by Christie's as one of the finest private collections formed this century. It enhances and complements the House and helps to create that special 'lived-in' feeling, providing the basis for what can be considered a fully furnished Georgian townhouse.

❖

CONTACT

Mr Peter Brown
Fairfax House
Castlegate
York
YO1 1RN

Tel: (01904) 655543

Fax: (01904) 652262

LOCATION

London 4 hours by car, 2 hours by train.

Fairfax House situated in the centre of York between the Castle Museum and the Jorvik Centre.

Rail: York Railway Station 10 minutes walk.

Taxi: Station Taxis (01904) 623332

SUITABILITY FOR OTHER EVENTS
Suitable for filming.

EXTRA FACILITIES
By prior arrangement the group on a Connoisseur's Tour can be met by one of the trustees. Lectures can be given on the House, its contents and history. The lectures can be given in the hotel in which the group is staying. A screen and projector for such a lecture can be provided by Fairfax House.

For groups of up to 50 people a buffet can be arranged. The Dining Room may be used on certain evenings for special formal dinners. Limited to groups of up to 25 people.

ADVICE TO COURIERS & DRIVERS
Please telephone to arrange for map showing the nearest coach park and approach to the House. No photography inside the House.

FACILITIES FOR THE DISABLED
Disabled and elderly visitors may alight at the door of the property prior to parking in adjacent public car park. No toilet facilities at the House.

PARKING FOR COACHES & CARS
Capacity of the public car park - 300 cars, 50 yds from House. Coach park is $^1\!/_2$ mile away, parties are dropped off.

GIFT SHOP
Open every day except Friday from 1 March - 1 January, 11am-5pm. Items include catalogues, tapes, gifts & antiques.

GUIDE BOOKS
Colour guide book, £3.50. Translations in French available. A 150 page catalogue on the furniture collection available at £19.95, softback £14.95.

SCHOOL VISITS/CHILDREN
A guided tour for school children can be arranged at a cost of £1.00 per head.

GUIDED TOURS
Connoisseur Tour - Guided tour showing secret drawers etc. Wine/sherry to follow tour. Parties split into groups of approx 12 persons, £10.00 per person (Min charge £100).

Evening Guided Tour - Guided tour plus wine/sherry to follow (secret drawers not included). Parties split into groups of approx 20, £5.00 per person (Min. charge £75).

Evening Guided Tour - Guided Tour only (does not include secret drawers, wine or sherry). Parties split into groups of approx 20/25, £4.00 per person (Min charge £60).

Daytime Parties - Guided - Accepted only within limits of staff availability/ number involved/other bookings etc. Children admitted only at a ratio of 8 to 1 adult. Adult parties split into groups of 20/25, £4 per person (Min charge £60).

Daytime Parties - Without Guide - To be arranged according to number involved and other bookings. Parties split into smaller groups, special party rate for pre-booked tour of 15 or more persons.

Tours available in French and German. The duration of the tour is approx 1$^1\!/_2$ hours.

FOUNTAINS ABBEY & STUDLEY ROYAL
Ripon

One of the most remarkable sites in Europe, sheltered in a secluded valley, Fountains Abbey and Studley Royal, a World Heritage Site, encompasses the spectacular ruin of a 12th century Cistercian Abbey, a Jacobean Mansion, and one of the best surviving examples of a Georgian Green Water Garden. Elegant ornamental lakes, avenues, temples and cascades provide a succession of unforgettable eye-catching vistas in an atmosphere of peace and tranquillity. St Mary's Church, built by William Burges in the 19th century, provides a dramatic focal point to the medieval deer park with over 700 deer.

Audio visual programme and exhibition at the Visitor Centre. Small museum near to the Abbey. Exhibitions in Fountains Hall and Swanley Grange.

The Abbey is maintained by English Heritage. St Mary's Church is owned by English Heritage and managed by the National Trust.

CONTACT

The National Trust
Fountains Abbey &
Studley Royal
Ripon
N. Yorkshire HG4 3DY

Tel: Weekdays
(01765) 608888
Weekends
(01765) 601005

Fax: (01765) 608889

LOCATION

4 miles W of Ripon off
B6265

8 miles W of A1

OPENING TIMES

All Year
except 24/25 December
and Fridays Nov - Jan

April - September
10.00am - 7.00pm

January - March &
October - December
10.00am - 5.00pm

Last admission 1 hour
before closing.

Closes at 4.00pm on
6 July, 1996.

ADMISSION

Adult £4.00
Child £2.00
Family £8.00

Groups over 15
Adult £3.50
Child £1.70
Groups over 40
Adult £3.00
Child £1.50

Group discount
applicable only with
prior booking.

SUITABILITY FOR OTHER EVENTS
Large and small events held throughout the year.

EXTRA FACILITIES
Exhibitions, walks, free guided tours and audio visual programme. Corporate hospitality seminar facilities.

ADVICE TO COURIERS & DRIVERS
Use Visitor Centre entrance only. Must be pre-booked. Contact Group Visit Organiser (01765) 601005.

FACILITIES FOR THE DISABLED
Batricars and wheelchairs available, pre-book on (01765) 601005. Adapted WC. Guided tours for visually impaired - please book.

CATERING
Refreshments available all day. Hot lunches 12 noon - 2.30pm.

GIFT SHOP
Two gift shops - open all day.

GUIDE BOOKS
There are guide books covering the whole Estate.

GUIDED TOURS
Free guided tours of Abbey and Water Garden.

SCHOOL VISITS /CHILDREN
Welcome by prior arrangement.
Contact Group Visit Organiser on (01765) 601005.

HAREWOOD HOUSE
Leeds

CONTACT

Gerald Long
The Estate Office
Harewood
Leeds
West Yorkshire
LS17 9LQ

Tel: (0113) 288 6331
Fax: (0113) 288 6467

LOCATION

A1 N or S to Wetherby,

A659 via Collingham, Harewood is on the A61 between Harrogate and Leeds. It is easily reached from A1, M1, M62 and M18 motorways.

Harewood House is 15 mins from the centre of Leeds or Harrogate.

Rail: Leeds Station 7 miles.

Bus: No. 36 from Leeds or Harrogate

HAREWOOD House, the Yorkshire home of the Earl and Countess of Harewood, is much more than a historic house, it is also the home of one of England's most distinguished families - designed by John Carr in 1759, it has been continually lived in by the Lascelles family ever since. The magnificent interior, created by Robert Adam, has superb ceilings and plasterwork and contains a noteworthy collection of English and Italian paintings. The furniture throughout the house reflects what many experts have described as 'the richest collection of Chippendale in the world', much of which was made especially for Harewood. Newly refurbished dedicated Watercolour Rooms showcase key historic works.

The Earl of Harewood is the son of the late Princess Mary, daughter of King George V, and is a cousin of Queen Elizabeth II. Princess Mary lived at Harewood for many years and some of her pictures and possessions are on display in her rooms.

TERRACE GALLERY
The Terrace Gallery was established in 1989 as a venue for exhibitions showing the best of contemporary art.

GROUNDS AND BIRD GARDEN
In the grounds, landscaped by 'Capability' Brown, are lakeside and woodland walks and Sir Charles Barry's parterre design on the Terrace has recently been restored to its original condition of intricate patterns made with box, bedding and white chippings. Two hugely popular Adventure Playgrounds provide endless fun for younger visitors - from toddlers to teenagers. Harewood Bird Garden has one of the most comprehensive collections in the north of England including exotic species, many endangered, from Africa, America and Australia.

CATERING & CORPORATE HOSPITALITY
Available for quality corporate entertaining and offers: State Dining Room dinners (32 max.); Gallery Banqueting (96 max); Drinks reception/buffets; Concerts (175 max); Wedding receptions, Marquee events, Product launches.

The Courtyard Suite, recently refurbished, has an exciting theme able to cater for all conferences, exhibitions, product launches and functions held within the Courtyard or the magnificent grounds.

An ideal venue for any gathering, the Courtyard Suite seats a max. of 120 theatre style. Conference organisers may wish to also use the Study Centre directly overhead for a meeting then retire to the Courtyard Suite for a meal. The Drawing Room can be incorporated to provide a reception area, additional dining area or exhibition space. The latest conference equipment is available for varied requirements.

Large launches etc. can be accommodated by using the full extent of the Courtyard area which can be covered by a 20'x24' marquee. This flexible approach has proven highly successful giving a maximum dinner seating of 400. Marquees of any size can be completely accommodated within the grounds.

CORPORATE HOSPITALITY
The beautiful grounds, provide the ideal setting to incorporate outside activities in your programme, a wide range of options are open from clay shoots to ballooning, jousting to a cricket match on Harewood's private ground - the management team will help to make your conference a success.

EXTRA FACILITIES
Grand piano, cricket and football pitch. Subject to availability lectures on the property, its gardens and history for up to 70. Projector and screen can be provided.

ADVICE TO COURIERS & DRIVERS
No unaccompanied children in the Bird Garden. Dogs on leads in grounds but not House (except Guide Dogs) or Bird Garden. Unlimited parking 400 yds from House and for 50+ coaches 500 yds from House.

FACILITIES FOR THE DISABLED
Disabled and elderly may alight at entrance to House, before parking in allocated areas. Guide dogs allowed in the House. Most facilities are accessible and a wheelchair is available at House and Bird Garden. The toilet is near the car park shop. Special concessions apply to disabled groups.

GIFT SHOP
Gift Shops and Plant Centre are open as Park. Items include Leeds pottery, flower pictures, glass, perfume and toys. Full colour guide book price £3.00.

AUDIO TOUR OF HOUSE
Hire charge £1.50.

OPENING TIMES

Summer
16 March - 27 October

BIRD GDN & GROUNDS
Daily from 10.00am

HOUSE
Daily from 11.00am

Closed to the public 17 May, 1996.

Winter
Nov-Mar: House Closed
Nov/Dec: Grounds & Gdns open weekends (ring to confirm times)

Certain rooms available for corporate entertaining plus Courtyard Suite for Conferences/ Product launches.

ADMISSION

ALL ATTRACTIONS
Adult £6.00
OAP £5.00
Child (4 - 15) £4.00
Family (2A+3C) .£18.00
Groups of 20+
Adult £5.25
OAP £5.00
Child (4 - 15) . . . . Free
(If accompanied)

BIRD GDN & GROUNDS
Adult £5.00
OAP £4.00
Child (4-15) £3.00
Family (2A+3C) .£14.00

GROUNDS & ADVENTURE PLAYGROUNDS
Adult £4.00
OAP £3.00
Child (4 - 15) . . .£2.00

HOVINGHAM HALL
York

HOVINGHAM HALL is a Palladian country house in the heart of Yorkshire overlooking the oldest private cricket ground in England. Built in warm local limestone, its unique design reflects the twin interests of its builder Thomas Worsley, architecture and horses. It is entered through a huge Riding School; extensive halls, originally designed as stables, lead into the gracious family rooms. Portraits of many generations look down.

Hovingham Hall remains a family home in the heart of an agricultural estate famous for its woodlands. It is the birthplace of HRH The Duchess of Kent, sister of Sir Marcus Worsley who now lives in the Hall.

The gardens at Hovingham Hall reflect their long history. Great yew hedges planted in the 18th century give a framework to lawns and borders with a wide variety of plants new and old. Recently a former kitchen garden has been laid out as an ornamental orchard, where golden hops reflect its ancient name, the Hop Garden. Roses are a particular family favourite and provide the background to matches on the cricket ground which gives the Hall its setting.

SUITABILITY FOR OTHER EVENTS
Fashion shows, air displays, archery, clay pigeon shooting, equestrian events, garden parties, shows, rallies, filming.

EXTRA FACILITIES
Grand piano, parkland, cricket pitch, squash court, croquet. 18th century Riding School, 98' x 35', suitable for promotions etc. Easy access from road. A lecture room is available and talks on the history of the property, its contents and history can be given. Contact Administrator for details.

ADVICE TO COURIERS & DRIVERS
No unaccompanied children, no dogs, no photography. Park outside Riding School entrance in centre of village. Free tour of house for couriers/drivers.

FACILITIES FOR THE DISABLED
Disabled or elderly visitors may alight at the entrance to the property, before parking in the allocated areas. The house is not suitable for the disabled and there are no special toilet facilities.

CATERING
Restaurant seating 42. Groups must book in advance - menus on request. Light refreshments. Buffets, lunches, dinners can be arranged, also catering for conferences, meetings etc.

GIFT SHOP
A small gift shop is open at all times when the Hall is open.

GUIDE BOOKS
Colour guide book available.

GUIDED TOURS
Guided tours available. It is sometimes possible for the owner to meet groups visiting the House. Average time for a tour is 45 minutes. Tours can also be arranged in French or Dutch.

ACCOMMODATION
We work in conjunction with the two rosette Worsley Arms Hotel and are able to offer them rooms for their functions and conferences. The Worsley Arms is a delightful Country House Hotel within short walking distance of the Hall.

CONTACT

Mrs Lamprey
Hovingham Hall
York
YO6 4LU

Tel: (01653) 628206
Fax: (01653) 628668

LOCATION

London A1/M1, A64 then to Hovingham 3$^{1}/_{2}$ hours.

Malton 10 minutes, York 30 minutes.

Rail: York 17 miles

Air: Leeds/Bradford airport 40 miles. Teeside Airport 40 miles

Taxis: Rydale Taxis, Malton, N. Yorks Tel: 01653 600030

OPENING TIMES

16 April - 26 September

BY PRE-BOOKED APPOINTMENT ONLY

Tues, Wed, Thurs 11.00am - 7.00pm

Arrangements can occasionally be made to open on other days.

ADMISSION

HOUSE & GARDEN

Adult £3.00
Child* £1.50

*Under 16 years

Groups by pre-booked appointment only. Minimum payment £45 (15 people).

CONFERENCE AND FUNCTION FACILITIES

ROOM	DIMENSIONS	CAPACITY	LAYOUT	POWER POINTS	SUITABLE FOR A/V
Ballroom	40' x 40'	130	Theatre	4	
Ionic Room	40' x 20'	90	Theatre	2	✓
Hunting Hall	36' x 21'	100	Buffets	2	
		42	Lunch/Dinner		
Dining Room	35' x 19'	24	Lunch/Dinner	3	

NEWBY HALL
Ripon

NEWBY HALL, the Yorkshire home of Mr and Mrs Robin Compton, is a late 17th century house built in the style of Sir Christopher Wren. William Weddell, an ancestor of Mr Compton, made the Grand Tour in the 1760's and amongst the treasures he acquired were magnificent classical statuary and a superb set of Gobelin Tapestries. To house these treasures, Weddell commissioned Robert Adam to create the splendid domed Sculpture Gallery and Tapestry Room that we see today. The Regency Dining Room and Billiards Room were added later. There is much fine Chippendale furniture and in recent years Mrs Compton has restored the decoration of the house, painstakingly researching colour and decor of the Adam period.

GARDENS

25 acres of glorious gardens contain rare and beautiful shrubs and plants. Newby's famous double herbaceous borders, flanked by great bastions of yew hedges, sweep down to the River Ure. Formal gardens such as the Autumn and Rose Gardens - each with splashing fountains - a Victorian Rock Garden, the tranquillity of Sylvia's Garden, Pergolas and even a Tropical Garden, make Newby a 'Garden for all Seasons'. Newby holds the National Collection of the Genus Cornus and in 1987 won the Christies'/ HHA Garden of the Year Award. The Gardens also incorporate an exciting children's Adventure Garden and Miniature Railway.

SUITABILITY FOR OTHER EVENTS

Individual requests considered. Newby Hall offers filming possibilities and is suitable for special events such as Craft & Country Fairs, Vehicle Rallies etc. The Grantham Room is available for wedding receptions, promotions and lectures.

ADVICE TO COURIERS & DRIVERS

Allow a full day for viewing House and Gardens. Dogs in picnic area only, no photography inside House.

FACILITIES FOR THE DISABLED

5 wheelchairs available on request. Access around ground floor of house and key areas in gardens. Toilet for the disabled at Restaurant.

PARKING FOR COACHES & CARS

Unlimited parking near House and Gardens.

CATERING

In Garden Restaurant, teas, hot and cold meals. Pre-booked parties in Grantham Room. Menus/rates on request.

THE NEWBY SHOP

Excellent, open from 11am - 5.30pm.

GUIDE BOOKS

Colour guide books of the House and Gardens. Illustrated leaflets for the Gardens and Woodland Discovery Walk can be bought at the shop and plant stall.

SCHOOL VISITS/CHILDREN

School groups welcome. Rates on request. Grantham Room for use as wet weather base subject to availability. Of special interest: Woodland Discovery Walk, Adventure Gardens and train rides on 10¼" gauge railway.

CONTACT

The Opening
Administrator
Newby Hall
Ripon
North Yorkshire
HG4 5AE

Tel: (01423) 322583

Fax: (01423) 324452

LOCATION

Midway between London and Edinburgh, 4 miles west of A1, towards Ripon.

Taxi: Ripon Taxi Rank (01765) 601283.

Bus: On Ripon-York route.

OPENING TIMES

Summer
April - September
HOUSE
Daily except Mondays
(Bank Hols Mons only)
12 noon - 5.00pm
Last admission 4.30pm.

GARDEN
Daily except Mondays
(Bank Hols Mons only)
11.00am - 5.30pm
Last admission 5.00pm.

Winter
October - end March
Closed.

ADMISSION

HOUSE & GARDEN
Adult £5.40
Child* £3.20
OAP £4.50
Disabled £3.20
Group**
Adult £4.50
Child*** £3.00

GARDEN ONLY
Adult £3.80
Child* £2.50
OAP £3.30
Disabled £2.50
Group**
Adult £3.30
Child*** £2.30
Additional charges made for train.

*   Age 4-16

** Minimum 0 people

*** Details from Administrator

CONFERENCE AND FUNCTION FACILITIES

ROOM	DIMENSIONS	CAPACITY	LAYOUT	POWER POINTS	SUITABLE FOR A/V
Grantham Room	200	Theatre	✓	✓	
	200	Reception			
	100	Lunch/Dinner			

NOSTELL PRIORY
Wakefield

This Palladian Mansion is still the family home of Lord and Lady St Oswald. Inside you can see superb plasterwork ceilings in the state rooms designed and decorated in the middle of the 18th century.

Chippendale, England's most famous cabinet maker, designed furniture especially for the house. Only at Nostell can you find his furniture in such a variety of styles: the magnificent mahogany library table and richly lacquered green and gold 'chinoiserie' furniture.

Nostell is also home to many art treasures: the Brussels tapestries by Van der Borcht, and the famous paintings of The Family of Sir Thomas More and The Procession to Calvary by Pieter Breughel the Younger. These are just some of the many collections that you can enjoy.

Can you imagine who might have played with the remarkable six foot high 18th century doll's house? It is still complete with its original fittings and furniture and is always a great attraction for our visitors.

You can test your knowledge of roses in the old walled garden, where many varieties are laid out in ornamental beds originally designed by the renowned architect Robert Adam as a soft fruit garden.

A gentle lakeside walk leads you to the secluded summer house from where the beautiful flowering magnolia trees can be enjoyed in early summer.

The craft centre in the stable block is where you can find crafts people demonstrating and selling samples of their work. Close by is Wragby church which is also open to visitors.

Next to the adventure playground is a picnic area, an ideal place to enjoy lunch.

SUITABILITY FOR OTHER EVENTS
Varied programme of events throughout the year, eg craft fairs, field events.

CONFERENCES/FUNCTIONS
The Old Riding School, and the Old Coach House (with arched windows on to the terrace) - available for concerts, family weddings, dinner dances, exhibitions, conferences, workshops and training days.

EXTRA FACILITIES
Lakeside walk, rose garden, extensive parkland, adventure playground, craft centre.

ADVICE TO COURIERS & DRIVERS
Please advise us of any major unavoidable delays en route.

PARKING FOR COACHES & CARS
Ample free parking. Coaches may set down & pick up at front doors.

FACILITIES FOR THE DISABLED
Tactile books, taped guides, Batricar, toilets for disabled, lift, wheelchairs.

CATERING (NOT NT)
Light refreshments & afternoon teas in the stable tearoom.

GIFT SHOP
Souvenir & Gift shops - one in grounds, the other in house.

GUIDE BOOK
For sale at both shops.

GUIDED TOURS
Weekdays and for special party bookings only.

SCHOOL VISITS/CHILDREN
Welcomed - please pre-book - party rates.

CONTACT

The Administrator
Nostell Priory
Wakefield
W. Yorkshire WF4 1QE

Tel: (01924) 863892
Fax: (01924) 865282

Conference &
Function facilities:
Mrs Barbara Bolton
Tel: (01924) 864287

LOCATION

6 miles SE of Wakefield, off A638 Wakefield to Doncaster road

J40 off M1 to Wakefield, then A638

J38 off A1(M) then A638

Take junction off M62 to Pontefract A628/A638

OPENING TIMES

30 March - 31 October

April - June
September - October
Sat & Sun
11.00am - 5.00pm

1 July - 12 September
Daily except Fridays
11.00am - 5.00pm

BH Mons and Tues.
Not Good Friday.

ADMISSION

HOUSE & GROUNDS
Adult £3.80
Child £2.00
Family £7.60

GROUNDS ONLY
Adult £2.50
Child £1.30
Family £5.00

Groups of 30+
Adult £3.30
Child £1.70

CONFERENCE AND FUNCTION FACILITIES

ROOM	DIMENSIONS	CAPACITY	LAYOUT	POWER POINTS	SUITABLE FOR A/V
Old Riding School	22m x 12m	202	Dance floor with bar and stage	✓	✓
Old Coach House	10m x 17m	120	Theatre	✓	✓
		90	Dining		

RIPLEY CASTLE
Harrogate

RIPLEY CASTLE has for twenty eight generations been the home of the Ingilby family and it retains that 'much loved and very much alive' feeling of a family home. The guides whilst being very knowledgeable, all have an excellent sense of humour, and the tours which take approximately one hour, are not only informative but great fun. The Castle contains fine portraits, paintings, furnishing and chandeliers and in the old (1555) tower, some splendid armour, books, panelling and a secret hiding place.

The extensive walled gardens have recently been transformed and now house The National Hyacinth Collection and fabulous Ripley tropical plant collection, which includes many rare and exotic species, 85,000 spring flowering bulbs create a blaze of colour in April/May, and are followed by the Bluebells and Rhododendrons, Delphiniums, Roses and Herbaceous Borders. Ripley village, on the Castle's doorstep is also very beautiful, with many interesting shops, an Art Gallery and Farm Museum.

❖

SUITABILITY FOR OTHER EVENTS
Wedding Receptions, Dinners, Dances, Banquets, Outdoor Concerts, Meetings, Activity Days, Medieval Banquets, Management Training Courses.

EXTRA FACILITIES
Conference, Training and Syndicate Rooms, Clay Pigeon Shooting, Archery, Buggies and Hovercraft, Fishing, Cricket, Tennis, Croquet, Infra-Red Combat. Marquee events any size.

ADVICE TO COURIERS & DRIVERS
Dogs prohibited (except Guide Dogs). No photography inside Castle unless prior written consent.

FACILITIES FOR THE DISABLED
5/7 rooms accessible for the disabled. Gardens easily accessible (except Tropical Collection). Toilets for the disabled at Hotel (100 yards) and in village car park (150 yards). Disabled parking 50 yards from Castle front door.

PARKING FOR COACHES & CARS
Free parking for 290 cars within 300 yards of the Castle entrance. Coach parking 50 yards from Castle entrance.

CATERING
Morning and Afternoon Tea and refreshments at Cromwell's Eating House (seats 80) outside Castle walls. Pub lunches or Dinner at Hotel (100 yards). VIP lunches and dinners (maximum 66) inside Castle, unlimited in Marquees. Parties of 15+ must book in advance for Cromwell's Eating House and Hotel.

ACCOMMODATION
At the Boar's Head Hotel (RAC****) 100 yards from Castle. Owned and managed by the Estate.

GIFT SHOP
Open daily April to October, weekends only November-March - 10.30am - 5pm.

GUIDE BOOKS
Colour guide book, £2.50. Special children's guide book is available price 99p.

GUIDED TOURS
Guided tours standard, and included in price.

SCHOOL VISITS/CHILDREN
Groups are welcome all year round, by prior arrangement, between 10.30am - 7.30pm.

CONTACT
Tours: Elizabeth Liddle
Meetings/Dinners:
Chloe Evans
Ripley Castle, Ripley
Harrogate
North Yorkshire
HG3 3AY
Tel: (01423) 770152
Fax: (01423) 771745

LOCATION
Just off A61, 3½ mls N of Harrogate, 8 mls S of Ripon. M1 18 mls South, M62 20 mls South.
Taxi: Blueline taxis Harrogate 503037

OPENING TIMES

CASTLE & GARDENS
April, May and October
Sat & Sun
11.30am - 4.30pm

Good Fri. & Bank Hols.
11.00am - 4.30pm

June & September
Thurs, Fri, Sat & Sun
11.30am - 4.30pm

July and August
Daily: 11.30am - 4.30pm

GARDENS ONLY
March
Thurs, Fri, Sat & Sun
11.00am - 4.00pm

April - October
Daily: 11.00am - 5.00pm

Nov - Dec 23rd
Daily: 11.00am - 3.30pm

Winter
Pre-booked parties of 15+. (except 25 Dec)
10.30am - 7.30pm

ADMISSION

All Year

CASTLE & GARDENS
Adult £4.00
Child* £2.00
OAP £3.00
Groups**
Adult £3.00
Child* £1.75

GARDENS ONLY
Adult £2.25
Child* £1.00
OAP £1.75
Groups**
Adult £1.75
Child* £1.00

* Under 16.
** Min. 25 people.

ROOM	DIMENSIONS	CAPACITY	LAYOUT	POWER POINTS	SUITABLE FOR A/V
Morning Room	27' x 22'	32 42 70 66	U-Shape Boardroom Theatre Lunch/Dinner	6	✓
Large Drawing Room	30 'x 22'	29 36 80 60	U-Shape Boardroom Theatre Lunch/Dinner	4	✓
Library	31 x 19'	26 36 75 48	U-Shape Boardroom Theatre Lunch/Dinner	3	✓
Tower Room	33' x 21'	26 36 75	U-Shape Boardroom Theatre	3	✓
Map Room	19' x 14'	10 16 24 16	U-Shape Boardroom Theatre Lunch/Dinner	6	✓
Dining Room	23' 3" x 19' 6"	16 16	Boardroom Lunch/Dinner	2	✓

SKIPTON CASTLE
Skipton

Guardian of the gateway to the Yorkshire Dales for over 900 years, this is one of the most complete and well-preserved medieval castles in England. From 1310 stronghold of the Cliffords, two Lords of Skipton went out from here to die on Roses battlefields. In the Civil War this was the last Royalist bastion in the North, falling after a three year siege. Every phase of this turbulent history has left its mark, from the Norman entrance arch and gateway towers to the beautiful early Tudor courtyard built in the heart of the Castle by 'The Shepherd Lord'; it was there, in 1659, that Lady Anne Clifford planted a yew tree (in whose shade you can sit today) to mark the completion of her repairs after the Civil War. Thanks to her – and to Cromwell, who permitted them on condition that the roofs should not be able to support cannon – the

Castle is still fully roofed, making a visit well worthwhile at any time of year.

The gatehouse of the Castle contains the Shell Room, decorated in 1620 with shells and Jamaican coral said to have been brought home by Lady Anne's father, George Clifford, 3rd Earl of Cumberland, Champion to Queen Elizabeth and one of her Admirals against the Armada; he lies beneath a splendid tomb in Skipton's Parish Church, a few yards from the Castle gates.

On leaving the Castle, the visitor is at once in the town's bustling High Street, with its four market days every week (and lots of other good shopping) and a great variety of pubs and restaurants. Close by, the Leeds & Liverpool Canal presents a lively scene.

❖

CONTACT

Judith Parker
Skipton Castle
Skipton
North Yorkshire
BD23 1AQ

Tel: (01756) 792442

LOCATION

In the centre of Skipton, at the head of the High Street.

Skipton is 20 miles west of Harrogate on the A59 and 26 miles NW of Leeds on A65.

OPENING TIMES

All Year

Daily (except 25 Dec)

from 10am
(Suns from 2pm)

Last admissions: 6pm
(Oct - Mar 4pm)

ADMISSION

Adult £3.40
OAP £2.90
with illustrated
tour sheet.
Child (6-18) £1.70
with badge and
illustrated tour sheet.
Child (0 - 5) . . . .Free

Groups of 15+
Adult . . . . . .less 10%

School Groups
Students £1.70
Teachers . . . . . . .Free

Groups welcome:
Guides available for
pre-booked parties
at no extra charge.

ADVICE TO COURIERS & DRIVERS
Large public coach and car park off nearby High Street. Coach drivers' rest room at the Castle.

CATERING
Soft drinks and ice creams are sold in the Castle Shop. There is a wide choice of cafés and pubs in the town.

GUIDE BOOKS
A colour guide book is available.

SCHOOL VISITS/CHILDREN
Teachers find that a visit to Skipton has considerable educational value and is popular with the children. Our guides are adept at suiting both tour and commentary to the age of the group. Pre-booking is essential. Teachers enter free – both with their class and on pre-view visits to assess educational potential.

ABBEY HOUSE MUSEUM

Tel: 01532 755821

Abbey Road, Kirkstall, Leeds, Yorkshire LS5 3EH
Owner: Leeds City Council   **Contact:** S. Flavin
The house which still includes the Norman Hall, enables visitors to explore the life of the people of Leeds at work and play. Shops and Georgian and Victorian streets recreated.
Location: On A65 3m out of Leeds city centre.
Opening Times: Tue - Sat: 10am - 5pm. Sun 1 - 5pm. Closed Mondays.
Admission: Adult £2.00, Child 50p, Conc/ Groups £1.00.

AMPLEFORTH COLLEGE JUNIOR SCHOOL

Tel: 01439 788238   **Tel:** 01439 788538

The Castle, Gilling East, York, Yorkshire YO6 4HP
Owner: Ampleforth Abbey Trustees   **Contact:** Fr Jeremy Sierla
Not suitable for wheelchairs. No public toilets.
Location: 20m N of York on Helmsley Road.
Opening Times: House: term time, 10am - 12 noon & 2 - 4pm. Gardens - All year: dawn - dusk.
Admission: Gardens: Adult 75p. House: Free (Great Hall & Entrance Hall only).

ASKE HALL

RICHMOND, NORTH YORKSHIRE DL10 5HJ

Owner: The Marquess of Zetland   *Contact:* Debbie Walker

Tel: 01748 823222   **Fax:** 01748 823252
Nestling in 'Capability' Brown landscaped parkland and dating back to medieval times, Aske Hall has been the family seat of the Dundas family since 1762. There is an impressive collection of exquisite furniture, paintings and porcelain, including Chippendale furniture and Zoffany and Gainsborough paintings.

Alterations over the centuries reflect architectural trends. The present Hall incorporates the original 15th century Peel Tower as well as a remodelled Jacobean tower and a chapel - converted from John Carr's old stable block in Victorian times. There is a coach house, with clock tower, where the family's carriage is kept and in the grounds there is a Gothic style folly known as The Temple and an elaborate stable block built in the Victorian era. Facilities available for corporate hospitality, business promotion, film and many other events.
Location: 2 miles from the A1 at Scotch Corner, on the outskirts of Richmond, on the Gilling West road (B6274).
Opening Times: All year for groups of 15+ by appointment only.
Admission: House & Grounds: £3.50 per person.

BAYSGARTH HOUSE MUSEUM

Tel: 01652 632318

Caistor Road, Barton on Humber, Humberside DN18 6AH
Owner: Glanford Borough Council   **Contact:** Mr D J Williams
18th century town house and park. Displays of porcelain and local history.
Location: Caistor Road, Barton on Humber.
Opening Times: Thurs, Fri and Bank Holidays: 10am - 4pm. Sat and Sun, 10am - 5pm.
Admission: Free.

BENINGBROUGH HALL

Tel: 01904 470666

Shipton-by-Beningbrough, Yorkshire YO6 1DD
Owner: The National Trust   **Contact:** The Administrator
This handsome Georgian house has been completely restored and in the principal rooms are one hundred famous portraits on loan from the National Portrait Gallery. Victorian laundry, potting shed and exhibitions. Garden and wilderness play area.
Location: 8m NW of York, 3m W of Shipton A19, 2m SE of Linton-on-Ouse, follow signposted route.
Opening Times: 30 March - 31 October: Sat - Wed and Good Friday. Also Fridays in July & August. House: 11am - 5pm. Last admission 4.30pm.
Admission: House, Garden and Exhibition: Adult £4.50, Child £2.30, Family 9.00. Garden and Exhibition: Adult £3.00, Child £1.50, Family £6.00.

BEVERLEY MINSTER

Tel: 01482 887520

Beverley, Yorkshire, HU17 0DP
           Contact: Mr R I Shaw
Ancient Medieval Minster dating from 1220. A very fine example of Gothic architecture. Fine set of 68 misericords. Saxon Sanctuary chair, famous Percy tomb canopy.
Location: 8m N of Hull, 30m E of York.
Opening Times: Sept - Mar: 9am - 4pm. Apr & May: 9am - 5pm. May - Aug: 9am - 7pm. Service: 8am, 10.30am and 6.30pm, Thurs 7.30pm.
Admission: Donation of at least £1.00.

BISHOPS HOUSE

Tel: 01142 557701

Meersbrook Park, Norton Lees Lane, Sheffield, Yorkshire S8 9BE
Owner: Sheffield City Council   **Contact:** Ms K Streets
Built around 1500, this beautiful timber-framed farmhouse is set in parkland and commands panoramic views over the city of Sheffield. Period rooms and displays contain local furniture, plasterwork and embroidery, and explore everyday life in Tudor and Stuart times. Temporary exhibitions and events programme on local historical themes throughout the year. Guided tours available by appointment.
Location: A61, 2 miles S off Chesterfield Road
Opening Times: All year: Wed - Sat 10am - 4.30pm; Sun 11am - 4.30pm.
Admission: Adult £1.00, Child 50p, Senior Citizen 50p. Unemployed free.

BOLTON CASTLE

OPEN

March to
end of October

Daily
10.00am - 5.00pm

Tel: 01969 623981
Fax: 01969 623332

LEYBURN, NORTH YORKSHIRE DL8 4ET

Owner: Hon Mr & Mrs Harry Orde-Powlett   *Contact:* Mr & Mrs Harry Orde-Powlett

Medieval castle with fine views over Wensleydale. Home of the Scrope family. Mary Queen of Scots was imprisoned here. Well preserved roof and some furnished rooms. Major restoration work was completed in the Spring of 1995. Medieval gardens are being developed. Tea room and well stocked gift shop. Good all weather entertainment.
Location: Approx 6 miles from market town of Leyburn heading W off the A684.
Admission: Adult £3, OAP/Child £2. Guided tours available when pre-booked.

BOWLING HALL MUSEUM

Tel: 01274 723057 **Fax:** 01274 726220

Bowling Hall Road, Bradford, Yorkshire BD4 7LP
Owner: City of Bradford Metropolitan District Council   **Contact:** Mrs A Bickley
A good example of local, domestic architecture ranging in date from the 15th to 18th century. The rooms are furnished appropriately for this period.
Location: In Bradford.
Opening Times: Please telephone the Museum for the 1996 opening times.
Admission: Free.

KEY TO SYMBOLS:  THE NATIONAL TRUST   ENGLISH HERITAGE   HISTORIC HOUSES ASSOCIATION

BRAMHAM PARK

Tel: 01937 844265 **Fax:** 01937 845923

Wetherby, West Yorkshire LS23 6ND

Owner: Mr and Mrs George Lane Fox **Contact:** Mr and Mrs George Lane Fox

A splendid Queen Anne mansion set in the peaceful tranquillity of 66 acres of formal gardens. Collections of furniture, porcelain and paintings. The gardens are famous for their "grand vista" design.

Location: Bramham, Nr. Wetherby.

Opening Times: Gardens, Sats - Mon at Easter, May Day and Spring Bank Holiday weekends. House and Gardens: 16 June - 1 September: Sun, Tues, Wed, Thurs and August Bank Holiday Monday. 1.15 - 5.30pm. Last admissions 5pm.

Admission: House and Gardens: Adult £3.50, Child £1.50, OAP £2.50. Grounds: Adult £2.00, Child £1.00, OAP £1.50. Reduced rates for 20+.

BRODSWORTH HALL ⌗

See Page 227 for full page entry.

BROUGHTON HALL

See Page 228 for full page entry.

BURTON AGNES HALL

DRIFFIELD, YORKSHIRE YO25 0ND

Owner: Burton Agnes Hall Preservation Trust Ltd *Contact: Mrs Susan Cunliffe-Lister*

Tel: 01262 490324 **Fax:** 01262 490513

A lovely Elizabethan Hall containing treasures collected by the family over four centuries from the original carving and plasterwork to modern and Impressionist paintings. The Hall is surrounded by lawns and topiary yew. The old walled garden has been recently redeveloped and now contains a maze, potager, jungle garden, campanula collection and colour gardens incorporating giant game boards. Licensed cafe, ice-cream parlour, plant sales, gift shop, herb and flower shop and children's corner.

Location: Off A166 between Driffield and Bridlington.

Opening Times: 1 April - 31 October: Daily 11am - 5pm.

Admission: House & Gardens: Adult £3.50, OAP £3.00, Child £2.00. Grounds only: Adult £1.80, OAP £1.50, Child 80p. (10% reduction for parties 30+).

BURTON AGNES MANOR HOUSE ⌗

Tel: 0191 261 1585

Burton Agnes, Bridlington, Humberside

Owner: English Heritage **Contact:** The North Regional Office

A rare example of a Norman house, altered and encased in brick in the 17th and 18th centuries.

Location: Burton Agnes village, 5m SW of Bridlington on A166.

Opening Times: 1 Apr - 31 Oct: Daily 10am - 6pm or dusk if earlier. 1 Nov - 31 Mar: Daily 10am - 4pm. Closed 24 - 26 Dec, 1 Jan.

BURTON CONSTABLE HALL

OPEN

Easter Sun - 30 Sept.
Suns - Thur
Also Sats in
July & Aug.

Grounds &
Tea Room
open 12 noon

Hall 1.00 - 4.15pm
(Last admission)

Tel: 01964 562400
Fax: 01964 563229

NR. HULL, NORTH HUMBERSIDE HU11 4LN

Owner: Burton Constable Foundation *Contact: David Wrench*

Burton Constable, a magnificent 16th century house with 18th century additions by Adam, Lightoler and others. The collections include pictures, English furniture and scientific instruments and guns collected in the 18th century by William Constable. With nearly 30 rooms open, a unique insight is possible into the patronage of the Constable family who have lived here since it was built.

Location: 14 mls from Beverley via A165 Bridlington Road, follow Historic House signs. 7 mls from Hull via A1238 to Sproatley then follow Historic House signs.

Admission: Adult £3.50, Senior Citizen £2.75, Child £1.50. Group rates available.

BYLAND ABBEY ⌗

Tel: 01347 868614

Coxwold, Helmsley, North Yorkshire YO6 4BD

Owner: English Heritage **Contact:** The Custodian

A hauntingly beautiful ruin, set in peaceful meadows in the shadow of the Hambleton Hills. It illustrates later development of Cistercian churches, including a beautiful floor of mosaic tiles.

Location: 2m S of A170 between Thirsk and Helmsley, near Coxwold village.

Opening Times: 1 Apr - 30 Sept: Daily 10am - 6pm. 1 - 31 Oct: Daily 10am - 6pm or dusk if earlier. (Closed lunch 1 - 2pm).

Admission: Adult £1.40, Child 70p, Conc £1.10.

CASTLE HOWARD

See Page 229 for full page entry.

CLIFFORD'S TOWER ⌗

Tel: 01904 646940

Clifford Street, York, Yorkshire YO1 1SA

Owner: English Heritage **Contact:** The Custodian

A 13th century tower on one of two mottes thrown up by William the Conqueror to hold York. There are panoramic views of the city from the top of the tower.

Location: In Tower Street.

Opening Times: 1 Apr - 30 Sept: Daily 10am - 6pm. 1 - 31 Oct: Daily 10am - 6pm or dusk if earlier. 1 Nov - 31 Mar: Daily 10am - 4pm.

Admission: Adult £1.60, Child 80p, Conc £1.20.

CONISBROUGH CASTLE ⌗

Tel: 0191 261 1585

Conisbrough, Yorkshire

Owner: English Heritage **Contact:** The North Regional Office

The spectacular white circular keep of this 12th century castle rises majestically above the River Don. The oldest circular keep in England and one of the finest medieval buildings.

Location: NE of Conisbrough town centre off A630, 4¹/₂ m SW of Doncaster.

Opening Times: 1 Apr - 30 Sept: Daily 10am - 5pm (6pm at weekends). 1 - 31 Oct: Daily 10am - 4pm. 1 Nov - 31 Mar: Daily 10am - 4pm. Closed 25 - 26 Dec, 1 Jan.

Admission: Adults £1.80, Child £1.35, Conc 90p.

CONSTABLE BURTON HALL GARDENS

Tel: 01677 450428 **Fax:** 01677 450622

Leyburn, North Yorkshire DL8 5LJ

Owner: M C A Wyvill Esq **Contact:** M C A Wyvill Esq

A delightful terraced woodland garden of lilies, ferns, hardy shrubs, roses and wild flowers attached to a beautiful Palladian house designed by John Carr (not open). Near to the entrance drive is a stream, bog garden and rockery. Impressive spring display of daffodils, aconites and snowdrops.

Location: 3 m E of Leyburn off the A684.

Opening Times: Garden only: 1 April - 20 October: Daily 9am - 6pm.

Admission: Adult £2.00, OAP £1.50, Children (under 16) 50p.

DUNCOMBE PARK

See Page 230 for full page entry.

EASBY ABBEY

Tel: 0191 261 1585

Richmond, Yorkshire
Owner: English Heritage **Contact:** The North Regional Office
Substantial remains of the medieval abbey buildings stand in a beautiful setting by the River Swale near Richmond.
Location: 1 m SE of Richmond off B6271.
Opening Times: Any reasonable time.

ELSHAM HALL COUNTRY AND WILDLIFE PARK

Tel: 01652 688698 **Fax:** 01652 688738

Elsham, Brigg, Humberside DN20 0QZ
Owner: Capt Jeremy Elwes/Robert Elwes **Contact:** Robert Elwes
Winner of ten Awards for Tourism. Attractions include Falconry, the Mini Zoo, Georgian Courtyard, Arboretum, Granary Tearooms/Restaurant, Theatre and Conference Centre, Clocktower Museum and beautiful lakeside gardens.
Location: 10 minutes from Junction 5 of the M180, Humber Bridge turn-off.
Opening Times: Easter - mid Sept: 11am - 5pm every day including Suns and Bank Holidays. Art Gallery: 12 noon - 5pm. Mid-Sept - Easter: Closed.
Admission: Adult £3.95, Child £2.50, OAP £3.50, under 3 years free. Party rates available for groups of over 20.

EPWORTH OLD RECTORY

Tel: 01427 872268

1 Rectory Street, Epworth, Doncaster, South Yorkshire DN9 1HX
Owner: World Methodist Council **Contact:** C J Barton (Warden)
1709 Queen Anne period house, John and Charles Wesley's boyhood home. Portraits, period furniture, Methodist memorabilia. Guided tours, garden, picnic facilities, toilets, car park. Cinematic presentation. Souvenir Shop. Refreshments. Accommodation may be booked.
Location: Epworth lies on A161, 3 miles South of J2 of M180.
Opening Times: 1 Mar - 31 Oct: Daily Mon - Sat 10am - 12 noon, 2 - 4pm. Suns 2 - 4pm.
Admission: Adult £2.00, Children in full-time education £1.00.

FAIRFAX HOUSE

See Page 231 for full page entry.

FOUNTAINS ABBEY & STUDLEY ROYAL

See Page 232 for full page entry.

THE GEORGIAN THEATRE ROYAL

Tel: 01748 823710 **Fax:** 01748 823710

Richmond, Yorkshire DL10 4DW
Owner: Georgian Theatre Royal Trust **Contact:** Bill Sellars
Brochure on request. Built in 1788, this is the country's oldest theatre in original form.
Location: 6m from Scotch Corner
Opening Times: Museum: 1 Apr - 31 Oct: Mon - Sat 11am - 4.45pm. Sun 2.30 - 4.45pm. Theatre performances; Apr - Dec.
Admission: Museum: Adult £1, Child 50p, Conc 70p, Groups by arrangement. Theatre: £3 - £8.

HAREWOOD HOUSE

See Page 233 for full page entry.

HARLOW CARR BOTANICAL GARDENS

Tel: 01423 565418
Fax: 01423 530663

Crag Lane, Harrogate, North Yorkshire HG3 1QB
Owner: Northern Horticultural Society **Contact:** Ms. Jennifer Lister
68 acre headquarters of the Northern Horticultural Society. Vegetable, fruit and flower trials; rock, foliage, winter and heather gardens; alpines; herbaceous beds; streamside; woodland and arboretum. National collections; exhibitions and displays; guided walks; lectures. Museum of Gardening; model village; children's play area; plant centre and gift shop. Shelters and seating. Ample parking.
Location: Off Otley Road (B6162) 1 1/2 miles from town centre.
Opening Times: Daily from 9.30am. Last admission 6pm or dusk if earlier.
Admission: Adult £3.30, OAP £2.50. Children free.

HELMSLEY CASTLE

Tel: 014397 70442

Helmsley, North Yorkshire YO6 5AB
Owner: English Heritage **Contact:** The Custodian
Close to the market square, with a view of the town, is this 12th century castle. Spectacular earthworks surround a great ruined Norman keep. There is an exhibition and tableau on the history of the castle.
Location: Near town centre.
Opening Times: 1 Apr - 30 Sept: Daily 10am - 6pm. 1 - 31 Oct: Daily 10am -6pm or dusk if earlier. 1 Nov - 31 Mar: Wed - Sun, 10am - 4pm (Closed lunch 1 - 2 Nov - Mar).
Admission: Adult £2.00, Child £1.00, Conc £1.50.

HOVINGHAM HALL

See Page 234 for full page entry.

KIRKHAM PRIORY

Tel: 01653 618768

Kirkham, Whitwell-on-the-Hill, Yorkshire YO6 7JS
Owner: English Heritage **Contact:** The Custodian
The ruins of this Augustinian priory include a magnificent carved gatehouse.
Location: 5 m SW of Malton on minor road off A64.
Opening Times: 1 Apr - 30 Sept: Daily 12 noon - 5pm.
Admission: Adult £1.40, Child 70p, Conc £1.10.

KNARESBOROUGH CASTLE

Tel: 01423 503340 **Fax:** 01423 840026

Knaresborough, North Yorkshire
Owner: Duchy of Lancaster **Contact:** Ms. Mary Kershaw
Ruins of 14th century castle standing high above the town. Local history museum housed in Tudor Courthouse. Gallery devoted to the Civil War.
Location: 5m E of Harrogate, off A59.
Opening Times: Easter BH w/e, 1 May - 30 Sept.
Admission: Adult £1.50, Child 75p, Family £3.50, Senior citizen 75p, Group £1.00.

LOTHERTON HALL

Tel: 0113 281 3259 **Fax:** 0113 260 2285

Aberford, Leeds, Yorkshire LS25 3EB
Owner: Leeds City Council **Contact:** Adam White Esq
Magnificent former home of the Gascoigne family. Fine furniture, paintings, silver, pottery, porcelain and displays of costume.
Location: Just off A1. 12 m NE of Leeds city centre.
Opening Times: Easter - Late Oct: 1 - 5pm. Groups at other times by appointment only.
Admission: Adult £2.00, Child accompanied by adults 50p (Leeds schools free), Conc £1.00.

MERCHANT ADVENTURERS' HALL

OPEN

16 Mar - 9 Nov
Daily
8.30am - 5.00pm

11 Nov - 14 Mar
1997(except Suns)
8.30am - 3.30pm

Closed Christmas/
New Year week

Tel: 01904 654818

FOSSGATE, YORK YO1 2XD

Owner: The Company of Merchant Adventurers *Contact: Ivison S Wheatley*

The finest medieval guild hall in Europe, built in 1357/61 and substantially unaltered. In it the Merchants transacted their business, as their successors still do today. On the ground floor was their hospice where they cared for the poor, and their private chapel, a unique survival in England. There are good collections of early portraits, furniture, silver and other objects used by the Merchants over the centuries when their wealth and influence helped to make York the second city in England, after London.
Location: On Piccadilly. Main entrance in Piccadilly, other entrance on Fossgate.
Admission: Adult £1.80, OAP £1.50, Child 60p.

MIDDLEHAM CASTLE

Tel: 01969 623899

Middleham, Leyburn, Yorkshire DL8 4QG
Owner: English Heritage **Contact:** The Custodian
This childhood home of Richard III stands controlling the river that winds through Wensleydale. There is a massive 12th century keep with splendid views of the surrounding countryside from the battlements.
Location: At Middleham, 2m S of Leyburn of A6108.
Opening Times: 1 Apr - 30 Sept: Daily 10am - 6pm. 1 - 31 Oct: Daily 10am - 6pm or dusk if earlier. 1 Nov - 31 Mar: Wed - Sun 10am - 4pm (closed for lunch 1 - 2pm Nov - Mar).
Admission: Adult £1.60, Conc £1.20, Child 80p.

MONK BRETTON PRIORY

Tel: 01226 204089

Barnsley, Yorkshire.
Owner: English Heritage **Contact:** The Custodian
Grime-stained blocks of red sandstone mark the peaceful ruin of this Cluniac monastery founded in 1153. Extensive remains of the fully restored 14th century Gatehouse.
Location: 1 M E of Barnsley town centre off A633.
Opening Times: Any reasonable time.
Admission: Free.

MOUNT GRACE PRIORY

SADDLE BRIDGE, NORTH YORKSHIRE DL6 3JG
Owner: *English Heritage*
Contact: *The Custodian*
Tel: 01609 883494

Hidden in tranquil wooded countryside at the foot of the Cleveland Hills, one of the loveliest settings of any English Priory, and the best preserved Carthusian monastery in England. Monks lived as hermits in their cells and one cell, recently restored, is furnished to give a clear picture of their austere routine of work and prayer. Visitors enter through the manor built by Thomas Lascelles in 1654 on the site of the monastery guest house. It was rebuilt at the turn of the century using traditional techniques, typical of the Arts and Crafts movement.

Location: 12 mls N of Thirsk, 7 mls NE of Northallerton on A19.

Admission: Adult £2.40, Conc. £1.80. Child £1.20. 15% discount on parties 11+.

OPEN

1 Apr - 30 Sept: Daily 10am - 6pm
1 - 31 Oct: Daily 10am - 6pm or dusk if earlier.

1 Nov - 31 Mar: Wed - Sun 10am - 4pm (closed lunch 1 - 2pm)

NEWBURGH PRIORY
Tel: 01347 868435

Coxwold, Yorkshire YO6 4AS
Owner: Sir George Wombwell Bt   **Contact:** Sir George Wombwell
Augustinian priory founded in 1145 converted into Tudor mansion, and again later in 18th century. Beautiful water garden.
Location: 7m SE Thirsk.
Opening Times: Apr - end Jun: Wed, Sun & Bank Hols: House: 2.30 - 4.45pm, Garden: 2 - 6pm.. Guided tours approx 60 mins. (Best to check first).

NEWBY HALL
See Page 235 for full page entry.

NORTON CONYERS
Tel: 01765 640333

Nr. Ripon, North Yorkshire HG4 5EH
Owner: Sir James and Lady Graham   **Contact:** Lady Graham
Visited by Charlotte Brontë in 1839, Norton Conyers is an original of the 'Thornfield Hall' in *Jane Eyre* and a family legend was an inspiration for the mad Mrs. Rochester. Building is late medieval with Stuart and Georgian additions. Family pictures, furniture and costumes. Friendly atmosphere, resulting from over 370 years of ownership by the same family. 18th century walled garden 100 yards from house, with an Orangery and herbaceous borders. Pick your own fruit.
Location: 4m NW of Ripon. 3m from the A1.
Opening Times: House & Garden: Bank Hol Suns & Mons. 23 Jun - 1 Sept: Suns 2 - 5pm. July: Mons 2 - 5pm, 23 - 27 July: Daily 2 - 5pm.
Admission: Adult £2.95, Child (10 - 16) £2.50, OAP/Student £2.00. Parties (20+) by arrangement. Garden is free, donations are welcome.

NOSTELL PRIORY
See Page 236 for full page entry.

NUNNINGTON HALL ❧
Tel: 01439 748283

Nunnington, Yorkshire YO6 5UY
Owner: National Trust   **Contact:** The Visitor Services Manager
16th century manor house with fine panelled hall and staircase. Carlisle collection of miniature rooms on display.
Location: In Ryedale, 4½m SE of Helmsley, 1½m S of B1257.
Opening Times: 30 March - 31 October: April, May, Sept, Oct: Tues, Wed, Thur, Sat, Sun & Good Friday 2 - 6pm; BH Mons, 1 - 6pm. June, July & Aug: Daily except Mons 1 - 6pm. Last admission 5.00pm.
Admission: House and Garden: Adult £3.50, Child £1.50. Family £7.00. Garden only: Adult £1.00, Child free.

THE OLD GRAMMAR SCHOOL
Tel: 01482 593902 **Fax:** 01482 593710

Market Place, Hull
Owner: Hull City Council   **Contact:** S R Green
Hull's oldest secular building now houses the social history exhibition "The Story of Hull and its People", an exploration of the fascinating lives of the people of Hull through the centuries. This history is explored using the themes common to all of us such as childhood, education, courtship, marriage and work. Visitors can participate by playing the 'game of life', following fictional characters making their way from birth to death. Various temporary exhibitions are displayed in the museum.
Location: 83 Alfred Gelder St, Hull.
Opening Times: Mon - Sat: 10am - 5pm, Sun: 1.30 - 4.30pm (Last adm. 15 minutes prior).

ORMESBY HALL ❧
Tel: 01642 324188

Church Lane, Ormesby, Middlesbrough, Yorkshire TS7 9AS
Owner: National Trust   **Contact:** The House Manager
A mid 18th century house with opulent decoration inside, including fine plasterwork by contemporary craftsmen. A Jacobean doorway with a carved family crest survives from the earlier house on the site. The stable block, attributed to Carr of York, is a particularly fine mid 18th century building with an attractive courtyard leased to the Mounted Police, also an attractive 5 acre garden with holly walk.
Location: 3m SE of Middlesbrough.
Opening Times: 30 Mar - 31 Oct: Wed, Thur, Sat, Sun, BH Mon & Good Friday, 2 - 5.30pm. July & August 1 - 5.30pm. Last admission 5pm.
Admission: House, Garden, Railway and Exhibitions: Adult £3.00, Child £1.50, Family £6.00. Garden, Railway and Exhibitions: Adult £2.00, Child £1.00.

PICKERING CASTLE ⌗
Tel: 01751 474989

Pickering, North Yorkshire YO18 7AX
Owner: English Heritage   **Contact:** The Custodian
A splendid motte and bailey castle, once a royal ranch. It is well preserved, with much of the original walls, towers and keep, and there are spectacular views over the surrounding countryside. There is an exhibition on the castle's history.
Location: In Pickering, 15m SW of Scarborough.
Opening Times: 1 Apr - 30 Sept: Daily 10am - 6pm. 1 - 31 Oct: Daily 10am - 6pm or dusk if earlier. 1 Nov - 31 Mar: Wed - Sun 10am - 4pm (closed for lunch 1 - 2pm).
Admission: Adult £2.00, Child £1.00, Conc £1.50.

RICHMOND CASTLE ⌗
Tel: 01748 822493

Richmond, North Yorkshire DL10 4QW
Owner: English Heritage   **Contact:** The Custodian
A splendid medieval fortress, with a fine 12th century keep and 11th century remains of the curtain wall and domestic buildings. There are magnificent views from the 100 feet high keep.
Location: In Richmond.
Opening Times: 1 Apr - 30 Sept: Daily 10am - 6pm. 1 - 31 Oct: Daily 10am - 6pm or dusk if earlier. 1 Nov - 31 Mar: Wed - Sun 10am - 4pm (closed for lunch 1 - 2pm).
Admission: Adult £1.80, Child 90p, Conc £1.40.

RIEVAULX ABBEY ⌗
Tel: 01439 798228

Rievaulx, Nr. Helmsley, North Yorkshire YO6 5LB
Owner: English Heritage   **Contact:** The Custodian
In a deeply wooded valley by the River Rye you can see some of the most spectacular monastic ruins in England, dating from the 12th century. The church has the earliest large Cistercian nave in Britain. A fascinating exhibition shows how successfully the Cistercians at Rievaulx ran their many businesses and explains the part played by Abbot Ailred, who ruled for twenty years.
Location: 2¼m W of Helmsley on minor road off B1257.
Opening Times: 1 Apr - 30 Sept: Daily 10am - 6pm. 1 - 31 Oct: 10am - 6pm or dusk if earlier. 1 Nov - 31 Mar: 10am - 4pm.
Admission: Adult £2.50, Child £1.30, Conc £1.90.

RIEVAULX TERRACE AND TEMPLES ❧
Tel: 01439 798340

Rievaulx, Helmsley, Yorkshire YO6 5LJ
Owner: The National Trust   **Contact:** The Visitor Services Manager
A ½m long grass-covered terrace and adjoining woodlands with vistas over Rievaulx Abbey and Rye valley to Ryedale and the Hambleton Hills. There are two mid 18th century temples: the Ionic Temple has elaborate ceiling paintings and fine 18th century furniture. A permanent exhibition in the basement is on English landscape design in the 18th century.
Location: 2¼m NW of Helmsley on B1257.
Opening Times: 30 March - 31 October: Daily 10.30am - 6.pm or dusk if earlier. Last admission 5pm. No access to Abbey from Terrace.
Admission: Adult £2.50, Child £1.00, Family £5.00.

RIPLEY CASTLE 🏛
See Page 237 for full page entry.

RIPON CATHEDRAL

Tel: 01765 602609 (information or tours etc.)

Ripon, Yorkshire HG4 1QR

Contact: Rev. David Murfet

One of the oldest crypts in Europe (672). Marvellous choir stalls and misericords (500 years old). Almost every type of architecture. Treasury.

Location: 5m W signposted off A1, 12m N of Harrogate.
Opening Times: All year: 8am - 6pm.
Admission: Donation.

ROCHE ABBEY

Tel: 01709 812739

Maltby, Rotherham, South Yorkshire S66 8NW
Owner: English Heritage.   **Contact:** The Custodian
This Cistercian monastery, founded in 1147, lies in a secluded landscaped valley sheltered by limestone cliffs and trees. Some of the walls still stand to their full height and excavation has revealed the complete layout of the abbey.
Location: 1 1/2 m S of Maltby off A634.
Opening Times: 1 Apr - 30 Sept: Daily 10am - 6pm. 1 - 31 Oct: Daily 10am - 6pm or dusk if earlier (closed lunch 1 -2pm).
Admission: Adult £1.40, Child 70p, Conc £1.10.

SCARBOROUGH CASTLE

Tel: 01723 372451

Castle Road, Scarborough, North Yorkshire YO11 1HY
Owner: English Heritage   **Contact:** The Custodian
From the walls of this enormous 12th century castle you will have spectacular coastal views. The buttressed castle walls stretch out along the cliff edge and the remains of the great rectangular stone keep still stand to over three storeys high. There is also the site of a 4th century Roman signal station. The castle was frequently attacked, but despite being blasted by cannons of the Civil War and bombarded from the sea during World War I, it is still a spectacular place to visit.
Location: Castle Road, E of town centre.
Opening Times: 1 Apr - 30 Sept: Daily 10am - 6pm. 1 - 31 Oct: Daily 10am - 6pm or dusk if earlier. 1 Nov - 31 Mar: Wed - Sun 10am - 4pm(closed for lunch 1 - 2pm Nov - Mar).
Admission: Adult £1.80, Child 90p, Conc £1.40.

SEWERDY HALL

Tel: 01262 677874   **Fax:** 01262 674265

Bridlington, Humberside Y15 1EA
Owner: Borough of East Yorkshire   **Contact:** The Administrator
Early 18th century house, now an art gallery. Large gardens of some interest.
Location: 2m N of Bridlington.
Opening Times: Summer 10am - 6pm. Winter: Sat - Tues, 11am - 4pm. Closed 10 Jan - 3 Mar.
Admission: Adult £2.50, Child £1.00, Senior citizens £2.00, Groups over 10 50% discount.

SHERIFF HUTTON PARK

Tel: 01347 878442   **Fax:** 01347 878442

Sheriff Hutton, York, Yorkshire YO6 1RH
Owner: East Fifteen Acting School   **Contact:** Pauline Simmons
Red-brick mansion in Queen Anne style from the outside. Jacobean and early Georgian rooms within. The garden also displays Jacobean features.
Location: A64 to 5m N of York; Sheriff Hutton exit to left. Rail: York station 10m.
Opening Times: Mon - Fri (except BHs) 10am - 4.30pm. Closed mid-Dec - mid-Jan.
Admission: Grounds: Adult £2.35, Child £1.20 Family £6, Conc £1.75. Party reductions. House: by prior arrangement only.

SHIBDEN HALL

Tel: 01422 352246   **Fax:** 01422 348440

Lister's Road, Halifax, West Yorkshire HX3 6XG
Owner: Calderdale MBC   **Contact:** Ms R Westwood
A half-timbered Manor House, the home of Anne Lister set in a landscaped park. Oak furniture, carriages and an array of objects make Shibden an intriguing place to visit. Cafe and Shop.
Location: 1 1/2m East of Halifax off A58.
Opening Times: 1 Mar - 30 Nov: Mon - Sat 10am - 5pm. Sun 12 noon - 5pm. Last adm. 4.30pm. For Winter opening please telephone.
Admission: Adult £1.60, Child/OAP/Conc 80p, Family £4.50.

OPEN

17 Mar - 31 Oct

Hall: Daily 12.30 - 4.30pm
Wed - Sun & all BH Mons.

Birds of Prey, Grounds:
Daily 10.30am - 5.30pm
Granary & Visitor Centre:
Tues - Suns
10.30am - 5.30pm

Tel: 01845 587206
Fax: 01845 587486

KIRBY WISKE, NORTH YORKSHIRE YO7 4EU

Owner: H.W. Mawer Trust   *Contact:* John D. Bridges

Charming, Edwardian mansion designed by Brierley – the 'Lutyens of the North' - has RIBA accolade for outstanding architectural merit. This Award Winning mansion has an eclectic Mawer collection of furniture, porcelain, clocks, paintings and period costume displays in 20 room settings - the most comprehensive in the north. Falconry in the Victorian walled garden - daily flying displays. Granary Tearoom. Visitor Centre and woodland walks.
Location: Signed off A167. 6 mls S of Northallerton, 4 mls W of Thirsk, 8 mls E of A1 via A61.
Admission: Hall: Adult £3.75, Conc. £3.00, Child £2.00. Birds: Adult £4.00, Conc. £3.00, Child £2.00. Grounds only: £1.00. Combined: Adult £6.75, Concession £5.00, Child £3.00. Groups Feb - Nov: any time by arrangement.

SKIPTON CASTLE   See Page 238 for full page entry.

SLEDMERE HOUSE

SLEDMERE, DRIFFIELD, EAST YORKSHIRE YO25 0XG

Owner: Sir Tatton Sykes   *Contact:* Mrs Anne Hines

Tel: 01377 236637   **Fax:** 01377 236560
Sledmere House is the home of Sir Tatton Sykes, 8th Baronet. There has been a manor house at Sledmere since medieval times. The present house was designed and built by Sir Christopher Sykes, 2nd Baronet, a diary date states 'June 17th, 1751 laid the first stone of the new house at Sledmere.' Sir Christopher employed a fellow Yorkshireman, Joseph Rose, the most famous English plasterer of his day to execute the decoration of Sledmere. Rose's magnificent work at Sledmere was unique in his career. A great feature at Sledmere is the 'Capability' Brown parkland and the beautiful 18th century walled rose gardens. Also worthy of note is the recently laid out knot-garden. Exhibition Centre, Museum, Cafe and Gift Shop.
Location: Off the A166 between York and Bridlington on scenic route.
Opening Times: 4 - 8 April, Suns in April then from 4 May - 24 Sept (closed Mon and Fri) House opens 1 - 4.30pm, Park & Gardens 11am - 5pm. Evenings and mornings by appointment.
Admission: Adult £3.50, OAP £3.00, Child £1.75. Park & Gardens: Adult £1.50, Child £1.00.

SPOFFORTH CASTLE

Tel: 0191 261 1585

Harrogate, Yorkshire.
Owner: English Heritage   **Contact:** The North Regional Office
This manor house has some fascinating features including an undercroft built into the rock. It was once owned by the Percy family.
Location: 3 1/2 m SE of Harrogate on minor road off A661 at Spofforth.
Opening Times: 1 Apr - 30 Sept: Daily 10am - 6pm. 1 - 31 Oct: Daily 10am - 6pm or dusk if earlier. 1 Nov - 31 Mar: 10am - 4pm.

STOCKELD PARK

OPEN
4 April - 10 Oct

Thursdays only.
2.00 - 5.00pm

Tel: 01937 586101
Fax: 01937 580084

WETHERBY, YORKSHIRE LS22 4AH
Owner: Mr and Mrs. P.G. F. Grant   *Contact: Mrs. L. A. Saunders*

Stockeld is a small and beautifully proportioned Palladian villa designed for Middletons by James Paine in 1763. The present family have lived at Stockeld for over a century and it is still very much a home, housing a good collection of 18th and 19th century furniture and paintings. Stockeld is set in beautiful parkland and has well established gardens and woodland.
Location: York 12 miles, Harrogate 5 miles, Leeds 12 miles.
Admission: Adult £2.00, Child £1.00, OAP £1.50.

ST WILLIAM'S COLLEGE
Tel: 01904 637134   **Fax:** 01904 654604

5 College Street, York, Yorkshire YO1 2JF
Owner: The Dean and Chapter of York   **Contact:** Sandie Clarke
15th century medieval home of Minster Chantry Priests. Three large medieval halls, available for functions, conferences, weddings, medieval banquets, etc. Halls open to view when not in use. Also available Shop, Minster restaurant, Information Centre, toilets.
Location: College Street, York.
Opening Times: 10am - 5pm
Admission: Adult 60p, Child 30p. For further details please telephone.

STUDLEY ROYAL: ST MARY'S CHURCH
Tel: 01765 608888

Ripon,   Yorkshire
Owner: English Heritage   **Contact:** The Custodian
A magnificent Victorian church, designed by William Burges in the 1870s with a highly decorated interior. Coloured marble, stained glass, gilded and painted figures and a splendid organ.
Location: 2¹/₂ m W of Ripon off B6265, in grounds of Studley Royal estate.
Opening Times: 1 Apr - 30 Sept : Daily, 1 - 5pm.

SUTTON PARK
Tel: 01347 810249

Sutton on the Forest, York, Yorkshire YO6 1DP
Owner: Mrs Sheffield   **Contact:** Mrs A. Wilkinson
Charming example of early Georgian architecture with rich collection of furniture and paintings put together with great style.
Location: 8m N of York on B1363 Helmsley Road.
Opening Times: Gardens: Daily Easter - Oct: 11am - 5.30pm.
Admission: Gardens: Adult £1.50, Child 50p. House: Private parties only.
Contact Administrator £5pp, £4.50 if group is 25+.

TEMPLE NEWSAM HOUSE
Tel: 0113 264 7321   **Fax:** 0113 260 2285

Leeds, Yorkshire LS15 0AE
Owner: Leeds City Council   **Contact:** Mrs C Stokes
Tudor and Jacobean mansion with extensive collections of decorative arts in their original room settings, including incomparable Chippendale collection.
Location: 5m E of city centre, off A63 Leeds/ Selby Road.
Opening Times: End Mar - end Oct: Daily except Mons 1 - 5pm. Nov - end Mar: Sats & Suns only, 12 noon - 4pm.
Admission: Adult £2.00, Child 50p, Conc £1.00, Pre-booked groups £1.00.

THORNTON ABBEY
Tel: 0191 261 1585

Scunthorpe, Humberside
Owner: English Heritage   **Contact:** The North Regional Office
The magnificent brick gatehouse of this ruined Augustine priory stands three storeys high, with a façade ornamented with finely carved details including some surviving 14th century statues.
Location: 18 m NE of Scunthorpe on minor road N of A160. 7 m SE of Humber Bridge on minor road E of A1077.
Opening Times: 1 Apr - 30 Sept: Daily 10am - 6pm. 1 - 31 Oct: Daily 10am - 6pm or dusk if earlier. 1 Nov - 31 Mar: Daily 10am - 4pm. Gatehouse: summer season, 1st & 3rd Sun of every month. 1 - 5pm or dusk if earlier. Gatehouse: winter season 3rd Sun of every month, 1 - 4pm or dusk if earlier.

TREASURER'S HOUSE
Tel: 01904 624247

Chapter House Street, York, Yorkshire YO1 2JD
Owner: The National Trust   **Contact:** The Administrator
A large 17th century house of great interest. Fine furniture and paintings. Exhibition.
Location: In Minster Yard on N side of Minster.
Opening Times: 30 March - 31 October: Daily 10.30am - 5.00pm. Last admission 4.30pm.
Admission: Adult £3.00, Child £1.50. Families £6.00.

WAKEFIELD CATHEDRAL

THE CATHEDRAL CHURCH OF ALL SAINTS, NORTHGATE, WAKEFIELD, WEST YORKSHIRE WF1 1HG

Owner: Church of England
Contact: Mr M.E. Ledger, Chapter Clerk

Tel: 01924 373923
Fax: 01924 215054

Built on the site of a previous Saxon church, this 14th century Parish Church became a cathedral in 1888 and was extended by Pearson and completed by his son. It is an oasis of tranquillity situated in a recently constructed award winning city precinct. It contains fine examples of stained glass, depicting a lifetime's work by Kempe and an intricately carved Rood Screen. It also boasts, at 200ft, the highest spire in Yorkshire. Bookshop.
Location: Wakefield city centre. M1 J39-41; M62 J29 W, J30 E.
Admission: Free admission. Donations welcome.

OPEN
Mon - Sat: 8am - 5pm. Sun: For services only
Guided Tours by prior arrangement
SUNDAY SERVICES: 8am Holy Communion. 9.15am Parish Eucharist. 11am Solemn Eucharist. 4pm Choral Evensong (Winter). 6.30pm Choral Evensong (Summer)
DAILY SERVICES: 8am Holy Communion. 10.30am Holy Communion - Wed & Sat. 12.30pm Holy Communion Fri 6.30pm Choral Evensong Thurs 5pm, Said Evensong Fri - Wed 5pm.

WHITBY ABBEY
Tel: 01947 603568

Whitby, Yorkshire YO22 4JT
Owner: English Heritage   **Contact:** The Custodian
This in an ancient holy place, once a burial place of kings and an inspiration for saints. A religious community was first established at Whitby in 657 by Abbess Hilda and was the home of Caedmon, the first English poet. The remains we can see today are of a Benedictine church built in the 13th and 14th centuries, and include a magnificent three-tiered choir and north transept. It is perched high above the picturesque harbour town of Whitby.
Location: On cliff top E of Whitby town centre.
Opening Times: 1 Apr - 30 Sept: Daily 10am - 6pm. 1 - 31 Oct: Daily 10am - 6pm or dusk if earlier. 1 Nov - 31 Mar: 10am - 4pm.
Admission: Adult £1.60, Child 80p, Conc £1.20.

WILBERFORCE HOUSE
Tel: 01482 593902   **Fax:** 01482 593710

High Street, Hull, Yorkshire HU1 1EP
Owner: Hull City Council   **Contact:** S R Green
Built c1656 the house has been a museum to the memory of William Wilberforce, slavery abolitionist, since 1906. The main display tells the horrific story of slavery and Wilberforce's struggle to abolish it. The house also holds many other fascinating displays such as the Victorian parlour, the famous Hull Silver and Georgian rooms.
Location: High Street, Hull.
Opening Times: Mon - Sat, 10am - 5pm. Sun 1.30 - 4.30pm. Closed Good Friday and Christmas Day.
Admission: Free.

Where to Stay
For Private Accommodation and Johansens recommended Hotels, see Accommodation Section.

SPECIAL EVENTS

❖ **HAREWOOD HOUSE** Concert in the Gallery	**22 MARCH**
❖ **SHIBDEN HALL** Demonstrating Craft weekend	**23 – 24 MARCH**
❖ **HAREWOOD HOUSE** Easter Weekend Events	**6 – 8 APRIL**
❖ **RIPLEY CASTLE** Spring Bulb Festival	**22 APRIL – 6 MAY**
❖ **HAREWOOD HOUSE** Yorkshire Dales Country & Western Festival	**2 – 6 MAY**
❖ **HAREWOOD HOUSE** Yorkshire Post Family Fun Day	**4 MAY**
❖ **HOVINGHAM HALL** YSCGP Spring Plant Fair	**12 MAY**
❖ **HAREWOOD HOUSE** Closed to the Public	**17 MAY**
❖ **HAREWOOD HOUSE** Festival of Craft, Fashion and Design	**25 – 28 MAY**
❖ **DUNCOMBE PARK** Country Fair	**27 MAY**
❖ **HAREWOOD HOUSE** Open Air Concert - Midsummer Classics	**2 JUNE**
❖ **RIPLEY CASTLE** Homes & Gardens Magazine Grand Summer Fair	**6 – 9 JUNE**
❖ **BURTON AGNES HALL** Gardeners' Fair	**8 – 9 JUNE**
❖ **DUNCOMBE PARK** Antiques Fair	**14 – 16 JUNE**
❖ **HAREWOOD HOUSE** Harewood Classic Car Show (Fathers' Day)	**16 JUNE**
❖ **HAREWOOD HOUSE** Singer Owners Club Rally	**23 JUNE**
❖ **HOVINGHAM HALL** Gardens open for charity	**23 JUNE**
❖ **RIPLEY CASTLE** Country Fair	**29 – 30 JUNE**
❖ **HAREWOOD HOUSE** Morris Minor Owners Club Northern Regional Rally	**30 JUNE**
❖ **HOVINGHAM HALL** Gardens open for charity	**30 JUNE**
❖ **HOVINGHAM HALL** 'Macbeth' - Box Hedge Co.	**30 JUNE**
❖ **HOVINGHAM HALL** Ball in aid of St John Ambulance	**6 JULY**
❖ **DUNCOMBE PARK** Steam Fair	**6 – 7 JULY**
❖ **HAREWOOD HOUSE** MG Rally	**6 – 7 JULY**
❖ **RIPLEY CASTLE** Performing Arts Concert with Fireworks	**7 JULY**
❖ **HAREWOOD HOUSE** Wellbeing Cricket Match	**7 JULY**
❖ **SHIBDEN HALL** Demonstrating Craft weekend	**13 – 14 JULY**
❖ **HAREWOOD HOUSE** Jaguar Rally	**14 JULY**
❖ **HAREWOOD HOUSE** Leeds Championship Dog Show	**27 – 29 JULY**
❖ **HAREWOOD HOUSE** Open Air Concert (Provisional)	**2 AUGUST**
❖ **HAREWOOD HOUSE** Koi Festival (Provisional on Saturday)	**3 – 4 AUGUST**
❖ **HAREWOOD HOUSE** Open Air Concert (Provisional)	**4 AUGUST**
❖ **HAREWOOD HOUSE** BMW Rally	**4 AUGUST**
❖ **HAREWOOD HOUSE** Rolls Royce Rally	**11 AUGUST**
❖ **HAREWOOD HOUSE** Steam Rally	**24 – 26 AUGUST**
❖ **RIPLEY CASTLE** North of England Hot Air Balloon Festival	**24 – 26 AUGUST**
❖ **HAREWOOD HOUSE** Open Air Concert - Last Night of the Proms	**1 SEPTEMBER**
❖ **HAREWOOD HOUSE** Alvis Owners Club	**8 SEPTEMBER**
❖ **SHIBDEN HALL** Demonstrating Craft weekend	**14 – 15 SEPTEMBER**
❖ **DUNCOMBE PARK** Antiques Fair	**1 – 3 NOVEMBER**
❖ **SHIBDEN HALL** Demonstrating Craft weekend	**16 – 17 NOVEMBER**
❖ **DUNCOMBE PARK** Christmas Craft Fair	**7 – 8 DECEMBER**

For National Trust and English Heritage Events see separate section.

WILLIAM MORRIS CENTENARY

The life and work of the charismatic and internationally influential British designer William Morris who was also a poet, craftsman and socialist will be the subject of a major exhibition at London's Victoria and Albert Museum from 9 May to 1 Sept 1996 to mark the centenary of his death. Other events at Kelmscott, near Lechlade (see page 71) on 3 Oct and 6 Oct 1996 will include the commemoration of Morris's death and funeral. Kelmscott Manor was his country home from 1871 until his death. The house contains an interesting collection of the possessions and works of Morris and his associates including furniture, textiles, carpets and ceramics.

SCOTLAND

This edition of Hudson's has placed entries under the existing Local Authority Regions. Following Local Government re-organisation, these regions will be replaced by new councils in April 1996.

EXISTING COUNCIL Regional & District	THE NEW COUNCIL	EXISTING COUNCIL Regional & District	THE NEW COUNCIL
BORDERS		**LOTHIAN**	
Berwickshire		East Lothian	East Lothian Council
Ettrick & Lauderdale	The Scottish Borders Council	City of Edinburgh	City of Edinburgh Council
Roxburgh		Midlothian	Midlothian Council
Tweeddale		West Lothian	West Lothian Council
CENTRAL		**STRATHCLYDE**	
Clackmannan	Clackmannanshire Council	Argyll & Bute	Argyll & Bute Council
Falkirk	Falkirk Council	Bearsden & Milngavie	East Dunbartonshire Council
Stirling	Stirling Council	Clydebank	West Dunbartonshire Council
DUMFRIES & GALLOWAY		Clydesdale	South Lanarkshire Council
Annandale & Eskdale		Cumbernauld & Kilsyth	North Lanarkshire Council
Nithsdale		Cumnock & Doon Valley	East Ayrshire Council
Stewartry	Dumfries & Galloway Council	Cunninghame	North Ayrshire Council
Wigtown		Dumbarton	West Dunbartonshire Council
FIFE		East Kilbride	South Lanarkshire Council
Dunfermline		Eastwood	East Renfrewshire Council
Kirkcaldy	Fife Council	City of Glasgow	City of Glasgow Council
North East Fife		Hamilton	South Lanarkshire Council
GRAMPIAN	City of Aberdeen Council	Inverclyde	Inverclyde Council
City of Aberdeen		Kilmarnock & Loudoun	East Ayrshire Council
Banff & Buchan		Kyle & Carrick	South Ayrshire Council
Gordon	Aberdeenshire Council	Monklands	North Lanarkshire Council
Kincardine & Deeside		Motherwell	North Lanarkshire Council
Moray	Moray Council	Renfrew	Renfrewshire Council
HIGHLAND		Strathkelvin	East Dunbartonshire Council
Badenoch & Strathspey		**TAYSIDE**	
Caithness		Angus	Angus Council
Inverness		City of Dundee	City of Dundee Council
Lochaber	Highland Council	Perth & Kinross	Perth & Kinross Council
Nairn		Orkney Islands Council	Orkney Islands Council
Ross & Cromarty		Shetland Islands Council	Shetland Islands Council
Skye & Lochalsh		Western Isles Islands Council	Western Isles Council
Sutherland			

Newly Opened

The Scottish ancestral home of the Marquess of Bute - whose lineage dates back to King Robert II in the 14th century - will have its first full open season this year.

Palatial Mount Stuart House (pg. 277) on the Isle of Bute off the west coast of Scotland is one of the finest examples of Victorian neo-Medieval architecture. Its lavish interiors and art treasures reflect the fantasy of the 3rd Marquess who had the house rebuilt following a fire in 1877. It is set in 300 acres of landscaped grounds, established in the 18th century by the 3rd Earl of Bute who helped set up London's Kew Gardens.

KEY TO SYMBOLS:

 THE NATIONAL TRUST FOR SCOTLAND

 HISTORIC SCOTLAND

 HISTORIC HOUSES ASSOCIATION

BOWHILL
Selkirk

Scottish Borders home of the Duke and Duchess of Buccleuch, dating mainly from 1812 and christened 'Sweet Bowhill' by Sir Walter Scott in his 'Lay of the Last Minstrel'.

Many of the works of art were collected by earlier Montagus, Douglases and Scotts or given by Charles II to his natural son James Duke of Monmouth and Buccleuch. Paintings include Canaletto's "Whitehall", works by Guardi, Claude, Ruysdael, Gainsborough, Raeburn, Reynolds, Van Dyck and Wilkie. Superb French furniture, Meissen and Sèvres porcelain, silver and tapestries.

Historical relics include Monmouth's saddle and execution shirt, Sir Walter Scott's plaid and some proof editions, Queen Victoria's letters and gifts to successive Duchesses of Buccleuch, her Mistresses of the Robes.

Completely restored Victorian Kitchen, 19th century horse-drawn fire engine, 'Bowhill Little Theatre', a lively centre for the performing arts and where, prior to touring the house, visitors can see 'The Quest for Bowhill', a 20 minute audio-visual by Dr Colin Thompson.

Conference Centre, Arts Courses, Education Service, Mountain Bike Hire, Visitor Centre. Shop, Tearoom, Adventure Playground, Woodland Walks, Nature Trails, Picnic Areas. Garden and landscape designed by John Gilpin.

SUITABILITY FOR OTHER EVENTS
Fashion shows, air displays, archery, clay pigeon shooting, equestrian events, charity garden parties, shows, rallies, filming, all requests considered. By prior arrangement.

EXTRA FACILITIES
As "education" is the prime function of the Buccleuch Heritage Trust, with emphasis on outstanding works of art and their relationship to their historic associations, the House is opened specially by appointment, outside the scheduled public hours, to groups of any age led by officials of a recognised museum, gallery or educational establishment. Lecture theatre and equipment available on request.

ADVICE TO COURIERS & DRIVERS
Photography prohibited inside the House. Free parking for 60 cars and 6 coaches within 50yds of House.

FACILITIES FOR THE DISABLED
Disabled and elderly visitors may alight at the House entrance. Special toilet facilities in the Stables Courtyard. Wheelchair visitors admitted free of charge.

CATERING
Restaurant (seating 72). Parties can be booked in advance for tea and other meals. Inside caterers normally used but outside caterers considered. Special rates for groups, menus on request.

GUIDED TOURS
Available for groups. Average time taken to see the House 1 hour 15 minutes.

GIFT SHOP
Open at the same time as the House, or by appointment. Mini shop open when grounds only open.

SCHOOL VISITS/CHILDREN
Groups welcome, £1 per child. The services of Education Officers are provided free and a schoolroom is available. Areas of interest include: projects in Bowhill House and Victorian Kitchen, Ranger-led Nature Walks. Adventure Playground. Please telephone to discuss requirements.

CONTACT

Mrs M Carter
Buccleuch Heritage Trust
Bowhill House & Country Park
Bowhill
Selkirk
Scotland
TD7 5ET

Tel: (01750) 22204

Fax: (01750) 22204

LOCATION

3 mls W of Selkirk off A708 Moffat Road, A68 from Newcastle, A7 from Carlisle or Edinburgh.

Bus: 3 miles Selkirk.

Taxi: (01750) 20354

OPENING TIMES

Summer
27 Apr - late Summer Bank Hol (UK)

COUNTRY PARK
Daily except Fridays (open Fridays in July)
12 noon - 5.00pm

HOUSE
July only.

Daily
1.00 - 4.30pm

Winter
By appointment only, for educational groups.

ADMISSION

Summer

HOUSE AND
COUNTRY PARK
Adult £4.00
Child* £1.00
OAP/Student . . .£3.50
Group** £3.50

COUNTRY PARK ONLY
All ages £1.00

* 5 - 16yrs.
** Min. 20 persons

Winter

HOUSE AND
COUNTRY PARK
Adult £4.50
Child* £1.00

Pre-booked educational groups over 20 persons welcomed.

CONFERENCE AND FUNCTION FACILITIES

ROOM	DIMENSIONS	CAPACITY	LAYOUT	POWER POINTS	SUITABLE FOR A/V
Bowhill Little Theatre		72	Theatre	✓	✓
		72	Buffet		
		72	Lunch/Dinner		

FLOORS CASTLE
Kelso

CONTACT

Frances Cowan
Roxburghe Estates Office
Kelso
Roxburghshire
Scotland
TD5 7SF

Tel: (01573) 223333

Fax: (01573) 226056

LOCATION

From South A68, A698.

From N A68, A697/9.
In Kelso follow signs.

Bus: Kelso Bus Stn
1 mile

Rail: Berwick 20 miles.

FLOORS CASTLE, home of the Duke and Duchess of Roxburghe is situated in the heart of the Scottish Border Country. It is reputedly the largest inhabited Castle in Scotland. Designed by William Adam, who was both masterbuilder and architect, for the first Duke of Roxburghe, building started in 1721.

It was the present Duke's great-great-grand-father, James the 6th Duke, who embellished the plain Adam features of the building. In about 1849 Playfair, letting his imagination and talent run riot, transformed the Castle, creating a multitude of spires and domes.

Externally the Castle has not been altered since the 6th Duke's time, but internally, several of the rooms, including the Dining Room and Ballroom were remodelled at the turn of the century. These apartments now display the outstanding collection of French 17th and 18th century furniture, magnificent tapestries, Chinese and European porcelain and the many other fine works of art. Many of the treasures in the Castle today were collected by Duchess May, American wife of the 8th Duke.

The Castle has been seen on cinema screens worldwide in the film 'Greystoke', as the home of Tarzan, the Earl of Greystoke.

GARDENS

The extensive parkland and gardens overlooking the Tweed provide a variety of wooded walks. The Walled Garden contains splendid herbaceous borders and in the outer walled garden a summerhouse built for Queen Victoria's visit in 1867 can still be seen. An excellent children's playground and picnic area is very close to the Castle.

❖

SUITABILITY FOR OTHER EVENTS
Gala dinners, conferences, product launches, incentive groups, 4 x 4 driving, highland games and other promotional events.

EXTRA FACILITIES
Include: extensive park, helicopter pad, fishing, clay pigeon shooting and pheasant shooting.

ADVICE TO COURIERS & DRIVERS
Coaches can be driven to the front door of the Castle, there is a waiting area close to the Restaurant exit. Coach drivers are offered a choice of lunch or tea. No photography inside the Castle. No dogs. Unlimited parking for cars, 100 yards away from the Castle, coach park situated 50 yards from the Castle. Guide book in French, German and Italian £1.50.

FACILITIES FOR THE DISABLED
Disabled and elderly visitors may alight at the entrance to the property, before parking in the allocated areas. Toilets for the disabled.

CATERING
There is a self-service, licensed restaurant seating 125 open from 10am, where coffee, lunch and tea are served. Groups can book in advance.

GIFT SHOP
Same hours as the Castle. Wide range of quality goods.

GUIDED TOURS
Tours lasting $1^{1}/_{4}$ hrs available on request for up to 100.

SCHOOL VISITS/CHILDREN
School visits are welcome and a guide will be provided. Cost per child £2.00. Playground facilities.

OPENING TIMES

Summer

Easter - September
Daily
10am - 4.30pm

October
Sunday & Wednesday
10am - 4.00pm

Winter

November to March
Closed to the general public.

ADMISSION

Summer
Adult £3.90
OAPs £3.50
Child* £2.20
Family £10.60

Groups
Adult £3.10
OAPs £2.90
Child* £1.90

* Aged 5-15

CONFERENCE AND FUNCTION FACILITIES

ROOM	DIMENSIONS	CAPACITY	LAYOUT	POWER POINTS	SUITABLE FOR A/V
Dining Room	18.3m x 7.3m	150	Theatre	✓	✓
		90	Lunch/Dinner		
		50	Boardroom		
Ballroom	21.1m x 7.9m	150	Theatre	✓	✓
		50	Boardroom		
Roxburghe Room (In Sunlaws House Hotel)		25	Boardroom	✓	✓

MANDERSTON
Duns

MANDERSTON, together with its magnificent stables, stunning marble dairy and 56 acres of immaculate garden, forms an ensemble which must be unique in Britain today.

The House was completely rebuilt between 1903 and 1905, with no expense spared.

Visitors are able to see not only the sumptuous State Rooms and bedrooms, decorated in the Adam manner, but also all the original domestic offices, in a truly 'Upstairs Downstairs' atmosphere. Manderston boasts a unique and recently restored silver staircase.

There is a special museum with a nostalgic display of valuable tins made by Huntley and Palmers from 1868 to the present day. *Winner of the AA/NPI Bronze Award UK 1994.*

GARDENS
Outside, the magnificence continues and the combination of formal gardens and picturesque landscapes is a major attraction: unique amongst Scottish houses.

The stables, still in use, have been described by *Horse and Hound* as "probably the finest in all the wide world."

SUITABILITY FOR OTHER EVENTS
Fashion shows, air displays, archery, clay pigeon shooting, equestrian events, garden parties, shows, rallies, filming, wedding receptions, product launches and marathons. Almost anything is possible by arrangement.

EXTRA FACILITIES
Two airstrips for light aircraft, approx 5 mls. Grand Piano, Full-size Billiard Table. Fox hunting, pheasant shoots (up to 600 birds per day). Sea angling on coast, salmon on River Tweed. Stabling for 20 horses, cricket pitch, tennis court, lake. Nearby: 9 hole golf course, indoor swimming pool, squash court.

ACCOMMODATION
Manderston offers : 5 twin, 4 doubles and 1 single.

ADVICE TO COURIERS & DRIVERS
It is appreciated and helpful if party fees can be paid by one person on arrival. Dogs (grounds only) on leads. No photography inside House. Please allow plenty of time as there is so much to see. Parking for 400 cars, 125 yds from House, 30 coaches 5 yds from the House.

FACILITIES FOR THE DISABLED
Cars containing disabled visitors can park outside the House. No special toilet facilities.

CATERING
Tea Room (capacity 80) open during day, waitress service. Afternoon Tea from £2.50, £10-£35 other meals. Meals can be booked in advance. Menus upon request. Menu can include local smoked trout pate, pheasant in mushroom and red wine sauce and strawberry mousse, prices include pre-meal cocktails and wines. For special functions/ conferences, buffets, lunches and dinners can be arranged.

GIFT SHOP
Open same time as House, other times by arrangement. Colour guide book, £2.00.

GUIDED TOURS
At no additional cost, tours available in French and English. When House is open, guides posted in most rooms. If requested, the owner may meet groups. Average time for tour 1¼ hours.

SCHOOL VISITS / CHILDREN
Groups welcome, £1.50 per child, min. £45. A guide can be provided. The Biscuit Tin Museum is of particular interest.

CONTACT

The Lord or Lady Palmer
Manderston
Duns
Berwickshire
Scotland
TD11 3PP

Tel: (01361) 883450
(01361) 882636
Fax: (01361) 882010

WWW No: http://www. twisel.co.uk/borders/shomes/ manderston.html

LOCATION

From Edinburgh
47 miles, 1 hour

Bus: 400 yards

Rail: Berwick Station
12 miles

Taxi: Chirnside 818216

Airport: Edinburgh or Newcastle both 60 mls or 80 mins.

OPENING TIMES

Summer
Mid May - end Sept

Thursdays & Sundays
2.00 - 5.30pm

Bank Holiday Mons of end May & end Aug
2.00 - 5.30pm

Group visits at other times by arrangement.

Winter
September - May
Visits by arrangement.

ADMISSION

HOUSE & GROUNDS
Adult £5.00
Child £1.00
Groups (min 20 people on open days)
Per person £3.00
School child . . . £1.50
(Min Student group £45.00)

GROUNDS ONLY
Including Stables & Marble Dairy
Adult £2.50
Child £0.50
Groups (min 20 people)
Per person £2.00

On days when the House is closed to the public, parties viewing by appointment will have personally conducted tours of the House and the Gift Shop will be open. On these occasions however, the above reduced party rates (except for school-children) will not apply. Group visits other than open days are £5.00 per person (min £100.00). Cream teas on open days only.

CONFERENCE AND FUNCTION FACILITIES

ROOM	DIMENSIONS	CAPACITY	LAYOUT	POWER POINTS	SUITABLE FOR A/V
Dining Room	22'x35'	22	Boardroom	✓	✓
		100	Buffet		
		60	Lunch/Dinner		
Ballroom	34'x21'	150	Theatre	✓	✓
Hall	22'x38'	130	Theatre	✓	✓
Drawing Room	35'x21'	150	Theatre	✓	✓

TRAQUAIR
Peeblesshire

TRAQUAIR, situated amidst beautiful scenery and close by the River Tweed, is the oldest inhabited house in Scotland - visited by twenty-seven kings. Originally a Royal Hunting Lodge, it was owned by the Scottish Crown until 1478 when it passed to a branch of the Royal Stuart family whose descendants still live in the house today.

From a single tower block the building grew, reflecting the growth and importance of the Stuarts of Traquair and no exterior alterations were made after the end of the 17th century. At the end of the tree lined avenue leading to the House are the famous Bear Gates closed since 1745 when the last person to pass through them was Bonnie Prince Charlie (not to be opened again until the restoration of the Stuarts).

Nearly ten centuries of Scottish political and domestic life can be traced from the collection of treasures in the House. It is particularly rich in associations with the Catholic Church in Scotland, Mary Queen of Scots and the Jacobite Risings.

GARDEN

70 acres of grounds with peacocks, ducks and other wildlife. In spring there is a profusion of daffodils followed by rhododendrons, wild flowers and herbaceous plants. A maze in Beech/Leylandi Cyprus is behind the House.

❖

CONTACT

Ms C Maxwell Stuart
Traquair House
Innerleithen
Peeblesshire
EH44 6PW

Tel: (01896) 830323
Fax: (01896) 830639

LOCATION

From Edinburgh 1 hour, Glasgow $1^1/2$ hours, Carlisle $1^1/2$ hours, Newcastle $2^1/2$ hours. On B709 near Junction with A72.

Rail: Edinburgh Waverley 30 miles.

Bus: Hourly bus service from Edinburgh to Innerleithen. Enquiries Eastern Scottish (031) 558 1616.

Taxi: Leithen Valley Taxis (01896) 830486

SUITABILITY FOR OTHER EVENTS
Garden parties, weddings, receptions, product launches, filming, archery, clay-pigeon shooting, theatre, son et lumière.

EXTRA FACILITIES
18th century fully operational Brewhouse, ale tasting every Friday between 3 - 4pm. 17th century harpsichord in Drawing Room, croquet (mallets can be hired). Lectures provided on the property, contents , history and grounds.

ACCOMMODATION
Traquair offers 2 fourposter suites with bathroom. One self-catering flat with double bedroom.

ADVICE TO COURIERS & DRIVERS
Coaches preferably booked in advance. Drivers please apply for vouchers on arrival. Dogs on leads in grounds. No photography in House. Introductory talks can be given to groups. Out of hours visits with meals / refreshments by prior arrangement.

PARKING FOR COACHES & CARS
Capacity of car park: 200 cars and 5 coaches 85 yards from the House. (Advance booking requested for coaches).

FACILITIES FOR THE DISABLED
Disabled/elderly visitors may alight at the entrance before parking in the allocated area. Toilets for the disabled.

GIFT SHOP
As House, selling Traquair House Ale, wine and crafts.

CATERING
Licensed self-service 1745 Cottage Tearoom. On fine days lunches and teas can be taken outdoors. Marquee (lined and floored) available for receptions, weddings, etc., in the gardens or the courtyard. Parties of up to 45 can be served in the Bear Cottage. Lunches and dinners in the house dining room from £25 by special arrangement.

GUIDE BOOKS
Colour guide book, £2.00. Translations in French, Spanish, German, Dutch, Swedish, Japanese & Italian. Children's guide books and quiz sheets.

GUIDED TOURS
Tours only outside opening hours £4.00 per person (£80 min).

OPENING TIMES

Summer
6 April - 30 Sept
Daily: 12.30 - 5.30pm

July & August
10.30am - 5.30pm
Last adm. 5.00pm

October: Fris - Suns
2.00 - 5.00pm

Restaurant: July & Aug.
12 noon - 11.00pm

Winter
1 November - Easter
Open by arrangement.

ADMISSION

Summer
HOUSE & GARDEN
Adult £3.80
Child* £1.80
Groups**
Adult £3.10
Child* £1.50

GARDEN ONLY
Adult £1.50
Child* £1.00

* Under 15 years.
** Minimum payment £60.00 when House open £80.00 when closed.

Winter
£6.00 per person.
Includes glass of wine/whisky/ Traquair Ale and shortbread. Minimum charge £100.

CONFERENCE AND FUNCTION FACILITIES

ROOM	DIMENSIONS	CAPACITY	LAYOUT	POWER POINTS	SUITABLE FOR A/V
Dining Room	33' x 18'	22	Lunches	3	✓
		16	Schoolroom		
		30	Buffet		
Drawing Room (with Harpsichord)	27' x 24'	50/60	Lunch/Dinner Drinks	3	✓
		50/60	Music Recitals		

ABBOTSFORD HOUSE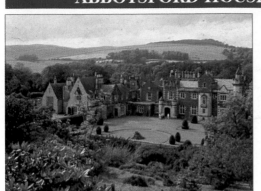

OPEN

19 Mar - 31 Oct

10am - 5pm
weekdays

2.00 - 5.00pm
Sundays

Tel: 01896 752043

MELROSE, ROXBURGHSHIRE TD6 9BQ

Owner: Mrs P Maxwell-Scott OBE   *Contact: Mrs P Maxwell-Scott*

Sir Walter Scott purchased the Cartley Hall farmhouse on the banks of the Tweed in 1812. Together with his family and servants he moved into the farm which he renamed Abbotsford. Scott had the old house demolished in 1822 and replaced it with the main block of Abbotsford as it is today. Scott was a passionate collector of historic relics including an impressive collection of armour and weapons and over 9,000 rare volumes in his library.

Location: 35m S of Edinburgh.

Admission: Adult £3.00, Child £1.50 (under 5 free).

DUNS CASTLE

OPEN

Not open to the public except by arrangement and for individuals, groups and companies for day or residential stays. Available all year.

Tel: 01361 883211
Fax: 01361 882015

DUNS, BERWICKSHIRE TD11 3NW

Owner: Alexander Hay of Duns   *Contact: Mrs Aline Hay*

This historical 1320 peel tower has been home to the Hay family since 1696, and the current owners Alexander and Aline Hay offer it as a welcoming venue for individuals, groups and corporate guests to enjoy. They have renovated it to produce the highest standards of comfort while retaining all the character of its rich period interiors. Wonderful lakeside and parkland setting.

Location: 10m off the A4. Rail: Berwick station 16 miles. Airports: Newcastle & Edinburgh, 1 hour.

Admission: Rates for private & corporate visits, weddings, filming by arrangement.

AYTON CASTLE

OPEN

5 May - 15 Sept
Sundays
2.00 - 5.00pm
or by appointment

Tel: 018907 81212
or 018907 81550

AYTON, BERWICKSHIRE TD14 5RD

Contact: The Curator

Built in 1846 by the Mitchell-Innes family and designed by the architect James Gillespie Graham. Over the last ten years it has been fully restored and is now a family home. It is a unique restoration project and the quality of the original and restored workmanship is outstanding. The Castle stands on an escarpment surrounded by mature woodlands containing many interesting trees and has been a film-making venue due to this magnificent setting.

Location: 7 miles north of Berwick-on-Tweed on Route A1.

Admission: Adult £2.00, Children under 5 Free.

FLOORS CASTLE   See Page 248 for full page entry.

HERMITAGE CASTLE   **Tel:** 013873 76222

Liddesdale, Newcastleton

Owner: Historic Scotland   **Contact:** The Custodian

Eerie fortress at the heart of the bloodiest events in the history of the Borders. Mary Queen of Scots made her famous ride here to visit her future husband.

Location: In Liddesdale 5½ m NE of Newcastleton, B6399.

Opening Times: 1 Apr - 30 Sept. Mon - Sat 9.30am - 6.30pm, Sun 2 - 6.30pm
1 Oct - 31 Mar: Sat 9.30am - 4.30pm, Sun 2 - 4.30pm. Last adm. ½ hour before closing.

Admission: Adult £1.20, Conc £75p, Child 75p.

THE HIRSEL GARDENS   **Tel:** 01890 882834   **Fax:** 01890 882834

Coldstream, Berwickshire TD12 4LP

Contact: Hirsel Estate Office

Wonderful spring flowers and rhododendrons. Homestead museum and crafts centre.

Location: Immediately W of Coldstream off A697.

Opening Times: Grounds - All year: Daily during daylight hours. Museum and Craft Shop open 10am - 5pm weekdays, 12 noon - 5pm weekends.

Admission: Parking charge only.

MANDERSTON   See Page 249 for full page entry.

MELLERSTAIN HOUSE

BOWHILL   See Page 247 for full page entry.

DAYWYCK BOTANIC GARDEN   **Tel:** 01721 760254   **Fax:** 01721 760214

Stobo, Peebles EH45 9JU

Contact: Assistant Curator

Historic landscaped woodland garden. An impressive collection of majestic trees, colourful shrubs and herbaceous plants with landscaped burnside walks.

Location: 8m SW of Peebles on B712.

Opening Times: 15 Mar - 22 Oct: Daily 10am - 6pm.

Admission: Adult £2.00, Child 50p, Family £4.50, Conc £1.50, Groups 11+ 10% discount.

DRYBURGH ABBEY   **Tel:** 01835 822381

St Boswells, Melrose

Owner: Historic Scotland   **Contact:** The Custodian

The ruins of Dryburgh Abbey are remarkably complete. The burial place of Sir Walter Scott and Field Marshal Earl Haig. Perhaps the most beautiful of all the Border Abbeys.

Location: 5m SE of Melrose on B6404.

Opening Times: 1 Apr - 30 Sept: Mon - Sat 9.30am - 6.30pm, Sun 2 - 6.30pm, last adm. 6pm.
1 Oct - 31 Mar: Mon - Sat 9.30am - 4.30pm, Sun 2 - 4.30pm, last adm. 4pm.

Admission: Adult £2.00, Conc. £1.25, Child 75p.

OPEN

Easter weekend (Fri - Mon)

1 May - 30 Sept
Daily except
Saturdays
12.30 - 5.00pm

Groups at
other times by
appointment.

Tel: 01573 410225

MELLERSTAIN, GORDON, BERWICKSHIRE TD3 6LG

Owner: The Earl of Haddington   *Contact: Mrs. F. Turnbull*

One of Scotland's great Georgian houses and a unique example of the work of the Adam family; the two wings built in 1725 by William Adam, the large central block by his son, Robert 1770-78. Rooms contain fine plasterwork, colourful ceilings and marble fireplaces. The Library is considered as Robert Adam's finest creation. Many fine paintings and period furniture.

Location: From Edinburgh A68 to Earlston, turn left 5m, signposted.

Admission: Adult £4.00, OAP £3.00, Child £1.50. Groups (Min. 20) £3.00.

MELROSE ABBEY
Tel: 01896 822562

Melrose

Owner: Historic Scotland   **Contact:** The Custodian

Its 14th to 16th century remains retain a unique elegance. Said to be the burial place of Robert the Bruce's Heart. Founded around 1136 as a Cistercian Abbey by David I.

Location: In Melrose off the A7 or A68.

Opening Times: 1 Apr - 30 Sept: Mon - Sat 9.30am - 6.30pm, Sun 2 - 6.30pm.
1 Oct - 31 Mar: Mon - Sat 9.30am - 4.30pm, Sun 2 - 4.30pm. Last adm. 1/2 hr before closing.

Admission: Adult £2.50, Conc £1.50, Child £1.00. Includes audio tour.

MERTOUN GARDENS
Tel: 01835 823236   **Fax:** 01835 822474

St Boswells, Melrose, Roxburgh TD6 0EA

Owner: The Duke of Sutherland   **Contact:** Miss Miller

26 acres of beautiful grounds. Walled garden and well preserved circular dovecote.

Location: Entrance off B6404 2m NE of St Boswells.

Opening Times: Apr - Sept: weekends only with Bank Holiday Mondays 9am - 5.30pm. Last admission 5pm.

Admission: Adult £1.00, Child 50p, Groups by arrangement.

NEIDPATH CASTLE
Tel: 01721 720333

Peebles EH45 8NW

Owner: Lady Elizabeth Benson   **Contact:** The Administrator

Medieval castle dramatically situated above the River Tweed. Good example of how such a fortress could be adapted to the more civilised living conditions of the 17th century.

Location: 1m W of Peebles on A72.

Opening Times: Easter - 30 Sept: Mon - Sat 11am - 5pm. Sun 1 - 5pm.

OLD GALA HOUSE
Tel: 01750 20096

Scot Crescent, Galashiels TD1 3JS

Owner: Mr Ian Brown   **Contact:** Mr Ian Brown

Dating from 1583 the former house the Laird of Gala includes displays on the history of the house and its inhabitants and the early growth of Galashiels. Particularly memorable is the painted ceiling dated 1635.

Location: Off town centre. Sign posts from A7.

Opening Times: Late Mar - early November: Mon - Sat 10am - 4pm, Sunday 2 - 4pm (as at time of publication).

ROBERT SMAIL'S PRINTING WORKS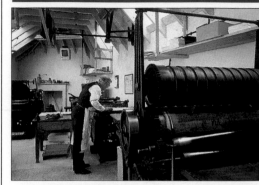

OPEN

1 May - 30 Sept
Mon - Sat
10am - 1pm
and
2pm - 5pm

Sun 2 - 5pm

Weekends in Oct:
Sats: 10am - 1pm
and 2 - 5pm
Suns: 2 - 5pm

Tel: 01896 830206

HIGH STREET, INNERLEITHEN, PEEBLESSHIRE EH44 6HA

Owner: The National Trust for Scotland   *Contact: Edward Nicol*

A printing time-capsule featuring a completely restored Victorian printing works. Visitors can experience the almost forgotten craft of hand typesetting. They will discover the secrets of the printing works from the archive-based posters and see the fully restored machines in action. The buildings also contain the Victorian office with its acid-etched windows, reconstructed waterwheel and many historic items which provide an insight into the history of the Border town of Innerleithen.

Location: In High Street, Innerleithen, 30m S of Edinburgh.

Admission: Adult £2.10, Child £1.40. Parties: Adult £1.70, School £1. Family £5.60.

SMAILHOLM TOWER
Tel: 01573 460365

Smailholm, Kelso

Owner: Historic Scotland   **Contact:** The Custodian

Set on a high rocky knoll this well preserved 16th century tower houses an exhibition of tapestries and costume dolls depicting characters from Sir Walter Scott's 'Minstrelsy of the Scottish Borders.'

Location: Nr Smailholm Village, 6m W of Kelso on B6937.

Opening Times: 1 Apr - 30 Sept: Mon - Sat 9.30am - 6.30pm, Sun 2 - 6.30pm. Last admission 1/2 hour before closing. Winter closed.

Admission: Adult £1.50, Conc £1.00, Child 75p.

PAXTON HOUSE

OPEN

5 Apr - 31 Oct.
Grounds:
10am - Sunset
House:
12 noon - 5pm
Last house tour
4.15pm

Open to groups/
schools all year by
appointment

Tel: 01289 386291
Fax: 01289 386660

BERWICK-UPON-TWEED TD15 1SZ

Owner: The Paxton Trust   *Contact: Martin Purslow*

Built in 1756 by John and James Adam, the house boasts the pre-eminent collection of Chippendale furniture on view in Scotland, the largest picture gallery in a Scottish country house, designed by Robert Reid in 1818, which now functions as an outstation for the National Galleries of Scotland, and a fine collection of Regency furniture by Trotter of Edinburgh. Other features include over 80 acres of woodland, parkland, gardens and riverside walks to explore, an adventure playground, tearoom, shop, temporary exhibitions, highland cattle, croquet and a function suite for hire.

Location: 3m from the A1 Berwick-upon-Tweed on the B6461.

Admission: Adult £4.00, Child £2.00. Grounds only: Adult £1.75, Child £1.00. Free parking.

THIRLESTANE CASTLE

OPEN

Easter 5 - 12 April

1 May - 30 Sept
Sun, Mon, Wed, Thur
afternoons
from 2.00pm
Last Admission
4.30pm

July & Aug.
every afternoon
except Sat.

Tel: 01578 722430
Fax: 01578 722761

THIRLESTANE, LAUDER, BERWICKSHIRE TD2 6RU

Owner: Thirlestane Castle Trust   *Contact: Peter Jarvis*

One of Scotland's oldest and finest castles standing in lovely Border countryside. Thirlestane was the seat of the Earls and Duke of Lauderdale and is still home to the Maitland family. Unsurpassed 17th century ceilings, fine portrait collection, large collection of historic toys, country life exhibitions. Tearoom, gift shop, woodland walks. STB commended. MGC Registered. State rooms available for functions.

Location: Off A68 at Lauder, 28 miles south of Edinburgh.

Admission: Adult £4.00, Family £10.00. Party £3.00. Grounds only £1.00.

PRIORWOOD GARDEN & DRIED FLOWER SHOP
Tel: 01896 822493

Melrose TD6 9PX

Owner: The National Trust for Scotland   **Contact:** Mrs Cathy Ross

Overlooked by the Abbey's 15th century ruins is this unique garden, where most of the plants are suitable for drying. With the aid of volunteers, Priorwood Garden markets a wide variety of dried flower arrangements through its own dried flower shop.

Location: In the Border town of Melrose, beside the Abbey.

Opening Times: 1 Apr - 30 Jun & 1 - 30 Sept: Mon - Sat 10am - 5.30pm, Sun 1.30 - 5.30pm. 1 Jul - 31 Aug: Mon - Sat 10am - 6.30pm, Sun 1.30 - 6.30pm. 1 Oct - 24 Dec: Mon - Sat 10am - 4pm, Sun 1.30 - 4pm.

Admission: Honesty box £1.00.

TRAQUAIR
See Page 250 for full page entry.

DRUMLANRIG CASTLE
Thornhill

DRUMLANRIG CASTLE, Gardens & Country Park, the home of the Duke of Buccleuch and Queensberry KT was built between 1679 and 1691 by William Douglas, 1st Duke of Queensberry. Drumlanrig is rightly recognised as one of the first and most important buildings in the grand manner in Scottish domestic architecture. James Smith, who made the conversion from a 15th century castle, made a comparable transformation at Dalkeith a decade later.

The Castle, of local pink sandstone offers superb views across Nithsdale. It houses a renowned art collection, including work by Leonardo, Holbein, and Rembrandt, as well as cabinets made for Louis XIV's Versailles, relics of Bonny Prince Charlie and a 300 year old silver chandelier.

The story of Sir James Douglas, killed in Spain while carrying out the last wish of Robert Bruce, pervades the Castle in the emblem of a winged heart, found throughout the building.

The gardens, now being restored to the plan of 1738 add to the overall effect. The fascination of Drumlanrig as a centre of art, beauty and history is complemented by its role in the Queensberry Estate, a model of dynamic and enlightened land management.

CONTACT

A Fisher
Drumlanrig Castle
Thornhill
Dumfriesshire
DG3 4AQ

Tel: (01848) 330248

Fax: (01848) 600244

LOCATION

18m N of Drumfries,
3m N of Thornhill
off A76.
16m from M74 at
Elvanfoot.
Approx. 1$\frac{1}{2}$ hrs
by road from
Edinburgh, Glasgow
and Carlisle.

OPENING TIMES

Summer
CASTLE
27 April - 26 August
11am - 5pm

Last entry to Castle
4.15pm.

Castle closed Thursdays

GARDENS &
COUNTRY PARK:

11am - 6pm throughout

Winter
By arrangement only.

ADMISSION

Summer
Adult	£4.00
Child	£2.00
OAP	£2.50
Family	£10.00

Groups
Adult	£2.50
Child	£2.00
OAP	£2.50

ADVICE TO COURIERS & DRIVERS
No photography inside the Castle. Restricted route in Castle 12 - 14 July.

PARKING FOR COACHES & CARS
Adjacent to the Castle.

FACILITIES FOR THE DISABLED
Disabled visitors welcome. Please enquire about facilities before visit.

CATERING
Tearoom inside Castle. Snacks, lunches and teas during Castle opening hours.

GIFT SHOP
Open Castle hours. Wide range of quality goods.

GUIDED TOURS
Available in the early season and by prior arrangement.

GUIDE BOOK
Full colour. Price £2.00.

SCHOOL VISITS / CHILDREN
Children's quiz and worksheets. Ranger led activities, including woodlands, forestry etc. Adventure playground. Bird of Prey centre.

CONFERENCE AND FUNCTION FACILITIES

ROOM	DIMENSIONS	CAPACITY	LAYOUT	POWER POINTS	SUITABLE FOR A/V
Visitors' Centre	6m x 13m	50		✓	✓

ARBIGLAND GARDENS

OPEN

1 May - 30 Sept

Tues - Sun
plus Bank Holiday
Mondays
2.00 - 6.00pm

House open
Fri 24 May -
Sun 2 Jun
and by
appointment.

Tel: 01387 880283

KIRKBEAN, DUMFRIES & GALLOWAY DG3 4DX

Owner: *Capt & Mrs Beauchamp Blackett* **Contact:** *Capt & Mrs Beauchamp Blackett*

Formal wooded and water gardens which have evolved through three centuries. The ideal family outing garden as the gardens run down to a sheltered sandy bay where the younger members (and dogs) can let off steam. 400 yards from the John Paul Jones Birthplace Museum, whose father created the gardens circa 1750.

Location: 15m from Dumfries off A710 'Solway Coast Road'.

Admission: Adult £2.00, OAP £1.50, Child 50p, Toddlers Free.

BROUGHTON HOUSE & GARDEN

OPEN

House & Garden:
1 Apr - 31 Oct

Daily
1.00 - 5.30pm

Last admission
4.30pm

Tel: 01557 330437

HIGH STREET, KIRKCUDBRIGHT DG6 4JX

Owner: *The National Trust for Scotland (in process of transfer)* **Contact:** *Frances Scott*

This fascinating 18th century house in the pleasant coastal town of Kirkcudbright was the home and studio from 1901 to 1933 of the artist E A Hornel, one of the "Glasgow Boys". It contains a superb collection of his work, along with paintings by other contemporary artists, and an extensive library of rare Scottish books, including valuable editions of Burns's works.

Location: Off A711 / A755, in Kirkcudbright, at 12 High Street.

Admission: Adult £2.10, Child £1.40. Parties: Adult £1.70, School £1. Family £5.60.

CAERLAVEROCK CASTLE

Tel: 01387 770244

Dumfries

Owner: Historic Scotland   **Contact:** The Custodian

Caerlaverock (Lark's Nest) is everyone's idea of a medieval fortress. Its most remarkable features are the twin-towered Gatehouse and the Nithsdale Lodging, a splendid Renaissance Range dating from 1638. The scene of two famous sieges. This moated castle has a children's adventure park and model siege engine in its grounds.

Location: 8m SE of Dumfries on the B725.

Opening Times: 1 Apr - 30 Sept: Mon - Sat 9.30am - 6.30pm, Sun 2 - 6.30pm.
1 Oct - 31 Mar: Mon - Sat 9.30am - 4.30 pm, Sun 2 - 4.30pm. Last adm. ¹/₂ hr before closing.
Admission: Adult £2.00, Conc £1.25, Child 75p.

CARDONESS CASTLE

Tel: 01557 814427

Gatehouse of Fleet

Owner: Historic Scotland   **Contact:** The Custodian

The well preserved ruin of a four storey tower house of 15th century date standing on a rocky platform above the Water of Fleet. It is the ancient home of the McCullochs. Very fine fire places.

Location: 1m SW of Gatehouse of Fleet.

Opening Times: 1 Apr - 30 Sept: Mon - Sat 9.30am - 6.30pm, Sun 2 - 6.30pm. 1 Oct - 31 Mar:
Sat 9.30am - 4.30pm, Sun 2 - 4.30pm. Last admission ¹/₂ hour before closing.
Admission: Adult £1.20, Conc 75p, Child 75p.

CARLYLE'S BIRTHPLACE

Tel: 01576 300666

Ecclefechan, Dumfriesshire

Owner: The National Trust for Scotland   **Contact:** Mr Ross Walter

Thomas Carlyle was born here in The Arched House in 1795, the year before Burns died. Carlyle was a brilliant essayist, historian, social reformer, visionary and literary giant. When he was 14 he walked the 84 miles to Edinburgh University - it took him three days. Upstairs is the bedroom in which Carlyle was born. There is also a little museum with a notable collection of photographs, manuscripts and other documents.

Location: Off M74, 5m SE of Lockerbie.

Opening Times: 1 May - 30 Sept: Fri - Mon 1.30 - 5.30pm. Last adm. 5pm.
Other times by appointment.

Admission: Adult £1.60, Child £1.00. Parties: Adult £1.30, School £1.00. Family £4.20.

CASTLE KENNEDY GARDENS

OPEN

1 April - 30 Sept.

Daily
10.00am - 5.00pm

Gardens only

Tel: 01776 702024
Fax: 01776 706248

STAIR ESTATES, REPHAD, STRANRAER, DUMFRIES & GALLOWAY DG9 8BX

Owner: *Lochinch Heritage Estate*   **Contact:** *Estate Office*

Outstanding garden in south west Scotland. Set between two lochs in beautiful countryside. These extensively landscaped gardens extend over 70 acres between the ruined Castle Kennedy and Lochinch Castle, the home of the Earl of Stair. Famous for Rhododendrons, Embothriums and Azaleas, many from original stock. Terraces and mounds built by man and horse provide spectacular views above gardens and water.

Location: 5m E of Stranraer on A75 Dumfries-Stranraer road.

Admission: Adult £2.00, OAP £1.50, Child £1.00. 20% reduction for groups of 20+.

DRUMLANRIG CASTLE

See Page 253 for full Page entry.

DUNDRENNAN ABBEY

Tel: 01557 500262

Kirkcudbright

Owner: Historic Scotland   **Contact:** The Custodian

Mary Queen of Scots spent her last night on Scottish soil in this Cistercian Abbey founded by David I. The Abbey stands in a small and secluded valley. Built in the second half of the 12th century.

Location: 6¹/₂m SE of Kirkcudbright on the A711.

Opening Times: 1 Apr - 30 Sept: Mon - Wed & Sat, 9.30am - 6.30pm, Thur 9.30am - 12 noon,
Fri Closed, Sun 2 - 6.30pm. Last adm. ¹/₂ hour before closing. 1 Oct - 31 Mar: Closed.
Admission: Adult £1.20, Conc 75p, Child 75p.

GALLOWAY HOUSE GARDENS

Tel: 01988 600680

Garlieston, Newton Stewart, Wigtownshire DG8 8HF

Owner: Galloway House Gardens Trust   **Contact:** D Marshall
Location: 15m S of Newton Stewart on B7004.
Opening Times: 1 Mar - 31 Oct: 9m - 5pm.
Admission: Adult £1.00, Child 50p, Family £2.50, Conc 50p.

GLENLUCE ABBEY

Tel: 01581 300541

Glenluce

Owner: Historic Scotland   **Contact:** Historic Scotland

A Cistercian Abbey founded In 1190. Remains include a handsome 16th century Chapter House.

Location: 2m NW of Glenluce village off the A75.

Opening Times: 1 Apr - 30 Sept: Mon - Sat 9.30am - 6.30pm, Sun 2 - 6.30pm.
1 Oct - 31 Mar: Sat 9.30am - 4.30pm, Sun 2 - 4.30pm. Last adm. ¹/₂ hour before closing.
Admission: Adult £1.20, Conc 75p, Child 75p.

LOGAN BOTANIC GARDEN
Tel: 01776 860 231   **Fax:** 01776 860 333

Port Logan, Stranraer, Wigtownshire DG9 9ND
Owner: Royal Botanic Garden Edinburgh   **Contact:** B Unwin
A rich diversity of plants from South and Central America, southern Africa, Australasia and the Mediterranean seldom seen elsewhere in Britain. Water gardens and extensive woodland gardens provide interest all year round. Licensed Salad Bar for coffee, lunch and tea. Shop selling cards, books gifts and plants. Facilities for the disabled.
Opening Times: 15 Mar - 31 Oct: Daily 10am - 6pm. Other times by arrangement.
Admission: Adult £2, Child 50p, Family £4.50, Conc £1.50, Groups 11 + 10% discount.

MACLELLAN'S CASTLE
Tel: 01557 331856

Kirkcudbright
Owner: Historic Scotland   **Contact:** The Custodian
A handsome castellated mansion, built in 1577 using stone from an adjoining ruined monastery by the then Provost. Elaborately planned with fine architectural details, it has been a ruin since 1752.
Location: Centre of Kirkcudbright on the A711.
Opening Times: 1 Apr - 30 Sept: Mon - Sat 9.30am - 6.30pm, Sun 2 - 6.30pm.
1 Oct - 31 Mar: Sat 9.30am - 4.30pm, Sun 2 - 4.30pm. Last adm. ½ hour before closing.
Admission: Adult £1.20, Conc 75p, Child 75p.

MAXWELTON HOUSE

OPEN

1 Jun - end Sept: Open to the general public.
Easter - end Sept: Open for group visits only.

MONIAIVE, THORNHILL, DUMFRIES & GALLOWAY DG3 4DX
Owner: Maxwelton House Trust
Contact: Roderick Stenhouse

Tel: 01848 200384 or 01848 200385

The birthplace of Annie Laurie made famous by the well loved ballad. Glencairn Castle now Maxwelton House dates back to 1370, the home of the Earls of Glencairn. Stephen Laurie bought Glencairn Castle in 1611 and changed the name to Maxwelton. Annie Laurie was born here in 1682. The Laurie family remained in possession until 1968 when Mr and Mrs Hugh Stenhouse bought it and carried out one of the largest restorations to a private house within Scotland. The restoration took three years and the continuing labour of no less than 65 men. It was completed in 1972. House, Museum, Chapel, Garden Tearoom, Gift Shop. Free parking.
Location: Entrances on B729 near Wallaceton or A702 near Penpont.

NEW ABBEY CORN MILL
Tel: 01387 785260

New Abbey Village
Owner: Historic Scotland   **Contact:** The Custodian
This carefully renovated 18th century water-powered oatmeal mill is in full working order and regular demonstrations are given for visitors in the summer.
Location: 8m S of Dumfries on the A710.
Opening Times: 1 Apr - 30 Sept: Mon - Sat 9.30am - 6.30pm, Sun 2 - 6.30pm.
1 Oct - 31 Mar: Mon - Wed & Sat 9.30am - 4.30pm, Thur 9.30am - 12 noon, Fri Closed, Sun 2 - 4.30pm. Last admission ½ hour before closing.
Admission: Adult £2.00, Conc £1.25, Child 75p. Joint entry ticket with Sweatheart Abbey: Adult £2.50, Conc £1.50, Child £1.00.

SWEETHEART ABBEY
Tel: 01387 785397

New Abbey Village
Owner: Historic Scotland   **Contact:** The Custodian
Cistercian abbey founded in 1273 by Devorgilla, in memory of her husband John Balliol. The principal feature is the well preserved precinct wall enclosing 30 acres. She also founded Balliol College, Oxford.
Location: In New Abbey Village, on the A710 8m S of Dumfries.
Opening Times: 1 Apr - 30 Sept: Mon - Sat 9.30am - 6.30pm, Sun 2 - 6.30pm. 1 Oct - 31 Mar: Mon - Wed & Sat 9.30am - 4.30pm, Thur 9.30am - 12 noon, Fri Closed, Sun 2 - 4.30pm. Last admission ½ hour before closing.
Admission: Adult £1.00, Conc 50p, Child 50p. Joint entry ticket with New Abbey Corn Mill: Adult £2.50, Conc £1.50, Child £1.00.

THREAVE CASTLE
Tel: 01831 168512

Castle Douglas
Owner: The National Trust for Scotland   **Contact:** Historic Scotland
Built by Archibald the Grim in the late 14th century, early stronghold of the Black Douglases. Round its base is an artillery fortification built before 1455 when the castle was besieged by James II. Ring the bell and the custodian will come to ferry you over. Long walk to property. Owned by The National Trust for Scotland but under the guardianship of Historic Scotland.
Location: 1m W of Castle Douglas on the A75.
Opening Times: 1 Apr - 30 Sept: Mon - Sat 9.30am - 6.30pm, Sun 2 - 6.30pm. Last admission ½ hour before closing. 1 Oct - 31 Mar: Closed.
Admission: Adult £1.50, Conc £1.00, Child 75p. Charges include ferry trip.

THREAVE GARDEN
Tel: 01556 502575

Castle Douglas DG7 1RX
Owner: The National Trust for Scotland   **Contact:** Trevor Jones
The garden has a wide range of features and a good collection of plants. There are peat and woodland garden plants and a colourful rock garden. Summer months bring a superb show from the herbaceous beds and borders. The heather gardens give a splash of colour, along with bright berries in the autumn. Truly a garden for all seasons.
Location: Off A75, 1m W of Castle Douglas, Dumfries & Galloway.
Opening Times: Estate & Garden: All year, Daily 9.30am - sunset. Walled garden & glasshouses: all year 9.30am - 5pm.
Admission: Adult £3.60, Child £2.40. Parties: Adult £2.90, School £1.00. Family £9.60.

WHITHORN PRIORY
Tel: 01988 500508

Whithorn
Owner: Historic Scotland   **Contact:** The Project Manager
Part of the 'Whithorn Cradle of Christianity' attraction. The site of the first Christian church in Scotland. Founded as 'Candida Casa' by St Ninian in the early 5th century it later became the cathedral church of Galloway. In the museum is a fine collection of early Christian stones including the Monreith Cross. Visitor Centre and archaeological dig.
Location: At Whithorn on the A746.
Opening Times: 1 Apr - 31 Oct: Daily 10.30am - 5pm.
Admission: Adult £2.70, Conc £1.70, Family £7.50.

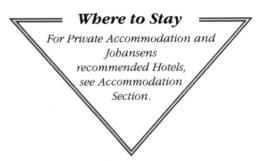

Where to Stay
For Private Accommodation and Johansens recommended Hotels, see Accommodation Section.

SPECIAL EVENTS

◇ **THREAVE GARDEN**   **10 MAY**
Concert "Three's Company". Popular mezzo-soprano Mary Sandeman, tenor James Nichol and composer/pianist John Moore. 8pm, tickets £7. Tel: 01556 502575.

ABERDOUR CASTLE

Tel: 01383 860519

Aberdour, Fife

Owner: Historic Scotland   **Contact:** The Custodian

A 14th century castle built by the Douglas family. The gallery on the first floor gives an idea of how it was furnished at the time. The castle has a 14th century tower extended in the 16th and 17th centuries, a delightful walled garden and a circular dovecote.

Location: In Aberdour 5m E of the Forth Bridge on the A921.

Opening Time: 1 Apr - 30 Sept: Mon - Sat 9.30am - 6.30pm, Sun 2 - 6.30pm. 1 Oct - 31 Mar: Mon - Wed & Sat 9.30am - 4.30pm, Thur 9.30am - 12 noon, Fri Closed, Sun 2 - 4.30pm. Last admission 1/2 hour before closing.

Admission: Adult £1.50, Conc £1.00, Child 75p.

BANNOCKBURN HERITAGE CENTRE

Tel: 01786 812664

Glasgow Road, Stirling FK7 0LJ

Owner: The National Trust for Scotland   **Contact:** Mrs Margaret Marshall

From this battlefield the Scots 'sent them homeward to think again', when Edward II's English army was soundly defeated by King Robert the Bruce. Inside the Heritage Centre there is a life-size statue of William Wallace, Bruce on his throne, a display enriched with replicas, vignettes of Scottish life and a panorama of historical characters.

Location: Off M80 / M9 at junction 9, 2m S of Stirling.

Opening Times: Site: All year: Daily. Heritage Centre & Shop: 1 - 31 Mar and 11 Nov - 23 Dec: Daily 11am - 3pm. 1 April - 31 Oct: Daily 10am - 5.30pm.

Admission: Adult £2.10, Child £1.40. Parties: Adult £1.70, School £1.00. Family £5.60.

BLACKNESS CASTLE

Tel: 01506 834807

Blackness

Owner: Historic Scotland   **Contact:** The Custodian

One of Scotland's most important strongholds. Built in the 14th century and massively strengthened in the 16th century as an artillery fortress, it has been a Royal castle and a prison armaments depot and film location for Hamlet. It was restored by the Office of Works in the 1920s. It stands on a promontory in the Firth of Forth.

Location: 4m NE of Linlithgow on the Firth of Forth, off the A904.

Opening Times: 1 Apr - 30 Sept: Mon - Sat 9.30am - 6.30pm, Sun 2 - 6.30pm. 1 Oct - 31 Mar: Mon - Wed & Sat 9.30am - 4.30pm, Thur 9.30am - 12 noon, Fri Closed, Sun 2 - 4.30pm. Last admission 1/2 hour before closing.

Admission: Adult £1.50, Conc £1.00, Child 75p.

CALLENDAR HOUSE

OPEN

Jan - Dec
Mon - Sat
10.00am - 5.00pm

April - Sept
Sundays
2.00 - 5.00pm

Open on
public holidays
Apr - Sept.

Tel: 01324 612134

CALLENDAR PARK, FALKIRK FK1 1YR

Owner: *Falkirk District Council*   **Contact:** *Mrs L. Anderson*

Imposing mansion set in attractive parkland with a 900 year history. Facilities include a working kitchen of 1825 where costumed interpreters carry out daily chores including cooking based on 1820's recipes. Exhibition area, "Story of Callendar House" plus two contemporary galleries with regularly changing exhibitions. There is also a history research centre, gift shop and Georgian Teashop at the Stables.

Location: To the E of Falkirk town centre on Callendar Road (A803).

Admission: Adult £1.60, OAP's and Children 80p.

CAMBO GARDENS

Tel: 01333 450313   **Fax:** 01333 450987

Cambo Estate, Kingsbarns, St Andrews, Fife KY16 8QD

Owner: Peter Erskine Esq   **Contact:** Catherine Erskine

Enchanting traditional walled garden in bloom from snowdrops to Autumn crocus. Blossoms, bulbs, lilies and 200 varieties of roses are a speciality. Gardened with joy to make it more fun than fossilised.

Location: 3m N of Crail.

Opening Times: All year: Daily except Christmas and New Year 10am - 4pm.

Admission: Adult £2.00, Child free.

CASTLE CAMPBELL

Tel: 01259 742408

Dollar Glen, Central District

Owner: The National Trust for Scotland   **Contact:** Historic Scotland

Known as 'Castle Gloom' this spectacularly sited 15th century fortress was the lowland stronghold of the Campbells. Stunning views from the parapet walk. Owned by The National Trust for Scotland but under the guardianship of Historic Scotland.

Location: At head of Dollar Glen, 10m E of Stirling on the A91.

Opening Time: 1 Apr - 30 Sept: Mon - Sat 9.30am - 6.30pm, Sun 2 - 6.30pm. 1 Oct - 31 Mar: Mon - Sat 9.30am - 4.30pm (except Thur afternoon and Fri all day) Sun 2 - 4.30pm. Last admission 1/2 hour before closing.

Admission: Adult £2.00, Conc. £1.25, Child 75p.

CHARLETON HOUSE

Tel: 01333 340249   **Fax:** 01333 340583

Colinsburgh, Fife KY9 1HG

Location: Colinsburgh.

Opening Times: Sept: 12 noon - 3pm. Admission every 1/2 hour with guided tours only.

Admission: Standard £5.00.

CULROSS PALACE

Tel: 01383 880359

Culross, Fife KY12 8JH

Owner: The National Trust for Scotland   **Contact:** Grace Murray

Relive the domestic life of the 16th and 17th centuries at this Royal Burgh fringed by the River Forth. Here the old buildings and cobbled streets create a time warp for visitors as they explore the old town. Enjoy too the Palace, dating from 1597 and the medieval garden.

Location: Off A985. 12m W of Forth Road Bridge and 4m E of Kincardine Bridge, Fife.

Opening Times: Palace: 1 Apr - 30 Sept: Daily 11am - 5pm. Town House & Study: same dates, 1.30 - 5pm. Weekdays in Oct: 11am - 5pm. Groups other times by appointment.

Admission: Adult £3.60, Child £2.40. Parties: Adult £2.90, School £1.00. Family £9.60.

DOUNE CASTLE

Tel: 01786 841742

Doune

Owner: Earl of Moray (leased to Historic Scotland)   **Contact:** The Custodian

The formidable 14th century courtyard castle was built for the Regent Albany. The striking keep-gatehouse also combines domestic quarters including the splendid Lord's Hall with its carved oak screen, musicians' gallery and double fireplace.

Location: In Doune, 8m S of Callendar on the A84.

Opening Times: 1 Apr - 30 Sept: Mon - Sat, 9.30am - 6.30pm, Sun 2 - 6.30pm. 1 Oct - 31 Mar: Mon - Wed & Sat 9.30am - 4.30pm, Thur 9.30am - 12 noon, Fri Closed, Sun 2 - 4.30pm. Last admission 1/2 hour before closing.

Admission: Adult £2.00, Conc £1.25, Child 75p.

DUNBLANE CATHEDRAL

Tel: 01786 823388

Dunblane

Owner: Historic Scotland   **Contact:** The Custodian

One of Scotland's noblest medieval churches. The lower part of the tower is Romanesque but the larger part of the building is of the 13th century. It was restored in 1889 - 93 by Sir Rowand Anderson.

Location: In Dunblane.

Admission: Free.

DUNFERMLINE ABBEY AND PALACE

Tel: 01383 739026

Dunfermline, Fife

Owner: Historic Scotland   **Contact:** The Custodian

The remains of the Benedictine abbey founded by Queen Margaret in the 11th century. The foundations of her church are under the 12th century Romanesque style nave. Robert the Bruce was buried in the choir. Substantial parts of the Abbey buildings remain, including the vast refectory.

Location: In Dunfermline off the M90.

Opening Times: 1 Apr - 30 Sept: Mon - Sat 9.30am - 6.30pm, Sun 2 - 6.30pm. 1 Oct - 31 Mar: Mon - Wed & Sat 9.30am - 4.30pm, Thur 9.30am - 12 noon, Fri Closed, Sun 2 - 4.30pm. Last admission 1/2 hour before closing.

Admission: Adult £1.50, Conc £1.00, Child 75p.

Where to Stay
*For Private Accommodation and
Johansens
recommended Hotels,
see Accommodation
Section.*

FALKLAND PALACE

FALKLAND KY15 7BU

Owner: The National Trust for Scotland   *Contact:* Mrs Veronica Woodman

Tel: 01337 857397

The Royal Palace of Falkland, set in the heart of a unique medieval village, was the country residence and hunting lodge of eight Stuart monarchs, including Mary, Queen of Scots. Built between 1502 and 1541, the Palace is an extremely fine example of Renaissance architecture. It includes the exceptionally beautiful Chapel Royal, and is surrounded by internationally known gardens, laid out in the 1950s. The Royal Tennis Court, reputedly the world's oldest, is still used today.

Location: A912, 11m N of Kirkcaldy.

Opening Times: Palace & Garden: 1 Apr - 31 Oct: Mon - Sat 11am - 5.30pm, Sun 1.30 - 5.30pm. Groups other times by appointment. Town Hall by appointment only.

Admission: Adult £4.10, Child £2.70. Parties: Adult £3.30, School £1. Family £10.90.

HILL OF TARVIT MANSIONHOUSE & GARDEN   **Tel:** 01334 653127

Cupar, Fife KY15 5PB

Owner: The National Trust for Scotland   **Contact:** Mrs June Pratt

This fine house was rebuilt in 1906 by Sir Robert Lorimer, the renowned Scottish architect, for a Dundee industrialist, Mr F B Sharp. The house still presents a perfect setting for Mr Sharp's notable collection of superb French, Chippendale and vernacular furniture. Fine paintings by Raeburn and Ramsay and a number of eminent Dutch artists are on view together with Chinese porcelain and bronzes. Don't miss the restored Edwardian laundry behind the house which is set in the midst of a delightful garden.

Location: Off A916, 2¹/₂m S of Cupar, Fife.

Opening Times: House: Good Fri - Easter Mon &1 May - 30 Sept: Daily, 1.30 - 5.30pm. Gdn & Grounds: 1 Apr - 31 Oct: Daily, 9.30am - 7pm. 1 Nov - 31 Mar: Daily, 9.30am - 4pm.

Admission: Adult £3.10, Child £2.00. Parties: Adult £2.50, School £1.00. Family £8.20. Honesty Box £1.

INCHCOLM ABBEY   **Tel:** 01383 823332

Inchcolm, Fife

Owner: Historic Scotland   **Contact:** The Custodian

Known as the 'Iona of the East'. This is the best preserved group of monastic buildings in Scotland, founded in 1123. Includes a 13th century octagonal chapter house.

Location: On Inchcolm in the Firth of Forth. Reached by ferry from South Queensferry (30 mins) Tel. 0131 331 4857, and from North Queensferry (weather permitting).

Opening Times: 1 Apr - 30 Sept: Mon - Sat 9.30am - 6.30pm, Sun 2 - 6.30pm. Last admission ¹/₂ hour before closing.

Admission: Adult £2.00, Conc £1.00, Child £1.00. Additional charge for ferries.

INCHMAHOME PRIORY   **Tel:** 01877 385294

Port of Menteith

Owner: Historic Scotland   **Contact:** The Custodian

A beautifully situated Augustinian priory on an island in the Lake of Menteith founded in 1238 with much of the building surviving. The five year old Mary Queen of Scots was sent here for safety in 1547.

Location: On an island in Lake of Menteith. Reached by ferry from Port of Menteith, 4m E of Aberfoyle off A81.

Opening Times: 1 Apr - 30 Sept: Mon - Sat 9.30am - 6.30pm, Sun 2 - 6.30pm. Last admission ¹/₂ hour before closing.

Admission: Adult £2.50, Conc £1.50, Child £1.00p. Charge includes ferry trip.

KELLIE CASTLE AND GARDEN

OPEN

Castle: Good Fri - Easter Mon and 1 May - 30 Sept Daily, 1.30 - 5.30pm

Weekends in Oct: 1.30 - 5.30pm

Garden & Grounds: 1 Apr - 31 Oct: Daily, 9.30am - 7pm

1 Nov - 31 Mar: Daily 9.30am - 4pm.

Tel: 01333 720271

PITTENWEEM, FIFE KY10 2RF

Owner: The National Trust for Scotland   *Contact:* Mrs Patricia Wigston

This very fine example of domestic architecture in Lowland Scotland dates from the 14th century and was sympathetically restored by the Lorimer family in the late 19th century. The Castle contains magnificent plaster ceilings and painted panelling as well as fine furniture designed by Sir Robert Lorimer. Of particular interest are the Victorian nursery and the old kitchen. The late Victorian garden features a fine collection of old fashioned roses and herbaceous plants which are cultivated organically.

Location: On B9171, 3m NW of Pittenweem, Fife.

Admission: Adult £3.10, Child £2. Parties : Adult £2.50, School £1. Family £8.20.

SCOTLAND'S SECRET BUNKER   **Tel:** 01333 310301   **Fax:** 01333 312040

Troywood, St Andrews KY16 8QH

Contact: Dr J Fox

Set 100ft under ground is the secret bunker where the Government would have gone in the event of a nuclear war. Operations room. Cinemas. Restaurants. An unique family day out.

Location: Off the B940, 6m S of St Andrews. Thistle signs.

Opening Times: Good Fri - 31 Oct: 11am - 6pm. Last adm. at 5pm. (1995 times)

Admission: Adult £4.00, Conc £3.00, Family £11.00, Tours £5.00, Evening curator's tours by arrangement £5.00 per person. (1995 prices)

ST ANDREWS CASTLE   **Tel:** 01334 47/196

St Andrews, Fife

Owner: Historic Scotland   **Contact:** The Custodian

The ruins of the castle of the Archbishops of St Andrews. An exhibition in the visitor centre brings the history of the Castle and the Cathedral to life.

Location: In St Andrews on the A91.

Opening Times: 1 Apr - 30 Sept: Mon - Sat 9.30am - 6.30pm, Sun 2 - 6.30pm. 1 Oct - 31 Mar: Mon - Sat 9.30am - 4.30pm, Sun 2 - 4.30pm. Last adm. ¹/₂ hr before closing.

Admission: Adult £2.00, Conc £1.25, Child 75p. Joint entry ticket for St Andrews Castle with St Andrews Cathedral: Adult £3.00, Conc £1.75, Child £1.00.

ST ANDREWS CATHEDRAL   **Tel:** 01334 472563

St Andrews, Fife

Owner: Historic Scotland   **Contact:** The Administrator

The remains still give a vivid impression of the scale of what was once the largest cathedral in Scotland along with the associated domestic ranges of the priory. The precinct walls are particularly well preserved. Climb St Rule's Tower for a magnificent view of the town and visit the Cathedral's collection of Celtic and medieval carved stones and other relics found on the site.

Opening Times: 1 Apr - 30 Sept: Mon - Sat 9.30am - 6.30pm, Sun 2 - 6.30pm. 1 Oct - 31 Mar: Mon - Sat 9.30am - 4.30pm, Sun 2 - 4.30pm. Last adm. ¹/₂ hr before closing.

Admission: Adult £1.50, Conc £1.00, Child 75p. Joint entry ticket available for St Andrews Cathedral and St Andrews Castle: Adult £3.00, Conc £1.75, Child £1.00.

STIRLING CASTLE   **Tel:** 01786 450000

Stirling

Owner: Historic Scotland   **Contact:** The Administrator

Considered by many as the grandest of all Scotland's castles with strong links to Mary Queen of Scots. She was crowned in the chapel in 1543 and narrowly escaped death by fire in 1561.

Location: At the head of Stirling's historic old town off the M9.

Opening Times: 1 Apr - 30 Sept: Daily 9.30am - 6pm. 1 Oct - 31 Mar: Daily 9.30am - 5pm. Last admission 45 minutes before closing time.

Admission: Adult £3.50, Conc £2.00, Child under 16 £1.00. Parking up to 3 hours: cars £2.00, coaches £5.00.

SPECIAL EVENTS

❖ **HILL OF TARVIT**   **31 MAY**
Concert "Three's Company". Popular mezzo-soprano Mary Sandeman, tenor James Nichol and composer/pianist John Moore. 8pm, tickets £7. Tel: 01334 653127.

BALLINDALLOCH CASTLE 🏛
Grantown-on-Spey

BALLINDALLOCH is one of the most beautiful and romantic castles in Scotland. It is first and foremost a much loved family home and has been lived in continuously by its original family, the Macpherson-Grants since 1546. It is set in the magnificent surroundings of the Spey valley and lies in the heart of whisky country with the distilleries of Glenlivet, Glenfarclas and Glenfiddich within ten miles.

Known as the "Pearl of the North" it is a warm and welcoming castle. It exemplifies the transition from the stark Tower house, necessary for survival in 16th century Scotland, to the elegant and comfortable country house so beloved of Victorians in the Highlands. The Castle is filled with family memorabilia and houses a fine collection of 17th century Spanish paintings built up by Sir John Macpherson-Grant in 1850.

Ballindalloch is also the home of the famous Aberdeen-Angus herd of cattle founded by Sir George Macpherson-Grant in 1860 and is the oldest herd in the world.

GARDENS

The Castle is surrounded by beautiful trees and parkland with wonderful walks by the Rivers Spey and Avon which run through the grounds. Visitors can relax in the delightful rock garden or walk to the newly renovated walled garden which has been landscaped into a 'Rose and water garden'. 1996 is the 450th anniversary of Ballindalloch, 1546-1996.

❖

CONTACT

Mrs. Clare Russell
Ballindalloch Castle
Grantown-on-Spey
Banffshire
AB37 9AX

Tel: (01807) 500206

Fax: (01807) 500210

LOCATION

14 miles north
of Grantown-on-Spey
on A95
22 miles south of
Elgin on A95

OPENING TIMES

Summer
Easter - 30 Sept
Daily:10.00am - 5.30pm.
Last admission 4.45pm.

Winter
Closed.

ADMISSION

Summer

CASTLE & GARDENS
Adult £3.95
Child (5 & under) . . FREE
Child (6 - 16yrs.) . . . £2.00
Disabled £1.50

Groups (min. 12 persons)
Adult £3.50
OAP £3.00

Season Tickets
Per person £5.00

GARDENS ONLY
Per person £1.50

SUITABILITY FOR OTHER EVENTS
Dinners, receptions, filming, product launches, rallies and whisky tasting.

EXTRA FACILITIES
Audio-visual, woodturner, artist/cartoonist, salmon fishing on Rivers Spey and Avon, pheasant and grouse shooting, roe stalking.

ADVICE TO COURIERS & DRIVERS
Pre-book if possible. Coach drivers and couriers free. Refreshments in tea shop. No photography/videos inside. Dogs in dog walking area only.

FACILITIES FOR THE DISABLED
Disabled visitors may alight at entrance to castle. Audio visual and 4 rooms in castle. Toilets for the disabled.

PARKING FOR COACHES AND CARS
200 cars and 4 coaches.

CATERING
Tea room / Light lunches. All home-cooking and baking.

GIFT SHOP
Open at same time as castle selling products from the estate and a range of Scottish goods.

GUIDED TOURS
On request and pre-booked. Room notes in four languages.

GUIDE BOOKS
Colour guide books available.

SCHOOL VISITS / CHILDREN
School visits welcome. Playground and magic drawer for small children.

CONFERENCE AND FUNCTION FACILITIES

ROOM	DIMENSIONS	CAPACITY	LAYOUT	POWER POINTS	SUITABLE FOR A/V
Dining Room	30' x 14'	24			

ARBUTHNOTT HOUSE

Tel: 01561 361226 **Fax:** 01561 320476

Arbuthnott, Laurencekirk, Kincardineshire AB30 1PA
Owner: The Viscount of Arbuthnott   **Contact:** The Viscount of Arbuthnott
Arbuthnott family home for 800 years with formal 17th century walled garden on unusually steep south facing slope. Well maintained grass terraces, herbaceous borders, shrubs and greenhouses.
Location: Off B967 between A90 and A92, 25m S of Aberdeen.
Opening Times: House: 26 & 27 May, 14, 15, 28, 29 Jul, 24, 26 Aug & 1, 2 Sept: 2 - 5pm. Guided tours. Garden: All year, 9am - 5pm. No dogs please. (1995 information)
Admission: House: £3.00 (concessions available). Garden: £1.50.

BALLINDALLOCH CASTLE

See Page 258 for full page entry.

BALMORAL CASTLE (GROUNDS & EXHIBITION)

Tel: 013397 42334 **Fax:** 013397 42471

Balmoral, Ballater, Aberdeenshire AB35 5TB
Owner: HM The Queen   **Contact:** Capt J R Wilson
Family holiday home of the Royal Family, bought by Prince Albert in 1852. Grounds and exhibition of paintings and works of art in the Ballroom.
Location: Off A93 between Ballater and Braemar.
Opening Times: 1 May - 31 Jul: Mon - Sat 10am - 5pm. (1995 information)
Admission: Adult £2.50, OAPs £2.00, Child under 16 free.

BALVENIE CASTLE

Tel: 01340 820121

Dufftown
Owner: Historic Scotland   **Contact:** The Custodian
Picturesque ruins of 13th century moated stronghold originally owned by the Comyns. Visited by Edward I in 1304 and by Mary Queen of Scots in 1562. Occupied by Cumberland in 1746.
Location: At Dufftown on the A941.
Opening Times: 1 Apr - 30 Sept: Mon - Sat, 9.30am - 6.30pm, Sun 2 - 6.30pm. Last admission 1/2 hour before closing.
Admission: Adult £1.20, Conc 75p, Child 75p.

BRAEMAR CASTLE

Tel: 01339 741224

Braemar, Aberdeenshire AB5 4EX
Owner: Capt A A C Farquharson of Invercauld   **Contact:** Capt Farquharson
Turreted stronghold built in 1628 by the Earl of Mar and burnt by Farquharson of Inverey in 1689. Rebuilt in 1748 when garrisoned by Hanoverian troops. Now a fully furnished family residence.
Location: 1/2 m NE of Braemar.
Opening Times: Easter - Oct: Sat - Thur, 10am - 6.pm.
Admission: Adult £1.90, OAPs/Coaches £1.50, Child 90p.

CASTLE FRASER AND GARDEN

OPEN
Castle:
Good Fri - Easter Mon
1 May - 30 Jun
1 - 30 Sept:
Daily:1.30 - 5.30pm
1 Jul - 31 Aug
Daily: 11am - 5.30pm
Weekends in Oct:
1.30 - 5.30pm

Garden: All year
Daily: 9.30am - sunset

Tel: 01330 833463

SAUCHEN, INVERURIE AB51 7LD
Owner: The National Trust for Scotland   *Contact: Eric Wilkinson*
Over 400 years of history could be told if the stout walls of Castle Fraser could speak. Begun in 1575 by the 6th Laird, Michael Fraser, the two low wings contribute to the scale and magnificence of the towers rising above them, combining to make this the largest and most elaborate of the Scottish castles built on the 'Z' plan. The stunning simplicity of the Great Hall, which occupies the entire first floor of the main block, with its striking fireplace, almost 3 meters wide, immediately creates for the visitor the atmosphere of past centuries.
Location: Off A944, 4m N of Dunecht and 16m W of Aberdeen.
Admission: Castle: Adult £3.60, Child £2.40. Parties: Adult £2.90, Child £2.90, Family £9.60. Garden: Adult £1.60, Child £1.00. Parties: Adult £1.30, School £1.00.

CORGARFF CASTLE

Tel: 01975 651460

Strathdon
Owner: Historic Scotland   **Contact:** The Custodian
A 16th century tower house converted into a barracks for Hanoverian troops in 1748. Its last military use was to control the smuggling of illicit whisky between 1827 and 1831. Still complete and with star shaped fortification.
Location: 8m W of Strathdon village on the A939.
Opening Times: 1 Apr - 30 Sept: Mon - Sat 9.30am - 6.30pm, Sun 2 - 6.30pm. 1 Oct - 31 Mar: Sat 9.30am - 4.30pm. Sun 2 - 4.30pm. Last admission 1/2 hour before closing.
Admission: Adult £2.00, Conc £1.25, Child 75p.

CRAIGIEVAR CASTLE

Tel: 013398 83635

Alford AB33 8JF
Owner: The National Trust for Scotland   **Contact:** David Mackay
Location: On A980, 6m S of Alford and 26m W of Aberdeen.
Opening Times: Controlled access times during 1 May - 30 Sept. Please enquire.
Admission: Castle: Adult £5.20, Child £3.40, no groups. Family £13.80.

CRATHES CASTLE

BANCHORY AB31 3QJ
Owner: The National Trust for Scotland   *Contact: William Bowman*

Tel: 01330 844525

Fairytale-like turrets, gargoyles of fantastic design, superb painted ceilings and the ancient Horn of Leys given in 1323 to Alexander Burnett by King Robert the Bruce, are just a few of the exciting features at this most picturesque castle. The building of the castle began in 1553 and took 40 years to complete. Just over 300 years later, Sir James and Lady Burnett began developing the walled garden and created not just one but eight superb gardens which now provide a riot of colour throughout the summer.
Location: On A93, 3m E of Banchory and 15m W of Aberdeen.
Opening Times: 1 Apr - 31 Oct: Daily 11am - 5.30pm. Other times by appointment only. Garden & Grounds: All year: Daily 9.30am - sunset.
Admission: Adult £4.10, Child £2.70. Parties: Adult £3.30, School £1.00. Family £10.90.

CRUICKSHANK BOTANIC GARDEN

Tel: 01224 272704 **Fax:** 01224 272703

St Machar Drive, Aberdeen AB9 2UD
Owner: University of Aberdeen   **Contact:** R B Rutherford
Extensive collection of shrubs, herbaceous and alpine plants and trees. Rock and water gardens.
Location: In old Aberdeen.
Opening Times: All year: Mon - Fri, 9am - 4.30pm. May - Sept: Sat and Sun only 2 - 5pm.
Admission: Free.

DALLAS DHU DISTILLERY

Tel: 01309 676548

Forres

Owner: Historic Scotland   **Contact:** The Custodian

A completely preserved time capsule of the distiller's craft. Wander at will through this fine old Victorian distillery then enjoy a dram. Visitor centre, shop and audio-visual theatre.

Location: 1m S of Forres off the A940.

Opening Times: 1 Apr - 30 Sept: Mon - Sat 9.30am - 6.30pm, Sun 2 - 6.30pm. 1 Oct - 31 Mar: Mon - Wed & Sat 9.30am - 4.30pm, Thur 9.30am - 12 noon, Fri Closed, Sun 2 - 4.30pm. Last admission 1/2 hour before closing.

Admission: Adult £2.00, Conc £1.25, Child 75p.

DELGATIE CASTLE

OPEN

Apr - Oct

11.00am - 5.00pm

Tel: 01888 563479

TURRIFF, ABERDEENSHIRE AB53 8ED

Owner: Captain Hay of Delgatie   *Contact: Mrs Joan Johnson*

11th century castle. Painted ceilings dated 1592 and 1597. Widest turnpike stair of its kind in Scotland. Lake and woodland walks. Tearoom and shop.

Location: Off A947 Aberdeen to Banff Road.

Admission: Adults £2.50, OAP's & children £1.50

DRUM CASTLE

Tel: 01330 811204

Drumoak, by Banchory AB31 3EY

Owner: The National Trust for Scotland   **Contact:** Mrs Krista Chisholm

The combination over the years of a 13th century square tower, a very fine Jacobean mansionhouse and the additions of the Victorian Lairds make Drum Castle unique among Scottish Castles. Owned for 653 years by one family, the Irvines, every stone and every room is steeped in history. Superb furniture and paintings provide a visual feast for the visitor. In the 16th century Chapel, the stained glass windows, the font copied from the Saxon one in Winchester Cathedral and the Augsburg silver Madonna, all add immense interest for the visitor.

Location: Off A93, 3m W of Peterculter and 10m W of Aberdeen.

Opening Times: Castle: Good Fri - Easter Mon & 1 May - 30 Sept: Daily, 1.30 - 5.30pm. Weekends in Oct: 1.30 - 5.30pm. Garden: Same dates:Daily 10am - 6pm. Grounds: All year: Daily, 9.30am - sunset.

Admission: Adult £3.60, Child £2.40. Parties: Adult £2.90, School £1.00. Family £9.60.

DUFF HOUSE

OPEN

1 Apr - 30 Sept:
10am - 5pm
(closed Tuesdays)

1 Oct - 31 Mar:
10am - 5pm
(closed Mon - Wed)

Closed 25 & 26 Dec,
1 & 2 Jan

Tel: 01261 818181
Fax: 01261 818900

BANFF AB45 3SX

Contact: The Manager

A magnificent example of baroque architecture, designed by William Adam in 1735. Has recently been extensively refurbished and now operates as an out-station of the National Galleries of Scotland. Woodland walks, icehouse, mausoleum, cafe, shop, audio-visual room and ample parking.

Location: Banff.

Admission: Adult £2.50, Conc £1.00.

DUNNOTTAR CASTLE

Tel: 01569 762173

The Lodge, Stonehaven AB3 2TL

Contact: P McKenzie

Impressive ruined fortress on rock cliff 160 feet above the sea.

Location: Just off A92.

Opening Times: Easter - Oct: Mon - Sat, 9am - 6pm. Sun 2 - 5pm. Nov - Easter: Mon - Fri, 9am - sunset. Closed weekends. Last adm: 30 mins before closing.

Admission: Adult £3.00, Child £1.00.

ELGIN CATHEDRAL

Tel: 01343 547171

Elgin

Owner: Historic Scotland   **Contact:** The Custodian

When entire this was perhaps the most beautiful of Scottish cathedrals, known as the Lantern of the North. 13th century, much modified after almost being destroyed in 1390 by Alexander Stewart, the infamous 'Wolf of Badenoch'. The octagonal chapterhouse is the finest in Scotland. You can see the Bishop's home at Spynie Palace, 2mls north of the town.

Location: In Elgin on the A96.

Opening Times: 1 Apr - 30 Sept: Mon - Sat 9.30am - 6.30pm, Sun 2 - 6.30pm. 1 Oct - 31 Mar: Mon - Wed & Sat 9.30am - 4.30pm, Thur 9.30am - 12 noon, Fri Closed, Sun 2 - 4.30pm. Last admission 1/2 hour before closing.

Admission: Adult £1.50, Conc £1.00, Child 75p. Joint entry ticket with Spynie Palace: Adult £2.50, Conc. £1.50, Child £1.20.

FASQUE

FETTERCAIRN, KINCARDINESHIRE AB30 1DJ

Owner: Charles Gladstone   *Contact: The Administrator*

Tel: 01561 340202 or 340569 **Fax:** 01561 340325

A spectacular example of a Victorian 'upstairs - downstairs' stately home. Home to William Gladstone, four times Prime Minister, for much of his life. Inside very little has changed since Victorian times. See the famous double cantilever staircase, William Gladstone Library, the extraordinary kitchen, and visit the family church. Shop, tea room, deer park, picnic site and walks.

Location: On the B974, 1/2m N of Fettercairn, 4m from A90. Aberdeen/Dundee 30 mins.

Opening Times: 1 May - 30 Sept: Daily 11am - 5.30pm. Groups by arrangement any time.

Admission: Adult £3.50, Child £1.50, Conc £2.50.

FYVIE CASTLE

Tel: 01651 891266

Turriff, Aberdeenshire AB53 8JS

Owner: The National Trust for Scotland   **Contact:** Donald Little

The south front of this magnificent building employs a plethora of crow-stepped gables, turrets, sculpted dormers and finials in the form of musicians, to create a marvellous façade. The five towers of the castle bear witness to the five families who have owned it. Fyvie Castle boasts the finest wheel stair in Scotland and there is a superb collection of arms and armour and paintings, including works by Batoni, Raeburn, Romney, Gainsborough, Opie and Hoppner.

Location: Off A947, 8m SE of Turriff, and 25m N of Aberdeen.

Opening Times: Castle: 1 Apr - 30 Jun & 1 - 30 Sept: Daily, 1.30 - 5.30pm. 1 Jul - 31 Aug: Daily 11am - 5.30pm. Weekends in Oct: 1.30 - 5.30pm. Grounds: All year Daily 9.30 - sunset.

Admission: Adult £3.60, Child £2.40. Parties: Adult £2.90, School £1.00. Family £9.60.

HADDO HOUSE

Tel: 01651 851440

Tarves, Ellon, Aberdeenshire AB41 0ER

Owner: The National Trust for Scotland **Contact:** Tony Ashby

This appealing house was designed by William Adam in 1731 for William, 2nd Earl of Aberdeen. Much of the splendid interior is 'Adam Revival' carried out about 1880 for John, 7th Earl and 1st Marquess of Aberdeen and his Countess, Ishbel. It is arguably the most elegant house in the north east, a classic English-style stately home transplanted to Scotland. Features of the house include the Italiante sweeping twin staircases at the front of the house, the atmospheric library and the subtlety of the great curving corridor.

Location: Off B999, 4m N of Pitmedden and 19m N of Aberdeen.

Opening Times: House: Good Fri - Easter Mon and 1 May - 30 Sept: daily 1.30 - 5.30pm. Weekends in Oct: 1.30 - 5.30pm. Garden & Country Park: all year, daily, 9.30am - sunset.

Admission: Adult £3.60, Child £2.40. Parties Adult £2.90, School £1.00. Family £9.60.

HUNTLY CASTLE

Tel: 01466 793191

Huntly.

Owner: Historic Scotland **Contact:** The Custodian

Known also as Strathbogie Castle, this glorious ruin stands in a beautiful setting on the banks of the River Deveron. Famed for its fine heraldic sculpture and inscribed stone friezes.

Location: In Huntly on the A96.

Opening Times: 1 Apr - 30 Sept: Mon - Sat, 9.30am - 6.30pm, Sun 2 - 6.30pm. 1 Oct - 31 Mar: Mon - Wed & Sat 9.30am - 4.30pm, Thur 9.30am - 12 noon, Fri Closed, Sun 2 - 4.30pm. Last admission 1/2 hour before closing.

Admission: Adult £2.00, Conc £1.25, Child 75p.

KILDRUMMY CASTLE

Tel: 01975 571331

Alford, Aberdeenshire

Owner: Historic Scotland **Contact:** The Custodian

Though ruined, the best example in Scotland of a 13th century castle with a curtain wall, four round towers, hall and chapel of that date. The seat of the Earls of Mar, it was dismantled after the first Jacobite rising in 1715.

Location: 10m SW of Alford on the A97.

Opening Times: 1 Apr - 30 Sept: Mon - Sat 9.30am - 6.30pm, Sun 2 - 6.30pm. Last admission 1/2 hour before closing.

Admission: Adult £1.50, Conc £1.00, Child 75p.

KILDRUMMY CASTLE GARDEN

Tel: 01975 571203 / 571277

Kildrummy, Aberdeenshire

Contact: Alastair J Laing

Ancient quarry shrub and alpine gardens renowned for their interest and variety. Water gardens below ruined castle.

Location: On A97 off A944 10m SW of Alford.

Opening Times: Apr - Oct: daily, 10.00am - 5.00pm.

Admission: Adult £1.70, Child 50p.

LEITH HALL

Tel: 01464 831216

Huntly, Aberdeenshire AB54 4NQ

Owner: The National Trust for Scotland **Contact:** The Custodian

This mansion house is built around a courtyard and was the home of the Leith family for almost 400 years. With an enviable family record of military service over the centuries, the house contains a unique collection of military memorabilia displayed in an exhibition *'For Crown and Country'*. The graciously furnished rooms are a delight to wander through and present a fine impression of the lifestyle of the Leith family.

Location: On B9002, 1 m W of Kennethmont and 34m NW of Aberdeen.

Opening Times: Good Fri - Easter Mon & 1 May - 30 Sept: Daily 1.30 - 5.30pm. Weekends in Oct: 1.30 - 5.30pm. Garden & Grounds: All year, Daily 9.30am - sunset.

Admission: Garden: Adult £1.60, Child £1.00. Parties: Adult £1.30, School £1.00. House: Adult £3.60, Child £2.40. Parties: Adult £2.90, Child £1.00. Family £9.60.

MONYMUSK WALLED GARDEN

Tel: 01467 651543

Home Farm, Monymusk, Aberdeen AB51 7H.

Owner: Mrs M Coleman **Contact:** Mrs M Coleman

Mainly herbaceous plants in walled garden setting.

Opening Times: Times unconfirmed at going to press.

Admission: Donations welcome.

PITMEDDEN GARDEN

OPEN

1 May - 30 Sept:

Daily

10am - 5.30pm

Last admission 5pm.

Tel: 01651 842352

ELLON, ABERDEENSHIRE AB41 0PD

Owner: *The National Trust for Scotland* **Contact:** *Douglas Westland*

The centrepiece of this property is the Great Garden which was originally laid out in 1675 by Sir Alexander Seton, 1st Baronet of Pitmedden. The elaborate designs inspired by the garden at the Palace of Holyroodhouse in Edinburgh have been painstakingly recreated for the enjoyment of visitors. In the 100 acre estate, is situated the very fine Museum of Farming Life which presents a vivid picture of the lives and times of bygone days when the horse was the power in front of the plough and farm machinery was less complicated than today's.

Location: On A920 1m W of Pitmedden village and 14m N of Aberdeen.

Admission: Adult £3.10, Child £2. Parties: Adult £2.50, School £1. Family £8.20.

SPYNIE PALACE

Tel: 01343 546358

Elgin

Owner: Historic Scotland **Contact:** The Custodian

Spynie Palace was the residence of the Bishops of Moray from the 14th century to 1686. The site is dominated by the massive tower built by Bishop David Stewart (1461-77) and affords spectacular views across Spynie Loch.

Location: 2 m N of Elgin off the A941.

Opening Times: 1 Apr - 30 Sept: Mon - Sat 9.30am - 6.30pm, Sun 2 - 6.30pm. 1 Oct - 31 Mar: Sat 9.30am - 4.30pm, Sun 2 - 4.30pm. Last admission 1/2 hour before closing.

Admission: Adult £1.50, Conc £1.00, Child 75p. Joint entry ticket with Elgin Cathedral: Adult £2.50, Conc. £1.50, Child £1.20.

ST MACHAR'S CATHEDRAL TRANSEPTS

Tel: 0131 668 8800

Old Aberdeen

Owner: Historic Scotland

The nave and towers of the Cathedral remain in use as a church, and the ruined transepts are in care. In the south transept is the fine altar tomb of Bishop Dunbar (1514 - 32).

Location: In old Aberdeen. Free site.

TOLQUHON CASTLE

Tel: 01651 851286

Aberdeenshire

Owner: Historic Scotland **Contact:** The Custodian

Tolquhon was built for the Forbes family. The early 15th century tower was enlarged between 1584 and 1589 with a large mansion round the courtyard. Noted for its highly ornamented gatehouse and pleasance.

Location: 15 m N of Aberdeen on the A920.

Opening Times: 1 Apr - 30 Sept: Mon - Sat 9.30am - 6.30pm, Sun 2 - 6.30pm. 1 Oct - 31 Mar: Sat 9.30am - 4.30pm, Sun 2 - 4.30pm. Last adm. 1/2 hour before closing.

Admission: Adult £1.50, Conc £1.00, Child 75p.

SPECIAL EVENTS

❖ **CASTLE FRASER** **24 MAY**
Concert "A Rantin' Roarin' - Bravo Burns!". An evening of Burns in poetry and song presented by The Lallan' Voices. 7.30pm. Tel: 01330 833463.

❖ **HADDO HOUSE** **28 JUNE**
Concert "An Evening with Noel Coward" presented by Cameo. 7.30pm. Tel: 01651 851440.

❖ **DELGATIE CASTLE** **4 AUGUST**
Clan hay gathering and games.

❖ **CASTLE FRASER** **9 AUGUST**
Concert "Three's Company". Popular mezzo-soprano Mary Sandeman, tenor James Nichol and composer/pianist John Moore. 8pm, tickets £7. Tel: 01330 833463.

❖ **FYVIE CASTLE** **23 AUGUST**
Concert "An Evening of New Orleans Jazz" with Violet Milne's Spirits of Rythm. 7.30pm. Tickets £12.30. Tel: 01651 891266.

❖ **FYVIE CASTLE** **27 SEPTEMBER**
Concert "The Oxford Concert Party". Europe's only Baroque and Tango Orchestra! 7.30pm. Tel: 01651 891266.

CAWDOR CASTLE
Nairn

This splendid romantic castle dating from the late 14th century was built as a private fortress by the Thanes of Cawdor, and remains the home of the Cawdor family to this day. The ancient medieval tower was built around the legendary holly-tree.

Although the house has evolved over 600 years, later additions mainly of the 17th century were all built in the Scottish vernacular style with slated roofs over walls and crow-stepped gables of mellow local stone. This style gives Cawdor a strong sense of unity, and the massive, severe exterior belies an intimate interior that gives the place a surprisingly personal, friendly atmosphere.

Good furniture, fine portraits and pictures, interesting objects and outstanding tapestries are arranged to please the family rather than to echo fashion or impress. Memories of Shakespeare's 'Macbeth' give Cawdor an elusive, evocative quality that delights visitors.

GARDENS
The Flower Garden also has a family feel to it, where plants are chosen out of affection rather than affectation. This is a lovely spot between spring and late summer. The Walled Garden has been restored with a holly maze, paradise garden, knot garden and thistle garden. The Wild Garden beside its stream leads into beautiful trails through a spectacular mature mixed woodland, through which paths are helpfully marked and colour-coded.

SUITABILITY FOR OTHER EVENTS
Conferences and day functions.

EXTRA FACILITIES
9 hole golf course, putting green, golf clubs for hire. Special arrangements can be made for groups to include lunches, sherry or champagne receptions, whisky tasting, musical entertainments. Specialised garden visits.

ADVICE TO COURIERS & DRIVERS
Two weeks advance notice for group catering. Coach drivers/couriers free. Refreshments or lunch in restaurant. Drivers entered in monthly prize draw. No photography, video photography or tripods inside. No dogs. Parking for 250 cars and 25 coaches.

FACILITIES FOR THE DISABLED
Disabled and elderly visitors may alight at the entrance to the Castle, before parking in the allocated areas. Toilets for the disabled.

CATERING
The licensed Castle Buttery provides hot meals, snacks and home baking from May to October, capacity 50. Groups should book in advance, Tel: (01667) 404615. Menus on request.

GIFT SHOP
There are three shops open at the same time as Castle. The Gift Shop items include: cashmere, china, leather goods, children's toys, sweets and a wide selection of products made in Scotland, many exclusively for Cawdor Castle. The Book Shop sells a wide and unusual selection of books, prints, stationery and cards. The Wool Shop: the best of Scottish cashmere, capes, ponchos and a large collection of sweaters and children's clothes including tartans.

GUIDE BOOKS
Colour guide book and room notes. French, German, Italian and Japanese translations available.

SCHOOL VISITS/CHILDREN
School groups are welcome, £2.50 per child. Room notes, quiz and answer sheet can be provided. Of particular interest: Ranger service and nature trails.

CONTACT

The Secretary
Cawdor Castle
Nairn
Scotland
IV12 5RD

Tel: (01667) 404615

Fax: (01667) 404674

LOCATION

From Edinburgh
A9 3½ hours,
Inverness 20 minutes,
Nairn 10 minutes.

Main road: A9 14 miles.

Rail: Nairn Station
5 miles.

Bus: Inverness to Nairn
bus route 200 yards.

Taxi: Piperhill Taxis
(01667) 404680.

Air: Inverness Airport
5 miles.

OPENING TIMES

Summer
1 May - 13 October

Daily 10am - 5.30pm

Last admission 5pm.

Winter
14 October - 30 April
Closed

ADMISSION

Summer
HOUSE & GARDEN

Adult £4.70
Child* £2.50
OAP £3.70
Family (2+5) £13.00

Groups (Min 20 people)
Adult £4.20
Child* £2.50

GARDEN ONLY

Adult £2.50
Child* £2.50
OAP £2.50

*Age 5 - 15

CONFERENCE AND FUNCTION FACILITIES

ROOM	DIMENSIONS	CAPACITY	LAYOUT	POWER POINTS	SUITABLE FOR A/V
Cawdor Hall		40	Boardroom Lunch/Dinner	✓	✓

DUNVEGAN CASTLE
Isle of Skye

DUNVEGAN is unique. It is the only Great House in the Western Isles of Scotland to have retained its family and its roof. It is the oldest home in the whole of Scotland continuously inhabited by the same family - the Chiefs of the Clan Macleod. A Castle placed on a rock by the sea - the curtain wall is dated before 1200 A.D. - its superb location recalls the Norse Empire of the Vikings, the ancestors of the Chiefs.

Dunvegan's continuing importance as a custodian of the Clan spirit is epitomised by the famous Fairy Flag, whose origins are shrouded in mystery but whose ability to protect both Chief and Clan is unquestioned.

To enter Dunvegan is to arrive at a place whose history combines with legend to make a living reality.

GARDENS

The gardens and grounds extend over some ten acres of woodland walks, peaceful formal lawns and a water garden dominated by two spectacular natural waterfalls. The temperate climate aids in producing a fine show of rhododendrons and azaleas, the chief glory of the garden in spring. Always one is aware of the proximity of the sea and many garden walks finish at the Castle Jetty, from where traditional boats make regular trips to view the delightful Seal Colony.

CONTACT

The Administrator
Dunvegan Castle
Isle of Skye
IV55 8WF

Tel: (01470) 521206
Fax: (01470) 521205

LOCATION

1 mile north of village.

From Inverness A82 to Invermoriston, A887 to Kyle of Lochalsh 82 miles. From Fort William A82 to Invergarry, A87 to Kyle of Lochalsh 76 miles.

Kyle of Lochalsh to Dunvegan 45 miles.

Ferry: to the Isle of Skye, 'roll-on, roll-off'; 4 minute crossing.

Rail: Inverness to Kyle of Lochalsh 3/4 trains per day - 45 miles.

Bus: Portree 25 miles, Kyle of Lochalsh 45 miles.

Paul Tomkins

EXTRA FACILITIES
Seal colony. $^1/_2$ mile from Castle. Boat trips to see seals at frequent intervals from the Castle Jetty. The Seals are generally un-disturbed by people in our small boats and are a joy to study and photograph at close quarters. Loch Cruises on 35 seater motor vessel $1^1/_2$hrs. Cruises throughout the day. Also available for charter and fishing trips. Herd of pedigree Highland Cattle.

ACCOMMODATION
Dunvegan offers 4 self-catering units, 3 of which sleep 6 and 1 of which sleeps 7.

ADVICE TO COURIERS & DRIVERS
Please park in Coach Park, 150 metres walk from Castle. DO NOT attempt to take passengers to Castle Jetty, it is a further 50m walk. Allow at least 1hr preferably 2. If possible please book in advance, particularly if it is intended to include the Seal Boat Trip. However, this facility is dependent upon the weather and can not be pre-booked. Dogs allowed in grounds only and must be kept on a leash. No photography within Castle. Parking for 120 cars and 10 coaches 150 yards from the Castle.

FACILITIES FOR THE DISABLED
Disabled & elderly visitors may be left at entrance to Castle before parking in allocated areas. Toilets for the disabled.

CATERING
Licensed restaurant. The Castle Restaurant provides snacks and hot meals throughout the season. Seating 70, special rates are offered to groups, menus upon request. Tel: (01470) 521310. Open late at height of season for evening meals.

GUIDED TOURS
Tours available by appointment in English or Gaelic at no extra charge. If requested the owner may meet groups. Average time for tour is 45 minutes.

GIFT SHOPS
2 Gift and Craft Shops, one in car park, the other in the Castle. Shops open 10am-5.30pm seven days a week.

GUIDE BOOKS
Full colour guide book £1.70. Translations in French, German, Spanish, Italian and Japanese.

SCHOOL VISITS/CHILDREN
Groups of children are welcome by arrangement. If requested a guide can be available.

OPENING TIMES

Summer

25 March - 31 October

Daily 10.00am - 5.30pm
Last entry 5.00pm

Winter
November - March
By appointment.

ADMISSION

Summer

CASTLE
  Adult £4.50
  Child (Under 16) . . £2.50
  OAP/Student . . . £4.00
  Group £4.00

GARDEN
  Adult £3.00
  Child (Under 16) . . £1.50

SEAL BOATS
  Adult £3.50
  Child (Under 16) . . £2.50

LOCH CRUISES*
  Adult £7.00
  Child £2.50
  Concessions . . . £5.00

* Aboard the motor vessel "MacLeod of MacLeod".

Winter
By Appointment.
No Boat Trips.

BISHOP'S & EARL'S PALACES

Tel: 01856 875461

Kirkwall, Orkney

Owner: Historic Scotland   **Contact:** The Custodian

The Bishop's Palace is a 12th century hall-house with a round tower built by Bishop Reid in 1541-48. The adjacent Earl's Palace built in 1607 has been described as the most mature and accomplished piece of Renaissance architecture left in Scotland.

Location: In Kirkwall on the A960.

Opening Times: 1 Apr - 30 Sept: Mon - Sat 9.30am - 6.30pm, Sun 2 - 6.30pm. Last admission 1/2 hour before closing.

Admission: Adult £1.20, Conc 75p, Child 75p. Joint entry ticket available for all the Orkney monuments: Adult £6.00, Conc £3.50, Child £2.00.

BLACK HOUSE

Tel: 01851 710395

Arnol, Isle of Lewis

Owner: Historic Scotland   **Contact:** The Custodian

A traditional Lewis thatched house, fully furnished, complete with attached barn, byre and stockyard. A peat fire burns in the open hearth.

Location: In Arnol village, Isle of Lewis, 11m NW of Stornoway on the A858.

Opening Times: 1 Apr - 30 Sept: Mon - Sat 9.30am - 6.30pm, Sun closed. 1 Oct - 31 Mar: Mon - Thur & Sat 9.30am - 4.30 pm. Last admission 1/2 hour before closing.

Admission: Adult £1.50, Conc £1.00, Child 75p.

BROCH OF GURNESS

Tel: 01831 579478

Aikerness, Orkney

Owner: Historic Scotland   **Contact:** The Custodian

Protected by three lines of ditch and rampart, the base of the broch is surrounded by a warren of Iron Age buildings.

Location: At Aikerness, about 14m NW of Kirkwall on A966.

Opening Times: 1 Apr - 30 Sept: Mon - Sat 9.30am - 6.30pm, Sun 2 - 6.30pm. Last admission 1/2 hour before closing.

Admission: Adult £2.00, Child £75p, Conc. £1.25. Joint entry ticket available for all Orkney monuments: Adult £6.00, Conc £3.50, Child £2.00.

BRODIE CASTLE

OPEN

1 Apr - 30 Sept:
Mon - Sat
11am - 5.30pm

Sun 1.30 - 5.30pm

Weekends in Oct:
Sat, 11am - 5.30pm
Sun, 1.30 - 5.30pm

Other times by appointment.

Grounds: All year, daily 9.30am - sunset.

Tel: 01309 641371

FORRES, MORAY IV36 0TE

Owner: The National Trust for Scotland   *Contact:* Dr Stephanie Blackden

This imposing Castle stands in rich Morayshire parkland. The lime harled building is a typical 'Z' plan tower house with ornate corbelled battlements and bartizans, with 17th & 19th century additions. The interior has unusual plaster ceilings, a major art collection, porcelain and fine furniture. There is a woodland walk by a large pond with access to wildlife observation hides. In springtime the grounds are carpeted with many varieties of daffodils for which Brodie Castle is rightly famous.

Location: Off A96 4 1/2m W of Forres and 24m E of Inverness.

Admission: Adult £3.60, Child £2.40. Parties: Adult £2.90, School £1.00. Family £9.60.

CAWDOR CASTLE

See Page 262 for full page entry.

CLAN DONALD VISITOR CENTRE & ARMADALE GARDENS

Tel: 01471 844305   **Fax:** 01471 844275

Armadale, Isle of Skye IV45 8RS

Owner: Clan Donald Lands Trust   **Contact:** R McDonald Parker

Part of Armadale Castle houses a visitor centre telling the story of the Macdonalds and the Lord of the Isles. 40 acres 19th century woodland garden.

Location: 1m from Mallaig - Armadale ferry terminal.

Opening Times: Apr - Oct: Daily 9.30am - 5.30pm.

Admission: Adult £3.40, Child £2.20, Conc £2.20, Groups £2.20.

CROMARTY COURTHOUSE

Tel: 01381 600418   **Fax:** 01381 600408

Church Street, Cromarty IV11 8XA

    Contact: David Alston

18th century village courthouse, visitor centre and museum.

Location: 25m N of Inverness.

Opening Times: Closed for annual maintenance at time of going to press, please phone for further details.

CULLODEN

INVERNESS IV1 2ED

Owner: The National Trust for Scotland   *Contact:* Ross MacKenzie

Tel: 01463 790607

No name in Scottish history evokes more emotion than that of Culloden, the bleak moor which in 1746 saw the hopes of the young Prince Charles Edward Stuart crushed, and the end of the Jacobite Rising, the 'Forty-Five'. The Prince's forces, greatly outnumbered by those of the brutal Duke of Cumberland, nevertheless went into battle with a courage which has passed into legend.

Location: On B9006, 5m E of Inverness, Highland.

Opening Times: Site: All year Daily. Visitor Centre: 3 Feb - 31 Mar & 1 Nov - 30 Dec: Daily 10am - 4pm. 1 Apr - 31 Oct: Daily 9am - 6pm. *Swords and Sorrows* exhibition 16 April - 20 Sept.

Admission: Adult £2.60, Child £1.70. Parties: Adult £2.10, School £1. Family £9.60.

DOCHFOUR GARDENS

Tel: 01463 861218

Dochgarroch, Inverness IV3 6JY

Owner: The Lord Burton   **Contact:** The Lord Burton

Victorian terraced garden near Inverness with panoramic views over Loch Dochfour. Magnificent specimen trees, naturalised daffodils, rhododendrons, water garden, yew topiary. Integral nursery selling shrubs, herbaceous, alpines.

Location: 6m SW of Inverness on A82 to Fort William.

Opening Times: Gardens: All year: Mon - Fri, Sat & Sun, 10am - 5pm. House not open.

Admission: Garden Walk - £1.50.

DUNROBIN CASTLE

OPEN
Easter - 31 May
Mon - Sat
10.30am - 4.30pm
Sun: 1.00 - 4.30pm
1 Jun - 30 Sept Mon -
Sat 10.30am - 5.30pm
Sun: 12 - 5.30pm
July & Aug: 10.30am
1 - 15 Oct: as May
Last Admission ½ hr
before closing

Tel: 01408 633177
or 01408 633268
Fax: 01408 634081

GOLSPIE, SUTHERLAND KW10 6SF

Owner: The Sutherland Trust   *Contact: Keith Jones, Curator*

Dates from the 13th century with additions in the 17th, 18th and 19th centuries. Wonderful furniture, paintings, library, ceremonial robes and memorabilia. Tearoom and gift shop. Victorian museum in grounds with a fascinating collection including Pictish stones. Set in fine woodlands overlooking the sea. Magnificent formal gardens, one of few remaining French/Scottish formal parterres.
Location: 50m N of Inverness on the A9.

Admission: Adult £4.50, Conc £2.80, Family £12.50. Group: Adult £4.20, Group Concessions: £2.50.

DUNVEGAN CASTLE

See Page 263 for full page entry.

EILEAN DONAN CASTLE

Tel: 01599 555202

Dornie, Kyle, Wester IV40 8DX

Contact: The Administrator

Picturesque castle on an islet dating back to 1220.
Location: On A87 8m E of Skye Ferry.
Opening Times: 1 Apr - end Oct: 10am - 5.30pm. (unconfirmed for 1996, check details)
Admission: Adult £1.50, Child 75p, Group £1.25. (unconfirmed for 1996)

FORT GEORGE

Tel: 01667 462777

Ardersier, Inverness-shire
Owner: Historic Scotland   **Contact:** The Custodian
Completed in 1769 following the Battle of Culloden as a Highland fortress for the army of George II. Fort George is still an active army barracks which houses the Regimental Museum of the Queen's Own Highlanders.
Location: 10m W of Nairn, 11m NE of Inverness off the A96.
Opening Times: 1 Apr - 30 Sept: Mon - Sat, 9.30am - 6.30pm, Sun 2 - 6.30pm. 1 Oct - 31 Mar: Mon - Sat, 9.30am - 4.30 pm, Sun 2 - 4.30pm.
Admission: Adult £2.50, Conc £1.50, Child £1.00.

GLENFINNAN

OPEN

Site: All year
Daily

Visitor Centre
1 Apr - 18 May &
1 Sept - 31 Oct:
Daily, 10am - 1pm
& 2 - 5pm

19 May - 31 Aug:
Daily 10am - 6pm

Tel: 01397 722250

INVERNESS-SHIRE PH37 4LT

Owner: The National Trust for Scotland   *Contact: Mrs Lillias Grant*

The monument, situated on the scenic road to the Isles, is set amid superb Highland scenery at the head of Loch Shiel. It was erected in 1815 in tribute to the clansmen who fought and died in the Jacobite cause. Prince Charles Edward Stuart's standard was raised near here 250 years ago in 1745. Despite its inspired beginnings, the campaign came to a grim conclusion on the Culloden battlefield in 1746.
Location: On A830, 18m W of Fort William, Lochaber.
Admission: Adult £1.00, Child 60p. Family £2.60.

HUGH MILLER'S COTTAGE

Tel: 01381 600245

Cromarty IV11 8XA
Owner: The National Trust for Scotland   **Contact:** Ms Frieda Gostwick
Furnished thatch cottage of c.1711, birthplace of eminent geologist and writer Hugh Miller. Exhibition and video.
Location: Via Kessock Bridge and A832, in Cromarty, 22m NE of Inverness.
Opening Times: 1 May - 30 Sept: Mon - Sat, 10am - 1pm and 2 - 5.30pm. Sun 2 - 5.30pm.
Admission: Adult £1.60, Child £1.00. Parties: Adult £1.30, School £1.00. Family £4.20.

INVEREWE GARDEN

POOLEWE, ROSS & CROMARTY IV22 2LQ

Owner: The National Trust for Scotland   *Contact: Kath Gamm*

Tel: 01445 781200

Where in Scotland will you see the tallest Australian gum trees in Britain, sweetly scented Chinese rhododendrons, exotic trees from Chile and Blue Nile lilies from South Africa, all growing on a latitude more northerly than Moscow? The answer is Inverewe. Miraculous? Yes and no, because although you are in a remote corner of Wester Ross, you are also in a sheltered garden, blessed by the North Atlantic Drift. In a spectacular lochside setting among pinewoods, Osgood Mackenzie's Victorian dreams have produced a glorious 50 acre mecca for garden lovers.
Location: On A832, by Poolewe, 6m NE of Gairloch, Highland.
Opening Times: 1 Apr - 31 Oct: Daily 9.30am - 9pm. 1 Nov - 31 Mar: Daily 9.30am - 5pm. Visitor Centre and Shop: 1 Apr - 31 Oct: Daily 9.30am - 5.30pm.
Admission: Adult £3.60, Child £2.40. Parties: Adult £2.90, School £1.00. Family £9.60.

JARLSHOF PREHISTORIC & NORSE SETTLEMENT **Tel:** 01950 460112

Shetland
Owner: Historic Scotland   **Contact:** The Custodian
Over 3 acres of remains spanning 3,000 years from the Stone Age. Oval shaped Bronze Age houses, Iron Age broch and wheel houses. Viking long houses, medieval farmstead and 16th century laird's house.
Location: At Sumburgh Head, 22m S of Lerwick on the A970.
Opening Times: 1 Apr - 30 Sept: Mon - Sat 9.30am - 6.30pm, Sun 2 - 6.30pm. Last admission ½ hour before closing. 1 Oct - 31 March: Closed.
Admission: Adult £2.00, Conc £1.25, Child 75p.

MAES HOWE

Tel: 01856 761606

Orkney
Owner: Historic Scotland   **Contact:** The Custodian
This world famous tomb was built in Neolithic times, before 2700 BC. The large mound covers a stone-built passage and a burial chamber with cells in the walls. Runic inscriptions tell of how it was plundered of its treasures by Vikings.
Location: 9m W of Kirkwall on the A965.
Opening Times: 1 Apr - 30 Sept: Mon - Sat 9.30am - 6.30pm, Sun 2 - 6.30pm. 1 Oct - 31 Mar: Mon, Tue, Fri, Sat 9.30am - 4.30pm, Wed, Thur & Sun 2 - 4.30pm. Last adm.½ hour before closing.
Admission: Adult £2.00, Conc £1.25, Child £75p. Joint entry ticket available for all Orkney monuments: Adult £6.00, Conc £3.50, Child £2.00. Admission, shop and refreshments at nearby Tormiston Mill.

ROTHIEMURCHUS

OPEN

May - Aug
Grounds:
Mondays
10am - 12.30pm
and
2 - 4.30pm.
Also first Mon of the
month in Winter.

Tel: 01479 810858
Fax: 01479 811778

THE DOUNE OF ROTHIEMURCHUS, BY AVIEMORE PH22 1QH

Owner: J P Grant of Rothiemurchus   *Contact:* Rothiemurchus Visitor Centre

The family home of The Grants of Rothiemurchus was nearly lost as a ruin and has been under an ambitious repair programme since 1975. This exciting project may be visited on selected Mondays throughout the year. Book with the Visitor Centre for a longer 2 hr 'Highland Lady' tour which explores the haunts of Elizabeth Grant of Rothiemurchus, born 1797, author of 'Memoirs of a Highland Lady', who vividly described the Doune and its surroundings from the memories of her childhood.

Location: Inverness-shire.

Admission: Doune Grounds: £1.00 per person. Guided Highland Lady Tour: £5.00 per person, min charge of £20. Booking is essential.

SKARA BRAE

Tel: 01856 841815

Orkney

Owner: Historic Scotland   **Contact:** The Custodian

Uncovered by a storm in 1850 Skara Brae is one of the best preserved groups of Stone Age houses in western Europe. The houses contain stone furniture, hearths and drains and present a remarkable picture of life in Neolithic times.

Location: 19m NW of Kirkwall on the B9056.

Opening Times: 1 Apr - 30 Sept: Mon - Sat, 9.30am - 6.30pm. Sun 2 - 6.30pm. 1 Oct - 31 Mar: Mon - Sat, 9.30am - 4.30pm. Sun 2 - 4.30pm. Last admission ½ hour before closing.

Admission: Adult £2.50, Conc £2.50, Child £1.00. Joint entry ticket available for all Orkney monuments: Adult £6.00, Conc £3.50, Child £2.00.

URQUHART CASTLE

Tel: 01456 450551

Drumnadrochit, Loch Ness

Owner: Historic Scotland   **Contact:** The Custodian

The remains of one of the largest castles in Scotland dominate a rocky promontory on Loch Ness. It fell into decay after 1689. Most of the existing buildings date from the 16th century. A popular viewpoint for monster spotting. Splendid views up and down the Loch.

Location: On Loch Ness, near Drumnadrochit on the A82.

Opening Times: 1 Apr - 30 Sept: Mon - Sun, 9.30am - 6.30pm. 1 Oct - 31 Mar: Mon - Sat, 9.30am - 4.30pm. Sun 11.30am - 4.30pm. Last admission ½ hour before closing.

Admission: Adult £3.00, Conc £2.00, Child £1.00.

SPECIAL EVENTS

❖ **CULLODEN VISITOR CENTRE**   **16 APRIL**
Exhibition "The Sword and The Sorrows". Until 20th Sept. Weaponry and other memorabilia connected with the 250th anniversary of Battle of Culloden. Tel: 01463 790607.

❖ **BRODIE CASTLE**   **1 – 2 JUNE**
Northern Craft Fair in Castle grounds. Tel: 01309 641371.

❖ **BRODIE CASTLE**   **1 JUNE**
Concert "Coronach" Scottish Renaissance Music. Tel: 01309 641371

❖ **BRODIE CASTLE**   **10 AUGUST**
Concert "Three's Company". Popular mezzo-soprano Mary Sandeman, tenor James Nichol and composer/pianist John Moore. 8pm, tickets £7. Tel: 01309 641371.

❖ **BRODIE CASTLE**   **10 AUGUST**
"Taste of Moray" organised by Forres Rotary Club. Major event in Castle and grounds with entertainment, food & craft fair. All day. Tel: 01309 641371

Where to Stay

For Private Accommodation and Johansens recommended Hotels, see Accommodation Section.

Ballindalloch ~ 450th Anniversary

1996 is the 450th anniversary of Ballindalloch Castle, near Grantown-on-Spey (see pg. 258).

It has been lived in continuously by its original family the Macpherson-Grants since 1546.

It lies in the heart of Whisky country with the distilleries of Glenfiddich, Glenfarclas and Glenlivet nearby.

The setting is magnificent: surrounded by hills with the tumbling waters of the River Spey and Avon flowing through the grounds.

HARBURN HOUSE
West Calder

HARBURN HOUSE offers its guests the perfect alternative to a first class hotel. This privately owned Georgian mansion surrounded by its own 3000 acre sporting and leisure estate is ideally situated offering unparalleled accessibility.

Harburn is essentially small and very personal. It is therefore frequently taken over exclusively for conferences, incentive travel, training seminars and product launches, etc. In this way guests may enjoy the luxury of a five star hotel, combined with the comfort and privacy of their own home.

A stay at Harburn is a very relaxed and informal affair. The staff are first class and the atmosphere is one of a private house party.

The estate provides the full range of sporting and leisure activities including, golf, game shooting, fishing, clay pigeon shooting, tennis, riding and archery to name but a few. Our guests are automatically members of our local country club and Harburn Loch together with 'Robinson Island' is a Bar-B-Quer's paradise.

The complete privacy and outstanding scenery, so accessible to the major cities and beauty spots, makes Harburn the ultimate choice for the discerning event or conference organiser.

❖

SUITABILITY FOR OTHER EVENTS
Weddings, filming, conferences, activity days, game shooting, product launches.

EXTRA FACILITIES
Any form of leisure facility available; i.e. Golf, Riding, Fishing, Archery, Buggies, Shooting, Falconry, etc. Also all guests can use the nearby Golf and Country Club.

ACCOMMODATION
We offer: 8 double/twin rooms (available for single or double occupancy) with bathrooms, 2 four-poster suites and 2 other units (1 for 8, 1 for 4/6). All with other private facilities.

The House is always exclusive to one party. The grounds are available for almost any leisure pursuit. The bedrooms are . All catering is done by our own staff.

ADVICE TO COURIERS & DRIVERS
Dogs on leads. Follow one way system and 20 mile/hr speed limit. Vehicles should not park on grass verges. Parking for up to 300 cars/coaches 100 yds from house in the summer or 50 cars/coaches during winter.

FACILITIES FOR THE DISABLED
Ground floor bedroom, dining room and drawing room.

CATERING
High quality in-house catering by our own top chef. Prices and menus on request.

CONTACT

Rozi Spurway
Harburn House
Harburn
West Calder
West Lothian
EH55 8RN

Tel: (01506) 461818
Fax: (01506) 416591

LOCATION

Almost equidistant between Glasgow and Edinburgh and well within one hour of Perth, Stirling or Dundee and the Border country.

OPENING TIMES

All Year

ADMISSION

The exclusive use of House and Grounds for activity days with no accommodation

Per day £600.00

Accommodation Rates:
Single w/bath . . £80.00

Double w/bath £120.00

Dinner, bed & breakfast
Single £100.00
Double (pp) . .£100.00

Day Delegate Rate . . . .
£33.00

VAT is not included in the above rates

CONFERENCE AND FUNCTION FACILITIES

ROOM	DIMENSIONS	CAPACITY	LAYOUT	POWER POINTS	SUITABLE FOR A/V
Conference Room	30' x 18'	20	Boardroom	6	✓
		20	Lunch/Dinner		
Drawing Room	30' x 18'	30	Schoolroom	10	✓
		20	Boardroom		
		40	Theatre		
Dining Room	30' x 18'	30	Schoolroom	6	✓
		20	Boardroom		
		40	Theatre		
		40	Lunch/Dinner		
Library	14' x 12'	10	Schoolroom	4	✓
		8	Boardroom		
		15	Theatre		
Morning Room	16' x 15'	12	Schoolroom		✓
		12	Boardroom		
		20	Theatre		
WHOLE HOUSE	All above rooms	80	Buffet		
		60	Lunch/Dinner		✓
Marquee	120' x 40' MAX	400	Schoolroom	As required	✓
		500	Buffet		
		500	Theatre		
		400	Lunch/Dinner		

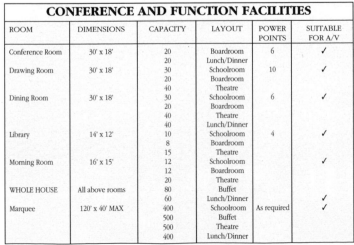

HOPETOUN HOUSE
Edinburgh

HOPETOUN HOUSE, 'Scotland's Finest Stately Home', is a gem of Europe's architectural heritage. Set in a hundred acres of parkland on the shores of the Forth with fine views of the famous Forth bridge to the east.

Hopetoun has been the home of the Hope family since it was built. The head of the family, formerly known as the Earl of Hopetoun was created Marquess of Linlithgow in 1901 after serving as the first Governor General of Australia. The 2nd Marquess served as Viceroy of India from 1936-1943. The present head of the family, Adrian, the 4th Marquess of Linlithgow lives in a private wing of the House.

The original House was designed by Sir William Bruce and built between 1699 and 1702. Enlargements were made by William Adam and his 3 sons John, Robert and James from 1721. Much of the original furniture made for the rooms in the 1760's survives today. Paintings by many famous artists adorn the State Apartments and there is a fine collection of 17th century tapestries and Meissen ornaments.

Separate exhibitions include 'The Building of Hopetoun', 'Horse and Man in Scotland' and 'Wildlife', a seasonal display of particular interest to children. To the west of the House there are magnificent woodland walks, a Red Deer Park, nature trails and a profusion of wild flowers. A Countryside Ranger is in attendance.

❖

SUITABILITY FOR OTHER EVENTS
A major venue in Scotland for private functions and special events throughout the year; Receptions, Gala Dinners, Antique Fairs, Concerts, Scottish Gala Evenings, Conferences.

EXTRA FACILITIES
Grand piano in Library. Boules (Petanque), Piste and Croquet Lawn. Helicopter landing.

ADVICE TO COURIERS & DRIVERS
Pre-book if possible. No smoking or flash photography in House. No dogs in house but welcome (on leads) in Grounds. Free parking close to the house.

CATERING
The Tapestry Room licensed Restaurant caters for 50-60 people. Groups (up to 250) can book in advance for lunch, afternoon tea and other meals in the Ballroom. Menus available on request (Tel: Banqueting Dept. 0131 331 4305)

FACILITIES FOR THE DISABLED
Restaurant, toilet facilities and exhibitions all on ground floor and easily accessible.

GIFT SHOP
Daily 10.30am-5.30pm. Wide range of quality Scottish goods.

GUIDED TOURS
Normally visitors tour at leisure but special guided tours can be arranged in advance. Foreign language guides usually available.

SCHOOL VISITS/CHILDREN
Holders of 2 Sandford Awards for Heritage Education. Special tours of House and/or Grounds for different age/interest groups. Of particular interest: Family life in Georgian and Victorian times, Nature trails with Countryside Ranger, Red Deer Park. Teachers' information pack available. Children's Guide Book.

CONTACT

Mr Paul Normand
Hopetoun House
South Queensferry
Edinburgh
West Lothian
EH30 9SL

Tel: (0131) 331 2451
Fax: (0131) 319 1885

LOCATION

2½ miles west of Forth Road Bridge.

12 miles west of Edinburgh
(25 mins. drive).

34 miles east of Glasgow
(50 mins. drive).

OPENING TIMES

Summer
5 April - 6 October
Daily 10.00am - 5.30pm
Last entry 4.30pm

Earlier admission for parties by prior arrangement. Booking for large groups advisable.

Winter
7 October - Easter
Closed except for group visits by prior arrangement.

Open throughout the year for booked functions.

ADMISSION

HOUSE & GROUNDS
Adult £4.20
Child * £2.10
OAP £3.50
Student £3.50
Groups (min 20)) . . £3.30

GROUNDS ONLY
Adult £3.50
Child * £1.90
OAP £3.50
Student £3.50
*Age 5 - 16. Under 5's Free

Guided Tours (Max 20 per guide) £10.00.

Winter
Out of season rates.

CONFERENCE AND FUNCTION FACILITIES

ROOM	DIMENSIONS	CAPACITY	LAYOUT	POWER POINTS	SUITABLE FOR A/V
Ballroom	92' x 35' Height 28'	350 250 370	Theatre/Buffet Dinner/Dance Lunch/Dinner	✓	✓
Tapestry Room (adjacent to Ballroom)	37' x 24' Height 28'	100 50 70	Theatre U-Shape/Boardroom/ Dinner/Dance Lunch/Buffet	✓	✓
*Red Drawing Room	44' x 24' Height 22'	100 40 60	Theatre U-Shape/Boardroom Lunch/Dinner	✓	
*State Dining Room * (In Main House)	39' x 23' 16"	20	Lunch/Dinner	✓	

ARNISTON HOUSE

OPEN

2 July - 15 Sept

Sundays, Tuesdays and Thursdays
2.00 - 5.00pm

Guided tours.

Pre-arranged groups
10-50 people
accepted
throughout
the year.

Tel: 01875 830238
Fax: 01875 830573

GOREBRIDGE, MIDLOTHIAN EH23 4RY
Owner: Mrs. A Dundas-Bekker   **Contact:** Mrs. A Dundas-Bekker

Magnificent William Adam mansion started in 1726. Fine plasterwork, Scottish portraiture, period furniture and other fascinating contents. Beautiful country setting beloved by Sir Walter Scott. Home-baked teas are also available.

Location: 11m from Edinburgh, off 6372, 1m from A7.
Admission: Adult £3.00, Child under school age free.

DALMENY HOUSE

OPEN

30 Jun - 3 Sept:

Sun: 1 - 5.30pm

Mon & Tues:
12 noon - 5.30pm

Last admission
4.45pm

Open at other times
by prior arrangement.

Tel: 0131 331 1888
Fax: 0131 331 1788

SOUTH QUEENSFERRY, EDINBURGH EH30 9TQ
Owner: The Earl of Rosebery   **Contact:** Mrs L Morison, The Administrator

Beautiful setting by shore, family home of the Earls of Rosebery, superb collections of porcelain and tapestries. Notable paintings by Gainsborough, Raeburn, Reynolds and Lawrence. Exquisite collection of 18th century French furniture. Important Napoleonic collection. Excellent for all corporate events including meetings, lunches, dinners. June - Sept: self service, light lunches and afternoon teas.

Location: 7miles N of Edinburgh, signposted off A90.
Admission: Summer: Adult £3.50, Child £1.80 (10 - 16 yrs), Student £2.80, OAP £3.00, Group £2.80 (min 20 people).

ARTHUR LODGE
               Tel: 0131 667 5163

60 Dalkeith Road, Edinburgh EH16 5AD
Owner: S Roland Friden   **Contact:** S Roland Friden

A neo-classical 'Greek Revival' villa, designed by Thomas Hamilton in 1827, Arthur Lodge is a vision of a gentleman's country residence in town. In a beautiful setting, which includes a White Garden and an Italianate sunken garden, the house itself has been imaginatively restored and decorated. Unique in Edinburgh, Arthur Lodge offers visitors the opportunity to experience an exquisite, and often surprising, private residence.

Location: Edinburgh southside, opposite the Commonwealth Pool.
Opening Times: Jun - Jul: Wed & Sat afternoons. Aug - Sept: Wed afternoon only. Tours at 2.15pm, 3.15pm and 4.15pm.
Admission: Visits by guided tour only: Adult £3.00, Conc £2.00, including tour.

CRAIGMILLAR CASTLE
               Tel: 0131 661 4445

Edinburgh
Owner: Historic Scotland   **Contact:** The Custodian

Mary Queen of Scots fled to Craigmillar after the murder of Rizzio and it was here that the plot was hatched for the murder of her husband Lord Darnley. This handsome structure with courtyard and gardens covers an area of one and a quarter acres. Built round an L plan tower house of the early 15th century including a range of private rooms linked to the hall of the old tower.

Location: 2½ m SE of Edinburgh off the A68.
Opening Times: 1 Apr - 30 Sept: Mon - Sat 9.30am - 6.30pm, Sun 2 - 6.30pm. 1 Oct - 31 Mar: Mon - Wed & Sat 9.30am - 4.30pm, Thur 9.30am - 12 noon, Fri Closed, Sun 2 - 4.30pm. Last admission ½ hour before closing.
Admission: Adult £1.50, Conc £1.00, Child 75p.

CRICHTON CASTLE
               Tel: 01875 320017

Pathhead
Owner: Historic Scotland   **Contact:** The Custodian

A large and sophisticated castle with a spectacular façade of faceted stonework in an Italian style added by the Earl of Bothwell between 1581 and 1591 following a visit to Italy. Mary Queen of Scots attended a wedding here.

Location: 2½ m SSW of Pathhead off the A68.
Opening Times: 1 Apr - 30 Sept: Mon - Sat 9.30am - 6.30pm, Sun 2 - 6.30pm. Last admission ½ hour before closing.
Admission: Adult £1.20, Conc 75p, Child 75p.

DALKEITH PARK
               Tel: 0131 665 3277

Dalkeith, Midlothian EH22 2NJ
             Contact: J C Manson

Extensive grounds of Dalkeith Palace. 18th century bridge and orangery. New tearoom, shop and interpretation area.

Location: 7m SE of Edinburgh.
Opening Times: Mar - Oct: 10am - 6pm.
Admission: Adult £1.50, Child £1.50, Family £4.00, Groups £1.00.

DIRLETON CASTLE AND GARDENS
               Tel: 01620 850330

Dirleton
Owner: Historic Scotland   **Contact:** The Custodian

Romantic castle besieged by Edward I in 1298, rebuilt, expanded and then destroyed in 1650. The gardens, added in the 16th century, include an Arts and Crafts herbaceous border and Victorian garden.

Location: In Dirleton village 2m W of North Berwick on the A198.
Opening Times: 1 Apr - 30 Sept: Mon - Sat 9.30am - 6.30pm, Sun 2 - 6.30pm. 1 Oct - 31 Mar: Mon - Sat 9.30am - 4.30pm, Sun 2 - 4.30pm. Last admission ½ hour before closing.
Admission: Adult £2.00, Conc £1.25, Child 75p.

THE DRUM
               Tel: 01316 647215   **Fax:** 01316 581944

Gilmerton, Edinburgh EH17 8RX
Owner: G A More-Nisbett Esq   **Contact:** Mrs More-Nisbett

William Adams' most sumptuous villa, superb high relief plasterwork by Thomas Clayton and Samuel Calderwood, attached to 15th century Tower house.

Location: ½m N of city bypass between A7 and A722.
Opening Times: By arrangement only.

DUNGLASS COLLEGIATE CHURCH
               Tel: 0131 668 8800

Cockburnspath
Owner: Historic Scotland

Founded in 1450 for a college of canons by Sir Alexander Hume. A handsome cross-shaped building with vaulted nave, choir and transepts.

Location: 1m NW of Cockburnspath.

EDINBURGH CASTLE
               Tel: 0131 225 9846

Edinburgh, Lothian
Owner: Historic Scotland   **Contact:** The Visitors Services Manager

This most famous of castles dominates Scotland's capital and gives stunning views of the city and countryside. The oldest parts of the castle date from the Norman period. St Margaret's Chapel, the enormous 500 year old siege cannon Mons Meg, the Great Hall built by James IV, the Half Moon Battery built by the Regent Morton in the late 16th century, the Royal Palace and the Scottish National War Memorial are here together with the highly acclaimed 'Honours of the Kingdom' exhibition which traces the history of Scotland's Crown Jewels and culminates in a visit to the Crown Room. The Vaults where foreign prisoners-of-war were held, particularly those captured in the wars with France in the 18th and 19th centuries. Some of the graffiti scrawled by the prisoners can still be seen. Courtesy vehicle can take disabled visitors to the top of the castle (sponsored by the Bank of Scotland). Restaurant offering self and table service.

Location: Edinburgh centre.
Opening Times: 1 Apr - 30 Sept: Daily 9.30am - 6pm. 1 Oct - 31 Mar: Daily 9.30am - 5pm. Last admission 45 mins before closing. Hours may be altered during the Tattoo or for State and military events.
Admission: Adult £5.50, Conc £3.50, Child under 16 £1.50. Parking for up to 2 hours: Cars £2.00, Coaches £5.00. There is no discount for parties. Members of HM Forces will be admitted free on production of their Identity Card. Guided tours are normally available but cannot be reserved in advance.

THE GEORGIAN HOUSE

OPEN

1 Apr - 31 Oct:

Mon - Sat:
10am - 5pm

Sun: 2 - 5pm

Tel: 0131 225 2160

7 CHARLOTTE SQUARE, EDINBURGH EH2 4DR
Owner: The National Trust for Scotland   *Contact: The Countess of Wemyss*

The north side of Charlotte Square is Robert Adam's masterpiece of urban architecture - a splendid example of the neo-classical 'palace front'. The three floors of No.7, The Georgian House, are delightfully furnished as they would have been around 1796. There is a fascinating array of china and silver, pictures and furniture, gadgets and utensils from the decorative to the purely functional.
Location: In Edinburgh's city centre, at 7 Charlotte Square.
Admission: Adult £3.60, Child £2.40. Parties: Adult £2.90, School £1.00. Family £9.60.

GLADSTONE'S LAND
Tel: 0131 226 5856

477b Lawnmarket, Royal Mile, Edinburgh EH1 2NT
Owner: The National Trust for Scotland   **Contact:** Mrs Alison Butler
Gladstone's Land was the home of a prosperous Edinburgh merchant in the 17th century. On the Royal Mile, near the Castle, it is decorated and furnished with great authenticity to give visitors an impression of life in Edinburgh's Old Town some 300 years ago. Features of the 6 storey building are the painted ceilings and the reconstructed shop booth complete with replicas of 17th century goods.
Location: In Edinburgh's Royal Mile, near the Castle.
Opening Times: 1 Apr - 31 Oct: Mon - Sat, 10am - 5pm, Sun 2 - 5pm.
Admission: Adult £2.60, Conc/Child £1.70. Parties: Adult £2.10, Child/School £1.00. Family £6.90.

GOSFORD HOUSE

OPEN

June & July

Wed, Sat & Sun

2.00 - 5.00pm

Tel: 01875 870200
Fax: 01875 870376

LONGNIDDRY, EAST LOTHIAN EH32 0PX
Owner: The Earl of Wemyss   *Contact: The Earl of Wemyss*

Robert Adams designed the central block and wings. These wings were later demolished. 1800 roof recently restored which was partly burnt in 1940 during military occupation. Two wings, rebuilt in 1890 by William Young. The south wing is the family home and contains the famous Marble Hall (Staffordshire alabaster). Parts of south wing and central block open. Fine collection of paintings and works of art. Surrounding gardens are being redeveloped, extensive policies, artificial ponds, geese and other wildfowl breeding.
Location: Longniddry.
Admission: Adult £2.50, Child 75p.

HAILES CASTLE
Tel: 0131 668 8800

East Linton
Owner: Historic Scotland
Beautifully sited ruin incorporating a fortified manor of 13th century date. It was extended in the 14th and 15th centuries. There are two vaulted pit prisons.
Location: 1¹/₂m SW of East Linton.

HARBURN HOUSE
See Page 267 for full page entry.

HOPETOUN HOUSE
See Page 268 for full page entry.

HOUSE OF THE BINNS
Tel: 0150 683 4255

Linlithgow, West Lothian EH49 7NA
Owner: The National Trust for Scotland   **Contact:** Tam and Kathleen Dalyell
Here is a historic house dating from the 17th century which has been the home of the Dalyells, one of Scotland's great families, since 1612. Here in 1681, General Tam Dalyell raised the Royal Scots Greys Regiment, so named after the colour of their uniforms. The house contains fine Italian-style plasterwork and outstanding collection of family paintings.
Location: Off A904, 15m W of Edinburgh.
Opening Times: House: 1 May - 30 Sept: Daily except Fri, 1.30 - 5.30pm.
Parkland: 1 Apr - 31 Oct: Daily 9.30am - 7pm. 1 Nov - 31 Mar: Daily 9.30am - 4pm.
Admission: Adult £3.10, Child £2.00, Adult Party £2.50, School Party £1.00. Family £8.20.

INVERESK LODGE GARDEN
Tel: 0131 683 1855

24 Inveresk Village, Musselburgh, East Lothian EH21 7TE
Owner: The National Trust for Scotland   **Contact:** Head Gardener
Small garden in grounds of 17th century house, with large selection of plants.House closed.
Location: A6124, S of Musselburgh, 6m E of Edinburgh.
Opening Times: 1 Apr - 30 Sept: Mon - Fri, 10am - 4.30pm, Sat - Sun, 2 - 5pm.
1 Oct - 31 Mar: Mon - Fri, 10am - 4.30pm, Sun 2 - 5pm.
Admission: £1.00 (honesty box).

LAURISTON CASTLE
Tel: 0131 336 2060

2a Cramond Road South, Edinburgh EH4 5QD
Owner: City of Edinburgh Council   **Contact:** R Barnes
A beautiful house overlooking the Firth of Forth. The oldest part is a 16th century tower house. William Burn designed the early 19th century exteriors, which were modernised and furnished around 1900 by the important Edinburgh interior designer William Reid. The Reids also used the house to display their collections of furnishings.
Location: At Davidson's Mains, off Queensferry Road, 10 mins by car from Edinburgh centre.
Opening Times: 1 Apr - 31 Oct: Daily except Fri, 11am - 5pm. 1 Nov - 31 Mar: Sat - Sun, 2 - 4pm. Gardens: Dawn to dusk, all year.
Admission: Adult £3.00, Conc £2.00, Family £8.00.

LENNOXLOVE HOUSE
Tel: 01620 823720 **Fax:** 01620 825112

Haddington, East Lothian EH41 4NZ
Owner: His Grace The Duke of Hamilton   **Contact:** House Opening Administrator
Originally called Lethington Tower, and for centuries belonged to the Maitlands. Of interest because of its architecture, association of its proprietors with the Royal House of Stuart, and the Hamilton Palace collection of portraits, furniture and porcelain.
Location: 1¹/₂m S of Haddington on B6369, 18 m E of Edinburgh off A1.
Opening Times: Easter weekend & May - Sept: Sat, Sun and Wed, 2 - 5pm.
Admission: Adult £3.00, Child £1.50, Groups £2.00 pp (min 15).

LINLITHGOW PALACE
Tel: 01506 842896

Linlithgow
Owner: Historic Scotland   **Contact:** The Custodian
Magnificent ruin of a great Royal Palace, set in its own park. All the Stuart Kings lived here. In 1542 Mary Queen of Scots was born at Linlithgow while her father James V lay dying at Falkland Palace.
Location: In Linlithgow off the M9.
Opening Times: 1 Apr - 30 Sept: Mon - Sat, 9.30am - 6.30pm, Sun, 2 - 6.30pm.
1 Oct - 31 Mar: Mon - Sat 9.30am - 4.30pm, Sun 2 - 4.30pm. Last adm. ¹/₂ hr before closing.
Admission: Adult £2.00, Conc £1.25, Child 75p.

NEWLISTON
Tel: 0131 333 3231 **Fax:** 0131 335 3596

Kirkliston, West Lothian EH29 9EB
Owner: J S Findlay Esq   **Contact:** J S Findlay
Late Robert Adam house. Costumes on display. 18th century designed landscape, rhododendrons, azaleas and water features. On Saturdays tea is in the Edinburgh Cookery School which operates in the William Adam Coach House. Also on Sundays there is a ride-on steam model railway from 2 - 5pm. Teas.
Location: 8m W of Edinburgh, 3m S of Forth Road Bridge, off B800.
Opening Times: 1 May - 2 Jun: Wed - Sun, 2 - 6pm. Also by appointment.
Admission: Adult £1.00, Child 50p, Senior citizens 50p.

PALACE OF HOLYROODHOUSE

Tel: 0131 556 1096 (24hrs)

Edinburgh EH8 8DX

Owner: HM The Queen　　　　**Contact:** The Superintendent

The Palace stands against the backdrop of Salisbury Crag. Throughout history Holyroodhouse has been the scene of turbulent and extraordinary events, yet the Palace retains a modern appeal appropriate to a Royal residence still in regular use.

Location: Central Edinburgh.

Opening Times: 1 Apr - 31 Oct: Mon - Sat, 9.30am - 5.15pm (last admission), Sun, 9.30am - 4.30pm (last admission). 1 Nov - 31 Mar: Daily 9.30am - 3.45pm (last admission). Closed: 5 Apr, 14 - 25 May, 24 Jun - 7 Jul, 25 & 26 Dec inc.

Admission: Adult £5.00, Over 60s £3.50, Under 17s £2.50, Family £12.50.

PRESTON MILL

OPEN

1 May - 30 Sept:
Mon - Sat
11am - 1pm
and
2 - 5.30pm
Sun 1.30 - 5.30pm

Weekends in Oct:
1.30 - 4pm.

Tel: 01620 860426

EAST LINTON, EAST LOTHIAN EH40 3DS
Owner: The National Trust for Scotland　　*Contact: Miss Clare White*

For centuries there has been a mill on this site and the present one operated commercially until 1957. While the interior of the mill is exciting, the exterior is extremely evocative and much favoured by artists who come from near and far to paint the attractive old buildings with their red pantile roofs fringed by the tranquillity of the mill pond with its ever present ducks.

Location: Off the A1, in East Linton, 23m E of Edinburgh.

Admission: Adult £1.60, Child £1.00, Parties: Adult £1.30, School £1.00, Family £4.20.

ROSSLYN CHAPEL

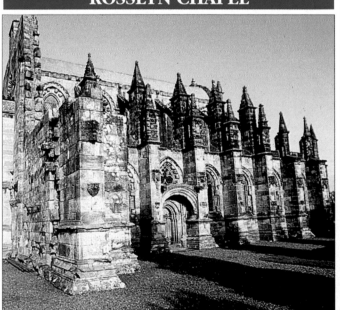

ROSLIN, MIDLOTHIAN EH25 9PU
Owner: The Earl of Rosslyn　　*Contact: Judith Fisken*

Tel: 0131 440 2159 **Fax:** 0131 448 2948

This most remarkable of churches was founded in 1446 by William St Clair, Prince of Orkney. Set in the woods of Roslin Glen and overlooking the River Esk, the Chapel is renowned for its richly carved interior and world famous apprentice pillar. Visitors to the Chapel, tea room and gift shop can enjoy a walk in some of Scotland's most romantic scenery. As Sir Walter Scott wrote, 'A morning of leisure can scarcely be anywhere more delightfully spent than in the woods of Rosslyn'. The chapel is available for weddings throughout the year.

Location: 6m S of Edinburgh off A701. Signposted.

Opening Times: 1 Apr - 31 Oct: Mon - Sat, 10am - 5pm, Sun 12 noon - 4.45pm. Please telephone for winter opening hours.

Admission: Adult £2.25, Conc £1.75, Child 75p.

ROYAL BOTANIC GARDEN

Tel: 0131 552 7171 **Fax:** 0131 552 0382

Inverleith Row, Edinburgh EH3 5LR

Contact: Angela Kilday

Exotic, bizarre and beautiful plants in 70 acres of superbly landscaped grounds. Rockgarden, Peat and Woodland gardens. Arboretum and Glasshouse.

Location: At Inverleith, 1 mile N of city centre.

Opening Times: Nov - Feb: 10am - 4pm (not 25 Dec /1 Jan). Mar - Apr: 10am - 6pm. May - Aug: 10am - 8pm. Sept - Oct: 10am - 6pm.

Admission: Free. Donations welcome.

ST. MARY'S CATHEDRAL

Tel: 0131 225 6293 **Fax:** 0131 225 3181

Edinburgh EH12 5AW

Contact: Cathedral Secretary

Neo-Gothic grandeur in the classical new town.

Location: 1/2m W of west end of Princes Street.

Opening Times: 7.30am - 6pm. Sun services: 8am, 10.30am and 3.30pm. Weekday services: 7.30am, 1.05pm and 5.30pm.Sat service: 7.30am.

TANTALLON CASTLE

Tel: 01620 892727

North Berwick

Owner: Historic Scotland　　　　**Contact:** The Custodian

Set on the edge of the cliffs looking out to the Bass Rock this formidable castle was a stronghold of the Douglas family. It features earthwork defences and a massive 50 foot high 14th century curtain wall with towers. During the 16th century the castle was strengthened to resist artillery.

Location: 3m E of North Berwick off the A198.

Opening Times: 1 Apr - 30 Sept: Mon - Sat 9.30am - 6.30pm, Sun 2 - 6.30pm. 1 Oct - 31 Mar: Mon - Wed & Sat 9.30am - 4.30pm, Thur 9.30am - 12 noon, Fri Closed, Sun 2 - 4.30pm. Last admission 1/2 hour before closing.

Admission: Adult £2.00, Conc £1.25, Child 75p.

WINTON HOUSE

Tel: 01875 340222

Pencaitland, Tranent, East Lothian EH34 5AT

Owner: Sir David Ogilvy's 1968 Trust　　　　**Contact:** Lady Ogilvy

Built 1620. Famous twisted stone chimneys and beautiful plaster ceilings in honour of Charles I's visit. Enlarged 1800. Fine pictures and furniture. Terraced gardens.

Location: Wrought-iron gates and lodges in Pencaitland (A6093) and New Winton Village B6355.

Opening Times: Restricted to groups of 10 or more (and others very specially interested) at any time by prior arrangement with the owners.

Admission: £3.50.

Where to Stay

For Private Accommodation and Johansens recommended Hotels, see Accommodation Section.

BLAIRQUHAN CASTLE
Maybole

BLAIRQUHAN is the home of James Hunter Blair, the great great grandson of Sir David Hunter Blair, 3rd Baronet for whom it was designed by William Burn and built in 1821-24.

All the Regency furniture bought for the house remains and the house has not been altered except discreetly to bring it up to date. There are 10 double bedrooms, including four-posters, with bathrooms en suite, five singles and many public rooms which can be used for conferences and every sort of occasion.

The Castle is approached by a 3 mile private drive along the River Girvan and it is situated in one of the most charming parts of South West Scotland. There is a well-known collection of pictures. The River Girvan runs through the Estate and five miles of it is available for fishing for salmon and sea trout.

Blairquhan is only 50 miles from Glasgow and Glasgow Airport. It is within about half an hour's driving distance of the famous golf courses of Prestwick, Troon and Turnberry - the last two of which are venues for the British Open Golf Championships.

❖

CONTACT

James Hunter Blair
Blairquhan Castle
Straiton
Maybole
Ayrshire
KA19 7LZ
Tel: (01655) 770239
Fax: (01655) 770278

LOCATION

From London M6 to Carlisle, A76 to Dumfries, A75 to Crocketford, A712 to A71 near New Galloway, B741 to Straiton on B7045 to Ayr. Turn left.

Rail: Maybole 7 miles.

SUITABILITY FOR OTHER EVENTS
Fashion shows, air displays, archery, clay pigeon shooting, equestrian events, garden parties, shows, rallies, filming, wedding receptions.

EXTRA FACILITIES
Grand piano, snooker, tennis, fishing, shooting. Slide projector, overhead projector, screen, and secretarial assistance available for meetings.

ACCOMMODATION
Blairquhan offers 10 Doubles (4 4-posters) with bathrooms en suite, 5 Singles. The Dower House at Milton has 8 Doubles, 2 Singles, 5 bathrooms. 7 holiday cottages on the Estate.

ADVICE TO COURIERS & DRIVERS
No photography within the Castle. Unlimited parking.

FACILITIES FOR THE DISABLED
Disabled and elderly visitors may alight at the entrance to the Castle. Toilets for the disabled.

CATERING
Restaurant: Afternoon teas, lunches, buffets and dinners. Groups can book in advance for tea and other meals. Special rates for groups. Prices start at £1.70 per person.

GIFT SHOP
The small shop is open when required.

GUIDED TOURS
Can be arranged at no extra charge for up to 100 people – duration 1 hour. Also available in French.

SCHOOL VISITS/CHILDREN
School visits are welcome. A guide and schoolroom can be provided. Cost negotiable.

OPENING TIMES

Summer

14 July -11 August

Daily except Mondays

Open at all other times by appointment.

Winter
Open by pre-booked appointment.

ADMISSION

Summer & Winter

HOUSE & GARDEN
Adult £3.50
Child** £2.00
OAP £2.50

Groups*
Negotiable

*   Minimum payment £20.
** Age 5 - 14

CONFERENCE AND FUNCTION FACILITIES

ROOM	DIMENSIONS	CAPACITY	LAYOUT	POWER POINTS	SUITABLE FOR A/V
Drawing Rooms (2 rooms)	1200 sq ft	100	Theatre	4	3
		50	Schoolroom		
		30	U-Shape		
		20	Boardroom		
		100	Dinner/Dance		
		100	Buffet/Lunch/Dinner		
		50	Seated Lunch/Dinner		
Dining Room	750 sq ft	100	Dinner/Dance	4	3
		100	Buffet/Lunch/Dinner		
		50	Seated Lunch/Dinner		
Library	400 sq ft	25 up to 100	(Using other rooms 100)		
Saloon	600 sq ft	100	Dinner Dance		
		100	Buffet/Lunch/Dinner		
		50	Seated Lunch/Dinner		
Meeting Room	255 sq ft	50	Buffet/Lunch/Dinner		

INVERARAY CASTLE
Argyll

The Duke of Argyll's family have lived in Inveraray since the early 15th century. The present Castle was built between 1740 and 1790.

The ancient Royal Burgh of Inveraray lies about 60 miles north west of Glasgow by Loch Fyne in an area of spectacular natural beauty combining the ruggedness of highland scenery with the sheltered tidal loch 90 miles from the open sea.

The Castle is the home of the Duke and Duchess of Argyll. Its fairy tale exterior belies the grandeur of its gracious interior. The building was designed by Roger Morris and decorated by Robert Mylne, the clerk of works being William Adam, father of Robert and John, who did much of the laying out of the present Royal Burgh, an unrivalled example of an early planned town.

Visitors to the Castle may see the famous Armoury Hall containing some 1300 pieces, French tapestries made especially for the Castle, fine examples of Scottish, English and French furniture together with a wealth of other works of art including china, silver and family artifacts, all of which form a unique collection spanning the generations which are identified by a magnificent genealogical display in the Clan Room.

ADVICE TO COURIERS & DRIVERS
It is preferable that party bookings are made in advance. No dogs and no photography.

PARKING FOR COACHES & CARS
Parking for approx. 100 cars. Separate coach park close to Castle.

FACILITIES FOR THE DISABLED
Disabled and elderly visitors may alight at the entrance to the castle before parking in the car park close by. There is a wheelchair ramp to the Castle plus two steps. All main public rooms may be visited by the infirm and those in wheelchairs, but there are two long flights of stairs to the smaller rooms upstairs. Toilet facilities are suitable for disabled visitors although not specially adapted.

CATERING
The Tea Room seats up to 50 people for afternoon tea and other meals. Menus are available on request and groups can book in advance. Telephone (01499) 302112.

GIFT SHOP
Open at the same time as the Castle.

GUIDE BOOKS
Colour guide book, £2.00. French, Italian, Japanese and German translations available.

GUIDED TOURS
Tours can be arranged for up to 100 people at no additional cost. Average time taken 1 hour.

SCHOOL VISITS/CHILDREN
School parties are welcome. £1.50 per child in organised party. If requested a guide can be provided. Areas of interest include a nature walk, special school project, wildlife park (nearby) and War Museum.

CONTACT

The Factor
Dept HHD
Argyll Estates Office
Cherry Park
Inveraray
Argyll
PA32 8XE

Tel: (01499) 302203

Fax: (01499) 302421

LOCATION

From Edinburgh 2¹/₂ - 3 hours via Glasgow.

Bus: Bus route stopping point within ¹/₂ mile.

OPENING TIMES

Summer
6 April - 13 October
Apr, May, Jun, Sept, Oct.
Mon, Tues, Wed, Thurs
& Sats 10.00am - 1.00pm
and 2.00 - 5.45pm
Fridays Closed
Sundays 1.00 - 5.45pm

July - August
Daily: 10am - 5.45pm
(Inc. Fridays)
Sundays 1.00 - 5.45pm

Last admissions
12.30 & 5.00pm

ADMISSION

Summer
HOUSE ONLY
Adult £4.00
Child* £2.00
OAP £3.00
Family (2+2) . . . £10.00
Groups (Min 20 people)
20% Discount

*Under 16

Winter
Closed

CONFERENCE AND FUNCTION FACILITIES

ROOM	DIMENSIONS	CAPACITY	LAYOUT	POWER POINTS	SUITABLE FOR A/V
State Dining Room	30' x 22'	50	Lunch/Dinner	3	
Tapestry Drawing Room	45' x 21'	200	Lecture Room	4	✓
		90	Lunch/Dinner		
Armoury Hall	23' x 31'	120	Assembly	2	✓
Saloon	24' x 44'	200	Lecture	2	✓

KELBURN CASTLE
Fairlie

The historic home of the Boyle family, later Earls of Glasgow, Kelburn is situated on the picturesque north Ayrshire coast. Kelburn Castle dates from the 13th century and is thought to be the oldest Castle in Scotland to be inhabited by the same family throughout its history.

The original 1200 Norman Keep was extended in 1580 by a Tower House, and an elegant William and Mary Mansion House was added in 1700 by David Boyle, who was created 1st Earl of Glasgow by Queen Anne in 1703 for his role in persuading reluctant Jacobite nobles to sign the Act of Union. A Victorian wing was built in 1879. Kelburn's essential charm is its informal family atmosphere, varied interior decor, and stunning location.

The grounds at Kelburn are quite lovely. Romantic Kelburn Glen with winding woodland trails, waterfalls and deep gorges. Featured gardens are the Plaisance, a formal walled garden dominated by two magnificent 1,000 year old Yew trees, and the Children's Garden which is planted in the shape and colours of the Saltire. An extraordinary mutant Weeping Larch, Scotland's oldest and tallest Monterey Pine, a Robert Adam Monument, 18th century Sundial and Ice House are among Kelburn's featured natural and historical attractions. Kelburn's newest attraction, THE SECRET FOREST, features unusual follies such as The Maze of The Green Man, a Chinese Pagoda, Gingerbread House, Grotto, Crocodile Swamp and Chinese Garden.

Within the Country Centre there is The Kelburn Story Cartoon Exhibition, a family Museum, Horse Riding, Adventure Play Areas, Commando Assault Course, Soft Play Room, Pets Corner, Nature Centre, Activity Workshop, Information Centre, Ranger Service and Picnic Areas. Birds of Prey display May - August. Events every weekend July, August & Sept.

❖

SUITABILITY FOR OTHER EVENTS
The property is suitable for a variety of indoor and outdoor events. Consideration given to all enquiries, rates negotiable.

EXTRA FACILITIES
Gardens, Grounds. Golf Club adjacent. The pavilion is available for buffets, exhibitions, nature activities and barbecues.

ADVICE TO COURIERS & DRIVERS
Coach passengers can alight at the Castle forecourt. The coach must then leave and return via the estate exit and use Country Centre car park. This is approx 5/10 mins walk from the Castle, next to the Country Centre buildings.

PARKING FOR COACHES & CARS
Ample parking for coaches and cars.

FACILITIES FOR THE DISABLED
Elderly/disabled visitors may alight at the entrance to the Castle before vehicles are parked. Toilets for the disabled.

CATERING
There is a licensed restaurant and a cafe at the country centre. Groups can book in advance. Special rates offered to groups. Full catering facilities for special functions/conferences in the Castle, outside caterers may also be used.

GIFT SHOP
The gift shop in the country centre carries souvenirs, craft items etc. Open throughout the summer season.

GUIDED TOURS
Maximum party size of 25 at no additional cost. Average time for a tour is 45 minutes. With prior notice lectures can be provided on the Castle, grounds, history etc.

SCHOOL VISITS/CHILDREN
Groups welcome £1.75 per child. Teachers free at ratio of 1:10 pupils, thereafter £1.75 ea. Countryside Ranger Service available for Guided Walks and Nature Activities, also Worksheets, Pets Corner, Pony Rides/Treks, Adventure Play Areas.

CONTACT

Earl of Glasgow
Kelburn Castle &
Country Centre
South Offices
Fairlie, Ayrshire
KA29 0BE

Tel: County Centre:
(01475) 568685
Castle:
(01475) 568204

Fax: County Centre:
(01475) 568121
Castle:
(01475) 568328

LOCATION

M8 Edinburgh to Glasgow, M8 Glasgow to Greenock, A78 to Largs, A78 main coastal trunk road.
Rail: Largs station 2 miles.
Bus: A78 main bus route to Ayr, stop adjacent to property.
Taxis: A2B taxis (01475) 673976.

OPENING TIMES

Summer
CASTLE
July and August
Tours: 1.45, 3.00 and 4.15pm. (Except when there are afternoon functions)

Tours can be arranged at other times of the year.

COUNTRY CENTRE & GARDENS
Easter - end October
Daily: 10.00am - 6.00pm.

Winter
CASTLE
By special arrangement only.

COUNTRY CENTRE
End October - Easter
11.00am - 5.00pm
Grounds only.

ADMISSION

Summer
CASTLE ONLY
Per person £1.50
Student £1.20
Per person £1.20
(These prices do not include entry fee to Centre)

COUNTRY CENTRE
Adult £4.00
Child* £2.50
OAP £2.50
Student £2.50
Groups (min 12 people)
Adult £2.50
Child* £1.75
OAP £1.75
Student £1.75

Winter
CASTLE ONLY
As Summer rates

COUNTRY CENTRE
Adult £1.75
Child* £1.00

* Accompanied children 2 - school age.

CONFERENCE AND FUNCTION FACILITIES

ROOM	DIMENSIONS	CAPACITY	LAYOUT	POWER POINTS	SUITABLE FOR A/V
Drawing Room Dining Room	33' x 24'	60	Lunch/Dinner		
		53	Seated Dinner		
		120	Buffet		
PRESENTLY THERE ARE NO FORMAL CONFERENCE FACILITIES.					

ACHAMORE HOUSE

Tel: 01583 505254/505267

Isle of Gigha, Argyll PA41 7AD
Owner: Mr and Mrs Derek Holt   **Contact:** Mr William Howden
Gardens only open. Sub-tropical gardens created by Sir James Horlick who bought Gigha in 1944.
Location: Off the Mull of Kintyre. Ferry from Tayinloch and from Tayinloan.
Opening Times: Dawn until dusk every day.
Admission: Adults £2.00, Child £1.00.

ARDCHATTAN PRIORY

Tel: 01631 750274

Oban, Argyll PA37 1RQ
Owner: Mrs Sarah Hope Troughton   **Contact:** Lt Col R Campbell Preston
The oldest inhabited house in Scotland. 3 acre garden, wild garden to west of house, formal garden in front, two herbaceous borders, 3 shrub borders, 1 rose garden. Fine variety of shrubs, trees and roses. Tea and light lunch room, gift shop.
Location: 5m E Connel Bridge, North side.
Opening Times: 1 Apr - 31 Oct: Dawn - dusk (9am - 9pm).
Admission: Adult £1.00, Child free, OAP £1.00. (Charges may vary from May - Aug).

ARDANAISEIG GARDENS

Tel: 01866 833333   **Fax:** 01866 833222

Oban, Argyll PA35 1HE
Owner: S B Gray   **Contact:** Nigel Liston
Woodland garden with fine trees and a great variety of rhododendrons, azaleas and other flowering shrubs surrounding one acre walled garden with large herbaceous border.
Location: 9 m S of Taynuilt on B845.
Opening Times: 30 Mar - mid Oct: 9am - 9pm.
Admission: Adult £1.00, Child free.

ARDUAINE GARDEN

Tel: 01852 200366

Arduaine, by Oban, Argyll PA34 4XQ
Owner: The National Trust for Scotland   **Contact:** Maurice Wilkins
Surprises await you in this west coast garden where plants, commonplace in smaller proportions elsewhere, can grow to a gigantic size in Arduaine's micro-climate, sheltered from the strong winds of the Western Isles. There are glorious bursts of colour in late spring and early summer from its rhododendrons and azaleas.
Location: On A816, 20m S of Oban and 17m N of Lochgilphead.
Opening Times: All year: Daily 9.30am - sunset.
Admission: Adult £2.10, Child £1.40. Parties:Adult £1.70, School £1.00, Family £5.60.

BACHELORS' CLUB

Tel: 01292 541940

Sandgate Street, Tarbolton KA5 5RB
Owner: The National Trust for Scotland   **Contact:** David Rodger
17th century thatched house in which poet Robert Burns and friends formed a debating society in 1780. Burns mementos and relics, period furnishings.
Location: In Tarbolton, B744, 7 1/2m NE of Ayr, off B743.
Opening Times: Good Fri - Easter Mon & 1 May - 30 Sept: Daily 1.30 - 5.30pm. Weekends in Oct: 1.30 - 5.30pm. Other times by appointment.
Admission: Adult £1.60, Conc £1.00. Parties: Adult £1.30, School £1.00. Family £4.20.

BALLOCH CASTLE COUNTRY PARK

OPEN

Visitor Centre
Apr - Oct:
Daily
10am - 6pm

Country Park:
All year
Dawn - Dusk

Tel: 01389 758216
Fax: 01389 755721

BALLOCH, DUNBARTONSHIRE G83 8LX
Contact: *Loch Lomond Park Authority Ranger Service*
Balloch Castle is a 200 acre Country Park situated on the bonnie banks of Loch Lomond. It is one of the finest Parks in the whole of the country. Steeped in history and with breathtaking views of Loch Lomond, this ancient seat of the Lennox offers the visitor a chance to blend the wild, natural beauty of Scotland with the formal glory of the ornamental gardens and splendid trees of former estate days. Balloch Castle, now the Visitor Centre, was built in 1808 and is built in the 'castle-gothic' style of architecture and was one of the first of its type built in Scotland.
Location: SE shore of Loch Lomond, off A82 for Balloch or A811 for Stirling.
Admission: Free for both visitor centre and country park.

BLAIRQUHAN CASTLE

See Page 272 for full page entry.

See Page 272 for full page entry.

BONAWE IRON FURNACE

Tel: 01866 822432

Taynuilt, Argyll
Owner: Historic Scotland   **Contact:** The Custodian
Founded in 1753 by Cumbrian iron masters this is the most complete remaining charcoal fuelled ironworks in Britain. Displays show how iron was once made here.
Location: By the village of Taynuilt off the A85.
Opening Times: 1 Apr - 30 Sept: Mon - Sat 9.30am - 6.30pm, Sun 2 - 6.30pm. Last admission 1/2 hour before closing.
Admission: Adult £2.00, Conc £1.25, Child 75p.

BOTHWELL CASTLE

Tel: 01698 816894

Uddingston, Strathclyde
Owner: Historic Scotland   **Contact:** The Custodian
The largest and finest 13th century stone castle in Scotland, much fought over during the Wars of Independence. Part of the original circular keep survives, but most of the castle dates from the 14th and 15th centuries. In a beautiful setting overlooking the Clyde.
Location: At Uddingston off the B7071.
Opening Times: 1 Apr - 30 Sept: Mon - Sat, 9.30am - 6.30pm, Sun, 2 - 6.30pm. 1 Oct - 31 Mar: Mon - Wed & Sat 9.30am - 4.30pm, Thur 9.30am - 12 noon, Fri Closed, Sun 2 - 4.30pm. Last admission 1/2 hour before closing.
Admission: Adult £1.50, Conc £1.00, Child 75p.

BRODICK CASTLE & COUNTRY PARK

OPEN

CASTLE
1 Apr - 31 Oct:
Daily
11.30am - 5pm

GARDEN &
COUNTRY PARK
All year
Daily
9.30am - Sunset

Tel: 01770 302202

ISLE OF ARRAN KA27 8HY
Owner: *The National Trust for Scotland*   **Contact:** *Mrs Olive Raymond*
This is a castle you will never forget ! The tall, stately building beckons you with the glow of its warm red sandstone. The setting is staggering, fronted by the sea, bedecked with gardens and overlooked by the majestic mountain of Goatfel. The castle was built on the site of a Viking fortress and dates from the 13th century. The contents are magnificent and include superb silver, porcelain, paintings and sporting trophies. The woodland garden ranks as one of Europe's finest.
Location: Isle of Arran. Ferries from Ardrossan & Claonaig and Kintyre.
Ferry enquiries: 01475 650100
Admission: Adult £4.10, Child £2.70. Parties: Adult £3.30, School £1. Family £10.90.

BURNS COTTAGE

Tel: 01292 441215

Alloway, Ayrshire KA7 4PY
     Contact: J Manson
Thatched cottage, birthplace of Robert Burns in 1759. Now a museum.
Location: 2m SW of Ayr.
Opening Times: Apr - May: Mon - Sat, 10am - 5pm. Sun 1 - 5pm. Jun - Aug: Mon - Sat, 10am - 5pm. Sun 1 - 5pm. Nov - Mar: 9am - 4pm. Sun 10am - 6pm. Sept - Oct: 10am - 4pm. Closed Sun.
Admission: Adult £2.50, Child £1.25, Family £6.00, Senior citizens £1.85. Admission charge includes entry to Burns Monument and Gardens.

CHATELHERAULT HUNTING LODGE   **Tel:** 01698 426213   **Fax:** 01698 421532

Ferniegair, by Hamilton ML3 7UE
Owner: South Lanarkshire District Council   **Contact:** Tom McCormack
Built for James, 5th Duke of Hamilton, designed by William Adam, completed around 1744. Set in 500 acre country park.
Location: On A72, 1 1/2m SE of Hamilton.
Opening Times: All year except Christmas and New Year.

COLZIUM HOUSE & WALLED GARDEN   **Tel:** 01236 823281   **Fax:** 01236 823281

Colzium - Lennox Estate, off Stirling Road, Kilsyth   G65 0RZ

Owner: Cumbernauld & Kilsyth District Council   **Contact:** A C Spiers

A walled garden with an extensive collection of conifers, rare shrubs and trees. Kilsyth Heritage Museum, curling pond, tea room, picnic tables, pitch and putt, woodland walks.

Location: Off A803 Banknock to Kirkintilloch Road.

Opening Times: Walled garden: 12 noon - 7pm. Easter - Sept: Museum in House: 2 - 5pm, Wed. Apr - Sept or by appointment.

Admission: Free. Charge for pitch and putt.

CRAIGNETHAN CASTLE   **Tel:** 01555 86364

Lanark, Strathclyde

Owner: Historic Scotland   **Contact:** The Custodian

In a picturesque setting overlooking the River Nethan and defended by a wide and deep ditch with an unusual caponier, a stone vaulted artillery chamber, unique in Britain.

Location: 5¹/₂ m WNW of Lanark off the A72.

Opening Times: 1 Mar - 31 Oct: Mon - Wed & Sat 9.30am - 6.30pm, Thur 9.30am - 12 noon, Fri Closed, Sun 2 - 6.30pm. Last admission ¹/₂ hour before closing.

Admission: Adult £1.50, Conc £1.00, Child 75p.

CROSSRAGUEL ABBEY   **Tel:** 01655 883113

Maybole, Strathclyde

Owner: Historic Scotland   **Contact:** The Custodian

Founded in the early 13th century by the Earl of Carrick. Remarkably complete remains include church, cloister, chapter house and much of the domestic premises.

Location: 2m S of Maybole on the A77.

Opening Times: 1 Apr - 30 Sept: Mon - Wed & Sat 9.30am - 6.30pm, Thur 9.30am - 12 noon , Fri Closed, Sun 2 - 6.30pm. Last adm. ¹/₂ hour before closing.

Admission: Adult £1.20, Conc 75p, Child 75p.

CULZEAN CASTLE & COUNTRY PARK

MAYBOLE KA19 8LE

Owner: The National Trust for Scotland   *Contact:* Jonathan Cardale

Tel: 01655 760274

Robert Adam's 18th century masterpiece, a real 'castle in the air', is perched on a cliff high above the crashing waves of the Firth of Clyde. Arrow slits and mock battlements give medieval touches to the sturdy exterior, and on the seaward-side front is the imposing drum tower. The interior is the epitome of the disciplined elegance, crowned by the spectacular oval staircase ascending through ornamental pillars & ironwork balustrading. Adam also designed many interior fittings. The exterior grounds encompass Scotland's first country park.

Location: 12m S of Ayr, on A719, 4m W of Maybole, off A77.

Opening Times: 1 Apr - 31 Oct: Daily 10.30am - 5.30pm. Other times by appointment. Country Park: All year Daily 9.30am - sunset.

Admission: Castle & Park: Adult £5.50, Child £3. Party: Adult £4.50. Family £15.

DUART CASTLE

OPEN

1 May - 14 Oct

10.30am - 6.00pm

Tel: 01680 812309
Fax: 01577 830311

ISLE OF MULL, ARGYLL PA64 6AP

Owner: Sir Lachlan Maclean Bt   *Contact:* Sir Lachlan Maclean Bt

Duart Castle has been a Maclean stronghold since the 12th century. The keep was built by Lachlan Lubanach, 5th Chief, in 1360. Burnt by the English in 1758, the castle was restored in 1912 and today is still the home of the Chief of the Clan Maclean. It has a spectacular position overlooking the Sound of Mull.

Location: Off A849 on the east point of the Isle of Mull.

Admission: Adult £3.30, Child £1.65, OAP £2.20, Student £2.75, Family £8.25.

DUMBARTON CASTLE   **Tel:** 01389 732167

Dumbarton, Strathclyde

Owner: Historic Scotland   **Contact:** The Custodian

Location: In Dumbarton on the A82.

Opening Times: 1 Apr - 30 Sept: Mon - Sat 9.30am - 6.30pm, Sun 2 - 6.30pm. 1 Oct - 31 Mar: Mon - Wed & Sat 9.30am - 4.30pm, Thur 9.30am - 12 noon, Fri Closed, Sun 2 - 4.30pm. Last admission ¹/₂ hour before closing.

Admission: Adult £1.50, Conc £1.00, Child 75p.

DUNSTAFFNAGE CASTLE AND CHAPEL   **Tel:** 01631 562465

Oban, Argyll

Owner: Historic Scotland   **Contact:** The Custodian

A very fine 13th century castle built on a rock with a great curtain wall. Close by are the remains of a chapel with beautiful architectural detail.

Location: 3¹/₂ m from Oban off the A85.

Opening Times: 1 Apr - 30 Sept: Mon - Sat 9.30am - 6.30pm, Sun 2 - 6.30pm. Last admission ¹/₂ hour before closing.

Admission: Adult £1.50, Conc £1.00, Child 75p.

FINLAYSTONE HOUSE   **Tel:** 01475 540285 / 01475 540508

Langbank, Renfrewshire PA14 6TJ

Owner: George MacMillan Esq   **Contact:** George MacMillan

House has connections with John Knox and Robert Burns and contains Victorian items on display. Gardens overlooking the river Clyde have special interest at any time of the year with woodland walks and play areas. Visitor Centre with Clan MacMillan Doll and Toy Museum and Celtic Art Display.

Location: On A8, 10 minutes W of Glasgow Airport.

Opening Times: House: Apr - Aug: weekends. Alternatively by appointment. Gardens / woodlands: 10.30am - 5pm all year.

Admission: Adult £2.00, plus £1.50 for house, Child £1.20, plus £1 for house, Conc £1.00.

GLASGOW CATHEDRAL   **Tel:** 0141 552 6891

Glasgow

Owner: Historic Scotland   **Contact:** The Custodian

The only Scottish mainland medieval cathedral to have survived the Reformation complete. Built over the tomb of St Kentigern. Notable features in this splendid building are the elaborately vaulted crypt, the stone screen of the early 15th century and the unfinished Blackadder Aisle.

Location: In central Glasgow.

GLENCOE

BALLACHULISH, ARGYLL PA39 4HX

Owner: The National Trust for Scotland   *Contact:* Derrick Warner

Tel: 01855 811307

This is a breathtaking, dramatic glen with jagged peaks incised on either side by cascading water. In 1692 many of the MacDonald clan were massacred by soldiers of King William's army, to whom they had given hospitality. Wildlife abounds and herds of red deer, wildcat and golden eagle enjoy this wilderness area.

Location: Off A82, 17m S of Fort William.

Opening Times: Site: All year, daily. Visitor Centre: 1 Apr - 18 May and 1 Sept - 31 Oct: Daily, 10am - 5pm. 19 May - 31 Aug: Daily. 9.30am - 5.30pm

Admission: Adult 50p, Child 30p.

GREENBANK

OPEN

All Year
Daily
9.30am - sunset
except: 25, 26 Dec
& 1, 2 Jan

House
1 Apr - 31 Oct
Sundays only
2.00 - 4.00pm
and during
special events

Tel: 0141 639 3281

CLARKSTON, GLASGOW G76 8RB

Owner: The National Trust for Scotland   *Contact:* Jim May

Be allured by the beautiful bronze water nymph 'Foam' whose exquisite form complements the circular pool and surrounding greenery. There are several small gardens including a parterre layout illustrating different aspects of gardening. The larger borders contain a wide range of shrub roses and perennial & annual flowers.

Location: Flenders Road, off Mearns Road, Clarkston. Off A77 and A726, 6m S of Glasgow city centre.

Admission: Adult £2.60, Child £1.70. Parties: Adult £2.10, School £1. Family £6.90.

THE HILL HOUSE

OPEN

1 Apr - 31 Oct
Daily
1.30 - 5.30pm

Tel: 01436 673900

UPPER COLQUHOUN STREET, HELENSBURGH G84 9AJ

Owner: The National Trust for Scotland   *Contact:* Mrs Anne Ellis

Certainly the finest domestic creation of the famous Scottish architect and artist, Charles Rennie Mackintosh. He set this 20th century masterpiece high on a hillside overlooking the Firth of Clyde. Mackintosh also designed furniture, fittings and decorative schemes to complement the house, and suggested a layout for the garden which has been renovated by the Trust.

Location: Off B832, between A82 and A814, 23m NW of Glasgow.

Admission: Adult £3.60, Child £2.40. Parties: Adult £2.90, School £1. Family £9.60.

HUTCHESONS' HALL

Tel: 0141 552 8391   **Fax:** 0141 552 7031

158 Ingram Street, Glasgow G1 1EJ

Owner: The National Trust for Scotland   **Contact:** Jeanette Macaulay

Described as one of Glasgow City Centre's most elegant buildings, the Hall by David Hamilton, replaced the earlier 1641 hospice founded by George & Thomas Hutcheson. Reconstructed in 1876, the building is now "A-Listed" as being of national importance. Available for functions.

Location: Glasgow city centre, Ingram Street, near SE corner of George Square.

Opening Times: Visitor Centre/Function Hall: all year (except public holidays and 24 Dec - 3 Jan), Mon - Sat 10am - 5pm. (Hall on view subject to functions in progress). Shop: same dates 10am - 4pm.

Admission: Free.

INVERARAY CASTLE

See Page 273 for full page entry.

INVERARAY JAIL

Tel: 01499 302381   **Fax:** 01499 302195

Church Square, Inveraray, Argyll PA32 8TX

Owner: Visitor Centres Ltd   **Contact:** J Linley

A living 19th century prison! Uniformed prisoners and wardens, life-like figures, imaginative exhibitions, sounds, smells and trials in progress, bring the 1820 courtroom and former County Prison back to life.

Location: Church Square, Inveraray, Argyll.

Opening Times: Apr - Oct: 9.30am - 6pm, last adm. 5pm. Nov - Mar: last adm. 4pm.

Admission: Adult £3.95, Child £2.00, Family £10.90, Senior citizens £2.50, Groups £3.20, Senior Citizens £2.00.

KELBURN CASTLE

See Page 274 for full page entry.

SPECIAL EVENTS

◇ **CULZEAN CASTLE**   **28 APRIL**
"Family Fun Run 1996" - up to 500 entrants negotiate their way over possibly the most scenic fun run course in Britain. Team and individual entries accepted. Tel: 01655 760274.

◇ **KELBURN CASTLE & COUNTRY PARK**   **28 – 29 APRIL**
Woodcraft and Forestry Fair. Wide ranging event with indoor and outdoor displays and demonstrations of Woodturning, Carving, Coopering, Pole Lathe Turning, Cane Furniture Making, Basket Weaving, Working Sawmill, Tree Surgery, Felling, Chainsaw Sculpture. Daily, 11am - 5pm.

◇ **KELBURN CASTLE & COUNTRY PARK**   **11 – 12 MAY**
West of Scotland Field Sports Fair. Country pursuits, displays, competitions including Birds of Prey, Sheepdog Display, Terrier Racing, Gun Dog Handling, Flycasting, Exemption Dog Show, Country Fare, Country Crafts, Outdoor Clothing Stands. 10am - 6pm Daily.

◇ **KELBURN CASTLE & COUNTRY PARK**   **25 – 27 MAY**
Festival of Flight. Exhibitions, workshops, displays on various aspects of flight including Model Rockets, Kites, Balloons, Model Aeroplanes, etc.

MOUNT STUART HOUSE & GARDENS

ISLE OF BUTE PA20 9LR

Owner: The Mount Stuart Trust
Contact: The Administrator

Tel: 01700 503877
Fax: 01700 505313

Spectacular High Victorian Gothic house, ancestral home of the Marquesses of Bute. Splendid interiors, art collection and architectural detail, set in 300 acres of stunning woodlands, mature Victorian Pinetum, arboretum and exotic gardens. Tearoom, shop, scenic picnic areas and car park. Scottish Tourism Oscar winner 1995.

Location: 5m S of Rothesay Pierhead, local bus service to house. Frequent ferry service from Wemyss Bay, Renfrewshire & Colintraive, Argyll.

Admission: House & Gardens: Adult £5.50, Child £2.50, Family £15. Gardens: Adult £3, Child £2, Family £8. Conc & group rates given. Pre-booked guided tours available.

OPEN

House - 1 May - 30 Sept: Daily
(except Tue & Thur), 11am - 5pm

Gardens - April: Sat & Sun. 1 May - 30 Sept: Mon, Wed, Fri, Sat & Sun. Oct: Sat & Sun, 10am - 5pm
Last admission 4.30pm

NEWARK CASTLE

Tel: 01475 741858

Port Glasgow, Strathclyde
Owner: Historic Scotland
Contact: The Custodian
The oldest part of the castle is a tower built soon after 1478 with a detached gatehouse, by George Maxwell. The main part was added in 1597 - 99 in a most elegant style. Enlarged in the 16th century by his descendent, the wicked Patrick Maxwell who murdered two of his neighbours.
Location: In Port Glasgow on the A8.
Opening Times: 1 Apr - 30 Sept: Mon - Sat 9.30am - 6.30pm, Sun 2 - 6.30pm. Last admission $\frac{1}{2}$ hour before closing.
Admission: Adult £1.50, Conc £1.00, Child 75p.

POLLOK HOUSE

Tel: 0141 632 0274   **Fax:** 0141 649 0823

Glasgow G43 1AT
Owner: City of Glasgow District Council
Contact: The Administrator
Early 18th century house, containing the remarkable Stirling Maxwell collection of Spanish paintings. Nearby in Pollok Park is the Burrell collection.
Location: 2m S of Glasgow city centre.
Opening Times: Mon - Sat, 10am - 5pm. Sun 11am - 5pm. (unconfirmed for 1996).
Admission: Free.

ROTHESAY CASTLE

Tel: 01700 502691

Rothesay, Isle of Bute
Owner: Historic Scotland
Contact: The Custodian
A favourite residence of the Stuart Kings, this is a wonderful example of a 13th century circular castle of enclosure with 16th century forework containing the Great Hall. Attacked by Vikings in its earlier days.
Location: In Rothesay, Isle of Bute. Ferry from Wemyss Bay on the A78.
Opening Times: 1 Apr - 30 Sept: Mon - Sat 9.30am - 6.30pm, Sun 2 - 6.30pm. 1 Oct - 31 Mar: Mon - Wed & Sat 9.30am - 4.30pm, Thur 9.30am - 12 noon, Fri Closed, Sun 2 - 4.30pm. Last admission $\frac{1}{2}$ hour before closing.
Admission: Adult £1.50, Conc £1.00, Child 75p.

SORN CASTLE

Tel: 01292 268181

Ayrshire KA5 6HR
Owner: Mrs R G McIntyre
Contact: Mrs R G McIntyre
Originally 14th century castle. James V visited the castle then owned by the Earl of Winton in 1598. The castle has been enlarged several times, most recently in 1908.
Location: 4m E of Mauchline on B743.
Opening Times: By appointment.

SOUTER JOHNNIE'S COTTAGE

Tel: 01655 760603

Main Road, Kirkoswald KA19 8HY
Owner: The National Trust for Scotland
Contact: Ms Jan Gibson
The home of John Davidson, original "Souter" (cobbler) of Robert Burns famous narrative poem "Tam O' Shanter". Burns mementos and restored cobbler's workshop. Life-sized stone figures in adjacent "ale-house".
Location: On A77, in Kirkoswald village, 4m SW of Maybole.
Opening Times: Good Fri - Easter Mon & 1 May - 30 Sept: Daily 1.30 - 5.30pm. Weekends in October: 1.30 - 5.30pm (last admission 5pm). Other times by appointment.
Admission: Adult £1.60, Conc £1.00. Parties: Adult £1.30, School £1.00. Family £4.20.

ST ANDREW'S CATHEDRAL

Tel: 0141 2042409

Glasgow G1 4ER

Contact: Mgr. J. Clancy
The earliest Catholic church (post reformation) in the Glasgow area. Built in 1816.
Location: Clyde Street, central Glasgow on N Bank of Clyde.
Opening Times: All Year: 8am - 6pm. Sun services: 10am, 12 noon & 5pm. Weekday services: 8.15am, 1pm and 5.15pm.

ST BLANE'S CHURCH

Kingarth, Isle of Bute
Owner: Historic Scotland
Contact: The Administrator
This 12th century Romanesque chapel stands on the site of a 12th century Celtic Monastery.
Location: At the south end of the Isle of Bute.

ST MARY'S CATHEDRAL

Tel: 0141 3396691   **Fax:** 0141 3574544

300 Great Western Road, Glasgow G4 9JB

Contact: The Very Rev P Francis
Fine Gothic Revival church by Sir George Gilbert Scott, with outstanding contemporary murals by Gwyneth Leech.
Location: $\frac{1}{4}$m after taking the Dumbarton A82 exit from M8 motorway.
Opening Times: 9am - 5.45pm. Sun services: 8.30am, 10am, 12 noon and 6.30pm Weekday services: Tel 0141 3396691.

THE TENEMENT HOUSE

Tel: 0141 333 0183

145 Buccleuch Street, Glasgow G3 6QN
Owner: The National Trust for Scotland
Contact: Miss Lorna Hepburn
Here is a typical Victorian tenement flat of 1892, a fascinating time capsule of the first half of the 20th century. It was the home of an ordinary Glasgow shorthand typist, who lived up this 'wally close' for more than 50 years. It is exceptional as the gaslit flat retains many of its original fittings and items such as her mother's sewing machine.
Location: Garnethill, (three streets N of Sauchiehall Street, near Charing Cross), Glasgow.
Opening Times: 1 Mar - 31 Oct: Daily, 2 - 5pm. Groups at other times by appointment.
Admission: Adult £2.60, Child £1.70. Parties: Adult £2.10, School £1.00. Family £6.90.

WEAVER'S COTTAGE

Tel: 01505 705588

Shuttle Street, Kilbarchan, Renfrew PA10 2JG
Owner: The National Trust for Scotland
Contact: Mrs Irene MacDiarmid
Typical cottage of an 18th century handloom weaver contains looms, weaving equipment and domestic utensils. Attractive cottage garden. Occasional weaving demonstrations.
Location: Off A740 (off M8) and A737, at The Cross, Kilbarchan, (nr Johnstone, Paisley) 12m SW of Glasgow.
Opening Times: Good Fri - Easter Mon & 1 May - 30 Sept: Daily 1.30 - 5.30pm. Weekends in October: 1.30 - 5.30pm. Last adm. 5pm
Admission: Adult £1.60, Conc £1.00. Parties: Adult £1.30, School £1.00. Family £4.20.

YOUNGER BOTANIC GARDEN BENMORE

Dunoon, Argyll PA23 8QU

Tel: 01369 706261 **Fax:** 01369 706369
Contact: Assistant Curator
Rhododendrons, Conifers and Redwood Avenue.
Location: 7m N of Dunoon on A815.
Opening Times: 15 Mar - 31 Oct: Daily, 10am - 6pm.
Admission: Adult £2, Child 50p, Family £4.50, Conc £1.50. Groups of 11+s - 10% discount.

SPECIAL EVENTS

❖ **BLAIRQUHAN CASTLE**
Open for Scotland's Gardens Scheme
11 AUGUST

❖ **GREENBANK GARDEN & HOLMWOOD HOUSE**
"Doors Open Day". Both houses open to the public 10am - 4pm.
14 – 15 SEPTEMBER

BLAIR CASTLE
Pitlochry

BLAIR CASTLE has been the ancient home and fortress of the Earls and Dukes of Atholl for over 725 years. Its central location makes it easily accessible from all major Scottish centres in less than two hours.

The Castle has known the splendour of Royal visitations, submitted to occupation by opposing forces on no less than four occasions, suffered siege and changed its architectural appearance to suit the taste of successive generations.

Today 32 rooms of infinite variety display beautiful furniture, fine collections of paintings, arms, armour, china, costumes, lace and embroidery, masonic regalia, Jacobite relics and other unique treasures giving a stirring picture of Scottish life from the 16th to 20th Centuries.

The 10th Duke of Atholl, who still lives at Blair Castle, has the unique distinction of having the only remaining Private Army in Europe - The Atholl Highlanders.

GARDENS

Blair Castle is set in extensive parklands. Near the car and coach parks, there is a picnic area, a Deer Park and a unique two acre plantation of large trees known as 'Diana's Grove.' It has been said that "it is unlikely that any other two acres in the world contain such a number of different conifers of such heights and of such small age." A restored Victorian Garden will be open to visitors in 1996.

❖

SUITABILITY FOR OTHER EVENTS
Fashion shows, archery, clay pigeon shooting, equestrian events, garden parties, shows, rallies, filming, wedding receptions, Highland Balls, Charity Balls, Piping Championships, plus full range of concerts and banquets.

EXTRA FACILITIES
Grand piano, helicopter pad, cannon firing by Atholl Highlanders, resident piper, parkland, picnic areas. Special arrangements for groups touring House and gardens can include lunches, dinners and entertainment, highland balls, piper, cannon, needlework displays.

ADVICE TO COURIERS & DRIVERS
Coach drivers and couriers free, plus free meal and weekly free prize draw for bottle of whisky. On first visit drivers/couriers receive free information pack. No dogs or smoking. Parking for 200 cars and 20 coaches 100 yards from Castle.

FACILITIES FOR THE DISABLED
Disabled and elderly visitors may alight at the entrance of the Castle, before parking in the allocated areas. Limited toilet facilities for the disabled. Wheelchair available.

CATERING
Two restaurants, both 'no smoking'. Self-service area seats 112, 'The Old Gun Room' (waitress service) seats 48. Prices from £1.00 - £3.50 for tea, snacks from £3.00, lunches from £6.00. Buffets, Dinners and Banquets for 70-200 can be provided. Details on application.

GIFT SHOP
Open as Castle. Over 1,000 items sold, 72% Scottish made.

GUIDE BOOKS
Colour guide book in English, German, French, Dutch, Italian, Spanish & Japanese, £1.50. Special guide book for children.

GUIDED TOURS
Available in English, German and French at no extra cost. Maximum size 25. Average time for tour of house 1½ hours.

SCHOOL VISITS/CHILDREN
School parties welcome £3.50ea, Primary Schools £3.00ea. Of particular interest: nature walks, deer park, collection of children's games, pony trekking. Special guide book.

CONTACT

Brian H Nodes
Administrator
Blair Castle
Blair Atholl
Pitlochry
Perthshire
PH18 5TL

Tel: (01796) 481207
Fax: (01796) 481487

LOCATION

From Edinburgh (80 miles), M90 to Perth, A9, follow signs for Blair Castle. 1½ hours. Trunk Road A9 2 miles.

Bus: Bus stop 1 mile in Blair Atholl.

Train: 1 mile, Blair Atholl Euston-Inverness line.

Taxi: Elizabeth Yule, (01796) 472290

OPENING TIMES

Summer
1 April - 25 October

Daily: 10.00am - 6.00pm
Last entry 5.00pm.

Winter
Closed from
26 October - 31 March

ADMISSION

HOUSE
Adult £5.00
Child/Student** £4.00
OAP £4.00
Family £14.00

Groups*
Adult £4.50
Child** £3.50
OAP £3.50
Disabled £2.00

* Minimum payment £200 out of season.
** Age 5-16

GROUNDS & PARKING
Cars £2.00
Mini Buses £5.00
Coaches* £10.00
*unless pre-booked

FUNCTION FACILITIES					
ROOM	DIMENSIONS	CAPACITY	LAYOUT	POWER POINTS	SUITABLE FOR A/V
Ballroom	89' x 35'	400	Theatre	14	✓
		200	Schoolroom		
		200	Buffet		
		300	Dinner/Dance		
		200	Lunch/Dinner		
State Dining Room (Evenings only)	36' x 25'	200	Receptions only	4	
Library	27' x 15'	40	Theatre	6	

GLAMIS CASTLE
Glamis

GLAMIS CASTLE is the family home of the Earls of Strathmore and Kinghorne and has been a royal residence since 1372. It is the childhood home of Her Majesty Queen Elizabeth The Queen Mother, the birthplace of Her Royal Highness The Princess Margaret and the legendary setting of Shakespeare's play 'Macbeth'. Though the Castle is open to visitors it remains a family home lived in and loved by the Strathmore family.

The Castle, a five-storey 'L' shaped tower block, was originally a royal hunting lodge. It was remodelled in the 17th Century and is built of pink sandstone. It contains the Great Hall, with its magnificent plasterwork ceiling dated 1621, a beautiful family Chapel constructed inside the Castle in 1688, an 18th Century Billiard Room housing what is left of the extensive library once at Glamis, a 19th century Dining Room containing family portraits and the Royal Apartments which have been used by Her Majesty Queen Elizabeth The Queen Mother. The Castle stands in an extensive park, landscaped towards the end of the 18th Century, and contains the beautiful Italian Garden which reflects the peace and serenity of the Castle and grounds.

❖

SUITABILITY FOR OTHER EVENTS
Grand dinners, lunches, receptions, fashion shows, archery, clay pigeon shooting, equestrian events, garden parties, shows, rallies, filming, product launches, highland games and wedding receptions. New cricket pavilion and shopping complex.

EXTRA FACILITIES
Grand piano in the Great Drawing Room.

ADVICE TO COURIERS & DRIVERS
Coach drivers and couriers are admitted free of charge. No photography within the Castle. Beware the narrow gates, they are wide enough to take buses.

FACILITIES FOR THE DISABLED
Toilet for the disabled. Disabled visitors may alight at the Castle entrance. Those in wheelchairs will be unable to tour the Castle but may visit the Coach House Exhibition.

PARKING FOR COACHES & CARS
Capacity of the car park - 500 cars, 30 yards from Castle, 20 coaches 50 yards from Castle.

CATERING
Self-service, licensed restaurant serving morning coffees, light lunches and afternoon teas. Seating for 100 in old Castle Kitchen. The State Rooms are also available for grand dinners / lunches.

GIFT SHOP
Open when Castle is open to visitors. Items include: glass, china, books, pictures and small antiques. The Garden Shop is open at the same time.

GUIDE BOOKS
Full colour guide book in English, Dutch, French, German, Italian, Spanish and Japanese £2.50.

GUIDED TOURS
All visits are guided - average time 50/60 minutes. Tours can be conducted by prior arrangement in French, German, Italian, Spanish and Portuguese.

SCHOOL VISITS/CHILDREN
School groups are welcome with one teacher admitted free for every 10 children. Facilities include a nature trail, family exhibition room, Estate exhibition in Coach House, dolls house and play area.

CONTACT

Lt Col P J Cardwell Moore
Estates Office
Glamis Castle
Glamis
By Forfar
Angus
DD8 1RJ

Tel: (01307) 840393
Fax: (01307) 840733

LOCATION

From Edinburgh M90, A94, 81 miles.
From Forfar A94, 6 miles.
From Glasgow 101 miles.
Motorway: M90.
Rail: Dundee Station 12 miles.
Air: Dundee Airport 12 miles.
Taxi: B Morrison (01575) 572988

OPENING TIMES

Summer

31 March - 28 October

Daily: 10.30 - 5.30pm

Last admission 4.45pm.

Winter

By appointment, groups are welcome.

ADMISSION

Summer

HOUSE & GARDEN
Adult £4.70
Child* £2.50
OAP/Student . . .£3.60
Family £13.00

Groups (min 20 people)
Adult £4.30
Child* £2.20
OAP/Student . . .£3.20

GARDEN ONLY
Adult £2.20
Child* £1.10
OAP £1.10
Disabled . . . . . .FREE

Groups (min 20 people)
Adult £2.20
Child* £1.10
OAP £1.10

* Under 16.

Winter

By arrangement.

CONFERENCE AND FUNCTION FACILITIES

ROOM	DIMENSIONS	CAPACITY	LAYOUT	POWER POINTS	SUITABLE FOR A/V
Dining Room	84 sq.m.	120	Buffet	✓	✓
		120	Theatre		
Restaurant	140 sq.m.	100	Buffet	✓	✓
		100	Theatre		

SCONE PALACE
Perth

SCONE PALACE, just outside Perth is the home of the Earls of Mansfield. Here Kenneth MacAlpine united Scotland and in 838AD, placed the stone of Scone upon the Moot Hill which became the Crowning Place of Scottish Kings, including Macbeth and Robert the Bruce. Edward I moved the Coronation Stone to Westminster in 1296.

The Abbey of Scone and the Bishops' Palace were ransacked and burned in 1559. The Gowries built a new Palace in 1580, which was enlarged and embellished around 1804 by the Third Earl and houses a fabulous collection of French furniture, clocks, 16th Century needlework (including bed hangings, worked by Mary Queen of Scots), ivories, objets d'art and Vernis Martin and one of the finest collections of porcelain in the country.

GARDENS

Scone's famous Pinetum is a unique collection of rare pines, some of which are over 150 feet high and still growing. There are pleasant walks through 100 acres of Wild Garden which offer the visitor magnificent displays of daffodils, rhododendrons and azaleas.

There is a fine picnic area, adventure playground and a collection of veteran machinery. A cricket pitch and pavilion in an attractive setting is ideal for a variety of outdoor functions.

❖

CONTACT

Lt Cdr. A R Robinson
Scone Palace
Perth
PH2 6BD

Tel: (01738) 552300

Fax: (01738) 552588

LOCATION

From Edinburgh Forth Bridge M90, A93 1 hour.

Bus: 2 buses a day from Perth.

Rail: Perth Station 3 miles.

Motorway: M90 from Edinburgh.

Taxi: Perth Radio Cabs (01738) 628171.

OPENING TIMES

Summer
5 April - 14 October

Daily: 9.30am - 5.00pm

Evening tours by appointment.

Winter
15 October - 27 March
By appointment only.

ADMISSION

Summer

PALACE & GARDEN
Adult £4.70
Child* £2.60
OAP £3.90
Family £13.50
Groups (min 20 people)
Adult £4.20
Child* £2.30
OAP £3.60

GARDEN ONLY
Adult £2.35
Child* £1.30

*Age 5 - 16

Winter
Per person £8.50
(£170 min. payment)

SUITABILITY FOR OTHER EVENTS
Grand dinners, receptions, fashion shows, war games, archery, clay pigeon shooting, equestrian events, garden parties, shows, rallies, filming, shooting and fishing, floodlit tattoos, weddings, product launches, highland games.

EXTRA FACILITIES
Including organ, parkland, cricket pitch, airfield, helicopter landing and croquet. Speciality lectures can be arranged. Race course, polo field, firework displays, adventure playground.

ADVICE TO COURIERS & DRIVERS
Please advise in advance, especially if catering required. Couriers and drivers admitted free to all facilities, free meal available. Advisable to pre-book especially groups over 60. Advise ticket seller at coach park if handicapped visitors require transport to Palace. Couriers of booked parties receive token on last visit of season, value dependent on visits.

FACILITIES FOR THE DISABLED
All the State Rooms on one level. Special wheelchair access to Restaurants. Disabled and elderly visitors may alight at entrance. Toilet facilities for the disabled.

PARKING FOR COACHES & CARS
500 cars and 15 coaches 100 yards from the Palace.

CATERING
Two Restaurants/Tea Rooms capacity 54 and 66. Teas from £2.00, lunches from £5, dinners from £18. All meals can be pre-booked, menus upon request, special rates for groups. Grand dinners in State Rooms a speciality. Larger numbers can be accepted for buffets, receptions, weddings, cocktail parties, etc, all prepared by the Palace's own chef.

GIFT SHOP
Produce Shop & Gift Shop open as Palace. Guide book, £2.50, in 7 languages. 1 page introduction available in 10 languages.

GUIDED TOURS
Free. English speaking guides in all rooms. Out of hours parties have 1 guide per tour. Average time for tour 45 minutes. Personal French and German guides usually available by appointment for a £30.00 charge.

CONFERENCE AND FUNCTION FACILITIES

ROOM	DIMENSIONS	CAPACITY	LAYOUT	POWER POINTS	SUITABLE FOR A/V
Long Gallery	140' x 20'	250	Theatre/Buffet	8	✓
		90	Lunch/Dinner		
Queen Victoria's Room	20' x 20'	35	Theatre\Buffet	4	✓
		20	Schoolroom		
		24	U-Shape		
		18	Boardroom		
		16	Lunch/Dinner		
Drawing Room	50' x 24'	100	Theatre	20	✓

ANGUS FOLK MUSEUM

OPEN

Good Friday - Easter Monday
and
1 May - 30 Sept
Daily
11am - 5pm

Weekends in Oct
11am - 5pm

Tel: 01307 840288

KIRKWYND, GLAMIS, FORFAR, ANGUS DD8 1RT

Owner: The National Trust For Scotland   *Contact:* Isla MacLeod

Where you will find cruisie lamps, pirn winders, cloutie rugs, bannock spades and a thrawcrook? These fascinating items, and many more, are to be found in the Angus Folk Museum, one of Scotland's finest. The domestic section is housed in six charming 19th century cottages in Kirk Wynd, and the agricultural collection is in the farm steading opposite. The displays inside the building explain and illustrate changes in the Angus countryside in the last 200 years.

Location: Off A94, in Glamis, 5m SW of Forfar.
Admission: Adult £2.10, Child £1.40. Parties: Adult £1.70, School £1. Family £5.60.

ARBROATH ABBEY

Tel: 01241 878756

Arbroath, Tayside
Owner: Historic Scotland   **Contact:** The Custodian
The substantial ruins of a Tironensian monastery, notably the gate house range and the abbot's house. Arbroath Abbey holds a very special place in Scottish history. It was here in 1320 that Scotland's nobles swore their independence from England in the famous 'Declaration of Arbroath'.
Location: In Arbroath town centre on the A92.
Opening Times: 1 Apr - 30 Sept: Mon - Sat 9.30am - 6.30pm, Sun 2 - 6.30pm. 1 Oct - 31 Mar: Mon - Sat 9.30am - 4.30 pm, Sun 2 - 4.30pm. Last adm. ½ hour before closing.
Admission: Adult £1.50, Conc £1.00, Child 75p.

BARRIE'S BIRTHPLACE

Tel: 01575 572646

9 Brechin Road, Kirriemuir, Angus DD8 4BX
Owner: The National Trust for Scotland   **Contact:** Karen Gilmour
'Do you believe in fairies'? The creator of the eternal magic of Peter Pan, J M Barrie, was born here in 1860. He was the ninth of ten children born to David Barrie, a handloom weaver and his wife Margaret Ogilvy. See the imaginative exhibition about this famous novelist and dramatist with life-size figures, miniature stage sets, dioramas, theatre posters and stage costumes, while a darting light, 'Tinkerbell', moves around the room!
Location: On A926 / B957, in Kirriemuir, 6m NW of Forfar.
Opening Times: Good Fri - Easter Mon and 1 May - 30 Sept: Mon - Sat 11am - 5.30pm, Sun 1.30 - 5.30pm. Weekends in Oct: Sat 11am - 5.30pm, Sun 1.30 - 5.30pm (last adm. 5pm).
Admission: Adult £1.60, Child £1.00. Parties: Adult £1.30, School £1.00. Family £4.20.

BARRY MILL

Tel: 01241 856761

Barry, Carnoustie, Angus DD7 7RJ
Owner: The National Trust for Scotland   **Contact:** Peter Ellis
18th century mill. Demonstrations and displays.
Location: N of Barry village between A92 and A930, 2m W of Carnoustie.
Opening Times: Good Fri - Easter Monday & 1 May - 30 Sept: Daily 11am - 5pm. Weekends on Oct: 11am - 5pm.
Admission: Adult £1.60, Child £1.00. Parties: Adult £1.30, Schools £1.00.

BLAIR CASTLE

See Page 279 for full page entry.

BOLFRACKS GARDEN

Tel: 01887 820207

Aberfeldy, Perthshire PH15 2EX
Owner: J D Hutchison   **Contact:** J D Hutchison
A garden for all seasons overlooking the Tay Valley and the higher hills beyond.
Location: 2m W of Aberfeld on A827 towards Kenmore and Loch Tay.
Opening Times: 1 Apr - 31 Oct: Daily, 10am - 6pm.
Admission: Adult £2.00, Child under 16 years free.

BRANKLYN GARDEN

Tel: 01738 625535

Dundee Road, Perth PH2 7BB
Owner: The National Trust for Scotland   **Contact:** Bob Mitchell
Here is a small but magnificent garden with an impressive collection of rare and unusual plants. Among the most breathtaking is the Himalayan blue poppy, *Meconopsis X Sheldonii*. There is a rock garden with purple maple and the rare golden *Cedrus*. Seasonal highlights in May and June are the alpines and rhododendrons and in autumn the fiery red *Acer palmatum*.
Location: On A85 at 116 Dundee Road, Perth.
Opening Times: 1 Mar - 31 Oct: Daily, 9.30am - sunset.
Admission: Adult £2.10, Child £1.40, Parties: Adult £1.70, School £1.00. Family £5.60.

CASTLE MENZIES

Tel: 01887 820982

Weem, Aberfeldy, Perth PH15 2JD
Owner: Menzies Charitable Trust   **Contact:** R A Adam
Seat of Chiefs of Clan Menzies. 16th century fortified house. Bonnie Prince Charlie rested here en route for Culloden in 1746.
Location: 1½ m from Aberfeldy on B846.
Opening Times: 1 Apr - 12 Oct.
Admission: Adult £2.50, Child £1.00, Conc £2.00, Groups: Adults £2.25.

CLUNY HOUSE GARDENS

Tel: 01887 820795

Aberfeldy, Perthshire PH15 2JT

Contact: W Mattingley

Good Woodland garden including many rare Himalayan species.
Location: 3½ m from Aberfeldy on the Weem to Strathtay Road.
Opening Times: 1 Mar - 31 Oct: 10am - 6pm.
Admission: Adults £2.00, Child under 16 free, Groups £2.00 per person (guided tour).

DAMSIDE HERB GARDEN

Tel: 01561 361496

Montrose, Angus, Kincardine DD10 0HY
Owner: Ian Cruickshank Esq   **Contact:** Ian Cruickshank
Location: Signposted on A92 halfway between Stonehaven and Montrose.
Opening Times: Daily 10am - 5pm. Closed Jan & Feb.
Admission: Adult £1.00, Child 80p, Conc 80p, accompanied child under 12 free. Groups by arrangement.

DRUMMOND CASTLE GARDENS

MUTHILL, CRIEFF, PERTHSHIRE PH5 2AA

Owner: Grimsthorpe & Drummond Castle Trust   *Contact:* Joe Buchanan

Tel: 01764 681257   **Fax:** 01764 681550
Scotland's most important formal gardens, among the finest in Europe. The terraces overlook a magnificent parterre celebrating the saltire and family heraldry, surrounding the famous multiplex sundial by John Milne, Master Mason to Charles I. Featured in the United Artists Film 'Rob Roy'. Coach parties and wheelchairs by prior arrangement.
Location: 2m S of Crieff off the A822.
Opening Times: Easter then 1 May - 31 Oct: 2 - 6pm, last entry 5pm.
Admission: Adult £3.00, Child £1.50, OAP £2.00.

EDZELL CASTLE AND GARDEN

Tel: 01356 648631

Edzell, Angus

Owner: Historic Scotland   **Contact:** The Custodian

The beautiful walled garden at Edzell is one of Scotland's unique sights, created by Sir David Lindsay in 1604. The 'Pleasance' is a delightful formal garden with walls decorated with sculptured stone panels, flower boxes and niches for nesting birds. The fine tower house, now ruined, dates from the last years of the 15th century. Mary Queen of Scots held a council meeting in the castle in 1562 on her way north as her army marched against the Gordons.

Location: At Edzell, 6m N of Brechin on the B966.
Opening Times: 1 Apr - 30 Sept: Mon - Sat 9.30am - 6.30pm, Sun 2 - 6.30pm. 1 Oct - 31 Mar: Mon - Wed & Sat 9.30am - 4.30pm, Thur 9.30am - 12 noon, Fri Closed, Sun 2 - 4.30pm. Last admission $^{1}/_{2}$ hour before closing.
Admission: Adult £2.00, Conc £1.25, Child 75p.

ELCHO CASTLE

Tel: 0131 668 8800

Perth

Owner: Historic Scotland

This handsome and complete fortified mansion of 16th century date has four projecting towers. The original wrought-iron grilles to protect the windows are still in place.
Location: On the Tay, 3m SE of Perth.
Opening Times: Apr - Sept: Mon - Sat, 9.30am - 6.30pm. Sun 2 - 6.30pm.

GLAMIS CASTLE

See Page 280 for full page entry.

HOUSE OF DUN

MONTROSE, ANGUS DD10 9LQ

Owner: The National Trust For Scotland
Contact: David Sharland

Tel: 01674 810264

This beautiful Georgian house, overlooking the Montrose Basin, was designed by William Adam and built in 1730 for David Erskine, Lord Dun. Lady Augusta Kennedy-Erskine was the natural daughter of William IV and Mrs Jordan and House of Dun contains many royal mementos. The house features superb plasterwork by Joseph Enzer.

Location: 3m W Montrose on A935
Admission: Adult £3.10, Child £2, Parties: Adult £2.50, School £1.00. Family £8.20.

OPEN
House: Good Fri - Easter Mon & 1 May - 30 Sept: Daily: 1.30 - 5.30pm
Weekends in Oct 1.30 - 5.30pm.
Garden & Grounds: All year Daily: 9.30 - Sunset

HOUSE OF PITMUIES

OPEN

1 April - 31 Oct

Daily

10am - 5pm

Tel: 01241 828245

BY FORFAR, ANGUS DD8 2SN
Owner: Mrs Farquhar Ogilvie   *Contact: Mrs Farquhar Ogilvie*

Semi-formal walled gardens celebrated for their delphiniums, rose collection and herbaceous borders in summer. Cool woodland and riverside walks with fine trees and massed spring bulbs. Fine 18th century house (open by appointment) flanked by stone-roofed outbuildings with adjacent 'Gothick' wash house and unique turreted doo-cot.

Location: A932, 6$^{1}/_{2}$m from Forfar, 8m from Arbroath, 1$^{1}/_{2}$m from Friockheim.
Admission: Garden: Adult £2, Child (under 12) free. Free parking.

HUNTINGTOWER CASTLE

Tel: 01738 627231

Perth

Owner: Historic Scotland   **Contact:** The Custodian

The splendid painted ceilings are especially noteworthy in this castle, once owned by the Ruthven family. Scene of a famous leap between two towers by a daughter of the house who was nearly caught in her lover's room. The two towers are still complete, one of 15th - 16th century date, the other of 16th century origin. Now linked by a 17th century range.
Location: 3m NW of Perth off the A85.
Opening Times: 1 Apr - 30 Sept: Mon - Sat 9.30am - 6.30pm, Sun 2 - 6.30pm. 1 Oct - 31 Mar: Mon - Wed & Sat 9.30am - 4.30pm, Thur 9.30am - 12 noon, Fri Closed, Sun 2 - 4.30pm. Last admission $^{1}/_{2}$ hour before closing.
Admission: Adult £1.50, Conc £1.00, Child 75p.

LOCHLEVEN CASTLE

Tel: 01786 450000

Loch Leven, Kinross

Owner: Historic Scotland   **Contact:** The Regional Custodian

Mary Queen of Scots endured nearly a year of imprisonment in this 14th century tower before her dramatic escape in May 1568. During the First War of Independence it was held by the English, stormed by Wallace and visited by Bruce.
Location: On an island in Loch Leven reached by ferry from Kinross off the M90.
Opening Times: 1 Apr - 30 Sept: Mon - Sat 9.30am - 6.30pm, Sun 2 - 6.30pm. Last admission $^{1}/_{2}$ hour before closing.
Admission: Adult £2.50, Conc £1.50, Child £1.00. Prices include ferry trip.

MEGGINCH CASTLE GARDENS

Tel: 01821 642222   Fax: 01821 642708

Errol, Perthshire PH2 7SW

Owner: Captain Drummond of Megginch and Lady Strange

15th century castle, 1,000 year old yews, flowered parterre, double walled kitchen garden, topiary, astrological garden, pagoda dovecote in courtyard. Part used as a location for the film "Rob Roy" released in 1995.
Location: 8m E of Perth on A90.
Opening Times: Apr - Oct: Wed. August: daily 2.30 - 6.00pm.
Admission: Adult £2.00, Child £1.00.

MEIGLE SCULPTURED STONE MUSEUM

Tel: 01828 640612

Meigle

Owner: Historic Scotland   **Contact:** The Custodian

A remarkable collection of 25 sculptured monuments of the Celtic Christian period. This is one of the finest collections of Dark Age sculpture in Western Europe.
Location: In Meigle on the A94.
Opening Times: 1 Apr - 30 Sept: Mon - Sat 9.30am - 6.30pm, Sun 2 - 6.30pm. Last admission $^{1}/_{2}$ hour before closing.
Admission: Adult £1.20, Conc 75p, Child 75p.

SCONE PALACE

See Page 281 for full page entry.

Sealed Knot at Fyvie Castle, Grampian.

SPECIAL EVENTS

❖ **HOUSE OF DUN**   **1 JUNE**
Concert "Three's Company". Popular mezzo-soprano Mary Sandeman, tenor James Nichol and composer/pianist John Moore. 8pm, tickets £7. Tel: 01674 810264.

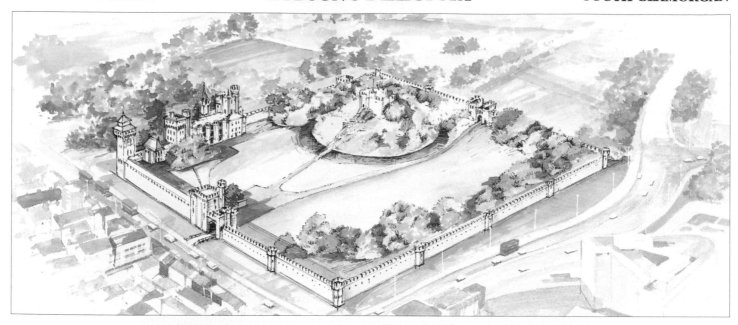

CARDIFF CASTLE
Cardiff

CARDIFF CASTLE at the centre of the capital city of Wales, occupies a large historic site that provides many levels of interest to the visitor.

Reconstructed Roman walls enclose the area, which contains the spectacular remains of mediaeval defences, including the 12th century shell keep which overlooks the grounds.

The Castle Lodgings, which partly date from the mid-15th century, were rebuilt during the 19th century and form perhaps the greatest creation of Art-Architect William Burges (1827 - 81), who transformed the Castle into a mediaevalist fantasy for his patron, the wealthy and cultured 3rd Marquess of Bute.

Access to the Lodgings is by public or pre-arranged specialist tours, and includes visits to some of Burges' magnificent and imaginative interiors which blend the medieval and the exotic to create some of the most extraordinary rooms in the country.

These include the Arab Room - a Burges vision of the Middle East which has sumptuous carved and gilded decoration, plus the three fantastic rooms of the Clock Tower, which celebrate themes of astrology and alchemy in a blaze of decorated tiles, marquetry and painting.

The superb Banqueting Hall recreated a uniquely Victorian vision of the mediaeval, and is available for functions.

CONTACT

Mrs J Brown
Cardiff Castle
Castle Street
Cardiff
South Glamorgan
CF1 2RB

Tel: (01222) 822083
Fax: (01222) 231417

LOCATION

The Castle is situated in central Cardiff. Signposted from the M4 motorway 'to City Centre'. From London M4 direct 2 hours.

Rail: Cardiff Central

Air: Cardiff Airport

OPENING TIMES

Summer
1 May - 30 September
Daily
10am - 6pm

Winter
March, April & October
10am - 5pm

November - February
10am - 4.30pm

ADMISSION

All Year
HOUSE & GROUNDS

Adult £3.70
Child* £1.80
OAP £1.80

GROUNDS ONLY

Adult £2.30
Child £1.20
OAP £1.20

Groups
10% reduction on parties of 20+. Tour operators and travel agents discount on request.

* under 16yrs

SUITABILITY FOR OTHER EVENTS
The Castle is suitable for a number of events and functions. Please apply to the Administrator for further details.

ADVICE TO COURIERS & DRIVERS
No photography of the interiors, except by special prior permission. The Lodgings are unsuitable for disabled / wheelchair visitors.

PARKING FOR COACHES & CARS
No parking facilities but there are public car parks nearby. Please contact the Administrator for advice on parking coaches.

FACILITIES FOR THE DISABLED
Disabled or elderly visitors may alight at the Castle's entrance. Toilet facilities for the disabled are available in the grounds. The Lodgings are unsuitable for disabled / wheelchair visitors.

CATERING
A Tea Room, seating 46, is available. Please note groups CANNOT book in advance.

NATIONAL TRUST SHOP
Shop open at same hours as Castle. Items include souvenirs, gifts, postcards, etc.

GUIDE BOOKS
Available from The National Trust shop.

SPECIALIST TOURS
Tours of Burges Interiors or the De Morgan Collection of ceramics available by the Keeper of Collections. Strictly by advance appointment and only for specialist groups. Tours of the interior by public guides. Maximum size for tour is 40.

The Banqueting Hall.

The Dining Room.

A SELECTION OF
THE IMPRESSIVE
FUNCTION FACILITIES
AT CARDIFF CASTLE

The Drawing Room.

The Library.

The Roof Garden in Summer.

CONFERENCE AND FUNCTION FACILITIES

ROOM	DIMENSIONS	CAPACITY	LAYOUT	POWER POINTS	SUITABLE FOR A/V
Banqueting Hall		110 - 150	Various	✓	
Drawing Room		50 - 60	Various	✓	
Small Dining Room		20	Various	✓	
George Thomas Suite		18 - 30	Various	✓	

TREDEGAR HOUSE
Newport

South Wales' finest country house, ancestral home of the Morgan dynasty for over 500 years.

Parts of a mediaeval house in stone remain, but Tredegar owes its reputation to lavish rebuilding in brick at the end of the 17th century. The new house was built on an exceptionally grand scale and included a glittering series of State Rooms complemented by a more intimate family wing, although the mediaeval courtyard plan was retained. The service wing was built in the 19th century.

The house and contents were sold in 1951 and for 23 years served as a school. Purchased by Newport Borough Council in 1974, it has been carefully restored and refurnished, often with original pieces. Visitors have a lively and entertaining tour through 40 rooms in a variety of historical decorative styles. Exquisite carving, plasterwork and decorations, fine painting and tapestries, and special attention to the accurate use of recreated fabrics, textiles and floor coverings are features of rooms above stairs, while a host of domestic bygones capture the visitor's imagination in the Great Kitchen, Housekeeper's Room, Servants' Hall and other rooms 'below stairs'.

GARDENS
The basic mediaeval garden plan survives on two sides of the house in a series of Walled Gardens currently undergoing restoration. Late 18th century landscaping by Mickle swept away all but one of the avenues of oak and chestnut radiating from the house. Ninety acres of parkland. The Sunken Garden has now been restored with an early 20th century planting scheme.

SUITABILITY FOR OTHER EVENTS
Press launches, concerts, lectures, filming & wedding receptions.

EXTRA FACILITIES
Park and gardens. Carriage rides, boating, adventure playground, craft workshops, camping and caravans.

ADVICE FOR COURIERS & DRIVERS
Please book in advance and allow at least three hours at the house for tours and refreshments. No dogs, unaccompanied children, photography, stilettos or smoking allowed in house.

PARKING FOR COACHES & CARS
Parking for 1800 cars and 10 coaches 150 yds from the house.

FACILITIES FOR THE DISABLED
Disabled access to ground floor and toilets. Free wheelchair loan. Please give advance warning.

CATERING
The Restaurant/Tea Room can cater for up to 80 people. Prices from £1.80 (tea), £5 (2 course lunch), £16 (3 course dinner). Groups can book in advance; menus available. Catering facilities available for special functions/conferences.

GIFT SHOPS
Visitor Centre Shop open daily 10.30am - 6pm. Housekeeper's Shop open as house. Including souvenirs, Welsh crafts, books, spices, toiletries and souvenirs.

GUIDED TOURS
Discounts for parties of 25+. Average time for tour 1¼ hours.

SCHOOL VISITS/CHILDREN
Groups welcome and guide available. £2 per child (house only). Areas of interest include: 'Below Stairs', boating, carriage rides, woodland walk, craft workshops and adventure play farm.

CONTACT

The Curator
Tredegar House & Park
Newport
Gwent
NP1 9YW

Tel: (01633) 815880

LOCATION

From London M4, signposted Junction 28 2½ hours. Newport 2 miles.

Rail: London to Newport station.

Bus: Bus within 300 yards of entrance.

Taxi: Dragon (01633) 216216.

OPENING TIMES

Summer
Good Friday - 30 Sept.

Bank Hol. Mons
11.00am - 5.00pm

Tuesdays during School Summer Hols only
11.30am - 4.00pm

Wed - Sun Tours
11.30am - 4.00pm.

NB Country Park open. Daily 8.00am - Dusk Evening tours by appointment only.

Winter
October only - weekend opening as Summer.

Day & Evening tours by appointment only. Christmas opening: Details from September

ADMISSION

HOUSE & GARDEN
Adult £3.80
Child £2.00
OAP £3.00
Student £3.00
Family £10.00

Prices correct at time of going to press.

CONFERENCE AND FUNCTION FACILITIES

ROOM	DIMENSIONS	CAPACITY	LAYOUT	POWER POINTS	SUITABLE FOR A/V
Morgan Room	58' x 20' x 8'	40 - 120	Various	4	✓
Tea Room & Bar	50' x 20' x 8'	30-80	Various	4	✓

CLWYD

BODELWYDDAN CASTLE

OPEN
30 Mar - 30 Jun &
7 Sept - 31 Oct: Daily
except Fri, 10am - 5pm.
Castle Gallery:
open 10.30am.
1 Jul - 6 Sept:
Daily: 10am - 5pm.
1 Nov - Easter 1997:
Daily except Mon & Fri,
11am - 4pm. Castle
Gallery: Open 11am.
Gardens: 10am - 4pm
(11am during winter)
Groups must pre-book.
Tel: 01745 584060

ST ASAPH, CLWYD
Owner: *Clwyd County Council*   ***Contact:*** *Karen Short*
Managed by Bodelwyddan Castle Trust - a Registered Charity

This magnificently restored Victorian mansion set in rolling parkland displays extensive collections from the National Portrait Gallery, furniture from the Victoria and Albert Museum, and John Gibson sculpture from the Royal Academy. Exhibitions of Victorian amusements and inventions and a programme of large and small indoor and outdoor events throughout the year. Winner of the Museum of the Year Award.
Location: Follow signs off A55 Expressway Nr. St Asaph, opposite Marble Church.
Admission: Castle & Grounds: Adult £4, OAP/Unemployed £3.50, Child/Student/Disabled £2.50, Family (2+3) £12. Grounds only: £2. Family (2+3) £7.50.
Check opening hours before travelling.

BODNANT GARDEN

Tel: 01492 650460   **Fax:** 01492 650448

Tal-y-Cafn, Colwyn Bay, Clwyd LL28 5RE
Owner: The National Trust   **Contact:** The Secretary
The 32-ha garden at Bodnant is one of the finest in the world, situated above the River Conwy and looking across the valley towards the Snowdon range. The garden is in two parts. The upper part around the house consists of the Terrace Gardens and informal lawns shaded by trees. The lower portion, The Dell, contains the Pinetum and Wild Garden. Masses of bulbs in spring make a colourful display. Rhododendrons, magnolias and camellias flower as well as splendid autumn colours. Plant centre and gift shop.
Location: 8m S of Llandudno and Colwyn Bay, off A470. Signposted from A55.
Opening Times: 16 Mar - 31 Oct: Daily, 10am - 5pm. Last admission ½ hr before close.
Admission: Adult £4.20, Child £2.10. Parties (20 or more) £3.80 pp.

BODRHYDDAN HALL 🏛

OPEN
June - September
inclusive.

Tue & Thur
2.00 - 5.30pm.

Coaches and
Special Parties
at any time by
appointment only
(minimum charge £40)

Tel: 01745 590414

RHUDDLAN, CLWYD LL18 5SB
Owner: *Colonel The Lord Langford OBE*   ***Contact:*** *Colonel The Lord Langford*

A Grade I listed family home, basically 17th century but traces of an earlier building exist. Additions by the famous Victorian architect William Eden Nesfield whose father William Andrews Nesfield designed the parterre. There are notable pieces of armour, pictures, period furniture and a 3,000 year old Mummy. Outside, a formal garden and a picnic area. Bodrhyddan is one of the few Grade I Houses in Wales still in private hands.
Location: On the A5151 midway between Dyserth and Rhuddlan.
Admission: Adult £2, Child £1. Free car park.

CHIRK CASTLE

Tel: 01691 777701   **Fax:** 01691 774706

Chirk, Wrexham, Clwyd LL14 5AF
Owner: The National Trust   **Contact:** The Property Manager
A magnificent Marcher fortress, completed in 1310, commanding fine views over the surrounding countryside. Elegant state rooms with elaborate plasterwork, superb Adam-style furniture, tapestries and portraits. In the formal gardens there are clipped yews, roses and a variety of flowering shrubs. Elaborate entrance gates made in 1719 by the Davies brothers. 18th century parkland.
Location: ½m W of Chirk village off A5, 8m S of Wrexham, signposted off A483.
Opening Times: 2 Apr - 30 Jun and 1 - 29 Sept: Daily except Mon & Sat but open BH Mon. Jul - Aug: Daily except Sat. 5 - 27 Oct: Sat & Sun only. Castle: 12 noon - 5pm. Garden: 11am - 6pm. 11 Aug - 15 Sept: Special opening of family apartments, 1 - 4.30pm (additional charge). Last admission ½ hour before close.
Admission: Adult £4, Child £2, Family (2x2) £10. Parties (20 or more) £3.20 pp. Garden only: Adult £2, Child £1. Family Apts: (inc. NT members) Adult £1.50, Child £1.

DENBIGH CASTLE

Tel: 01745 813979

Denbigh, Clwyd
Owner: CADW: Welsh Historic Monuments   **Contact:** The Administrator
Crowning the summit of a prominent outcrop dominating the Vale of Clwyd, the principal feature of this spectacular site is the great gatehouse dating back to the 11th century. Some of the walls can still be walked by visitors.
Location: Denbigh via A525 or B5382.
Opening Times: 1 May - 30 Sept: Daily 10am - 5pm.
Admission: Castle: Adult £1.70, Reduced £1.20, Family £4.

ERDDIG

Tel: 01978 355314   **Fax:** 01978 313333

Wrexham, Clwyd LL13 0YT
Owner: The National Trust   **Contact:** The Property Manager
This late 17th century house with 18th century additions, is the most evocative upstairs - downstairs house in Britain. The range of outbuildings includes laundry, bakehouse, stables, sawmill, smithy and joiner's shop, while the state rooms display most of the original 18th and 19th century furniture and furnishings. A large walled garden restored to its 18th century formal design with Victorian parterre and Yew Walk, also contains the National Ivy Collection. Surrounding parkland with extensive woods. 10min video programme. The Tapestry and Small Chinese rooms are open on Wed and Sat only.
Location: 2m S of Wrexham off A525 or A483.
Opening Times: 1 Apr - 2 Oct: Daily, except Thur & Fri, open Good Fri. House: 12 noon - 5pm. Gardens 11am - 6pm. Jul - Aug: 10am - 6pm. 5 Oct - 3 Nov: House: 12 noon - 4pm. Garden: 11am - 5pm. Last admission 1 hr before close.
Admission: Adult £5.20, Child £2.60. Party (15+) £4.20pp. Below stairs (incl. outbuildings & garden) Adult £3.40, Party £2.70 pp, Child £1.70. Family (2x2) £8.50.

ST ASAPH CATHEDRAL

Tel: 01745 583597

St Asaph, Clwyd LL17 0RL

Contact: The Dean
Smallest ancient cathedral in Great Britain. Founded 560AD. Present building dates from 13th century.
Location: Just off A55.
Opening Times: Summer: 7.30am - 6.30pm. Winter: 7.30am - dusk. Sun services: 8am, 11am, 3.30pm. (unconfirmed for 1996).

VALLE CRUCIS ABBEY ✤

Tel: 01978 860326

Llangollen, Clwyd
Owner: CADW: Welsh Historic Monuments   **Contact:** The Administrator
The lovely ruins of the 13th century Abbey are set at the foot of the Horseshoe Pass beside a stream.
Location: B5103 from A5, W of Llangollen, or A542 from Ruthin.
Opening Times: See CADW standard opening times pg. 291.
Admission: Adult £1.70, Reduced Rates £1.20. Family £4.00.

DYFED

CAREW CASTLE AND TIDAL MILL

Tel: 01646 651782   **Fax:** 01646 651782

Tenby, Pembrokeshire SA70 8SL
Owner: Pembrokeshire Coast National Park   **Contact:** G M Candler
A magnificent Norman castle which later became an Elizabethan country house. Royal links with Henry Tudor and the setting for the Great Tournament of 1507. The Mill is one of only four restored tidal mills in Britain. Introductory slide programme, automatic 'talking points' and special exhibition on 'The Story of Milling'.
Location: Off A477 between Tenby and Pembroke.
Opening Times: Apr - Oct: Daily, 10am - 5pm.
Admission: Adult £2.00, Child / OAP £1.30, Family £5.50.

CILGERRAN CASTLE   **Tel:** 01239 615136

Cardigan, Dyfed
Owner: CADW: Welsh Historic Monuments   **Contact:** The Administrator
Perched high up on a rugged spur above the River Teifi, Cilgerran Castle is one of the most spectacularly sited fortresses in Wales. It dates from the 11th - 13th centuries.
Location: Main roads to Cilgerran from A478 and A484.
Opening Times: See CADW standard opening times pg. 291.
Admission: Adult £1.70, Reduced Rate £1.20, Family £4.00.

COLBY WOODLAND GARDEN   **Tel:** 01834 811885 / 01558 822800

Amroth, Narberth, Pembrokeshire SA67 8PP
Owner: The National Trust   **Contact:** The Centre Manager
An attractive woodland garden. The early 19th century house is not open. There are walks through secluded valleys along open woodland pathways, one of which links the property with the nearby coastal resort of Amroth.
Location: ¹/₂m inland from Amroth beside Carmarthen Bay. Signposted from A477.
Opening Times: 29 Mar - 1 Nov: Daily, 10am - 5pm. Walled Garden: 1 Apr - 30 Oct: Daily 11am - 5pm.
Admission: Adult £2.60, Child £1.30, Family £6.50. Group: Adult £2.10, Child £1.10. Coaches welcome. Open evenings by arrangement.

CYMER ABBEY   **Tel:** 01341 422854

Dolgellau, Dyfed
Owner: CADW: Welsh Historic Monuments   **Contact:** The Administrator
This remote and tranquil setting is typical of locations sought by the austere Cistercian monks. It suffered badly during the Welsh wars and was finally closed during the reign of Henry VIII. However, it is still impressive and gives wonderful insight into Cistercian life.
Location: 2m NW of Dolgellau on A494.
Opening Times: See CADW standard opening times pg. 291.
Admission: Adult £1.20, Reduced rate 70p, Family £3.00.

DINEFWR PARK   **Tel:** 01558 823902

Llandeilo, Dyfed SA19 6RT
Owner: The National Trust   **Contact:** The Property Manager
A Victorian Gothic mansion within an 18th century landscaped park. Parts of the ground floor and basement will be open in 1996 and a small exhibition explains the history of Dinefwr. There is a Victorian garden currently under restoration at the rear of Newton House, and an ancient deer park with White Park cattle. There is limited access to a privately owned walled garden. The Dinefwr White Park cattle and herd of fallow deer can be seen from vantage points. Access to Dinefwr Castle. Footpaths through parts of 162 ha estate and outstanding views of Towy Valley.
Location: N of Llandeilo on A40. Take M4 from Swansea to Pont Abraham. A48 to Cross Hands and A476 to Llandeilo. Entrance by police station.
Opening Times: House & Park: 1 Apr - 31 Oct: Daily, 10.30am - 5pm.
Admission: Adult £2.00, Child £1.00. Family (2+2) £5.00. Party £1.80pp, Child/School groups 90p. Coaches by prior arrangement.

DYFI FURNACE   **Tel:** 01222 465511

Aberdyfi, Dyfed
Owner: CADW: Welsh Historic Monuments   **Contact:** The Administrator
This was built around 1755 and is probably the best preserved charcoal furnace in Britain. Set in beautiful woodland it also has a grand external water wheel in working order.
Location: On the A487 near Eglwsfach, 6m from Machynlleth.
Opening Times: 1 May - 30 Sept: Daily 10am - 5pm.
Admission: Adult £1.70. Reduced rate £1.20. Family £4.00.

LAMPHEY BISHOP'S PALACE   **Tel:** 01646 672224

Lamphey, Dyfed
Owner: CADW: Welsh Historic Monuments   **Contact:** The Administrator
Lamphey marks the place of the spectacular Bishops' Palace but it reached its height of greatness under Bishop Henry de Gower who raised the new great hall. Today the ruins of this comfortable retreat reflect the power enjoyed by the medieval bishops.
Location: A4139 from Pembroke or Tenby.
Opening Times: 1 May - 30 Sept: Daily, 10am - 5pm.
Admission: Adult £1.70, Reduced rate £1.20, Family £4.00.

ST DAVIDS BISHOP'S PALACE   **Tel:** 01437 720517

Pembroke, Dyfed
Owner: CADW: Welsh Historic Monuments   **Contact:** The Administrator
St. Davids Bishop's Palace was a grand and richly decorated building and one of the medieval buildings unique to Wales. The architecture includes superb arcaded parapets and sculpted heads. Exhibition: "Life in the Palace of a Prince of the Church".
Location: A487 to St. Davids, minor road past the Cathedral.
Opening Times: See CADW standard opening times pg. 291.
Admission: Adult £1.70, Reduced Rate £1.20, Family £4.00.

ST DAVID'S CATHEDRAL   **Tel:** 01437 720691   **Fax:** 01437 721885

St David's, Dyfed SA62 6QW
                                        Contact: Mr R G Tarr
St David's is Britain's smallest city by Royal Charter March 1994. Premier cathedral of church in Wales. Over eight centuries old. Many unique and "odd" features. Resited to be on site of St David's 6th century monastery.
Location: 5 - 10 minutes walk from car/coach parks signposted for pedestrians.
Opening Times: 7.30am - 7pm Sun: 12.30am - 5.30pm may be closed when services are in progress. Sun services: 8am, 9.30am, 11am and 6pm. Weekday services: 7.30am, 8am and 6pm.
Admission: Donations. Guided tours (Adult £2.00, Child 75p) must be booked in advance.

STRATA FLORIDA ABBEY

Dyfed
Owner: CADW: Welsh Historic Monuments   **Contact:** The Administrator
The Abbey was founded in the 12th century when the Norman baron Robert Fitz Stephen drew a colony of 13 monks from the Cistercian abbey Whitland and set up a new house in this tranquil location.
Location: Minor road from Pontrhydfendigaid reached from the B4340.
Opening Times: 1 Apr - 30 Sept: See CADW standard opening times pg. 291.
Admission: Adult £1.70, Reduced Rate £1.20, Family £4.00.

TUDOR MERCHANTS HOUSE   **Tel:** 01834 842279

Quay Hill, Tenby, Pembrokeshire SA70 7BX
Owner: The National Trust   **Contact:** The Administrator
A late 15th century townhouse, characteristic of the building tradition of south-west Wales. The ground-floor chimney at the rear of the house is a fine vernacular example, and the original scarfed roof-trusses survive. The remains of early frescos can be seen on three interior walls. Access to small herb garden, weather permitting. Furniture and fittings re-create the atmosphere from the time when a Tudor family was in residence.
Location: Tenby.
Opening Times: 31 Mar - 30 Sept: Mon - Fri, 10am - 5pm, Sun 1 - 5pm.
1 - 31 Oct: Mon - Fri, 10am - 3pm, Sun 12 noon - 3pm.
Admission: Adult £1.60, Child 80p, Group: Adult £1.30, Child 60p.

MID GLAMORGAN

CAERPHILLY CASTLE   **Tel:** 01222 833143

Caerphilly, Mid Glamorgan
Owner: CADW: Welsh Historic Monuments   **Contact:** The Administrator
This vast fortress is one of the great surviving castles of the medieval western world. It covers a massive 30 acres. Restoration began in the late 19th century and was completed in 1939 so that much of its magnificence remains today.
Location: A468 (from Newport) A469 (from Cardiff).
Opening Times: See CADW standard opening times pg. 291.*
Admission: Adult £2.20, Reduced £1.70, Family £6.00.

SOUTH GLAMORGAN

CARDIFF CASTLE   See Page 284 for full page entry.

CASTELL COCH   **Tel:** 01222 810101

Taff Wells, Cardiff, South Glamorgan
Owner: CADW: Welsh Historic Monuments   **Contact:** The Administrator
This breath-takingly decorated 19th century castle was the creation of the fabulously wealthy Lord Bute on the site of a medieval castle, set in the beech woods to the North of Cardiff. Wonderful murals of Aesop's fables.
Location: M4 (Jct 32), A470 then signposted Taff Wells.
Opening Times: See CADW standard opening times pg. 291.*
Admission: Adult £2.20, Reduced Rate £1.70, Family £6.00

DYFFRYN GARDENS

Tel: 01222 593328   **Fax:** 01222 591966

St Nicholas, Cardiff, South Glamorgan CF5 6SU

Owner: Mid & South Glamorgan County Council   **Contact:** Ms N Walby

55 acres of landscaped gardens, beautiful at most times of year. Numerous small theme gardens, heather bank, arboretum and glass houses.

Location: Exit junction 33/M4 - signposted Barry.

Opening Times: Mar: Weekends only 10.30am - 4.30pm. Apr - Oct: Daily, 10am - 5.30pm.

Admission: Adult £2.00, Child £1.50, Family £6.00, Conc £1.50, Groups £1.50.

MUSEUM OF WELSH LIFE

Tel: 01222 569441

St Fagans, Cardiff, South Glamorgan

Contact: The Administrator

St Fagans Castle, a 16th century building built within the walls of a 13th century castle. The grounds have numerous reconstructed old farmhouses, cottages and other buildings which together with the museum building represent the life and culture of Wales.

Location: St Fagans.

Opening Times: All year: Daily, 10am - 5pm.

Admission: Summer: Adult £5.00, Child £2.50, OAP £3.75, Family £12.50. Winter: Adult £4.00, Child £2.00, OAP £3.00, Family £10.00.

WEST GLAMORGAN

ABERDULAIS FALLS

Tel: 01639 636674

Aberdulais, Neath, West Glamorgan SA10 8EU

Owner: The National Trust   **Contact:** The Property Warden

For over 300 years this famous waterfall has provided the energy to drive the wheels of industry, from the first manufacture of copper in 1584 to present day remains of the tinplate works. It has also been visited by famous artists such as J M W Turner in 1796. The site today houses a unique hydro-electrical scheme which has been developed to harness the waters of the Dulais river. The Turbine House provides access to an interactive computer, fish pass, and display panels. A special lift has been installed to allow disabled visitors access to the roof level, which affords excellent views of the Falls. The new water wheel, the largest currently used in Britain to generate electricity, makes Aberdulais Falls self-sufficient in environmentally friendly energy.

Location: On A465, Heads of the Valleys road, 3m NE of Neath, 4m from M4 exit 43.

Opening Times: 1 Apr - 3 Nov: Mon - Fri, 10am - 5pm. Sat, Sun & BHs, 11am - 6pm. Last admission ½ hour before closing.

Admission: Adult £2.80, Child £1.40 (one child under 16 free with each adult), Party (min 15) by prior arrangement £2.20, Child £1.10.

CARREG CENNEN CASTLE

Tel: 01558 822291

Brecon Beacons National Park, Llandeilo, West Glamorgan

Owner: CADW: Welsh Historic Monuments   **Contact:** The Administrator

Carreg Cennen Castle occupies a spectacular defensive location and is one of the earliest stone-built castles and is a marvellous example of how a sophisticated castle was built despite the obstacles of such rugged terrain.

Location: Minor roads from A483(T) to Trapp village.

Opening Times: See CADW standard opening times pg. 291, plus Jun - Aug: Daily, 6.30pm - 8pm. Oct - Mar: Sun, 9.30am - 2pm.

Admission: Adult £2.20, Reduced £1.70, Family £6.00.

KIDWELLY CASTLE

Tel: 01554 890104

Kidwelly, West Glamorgan

Owner: CADW: Welsh Historic Monuments   **Contact:** The Administrator

Kidwelly Castle is built in a magnificent sweeping crescent set high above the River Gwendraeth making full use of the huge earthwork stronghold built in 1106. Outstanding example of later 13th century castle design.

Location: Kidwelly via A484: Kidwelly Rail Station 1m.

Opening Times: See CADW standard opening times pg. 291.*

Admission: Adult £2.20, Reduced £1.70, Family £6.00.

WEOBLEY CASTLE

Tel: 01792 390012

Gower, West Glamorgan

Owner: CADW: Welsh Historic Monuments   **Contact:** The Administrator

Weobley Castle is as much a medieval fortified manor house as a true castle. Visitors to Weobley can enjoy a fascinating exhibition about the castle high above the stark northern shore of the Gower Peninsula.

Location: B4271 or B4295 to Llanrhidian Village, then minor road.

Opening Times: See CADW standard opening times pg. 291.

Admission: Adult £1.70, Reduced Rates £1.20, Family £4.00.

GWENT

BLAENAVON IRONWORKS

Tel: 01495 792615

Near Brecon Beacons National Park, Blaenavon, Gwent

Owner: CADW: Welsh Historic Monuments   **Contact:** The Administrator

Blaenavon Ironworks is one of the most complete works to survive in the country and dates back to the 18th century. Furnaces can be viewed and are in varying stages of preservation.

Location: Via A4043 follow signs to Big Pit Mining Museum and Blaenavon Ironworks. Abergavenny 8m. Pontypool 8m.

Opening Times: 1 May - 30 Sept: Mon - Sat, 11am - 5pm, Sun 2 - 5pm.

Admission: Adult £1.20, Reduced Rate 70p, Family £3.00.

THE CASTLE HOUSE

Tel: 01291 672563

Usk, Gwent NP5 1SD

Owner: J H L Humphreys   **Contact:** J H L Humphreys

Medieval Gatehouse with 19th century interior and 13th century castle ruins, set in a series of gardens providing seasonal interest (donations to NGS).

Location: Off Monmouth Road in Usk, opposite fire station.

Opening Times: House: Prior written appointment with SAE. Bank Hol Weekends. Jun: Daily 12 noon - 5pm, except Mon. Guided tours only. Gardens & Castle Ruins: throughout the year by appointment.

Admission: House & Garden: Adult £3.50, Family £8.00. Castle & Garden: Adult £2.00, Child free.

CHEPSTOW CASTLE

Tel: 01291 624065

Chepstow, Gwent

Owner: CADW: Welsh Historic Monuments   **Contact:** The Administrator

Chepstow Castle is magnificently situated on the cliffs above the River Wye guarding one of the main crossings from England to Wales.

Location: Chepstow via A465, B4235. A48 or M4 (Jct 22).

Opening Times: See CADW standard opening times pg. 291.*

Admission: Adult £3.00, Reduced Rate £2.00, Family £8.00.

PENHOW CASTLE

OPEN
Summer
Good Fri - 30 Sept:
Wed - Sun & Bk Hols
Aug: Daily
10am - 5.15pm (last adm.)
Winter:
Wed, 10am - 4pm
Selected Sun, 1 - 4pm
Evening Candlelit Tours
all year by arrangement.
Christmas Tours
15 Nov - 5 Jan.

Tel: 01633 400800
Fax: 01633 400990

NR. NEWPORT, GWENT NP6 3AD

Owner: Stephen Weeks Esq   *Contact: Miss Kathleen Bull*

Wales' oldest lived-in Castle, the first home in Britain of the Seymour family. Now lovingly restored by the present owner, visitors explore the varied period rooms from battlements to kitchens. Discover the Norman bedchamber, 15th century Great Hall with minstrels' gallery, elegant panelled Carolean dining room, guided by the acclaimed 'Time Machine', audio tours included in the admission; also in French & German. Penhow holds 8 awards for careful restoration & imaginative interpretation.

Location: Midway between Chepstow and Newport on the A48. Use M4 J22 or 24.

Admission: Adult £3.15, Child £1.85, Family (2+2) £8.15. Groups by arrangement all year, 10% discount for 20+.

RAGLAN CASTLE

Tel: 01291690228

Raglan, Gwent

Owner: CADW: Welsh Historic Monuments   **Contact:** The Administrator

Situated on the Borders. Raglan Castle is famed for its striking hexagonal Great Tower. It is also unique as part of it is constructed of brick, probably the earliest use of this material in Wales. It was as much a product of social grandeur as it was of military necessity.

Location: Raglan, Gwent.

Opening Times: See CADW standard opening times pg. 291.*

Admission: Adult £2.20, Reduced Rate £1.70, Family : £6.00.

TINTERN ABBEY

Tel: 01291 689251

Tintern, Gwent
Owner: CADW: Welsh Historic Monuments   **Contact:** The Administrator
Originally founded in 1131 for the Cistercian monks and by 1536 was the richest Abbey in Wales. The great church is still gloriously intact and visitors will find the views both beautiful and unforgettable.
Location: Tintern via A466, from M4 (Jct 22). Chepstow 6m.
Opening Times: See CADW standard opening times pg. 291.*
Admission: Adult £2.20, Reduced Rate £1.70, Family £6.00.

TREDEGAR HOUSE

See Page 286 for full page entry.

WHITE CASTLE

Tel: 01606 85380

Brecon Beacons National Park, Gwent
Owner: CADW: Welsh Historic Monuments   **Contact:** The Administrator
Situated on a low hill about a mile from the village of Llantilio Crossenny, White Castle was built in the 11th century to control the southern March. It was given the name 'White Castle' because of the rendering, traces of which can be seen today.
Location: By minor roads from B4233 near Llantilio Crossenny. Abergavenny 8m.
Opening Times: 1 Apr - 30 Sept: Daily, 10am - 6pm.
Admission: Adult £1.70, Reduced Rate £1.20, Family £4.00

GWYNEDD

ABERCONWY HOUSE

Tel: 01492 592246

Castle Street, Conwy, Gwynedd LL32 8AY
Owner: The National Trust   **Contact:** The Custodian
Dating from the 14th century, this is the only medieval merchant's house in Conwy to have survived the turbulent history of this walled town for nearly six centuries. Furnished rooms and an audio-visual presentation show daily life from different periods in its history.
Location: At junction of Castle Street and High Street.
Opening Times: 31 Mar - 3 Nov: Daily except Tues, 10am - 5pm, last admission 4.30pm.
Admission: Adult £2.00, Child £1.00, Family (2+2) £5.00, Pre-booked groups £1.80pp.

BEAUMARIS CASTLE

Tel: 01248 810361

Beaumaris, Anglesey, Gwynedd WL58 8AP
Owner: CADW : Welsh Historic Monuments   **Contact:** The Administrator
Beaumaris is a World Heritage Listed Site. Built by Edward I in his conquest of Wales, it is the most sophisticated example of medieval military architecture.
Location: A545 (Menai Bridge), A5 (Bangor).
Opening Times: See CADW standard opening times pg. 291.*
Admission: Adult £1.70, Reduced £1.20, Family £4.00.

BRYN BRAS CASTLE

Tel: 01286 870210   **Fax:** 01286 870210

Llanrug, Caernarfon, Gwynedd LL55 4RE
Owner: Mr & Mrs N E Gray-Parry   **Contact:** Marita Gray-Parry
Built in the Neo-Romanesque style in 1830, on an earlier structure and probably designed by Thomas Hopper. Elegantly romantic family home with fine stained glass, panelling, interesting ceilings and richly carved furniture. The Castle stands in the beautiful Snowdonian range and the extensive gardens include herbaceous borders, walled knot garden, woodland walks, stream and pools, $^1/_4$m mountain walk with superb views of Snowdon, Anglesey and the sea. Welsh teas in the tearoom and tea garden. Picnic area.
Location: $^1/_2$ m off A4086 at Llanrug, $4^1/_2$m E of Caernarfon.
Opening Times: Spring Bk Hol weekend - mid Sept; Tue, Wed, Thu, Fri, 1 - 5pm. Mid Jul - end Aug: open 11am. (1995 times). Groups by prior appointment.
Admission: Adult £3.50, Child £1.75. Groups 10% discount by prior arrangement.

CAERNARFON CASTLE

Tel: 01286 677617

Caernarfon, Gwynedd LL55 2AY
Owner: CADW: Welsh Historic Monuments   **Contact:** The Administrator
Caernarfon Castle is a mighty medieval fortress built by Edward I and is undoubtedly one of Europe's finest. It became famous in modern times as the setting for the Prince of Wales investiture.
Location: In Caernarfon.
Opening Times: See CADW standard opening times pg. 291.*
Admission: Adult £3.80, Reduced £2.80, Family £10.00.

CONWAY CASTLE

Tel: 01492 592358

Conwy, Gwynedd
Owner: CADW: Welsh Historic Monuments   **Contact:** The Administrator
Conwy Castle is a masterpiece of medieval military architecture. Built between 1238 and 1289 by Edward I, it helped to complete the conquest of the Welsh princes in North Wales. World Heritage listed site.
Location: Conwy by A55 or B5106.
Opening Times: See CADW standard opening times pg. 291.*
Admission: Adult £3.00. Reduced Rate £2.00. Family £8.00.

CRICCIETH CASTLE

Tel: 01766 522227

Criccieth, Gwynedd
Owner: CADW: Welsh Historic Monuments   **Contact:** The Administrator
Criccieth is made impressive by the natural sea cliff defence and the construction of the earthworks. Overlooking Cardigan Bay its ruins are testament to Welsh castle building.
Location: A497 to Criccieth from Portmadoc or Pwelleli.
Opening Times: See CADW standard opening times pg. 291.
Admission: Adult £2.20, Reduced Rate £1.70, Family £6.00.

DOLWYDDELAN CASTLE

Tel: 01690 6366

Blaenau Ffestiniog, Gwynedd
Owner: CADW: Welsh Historic Monuments   **Contact:** The Administrator
Standing proudly on a ridge, this stern building remains remarkably intact and visitors cannot fail to be impressed with the great solitary square tower, built by Llewelyn the Great in the early 13th century.
Location: A470(T) Blaenau Ffestiniog to Betws-y-Coed.
Opening Times: See CADW standard opening times.
Admission: Adult £1.70, Reduced Rate £1.20, Family £4.00.

HARLECH CASTLE

Tel: 01766 780552

Harlech, Gwynedd
Owner: CADW: Welsh Historic Monuments   **Contact:** The Administrator
Set against the backdrop of Snowdonia, visitors will be struck by the awe-inspiring and majestic fortress of Harlech Castle which is now deservedly a World Heritage listed site. It was impregnable until captured by Owain Glyndwr during the Welsh uprising in 1404.
Location: Harlech, Gwynedd.
Opening Times: See CADW standard opening times pg. 291.*
Admission: Adult £3.00. Reduced Rate £2.00. Family £8.00.

PENRHYN CASTLE

Tel: 01248 353084   **Fax:** 01248 371281

Bangor, Gwynedd LL57 4HN
Owner: The National Trust   **Contact:** The Property Manager
A huge neo-Norman castle placed dramatically between Snowdonia and the Menai Strait. Built by Thomas Hopper between 1820 - 1845, the castle contains interesting Norman furniture, panelling and plasterwork designed by Hopper and houses the best private collection of paintings in North Wales. There is also an industrial railway museum, a doll museum, a countryside exhibition and a Victorian walled garden.
Location: 1m E of Bangor, at Llandegai on A5122. Signposted from A55 and A5.
Opening Times: 27 Mar - 3 Nov: Daily except Tues. Castle: 12 noon - 5pm. Jul - Aug: 11am - 5pm. Grounds & Exhibitions: 11am - 6pm. Jul - Aug: 10am - 6pm. Last adm. $^1/_2$ hr before closing. Last audio tour 4pm.
Admission: Adult £4.50, Child £2.25, Family £11.25, Party (20+) £3.60. Grounds & Exhibitions: Adult £3, Child £1.50.

PLAS BRONDANW GARDENS

Tel: 01766 770484 / 770814

Menna Angharad, Plas Brondanw, Llanfrothen, Gwynedd LL48 6SW
Owner: Trustees of the Second Portmeirion Foundation
Location: 3m N of Penrhyndeudraeth off A40A5, on Croesor Road.
Opening Times: All year: Daily, 9am - 5pm.
Admission: Adult £1.50, Child 25p, Group £1.00 (if pre-booked).

PLAS NEWYDD

Tel: 01248 714795

Llanfairpwll, Anglesey, Gwynedd LL61 6DQ
Owner: The National Trust   **Contact:** The Custodian
An impressive 18th century house by James Wyatt in unspoilt surrounding on the Menai Strait, with magnificent views of Snowdonia. The house contains Rex Whistler's largest wall painting and an exhibition about his work. In the military museum are campaign relics of the 1st Marquess of Anglesey and the Battle of Waterloo. There is a fine spring garden and parkland.
Location: 1m SW of Llanfairpwll and A5 on A4080 to Brynsiencyn; turn off A5 at W end of Britannia bridge.
Opening Times: House: 29 Mar - 30 Sept: Daily except Sat. 1 Oct - 3 Nov: Fri & Sun, 12 noon - 5pm. Garden: same as house, 11am - 5pm. Last admission 4.30pm.
Admission: Adult £4.00, Child £2.00, Family (2+2) £10. Pre-booked parties (20+) £3.20pp.

PLAS YN RHIW

Tel: 01758 780219

Rhiw, Pwllheli, Gwynedd LL53 8AB
Owner: The National Trust **Contact:** The Custodian
A small manor house, with garden and woodlands, overlooking the west shore of Porth Neigwl (Hell's Mouth Bay) on the Llyn Peninsula. The house is part medieval, with Tudor and Georgian additions, and the ornamental gardens have flowering trees and shrubs, divided by box hedges and grass paths, rising behind to the snowdrop wood.
Location: 12m from Pwllheli from B4413 to Aberdaron.
Opening Times: 1 Apr - 30 Sept:Daily (except Sat), 12 noon - 5pm, last adm. 4.30pm.
Admission: Adult £2.50, Child £1.25, Family (2+2) £6.25. Pre-booked parties evenings only £3.50pp.

PORTMEIRION

Tel: 01766 770228 **Fax:** 01766 771331

Portmeirion, Gwynedd LL48 6ET
Owner: Portmeirion Ltd **Contact:** Mr R Llywelyn
Fairy tale Italianate village on shores of Cardigan Bay built by the architect Sir Clough Williams Ellis.
Location: Off A487 at Minffordd between Penrhyndeudraeth and Porthmadog.
Opening Times: All Year (except Christmas Day): Daily, 9.30am - 5.30 .
Admission: Adult £3.20, Child £1.60, Family £8.60, OAP £2.60.

POWYS

GLANSEVERN HALL GARDEN

Tel: 01686 640200 **Fax:** 01686 640829

Berriew, Welshpool, Powys SY21 8AH
Owner: Mr & Mrs R N Thomas **Contact:** Mr & Mrs R N Thomas
A classic Greek revival house romantically positioned on banks of River Severn. 14 acres of mature gardens notable for variety of unusual tree species. Also much new planting. Lakeside and woodland walks, water and rock gardens, grotto, walled rose garden. Tea room and gift shop in stabled courtyard. Plants for sale.
Location: On A483, 4m W of Powis Castle, Welshpool.
Opening Times: May - Sept: Fri, Sat, Sun and Bank Holiday Mondays, 2 - 6pm.
Admission: Adult £2.00, Child (under 16) free.

POWIS CASTLE

Tel: 01938 554338 **Fax:** 01938 554336

Welshpool, Powys SY21 8RF
Owner: The National Trust **Contact:** The Property Manager
Perched on a rock above the late 17th century garden terraces, this medieval castle contains the finest country house collection in Wales. It was built c.1200 by Welsh princes, and has been owned and altered by successive generations of Herberts and Clives for 400 years. The garden is of the highest horticultural and historic importance. The Clive Museum displays treasures from India.
Location: 1m S of Welshpool. Pedestrian access from High Street A490.
Opening Times: Castle & Museum: 1 Apr - 30 Jun & 1 Sept - 3 Nov: Daily except Mon & Tue. Jul - Aug: Daily except Mon, 12 noon - 5pm. Open BH Mons during season. Garden: same days as Castle & Museum, 11am - 6pm. Last admission 1/2 hour before close.
Admission: Garden: Adult £4, Child £2, Family (2+2) £10. Parties £3.20pp. All-in ticket Adult £6, Child £3, Family £15. Parties for Castle, Museum & Garden: £5.50, Coach & school parties by appointment.

TREBINSHUN HOUSE

Tel: 01874 730653 **Fax:** 01874 730843

Brecon, Powys LD3 7PX
Owner: R Watson Esq **Contact:** R Watson
A medium sized 16th century manor house which underwent extensive restoration in 1800. Fine courtyard and walled garden.
Location: 7m SE of Brecon 1 1/2m from Bwlch A40.
Opening Times: 1 May - 31 Aug: Mon -Tue 10am - 5pm.

TRETOWER COURT AND CASTLE

Tel: 01874 730279

Brecon Beacons National Park, Crickhowell, Powys
Owner: CADW: Welsh Historic Monuments **Contact:** The Administrator
Tretower Court is a glorious late 15th century house made up of a group of medieval buildings. It is memorable for its magnificent roof and timbers as well as the ornamental garden that was created as recently as 1991.
Location: Signposted to Tretower Village, off A479, 3m NW of Crickhowell.
Opening Times: See CADW standard opening times pg. 291.*
Admission: Adult £2.20, Reduced rates £1.70, Family £6.00.

TREWERN HALL

Tel: 01938 570243

Trewern, Welshpool, Powys SY21 8DT
Owner: Murray Chapman **Contact:** Mrs Margaret Chapman
Trewern Hall is a Grade II* listed building standing in the Severn Valley. It has been described as 'one of the most handsome timber-framed houses surviving in the area'. The porch contains a beam inscribed RF1610, though it seems likely that parts of the house are earlier. The property has been in the ownership of the Chapman family since 1918.
Location: Off A458 Welshpool - Shrewsbury Road, 4m from Welshpool.
Opening Times: Last week in April. During May: Mon - Fri, 2 - 5pm.
Admission: Adult £2.00, Child £1.00, Groups by arrangement.

CADW - Welsh Historic Monuments
Standard Opening Times and Admission Prices

REDUCED: Children under 16 (under 5 free of charge), over 60s and students with student cards. For groups of 15 or more, a 10% discount will apply for the adult and reduced categories.

FAMILY: Up to 2 adults and 3 children.

STANDARD OPENING HOURS:

Summer: (late Mar - late Oct): Mon - Sun, 9.30am - 6.30pm

Winter: (late Oct - late Mar): Mon - Sat, 9.30am - 4pm,
     *Sun, 11am - 4pm
     or Sun 2 - 4pm

Wheelchair users and the visually handicapped, together with their assisting companion, will be admitted free of charge to all monuments.

Effective from 1 April 1996. Details may be subject to change.
Tel: (01222) 500242 or 500261 for further information.

CADW PROPERTIES

The opening times and admission prices included for CADW properties are those likely to apply, but at the time of going to press (Feb. 1996) they had not been fully confirmed by the Welsh Office.
CADW is a division of the Welsh Office and is therefore part of the Civil Service, unlike English Heritage which has a separate status. It manages properties in the care of the Secretary of State for Wales. Some of these are owned outright, some are held on lease and others remain the property of private owners under the guardianship of CADW.

SPECIAL EVENTS

❖	**ERDDIG** Illyria Theatre Company performing 'Much Ado About Nothing'	**7 MARCH**
❖	**LLANERCHAERON** Illyria Theatre Company performing 'Much Ado About Nothing'	**8 JUNE**
❖	**PENRHYN CASTLE** Illyria Theatre Company performing 'Macbeth'	**15 JUNE**
❖	**ERDDIG** Open Air Orchestral Concerts by Performing Arts Symphony Orchestra	**16 JUNE**
❖	**COLBY WOODLAND GARDEN** Illyria Theatre Company performing 'Much Ado About Nothing'	**27 JUNE**
❖	**ERDDIG** Illyria Theatre Company performing 'Much Ado About Nothing'	**27 JUNE**
❖	**POWIS CASTLE** Illyria Theatre Company performing 'Macbeth'	**28 JUNE**
❖	**POWIS CASTLE** Illyria Theatre Company performing 'Much Ado About Nothing'	**29 JUNE**
❖	**DINEFWR** Illyria Theatre Company performing 'Much Ado About Nothing'	**4 JULY**
❖	**CHIRK CASTLE** Open Air Concert by Performing Arts Symphony Orchestra	**21 JULY**
❖	**ERDDIG** Charity Opera Gala Evening	**3 AUGUST**
❖	**PLAS NEWYDD** Illyria Theatre Company performing 'Much Ado About Nothing'	**13 AUGUST**

ARDRESS HOUSE

Tel: 01762 851236

64 Ardress Road, Portadown, Co Armagh BT62 1SQ

Owner: The National Trust   **Contact:** The Administrator

Originally a 17th century farmhouse, the main front and garden façades were added in the 18th century by the owner-architect George Ensor. The house contains some particularly fine neo-Classical plasterwork as well as good furniture and pictures. There is a display of farm implements and livestock in the farmyard, an attractive garden and woodland walks.

Location: 7m from Portadown on Moy road B28, 5m from Moy, 3m from Loughgall intersection 13 on M1, 9m from Armagh.

Opening Times: House & Farmyard: Apr: weekends & Easter (5 - 9 Apr) 2 - 6pm. May & Sept: Sat, Sun & BH 2 - 6pm. Jun - end Aug: Daily except Tue 2 - 6pm. Farmyard also open weekdays (except Tue) May & Sept: 12 noon - 4pm.

Admission: Adult £2.10, Child £1.05, Family £5.25, Party £1.70. Parties outside opening times £3 per person.

THE ARGORY

Tel: 01868 784753 **Fax:** 01868 789598

Moy, Dungannon, Co Tyrone BT71 6NA

Owner: The National Trust   **Contact:** The Administrator

Set in over 130ha of woodland overlooking the Blackwater River, the house dates from 1820 and remains substantially unchanged since the turn of the century. Fascinating furniture and contents, including an 1824 Bishop's barrel organ. Imposing stableyard with a coach house and carriages, harness room, laundry and acetylene gas plant. Also an interesting sundial garden and extensive walks.

Location: 4m from Moy, 3m from M1, Exit 13 or 14.

Opening Times: Easter (5 - 9 Apr) Daily. May & Sept: Sun & BH. Jun - end Aug: Daily except Tue, all 2 - 6pm. Open 1 - 6pm on all BH. Last tour 5.15pm.

Admission: Adult £2.30, Child £1.15, Family £5.75, Party £1.70. Parties outside opening times £3 per person. Car park £1. Coaches must book.

CASTLE COOLE

Tel: 01365 322690 **Fax:** 01365 325665

Enniskillen, Co Fermanagh BT74 6JX

Owner: The National Trust   **Contact:** The Administrator

This very fine neo-classical late 18th century house with colonnaded wings was designed by James Wyatt. It contains original decoration and furniture dating from before 1830, and is set in a landscaped parkland with mature oak woodland. State Bedroom prepared for George IV in 1821. Exterior attractions include servants' tunnel, stables and nature display room in Grand Yard.

Location: 1/2m SE of Enniskillen on A4, Belfast - Enniskillen road.

Opening Times: Easter (5 - 9 Apr): Daily. Apr & Sept: Sat, Sun & BH only. May - end Aug: Daily (except Thurs), 1 - 6pm. Last tour 5.15pm. Grounds open during daylight hours.

Admission: Adult £2.60, Child £1.30. Parties £2.25pp. Family £6.40. Party after hours £3.00pp. Estate parking £1.50.

CASTLE WARD

Tel: 01396 881204 **Fax:** 01396 881729

Strangford, Downpatrick, Co Down BT30 7LS

Owner: The National Trust   **Contact:** The Administrator

Castle Ward is set in a 285ha country estate on the shores of Strangford Lough. This unique 18th century mansion has opposing façades in different styles. The west front is Classical and the east front Gothick. In the stableyard there is a Victorian laundry and theatre for visiting companies. Also formal and landscape gardens with specimen shrubs and trees, fortified towers, a sawmill and working cornmill. Strangford Lough Wildlife Centre, located on the water's edge, has audio visual shows (call to check opening times) . Caravan park, holding cottages and a basecamp for young people.

Location: 1m W of Strangford on A25 Downpatrick to Strangford.

Opening Times: Estate: dawn to dusk all year. House: Easter (5 - 14 April), Apr: weekends, May, Jun, Jul Aug: Daily except Thur all 1- 6pm.. Sept & Oct: weekends only 1 - 6pm.

Admission: Adult £2.60, Child £1.30. Family £6.50. Party £2.00 (after hrs £3). Estate parking £3.50.

FLORENCE COURT

Tel: 01365 348249 **Fax:** 01365 348873

Enniskillen, Co Fermanagh BT92 1DB

Owner: The National Trust   **Contact:** The Administrator

One of the most important houses in Ulster, built in the mid 18th century by John Cole, father of 1st Earl of Enniskillen. Contents include fine rococo plasterwork and good examples of 18th century furniture. There are pleasure grounds with an ice house and water-powered sawmill, plus walled garden and fine views over surrounding mountains.

Location: 8m SW of Enniskillen via A4 Sligo road and A32 Swanlinbar road.

Opening Times: Easter (5 - 9 April) Daily. Apr & Sept: Sat, Sun, BH only. May - end Aug: Daily except Tue, all 1 - 6pm. Last adm 5.15pm. Grounds: All year 10am - 7pm, Oct - Mar: 10am - 4pm. Closed Dec 25.

Admission: House: £2.60, Child £1.30, Family £6.50, Parties £2.25pp. Parties outside opening hours £3pp. Estate: £1.50.

GRAY'S PRINTING PRESS

Tel: 01504 884094

49 Main Street, Strabane, Co Tyrone BT82 8AU

Owner: The National Trust   **Contact:** The Administrator

An 18th century printing press, shop and stationers. It may be here that John Dunlap, the printer of the American Declaration of Independence, and James Wilson, grandfather of President Woodrow Wilson, learned their trade. There is a collection of 19th century hand printing machines, NT information in the stationer's shop and an audio visual display.

Location: Strabane centre.

Opening Times: Apr - end Sept: Daily, except Thur, Sun & BH, 2 - 5.30pm. At other times by prior arrangement.

Admission: Adult £1.50, Child 75p, Family £3.75, Party £1pp.

HEZLETT HOUSE

Tel: 01265 848567

107 Sea Road, Castlerock, Coleraine, Co Londonderry BT51 4TW

Owner: The National Trust   **Contact:** The Administrator

A 17th century thatched house, with an interesting cruck truss roof construction. Furnished in late Victorian style. Small museum of farm implements.

Location: 5m W of Coleraine on Coleraine - Downhill coast road A2.

Opening Times: Easter (5 - 9 Apr): Daily. Apr, May, Jun & Sept; Sat, Sun & BH only. Jul & Aug: Daily, except Tue all 1 - 6pm. Guided tours. Parties must book in advance.

Admission: Adult £1.50, Child 75p, Family £3.75, Party £1pp (outside hours £2pp).

MOUNT STEWART

OPEN

HOUSE
Easter (5 - 14 April):
Daily.

Apr & Oct:
Sat & Sun.

May - end Sept:
Daily except Tue,

1 - 6pm.
Last tour 5pm.

GARDEN
Mar: Sun only 2 - 5pm.

Apr - end Sept:
Daily 10.30am - 6pm.

Oct: Sat, Sun only,
10.30am - 6pm.

Tel: 01247 788387
or 01247 788487
Fax: 01247 788569

NEWTOWNARDS, CO. DOWN BT22 2AD

Owner: The National Trust   *Contact:* The Administrator

Fascinating 18th century house with 19th century additions, where Lord Castlereagh grew up. Gardens largely created by Edith, wife of 7th Marquess of Londonderry, with an unrivalled collection of plants, colourful parterres and magnificent vistas. The Temple of the Winds, James 'Athenian' Stuart's banqueting hall of 1785 overlooks Strangford Lough.

Location: 15m SE of Belfast on A20, 5m SE of Newtownards.

Admission: House, Garden & Temple: Adult £3.00, Child £1.50. Family £7.50. Party £2.60pp (after hours £4.30pp).

ROWALLANE GARDEN

Tel: 01238 510131 **Fax:** 01238 511242

Saintfield, Ballynahinch, Co Down BT24 7LH

Owner: The National Trust   **Contact:** The Administrator

21ha garden, with daffodils and rhododendrons in spring, summer-flowering trees and shrubs and herbaceous plants, fuchsias and shrub roses in the Wall Garden. The garden also includes a national collection of penstemons, and the rock garden with primulas, meconopsis, heathers and dwarf shrubs is interesting throughout the year. The are several areas of natural wild flowers to attract butterflies.

Location: 11m SE of Belfast, 1m S of Saintfield, W of the A7 Downpatrick road.

Opening Times: 1 Apr - end Oct: Daily (weekdays 10.30am - 6pm, Weekends 2 - 6pm). Nov - end Mar 97: Daily except Sat & Sun, 10.30am - 5pm. Closed 25, 26 Dec and 1 Jan.

Admission: Easter - Oct: Adult £2.50, Child £1.25, Family £6.25, Party £1.60 (after hours £2.80pp). Nov - end Mar 97: Adult £1.40 Child 70p, Party 80p.

SEAFORDE GARDENS

OPEN

Easter - end Sept
Mon - Sat
10am - 5pm.
Sun 2 - 6pm

Oct - Mar
Mon - Fri
10am - 5pm

Tel: 01396 811225
Fax: 01396 811370

SEAFORDE, CO DOWN BT30 8PG

Owner: *Patrick Forde*   ***Contact:*** *Patrick Forde*

Beautiful gardens and maze containing many rare plants, some tender, huge rhododendrons and the National Collection of eucryphias. Also a tropical butterfly house and nursery garden. Teas.

Location: 20m S of Belfast on the main road to Newcastle.
Admission: Adult £2.00, Child £1.20.

SPRINGHILL

Tel: 01648 748210

20 Springhill Road, Moneymore, Magherafelt, Co Londonderry BT45 7NQ
Owner: The National Trust   **Contact:** The Administrator
17th century 'Planter' house with 18th and 19th century additions. Springhill was the home of ten generations of a family which arrived from Ayrshire in the 17th century and the house contains family furniture, a refurbished nursery, paintings, ornaments, curios and 18th century hand-blocked wallpaper. Outbuildings house an extensive costume collection and there are walled gardens and woodland walks.
Location: 1m from Moneymore on B18.
Opening Times: Easter (5 - 9 Apr): Daily. Apr, May & Sept: Sat, Sun & BH only, all 2 - 6pm. Jun - Aug: Daily except Thur 2 - 6pm.
Admission: Adult £2.30, Child £1.15, Family £5.75, Party £1.70 (outside hours £3).

TEMPLETOWN MAUSOLEUM

Tel: 01238 510721

Templepatrick, Ballyclare, Co Antrim
Owner: The National Trust   **Contact:** The Administrator
Built in 1783 by Robert Adam in memory of the Hon Arthur Upton.
Location: In Castle Upton graveyard at Templepatrick on Belfast - Antrim road A6.
Opening Times: All year during daylight hours.

WELLBROOK BEETLING MILL

Tel: 01648 751735

20 Wellbrook Road, Corkhill, Cookstown, Co Tyrone BT80 9RY
Owner: The National Trust   **Contact:** The Administrator
A hammer mill powered by water for beetling, the final process in linen manufacture. Original machinery is in working order. The mill is situated in an attractive glen, with wooded walks along the Ballinderry River and by the mill race.
Location: 4m W of Cookstown, 1/2 m off Cookstown - Omagh road, from Cookstown turn right at Kildress Parish Church or follow Orritor Road A53 to avoid town centre.
Opening Times: Easter (5 - 9 April): Daily 2 - 6pm. Apr, May, Jun & Sept: Sat, Sun & BH only 2 - 6pm. July & Aug: Daily except Tue 2 - 6pm.
Admission: Adults £1.50, Child 75p, Family £3.75, Party £1pp (outside open hours £2pp).

Hudson's Choice

Accommodation in Privately Owned Historic Houses

Included are houses where accommodation is provided as an ancillary to the house's function as a family home.

Staying at one of these houses provides visitors with the opportunity to be private guests in comfortable, historic country houses. You will be made to feel at home as personal guests of your host and hostess.

Bedroom and bathroom arrangements are as you would find when staying in any private country residence. Often en-suite bathrooms are available; otherwise your bathroom will be close by, probably exclusive to you.

Because these houses are not hotels, visitors should observe usual courtesies as when staying with friends. The visits must be arranged in advance and hosts will want to know the time of your arrival which, because they may be out and about during the day, should not normally be much before 5pm. Meals, if available, will be served at normal times rather than on demand and on occasion it may not be possible for the hosts to provide dinner but visitors would be informed beforehand and recommended to a local restaurant if they so wish.

Locations are only approximate.

ENGLAND				
BEER FARM	1	LODGE DOWN	20	DRUIMNEIL	37
BERYL	2	MANTLE HILL	21	DUPPLIN CASTLE	38
BIRKSEY BROW	3	THE MOUNT HOUSE	22	FINNICH MALISE	39
BROMPTON HOUSE	4	THE OLD HOUSE	23	FOGORIG HOUSE	40
BROXWOOD COURT	5	THE OLD RECTORY	24	FORBES LODGE	41
CALLALY MAINS	6	THE OLD VICARAGE	25	FORTH LODGE	42
COLLEGE FARMHOUSE	7	SANDRIDGE PARK	26	GEDDES HOUSE	43
CONGHURST FARM	8	SPURSHOLT HOUSE	27	HOUSE OF URRARD	44
CRANBURY PARK	9	ST MARY HALL	28	KINKELL	45
CREED HOUSE	10	THORNBROUGH HIGH HOUSE	29	KNOCKHILL	46
CRUGSILLICK MANOR	11	TROTTON OLD RECTORY	30	MAINHILL	47
DEARNFORD HALL	12	NORTHBOURNE ROAD	56	NO 22 MURRAYFIELD GARDENS	48
DRAKESTONE HOUSE	13			NEWMILLS HOUSE	49
GLASCOED HALL	14	SCOTLAND		27A SCOTLAND STREET	50
GREENBANKS	15			SKIRLING HOUSE	51
HALSTOCK MILL	16	ABERCORN HOUSE	31	STROQUHAN	52
HARTLIP PLACE	17	ASHINTULLY CASTLE	32	TALISKER HOUSE	53
HOBSHORTS HOUSE	18	BALAVIL	33		
LAWRENCE HOUSE	19	BALGERSHO	34	WALES	
		BARDROCHAT	35	LLANWENARTH HOUSE	54
		CLEISH CASTLE	36	THE OLD RECTORY	55

Hudson's Choice

BEER FARM   1

PRICES
B & B: £24pp
Dinner: £15pp

OPEN
All year except
Christmas and
New Year.

HOST
Mrs Susan Morlock

Tel: 01458 250285

BERE ALLER, LANGPORT, SOMERSET TA10 0QX

Beer Farm is a predominantly Georgian stone farmhouse, fully central heated and comfortably furnished. It is surrounded by its interesting plantsman's garden with ancient woods on the hill above, and the unique Somerset levels with prospects to the Quantock, Blackdown and Polden hills below. Midway between the A303 and M5 it is a good staging post for travellers to and from the West Country. Local places to visit include Montacute House, Barrington Court, Wells Cathedral and many gardens of interest.

Location: From Langport take A372 to Bridgwater, through Aller, turn right signposted to Beer. Pass Bere Farm on right and take first left at the stone barn.

BERYL   2

PRICES
B & B: £32.50 - £37.50pp
Single: £45pp
Dinner: £18pp

OPEN
All year except
24 - 27 Dec

HOST
Eddie & Holly Nowell

Tel: 01749 678738
Fax: 01749 670508

WELLS, SOMERSET BA5 3JP

A small mansion built in Gothic revival style in its original parkland of 13 acres. The reception rooms and bedrooms are comfortably furnished with antiques and have ensuite facilities and direct dial telephone. Holly enjoys cooking using much of the produce from the 3/4 acre walled vegetable garden. Eddie, a senior member of the B.A.D.A. still keeps shop in Wells. They enjoy dining with their guests and serving local and well selected wines and drinks.

Location: 1m NE of Wells Cathedral.

BIRKSEY BROW   3

PRICES
B & B: £25 - £30pp
Dinner: £15pp
by prior booking

OPEN
All year

HOST
Robin & Dany Brown

Tel: 01539 443380

WINDERMERE, CROOK, CUMBRIA LA8 8LQ

Birksey Brow is a traditional stone built country house standing in its own grounds, surrounded by fields. Bedrooms are elegant and spacious and all rooms have magnificent views of the distant mountains. Situated at the entrance to the Lake District National Park, it is an ideal base from which to explore this fascinating and beautiful part of England. For the golfer, Windermere Golf Course is only one mile away. Robin is Cumbrian born and bred and would be delighted to advise you on the Lake District.

Location: From A591 take the B5284, through Crook village, Sun Inn on right, up the hill, past village hall and church on left. 1/2m on right from the church.

BROMPTON HOUSE   4

PRICES
B & B: £32 - £39pp
Dinner not available.

OPEN
All year except
Christmas and
New Year

HOST
David & Sue Selby

Tel: 01225 420972
Fax: 01225 420505

ST JOHNS ROAD, BATH BA2 6PT

Charming Georgian Rectory (1777) set in beautiful secluded mature gardens and conveniently situated only minutes level walk to city centre. Converted with exquisite care to provide tastefully furnished ensuite rooms equipped with colour TV, tea/coffee, direct dial telephone and hairdryers. A very friendly welcome into their home is assured from the Selby family making an atmosphere that is warm, relaxing and informal. All bedroom are non-smoking/ lounge only. Car park within grounds.

Location: Just off city centre. M4 exit 18. London 112 miles. Cotswolds 20 miles. Salisbury 50 miles.

BROXWOOD COURT   5

PRICES
B & B: £30 - £35pp
Dinner: £18pp

OPEN
All year
except Christmas

HOST
Mike & Anne Allen

Tel: 01544 340245
Fax: 01544 340573

BROXWOOD, LEOMINSTER, HEREFORDSHIRE HR6 9JJ

Broxwood Court occupies a commanding position with superb views of the Black Mountains and surrounding countryside. This 1200 acre estate has belonged to the family for over 300 years, the house having been rebuilt in 1954, whilst retaining the original courtyard and clock tower. The gardens with the lake, magnificent trees, sweeping lawns and peacocks, offer a unique atmosphere of peace and tranquillity. Ideally situated for Hay-on-Wye, Croft Castle, Berrington Hall and Hergest Croft Gardens.

Location: 10m W of Leominster, 3m NW off Weobley. Hereford 15m.

CALLALY MAINS   6

PRICES
B & B: £37.50pp
Dinner: £22.50pp

OPEN
All year
except Christmas
and New Year

HOST
Anne Fisher

Tel: 01665 574665

WHITTINGHAM, NORTHUMBERLAND NE66 4SZ

Callaly Mains is the former home farm and estate office of nearby Callaly Castle. Situated in the foothills of the Cheviots and the beautiful Vale of Whittingham. The house is lived in by someone whose family have been in the county for over 700 years and who is a passionate Northumbrian who can tell you what to see and do. Guests are treated as friends and every comfort is provided.

Location: Off A697 at Bridge of Aln Pub. In Whittingham take second left, fork left then take first left - the house is on the right. 2m from Whittingham which is signposted off A1. From west follow signs from Thropton near Rothbury.

Hudson's Choice

COLLEGE FARMHOUSE 7

PRICES
B & B: £25pp
Dinner: £15pp
by arrangement

OPEN
All year
except Christmas

HOST
Stephen & Sara Allday

Tel: 01295 811473
Fax: 01295 812505

KINGS SUTTON, BANBURY, OXON OX17 3PS

College Farmhouse is a fine period house, with lovely views, set in its own secluded grounds, which include a lake, tennis court and an organic vegetable garden. Ideally suited for visits to Oxford, Warwick, Stratford-upon-Avon and The Cotswolds. London Heathrow Airport 1¼ hrs. Excellent home produced food. Special diets catered for. Stephen and Sara have considerable local knowledge. They enjoy gardening, bridge and racing. You can be sure of a very comfortable and peaceful stay.

Location: 1m E of B4100, 15m N of Oxford, 10 mins from M40 motorway.

CONGHURST FARM 8

PRICES
B & B: £22.50pp
Dinner: £13pp

OPEN
Mar - Nov

HOST
Mrs Rosemary Piper

Tel: 01580 753331
Fax: 01580 754579

HAWKHURST, KENT TN18 4RW

Conghurst is set in peaceful, unspoilt countryside. It has been home to generations of Pipers and records in the local church date back to 1100. The oldest part of the house dates from 1400. The house is spacious, comfortable and delightfully furnished. Dinners, served in the elegant dining room, use local produce whenever possible. It is centrally situated from which to visit the many houses and gardens Kent and Sussex have to offer.

Location: On Kent - Sussex border, 15m S of Tunbridge Wells. 6m S of Cranbrook. Rye 12m.

CRANBURY PARK 9

PRICES
B & B: £70 /single
£140/couple
Dinner: £30pp

OPEN
1 April - 30 September

HOST
Penelope
Chamberlayne-
Macdonald

Tel: 01703 252617
Fax: 01703 262692

WINCHESTER, HAMPSHIRE SO21 2HL

Cranbury was built in 1780 by George Dance for his brother and sister-in-law Sir Nathaniel and Lady Dance-Holland. It was left to the Chamberlayne family in the early part of the 19th century when the pleasure grounds were laid out, and most of the paintings and furniture were acquired.

Location: 5m S of Winchester, off exit 12 on M3. Entrance lodge in Hocombe Road Chandlers Ford, 1m W of exit 12.

CREED HOUSE 10

PRICES
B & B: £25 - £30pp
Large selection
of local restaurants

OPEN
All year except
Christmas and
New Year

HOST
Mr & Mrs W Croggon

Tel: 01872 530372

CREED, GRAMPOUND, TRURO, CORNWALL TR2 4SL

A spacious Georgian Rectory built around 1730, set deep in beautiful countryside and standing amidst five acres of garden occasionally open to the public. Below the garden is the ancient church of St Crida and the River Fal flowing through tranquil meadows. The spectacular Cornish coast is less than five miles away with several famous gardens nearby. All the attractions of the Duchy are within easy reach. William and Lally offer a warm welcome and their local knowledge.

Location: Take A390 to Grampound, turn left beyond clock tower into Creed Lane. After 1m turn left at grass triangle, opposite church, house is on left.

CRUGSILLICK MANOR 11

PRICES
B & B: £35 - £44pp
Dinner: £20pp

OPEN
All year

HOST
Oliver & Rosemary
Barstow

Tel: 01872 501214
Fax: 01872 501214

RUAN HIGH LANES, ST MAWES, TRURO, CORNWALL TR2 5LJ

One of the oldest houses in Cornwall, this charming Grade II* listed Queen Anne Manor House was extended c.1710 from a pre-Elizabethan farmhouse. Now an elegant and comfortable home, it is beautifully furnished with family antiques. Only a short walk to the sea and coastal path it is also perfectly placed to explore Cornwall's historic houses and famous gardens. Enjoy delicious meals of local produce, seafood and homegrown vegetables in the friendly and peaceful atmosphere.

Location: In the Roseland Peninsular midway between St Mawes and Tregony.

DEARNFORD HALL 12

PRICES
B & B: £25pp
(£5 single
supplement)
Dinner: not available

OPEN
All year
excluding Christmas

HOST
Charles & Jane
Bebbington

Tel: 01948 662319
Fax: 01948 662319

WHITCHURCH, SHROPSHIRE SY13 3JJ

Dearnford Hall is an elegant country house constructed in 1690 in the style of William & Mary. It has been restored by its present owners to a high standard. Accommodation consists of two very spacious double bedrooms each with ensuite facilities, overlooking mature gardens and lawns. Fly fishing is available at their own 15 acre trout fishery. Golf courses and racing are within easy reach. Convenient for Hawkstone Park, Hodnet Hall, Powis and Chirk Castles, Hodnet Hall Gardens and Ironbridge Gorge Museum.

Location: 1m S of Whitchurch, 30mins from Chester and Shrewsbury. Manchester and Birmingham airports 1 hour.

DRAKESTONE HOUSE · 13

PRICES
B & B: £25.00pp
Dinner: £15.00pp

OPEN
April - October.

HOST
Hugh & Crystal
St. John Mildmay

Tel: 01453 542140

DRAKESTONE HOUSE, DURSLEY, GLOUCESTERSHIRE GL11 6AS

A fine listed Edwardian country house having links with the Arts and Craft Movement. Hugh's grandparents laid out the formal gardens with terraces and yew hedges before the First World War, and Hugh and Crystal since taking over the family home have been engaged in a steady process of restoration. Guests are offered a warm welcome and a relaxing atmosphere at Drakestone. It is an ideal centre for touring the Cotswolds and within easy reach of Bath and Bristol.

Location: Midway between Dursley and Wotton-under-Edge on B4060.

GLASCOED HALL · 14

PRICES
B & B: £32.00pp
Dinner: £17.00pp

OPEN
All Year except
Christmas and
New Year.

HOST
Ben & Louise
Howard- Baker.

Tel: 01691 791334

LLANSILIN, NR. OSWESTRY, SHROPSHIRE SY10 9BP

A Grade II listed Elizabethan Hall of historical interest, set in the beautiful foothills of the Welsh borders, yet within easy reach of Chester, Shrewsbury and numerous historic houses and castles. Ben and Louise enjoy entertaining guests in their home which features magnificent oak beams and staircase, open log fires and antique furniture. There is a heated outdoor swimming pool and a hard tennis court within the gardens.

Location: 5m SW of Oswestry, Shrewsbury 25 miles.

GREENBANKS · 15

PRICES
B & B: £26 - £29pp
Dinner: £16pp

OPEN
All year

HOST
Christopher & Tanda
Wilson-Clarke

Tel: 01691 623420
Fax: 01691 623420

COPTIVINEY, ELLESMERE, SHROPSHIRE SY12 0ND

Greenbanks is an attractive and comfortable Victorian house with a relaxed atmosphere, set within the tranquillity of its own 20 acres. The garden has interest throughout the year. From the doorstep are wonderful woodland walks. The market town of Ellesmere is at the heart of the Shropshire Lake District, which has abundant wildlife. Within easy reach are the cities of Shrewsbury and Chester as well as the great houses and gardens of Biddulph, Bodnant, Chirk, Erddig and Powis.

Location: Situated between Chester and Shrewsbury. Oswestry 10 miles.

HALSTOCK MILL · 16

PRICES
B & B: £22 - £25pp
Dinner: £14pp

OPEN
All year
except Christmas

HOST
Mrs Jane Spender

Tel: 01935 891278

HALSTOCK, YEOVIL, DORSET BA22 9SJ

17th century Halstock Mill, converted into a spacious country house of great charm and character, is surrounded by 400 acres of pastureland ensuring a peaceful, relaxing stay. Accommodation comprises 4 spacious ensuite bedrooms with CTV and tea & coffee making facilities. Jane Spender offers a superb 4 course dinner prepared with home/local produce. Ideal base for visiting gardens and houses in Devon, Somerset and Dorset.

Location: 4m off the A37 between Yeovil and Dorchester.

HARTLIP PLACE · 17

PRICES
B & B: £35pp
Dinner: £20pp
(to include wine)

OPEN
All year
except Christmas

HOST
Lt Col & Mrs John
Yerburgh

Tel: 01795 842583

HARTLIP, SITTINGBOURNE, KENT ME9 7TR

Fine Regency house, listed Grade II, set on the edge of the village facing south into 4½ acres of garden and woodland including a secret rose garden and large pond. The house has finely proportioned rooms furnished with antiques. The drawing room and dining room are for the exclusive use of guests. Food, where possible, is locally produced and of a very high standard. A pet Vietnamese pig and ornamental bantams wander around the grounds. Gillian Yerburgh is Chairman of the Kent Gardens Trust.

Location: 5 mins from M2 junct. 5, 45 mins from Gatwick, Dover & Folkestone. 1 hour from Heathrow and London. M20 is 15 mins away. Canterbury, Rochester and Leeds Castle and many other attractions within easy access.

HOBSHORTS HOUSE · 18

PRICES
B & B: £30pp
Dinner: £17.50pp

OPEN
All year

HOST
Mrs Brenda Weller

Tel: 01403 711821
Fax: 01403 711821

ROOKCROSS LANE, WEST GRINSTEAD, WEST SUSSEX RH13 8LL

14th century hall house, listed Grade II, with later additions set in the heart of the Sussex Weald in an idyllic position overlooking a pond and with extensive views to the South Downs. Convenient for the south coast, Lancing College, Ardingly and Hurstpierpoint Schools, it is also ideal for visiting Chichester, Goodwood, Petworth and Parham House. ½ hour from Gatwick and Hickstead All England Course. Well furnished house; cooking often includes game and home grown vegetables.

Location: 1¼m S of Buck Barn crossroads on A24 after crossing A272 and having passed Partridge Green turning, turn left into Rookcross Lane, continue for 1 mile ignoring Bassells Lane on left.

Hudson's Choice

LAWRENCE HOUSE 19

PRICES
B & B: £35pp
(single supplement)
Dinner: £18.50pp

OPEN
All year except
Christmas & New Year

HOST
John & Harriet
Highley

Tel: 01765 600947
Fax: 01765 601389
(please mention
Highley on fax)

STUDLEY ROGER, RIPON, NORTH YORKSHIRE HG4 3AY

Lawrence House is a Georgian Grade II listed house on the edge of the village of Studley Roger, which is 2 miles from the cathedral town of Ripon. 2 acres of fine garden adjoin Studley Royal deer park and Fountains Abbey. The Dales, Harrogate and York are all within easy driving distance. Lawrence House is beautifully furnished with many antiques and fine pictures, and in the winter is filled with roaring log fires. The bedrooms, with views over open countryside are spacious and beautifully furnished.

Location: Off A1 to Ripon, in Ripon take B6265 Pateley Bridge road. 2m out of Ripon take left turn into village of Studley Roger. Lawrence house is the last house on the right hand side of village.

LODGE DOWN 20

PRICES
B & B: £25pp single
£22pp double
Dinner: n/a

OPEN
All year

HOST
John & Sally Cook

Tel: 01672 540304
Fax: 01672 540304

LAMBOURN, HUNGERFORD, BERKSHIRE RG17 7BJ

Country house with luxury accommodation, ensuite bathrooms and spacious visitors lounge, set in lovely grounds with views over the Lambourn Gallops. Swimming pool (in season) excellent dining in surrounding villages, easy access to M4 motorway, junction 14/15 makes our location a central base for Heathrow (60m), Bath (43m), Oxford (26m) and The Cotswolds. Tourist Board 2 crowns, AA 4Q selected.

Location: Exit M4 junction 14, take Wantage road, 300 metres. Take 1st left to Baydon. Entrance to Lodge Down on right 1m before Baydon. House is 300 metres down the drive.

MANTLE HILL 21

PRICES
B & B: £24pp
Dinner: by
arrangement

OPEN
All year

HOST
Peter & Charlotte Loyd

Tel: 01434 220428
Fax: 01434 220113

HESLEYSIDE, BELLINGHAM, HEXHAM, NORTHUMBERLAND NE48 2LB

Mantle Hill is the 18th century Dower House to historic Hesleyside Hall. Set in the Northumberland National Park, it commands breathtaking views across the North Tyne Valley. The succulent lamb, fruit and vegetables are home grown and there is an extensive range of fine wines. Wonderful private walking is available to guests as is trout and salmon fishing in season. It is an ideal base from which to explore Hadrian's Wall, Kielder Water and the unspoiled Northumbrian countryside.

Location: 17m NW of Hexham. 50 mins to Newcastle.

THE MOUNT HOUSE 22

PRICES
B & B: £20 - £25pp
Dinner: unavailable

OPEN
All year
except Christmas

HQST
Julian & Diana Paul

Tel: 01959 563617
Fax: 01959 561296

BRASTED, WESTERHAM, KENT TN16 1JB

The Mount House, which is a family home, is a substantial Grade II listed village house dating from the early 18th century. Brasted, which is well known for its many antique shops is near Chartwell, the former home of Sir Winston Churchill. Other stately homes within easy reach include Knole, Hever Castle and Penshurst. There is a regular (3 an hour) fast train service to London throughout the day from Sevenoaks.

Location: Situated in the centre of Brasted village, 2m E of Westerham, 4m W of Sevenoaks.

THE OLD HOUSE 23

PRICES
B & B: £30pp
single £37pp
Dinner: £18 - £22pp

OPEN
All year except
Christmas & New Year

HOST
Bridget & Colin
Thompson

Tel: 01985 840344

SUTTON VENY, WARMINSTER, WILTSHIRE BA12 7AQ

This thatched 300 year old stone house has been thoroughly modernised but retains its charm. It is set in peaceful grounds of four acres and is within easy access of numerous National Trust properties as well as Bath and Salisbury. Colin works for a fine art auctioneer and both he and Bridget have a wide variety of interests and enjoy entertaining. There are log fires in winter and home grown vegetables in season.

Location: A36 Salisbury to Warminster. At roundabout to S of Warminster follow signs to Sutton Veny, at crossroads at Woolpack pub turn left. Duck Street is first turning on left past the church. Drive in first right.

THE OLD RECTORY 24

PRICES
B & B: £38pp
Dinner: £24pp
3 courses, cheese,
coffee & mints and
½ bottle of wine

OPEN
All year except Easter,
Christmas & New Year

HOST
Mrs Diana de Lisle

Tel: 01858 565330
Fax: 01858 565340

MEDBOURNE, MARKET HARBOROUGH, LEICESTERSHIRE LE16 8DZ

The Old Rectory dates from the 17th century with a pure Georgian front, reception and bedrooms added in 1810. The de Lisles bought and restored it completely 22 years ago. The house is secluded within its own walls and 3 acre garden, in the middle of the village and with a Medieval pond. It is decorated in a classic English country manor house style. Diana is a trained French cook and has extensive knowledge of surrounding areas and houses.

Location: Situated in the centre of the village of Medbourne between Market Harborough and Uppingham (7m each). M1 20m, A1 22m, Birmingham 40m.

Hudson's Choice

THE OLD VICARAGE   25

PRICES
B & B: £30 - £32.50pp
Dinner: £19.50pp

OPEN
All year

HOST
Major & Mrs Jeremy
Steele

Tel: 01636 705031
Fax: 01636 708728

LANGFORD, NR. NEWARK, NOTTINGHAMSHIRE NG23 7RT

Built in 1859 this fine Victorian Vicarage stands in 3 acres of secluded grounds in the middle of Civil War country next to one of the oldest and prettiest churches in Nottinghamshire. Belvoir Castle, Belton House and many more beautiful houses and gardens are nearby. Jeremy and Jillie are both well travelled, enjoy entertaining and home grown produce is used for delicious dinners.

Location: Off A1 on to A46 to Lincoln, first roundabout left A1133 to Gainsborough. After 1m drive through Langford, take left hand turning to Holme. The Old Vicarage is 100 yards on right next to church.

SANDRIDGE PARK   26

PRICES
B & B: £40pp
Dinner: £20pp

OPEN
All year
except Christmas

HOST
Annette
Hoogeweegen

Tel: 01225 706897
Fax: 01225 702838

SANDRIDGE MILL, MELKSHAM, WILTSHIRE SN12 7QU

Sandridge Park is a beautiful Victorian mansion with great views and tranquil park and gardens. The rooms are elegantly decorated and scattered with objets d'art. The bedrooms have everything for the guests' requirements; from bathrobes, bottled water and cotton buds to plastic ducks. The dining is en famille in a beautiful candlelit red lacquered dining room.

Location: Bath, Wilton House, Stourhead, Avebury, Stonehenge, Longleat and the Cotswolds are within easy reach.

SPURSHOLT HOUSE   27

PRICES
B & B: £20 - £30pp
Dinner: £12.50pp

OPEN
All year except
Christmas.

HOST
Anthea Hughes

Tel: 01794 512229
Fax: 01794 523142

SALISBURY ROAD, ROMSEY, HAMPSHIRE SO51 6DJ

This magnificent home dates from the 17th century with Victorian extensions for Lord Palmerston. The garden extends to 2 acres with paved terraces, topiary, a parterre, roses and a lily pool. Rooms are furnished with antiques. The bedrooms are spacious and oak panelled with extra-large comfortable beds, antiques, elegant sofas and garden views. The sitting room is available at all times with TV and telephone at hand. Tea/coffee facilities available. The dining room is handsomely furnished in Victorian style. 1 twin, 1 double, 1 family all either ensuite or with private bathrooms. Non smoking..

Location: ³/₄m from Romsey, equidistant from Winchester, Salisbury and Southampton.

ST MARY HALL   28

PRICES
B & B: £25 -£30pp
Dinner: £16 - £20pp

OPEN
2 Jan - 20 Dec

HOST
Mr & Mrs David Morse

Tel: 01787 237202

BELCHAMP WALTER, SUDBURY, SUFFOLK CO10 7BB

Although houses have stood on the site since Domesday Book and before, the present building dates mainly from the late 15th and early 16th Centuries. Catherine and David have made an attractive garden in the 5 acres surrounding the house which contains a tennis court and heated swimming pool. This is a convenient centre for visiting the "Wool towns' of South Suffolk, and also Bury St Edmunds, Cambridge and Ely. Stansted Airport is less than 40 minutes away, and Harwich Ferry Terminal about an hour.

Location: 5m from Sudbury off the minor road through Bulmer and Gestingthorpe leading to Great Yeldham on the A604, 1¹/₂ miles SW from crossroads in Belchamp Walter.

THORNBROUGH HIGH HOUSE   29

PRICES
B & B: £25 - £30pp
Dinner: £15pp

OPEN
Jan - Dec

HOST
Ben & Ailsa Speke

Tel: 01434 633080

CORBRIDGE, NORTHUMBERLAND NE45 5PR

This stone built Grade II listed farmhouse is situated on a small Northumberland estate and has outstanding views over the Tyne Valley. Large open fires and pretty bedrooms ensure a warm welcome with a wonderful relaxed atmosphere. Ailsa is a cordon bleu trained cook who enjoys entertaining. Hadrian's Roman Wall is just two miles away and there are several houses and gardens in the immediate area which are open to the public.

Location: 3m NE of Corbridge. Newcastle 15 miles.

TROTTON OLD RECTORY   30

PRICES
B & B: £35pp
Dinner: £20pp

OPEN
All Year

HOST
Captain & Mrs John
Pilley

Tel: 01730 813612
Fax: 01730 816831

NEAR PETERSFIELD, HAMPSHIRE GU31 5EN

This attractive Georgian former rectory with its curled slate roof and shutters is reminiscent of France and provides a relaxed, comfortable and peaceful atmosphere in summer and winter. The typical English garden with its rose beds designed by Hazel Le Rougetel, framed in a box and yew, has two levels with beautiful and interesting trees and shrubs running down to the lake and the River Rother. There is also a fruit and vegetable garden which supplies the house.

Location: At Trotton, on the A272. 2 miles form Midhurst and 5 miles from Petersfield. The drive is opposite the Church and just west of the bridge.

ABERCORN HOUSE 31

PRICES
B & B: £30pp
Dinner: £16pp
by prior arrangement

OPEN
Mar - Nov

HOST
Elizabeth Seligman

Tel: 0131 331 1065

SOUTH QUEENSFERRY, WEST LOTHIAN EH30 9SL

Abercorn House is situated on the Hopetoun Estate within walking distance of Hopetoun House and local places of interest. The house was originally the manse linked with Abercorn Church nearby. It is an ideal base for visits to Edinburgh and the Forth Valley. Dinner is available if pre-arranged. Situated in a special conservation area.

Location: 3m W of the Forth Road Bridge between South Queensferry and Linlithgow.

ASHINTULLY CASTLE 32

PRICES
B & B: £33pp
Dinner: £19pp

OPEN
Apr - Nov

HOST
John & Carol Steel

Tel: 01250 881237

KIRKMICHAEL, BLAIRGOWRIE, PERTHSHIRE PH10 7LT

The unique and charming 400 year old Ashintully Castle is tucked away in the hills of Highland Perthshire. Today it is the friendly, comfortable home of John and Carol Steel. They offer their guests a relaxing, welcoming atmosphere and delicious home cooking. Royal Deeside and the Central Highlands are both within easy driving distance with plentiful castles, National Trust properties, golf courses and other sporting activities. Ashintully itself has an all weather tennis court and there are lovely walks on the estate.

Location: On the B950, 4m from Kirkmichael and 7m from Bridge of Cally.

BALAVIL 33

PRICES
B & B: £30pp
Dinner: £15pp

OPEN
All year

HOST
Allan & Marjorie
Macpherson-Fletcher

Tel: 01540 661413
Fax: 01540 662021

KINGUSSIE, INVERNESS-SHIRE PH21 1LU

Balavil House is an Adam mansion providing elegant and comfortable accommodation at the centre of a 7,500 acres Highland sporting estate. Grouse and pheasant shooting, deer stalking and salmon fishing are all available on the estate which has been in the same family for over 200 years. The house has recently been totally renovated and now provides ideal family accommodation in the heart of Strathspey where skiing, golfing, sailing, pony trekking and other activities can be arranged.

Location: 2m N of Kingussie on the A9, 43m S of Inverness and 70m N or Perth.

BALGERSHO 34

PRICES
B & B: £30pp
Dinner: £18pp

OPEN
All year

HOST
Peter & Silla Keyser

Tel: 01828 627397
Fax: 01828 627397

COUPAR ANGUS, PERTHSHIRE PH13 9JE

The family home of Peter and Silla Keyser has a charming atmosphere, is exceptionally well equipped with fine reception rooms, believed to date from the 17th century with 19th century additions. Mature woodlands surround lawns and an outdoor heated swimming pool. Situated in the Vale of Strathmore with easy access to Perth and the Grampian Hills to the north. The area is renowned for its sport and excellent golf courses.

Location: 1 hour N of Edinburgh. 15m from Perth and 5m from Blairgowrie.

BARDROCHAT 35

PRICES
Dinner, overnight
accommodation,
breakfast: £140pp

OPEN
April - October

HOST
Mr & Mrs A McEwen

Tel: 01465 881242
Fax: 01465 881330

COLMONELL, AYRSHIRE KA26 0SG

Built by Robert Lorimer in 1893 for the present owner's grandfather, Bardrochat stands high on the south side of the Stinchar Valley. The house sleeps six couples in great comfort with their own bathrooms. The maximum is eighteen. Centrally situated for the great golf courses and gardens and with its own tennis court, croquet and salmon fishing. The Walled Garden provides all the vegetables for the house and memorable food. All drinks are included in the price. The house is open to the public by appointment between Apr and Oct.

Location: Nr. Colmonell, 10m S of Girvan off the A77.

CLEISH CASTLE 36

PRICES
B & B: £30pp
Dinner: by prior
arrangement

OPEN
All year

HOST
Mrs Judith Miller

Tel: 01577 850333
Fax: 01577 850366

CLEISH, KINROSS-SHIRE KY13 7LW

Cleish Castle is a classic L shaped tower house, steeped in Scottish history, located ¹/₂ mile west of the conservation village of Cleish. Squire Meldrum was the first recorded birth in 1492 and in 1568 Mary Queen of Scots visited the castle upon her escape from Loch Leven. The castle is now a beautifully furnished family home, providing an excellent base for visiting the many historic properties in Fife and Perthshire.

Location: Situated 2¹/₂m from J5 of M90, half way between Perth and the Forth Road Bridge

Hudson's Choice

DRUIMNEIL 37

PRICES
B & B: £30pp
Dinner: £19.50pp

OPEN
All year

HOST
Janet Glaisher

Tel: 01631 730228

DRUIMNEIL, PORT APPIN, ARGYLL PA38 4DQ

Druimneil is a very well appointed and spacious mid Victorian house which has been restored to a very high standard for the comfort of six guests. The present owners enjoy entertaining, their visitors particularly, preparing dinner in the elegant dining room. The gardens extend to some ten acres, in which there are many varieties of rhododendrons and other mature shrubs and trees.

Location: Situated midway between Oban and Fort William in the unspoilt village of Port Appin.

DUPPLIN CASTLE 38

PRICES
B & B: £45pp
single supplement
£15pp
Dinner: £28pp

OPEN
All year

HOST
Derek & Angela
Straker

Tel: 01738 623224
Fax: 01738 444140

BY PERTH, PERTHSHIRE PH2 0PY

Rebuilt on the site of the original castle in 1969 in private parkland. The balustraded terrace and rose garden have stunning views over the lovely Earn valley and the reception and bedrooms are elegantly furnished to a high standard. Ideally situated for the River Tay valley with shooting, roe stalking, fishing and golf (St Andrews, Rosemount at Blairgowrie, Auchterader) available by prior arrangement. Theatres in Perth & Pitlochry, Polo and National Hunt Racing at nearby Scone Palace. Derek and Angela make their guests feel at home and enjoy entertaining providing them with delicious food.

Location: From M90 roundabout, A93 towards Perth for 1 mile, sharp turn right B9112 to Fortevoit & Dunning after 2.7m the lodge and ornamental gates are on the right (N) side of the road. From Stirling/Glasgow ornamental gates appr. $3^1/_2$ m S of Perth on the E side of the A9. Perth 10 mins, Edinburgh & Glasgow 1 hr.

FINNICH MALISE 39

PRICES
B & B: £30pp
Dinner: not
normally available

OPEN
All year

HOST
Mr & Mrs Dewar-Durie

Tel: 01360 660257
Fax: 01360 660101

CROFTAMIE, STIRLINGSHIRE G63 0HA

Finnich Malise was built in 1806 in a superb position, surrounded by 200 acres of woods and parkland, but only 30 minutes drive north of Glasgow. Andrew and Marguerite Dewar-Durie have, in the last three years, transformed this beautiful Georgian house into a comfortable family home, with tall windows, panelled rooms and glorious views to Ben Lomond. Finnich Malise provides the perfect base to explore from Glasgow to Loch Lomond, The Trossacks and Stirling.

Location: Between Glasgow and Stirling, next to Drymen.

FOGORIG HOUSE 40

PRICES
B & B: £27pp
Dinner: not
available

OPEN
Feb - Nov

HOST
Mr & Mrs P J S Gray

Tel: 01890 840535

DUNS, BERWICKSHIRE TD11 3RB

A warm welcome awaits you at this lovely Georgian country house situated in the heart of the Scottish Borders, with magnificent views to the Cheviot Hills. The house is surrounded by a large mature garden which includes stables and a games room with table-tennis. Many local tourist attractions are within easy reach including Manderston, Thirlestane Castle and Abbotsford. Edinburgh is an hours drive and Berwick-upon-Tweed and the pretty village of St Abbs close by

Location: 15m W of Berwick-upon-Tweed on B6460 and 3m off A697, main Newcastle to Edinburgh road.

FORBES LODGE 41

PRICES
B & B: £40pp
Dinner: £18pp

OPEN
All Year

HOST
Lady Marioth Hay

Tel: 01620 81212

GIFFORD, HADDINGTON, EAST LOTHIAN EH44 4JE

A handsome 18th century house dating from 1763, just 18 miles from Edinburgh. It is a most stylish home with family portraits going back over 200 years. One of the bedrooms is sumptuous, with a bathroom of grand proportions in keeping with the whole house. It is a memorable experience staying with Lady Marioth whose enjoyment of entertaining, music and gardening complements the atmosphere of this delightful house. Castles are plentiful in the area as are golf courses including Muirfield and Gullane. There are also two very good restaurants located in the village.

Location: On the edge of Gifford. 4 miles from the A1.

FORTH LODGE 42

PRICES
B & B: £30pp
Dinner: Not available
as excellent
restaurants & pubs
within walking
distance.

OPEN
All year except
Christmas & New Year

HOST
Mrs Susannah Jackson

Tel: 01620 842136
Fax: 01620 842058

HILL ROAD, GULLANE, EAST LOTHIAN EH31 2BE

Forth Lodge stands within an acre of garden above Gullane beach with outstanding views over the Firth of Forth and Muirfield Golf Course. Tim and Susannah Jackson and their two sons have lived in this comfortable family house for twelve years. Forth Lodge is ideally situated for all the East Lothian golf courses and historic houses and castles and is in a prime bird watching area. Susie would be happy to advise on day excursions and is extremely knowledge-able about the museums and art galleries in Edinburgh.

Location: Gullane is 20m from Edinburgh on A198 between Aberlady / North Berwick. Take turning to Gullane Bents and 2nd left into Hill Road. Forth Lodge is half way up on right after junction with Hummel Road.

Hudson's Choice

GEDDES HOUSE   43

PRICES
B & B: £28pp
Dinner: £18pp

OPEN
April - October

HOST
Elizabeth
Mackintosh-Walker

Tel: 01667 452241
Fax: 01667 456707

NAIRN IV12 5QX

Geddes is a Georgian mansion house situated two miles from Cawdor and eight miles from Culloden. It is a family home set in a typical highland estate which offers a chance to enjoy walking, fishing and relaxation in the beautiful garden and house. Nearby is Nairn, famed for its beaches and championship golf courses. Elizabeth produces a welcoming atmosphere, her cooking of mainly home produce is delicious.

Location: A96 from Inverness turn right on to B9090, through Cawdor, on to B9101 then first right up drive. 15m from Inverness, 2^1/$_2$ m from Nairn.

HOUSE OF URRARD   44

PRICES
B & B: £30pp
Dinner: £20pp

OPEN
All year

HOST
Andrew & Jane
Mackinnon

Tel: 01796 473215
Fax: 01796 473215

KILLIECRANKIE, PITLOCHRY, PERTHSHIRE PH16 5LN

The House of Urrard was built in 1831 on the site of the old house in 1681 and where the Battle of Killiecrankie was fought in 1689. It has been a family home for over 300 years and has recently been completely modernised and beautifully done up, each bedroom having its own bathroom. Delicious food specialising in game from the estate and local produce help make it an ideal place to stay when visiting Scotland.

Location: Situated 5m N of Pitlochry on the B8079, first driveway on right after village of Killiecrankie between Pitlochry and Blair Atholl.

KINKELL   45

PRICES
B & B: £26 - £30pp
£10 single supplement
Dinner: £22pp

OPEN
All year

HOST
Sandy & Frippy Fyfe

Tel: 01334 472003
Fax: 01334 475248

ST ANDREWS, FIFE KY16 8PN

Kinkell is a family home on a farm close to St Andrews. Sandy and Frippy offer a warm welcome, good food and informal hospitality to their guests. Kinkell is ideally situated for St Andrews and the surrounding area whose attractions include a number of historic houses and buildings. The farm is close to the sea and has spectacular views of the coastline. The informal garden includes a large lawn, suitable for croquet and a hard tennis court.

Location: Kinkell is 2m from St Andrews on the left of the A917 to Crail. The drive is in the first line of trees on the left of the road after leaving St Andrews.

KNOCKHILL   46

PRICES
B & B: £25 - £27.50pp
Dinner: £15 by prior
arrangement

OPEN
Jan - Oct

HOST
Rupert & Yda Morgan

Tel: 01576 300232
Fax: 01576 300232

LOCKERBIE, DUMFRIESSHIRE DG11 1AW

Carved in stone over the front door: 'Too small for envy, for contempt too great' is an apt description of this charming Georgian country house. Knockhill is a comfortable family home and an interesting and elegant house, set in 35 acres of parkland where sheep and horses graze. Ideally placed for exploring Carlyle country, the Solway coast and Border Keeps. Five minutes off the main route from England to Edinburgh, Glasgow and the Highlands.

Location: Situated between Lockerbie and Annan, 5m S of Lockerbie and 2^1/$_2$m SW of Ecclefechan. Junction 19 on M74.

MAINHILL   47

PRICES
B & B: £25 - £30pp
Dinner: not available

OPEN
All year

HOST
Mrs Hugh Lee

Tel: 01835 823788

ST BOSWELLS, ROXBURGHSHIRE TD6 0HG

Mainhill is a late Georgian house facing south in the beautiful Border country. It is within easy reach of the attractive towns of Melrose and Kelso. Abbotsford, Bowhill, Floors Castle, Thirlestane Castle, Mellerstain and Ferniehurst Castle are within a twelve mile radius, also the Abbeys of Melrose, Kelso, Jedburgh and Dryburgh. Mertoun House Garden and Monteviot Garden are well worth a visit on a Sunday, as are a number of local gardens.

Location: ^{1}/$_2$m from the A68, South of St Boswells.

No. 22 MURRAYFIELD GARDENS   48

PRICES
B & B: £30pp
single supplement
Dinner: not available

OPEN
All year

HOST
Tim & Christine
MacDowel

Tel: 0131 337 3569
Fax: 0131 337 3569

EDINBURGH EH12 6DF

An elegant detached Victorian house surrounded by ornamental shrubs and trees. Unrestricted car parking (on or off street). Frequent buses to city centre and airport. Also easily accessible are The Castle, The National Gallery, Charlotte Square, National Gallery of Modern Art, Conference Centre, Murrayfield, Golf, Skating and the Zoo.

Location: 1^1/$_2$m due W of Princes Street.

Hudson's Choice

NEWMILLS HOUSE   49

PRICES
B & B: £25pp
Dinner: not available

OPEN
All year

HOST
Mrs Lois-May
Donaldson

Tel: 0131 449 4279

1 NEWMILLS ROAD, BALERNO, MIDLOTHIAN EH14 5AG

Newmills is a beautiful Georgian House close to Edinburgh where David and Lois-May offer a warm welcome and informal hospitality to their guests. The house is set in 1 acre of garden with an old yew hedge. Breakfast is served in a lovely conservatory. There are many stately homes and gardens nearby, including Malleny, Hopetoun and Dalmeny. There are also some good local restaurants.

Location: Edinburgh & Edinburgh airport 20 mins, Glasgow 50 mins and Glasgow airport 60 mins. W of Edinburgh on A70 Lanark Road. Newmills Road is on the right just before the village of Balerno.

27A SCOTLAND STREET   50

PRICES
B & B: £50 twin
£35 single
Dinner: not available

OPEN
All year

HOST
Mrs Rosemary
Maitland Hume

Tel: 0131 556 3024

EDINBURGH EH3 6PY

Ian and Rosemary Maitland Hume will give you a great welcome in their cosy garden flat in the classic Georgian 'Newtown' within a few minutes walk of the heart of this breathtaking world heritage city, and a wide variety of restaurants. Their flat is the ideal pied-à-terre and Ian specialises in Scottish history and ethnology at Edinburgh University, whilst Rosemary concentrates on artistic pursuits.

Location: In Edinburgh's 'Newtown', Princes Street 10 minutes.

SKIRLING HOUSE   51

PRICES
B & B: £25 - £35pp
Dinner: £15pp

OPEN
Mar - Dec

HOST
Bob & Isobel Hunter

Tel: 01899 860274
Fax: 01899 860255

SKIRLING, BY BIGGAR ML12 6HD

An 'Arts & Crafts' country retreat with fascinating original features and extensive grounds, set in picturesque Skirling village. This characterful house has recently been restored to provide elegant accommodation offering guests every comfort. Bob and Isobel pride themselves on serving imaginative food based on fresh, local produce. It is an ideal base for exploring the Borders and southern Scotland as well as being convenient for Edinburgh and Glasgow and well placed for a break en-route. STB 3 crowns, highly commended and accepted for 'Taste of Scotland'.

Location: On A72, 2m NE of Biggar.

STROQUHAN   52

PRICES
B & B: £28 - £34pp
Dinner: from £18pp

OPEN
All year except
Christmas & New Year

HOST
Andrew & Sarah
Lukas

Tel: 01387 820341
Fax: 01387 820582

DUNSCORE, DUMFRIESSHIRE DG2 0UP

This interesting Grade II listed house, standing in its own lovely grounds with spectacular views, is in the heart of Burns country. It is an ideally situated base for visiting the many fine houses and gardens in the South West of Scotland and the statues at Glenkiln (by Henry Moore, Rodin and Epstein) in their unsurpassed moorland setting. You are assured of a warm welcome, good food and a comfortable stay in this fine house.

Location: 1$^{1}/_{2}$m E of Dunscore. Take road signed to Corsock for 1$^{1}/_{2}$ miles, at junction go left to Dumfries for 200 yards, white gateway on right.

TALISKER HOUSE   53

PRICES
B & B: £30 - £40pp
Dinner: £18pp

OPEN
May - Oct

HOST
Jon & Ros Wathen

Tel: 01478 640245

CARBOST, ISLE OF SKYE IV47 8SF

A beautiful and historic home, dating from the 1720s and visited by Johnson and Boswell during their historic tour of the Hebrides in 1773, Talisker House celebrates ease and grace. With its fine trees and garden, under the imposing rock mass of Preshal Mhor, it offers superb views to the sea, and currently accommodates three couples in spacious and elegantly furnished comfort. All rooms have ensuite facilities. Carefully selected wines complement the fine dinners which feature the best of local produce. Hill and beach walking and fishing are favourite pursuits.

Location: On Skye's west coast, 5m from Carbost. Portree 20 miles.

Hudson's Choice

LLANWENARTH HOUSE   54

PRICES

B & B:£34 - £38pp Dble
B & B:£48 - £56pp Sgl.
Dinner: £22.50pp

OPEN

March - Mid January

HOST

Amanda & Bruce
Weatherill

Tel: 01873 830289
Fax: 01873 832199

GOVILON, ABERGAVENNY, GWENT NP7 9SF

The house which predates 1600 was the ancestral home of the Morgans; Privateer, Captain Henry (1635-1688) Governor of Jamaica being the best known. Now restored to something approaching its former splendour, it is the family home of the Weatherills, who with the children and friendly Lurcher dogs welcome guests. Aperitifs in the Georgian Drawing room are followed by dinner, utilising much home grown produce, accompanied by fine wine from the cellar. The history of the area embraces ancient castles and many relics of the Industrial Revolution.

Location: From junction of A40 Monmouth, A465 from Hereford and A4042 from Newport, east of Abergavenny follow A465 towards Merthyr Tydfil for 3^1/$_2$ miles to next roundabout. Take first exit to Govilon, and the ^{1}/$_2$ mile drive is 150 yards on right-hand side.

THE OLD RECTORY   55

PRICES

B & B: £37 - £57pp
Dinner: £27.50pp

OPEN

1 Feb - 20 Dec

HOST

Michael & Wendy
Vaughan

Tel: 01492 580611
Fax: 01492 584555

LLANSANFFRAID GLAN CONWY, CONWY, GWYNEDD LL28 5LF

This de luxe rated country house enjoys dramatic views of Snowdonia, Conwy Estuary and Castle from its beautiful gardens. Inside antiques and paintings abound in the elegant relaxing rooms where personal service is assured. Wendy Vaughan's cuisine deserves its praises by Egon Ronay and it is complemented by an award winning wine cellar. An AA Red Star and RAC Blue Ribbon award winning country house. "A beautiful haven of peace".

Location: Situated on A470, ^{1}/$_2$m S of its junction with A55, 3m N of Bodnant Gardens.

Late notification.

LONDON   56

22 NORTHBOURNE ROAD

22 Northbourne Road, Clapham, London SW4 7DJ

Owner: Mrs de Rougemont

Tel: 0171 720 4871.

Offering B&B in a large family house with homely atmosphere near Clapham Common. Easy access to West End by bus or underground.

Opening: All Year.

Price guide: £30.00/head.

Talisker House, Isle of Skye ~ which since last year has been joined to the mainland by a bridge.

ACCOMMODATION INDEX

Houses included in the county listings which provide accommodation

- **APPLEBY CASTLE**
  CUMBRIA 41
  3 singles without bathrooms

  9 doubles without bathrooms

  3 doubles with bathrooms

  Self-contained flat (sleeps 3)

- **AYTON CASTLE** *(shown above)*
  BERWICKSHIRE 251
  3 singles with bathrooms

  7 doubles with bathrooms

- **BLAIRQUHAN CASTLE**
  AYRSHIRE 272
  6 singles without bathrooms

  10 doubles (4 four poster) with bathrooms

  The Dower House has 8 doubles,
  2 singles, 5 bathrooms.

  7 self-catering cottages

- **BROUGHTON HALL**
  YORKSHIRE 228
  Only on special occasions by prior
  arrangement.

- **BUCKFAST ABBEY**
  DEVON 52
  4 singles without bathrooms

  8 doubles without bathrooms

- **CASTLE ASHBY** *(shown above)*
  NORTHAMPTONSHIRE 139
  Only available when attending
  Functions or Conferences

  17 doubles with bathrooms

  9 twins with bathrooms

- **CATTON HALL**
  DERBYSHIRE 47
  2 doubles without bathrooms

  7 doubles with bathrooms

- **COBHAM HALL**
  KENT 95
  24 singles without bathrooms

  18 singles with bathrooms

  24 doubles without bathrooms

  18 doubles with bathrooms

  200 beds in Dormitory style

- **COUGHTON COURT**
  WARWICKSHIRE 207
  1 single without bathroom

  3 doubles without bathroom

  1 single with bathroom

  3 doubles with bathroom

- **DEENE PARK**
  NORTHAMPTONSHIRE 140
  Residential conference facilities
  by arrangement.

- **DUNS CASTLE**
  BERWICKSHIRE 251
  2 singles without bathrooms

  6 twin/doubles with bathrooms

  4 four poster suites with bathrooms

  2 singles with bathrooms
  (for accompanying guides etc.)

- **EASTNOR CASTLE**
  HEREFORDSHIRE 84
  5 singles without bathrooms

  1 double without bathroom

  3 doubles with bathrooms

  1 twin with bathroom

- **EPWORTH OLD RECTORY**
  YORKSHIRE 241
  2 doubles without bathrooms

- **HARBURN HOUSE**
  MIDLOTHIAN 267
  (Groups only) 1 single with bathroom

  14 twin/doubles with bathrooms

  1 double without bathroom

- **HEVER CASTLE** *(shown top 3rd column)*
  KENT 98
  4 singles with bathrooms

  10 twins with bathrooms

  6 doubles with bathrooms

  Stable House offers 4 twin rooms
  and 1 double room

- **KINGSTONE LISLE PARK**
  OXFORDSHIRE 159
  1 single with bathroom

  4 doubles with bathrooms

  4 doubles without bathrooms

  Dinner, Bed and Breakfast
  Strictly by prior arrangement.

- **LEEDS CASTLE**
  KENT 101
  Only available when attending conferences.

  6 singles with bathrooms

  29 doubles with bathrooms

- **MANDERSTON**
  BERWICKSHIRE 249
  5 twins with bathrooms

  4 doubles with bathrooms

  1 single with bathroom

- **MAXWELTON HOUSE**
  DUMFRIES & GALLOWAY 255
  1 single without bathroom

  4 singles with bathrooms

  7 doubles with bathrooms

- **MOYNS PARK** *(shown above)*
  ESSEX 64
  9 principal bedrooms, all with
  private or en-suite bathrooms.

  Further secondary bedrooms
  available if required.

- **NOSELEY HALL**
  LEICESTERSHIRE 113
  Only if attending a function within the house
  2 doubles with en-suite bathrooms

  1 single without en-suite bathroom

- **OAKLEY HALL**
  SHROPSHIRE 166
  3 doubles with bathrooms

  1 twin with bathroom

- **SMEDMORE HOUSE**
  DORSET 59
  10 singles with bathrooms

  1 double with bathroom

- **SOMERLEY**
  HAMPSHIRE 77
  1 single with bathroom

  8 twin/doubles with bathrooms

  All rooms to be taken by House Party.
  Smaller numbers negotiable.

- **STOWE SCHOOL**
  BUCKINGHAMSHIRE 11
  170 singles

  80 twins

  5 suites with bathrooms

  Dormitory accommodation for 200

- **TRAQUAIR HOUSE**
  PEEBLESSHIRE 250
  2 four poster suites with bathrooms

  1 self catering flat with double bedroom.

- **WALCOT HALL**
  SHROPSHIRE 170
  2 singles without bathroom

  1 double without bathroom

  3 doubles with bathroom

- **WESTON PARK** *(shown below)*
  SHROPSHIRE 167
  (Group bookings of min. of 15 persons)

  3 singles with bathrooms

  16 doubles with bathrooms

  13 bedded suite

CIVIL WEDDING VENUES

Archbishop's Palace, Kent

Arley Hall & Gardens, Cheshire

Astley Hall, Lancashire

Belvoir Castle, Lincolnshire

Bentley Wildfowl & Motor Museum, Sussex

Berrington Hall, Herefordshire

Boughton Monchelsea Place, Kent

Burford House Gardens, Shropshire

Burgh House, London

Cardiff Castle, South Glamorgan

Chiddingstone Castle, Kent

Chillingham Castle, Northumberland

Clandon Park, Surrey

Cobham Hall, Kent

Cragside House & Garden, Northumberland

Duncombe Park, Yorkshire

Eastnor Castle, Herefordshire

Escot, Devon

Finchcocks, Kent

Goodwood House, Sussex

Groombridge Place Gardens, Kent

Hanbury Hall, Worcestershire

Hatfield House, Hertfordshire

Highclere Castle, Hampshire

Kirkley Hall Gardens, Northumberland

Knebworth House, Hertfordshire (Barns only)

Lamport Hall & Gardens, Northamptonshire

Layer Marney Tower, Essex

Leigh Court, Avon

Ludlow Castle, Shropshire

Lympne Castle, Kent

Naworth Castle, Cumbria

Newstead Abbey, Nottinghamshire

Painswick House, Gloucestershire

Penshurst Place, Kent

Powderham Castle, Devon

Prestwold Hall, Leicestershire

Ramster Gardens, Surrey

Ripley Castle, Yorkshire

Roman Bath and Pump Room, Avon

Royal Botanic Gardens, Surrey

The Royal Pavilion, Sussex

Royal Society of Arts, London

Shugborough Estate, Staffordshire

Stowe School, Buckinghamshire

Tabley House, Cheshire

Tonbridge Castle, Kent

Tredegar House, Gwent

The Vyne, Hampshire (closed Sept.'96 - mid 1998)

Waddesdon Manor, Buckinghamshire

Washington Old Hall, Tyne & Wear

Woburn Abbey, Bedfordshire

The Marriage Act 1995 which has resulted in many more wedding venues in England has not changed the situation in Scotland. In Scotland religious wedding ceremonies can take place anywhere subject to the Minister being prepared to perform them. Civil weddings however are still confined to Registry Offices.

Johansens
Recommended Hotels

Diversity and Excellence for the Discerning Traveller

(see details of Johansens Guides on Page II). Guides can be obtained by telephoning: UK: Freefone: 0800 269397   USA: Toll-Free: 1 800 786 9556

Channel Islands

• **Almorah Hotel**, One Almorah Crescent, Lower Kings Cliff, St Helier, Jersey JE2 3GU **Tel:** 01534 21648
• **Atlantic Hotel**, La Moye, St Brelade, Jersey JE3 8HE **Tel:** 01534 44101
• **Chateau La Chaire**, Rozel Bay, Jersey JE3 6AJ **Tel:** 01534 863354
• **Hotel La Place**, Route du Coin, La Haule, St Brelade, Jersey JE3 8BF **Tel:** 01534 44261
• **Hotel L'Horizon**, St Brelade Bay, Jersey JE3 8EF **Tel:** 01534 43101
• **La Favorita Hotel**, Fermain Bay,Guernsey GY4 6SD **Tel:** 01481 35666
• **Les Embruns House Hotel**, Route De La Margion, Vazon Bay, Castel, Guernsey GY5 7LZ **Tel:** 01481 64834
• **Longueville Manor**, St Saviour, Jersey JE2 7SA **Tel:** 01534 25501
• **St Pierre Park Hotel**, Rohais, St Peter Port, Guernsey GY1 1FD **Tel:** 01481 728282

Avon

• **Apsley House**, 141 Newbridge Hill Road, Bath BA1 3PT **Tel:** 01225 336966
• **Bath Lodge Hotel**, Norton St Philip,Bath BA3 6NH **Tel:** 01225 723040
• **Bloomfield House**, 146 Bloomfield Road, Bath BA2 2AS **Tel:** 01225 420105
• **Chelwood House**, Achelwood BS18 4NH **Tel:** 01761 490730
• **Combe Grove Manor & Country Club**, Brassknocker Hill, Monkton Combe, Bath BA2 7HS **Tel:** 01225 834644
• **Eagle House**, Church Street, Bathford BA1 7RS **Tel:** 01225 859946
• **Homewood Park**, Hinton Charterhouse, Bath BA3 6BB **Tel:** 01225 723731
• **Hunstrete House**, Hunstrete, Chelwood BS18 4NS **Tel:** 01761 490490
• **Irondale House**, 67 High Street, Rode, Bath BA3 6PB **Tel:** 01373 830730
• **Monkshill**, Shaft Road, Monkton Combe, Bath BA2 7HL **Tel:** 01225 833028
• **Newbridge House Hotel**, 35 Kelston Road, Bath BA1 3QH **Tel:** 01225 446676
• **Paradise House**, Holloway, Bath BA2 4PX **Tel:** 01225 317723
• **Petty France**, Dunkirk, Badminton GL9 1AF **Tel:** 01454 238361
• **Priory Hotel**, Weston Road, Bath BA1 2XT **Tel:** 01225 331922
• **Queensberry**, Russel Street, Bath BA1 2QF **Tel:** 01225 447928
• **Royal Crescent**, Bath BA1 2LS **Tel:** 01225 739955
• **Swallow Royal Hotel**, College Green, Bristol BS1 5TA **Tel:** 0117 9255100
• **Woolpack Inn**, Beckington BA3 6SP **Tel:** 01373 831244

Bedfordshire

• **Flitwick Manor**, Church Road, Flitwick MK45 1AE **Tel:** 01525 712242
• **Moore Place Hotel**, The Square, Aspley Guise MK17 8DW **Tel:** 01908 282000
• **Woodlands Manor**, Green Lane, Clapham, Bedford MK41 6EP **Tel:** 01234 363281

Berkshire

• **Bird In Hand**, Bath Road, Knowl Hill, Twyford RG10 9UP **Tel:** 0162882 6622/2781
• **Boulters Lock Hotel**, Boulters Island, Maidenhead SL6 8PE **Tel:** 01628 21291
• **Christopher Hotel**, High Street, Eton, Windsor SL4 6AN **Tel:** 01753 852359
• **Cliveden**,Taplow, Berkshire SL6 0JF **Tel:** 01628 668561
• **Donnington Valley Hotel & Golf Course**, Old Oxford Road, Donnington, Newbury RG14 3AG **Tel:** 01635 551199
• **Foley Lodge**, Stockcross, Newbury, Berks RG20 8JU **Tel:** 01635 528770
• **Frederick's Hotel & Restaurant**, Shoppenhangers Road, Maidenhead SL6 2PZ **Tel:** 01628 35934
• **French Horn**, Sonning-on-Thames, Berks RG4 0TN **Tel:** 01734 692204
• **Highwayman**, Exlade street, Checkendon, Berks RG8 0UA **Tel:** 01491 682020
• **Hollington House Hotel**, Woolton Hill, Berks RG20 9XA **Tel:** 01635 255100
• **Leatherne Bottel Riverside Inn & Restaurant**, The Bridleway, Goring-On-Thames, RG8 0HS **Tel:** 01491 872667
• **Monkey Island**, Bray-on-Thames, Maidenhead SL6 2EE **Tel:** 01628 23400

• **Oakley Court**, Windsor Road, Water Oakley, SL4 5UR **Tel:** 01753 609988
• **Royal Berkshire**, London Road, Sunninghill, Ascot SL5 0PP **Tel:** 01344 23322
• **Royal Oak Hotel**, Yattendon, Newbury, Berks RG16 0UF **Tel:** 01635 201325
• **Swan Diplomat**, Streatley-On-Thames, Berks RG8 9HR **Tel:** 01491 873737
• **Ye Olde Bell**, High Street, Hurley, Berks SL6 5LX **Tel:** 01628 825881

Buckinghamshire

• **Danesfield House**, Medmenham, Marlow, Bucks SL7 2EY **Tel:** 01628 891010
• **Fox Country Hotel**, Ibstone, Bucks HP14 3GG **Tel:** 01491 638289
• **Hartwell House**, Oxford Road, Bucks HP17 8NL **Tel:** 01296 747444
• **Mole & Chicken**, The Terrace, Long Crendon, Aylesbury HP18 9EY **Tel:** 01844 208387
• **Priory Hotel**, High St, Witchurch, Aylesbury, Bucks HP22 4JS **Tel:** 01296 641239

Cambridgeshire

• **Anchor Inn**, Sutton Gault, Sutton, Cambridge CB6 2BD **Tel:** 01353 778537
• **Duxford Lodge Hotel & Restaurant**, Duxford CB2 4RU **Tel:** 01223 836444
• **Haycock**, Wansford-In-England, Peterborough PE8 6JA **Tel:** 01780 782223
• **Old Bridge Hotel**, 1 High Street, Huntingdon PE18 6TQ **Tel:** 01480 452681
• **Panos Hotel & Restaurant**, 154/156 Hills Road CB2 2PB **Tel:** 01223 212958
• **Quy Mill Hotel**, Newmarket Road, Stow-Cum-Quy, Cambridge CB5 9AG **Tel:** 01223 293383

Cheshire

• **Alderley Edge Hotel**, Macclesfield Road, Alderley Edge SK9 7BJ **Tel:** 01625 583033
• **Bridge Hotel**, Prestbury SK10 4DQ **Tel:** 01625 829326
• **Broxton Hall Country House Hotel**, Whitchurch Road, Broxton, Chester CH3 9JS **Tel:** 01829 782321
• **Chester Grosvenor**, Eastgate, Chester, Cheshire CH1 1LT **Tel:** 01244 324024
• **Crabwall Manor**, Parkgate Road, Mollington, Chester CH1 6NE **Tel:** 01244 851666
• **Frogg Manor**, Nantwich Road, Fullers Moor, Broxton, Chester CH3 9JH **Tel:** 01829 782629
• **Higher Huxley Hall**, Huxley, Chester CH3 9BZ **Tel:** 01829 781484
• **Longview Hotel & Restaurant**, 51/55 Manchester Road, Knutsford WA16 0LX **Tel:** 01565 632119
• **Nunsmere Hall**, Tarporley Road, Sandiway CW18 2ES **Tel:** 01606 889100
• **Pheasant Inn**, Higher Burwardsley, Tattenhall, Chester CH3 9PF **Tel:** 01829 770434
• **Rookery Hall**, Worleston, Nantwich CW5 6DQ **Tel:** 01270 610016
• **Rowton Hall Hotel**, Whitchurch Road, Rowton, Chester CH3 6AD **Tel:** 01244 335262
• **Stanneylands Hotel**, Stanneylands Road, Wilmslow SK9 4EY **Tel:** 01625 525225
• **Willington Hall Hotel**, Willington CW6 0NB **Tel:** 01829 752321
• **Woodland Park Hotel**, Timperley, Altrincham WA15 7RG **Tel:** 0161 928 8631

Cornwall

• **Allhays Country House**, Talland Bay, Looe PL13 2JB **Tel:** 01503 272434
• **Budock Vean Golf & Country Club**, Mawnan Smith, Falmouth TR11 5LG **Tel:** 01326 250288
• **Coombe Farm**, Widegates PL13 1QN **Tel:** 01503 240223
• **Countryman At Trink Hotel & Restaurant**, Old Coach Road, St Ives TR26 3JQ **Tel:** 01736 797571
• **Garrack Hotel**, Burthallan Lane, St Ives TR26 3AA **Tel:** 01736 796199
• **Harbour Inn**, Commercial Road, Porthleven TR13 9JD **Tel:** 01326 573876
• **Jubilee Inn**, Pelynt PL13 2JZ **Tel:** 01503 220312
• **Lugger Hotel**, Portloe TR2 5RD **Tel:** 01872 501322
• **Meudon Hotel**, Mawnan Smith TR11 5HT **Tel:** 01326 250541
• **Nansidwell Country House**, Mawnan TR11 5HU **Tel:** 01326 250340
• **Nansloe Manor**, Meneage Road, Helston TR13 0SB **Tel:** 01326 574691
• **Nare Hotel**, Carne Beach, Veryan-In-Roseland, Truro TR2 5PF **Tel:** 01872 501279
• **Old Custom House Hotel**, South Quay, Padstow PL28 8ED **Tel:** 01841 532359
• **Pentire Rocks Hotel**, New Polzeath PL27 6US **Tel:** 01208 862213

• **Polurrian Hotel**, Mullion, Lizard Peninsula TR12 7EN **Tel:** 01326 240421
• **Port Gaverne Hotel**, PL29 3SQ **Tel:** 01208 880244
• **Rising Sun**, The Square, St Mawes TR2 5DJ **Tel:** 01326 270233
• **Rose-in-Vale Country House Hotel**, Mithian, St Agnes TR5 0QD **Tel:** 01872 552202
• **Seafood Restaurant & St Petroc's House**, Riverside, Padstow PL28 8BY **Tel:** 01841 532485
• **Talland Bay Hotel**, Talland-By-Looe PL13 2JB **Tel:** 01503 272667
• **Trebrea Lodge**, Trenale, Tintagel PL34 0HR **Tel:** 01840 770410
• **Tregildry Hotel**, Gillan Manaccan, Helston TR12 6HG **Tel:** 01326 231378
• **Treglos Hotel**, Constantine Bay PL28 8JH **Tel:** 01841 520727
• **Trelawne Hotel**, Mawnan Smith TR11 5HS **Tel:** 01326 250226
• **Trengilly Wartha Country Inn & Restaurant**, Nancenoy, Constantine, Falmouth TR11 5RP **Tel:** 01326 40332
• **Tyacks Hotel**, 27 Commercial Street, Camborne TR14 8LD **Tel:** 01209 612424
• **Tye Rock Hotel**, Loe Bar Road, Porthleven TR13 9EW **Tel:** 01326 572695
• **Well House**, St Keyne, Liskeard PL14 4RN **Tel:** 01579 342001
• **White Hart Hotel**, Church Street, St Austell PL25 4AT **Tel:** 01726 72100

Co Durham

• **Headlam Hall**, Headlam, Darlington DL2 3HA **Tel:** 01325 730238
• **Lumley Castle Hotel**, Chester-Le-Street DH3 4NX **Tel:** 0191 389 1111
• **Morritt Arms Hotel**, Greta Bridge DL12 9SE **Tel:** 01833 627232
• **Redworth Hall Hotel & Country Club**, Redworth DL5 6NL **Tel:** 01388 772442

Cumbria

• **Appleby Manor Country House Hotel**, Roman Road, Appleby-in-Westmorland CA16 6JB **Tel:** 017683 51571
• **Aynsome Manor Hotel**, Cartmel, Grange-Over-Sands LA11 6HH **Tel:** 015395 36653
• **Borrowdale Gates Country House Hotel**, Grange-in-Borrowdale, Keswick, CA12 5UQ **Tel:** 01768 777204
• **Crosby Lodge Country House Hotel**, High Crosby, Crosby-On-Eden, Carlisle CA6 4QZ **Tel:** 01228 573618
• **Dale Head Hall Lakeside Hotel**, Thirlmere, Keswick CA12 4TN **Tel:** 017687 72478
• **Farlam Hall Hotel**, Brampton, Cumbria CA8 2NG **Tel:** 016977 46234
• **Fayrer Garden House Hotel**, Lyth Valley Road, Bowness-On-Windermere LA23 3JP **Tel:** 015394 88195
• **Gilpin Lodge**, Crook Road LA23 3NE **Tel:** 015394 88818
• **Grange Country House Hotel**, Manor Brow, Keswick-On-Derwentwater CA12 4BA **Tel:** 017687 72500
• **Graythwaite Manor**, Fernhill Road, Grange-Over-Sands, Cumbria LA11 7JE **Tel:** 015395 32001
• **Hipping Hall**, Cowan Bridge, Kirkby Lonsdale LA6 2JJ **Tel:** 015242 71187
• **Holbeck Ghyll Country House Hotel**, Holbeck Lane, Windermere LA23 1LU **Tel:** 015394 32375
• **Kirkstone Foot Country House Hotel**, Kirkstone Pass Road, Ambleside LA22 9EH **Tel:** 015394 32232
• **Lakeside Hotel On Lake Windermere**, Lakeside, Newby Bridge LA12 8AT **Tel:** 015395 31207
• **Langdale Chase**, Windermere LA23 1LW **Tel:** 015394 32201
• **Laurel Villa**, Lake Road, Ambleside LA22 0DB **Tel:** 015394 33240
• **Linthwaite House Hotel**, Crook Road, Bowness-On-Windermere LA23 3JA **Tel:** 015394 88600
• **Lovelady Shield Country House Hotel**, Nenthead Road, Alston CA9 3LF **Tel:** 01434 381203
• **Michaels Nook**, Grasmere LA22 9RP **Tel:** 015394 35496
• **Mortal Man Hotel**, Troutbeck LA23 1PL **Tel:** 015394 33193
• **Nanny Brow Hotel**, Clappersgate, Ambleside LA22 9NF **Tel:** 015394 32036
• **New Dungeon Ghyll Hotel**, Great Langdale, Ambleside LA22 9JY **Tel:** 015394 37213
• **New House Farm**, Lorton, Cockermouth CA13 9UU **Tel:** 01900 85404

• **Old Vicarage Country House Hotel**, Church Road, Witherslack LA11 6RS **Tel:** 015395 52381
• **Pheasant Inn**, Casterton, Kirkby Lonsdale LA26 2RX **Tel:** 015242 71230
• **Rampsbeck Country House Hotel**, Watermillock, Lake Ullswater CA11 0LP **Tel:** 017684 86442
• **Red Lion Inn**, Hawkshead, Ambleside LA22 0MV **Tel:** 015394 36213
• **Rothay Manor**, Rothay Bridge, Ambleside LA22 0EH **Tel:** 015394 33605
• **Royal Oak Inn**, Bongate, Appleby-In-Westmorland CA16 6UN **Tel:** 017683 51463
• **Snooty Fox, Main Street**, Kirkby Lonsdale LA6 2AH **Tel:** 015242 71308
• **Swan Hotel**, Newby Bridge, Cumbria LA12 8NB **Tel:** 015395 31681
• **Swinside Lodge Hotel**, Grange Road, Newlands, Keswick CA12 5UE **Tel:** 017687 72948
• **Temple Sowerby House Hotel**, Temple Sowerby, Penrith CA10 1RZ **Tel:** 017683 61578
• **Tufton Arms Hotel**, Market Square, Appleby-In-Westmorland CA16 6XA **Tel:** 017683 51593
• **Underscar Manor**, Applethwaite CA12 PH **Tel:** 017687 75000
• **White Moss House**, Rydal Water, Grasmere LA22 9SE **Tel:** 015394 35295
• **Whoop Hall Inn**, Burrow-With-Burrow, Kirkby Lonsdale LA6 2HP **Tel:** 015242 71284
• **Wordsworth Hotel**, Grasmere LA22 9SW **Tel:** 015394 35592

Derbyshire

• **Beeches Farmhouse**, Waldley, Doveridge, Ashbourne DE6 5LR **Tel:** 01889 590288.
• **Biggin Hall**, Biggin-by-Hartington, Buxton SK17 0DH **Tel:** 01298 84451
• **Biggin Mill House**, Biggin-by-Hulland DE6 3FN **Tel:** 01335 370414
• **Boar's Head Hotel**, Lichfield Road, Sudbury DE6 5GX **Tel:** 01283 820344
• **Callow Hall**, Mappleton Road, Ashbourne DE6 2AA **Tel:** 01335 343403
• **Cavendish Hotel**, Baslow DE4 1SP **Tel:** 01246 582311
• **Chequers Inn**, Froggatt Edge S30 1ZB **Tel:** 01433 630231
• **Dannah Farm Country Guest House**, Bowman's Lane, Shottle DE56 2DR **Tel:** 01773 550273 / 630
• **East Lodge Country House Hotel**, Rowsley, Matlock DE4 2EF **Tel:** 01629 734474
• **Fischer's, Baslow Hall**, Calver Road, Baslow DE45 1RR **Tel:** 01246 583259
• **Hassop Hall**, Hassop DE45 1NS **Tel:** 01629 640488
• **Makeney Hall Country House Hotel**, Makeney, Milford DE56 0RU **Tel:** 01332 842999
• **Manor House Hotel & Restaurant**, High Street, Old Dronfield SY18 6PY **Tel:** 01246 413971
• **Maynard Arms**, Main Road, Grindleford S30 1HP **Tel:** 01433 630321
• **Mickleover Court**, Elwall Road, Mickleover **Tel:** 01332 521234
• **Peacock Hotel at Rowsley**, Rowsley DE4 2EB **Tel:** 01629 733518
• **Priest House**, Kings Mills, Castle Donington DE74 2RR **Tel:** 01332 810649
• **Riber Hall**, Matlock DE4 5JU **Tel:** 01629 582795
• **Riverside Country House Hotel**, Ashford-In-The-Water DE4 1QF **Tel:** 01629 814275
• **Twitchill Farm Cottages**, Edale Road, Hope S30 2RF **Tel:** 01433 621426
• **Underleigh House**, Off Edale Road, Hope S30 2RF **Tel:** 01433 621372
• **Waltzing Weasel**, New Mills Road, Birch Vale SK12 5BT **Tel:** 01663 743402
• **Wind In The Willows**, Derbyshire Level, Glossop SK13 9PT **Tel:** 01457 868001
• **Ye Olde Nags Head Hotel**, Cross Street, Castleton S30 2WH **Tel:** 01433 620248

Devon

• **Alston Hall Country House Hotel**, Alston, Holbeton PL8 1HN **Tel:** 01752 830555
• **Arundell Arms**, Lifton PL16 0AA **Tel:** 01566 784666
• **Barn Owl Inn**, Aller Mills, Kingskerswell TQ12 5AN **Tel:** 01830 872130
• **Bel Alp House**, Haytor TQ13 9XX **Tel:** 01364 661217
• **Bessemer Thatch**, Berrynarbor EX34 9SE **Tel:** 01271 882296
• **Blagdon Manor Country Hotel**, Ashwater EX21 5DF **Tel:** 01409 211224
• **Bolt Head Hotel**, South Sands, Salcombe TQ8 8LL **Tel:** 01548 843751
• **Bovey House**, Beer, Seaton EX12 3AD **Tel:** 01297 680 241

- **Brookdale House Restaurant & Hotel**, North Huish, South Brent TQ10 9NR **Tel:** 01548 821661
- **Buckland-Tout-Saints**, Goveton, Kingsbridge TQ7 2DS **Tel:** 01548 853055
- **Commodore**, Marine Parade, Instow EX39 4JN **Tel:** 01271 860347
- **Cridford Inn**, Trusham TQ13 0NR **Tel:** 01626 853694
- **Easton Court Hotel**, Easton Cross, Chagford TQ13 8JL **Tel:** 01647 433469
- **Eastwrey Barton Hotel**, Lustleigh, Newton Abbot TQ13 9SN **Tel:** 01647 277338
- **Edgemoor**, Haytor Road, Bovey Tracey TQ13 9LE **Tel:** 01626 832466
- **Foxdown Manor**, Horns Cross EX39 5PJ **Tel:** 01237 451325
- **George Hotel**, Market Street, Hatherleigh EX20 3JN **Tel:** 01837 810454
- **Gidleigh Park**, Chagford TQ13 8HH **Tel:** 01647 432367
- **Halmpstone Manor**, Bishop Tawton EX32 0EA **Tel:** 01271 830321
- **Holne Chase Hotel**, Devon TQ13 7NS **Tel:** 01364 631471
- **Home Farm Hotel**, Wilmington EX14 9JQ **Tel:** 01404 831278
- **Horn Of Plenty**, Gulworthy, Tavistock PL19 8JD **Tel:** 01822 832528
- **Hotel Riviera**, The Esplanade, Sidmouth EX10 8AY **Tel:** 01395 515201
- **Ilsington Hotel**, Ilsington, Newton Abbott TQ13 9RR **Tel:** 01364 661452
- **Kingston House**, Staverton, Totnes TQ9 6AR **Tel:** 01803 762 235
- **Leusdon Lodge Hotel**, Leusdon, Poundsgate TQ13 7PE **Tel:** 01364 631304
- **Lord Haldon Hotel**, Dunchideock EX6 7YF **Tel:** 01392 832483
- **Lynton Cottage Hotel**, North Walk, Lynton EX35 6ED **Tel:** 01598 752342
- **Manor House Hotel & Golf Course**, Moretonhampstead TQ13 8RE **Tel:** 01647 440355
- **Marsh Hall Country House Hotel**, South Molton EX36 3HQ **Tel:** 01769 572666
- **Moor View House**, Vale Down, Lydford EX20 4BB **Tel:** 0182 2820 220
- **Moorland Links Hotel & Restaurant**, Yelverton PL20 6DA **Tel:** 01822 852245
- **Nobody Inn**, Doddiscombsleigh EX6 7PS **Tel:** 01647 52394
- **Northcote Manor**, Burrington, Taw River Valley EX37 9LZ **Tel:** 01769 560501
- **Orestone Manor Hotel & Restaurant**, Rockhouse Lane, Maidencombe, Torquay TQ1 4SX **Tel:** 01803 328098
- **Osborne Hotel & Langtry's Restaurant**, Meadfoot Beach, Torquay TQ1 2LL **Tel:** 01803 213311
- **Oxenham Arms**, South Zeal, Devon, EX20 2JT **Tel:** 01837 840244/577
- **Palace Hotel**, Babbacombe Road, Torquay TQ1 3TG **Tel:** 01803 200200
- **Passage House Hotel**, Kingsteighton, Newton Abbot TQ12 3QH **Tel:** 01626 55515
- **Rising Sun**, Harbourside, Lynmouth EX35 6EQ **Tel:** 01598 753223
- **Sea Trout Inn**, Staverton TQ9 6PA **Tel:** 01803 762274
- **Soar Mill Cove Hotel**, Soar Mill Cove TQ7 3DS **Tel:** 01548 561566
- **St Olaves Court Hotel**, Mary Arches Street, Exeter EX4 3AZ **Tel:** 01392 217736
- **Thatched Cottage Country Hotel & Restaurant**, Sprytown, Lifton PL16 0AY **Tel:** 01566 784224
- **Thelbridge Cross Inn**, Thelbridge, Devon, EX17 4SQ **Tel:** 01884 860316
- **Tytherleigh Cot Hotel**, Chardstock, Axminster EX13 7BN **Tel:** 01460 221170
- **Watersmeet Hotel**, Mortehoe, Woolacombe EX34 7EB **Tel:** 01271 870333
- **Whitechapel Manor**, EX36 3EG **Tel:** 01769 573377
- **Wigham**, Morchard Bishop, Devon, EX17 6RJ **Tel:** 01363 877350
- **Woolacombe Bay Hotel**, South St, Woolacombe EX34 7BN **Tel:** 01271 870388

Dorset

- **Acorn Inn Hotel**, Fore Street, Evershot DT2 0JW **Tel:** 1935 83228
- **Beechleas**, 17 Poole Road, Wimborne Minster BH21 1QA **Tel:** 01202 841684
- **Carlton Hotel**, East Overcliff Drive, Bournemouth BH1 3DN **Tel:** 01202 552011
- **Chedington Court**, Chedington, Dorset DT8 3HY **Tel:** 01935 891265
- **Eastbury Hotel**, Long Street, Sherborne, Dorset DT9 3BY **Tel:** 01935 813131
- **Kemps Country House Hotel & Restaurant**, East Stoke, Wareham BH20 6AL **Tel:** 01929 462563
- **Langtry Manor**, Derby Road, East Cliff, Bournemouth BH1 3QB **Tel:** 01202 553887
- **Lodge**, Beaminster DT8 3BL **Tel:** 01308 863468
- **Manor Hotel**, West Bexington, Dorchester DT2 9DF **Tel:** 01308 897616
- **Mansion House**, Thames Street, Poole BH15 1JN **Tel:** 01202 685666
- **Plumber Manor**, Sturminster Newton DT10 2AF **Tel:** 01258 472507
- **Priory**, Church Green, Wareham BH20 4ND **Tel:** 01929 551666
- **Rectory House**, Fore Street, Evershot DT2 0JW **Tel:** 0193583 273
- **Summer Lodge**, Summer Lane, Evershot DT2 0JR **Tel:** 01935 83424
- **Yalbury Cottage Hotel**, Lower Bockhampton, Dorchester DT2 8PZ **Tel:** 01305 62382

Essex

- **Bauble**, Higham, Colchester CO7 6LA **Tel:** 01206 337254
- **Cricketers**, Clavering CB11 4QT **Tel:** 01799 550442
- **Five Lakes Hotel Golf & Country Club**, Colchester Road, Tolleshunt Knights, Maldon CM9 8HX **Tel:** 01621 868888
- **Hockley Place**, Frating, Colchester CO7 7HF **Tel:** 01206 251703
- **Maison Talbooth**, Stratford Road, Dedham, Colchester CO7 6HN **Tel:** 01206 322367
- **Pontlands Park Country Hotel & Restaurant**, West Hanningfield Rd, Great Baddow CM2 8HR **Tel:** 01245 476444
- **Starr Restaurant With Rooms**, Market Place, Great Dunmow CM16 1AX **Tel:** 01371 874321
- **White Hart Hotel & Restaurant**, Market End, Coggeshall CO6 1NH **Tel:** 01376 561654
- **Whitehall**, Church End, Broxted CM6 2BZ **Tel:** 01279 850603

Gloucestershire

- **Bell Hotel**, Church Street, Tewkesbury GL20 5SA **Tel:** 01684 293293
- **Bibury Court**, Bibury GL7 5NT **Tel:** 01285 740337
- **Burleigh Court**, Minchinhampton, GL5 2PF **Tel:** 01453 883804
- **Calcot Manor**, GL8 8YJ **Tel:** 01666 890391
- **Charingworth Manor**, GL55 6NS **Tel:** 01386 593555
- **Charlton Kings Hotel**, Charlton Kings, Cheltenham Gl52 6UU **Tel:** 01242 231061
- **Close Hotel**, Long Street, Tetbury GL8 8AQ **Tel:** 01666 502272
- **Corse Lawn House Hotel**, Corse Lawn GL19 4LZ **Tel:** 01452 780479/771
- **Cotswold House**, High Street, Chipping Campden GL55 6AN **Tel:** 01386 840330
- **Cotswold Park**, Woodmancote, Cirencester GL7 7EL **Tel:** 01285 831414
- **Dial House Hotel**, The Chestnuts, High Street, Bourton-On-The-Water GL54 2AN **Tel:** 01451 822244
- **Grapevine Hotel**, Sheep Street, Stow-On-The-Wold GL54 1AU **Tel:** 01451 830344
- **Greenway**, Shurdington, Cheltenham GL51 5UG **Tel:** 01242 862352
- **Halewell**, Halewell Close, Withington GL54 4BN **Tel:** 01242 890238
- **Hatton Court Hotel**, Upton Hill, Upton St Leonards GL4 8DE **Tel:** 01452 617412
- **Hinton House**, Ablington, Cirencester GL7 5NY **Tel:** 01285 740233
- **Hotel On The Park**, Evesham Road, Cheltenham GL52 2AH **Tel:** 01242 518898
- **Kingshead House Restaurant**, Birdlip GL4 8JH **Tel:** 01452 862299
- **Lords Of The Manor**, Upper Slaughter, Cheltenham GL54 2JD **Tel:** 01451 820243
- **Lower Brook House**, Blockley GL56 9DS **Tel:** 01386 700286
- **Lower Slaughter Manor**, Lower Slaughter GL54 2HP **Tel:** 01451 820456
- **Malt House**, Broad Campden GL55 6UU **Tel:** 01386 840295
- Manor House Hotel, Moreton-In-Marsh GL56 0LJ **Tel:** 01608 650501
- **Masons Arms**, Meysey Hampton GL7 5JT **Tel:** 01285 850164
- **Middle Lypiatt House**, Middle Lypiatt, Stroud GL6 7LW **Tel:** 01453 882151
- **New Inn**, Colne St-Aldwyns GL7 5AN **Tel:** 01285 750651
- Noel Arms, Chipping Campden GL55 6AT **Tel:** 01386 840317
- **Old Manse**, Victoria Street, Bourton-On-The-Water, GL54 2BX **Tel:** 01451 820082
- **Orchard House**, Aston Ingham Rd, Kilcot GL18 1NP **Tel:** 01989 720417
- **Puckrup Hall**, Puckrup, Tewkesbury GL20 6EL **Tel:** 01684 296200
- **Ragged Cot**, Hyde, Minchinhampton GL6 8PE **Tel:** 01453 884643 /-731333
- **Royalist Hotel**, Digbeth Street, Stow-On-The-Wold GL54 1BN **Tel:** 01451 830670
- **Snooty Fox**, Market Place, Tetbury GL8 8DD **Tel:** 01666 502436
- **Stonehouse Court**, Stonehouse GL10 3RA **Tel:** 01453 825155
- **Swan Hotel At Bibury**, Bibury GL7 5NW **Tel:** 01285 740695
- **Upper Court, Kemerton** GL20 7HY **Tel:** 01386 725351
- **Washbourne Court Hotel**, Lower Slaughter GL54 2HS **Tel:** 01451 822143
- **Wesley House**, The High St, Winchcombe GL54 5LJ **Tel:** 01242 602366
- **Wyck Hill House**, Wyck Hill, Stow-On-The-Wold GL54 1HY **Tel:** 01451 831936

Greater Manchester

- **Etrop Grange**, Thorley Lane, Manchester Airport, Gt Manchester M90 4EG **Tel:** 0161 499 0500

Hampshire

- **Careys Manor Hotel**, Brockenhurst SO42 7RH **Tel:** 01590 623551
- **Chewton Glen**, New Milton BH25 6QS **Tel:** 01425 275341
- **Esseborne Manor**, Hurstborne Tarrant, Andover SP11 0ER **Tel:** 01264 736444
- **George Hotel**, High Street, Odiham, Hook RG291LP **Tel:** 01256 702081
- **Gordleton Mill Hotel**, Silver Street, Hordle SO41 6DJ **Tel:** 01590 682219
- **Hotel Du Vin & Bistro**, 14 Southgate Street, Winchester SO23 9EF **Tel:** 01962 841414
- **Lainston House Hotel**, Sparsholt, Winchester SO21 2LT **Tel:** 01962 863588
- **Lions Court Restaurant & Hotel**, Fordingbridge SP6 1AS **Tel:** 01425 652006
- **Montagu Arms Hotel**, Beaulieu, New Forest SO42 7ZL **Tel:** 01590 612324
- **New Park Manor**, Lyndhurst Road, Brockenhurst SO42 7QH **Tel:** 01590 623467
- **Parkhill Hotel**, Beaulieu Road, Lyndhurst SO43 7FZ **Tel:** 01703 282944
- **Passford House Hotel**, Mount Pleasant Lane, Lymington, SO41 8LS **Tel:** 01590 682398
- **Rhinefield House Hotel**, Rhinefield Road, Brockenhurst, SO42 7QB **Tel:** 01590 622922
- **Thatched Cottage Hotel**, 16 Brookley Road, Brockenhurst SO42 7RR **Tel:** 01590 623090
- **Tylney Hall**, Rotherwick RG27 9AZ **Tel:** 01256 764881
- **Whitley Ridge & Country House Hotel**, Beaulieu Road, Brockenhurst SO42 7QL **Tel:** 01590 622354
- **Woodfalls Inn**, The Ridge, Woodfalls, Fordingbridge SP5 2LN **Tel:** 01725 513222
- **Wykeham Arms**, 75 Kingsgate St, Winchester SO23 9PE **Tel:** 01962 853834

Herefordshire

- **Allt-Yr-Ynys Hotel**, Walterstone, Herefordshire HR2 0DU **Tel:** 01873 890307
- **Chase Hotel**, Gloucester Road, Ross-On-Wye HR9 5LH **Tel:** 01989 763161
- **Feathers Hotel**, High Street, Ledbury HR8 1DS **Tel:** 01531 635266
- **Glewstone Court**, HR6 6AW **Tel:** 01989 770367
- **Hanbury Manor Hotel**, Ware SG12 0SD **Tel:** 01920 487722
- **Hope End Hotel**, Hope End, Ledbury HR8 1JQ **Tel:** 01531 633613
- **Lower Bache**, Kimbolton HR6 0ER **Tel:** 01568 750304
- **Pengethley Manor,** HR9 6LL **Tel:** 01989 730211
- **Penrhos Court**, Kington HR5 3LH **Tel:** 01544 230720
- **Peterstow Country House**, Peterstow, Ross-On-Wye HR9 6LB **Tel:** 01989 562826
- **Rhydspence Inn**, Whitney-On-Wye HR3 6EU **Tel:** 01497 831262
- **Rocks Place**, Rocks Place, Yatton, Ross-On-Wye HR9 7RD **Tel:** 01531 660218
- **Steppes**, Ullingswick HR1 3JG **Tel:** 01432 820424
- **Wheelbarrow Castle**, Stoke Prior, Leominster HR6 0NB **Tel:** 01568 612219
- **Ye Olde Salutation Inn**, Market Pitch, Weobley HR4 8SJ **Tel:** 01544 318443

Hertfordshire

- **Briggens House Hotel**, Stanstead Road, Stanstead Abbotts, SG12 8LD **Tel:** 01279 829955
- **Down Hall Country House Hotel**, Hatfield Heath CM22 7AS **Tel:** 01279 731441
- **Little Offley**, Hitchin SG5 3BU **Tel:** 01462 768243
- **Melbourn Bury**, Melbourn SG8 6DE **Tel:** 01763 261151
- **Pendley Manor Hotel & Conference Centre**, Cow Lane, Tring HP23 5QY **Tel:** 01442 891891
- **Sopwell House Hotel & Country Club**, Cottonmill Lane, Sopwell, St Albans, AL1 2HQ **Tel:** 01727 864477
- **St Michael's Manor Hotel**, Fishpool Street, St Albans AL3 4RY **Tel:** 01727 864444
- **West Lodge Park**, Cockfosters Road, Hadley Wood, Barnet EN4 0PY **Tel:** 0181 440 8311

Kent

- **Brandshatch Place Hotel**, Fawkham Valley Road, Fawkham DA3 8NQ **Tel:** 01474 872239
- **Chilston Park Country House**, Sandway, Lenham ME17 2BE **Tel:** 01622 859803
- **Eastwell Manor**, Boughton Lees, Ashford TN25 4HR **Tel:** 01233 219955
- **Harrow At Warren Street**, Warren Street ME17 2ED **Tel:** 01622 858727
- **Howfield Manor**, Chartham Hatch CT4 7HQ **Tel:** 01227 738294
- **Ringlestone Inn**, 'Twixt' Harrietsham & Wormshill, ME17 1NX **Tel:** 01622 859900
- **Romney Bay House**, Coast Road, Littlestone, New Romney TN28 8QY **Tel:** 01797 364747
- **Rowhill Grange**, Wilmington, Dartford DA2 7QH **Tel:** 01322 615136
- **Royal Wells Inn**, Mount Ephraim, Tunbridge Wells TN4 8BE **Tel:** 01892 511188
- **Spa Hotel**, Mount Ephraim, Royal Tunbridge Wells TN4 8XJ **Tel:** 01892 520331
- **Tanyard**, Wierton Hill, Boughton Monchelsea ME17 4JT **Tel:** 01622 744705
- **Wallett's Court**, West Cliffe, St. Margaret's-at-Cliffe CT15 6EW **Tel:** 01304 852424
- **Woodville Hall**, Temple Ewell, Dover CT16 1DJ **Tel:** 01304 825256

Lancashire

- **Gibbon Bridge Country House Hotel**, Chipping, Preston PR3 2TQ **Tel:** 01995 61456
- **Harrop Fold**, Bolton-By-Bowland, Clitheroe BB7 4PJ **Tel:** 01200 447600
- **Inn At Whitewell**, Forest Of Bowland, Clitheroe BB7 3AT **Tel:** 01200 448222
- **Kilhey Court**, Chorley Road, Standish, Wigan WM1 2XN **Tel:** 01257 472100
- **Old Bell Inn Hotel**, Huddersfield Road, Delph, Saddleworth OL3 5EG **Tel:** 01457 870130
- **Ye Horn's Inn**, Horn's Lane, Goosnargh PR3 2FJ **Tel:** 01772 865230

Leicestershire

- **Abbots Oak**, Greenhill, Coalville LE67 4UY **Tel:** 01530 832328
- **Barnacles Restaurant**, Watlins Street LE10 3JA **Tel:** 01455 633220
- **Barnsdale Lodge**, The Avenue, Rutland Water, Nr Oakham, Rutland LE15 8AH **Tel:** 01572 724678
- **Fernie Lodge Hotel**, Berridges Lane, Husbands Bosworth, Lutterworth LE17 6LE **Tel:** 01858 880551
- **Greyhound**, Market Street, Lutterworth LE17 4EJ **Tel:** 01455 553307
- **Hambleton Hall**, Hambleton, Oakham, Rutland LE15 8TH **Tel:** 01572 756991
- **Lake Isle**, 16 High St East, Uppingham, Rutland LE15 9PZ **Tel:** 01572 822951
- **Monckton Arms Hotel**, Glaston, Rutland LE15 9BP **Tel:** 01572 822326
- **Normanton Park Hotel**, Normanton Park, Rutland Water, Southshore LE15 8RP **Tel:** 01780 720315
- **Quorn Country Hotel**, 66 Leicester Rd, Quorn LE12 8BB **Tel:** 01509 415050
- **Quorn Grange**, 88 Wood Lane, Quorn LE12 8DB **Tel:** 01509 412167
- **Stapleford Park Country House Hotel**, Leicestershire LE14 2EF **Tel:** 01572 787522
- **White Wings**, Quaker Close, Fenny Drayton CV13 6DE **Tel:** 01827 716100

Lincolnshire

- **Black Horse Inn**, Grimsthorpe, Bourne PE10 0LY **Tel:** 01778 591247
- **George Of Stamford**, St Martins, Stamford PE9 2LB **Tel:** 01780 55171
- **Hare & Hounds,** The Green, Fulbeck NG32 3JJ **Tel:** 01400 272090.
- **Petwood House Hotel**, Stixwould Road, Woodhall Spa LN10 6QF **Tel:** 01526 352411
- **Priory**, Church Road, Ketton, Stamford PE9 3RD **Tel:** 01780 720215
- **Washingborough Hall**, Church Hill, Washingborough, LN4 1BE **Tel:** 01522 790340

London

- **11 Cadogan Gardens**, Sloane Square, Knightsbridge SW3 2RJ **Tel:** 0171 730 3426
- **16 Sumner Place**, SW7 3EG **Tel:** 0171 589 5232
- **22 Jermyn Street,** SW1Y 6HL **Tel:** 0171 734 2353
- **Ascott Mayfair,** 49 Hill St W1X 7FQ **Tel:** 0171 499 6868
- **Basil St Hotel**, Basil St SW3 1AH **Tel:** 0171 581 3311
- **Beaufort**, 33 Beaufort Gardens, Knightsbridge SW3 1PP **Tel:** 0171 584 5252
- **Beaufort House Apts**, 45 Beaufort Gardens SW3 1PN **Tel:** 0171 584 2600
- **Berkeley**, Wilton Place, Knightsbridge SW1X 7RL **Tel:** 0171 235 6000
- **Blakes Hotel**, 33 Roland Gardens SW7 3PF **Tel:** 0171 370 6701
- **Cadogan**, Sloane Street SW1X 9SG **Tel:** 0171 235 7141
- **Cannizaro House**, West Side, Wimbledon Common SW19 4UE **Tel:** 0181 879 1464
- **Claridge's**, Brook Street, Mayfair W1A 2JQ **Tel:** 0171 629 8860
- **Dorchester**, Park Lane, Mayfair WIA 2HJ **Tel:** 0171 629 8888
- **Draycott House Apartments**, 10 Draycott Avenue, Chelsea SW3 3AA **Tel:** 0171 584 4659
- **Halcyon**, 81 Holland Pk W11 3RZ **Tel:** 0171 727 7288
- **Harrington Hall**, 5-25 Harrington Gardens SW7 4JW **Tel:** 0171 396 9696
- **Howard**, Temple Place, The Strand WC2 2PR **Tel:** 0171 836 3555
- **Leonard**, 15 Seymour St. W1H 5AA **Tel:** 0171 935 2010
- **Milestone**, 1-2 Kensington Court W8 5DL **Tel:** 0171 917 1000
- **Pembridge Court Hotel**, 34 Pembridge Gardens W2 4DX **Tel:** 0171 229 9977
- **Savoy**, The Strand WC2R 0EU **Tel:** 0171 836 4343
- **Sloane Hotel**, 29 Draycott House, Chelsea SW3 2SH **Tel:** 0171 581 5757

Merseyside

- **Tree Tops Country House Restaurant & Hotel**, Southport Old Road, Formby L37 0AB **Tel:** 01704 879651

•Woolton Redbourne Hotel, Acrefield Road, Woolton L25 5JN **Tel:** 0151 428 2152 /421 1500

Norfolk

•Barton Angler Country Inn, Irstead Road, Neatishead NR12 8XP **Tel:** 01692 630740
•Beeches Hotel & Victorian Gardens, 4-6 Earlham Road, Norwich NR2 3DB **Tel:** 01603 621167
•Beechwood Hotel, Cromer Road, North Walsham NR28 0HD **Tel:** 01692 403231
•Broom Hall, Richmond Road, Saham Toney, Thetford IP25 7EX **Tel:** 01953 882125
•Catton Old Hall, Lodge Lane, Catton, Norwich NR6 7HG **Tel:** 01603 419379
•Congham Hall, Grimston, King's Lynn PE32 1AH **Tel:** 01485 600250
•Garden House Hotel, Salhouse Road, Rackheath, Norwich, NR13 6AA **Tel:** 01603 720007
•Green Farm Restaurant & Hotel, North Walsham Road, Thorpe Market NR11 8TH **Tel:** 01263 833602.
•Hoste Arms Hotel, The Green, Burnham Market PE31 8HD **Tel:** 01328 738257
•Old Rectory, Gissing, Diss IP22 3XB **Tel:** 01379 677575
•Old Rectory, Fakenham NR12 0HP **Tel:** 01328 820597
•Park Farm Hotel & Leisure, Hethersett, Norwich NR9 3DL **Tel:** 01603 810264
•Petersfield House Hotel, Lower Street, Horning NR12 8PF **Tel:** 01692 630741
•Salisbury House, Victoria Road, Diss IP22 3JG **Tel:** 01379 644738
•Sculthorpe Mill, Sculthorpe NR21 9QG **Tel:** 01328 856161/86275
•Sprowston Manor Hotel, Sprowston Park, Wroxham Road, Norwich NR7 8RP **Tel:** 01603 410871
•Stower Grange, School Road, Drayton NR8 6EF **Tel:** 01603 860210

Northamptonshire

•Falcon Hotel, Castle Ashby NN7 1LF **Tel:** 01604 696200
•Windmill At Badby, Main Street, Badby NN11 6AN **Tel:** 01327 702363

Northumberland

•Blue Bell Hotel, Market Place, Belford NE70 7NE **Tel:** 01668 213543
•Breamish Country House Hotel, Powburn, Alnwick, NE66 4LL **Tel:** 01665 578544/578266
•Glenview, 6 Meadowfield Road, Stocksfield NE43 7QX **Tel:** 01661 843674
•Langar Hall, Langar NG13 9HG **Tel:** 01949 860559
•Linden Hall Hotel & Health Spa, Longhorsley, Morpeth NE65 8XF **Tel:** 01670 516611
•Slaley Hall, Slaley NE47 0BY **Tel:** 01434 673350
•Tillmouth Park, Cornhill-on-Tweed TD12 4UU **Tel:** 01890 882255
•Waren House Hotel, Waren Mill, Bamburgh NE70 7EE **Tel:** 01668 214581
•Wark Farm House, Wark, Cornhill-On-Tweed TD12 4RE **Tel:** 01890 883570

Nottinghamshire

•Hotel Des Clos, Old Lenton Lane NG7 2SA **Tel:** 01159 866566

Oxfordshire

•Bay Tree Hotel & Restaurant, Sheep Street, Burford OX18 4LW **Tel:** 01993 822791
•Cotswold Gateway Hotel, Cheltenham Road, Burford OX18 4HX **Tel:** 01993 822695
•Fallowfields, Kingston Bagpuize With Southmoor OX13 5BH **Tel:** 01865 820416
•Feathers Hotel, Market Street, Woodstock OX20 1SX **Tel:** 01993 812291
•George Hotel, High Street, Dorchester-On-Thames OX9 8HH **Tel:** 01865 340404
•Holcombe Hotel, High Street, Deddington OX15 0SL **Tel:** 01869 338274
•Jersey Arms, Middleton Stoney **Tel:** 01869 343234
•Kings Head Inn & Restaurant, The Green, Bledington OX7 6HD **Tel:** 01608 658365
•Lamb Inn, Sheep Street, Burford OX18 4LR **Tel:** 01993 823155
•Lamb Inn, Shipton-Under-Wychwood OX7 6DQ **Tel:** 01993 830465
•Le Manoir Aux Quat' Saisons, Great Milton OX44 7PD **Tel:** 01844 27888
•Mill & Old Swan, Minster Lovell OX8 5RN **Tel:** 01993 774441
•Mill House Hotel, Kingham OX7 6UH **Tel:** 01608 658188
•Plough, Bourton Road, Clanfield OX18 2RB **Tel:** 01367 810222
•Red Lion Inn, The Green, Adderbury OX17 3LU **Tel:** 01295 810269
•Shaven Crown Hotel, High Street, Shipton Under Wychwood OX7 6BA **Tel:** 01993 830330
•Springs Hotel, North Stoke, Wallingford OX10 6BE **Tel:** 01491 836687
•Stonor Arms, Stonor RG9 6HE **Tel:** 01491 638345
•Studley Priory, Horton-cum-Studley OX33 1AZ **Tel:** 01865 351203
•Talkhouse, Wheatley Road, Stanton-St-John OX33 1EX **Tel:** 01865 351648
•Thatchers Inn, 29-30 Lower High Street, Thame OX9 2AA **Tel:** 0184421 2146

•Wroxton House Hotel, Wroxton St Mary OX15 6QB **Tel:** 01295 730777

Shropshire

•Brakes, Downton SY8 2LF **Tel:** 01584 856485
•Buckatree Hall Hotel, The Wrekin, Wellington, Telford TF6 5AL **Tel:** 01952 641821
•Cross Lane House Hotel, Astley Abbots, Bridgnorth WV16 4SJ **Tel:** 01746 764887
•Delbury Hall, Diddlebury, Craven Arms SY7 9DH **Tel:** 01584 841267
•Dinham Hall, Ludlow SY8 1EJ **Tel:** 01584 876464
•Hundred House Hotel, Bridgnorth Road, Norton, Nr Shifnal, Telford TF11 9EE **Tel:** 01952 730353
•Madeley Court, Telford TF7 5DW **Tel:** 01952 680068
•Old Vicarage Hotel, Worfield, Bridgnorth WV15 5JZ **Tel:** 01746 716497
•Pen-y-Dyffryn Country Hotel, Rhydycroesau SY10 7DT **Tel:** 01691 653700
•Poppies At The Roebuck, Brimfield, Ludlow SY8 4NE **Tel:** 01584 711230
•Redfern Hotel, Cleobury Mortimer DY14 8AA **Tel:** 01299 270 395
•Rowton Castle Hotel & Restaurant, Halfway House, Shrewsbury SY5 9EP **Tel:** 01743 884044

Somerset

•Anchor Country Inn & Hotel, Exbridge TA22 9AZ **Tel:** 01398 23433
•Beacon Country House Hotel, Beacon Road, Minehead TA24 5SD **Tel:** 01643 703476
•Beryl, Wells BA5 3JP **Tel:** 01749 678738
•Castle At Taunton, Castle Green, Taunton TA1 1AF **Tel:** 01823 272671
•Crown Hotel, Exford, Exmoor National Park TA24 7PP **Tel:** 01643 831554/5
•Daneswood House Hotel, Cuck Hill, Shipham BS25 1RD **Tel:** 01934 843145
•Farthings Hotel & Restaurant, Hatch Beauchamp, Taunton TA3 6SG **Tel:** 01823 480664
•George Hotel, Market Place, Castle Cary BA7 7AH **Tel:** 01963 350761
•Glencot House, Glencot Lane, Wookey Hole BA5 1BH **Tel:** 01749 677160
•Kings Arms Inn & Restaurant, Montacute TA16 6UU **Tel:** 01935 822513
•Langley House Hotel, Langley Marsh, Wiveliscombe TA4 2UF **Tel:** 01984 623318
•Meadow House, Sea Lane, Kilve TA5 1EG **Tel:** 01278 741546
•Periton Park Hotel, Middlecombe TA24 8SW **Tel:** 01643 706885
•Pheasant Hotel, Seavington St Mary TA19 0HQ **Tel:** 01460 240502
•Royal Oak Inn, Exmoor National Park, Winsford TA24 7JE **Tel:** 01643 851 455
•Royal Oak Inn, Withypool, Exmoor National Park TA24 7QP **Tel:** 01643 831236
•Rumwell Manor Hotel, Rumwell, Taunton TA4 1EL **Tel:** 01823 461902
•Simonsbath House Hotel, Simonsbath, Exmoor TA24 7SH **Tel:** 01643 831259
•Ston Easton Park, Ston Easton, Bath BA3 4DF **Tel:** 01761 241631
•Walnut Tree, West Camel BA22 7QW **Tel:** 01935 851292.
•Webbington Hotel, Loxton BS26 2XA **Tel:** 01934 750100

Staffordshire

•Brookhouse, Rolleston on Dove DE13 9AA **Tel:** 01283 814188
•Hoar Cross Hall Health Spa Resort, Hoar Cross DE13 8QS **Tel:** 01283 575671
•Old Beams Restaurant with Rooms, Waterhouses ST10 3HW **Tel:** 01538 308254
•Old Vicarage, Main Street, Branston, Burton Upon Trent DE14 3EX **Tel:** 01283 533222
•Swinfen Hall, Swinfen WS14 9RS **Tel:** 01543 481494
•Three Horseshoes Inn & Restaurant, Buxton Rd, Blackshaw Moor ST13 8TW **Tel:** 01538 300296
•Wheatsheaf Inn At Onneley & La Puerta Del Sol Restaurante Espanol, Barhill Road, Onneley CW3 9QF **Tel:** 01782 751581

Suffolk

•Anchor, Walberswick IP18 6UA **Tel:** 01502 722112
•Angel Hotel, Bury St Edmunds IP33 1LT **Tel:** 01284 753926
•Belstead Brook Manor Hotel, Belstead Brook Park, Belstead Rd, Ipswich IP2 9HB **Tel:** 01473 684241
•Bradfield House Restaurant & Hotel, Bury St Edmunds IP30 0LR **Tel:** 01284 386301
•Chippenhall Hall, Fressingfield, Eye IP21 5TD **Tel:** 01379 588180
•Countrymen, The Green, Long Melford CO10 9DN **Tel:** 01787 312356
•Great House Restaurant & Hotel, Market Place, Lavenham CO10 9QZ **Tel:** 01787 247431
•Hintlesham Hall, Hintlesham, Ipswich IP8 3NS **Tel:** 01473 652268
•Otley House, Otley, Ipswich IP6 9NR **Tel:** 01473 890253
•Ravenwood Hall, Rougham, Bury St Edmunds IP30 9JA **Tel:** 01359 270345
•Seckford Hall, Woodbridge IP13 6NU **Tel:** 01394 385678

•St. Peter's House, Old Market, Beccles NR34 9AP **Tel:** 01502 713203
•Swan Hotel, Southwold IP18 6EG **Tel:** 01502 722186
•Wentworth Hotel, Wentworth Road, Aldeburgh IP15 5BD **Tel:** 01728 452312

Surrey

•Angel Posting House & Livery, 91 The High Street, Guildford GU1 3DP **Tel:** 01483 64555
•Chase Lodge, 10 Park Road, Hampton Wick, Kingston Upon Thames KT1 4AS **Tel:** 0181 943 1862
•Inn On The Lake, Ockford Road, Godalming GU7 1RH **Tel:** 01483 415575
•Langshott Manor, Langshott, Horley RH6 9LN **Tel:** 01293 786680
•Lythe Hill Hotel, Petworth Road, Haslemere GU27 3BQ **Tel:** 01428 651251
•Manor, Newlands Corner, Guildford GU4 8SE **Tel:** 01483 222624
•Nutfield Priory, Nutfield RH1 4EN **Tel:** 01737 822066
•Oatlands Park Hotel, 146 Oatlands Drive, Weybridge KT13 9HB **Tel:** 01932 847242
•Pennyhill Park Hotel & Country Club, London Road, Bagshot GU19 5ET **Tel:** 01276 471774
•Richmond Gate Hotel & Restaurant, Richmond Hill, Richmond-Upon-Thames TW10 6RP **Tel:** 0181 940 0061
•Stanhill Court Hotel, Stanhill Road, Charlwood RH6 0EP **Tel:** 01293 862166
•Woodlands Park Hotel, Stoke d'Abernon, Cobham KT11 3QB **Tel:** 01372 843933

Sussex

•Alexander House, Turner's Hill RH10 4QD **Tel:** 01342 714914
•Amberley Castle, Amberley BN18 9ND **Tel:** 01798 831992
•Angel Hotel, North Street, Midhurst GU29 9DN **Tel:** 01730 812421
•Ashdown Park Hotel, Wych Cross, Forest Row, Ashdown Forest RH18 5JR **Tel:** 01342 824988
•Bailiffscourt, Climping BN17 5RW **Tel:** 01903 723511
•Boathouse Brasserie, Houghton Bridge, Amberley, BN18 9LR **Tel:** 01798 831059
•Broomhill Lodge, Rye Foreign, Rye TN31 7UN **Tel:** 01797 280421
•Burpham Country Hotel, Old Down, Burpham, BN18 9RV **Tel:** 01903 882160
•Buxted Park, Buxted, Uckfield TN22 4AY **Tel:** 01825 732711
•Chequers At Slaugham, Slaugham RH17 6AQ **Tel:** 01444 400239/400996
•Chequers Hotel, Church Place, Pulborough RH20 1AD **Tel:** 01798 872486
•Country House At Winchelsea, Hastings Road, Winchelsea TN36 4AD **Tel:** 01797 226669
•Down House, Down Street, Nutley TN22 3LG **Tel:** 01825 712328
•Hooke Hall, High Street, Uckfield TN22 1EN **Tel:** 01825 761578
•Horsted Place Sporting Estate & Hotel, Little Horsted TN22 5TS **Tel:** 01825 750581
•Little Thakeham, Merrywood Lane, Storrington RH20 3HE **Tel:** 01903 744416
•Mermaid Inn, Mermaid Street, Rye TN31 7EU **Tel:** 01797 223065
•Millstream Hotel, Bosham PO18 8HL **Tel:** 01243 573234
•Ockenden Manor, Ockenden Lane, Cuckfield RH17 5LD **Tel:** 01444 416111
•Old Tollgate Restaurant & Hotel, The Street, Bramber, Steyning BN44 3WE **Tel:** 01903 879494
•Powdermills Hotel, Powdermill Lane, Battle TN33 0SP **Tel:** 01424 775511
•South Lodge Hotel, Brighton Road, Lower Beeding RH13 6PS **Tel:** 01403 891711
•Spread Eagle Hotel, South Street, Midhurst GU29 9NH **Tel:** 01730 816911
•Topps Hotel, 17 Regency Square, Brighton BN1 2FG **Tel:** 01273 729334
•White Horse Inn, Sutton RH20 1PS **Tel:** 01798 869 221
•White Lodge Country House Hotel, Sloe Lane, Alfriston BN26 5UR **Tel:** 01323 870265

Warwickshire

•Ardencote Manor Country Club, Lye Green Road, Claverdon CU35 8LS **Tel:** 01926 843111
•Arrow Mill Hotel & Restaurant, Arrow B49 5NL **Tel:** 01789 762419
•Baraset Barn Restaurant, Pimlico Lane, Alveston, Stratford-Upon-Avon CV37 7RF **Tel:** 01789 295510
•Billesley Manor, Billesley, Alcester B49 6NF **Tel:** 01789 279955
•Blue Boar Inn, Temple Grafton, Alcester B49 6NR **Tel:** 01789 750010
•Chapel House, Friars' Gate, Atherstone CV9 1EY **Tel:** 01827 718949
•Coombe Abbey, Brinklow Road, Binley CV3 2AB **Tel:** 01203 450450
•Ettington Park Hotel, Alderminster, Stratford-Upon-Avon CV37 8BS **Tel:** 01789 450123
•Glebe At Barford, Church Street, Barford CV35 8BS **Tel:** 01926 624218

•Golden Lion Inn of Easenall, Easenall CV23 0JA **Tel:** 01788 832265
•Marston Farm Hotel, Bodymoor Heath, Sutton Coldfield, Warwickshire, B76 9JD **Tel:** 01827 872133
•Nailcote Hall, Nailcote Lane, Berkswell CV7 7DE **Tel:** 01203 466174
•Nuthurst Grange, Hockley Heath B94 5NL **Tel:** 01564 783972
•Welcombe Hotel Golf Course, Warwick Road, Stratford-Upon-Avon CV37 0NR **Tel:** 01789 295252

West Midlands

•New Hall, Walmley Road, Royal Sutton Coldfield, West Midlands B76 8QX **Tel:** 0121 378 2442
•Swallow Hotel, 12, Hagley Road, Fiveways, Birmingham B16 8SJ **Tel:** 0121 452 1144

Wiltshire

•Bishopstrow House, Warminster BA12 9HH **Tel:** 01985 212312
•Blunsdon House Hotel, Blunsdon, Swindon SN2 4AD **Tel:** 01793 721701
•Box House, Box SN13 8NR **Tel:** 01225 744447
•Castle Inn, Castle Combe SN14 7HN **Tel:** 01249 783030
•Crudwell Court Hotel, Crudwell SN16 9EP **Tel:** 01666 577194
•Horse & Groom Inn, Charlton SN16 9DL **Tel:** 01666 823904
•Ivy House Hotel, High St, Marlborough SN8 1HJ **Tel:** 01672 515333
•Lucknam Park, Colerne SN14 8AZ **Tel:** 01225 742777
•Manor House, Castle Combe, Chippenham SN14 7HR **Tel:** 01249 782206
•Milford Hall Hotel & Restaurant, 206 Castle Street, Salisbury SP1 3TE **Tel:** 01722 417411
•Old Bell, Abbey Row, Malmesbury SN16 0AG **Tel:** 01666 822344
•Stanton Manor, Stanton Saint Quinton SN14 6DQ **Tel:** 01666 837552
•Whatley Manor, Easton Grey, Malmesbury SN16 0RB **Tel:** 01666 822888
•White Hart, Ford, Chippenham SN14 8RP **Tel:** 01249 782213
•Widbrook Grange, Trowbridge Road, Bradford-On-Avon BA15 1UH **Tel:** 01225 864750 / 863173
•Woolley Grange, Woolley Green, Bradford-On-Avon BA15 1TX **Tel:** 01225 864705

Worcestershire

•Brockencote Hall, Chaddersley Corbett DY10 4PY **Tel:** 01562 777876
•Buckland Manor, Buckland WR12 7LY **Tel:** 01386 852626
•Collin House Hotel, Collin Lane, Broadway WR12 7PB **Tel:** 01386 858354 & 852544
•Cottage In The Wood, Holywell Road, Malvern Wells WR14 4LG **Tel:** 01684 575859
•Crown At Hopton, Hopton Wafers, Cleobury Mortimer DY14 0NB **Tel:** 01299 270372
•Dormy House, Willersey Hill, Broadway WR12 7LF **Tel:** 01386 852711
•Evesham Hotel, Coopers Lane, Off Waterside, Evesham WR11 6DA **Tel:** 01386 765566
•Freshmans Restaurant, Church Hill, Belbroughton DY9 0DT **Tel:** 01562 730467
•Grafton Manor Country House Hotel, Grafton Lane, Bromsgrove B61 7HA **Tel:** 01527 579007
•Leasow House, Laverton Meadows, Broadway WR12 7NA **Tel:** 01386 584526
•Lygon Arms, Broadway WR12 7DU **Tel:** 01386 852255
•Mill At Harvington, Anchor Lane, Harvington, Evesham WR11 5NR **Tel:** 01386 870688
•Old Rectory, Church Street, Willersey WR12 7PN **Tel:** 01386 853729
•Old Rectory, Ipsley Lane, Redditch B98 0AP **Tel:** 01527 523000
•Riverside Restaurant & Hotel, The Parks, Offenham Road WR11 5JP **Tel:** 01386 446200
•Salford Hall Hotel, Abbot's Salford **Tel:** 01386 871300
•White Lion Hotel, High Street, Upton-Upon-Severn WR8 0HJ **Tel:** 01684 592551

Yorkshire

•4 South Parade, York YO2 2BA **Tel:** 01904 628229
•42 The Calls, Leeds LS2 7EW **Tel:** 0113 244 0099
•Appleton Hall, Appleton-Le-Moors YO6 6TF **Tel:** 01751 417227
•Bagden Hall Hotel & Golf Course, Wakefield Road, Scissett HD8 9LE **Tel:** 01484 865330
•Balmoral Hotel, Franklin Mount, Harrogate HG1 5EJ **Tel:** 01423 508208
•Bilbrough Manor, Bilbrough, York YO2 3PH **Tel:** 01937 834002
•Blue Lion, East Witton DL8 4SN **Tel:** 01969 624273
•Boar's Head Hotel, Ripley, Harrogate HG3 3AY **Tel:** 01423 771888
•Carlton Hotel, Albert Street, Hebden Bridge HX7 8ES **Tel:** 01422 844400
•Charnwood Hotel, 10 Sharrow Lane, Sheffield S11 8AA **Tel:** 0114 258 9411
•Chevin Lodge Country Park Hotel, Yorkgate, Otley LS21 3NU **Tel:** 01943 467818

• **Crathorne Hall Hotel**, Crathorne TS15 0AR **Tel:** 01642 700398
• **Devonshire Arms Country House Hotel**, Bolton Abbey, Skipton BD23 6AJ **Tel:** 01756 710441
• **Dunsley Hall**, Dunsley, Whitby YO21 3TL **Tel:** 01947 893437
• **East Ayton Lodge Country Hotel & Restaurant**, Moor Lane, Forge Valley, East Ayton, Scarborough, YO13 9EW **Tel:** 01723 864227
• **Feversham Arms Hotel**, Helmsley YO6 5AG **Tel:** 01439 770766
• **George & Dragon Hotel**, Market Place, Kirkbymoorside YO6 6AA **Tel:** 01751 433334
• **Grange Hotel**, Clifton, York YO3 6AA **Tel:** 01904 644744
• **Grants Hotel**, Swan Road, Harrogate HG1 2SS **Tel:** 01423 560666
• **Green Man**, 15 Market Street, Malton YO17 0LY **Tel:** 01653 600370
• **Hackness Grange**, North York Moors National Park, Scarborough YO13 0JW **Tel:** 01723 882345
• **Haley's Hotel & Restaurant**, Shire Oak Road, Headingley LS6 2DE **Tel:** 0113 278 4446
• **Hob Green Hotel & Restaurant**, Markington, Harrogate HG3 3PY **Tel:** 01423 770031
• **Holdsworth House**, Holdsworth Road, Holmfield, Halifax HX2 9TG **Tel:** 01422 240024
• **Kings Arms Hotel & Restaurant**, Market Place, Askrigg-In-Wensleydale DL8 3HQ **Tel:** 01969 650258
• **Linton Springs**, Sicklinghall Road, Wetherby LS22 4AF **Tel:** 01937 585353
• **Mallyan Spout Hotel**, Goathland YO22 5AN **Tel:** 01947 896486
• **Manor House**, Northlands, Walkington HU17 8RT **Tel:** 01482 881645
• **Middlethorpe Hall**, Bishopthorpe Road, York YO2 1QB **Tel:** 01904 641241
• **Milburn Arms Hotel**, Rosedale Abbey, Pickering YO18 8RA **Tel:** 01751 417312
• **Millers House Hotel**, Middleham, Wensleydale DL8 4NR **Tel:** 01969 622630
• **Monk Fryston**, Monk Fryston, Leeds LS25 5DU **Tel:** 01977 682369
• **Mount Royale Hotel**, The Mount, York YO2 2DA **Tel:** 01904 628856
• **Newstead Grange**, Norton-On-Derwent, Malton YO17 9PQ **Tel:** 01653 692502
• **Nidd Hall**, Nidd, Harrogate HG3 3BN **Tel:** 01423 771598
• **Old White Lion Hotel**, Keighley BD22 8DU **Tel:** 01535 642313
• **Parsonage Country House Hotel**, Escrick, York YO4 6LF **Tel:** 01904 728111
• **Pheasant**, Harome, Helmsley YO6 5YG **Tel:** 01439 771241 /770416.
• **Rock Inn Hotel**, Holywell Green, Halifax HX4 9BS **Tel:** 01422 379721
• **Rookhurst Georgian Country House Hotel**, West End, Gayle, Hawes DL8 3RT **Tel:** 01969 667454
• **Tempest Arms**, Elslack BD23 3AY **Tel:** 01282 842450
• **Victoria Hotel**, Bridge Street, Bradford BD1 1JX **Tel:** 01274 728706
• **Wensleydale Heifer Inn**, West Witton, Wensleydale DL8 4LS **Tel:** 01969 622322
• **Wentbridge House Hotel**, Wentbridge WF8 3JJ **Tel:** 01977 620444
• **Wheatsheaf Inn**, Egton YO21 1TZ **Tel:** 01947 895271
• **White House**, 10 Park Parade, Harrogate HG1 5AH **Tel:** 01423 501388
• **White Swan**, The Market Place, Pickering YO18 7AA **Tel:** 01751 472288.
• **Whitley Hall Hotel**, Elliot Lane, Grenoside, Sheffield S30 3NR **Tel:** 0114 245 4444
• **Wood Hall**, Linton LS22 4JA **Tel:** 01937 587271
• **Worsley Arms Hotel**, Hovingham, York YO6 4LA **Tel:** 01653 628234
• **Wrea Head Country Hotel**, Scalby YO13 0PB **Tel:** 01723 378211

Scotland

• **Allt-nan-Ros Hotel**, Onich, Fort William, Inverness-shire PH33 6RY **Tel:** 01855 821210
• **Altamount House Hotel**, Coupar Angus Road, Blairgowrie, Perthshire PH10 6JN **Tel:** 01250 873512
• **Ardanaiseig**, Kilchrenan by Taynuilt, Argyll PA35 1HE **Tel:** 01866 833333
• **Ardfillayne House & Restaurant**, West Bay, Dunoon, Argyll PA23 7QJ **Tel:** 01369 702267
• **Ardsheal House**, Kentallen Of Appin, Argyll PA38 4BX **Tel:** 01631 740227
• **Ardvourlie Castle**, Aird aMhulaidh, Isle Of Harris, Western Isles HS3 3AB **Tel:** 01859 502307
• **Arisaig House**, Beasdale, By Arisaig, Inverness-shire PH39 4NR **Tel:** 01687 450622
• **Balcary Bay Hotel**, Auchencairn, Dumfries & Galloway DG7 1QZ **Tel:** 01556 640217
• **Balgonie Country House**, Braemar Place, Royal Deeside, Ballater, Abdshire AB35 5RQ **Tel:** 013397 55482
• **Ballathie House Hotel**, Kinclaven By Stanley, Perthshire PH1 4QN **Tel:** 01250 883268
• **Baron's Craig Hotel**, Rockcliffe By Dalbeattie, Kirkcudbrightshire DG5 4QF **Tel:** 01556 630 225
• **Borthwick Castle**, Borthwick, North Middleton, Midlothian EH23 4QY **Tel:** 01875 820514
• **Bunchrew House Hotel**, Inverness, Inverness-shire IV3 6TA **Tel:** 01463 234917
• **Cairnbann Hotel**, By Lochgilphead, Argyll PA31 8SJ **Tel:** 01546 603668
• **Cally Palace Hotel**, Gatehouse Of Fleet, Dumfries & Galloway DG7 2DL **Tel:** 01557 814341
• **Cameron House**, Loch Lomond, Dunbartonshire G83 8QZ **Tel:** 01389 755565
• **Castleton House Hotel**, Glamis, By Forfar, Angus DD8 1SJ **Tel:** 01307 840340
• **Channings**, South Learmonth Gardens, Edinburgh, Mid Lothian EH4 1EZ **Tel:** 0131 315 2226
• **Comrie Hotel**, Comrie, Perthshire PH6 2DY **Tel:** 01764 670239/670330
• **Conchra House**, Ardelve, Kyle of Lochalsh, Invernessshire IV40 8DZ **Tel:** 01599 555233
• **Corrour House Hotel**, Inverdruie, Aviemore, Inverness-shire PH22 1QH **Tel:** 01479 810220
• **Craigmhor Lodge**, 27 West Moulin Road, Pitlochry, Perthshire PH16 5EF **Tel:** 01796 472123
• **Cringletie House Hotel**, Peebles, Peebleshire EH45 8PL **Tel:** 01721 730233
• **Cromlix House**, Kinbuck, By Dunblane, Perthshire FK15 9JT **Tel:** 01786 822125
• **Culcreuch Castle Hotel**, Fintry, Loch Lomond, Stirlingsshire G63 0LW **Tel:** 01360 860228
• **Culdearn House**, Woodlands Terrace, Grantown-On-Spey, Moray PH26 3JU **Tel:** 01479 872106
• **Culduthel Lodge**, 14 Culduthel Road, Inverness, Inverness-shire IV2 4AG **Tel:** 01463 240089
• **Culloden House Hotel**, Inverness, Inverness-shire IV1 2NZ **Tel:** 01463 790461
• **Dalhousie Castle Hotel & Restaurant**, Edinburgh, Bonnyrigg EH19 3JB **Tel:** 01875 820153
• **Dalmunzie House**, Spittal O'Glenshee, Blairgowrie, Perthshire PH10 7QG **Tel:** 01250 885224
• **Darroch Learg Hotel**, Braemar Road, Ballater, Aberdeenshire AB35 5UX **Tel:** 013397 55443
• **Dunfallandy House**, Logierait Road, Pitlochry, Perthshire PH16 5NA **Tel:** 01796 472648
• **Dupplin Castle**, Dupplin Estate, By Perth, Perthshire PH2 0PY **Tel:** 01738 623224
• **Ednam House Hotel**, Bridge Street, Kelso, Roxburghshire TD5 7HT **Tel:** 01573 224168
• **Enmore Hotel**, Marine Parade, Kirn, Dunoon, Argyll PA23 8HH **Tel:** 01369 702230
• **Farleyer House Hotel**, Aberfeldy, Perthshire PH15 2JE **Tel:** 01887 820332
• **Gleddoch House**, Langbank, Renfrewshire PA14 6YE **Tel:** 01475 540711
• **Glenisla Hotel**, Kirkton of Glenisla, By Alyth, Perthshire PH11 8PH **Tel:** 01575 582223
• **Greywalls**, Muirfield, Gullane, East Lothian EH31 2EG **Tel:** 01620 842144
• **Harlosh House**, By Dunvegan, Isle of Skye, Invernesshire IV55 8ZG **Tel:** 01470 521367
• **Hotel Eilean Iarmain or Isle Ornsay Hotel**, Eilean Iarmain, Sleat, Isle Of Skye IV43 8QR **Tel:** 01471833 332
• **Howard**, 36 Great King Street, Edinburgh EH3 6QH **Tel:** 0131 557 3500
• **Invercreran Country House Hotel**, Glen Creran, Appin, Argyll PA38 4BJ **Tel:** 01631 730 414
• **Isle Of Eriska**, Ledaig, By Oban, Argyll PA37 1SD **Tel:** 01631 720371
• **Johnstounburn House**, Humbie, East Lothian EH36 5PL **Tel:** 01875 833696
• **Kildrummy Castle Hotel**, Kildrummy, By Alford, Aberdeenshire AB33 8RA **Tel:** 019755 71288
• **Killiechronan**, Killiechronan, Argyll PA72 6JU **Tel:** 01680 300403
• **Killiecrankie Hotel**, Killiecrankie, By Pitlochry, Perthshire PH16 5LG **Tel:** 01796 473220
• **Kingsmills Hotel**, Culcabock Road, Inverness, Inverness-shire IV2 3LP **Tel:** 01463 237166
• **Kinloch House Hotel**, By Blairgowrie, Perthshire PH10 6SG **Tel:** 01250 884237
• **Kinnaird**, Kinnaird Estate, By Dunkeld, Perthshire PH8 0LB **Tel:** 01796 482 440
• **Kirroughtree Hotel**, Newton Stewart, Wigtownshire DG8 6AN **Tel:** 01671 402141
• **Knipoch Hotel**, By Oban, Argyll PA34 4QT **Tel:** 01852 316251
• **Knockie Lodge Hotel**, Whitebridge, Inverness-shire IV1 2UP **Tel:** 01456 486276
• **Knockinaam Lodge**, Portpatrick, Wigtownshire DG9 9AD **Tel:** 01776 810471
• **Knockomie Hotel**, Grantown Road, Forres, Moray IV36 0SG **Tel:** 01309 673146
• **Kylesku Hotel**, Kylesku, Via Lairg, Sutherland IV27 4HW **Tel:** 01971 502231/502200
• **Lake Hotel**, Port Of Menteith, Perthshire FK8 3RA **Tel:** 01877 385258
• **Letham Grange Hotel & Golf Course**, Colliston, By Arbroath, Angus DD11 4RL **Tel:** 01241 890373
• **Loch Torridon Hotel**, By Achnasheen, Wester-Ross, Inverness-shire IV22 2EY **Tel:** 01445 791242
• **Malmaison Hotel**, 1 Tower Place, Leith, Edinburgh EH6 7DB **Tel:** 0131 555 6868
• **Malmaison Hotel**, 278 West George Street, Glasgow G2 4LL **Tel:** 0141 221 6400
• **Manor House Hotel**, Gallanch Road, Oban, Argyllshire PA34 4LS **Tel:** 01631 562087
• **Mansion House Hotel & Country Club**, The Haugh, Elgin, Moray IV30 1AW **Tel:** 01343 548811
• **Montgreenan Mansion House Hotel**, Montgreenan Estate, Kilwinning KA13 7QZ **Tel:** 01294 557733
• **Murrayshall Country House Hotel**, Scone, Perthshire PH2 7PH **Tel:** 01738 551171
• **Nivingston House**, Cleish, Kinross-shire KY13 7LS **Tel:** 01577 850216
• **Norton House Hotel**, Ingliston, Edinburgh, Mid-Lothian EH28 8LX **Tel:** 0131 333 1275
• **One Devonshire Gardens**, Glasgow G12 0UX **Tel:** 0141 339 2001
• **Parklands Hotel & Restaurant**, St Leonard's Bank, Perth, Perthshire PH2 8EB **Tel:** 01738 622451
• **Piersland House Hotel**, Craig End Road, Troon, Ayrshire KA10 6HD **Tel:** 01292 314747
• **Polmaily House Hotel**, Drumnadrochit, Loch Ness, Inverness-shire IV3 6XT **Tel:** 01456 450343
• **Potarch Hotel**, By Banchory, Royal Deeside, Kincardineshire AB31 4BD **Tel:** 013398 84339
• **Roman Camp Hotel**, Callander, Perthshire FK17 8BG **Tel:** 01877 330003
• **Rufflets Country House & Garden Restaurant**, Stathkinness, St Andrews, Fife KY16 9TX **Tel:** 01334 472594
• **Sciberscross Lodge**, Strath Brora, Rogat, Sutherland IV28 3YO **Tel:** 01408 641246
• **Shieldhill House**, Quothquan, Biggar, Lanarkshire ML12 6NA **Tel:** 01899 220035
• **Summer Isles Hotel**, Achiltibuie, Ross-shire IV26 2YG **Tel:** 01854 622282
• **Sunlaws House Hotel**, Kelso, Roxburghshire TD5 8JZ **Tel:** 01573 450331
• **Town House Hotel**, West George Street, Glasgow G2 1NG **Tel:** 0141 332 3320
• **Uig Hotel**, Uig, Isle Of Skye IV51 9YE **Tel:** 01470 542205
• **Well View Hotel**, Ballplay Road, Moffat, Dumfriesshire DG10 9JU **Tel:** 01683 220184
• **Western Isles Hotel**, Tobermory, Isle Of Mull, Argyll PA75 6PR **Tel:** 01688 302012
• **Winnock Hotel**, The Square, Drymen, Stirlingshire G63 0BL **Tel:** 01360 660245

Wales

• **Berthlwyd Hall Hotel**, Llechwedd, Gwynedd LL32 8DQ **Tel:** 01492 592409
• **Bodfach Hall Country House Hotel**, Llanfyllin, Powys SY22 5HS **Tel:** 01691 648272
• **Bodysgallen Hall**, Llandudno, Gwynedd LL30 1RS **Tel:** 01492 584466
• **Bontddu Hall**, Bontddu, Gwynedd, LL40 2SU **Tel:** 01341 430661
• **Bron Eifion Country House Hotel**, Criccieth, Gwynedd LL52 0SA **Tel:** 01766 522385
• **Bryn Howel Hotel & Restaurant**, Clwyd LL20 7UW **Tel:** 01978 860331
• **Castle View Hotel**, 16 Bridge Street, Chepstow, Gwent NP6 5EZ **Tel:** 01291 620349
• **Cawdor Arms Hotel**, Llandeilo, Dyfed SA19 6EN **Tel:** 01558 823500
• **Celtic Manor Hotel & Golf Club**, Coldra Woods, Newport, Gwent NP6 2YA **Tel:** 01633 413000
• **Coed-Y-Mwstwr Hotel**, Coychurch, Mid Glamorgan CF35 6AF **Tel:** 01656 860621
• **Conrah Country House Hotel**, Rhydgaled, Chancery, Aberystwyth SY23 4DF **Tel:** 01970 617941
• **Crown At Whitebrook**, Whitebrook, Monmouth, Gwent, NP5 4TX **Tel:** 01600 860254
• **Cwrt Bleddyn Hotel**, Llangybi, Gwent NP5 1PG **Tel:** 01633 450521
• **Dolmelynllyn Hall**, Ganllwyd, Dolgellau, Gwynedd LL40 2HP **Tel:** 01341 440273
• **Dragon Hotel**, Montgomery, Powys SY15 6PA **Tel:** 01686 668359
• **Egerton Grey Country House Hotel**, Porthkerry, South Glamorgan CF6 9BZ **Tel:** 01446 711666
• **George III Hotel**, Penmaenpool, Dolgellau, Gwynedd LL40 1YD **Tel:** 01341 422525
• **Glangrwyney Court**, Glangrwyney, Powys NP8 1ES **Tel:** 01873 811288
• **Gliffaes Country House Hotel**, Crickhowell Powys NP8 1RH **Tel:** 01874 730371
• **Hotel Maes-Y-Neuadd**, Talsarnau, Gwynedd LL47 6YA **Tel:** 01766 780200
• **Hotel Portmeirion**, Portmeirion, Gwynedd LL48 6ET **Tel:** 01766 770228
• **Kinsale Hall Hotel**, Llanerchymor, Clwyd CH8 9DX **Tel:** 01745 560001
• **Lake Country House**, Llangammarch Wells, Powys LD4 4BS **Tel:** 01591 620202
• **Lake Vyrnwy Hotel**, Lake Vyrnwy , Llanwddyn, Montgomeryshire SY10 0LY **Tel:** 01691 870 692
• **Lion Hotel & Restaurant**, Berriew, Montgomeryshire SY21 8PQ **Tel:** 01686 640452
• **Llangoed Hall**, Llyswen, Brecon, Powys LD3 0YP **Tel:** 01874 754525
• **Llanwenarth House**, Govilon, Abergavenny, Gwent NP7 9SF **Tel:** 01873 830289
• **Miskin Manor**, Miskin, Mid-Glamorgan CF7 8ND **Tel:** 01443 224204
• **Mynydd Ednyfed Country House Hotel**, Caernarfon Road, Criccieth, Gwynedd LL52 0PH **Tel:** 01766 523269
• **Norton House Hotel & Restaurant**, Norton Road, Mumbles, Swansea SA3 5TQ **Tel:** 01792 404891
• **Old Gwernyfed Country Manor**, Felindre, Three Cocks, Brecon, Powys LD3 0SU **Tel:** 01497 847376
• **Old Rectory**, Llanrwst Road, Llansanffraid Glan Conwy, Gwynedd LL28 5LF **Tel:** 01492 580611
• **Palé Hall**, Palé Llandderfel, Bala, Gwynedd LL23 7PS **Tel:** 01678 530285
• **Parva Farmhouse & Restaurant**, Tintern, Chepstow, Gwent NP6 6SQ **Tel:** 01291 689411
• Penally Abbey, Penally,Tenby, Pembrokeshire SA70 7PY Tel: 01834 843033
• **Penmaenuchaf Hall**, Penmaenpool, Dolgellau, Gwynedd LL40 1YB **Tel:** 01341 422129
• **Penyclawdd Court**, Llanfihangel Crucorney, Abergavenny, Gwent NP7 7LB **Tel:** 01873 890719
• **Peterstone Court**, Llanhamlach, Brecon, Powys LD3 7YB **Tel:** 01874 86387
• **Plas Bach**, Glandwr, Nr Bontddu, Barmouth, Gwynedd LL42 1TG **Tel:** 01341 281234
• **Plas-Glyn-y-Mel**, Lower Town, Fishguard, Pembrokeshire SA65 9LY **Tel:** 01348 872296
• **Plough Inn**, Rhosmaen, Llandeilo, Carmarthenshire SA19 6NP **Tel:** 01558 823431
• **Porth Tocyn Country House Hotel**, Abersoch, Pwllheli, Gwynedd LL53 7BU **Tel:** 01758 713303
• **Seiont Manor Hotel**, Llanrug, Caernarvon, Gwynedd LL55 2AQ **Tel:** 01286 673366
• **Soughton Hall Country House Hotel**, Northop, Clwyd CH7 6AB **Tel:** 01352 840811
• **St Tudno Hotel**, Promenade, Llandudno, Gwynedd LL30 2LP **Tel:** 01492 874411
• **Stone Hall Hotel & Restaurant**, Welsh Hook, Haverford-west, Pembrokeshire SA62 5NS **Tel:** 01348 840212
• **Tan-y-Foel**, Capel Garmon, Gwynedd LL26 0RE **Tel:** 01690 710507
• **Tower**, Off Nercwys Road, Mold, Clwyd, CH7 4ED **Tel:** 01352 700220
• **Trearddur Bay Hotel**, Lon Issalt, Trearddur Bay, Anglesey, Gwynedd LL65 2UN **Tel:** 01407 860301
• **Tyddyn Llan Country House Hotel**, Llandrillo, Clwyd LL21 0ST **Tel:** 01490 440264
• **Tynycornel Hotel**, Tal-y-Llyn, Tywyn, Gwynedd LL36 9AJ **Tel:** 01654 782282
• **Ty'n Rhos Country House**, Llanddeiniolen, Caernarfon, Gwynedd LL55 3AE **Tel:** 01248 670489
• **Warpool Court Hotel**, St David's, Pembrokeshire SA62 6BN **Tel:** 01437 720300
• **Waterwynch House Hotel**, Waterwynch Bay, Tenby, Pembrokeshire SA70 8TJ **Tel:** 01834 842464
• **West Arms Hotel**, Llanarmon D C, Clwyd LL20 7LD **Tel:** 01696 00665
• **Ynyshir Hall**, Eglwysfach, Machynlleth, Powys SY10 8TA **Tel:** 01654 781209

Ireland

• **Adare Manor**, Adare, Co. Lim. **Tel:** 00 353 61 396566
• **Aghadoe Heights Hotel**, Aghadoe, Killarney, Co Kerry **Tel:** 0353 64 31766
• **Ashford Castle**, Cong, Co. Mayo **Tel:** 00353 92 46003
• **Barberstown Castle**, Straffan, Co. Kildare, **Tel:** 010 353 1 6288157
• **Beech Hill**, 23 Ballymoney Road, Craigantlet, Newtownards, Co Down BT23 4TG **Tel:** 01232 425892
• **Belcamp Hutchinson**, Balgriffin, Dublin 17, Co Dublin **Tel:** 010 353 1 846 0843
• **Castle Grove Country House**, Ramelton Road, Letterkenny, Co Donegal **Tel:** 010 353 745 1118
• **Coopershill House**, Riverstown, Co Sligo **Tel:** 010353 71 65108
• **Dromoland Castle**, Newmarket-On-Fergus, Co. Clare **Tel:** 00 353 61 368144
• **Edenvale House**, 130 Portaferry Road, Newtownards, Co Down, BT22 2AH **Tel:** 01247 814881
• **Galgorm Manor**, Ballymena, Co Antrim, BT42 1EA **Tel:** 01266 881001
• **Glenlo Abbey Hotel**, Bushy Park, Co Galway **Tel:** 00 353 91 526666
• **Hibernian**, Eastmoreland Place, Ballsbridge, Dublin **Tel:** 4 00 353 1 668 7666
• **Kelly's Resort Hotel**, Rosslare, Co Wexford **Tel:** 00 353 5332114
• **Kildare Hotel & Country Club**, At Straffan, Co Kildare **Tel:** 00 353 1 627 3333
• **Kinnitty Castle**, Kinnitty, Birr, Co Offaly **Tel:** 00 353 509 37318
• **Liss Ard Lake Lodge**, Skibbereen, Co.Cork **Tel:** 00 353 28 22365
• **Markree Castle**, Colooney **Tel:** 00 353 71 67800
• **Marlfield House**, Gorey, Co Wexford **Tel:** 00 353 21124
• **Mount Juliet House**, Thomastown, Co Kilkenny **Tel:** 00 353 56 24455
• **Nuremore Hotel & Country Club**, Carrickmacross, Co Monaghan **Tel:** 00 353 42 61438
• **Old Rectory**, Wicklow Town, Co Wicklow **Tel:** 00 353 404 67048
• **Park Hotel Kenmare**, Kenmare, Co Kerry **Tel:** 00 353 64 41200
• **Portaferry Hotel**, The Strand, Portaferry, Co Down, BT22 1PE **Tel:** 012477 28231
• **Renvyle House Hotel**, Renvyle, Connemara, Co Galway **Tel:** 00 353 95 43511
• **St David's Country House & Restaurant**, Puckane, Nenagh, Co Tipperary **Tel:** 00 353 67 24145
• **Tinakilly Country House Hotel & Restaurant**, Rathnew, Wicklow, Co Wicklow **Tel:** 00 353 40469274

The Landmark Trust

A CHARITY WHICH RESTORES HISTORIC BUILDINGS AND LETS THEM FOR HOLIDAYS

Over 150 places where you can become, for a short time, the owner of a fine historic building. No membership is required but you do need to buy The Landmark Handbook which illustrates every property with plans, location maps and black and white photographs (£8.50, refundable against your booking).

WARDEN ABBEY

NR. BIGGLESWADE, BEDFORDSHIRE

Landmarks are chosen for their historic interest or architectural importance, because they need our help, and also because many are in surroundings which give unexpected pleasure. Warden Abbey is a fragment of a great Cistercian Abbey and a Tudor House, set in fruitful countryside, once farmed by monks.

Accommodation:
Sleeps up to 5 people.

CULLODEN TOWER

RICHMOND, NORTH YORKSHIRE

The beauty of the Landmark solution is not only that a building is saved and put to good use, but also that the restoration respects its original design. For a short time it is possible to live with rooms in surprising places. At Culloden Tower, there are 68 steps between the bathroom and the main bedroom.

Accommodation:
Sleeps 4 people.

LANGLEY GATEHOUSE

ACTON BURNELL, SHROPSHIRE

Landmarks often lie off the beaten track. Langley is no exception, set in a remote valley with a view to the Wrekin. In our restorations, we prefer to repair the old, and avoid renewal, to preserve the building's texture. When the building is timber framed, this can be like trying to patch a cobweb!

Accommodation:
Sleeps 4 people.

EAST BANQUETING HOUSE

CHIPPING CAMPDEN, GLOUCESTERSHIRE

Some Landmarks, like this one, reflect a way of life from more gracious times and are connected with grand old families. All are furnished as appropriately as possible, with curtains designed and printed for each place, and furniture which is old, simple and good, with occasional extravagant flourishes.
Accommodation: Sleeps 4, a further 2 beds in the North Lodge.

VISA/MASTERCARD NUMBER: HD

☐☐☐☐ ☐☐☐☐ ☐☐☐☐ ☐☐☐☐

Expiry: ☐☐☐☐ Please send me ☐ copies @ ☐ each.

Name:

Address: . . . .

. . . .

. . . . Post Code: . . . .

Name and address of cardholder of different from above:

Name: . . . .

Address: . . . .

. . . .

. . . . Post Code: . . . .

The Landmark Trust Handbook Order Form

Order your copy by sending a sterling cheque drawn on a UK bank, Eurocheque or quoting your VISA or mastercard number.

Handbooks cost £8.50 including postage and packing when they are posted to an address in the UK, otherwise they cost: -£10.50 to Europe; £20.00 to the Americas**, Central Asia, Middle East and Africa; £25.00 to Australasia and Far East.

**Residents of the USA can order a copy for US$19.50 from our mailing house in the States. Contact; The Landmark Trust, 28 Birge Street, Brattleboro, Vermont 05301. Tel: (toll free for US calls) 1-800-848-347.

The cost of the Handbook is refundable against your next booking by using the voucher that comes with it.

Once you have bought a Handbook, you will automatically be put on our mailing list to receive up-to-date Price Lists and availability charts.

PAYMENT by credit card can be made by telephoning our Booking Office on (01628) 825925 or by filling in this order form and posting it to: The Landmark Trust (HD), Shottesbrooke, Maidenhead, Berkshire SL6 3SW Tel: (01628) 825925. Fax: (01628) 825417.

Charity Number: 243312

A SELECTION OF
NATIONAL TRUST EVENTS IN 1996

A list of these and other large summer events, with booking information, will be available from the end of March from the National Trust, PO Box 39, Bromley, Kent BR1 3XL. Please enclose an A5 25p SAE.

• CONCERT SERIES
SPONSORED BY HMSO BOOKS

Petworth House, West Sussex	May
Ham House, Surrey	June
Clumber Chapel, Nottinghamshire	20 July
Claydon House, Bucks	10 August**
Lyme Park (house), Cheshire	September
Clandon Park, Surrey	October

• OPEN AIR CONCERTS

Chartwell, Kent	15 June
Polesden Lacey, Surrey	16 June; 7 July
Petworth Park, West Sussex	28 – 30 June*
Belton House, Lincolnshire	29 June*
Bodiam Castle, East Sussex	29 June
Ickworth, Suffolk	10 – 12 July**
Gibside, Tyne & Wear	13 July*
Kingston Lacy, Dorset	19 July*
Stowe Landscape Garden, Buckinghamshire	19 – 21 July*
Wimpole Hall, Cambridgeshire	19 – 21 July*
Chirk Castle, Clwyd	21 July*
Killerton, Devon (Exeter Festival Event)	21 July*
Tatton Park, Cheshire	27 July*
Bateman's, East Sussex	3 – 4 August*
Castle Ward, Co Down	3 August*
Hatchlands Park, Surrey	9 August
Calke Abbey, Derbyshire	17 August*

• INDOOR CONCERTS

Charlecote Park, Warwickshire	20 26 June
Clandon Park, Guildford	4 July

• JAZZ AND POP CONCERTS

The Vyne, Hampshire	8 June; 19 – 20 July*
Wallington, Northumberland	22 June
Canons Ashby, Northamptonshire	29 June
Dyrham Park, Avon	5 – 6 July
Clumber Park, Nottinghamshire	13 July*; 3 August*
Claremont Landscape Garden, Surrey	14 July
Killerton, Devon (Exeter Festival event)	20 July
Lanhydrock, Cornwall	26 July*
Mottistone Manor, Isle of Wight	2 – 3 August*
Kingston Lacy, Dorset	9 August*
Emmetts Garden, Kent	10 August
Hatchlands Park, Surrey	10 August

• FETES CHAMPETRES

Fountains Abbey & Studley Royal, Yorkshire (Sponsored by Wolseley Centers Limited)	5 – 6 July
Packwood House, Warwickshire	5 – 6 July*
Claremont Landscape Garden, Surrey	10 – 13 July*
Stourhead Landscape Garden, Wiltshire	24 – 27 July*
Wimpole Hall, Cambridgeshire	17 August

• OPEN AIR OPERA

Avebury Manor Garden, Wiltshire	8 June
Scotney Castle Garden, Kent	11 – 14 July; 18 – 20 July
Ickworth, Suffolk	27 July
Polesden Lacey, Surrey	4 – 6 July
Erddig, Clwyd	3 August
Dyrham Park, Avon	10 August
Brownsea Island, Dorset	13 – 17 August

• OPEN AIR THEATRE

Llanerchaeron, Dyfed	8 June
Polesden Lacey, Surrey	between 16 June & 7 July
Fountains Abbey & Studley Royal, Yorkshire	19 – 22 June; 18 – 20 July
Cliveden, Buckinghamshire	26 – 30 June; 3 – 7 July
Wallington, Northumberland	26 – 30 June
Colby Woodland Garden, Dyfedd	27 June
Speke Hall, Merseyside	28 – 30 June
Golden Cap, Dorset	24 – 27 July
Brimham Rocks, Yorkshire	26 – 28 July; 1 – 3 August
Brownsea Island, Dorset	26 July – 9 August
Powis Castle, Powys	28 – 29 July
Plas Newydd, Gwynedd	13 – 14 August

• FAMILY EVENTS

Charlecote Park, Warwickshire	30 May
Aberdulais Falls, West Glamorgan	June
Cragside, Northumberland	2 June; 4 August
Cherryburn, Northumberland	7 July
Belton House, Lincolnshire	21 July
Hatfield Forest, Essex	3 August
Rhossili, West Glamorgan	20 August

• COUNTRY & CRAFT FAIRS, SHOWS & FLOWER SHOWS

Morden Hall Park, London	4 – 6 May
Bodiam Castle, East Sussex	5 – 6 May
Wimpole Hall, Cambridgeshire	18 – 19 May; 6 – 7 July; 1 September; 23 – 24 November
Shugborough, Staffordshire	25 – 27 May
Florence Court, Co. Fermanagh	26 May
Charlecote Park, Warwickshire	2 – 4 August
Emmetts Garden, Kent	17 – 18 August

• STEAM EVENTS

Patterson's Spade Mill, Co. Antrim	6 May
Quarry Bank Mill, Cheshire	15 – 16 June

• HORSE TRIALS

Belton House, Lincolnshire	13 – 14 April
Clumber Park, Nottinghamshire	4 – 5 May
Montacute House, Somerset	13 – 14 July

• PLANT SALES

Dunham Massey, Cheshire	19 May
Beningbrough Hall, Yorkshire	8 September

Above: Stourhead Landscape Garden, Wiltshire.

Below: Studley Royal, Yorkshire.

*   Fireworks

**   Candlelit

ENGLISH HERITAGE EVENTS 1996
Bringing history alive

2000 years of history are just a short step away ! Visit an exciting selection of displays, re-enactments, music and drama.
Absorbing, stimulating, entertaining and exciting - English Heritage events have something for everyone to enjoy and opportunities
on many occasions to try your hand at some of the activities if you wish.

For a free events diary containing details of **over 450 events and displays**, call: 0171-973-3396 or ask at any staffed property.

Highlights of the year include:

APRIL

1 GOOD FRI 5 TO BANK HOLIDAY MON 8
From Noon

MEDIEVAL MUSIC

◆ Misericordia

STOKESAY CASTLE, SHOPSHIRE
7 miles north west of Ludlow off the A49.

■ Lively medieval music played on authentic copies of instruments from the period, performed by a costumed musical duo making their debut at English Heritage sites this year.

● Normal admission prices, English Heritage members free.

▲ Enquiries: (01588) 672544

2 EASTER SUN 7 TO BANK HOL MON 8
From Noon

ENGLAND UNDER THREAT, 1746

◆ Lace Wars

DEAL CASTLE, KENT
In Deal.

■ British redcoats in garrison during the Jacobite rebellion, watching the Channel for a threatened French invasion.

● Adult £3.00, Concession £2.25, Child £1.50, English Heritage members free.

▲ Enquiries: (01304) 372762

3 EASTER SUN 7 TO BANK HOL MON 8
From Noon

THE PORTCHESTER GARRISON, FROM ROMANS TO REDCOATS

◆ Various performers

PORTCHESTER CASTLE, HAMPSHIRE
On the south side of Portchester off the A27.

■ Uniforms, drill and weaponry of the soldiers stationed at Portchester Castle from Roman times through to the Napoleonic Wars. Plus living history and encampments.

● Adult £4.00, Concession £3.00, Child £2.00, English Heritage members free.

▲ Enquiries: (01705) 378291

4 EASTER SUN 7 TO BANK HOL MON 8
From Noon

TUDOR LIVING HISTORY

◆ The Tudor Group

PORTLAND CASTLE, DORSET
Overlooking Portland harbour adjacent to the RN helicopter base.

■ The Castle in 1596 brought to life, including a working kitchen.

● Adult £2.50, Concession £1.75, Child £1.00, English Heritage members free.

▲ Enquiries: (01305) 820539

MAJOR EVENT

5 SAT 27 TO SUN 28
At 3pm

CIVIL WAR BATTLE

◆ The Sealed Knot

OLD SARUM, WILTSHIRE
2 miles north of Salisbury off the A345.

■ Hundreds of 17th century pikemen and musketeers, cavalry plus cannon, as the King and Parliament fight for victory.

● Adult £4.00, Concession £3.00, Child £ 2.00, English Heritage members free.

▲ Enquiries: (01722) 335398

MAY

6 SUN 5 TO BANK HOLIDAY MON 6
At 3pm

LEGENDS OF KING ARTHUR

◆ Labyrinth Productions

KENILWORTH CASTLE, WARWICKSHIRE
In Kenilworth.

■ Magical stories about King Arthur, brought to life by a colourful cast of characters including Arthur, Guinevere, Lancelot, Merlin, the Black Knight and the evil Morgan le Fay.

● Adult £4.00, Concession £3.00, Child £2.00, English Heritage members free.

▲ Enquiries: (01926) 852078

MAJOR EVENT

7 SUN 5 TO BANK HOLIDAY MON 6
From Noon

ARMIES THROUGH THE AGES, FROM THE ROMANS TO VE DAY

◆ Various performers

AUDLEY END HOUSE, ESSEX
1 mile west of Saffron Walden on the B1383 (M11 exits 8, 9 northbound only and 10).

■ Top re-enactment societies join together to present 2000 years of history in one afternoon! Enjoy a series of spectacular displays including Imperial Roman Army battle tactics, Saxons and Vikings, Royalists in battle against Cromwell's New Model Army, Napoleonic dragoons and a World War Two combat set after D-Day. Plus encampments and living history.

● Grounds and event Adult £5.00, Concession £4.00, Child £2.50, English Heritage members free.

House extra, subject to capacity.

▲ Enquiries: (01799) 522399/522842

8 SAT 25 TO BANK HOLIDAY MON 27
From 10am

HOMES & GARDENS SHOW

◆ Romor Exhibitions Limited

WREST PARK , BEDFORDSHIRE
In Silsoe, 10 miles S of Bedford off the A6.

■ Aspects of the home and garden from interior design to ornamental tables, from garden furniture to specialist plants.

● Adult £3.50, Concession £2.50, Child £1.50, English Heritage members free.

▲ Enquiries: (01525) 860152 weekends or (01536) 203230 weekdays

9 SUN 26 TO BANK HOLIDAY MON 27
From 11am

MONASTIC LIFE

◆ Horrarium

BYLAND ABBEY, NORTH YORKSHIRE
2 miles south of A170 between Thirsk and Helmsley, near Coxwold village.

■ A small yet fascinating recreation of monastic life in the 15th century, with a Latin mass, chapter meeting and even a midday meal held in silence. Also includes demonstrations of abbey crafts, medieval games for children and storytelling.

● Adult £3.00, Concession £2.25, Child £1.50, English Heritage members free.

▲ Enquiries: (01347) 868614

MAJOR EVENT

10 SUN 26 TO BANK HOLIDAY MON 27
From Noon

AMERICAN CIVIL WAR BATTLE AND LIVING HISTORY

◆ The Southern Skirmish Association

BATTLE ABBEY, EAST SUSSEX

Access and parking for vehicles via Powdermill Lane on the south side of Battle. Pedestrian and disabled visitors via main gates at the south end of Battle High Street.

■ A spectacular slice of American history with hundreds of Union and Confederate infantry, supported by artillery and cavalry. Witness a rebel raid on a Yankee encampment, enjoy living history and watch as the troops clash in battle at 3pm.

● Adult £5.00, Concession £4.00, Child £2.50, English Heritage members free.

▲ Enquiries: (01424) 773792

JUNE

11 FRI 7 TO SUN 9
From 10am

DOVER CASTLE PREPARES FOR WAR, 1475

◆ The Order of St. George and friends

DOVER CASTLE, KENT
To the east of Dover, overlooking the town.

■ Over 100 completely authentic 15th Century soldiers and civilians, including many from Europe, recreating preparations for an invasion of France. See drill, weapons, cannon firing,craftsmen, encampments, cooking and and all the paraphernalia of a medieval army. A fascinating chance to step back in time. With music by Hautbois.

● Normal admission prices, English Heritage members free.

▲ Enquiries: (01304) 201628/211067

MAJOR EVENT

12 SAT 15 TO SUN 16
From 11am

HISTORY IN ACTION !

◆ Various performers

KIRBY HALL, NORTHAMPTONSHIRE
4 miles north east of Corby off the A43.

■ English Heritage's most ambitious historical event of the year. A festival of displays and living history from the Romans to 20th Century featuring up to 1,000 top quality re-enactors from over 20 societies, impressive period encampments, plus a fascinating and unusual market with over 100 craftsmen selling accurate reproductions of period swords, armour, pewter, cloth, buttons, clothing and pottery - indeed, just about everything needed in order to authentically recreate the past! An event every history enthusiast should visit!

● Adult £5.00, Concession £4.00, Child £2.50, English Heritage members free.

▲ Enquiries: (01536) 203230

MAJOR EVENT

13 SAT 29 TO SUN 30
From 10am

CRAFTS AND COUNTRY SHOW

◆ Romor Exhibitions Limited.

AUDLEY END HOUSE, ESSEX
1 mile west of Saffron Walden on the B1383 (M11 exits 8, 9 northbound only and 10.)

● Adult £5.00, Concession £3.00, Child £1.00, English Heritage members free.

(House extra, subject to capacity)

▲ Enquiries: (01799) 522399/522842

JULY

14 **SAT 6 TO SUN 7**
From Noon

RICHARD III, THE MAN BEHIND THE MYTH

◆ The Stafford Household

MIDDLEHAM CASTLE, NORTH YORKSHIRE
In Middleham.

■ Meet the controversial monarch in the year 1484, along with members of his court and loyal soldiers. Also enjoy music by Hautbois, dance and games.

● Adult £4.00, Concession £3.00, Child £2.00, English Heritage members free.

▲ Enquiries: (01969) 623899

15 **SAT 13 TO SUN 14**
From Noon

SOLDIERS OF THE QUEEN

◆ Various performers

FRAMLINGHAM CASTLE, SUFFOLK
In Framlingham on the B1116.

■ Thrilling, colourful displays by infantry, cavalry and artillery of Queen Victoria's army in 1890. Uniforms, weaponry, equipment and tactics, plus encampment.

● Adult £4.00, Concession £3.00, Child £2.00, English Heritage members free.

▲ Enquiries: (01728) 724189

16 **SAT 20 JULY TO SUN 1 SEPTEMBER**

SUMMER HOLIDAY MINI EVENTS

◆ Various performers

■ On EVERY Saturday and Sunday from 20 July to 1 September plus Bank Holiday Monday 26 August, you'll be able to enjoy a special event or a summer holiday mini event at **over 40 English Heritage properties**. From armoured knights to storytelling, medieval music to Roman soldiers, there's lots to see, do and enjoy.

● Normal admission prices apply at all summer mini events (English Heritage members free).

▲ For details call 0171 973 3396 (weekdays).

17 **SAT 20 TO SUN 21**
From Noon

DOGS, FALCONS, SHEEP AND GEESE!

◆ Will Gray with Feather Perfect Falconry

WREST PARK, BEDFORDSHIRE
In Silsoe, 10 miles S of Bedford off the A6.

■ Falcons flying free, gun dogs and sheepdogs demonstrating their skills with sheep and geese.

● Adult £3.00, Concession £2.25, Child £1.50, English Heritage members free.

▲ Enquiries: (01525) 860152 weekends or (01536) 203230 weekdays

---

18 **SUN 28**
From 11am

THE BATTLE HISTORIC AND CLASSIC CAR SHOW

◆ The Rotary Club

BATTLE ABBEY, EAST SUSSEX
At the south end of Battle High Street.

■ A display of superb classic and vintage cars, plus motorcycles and commercial vehicles, with cavalcade at 3pm. In aid of local charities.

● Normal admission prices, English Heritage members free.

▲ Enquiries: (01424) 773792

AUGUST

MAJOR EVENT

19 **SAT 10 TO SUN 11**
From Noon

A GRAND REGENCY FAIR

◆ Various performers

WREST PARK, BEDFORDSHIRE
In Silsoe, 10 miles S of Bedford off the A6.

■ Enjoy entertainments and music from the year 1815. Meet the terrifying "wild man", be amazed by a mermaid or a talking pig, cheer the Royal Navy in its epic battle at Trafalgar and feel the earth shaken by the thundering hooves of the 12th Light Dragoons as gentry and country folk celebrate the defeat of Napoleon at Waterloo. Plus savage duellists, redcoats on parade, cannon and musket firing, soldiers' encampment and living history. Includes music by Hautbois.

● Adult £5.00, Concession £4.00, Child £2.50, English Heritage members free.

▲ Enquiries: (01525) 860152 weekends or (01536) 203230 weekdays

MAJOR 350TH ANNIVERSARY EVENT

20 **SAT 10 TO SUN 11**
From Noon

THE SIEGE OF GOODRICH CASTLE, 1646

◆ The English Civil War Society

GOODRICH CASTLE, HEREFORD AND WORCESTER
5 miles south of Ross-on-Wye off the A40.

■ Visit the siege lines of Parliament's army and defiant Royalist defenders as the Castle is battered by heavy cannon fire. With exciting skirmishes and living history encampments.

● Adult £5.00, Concession £4.00, Child £2.50, English Heritage members free.

▲ Enquiries: (01600) 890538

MAJOR 350TH ANNIVERSARY EVENT

21 **SAT 17 TO SUN 18**
From Noon

THE SIEGE OF PENDENNIS CASTLE, 1646

◆ The Sealed Knot

PENDENNIS CASTLE, CORNWALL
On Pendennis Head 1 mile south east of Falmouth

■ The final stages of this dramatic siege re-enacted, as the last Royalist garrison in Southern England continue a gallant but hopeless struggle for their King, Charles I.

● Adult £4.00, Concession £3.00, Child £2.00, English Heritage members free.

▲ Enquiries: (01326) 316594

MAJOR EVENT

22 **SAT 24 TO BANK HOLIDAY MON 26**
From 10am

WREST PARK CRAFT FESTIVAL

◆ Romor Exhibitions Ltd

WREST PARK, BEDFORDSHIRE
In Silsoe, 10 miles S of Bedford off the A6.

■ Large scale show with over 150 crafts people plus entertainment.

● Adult £4.00, Concession £3.00, Child £2.00, English Heritage members free.

▲ Enquiries: (01536) 203230 weekdays

MAJOR EVENT

23 **SUN 25 TO BANK HOLIDAY MON 26**
From 11am

DOVER CASTLE ON THE EVE OF D-DAY

◆ Various performers.

DOVER CASTLE, KENT
To the east of Dover, overlooking the town.

■ Hundreds of Allied soldiers, plus military vehicles and guns, workshops, offices, living quarters and even German POWs, evoke the preparations at Dover for the invasion of Europe in 1944. Includes firing of a pair of 25-pounder guns.

● Normal admission prices, English Heritage members free.

▲ Enquiries: (01304) 201628/211067

SEPTEMBER

24 **SAT 14 TO SUN 15**
From Noon

A TUDOR WEDDING

◆ The Tudor Group

MUCHELNEY ABBEY, SOMERSET
In Muchelney, 2 miles south of Langport.

■ A delightful small scale re-enactment of how a typical wedding of the 1580s might have looked, using an original wedding service, plus music, celebrations and living history.

● Adult £3.00, Concession £2.25, Child £1.50, English Heritage members free

▲ Enquiries: (01458) 250664

25 **SAT 14 TO SUN 15**
From 11am

MEDIEVAL ENTERTAINMENT

◆ The Lion Rampant

FRAMLINGHAM CASTLE, SUFFOLK
In Framlingham on the B1116.

■ The excitement and pageantry of the medieval world recreated with fighting knights, dances, music and drama.

● Adult £3.00, Concession £2.25, Child £1.50, English Heritage members free.

▲ Enquiries: (01728) 724189

26 **SAT 28 TO SUN 29**
From Noon

INVASION 1066 !

◆ The Vikings and Conquest

PEVENSEY CASTLE, EAST SUSSEX
In Pevensey.

■ A major event to commemorate the anniversary of the landing at Pevensey by Duke William of Normandy, exactly 930 years this weekend. See Norman Knights on horseback, men-at-arms, weapons and displays.

● Adult £4.00, Concession £3.00, Child £2.00, English Heritage members free.

▲ Enquiries: (01323) 762604

HUDSON'S DIRECTORY INDEX

Devon and Cornwall

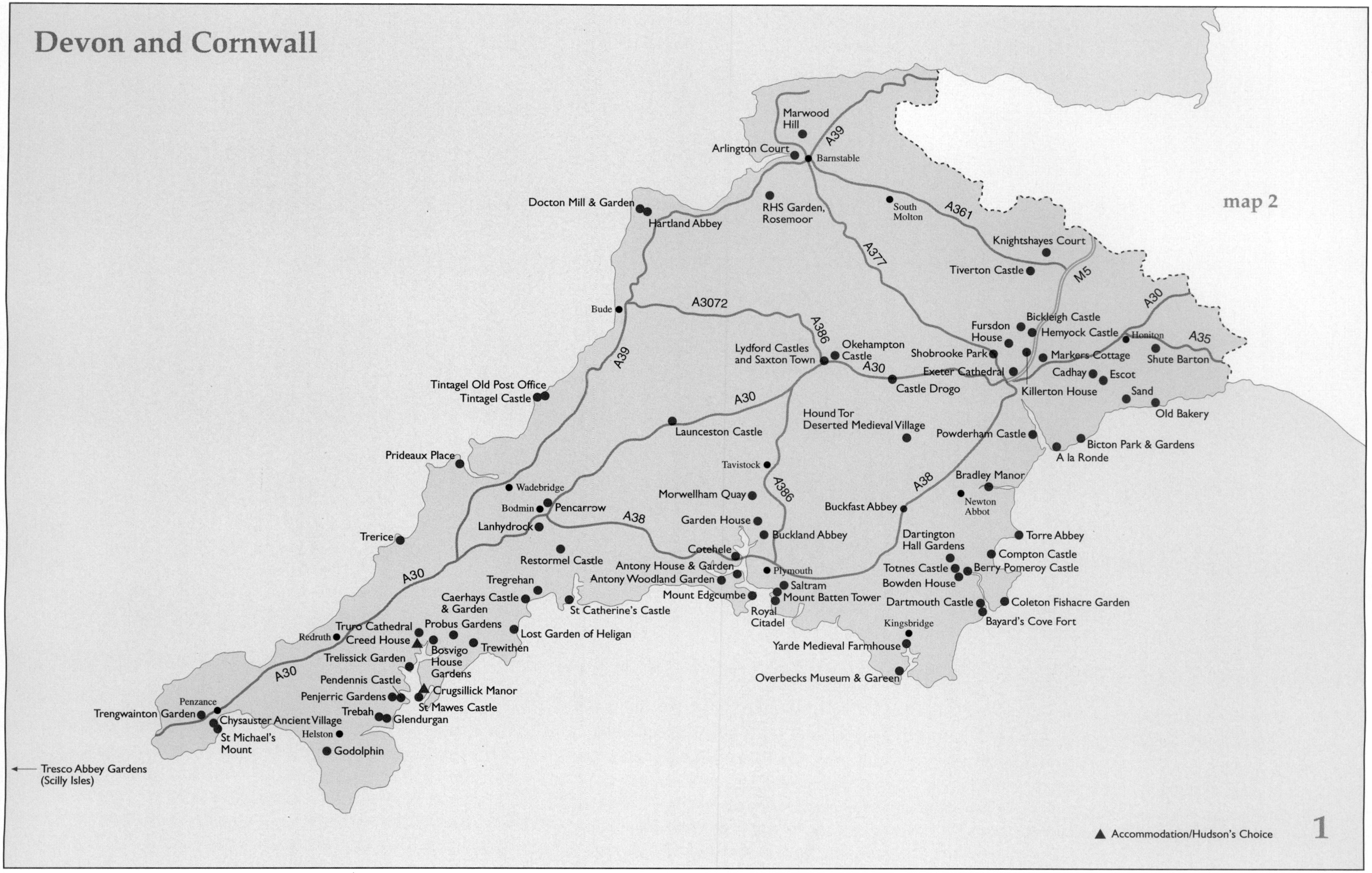

map 2

A35

Marwood Hill
Arlington Court
A39
Barnstable
A361
Knightshayes Court
RHS Garden, Rosemoor
South Molton
A377
Tiverton Castle
Fursdon House
Bickleigh Castle
Hemyock Castle
Markers Cottage
Cadhay
Escot
Honiton
Shute Barton
Sand
Old Bakery
Bicton Park & Gardens
A la Ronde
Shobrooke Park
Exeter Cathedral
Killerton House
Castle Drogo
Powderham Castle
Bradley Manor
Newton Abbot
Torre Abbey
Compton Castle
Berry Pomeroy Castle
Coleton Fishacre Garden
Bayard's Cove Fort
Okehampton Castle
A30
Hound Tor Deserted Medieval Village
A38
Dartington Hall Gardens
Totnes Castle
Bowden House
Dartmouth Castle
Buckfast Abbey
Kingsbridge
Yarde Medieval Farmhouse
Overbecks Museum & Gareen
Hartland Abbey
A3072
Lydford Castles and Saxton Town
A386
A30
Launceston Castle
Tavistock
Morwellham Quay
Garden House
Buckland Abbey
A386
Plymouth
Saltram
Mount Batten Tower
Royal Citadel
Doncton Mill & Garden
Bude
A39
Cotehele
Antony House & Garden
Antony Woodland Garden
Mount Edgcumbe
Tintagel Old Post Office
Tintagel Castle
Prideaux Place
Wadebridge
Bodmin
Pencarrow
Lanhydrock
Restormel Castle
St Catherine's Castle
Lost Garden of Heligan
A38
Tregrehan
Caerhays Castle & Garden
Probus Gardens
Lost Garden of Heligan
Trewithen
Bosvigo House Gardens
Crugsillick Manor
St Mawes Castle
Trerice
A30
Truro Cathedral
Creed House
Trelissick Garden
Pendennis Castle
Penjerric Gardens
Trebah
Glendurgan
Godolphin
Redruth
Helston
Chysauster Ancient Village
St Michael's Mount
Penzance
Trengwainton Garden

—— Tresco Abbey Gardens (Scilly Isles)

▲ Accommodation/Hudson's Choice

Avon, Somerset, Wiltshire and Dorset

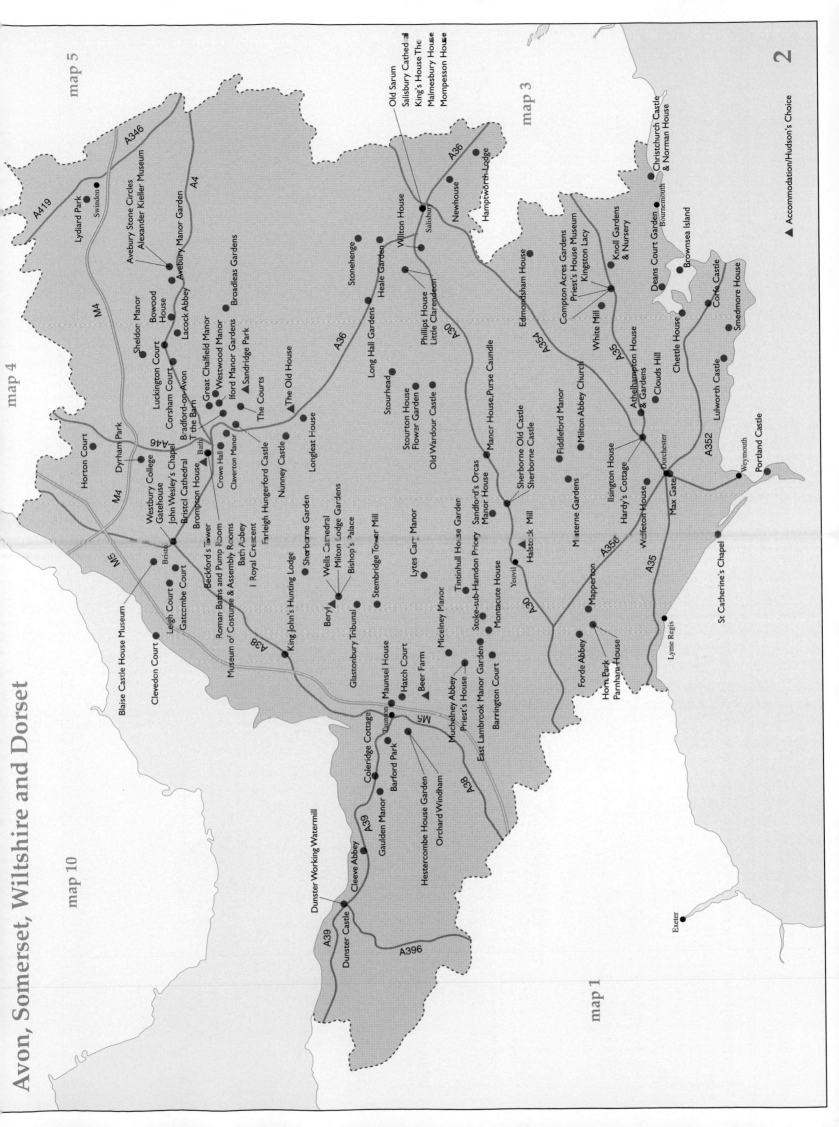

map 5

map 4

map 10

map 3

map 1

2

Old Sarum
Salisbury Cathedral
King's House The
Malmesbury House
Mompesson House

▲ Accommodation/Hudson's Choice

A419

Lydiard Park

Swindon

A346

M4

Avebury Stone Circles
Alexander Keiller Museum
Avebury Manor Garden

A4

Sheldon Manor
Bowood House

Broadleas Gardens

Luckington Court
Corsham Court
Lacock Abbey

Great Chalfield Manor
Westwood Manor
Iford Manor Gardens
▲Sandridge Park

Bradford-on-Avon
T the Barn

The Courts

Horton Court

A46

Dyrham Park

M4

M5

Bristol

Westbury College
Gatehouse
John Wesley's Chapel
Bristol Cathedral
Brompton House
Beckford's Tower
Museum of Costume & Assembly Rooms
Roman Baths and Pump Room
Bath Abbey
I Royal Crescent

Bath

Crowe Hall
Claverton Manor

Farleigh Hungerford Castle

Nunney Castle

▲The Old House

Longleat House

Stonehenge

Heale Garden

Wilton House

Salisbury

Newhouse

Hamptworth Lodge

A36

A36

Long Hall Gardens

Stourhead

Phillips House
Little Clarendon

Edmondsham House

Compton Acres Gardens
Priest's House Museum
Kingston Lacy

Christchurch Castle
& Norman House

Bournemouth

Deans Court Garden

Brownsea Island

Leigh Court
Gatcombe Court

Blaise Castle House Museum

Clevedon Court

A38

King John's Hunting Lodge

Sherborne Garden

Beryl ▲

Wells Cathedral
Milton Lodge Gardens
Bishop's Palace

Stembridge Tower Mill

Lytes Cary Manor

Glastonbury Tribunal

Maunsel House

Hatch Court

Beer Farm

Micelney Manor

Tintinhull House Garden

Muchelney Abbey
Priest's House

Stoke-sub-Hamdon Priory
Sandford's Orcas
Manor House

Montacute House

Yeovil

Halstock Mill ▲

East Lambrook Manor Garden

Barrington Court

Stourton House
Flower Garden
Old Wardour Castle

A36

A30

Manor House, Purse Caundle

Sherborne Old Castle
Sherborne Castle

A354

Fiddleford Manor

Milton Abbey Church

Materne Gardens

Ilsington House
Hardy's Cottage

Athelhampton House
& Gardens

Clouds Hill

Chettle House

White Mill

A35

Knoll Gardens
& Nursery

Corfe Castle

Smedmore House

Lulworth Castle

Dorchester

Max Gate

Welfeton House

A35

A352

Portland Castle

Weymouth

St Catherine's Chapel

Forde Abbey

Horn Park
Parnham House

Mapperton

A356

A358

A30

Lyme Regis

Exeter

Dunster Castle
Dunster Working Watermill

A39

Cleeve Abbey

A396

A39

Gaulden Manor

Barford Park

Coleridge Cottage

Hestercombe House Garden
Orchard Windham

Taunton

M5

A38

Clevedon Court

Horton Court

Hampshire, Surrey, West Sussex, East Sussex, Kent, Greater London and Isle of Wight

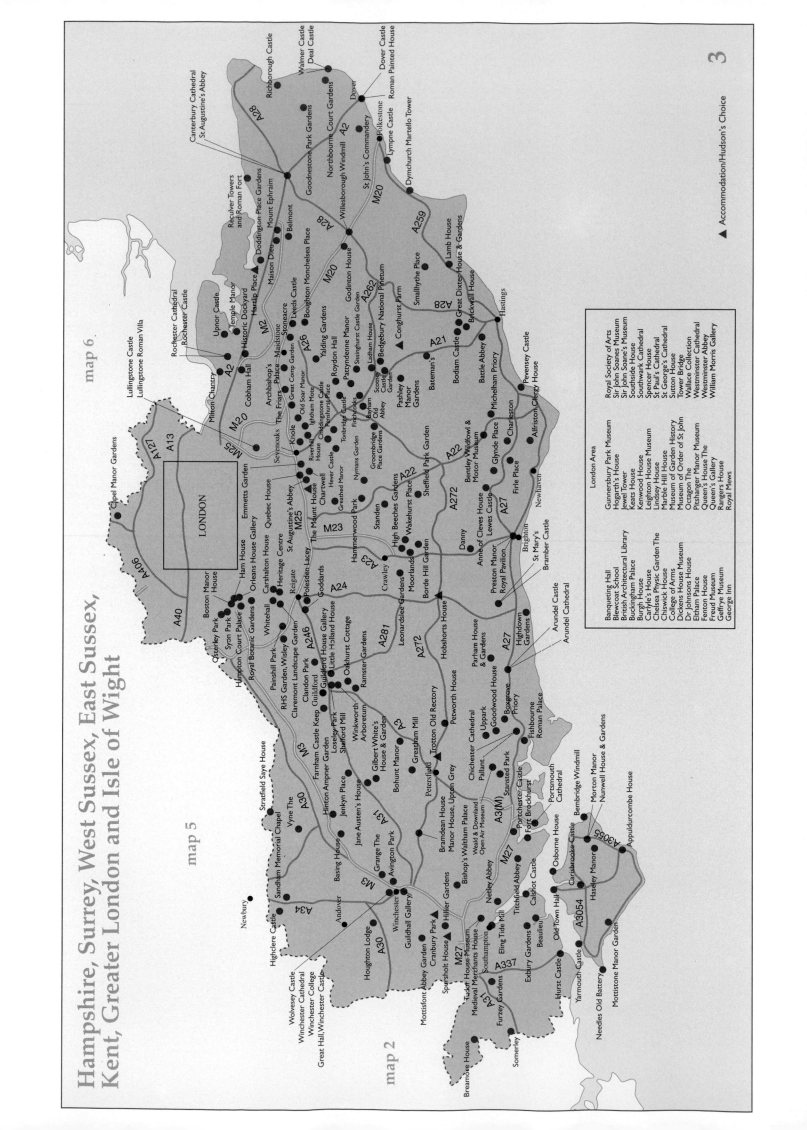

map 6.

map 5

map 2

LONDON

▲ Accommodation/Hudson's Choice

3

London Area

Banqueting Hall
Blewcoat School
British Architectural Library
Buckingham Palace
Burgh House
Carlyle's House
Chelsea Physic Garden The
Chiswick House
College of Arms
Dickens House Museum
Dr Johnsons House
Eltham Palace
Fenton House
Freud Museum
Geffrye Museum
George Inn

Gunnersbury Park Museum
Hogarth's House
Jewel Tower
Keats House
Kenwood House
Leighton House Museum
Lindsey House
Marble Hill House
Museum of Garden History
Museum of Order of St John
Octagon The
Pitshanger Manor Museum
Queen's House The
Queen's Gallery
Rangers House
Royal Mews

Royal Society of Arts
Sir John Soanes Museum
Sir John Soane's Museum
Southside House
Southwark Cathedral
Spencer House
St Paul's Cathedral
St George's Cathedral
Sutton House
Tower Bridge
Wallace Collection
Westminster Cathedral
Westminster Abbey
William Morris Gallery

Shropshire, Staffordshire, West Midlands, Hereford and Worcester, Warwickshire, and Gloucestershire

map 8

map 7

Biddulph Grange Garden

Ford Green Hall

Ancient High House
Izaak Walton's Cottage
Stafford Castle
Wolseley Garden Park

Greenbanks

Dearnford Hall

Combermere Abbey

Oakley Hall

Eccleshall Castle

Hawkstone Park

Sandon Hall

Glascoed Hall

Hodnet Hall Gardens

Moreton Corbet Castle

Stafford

Shugborough Estate

Burton-upon-Trent

Adcote School

Lichfield Cathedral
Samuel Johnson Birthplace Museum

Clive House Museum
Rowley's House Museum
Shrewsbury Abbey
Shrewsbury Castle

Haughmond Abbey

Weston Park

Attingham Park

Lilleshall Abbey

Shrewsbury

Wroxeter Roman City

Boscobel House

Tamworth Castle

Acton Burnell Castle

Benthall Hall

Buildwas Abbey

Chillington Hall

Langley Chapel

Ironbridge Gorge Museum
Iron Bridge

Moseley Old Hall

Wightwick Manor

Wilderhope Manor

Shipton Hall

Wenlock Priory

Halesowen Abbey

Aston Hall

Preen Manor Gardens

Upton Cressett Hall

Birmingham Botanical Gardens

Morville Hall

Hagley Hall

Arbury Hall

Dudmaston Hall

Birmingham

Blakesley Hall

Walcot Hall

Coventry

Clun Castle

Stokesay Castle

Coventry Cathedral

Ryton Organic Gardens

Ludlow Castle

map 10

Hartlebury Castle

Avoncroft Museum of Historic Buildings

Baddesley Clinton

Burford House Gardens

Packwood House

Kenilworth Castle

Croft Castle

Witley Court

Hanbury Hall

Lord Leycester Hospital
Warwick Castle

Berrington Hall

Warwick

Broxwood Court

Wichenford Dovecote

Coughton Court

Charlecote Park

Hawford Dovecote

Hergest Croft Gardens

Lower Brockhampton

Worcester

Stratford on Avon

Cwmmau Farmhouse

Elgar's Birthplace Museum

Ragley Hall

Shakespearean Properties

Upton House

Dinmore Manor

Madresfield Court

Spetchley Park Garden

Farnborough Hall

Brobury House Gardens

Weir The

Greyfriars The

Hidcote Manor Gardens

Honington Hall

Hereford

Leigh Court Barn

Kiftsgate Court Gardens

Hereford Cathedral
Rotherwas Chapel

Eastnor Castle

Snowshill Manor

Batsford Arboretum

Abbeydore Court Gardens

Stanway House

Longtown Castle

St Mary's Church

Sezincore

How Caple Court Gardens

Hailes Abbey

Ashleworth Tithe Barn

Sudeley Castle

Goodrich Castle

Whittington Court

Gloucester

Cheltenham

Blackfriars

Chedworth Roman Villa

map 5

Littledean Hall

Painswick Rococo Gardens

Woodchester Park Mansion

Westbury Court Garden

Misarden Park Gardens

Lydney Park Gardens

Owlpen Manor

Rodmarton Manor

Berkeley Castle

Drakestone House

Chavenage

Kelmscott Manor

Westonbirt Arboretum

Swindon

map 2

Bristol

Bath

▲ Accommodation/Hudson's Choice

4

Oxfordshire, Berkshire, Buckinghamshire, Bedfordshire, and Hertfordshire

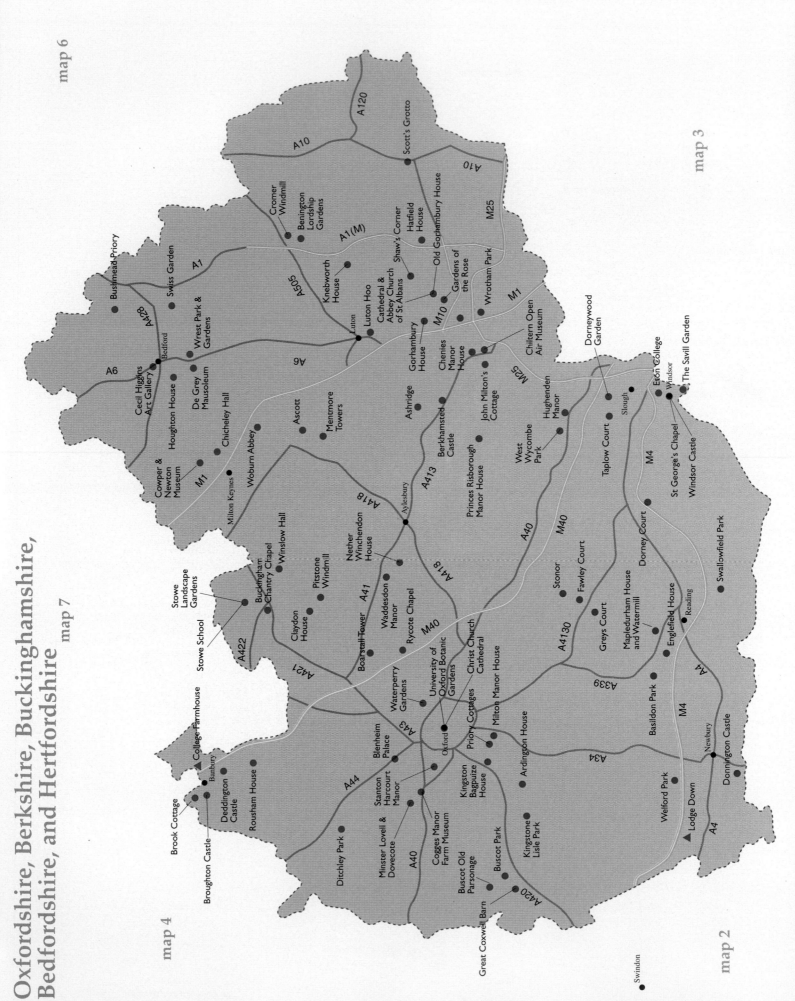

map 6

map 7

map 4

map 2

map 3

▲ Accommodation/Hudson's Choice

5

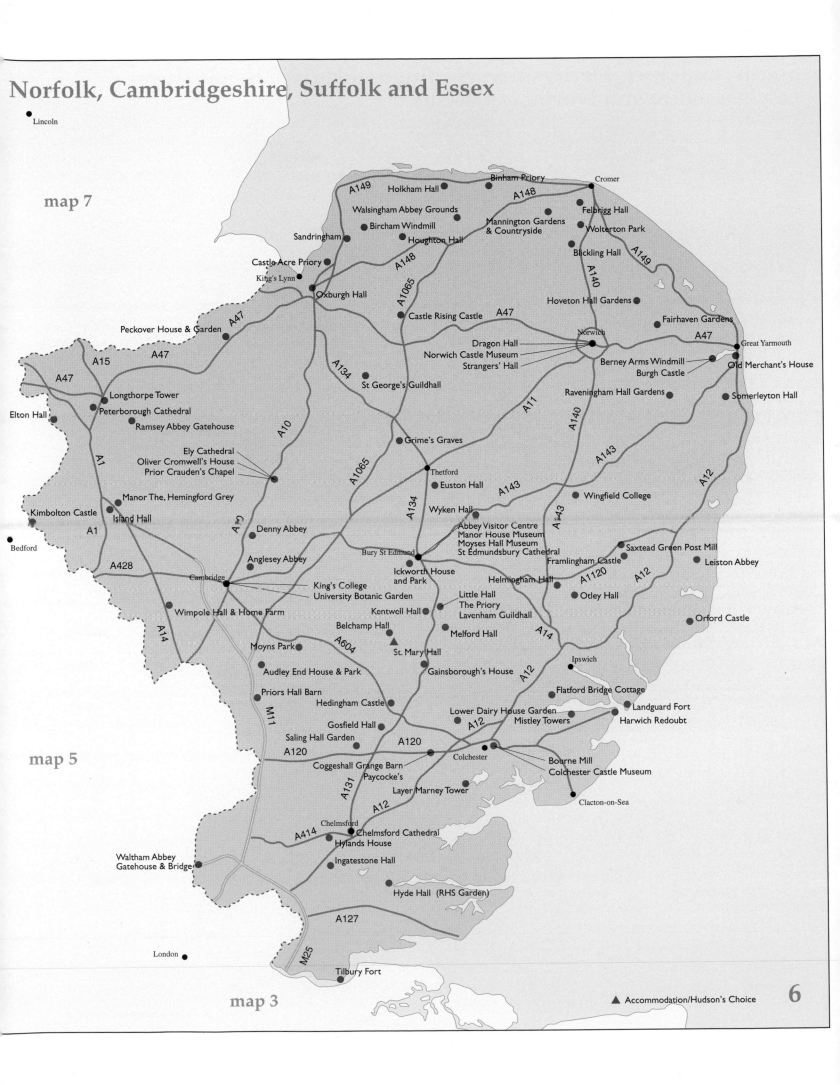

Norfolk, Cambridgeshire, Suffolk and Essex

map 7

Lincoln

A149
Holkham Hall
Binham Priory
Cromer
A148
Walsingham Abbey Grounds
Felbrigg Hall
Bircham Windmill
Mannington Gardens & Countryside
Wolterton Park
Sandringham
Houghton Hall
A148
Blickling Hall
A149
Castle Acre Priory
A1065
A140
King's Lynn
Oxburgh Hall
Hoveton Hall Gardens
Fairhaven Gardens
Castle Rising Castle
A47
A47
Peckover House & Garden
A47
A134
Norwich
Great Yarmouth
A15
Dragon Hall
Norwich Castle Museum
Strangers' Hall
Berney Arms Windmill
Burgh Castle
Old Merchant's House
A47
Longthorpe Tower
St George's Guildhall
A11
A140
Raveningham Hall Gardens
Somerleyton Hall
Peterborough Cathedral
Elton Hall
Ramsey Abbey Gatehouse
A10
A1065
Grime's Graves
A143
A12
Ely Cathedral
Oliver Cromwell's House
Prior Crauden's Chapel
Thetford
Euston Hall
A143
Wingfield College
Manor The, Hemingford Grey
A134
Wyken Hall
A143
Kimbolton Castle
Island Hall
Abbey Visitor Centre
Manor House Museum
Moyses Hall Museum
St Edmundsbury Cathedral
Saxtead Green Post Mill
A1
A428
Denny Abbey
Bury St Edmunds
Framlingham Castle
A1120
Leiston Abbey
Bedford
A1
Anglesey Abbey
Helmingham Hall
A12
Cambridge
King's College
University Botanic Garden
Little Hall
The Priory
Lavenham Guildhall
Otley Hall
Wimpole Hall & Home Farm
Kentwell Hall
Orford Castle
A14
Belchamp Hall
Melford Hall
A14
Moyns Park
A604
St. Mary Hall
Gainsborough's House
Ipswich
Audley End House & Park
A12
Flatford Bridge Cottage
Priors Hall Barn
Hedingham Castle
Lower Dairy House Garden
Landguard Fort
M11
Gosfield Hall
A12
Mistley Towers
Harwich Redoubt
Saling Hall Garden
A120
Bourne Mill
A120
Coggeshall Grange Barn
Paycocke's
Colchester
Colchester Castle Museum
A131
Layer Marney Tower
Clacton-on-Sea
A12
Chelmsford
Chelmsford Cathedral
Hylands House
A414
Ingatestone Hall
Waltham Abbey
Gatehouse & Bridge
Hyde Hall (RHS Garden)
A127
London
M25
Tilbury Fort

map 5

map 3

▲ Accommodation/Hudson's Choice

6

map 9

Monk Bretton Priory

A635

Brodsworth Hall

A628

M18

Elsham Hall Country & Wildlife Park

A1(M)

Doncaster

Conisbrough Castle

M1

M18

A1(M)

A57

Roche Abbey

Sheffield

A46

A16

Bishop's House

A57

Hodsock Priory Gardens

Peveril Castle

Eyam Hall

Gainsborough Old Hall

A57

A158

Revolution House

Renishaw Hall

Clumber Park

Bakewell Old House Museum

A619

Sutton Scarsdale Hall

Bishop's Old Palace

Lincoln Cathedral

Chatsworth

Bolsover Castle

Doddington Hall

Winster Market House

Haddon Hall

A6

A614

Lincoln

A61

A1

A46

Aubourn Hall

Hardwick Hall
Hardwick Old Hall
Hardwick Estate - Stainsby Mill

Carlton House

The Old Vicarage

Gunby Hall

Skegness

Rufford Abbey

A16

Winkburn Hall

Tattershall Castle

Sir Richard Arkwright's Cromford Mill

Norwood Park

Newark-on-Trent

A17

Fulbeck Hall

A15

Sibsey Trader Windmill

Newstead Abbey

A17

Wollaton Hall National History Museum

A52

Castle Museum & Art Gallery

Nottingham

Boston

Kedleston Hall

Melbourne Hall

Belton House Park and Gardens

Derby

Holme Pierrepont Hall

A52

Elvaston Castle Country Park

Thrumpton Hall

Belvoir Castle

Grantham

Sudbury Hall

A38

Catton Hall

Harlaxton Manor

A1

A15

Whatton House Garden

Woolsthorpe Manor

A151

A17

King's Lynn

A50

A6

A46

Grimsthorpe Castle, Park & Gardens

A16

Ashby de la Zouch Castle

M1

Prestwold Hall

A606

Burghley House

Kirby Muxloe Castle

Belgrave Hall

map 6

Leicester

A47

Prebendal Manor House

Noseley Hall

M69

Lyddington Bede House

A6

Rockingham Castle

A43

Southwick Hall

M1

Rushton Triangular Lodge

Stanford Hall

Lamport Hall & Gardens

Stratford on Avon

A43

Cambridge

map 4

M45

Northampton Cathedral

Northampton

A428

The Menagerie

Stoke Park Pavilions

Banbury

Sulgrave Manor

A43

Milton Keynes

map 5

▲ Accommodation/Hudson's Choice

7

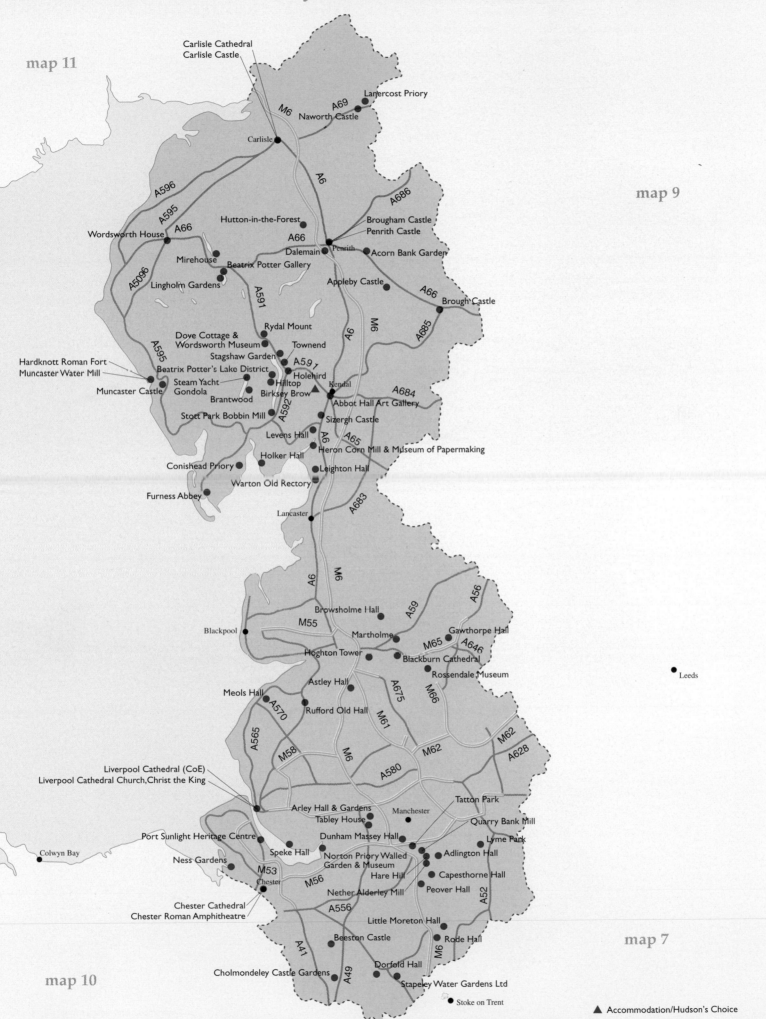

Cumbria, Lancashire, Merseyside, Cheshire and Greater Manchester

map 11

map 9

map 7

map 10

Carlisle Cathedral
Carlisle Castle

Lanercost Priory

A69

Naworth Castle

M6

Carlisle

A596

A595

A6

A686

Hutton-in-the-Forest

Brougham Castle
Penrith Castle

Wordsworth House

A66

A66

Dalemain

Penrith

Acorn Bank Garden

Mirehouse

Beatrix Potter Gallery

A5096

Lingholm Gardens

Appleby Castle

A66

A591

Brough Castle

A685

Rydal Mount

Dove Cottage &
Wordsworth Museum

Townend

A6

M6

Stagshaw Garden

A591

Hardknott Roman Fort
Muncaster Water Mill

Beatrix Potter's Lake District

Holehird

A595

Steam Yacht
Gondola

Hilltop

Kendal

A684

Muncaster Castle

Brantwood

Birksey Brow

Abbot Hall Art Gallery

A592

Stott Park Bobbin Mill

Sizergh Castle

Levens Hall

A6

A65

Heron Corn Mill & Museum of Papermaking

Holker Hall

Conishead Priory

Leighton Hall

Warton Old Rectory

Furness Abbey

Lancaster

A683

A6

M6

Browsholme Hall

A59

A56

Blackpool

M55

Martholme

Gawthorpe Hall

Hoghton Tower

M65

A646

Blackburn Cathedral

Rossendale Museum

Astley Hall

A675

M66

Meols Hall

A570

Rufford Old Hall

M61

Leeds

A565

M58

A6

M62

A628

Liverpool Cathedral (CoE)
Liverpool Cathedral Church, Christ the King

A580

M62

Tatton Park

Arley Hall & Gardens

Manchester

Quarry Bank Mill

Tabley House

Port Sunlight Heritage Centre

Dunham Massey Hall

Lyme Park

Colwyn Bay

Speke Hall

Norton Priory Walled
Garden & Museum

Adlington Hall

Ness Gardens

M53

Hare Hill

Capesthorne Hall

Chester

M56

Peover Hall

A52

Nether Alderley Mill

Chester Cathedral
Chester Roman Amphitheatre

A556

Little Moreton Hall

Beeston Castle

Rode Hall

M6

A41

Cholmondeley Castle Gardens

A49

Dorfold Hall

Stapeley Water Gardens Ltd

Stoke on Trent

▲ Accommodation/Hudson's Choice

8

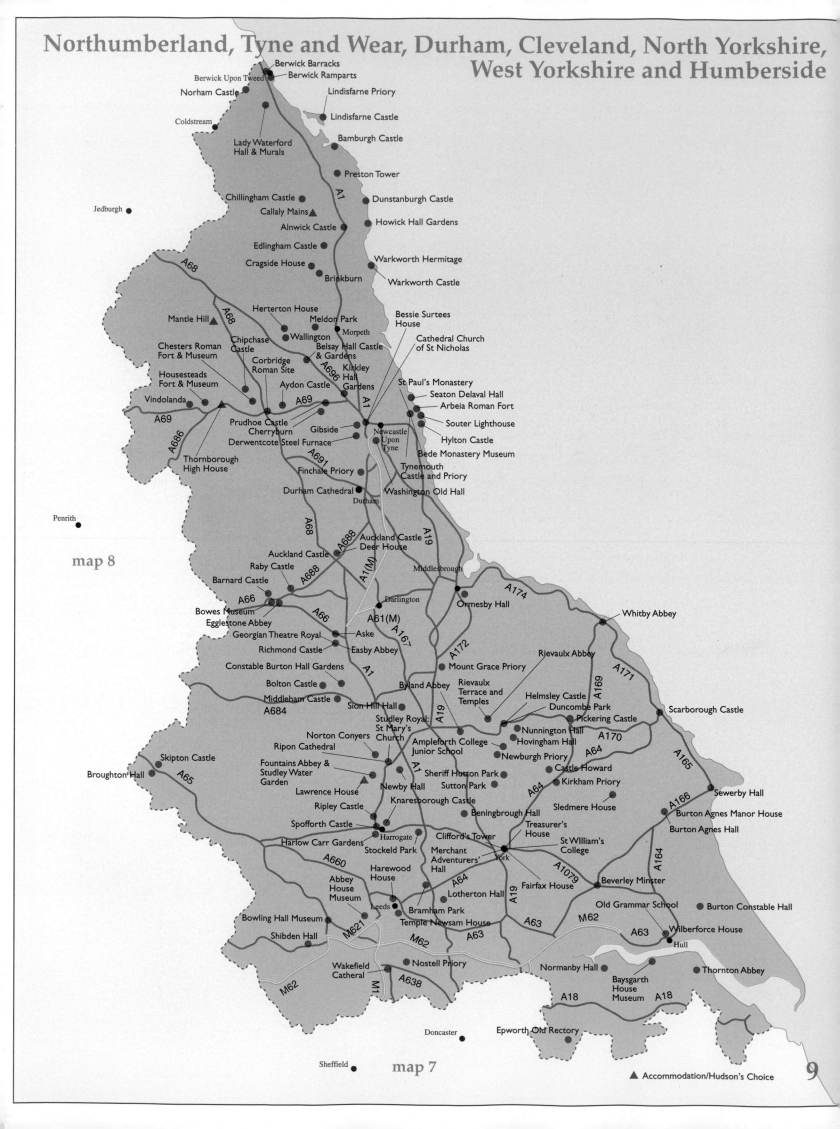

Northumberland, Tyne and Wear, Durham, Cleveland, North Yorkshire, West Yorkshire and Humberside

Berwick Barracks
Berwick Ramparts
Berwick Upon Tweed
Lindisfarne Priory
Norham Castle
Lindisfarne Castle
Coldstream
Bamburgh Castle
Lady Waterford Hall & Murals
Preston Tower
Jedburgh
Chillingham Castle
Dunstanburgh Castle
Callaly Mains
Howick Hall Gardens
Alnwick Castle
Edlingham Castle
Cragside House
Warkworth Hermitage
Brinkburn
Warkworth Castle
A68
Herterton House
Bessie Surtees House
Mantle Hill
Meldon Park
Cathedral Church of St Nicholas
A68
Chipchase Castle
Wallington
Morpeth
Chesters Roman Fort & Museum
Belsay Hall Castle & Gardens
Corbridge Roman Site
Kirkley Hall Gardens
St Paul's Monastery
Housesteads Fort & Museum
Aydon Castle
Seaton Delaval Hall
Arbeia Roman Fort
Vindolanda
A69
Souter Lighthouse
A69
Prudhoe Castle
Gibside
Newcastle Upon Tyne
Hylton Castle
A686
Cherryburn
Derwentcote Steel Furnace
Bede Monastery Museum
Thornborough High House
A691
Finchale Priory
Tynemouth Castle and Priory
Durham Cathedral
Washington Old Hall
Durham
Penrith
A68
A688
Auckland Castle Deer House
A19
map 8
Auckland Castle
Middlesbrough
Raby Castle
A688
Barnard Castle
A174
A66
Whitby Abbey
Bowes Museum
Darlington
Ormesby Hall
Egglestone Abbey
A61(M)
Georgian Theatre Royal
A66
Aske
A167
Rievaulx Abbey
A172
A171
Richmond Castle
Easby Abbey
Mount Grace Priory
A169
Constable Burton Hall Gardens
A1
Byland Abbey
Rievaulx Terrace and Temples
Helmsley Castle
Scarborough Castle
Bolton Castle
Duncombe Park
Middleham Castle
Pickering Castle
A684
Sion Hill Hall
A19
A170
Studley Royal: St Mary's Church
Nunnington Hall
Hovingham Hall
Norton Conyers
Ampleforth College Junior School
Newburgh Priory
A64
Skipton Castle
Ripon Cathedral
Castle Howard
A165
Broughton Hall
Fountains Abbey & Studley Water Garden
Sheriff Hutton Park
Kirkham Priory
A65
Lawrence House
Newby Hall
Sutton Park
Sledmere House
A166
Ripley Castle
Knaresborough Castle
Sewerby Hall
Spofforth Castle
Beningbrough Hall
Treasurer's House
Burton Agnes Manor House
Harlow Carr Gardens
Harrogate
Clifford's Tower
St William's College
Burton Agnes Hall
Stockeld Park
Merchant Adventurers' Hall
York
A164
A660
Harewood House
A64
Fairfax House
Beverley Minster
Abbey House Museum
A1079
Old Grammar School
Lotherton Hall
A19
Burton Constable Hall
Bowling Hall Museum
Leeds
Bramham Park
A63
M62
Wilberforce House
M621
Temple Newsam House
A63
Hull
Shibden Hall
Normanby Hall
Thornton Abbey
Wakefield Cathedral
Nostell Priory
Baysgarth House Museum
A18
M62
M1
A638
A18
Epworth Old Rectory
Doncaster
Sheffield
map 7

▲ Accommodation/Hudson's Choice

9

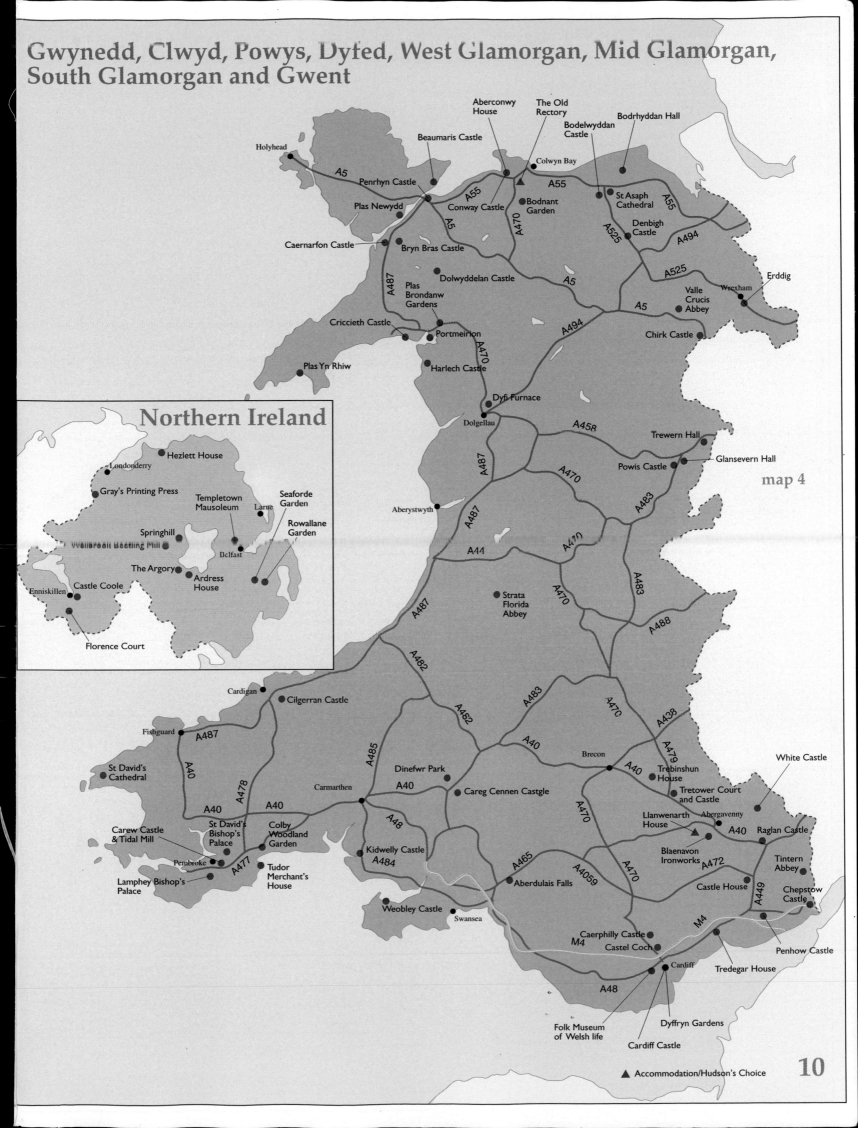

Gwynedd, Clwyd, Powys, Dyfed, West Glamorgan, Mid Glamorgan, South Glamorgan and Gwent

Holyhead

Beaumaris Castle

Aberconwy House

The Old Rectory

Bodelwyddan Castle

Bodrhyddan Hall

Colwyn Bay

Penrhyn Castle

Conway Castle

St Asaph Cathedral

Plas Newydd

Bodnant Garden

Denbigh Castle

Caernarfon Castle

Bryn Bras Castle

Dolwyddelan Castle

Valle Crucis Abbey

Wrexham

Erddig

Plas Brondanw Gardens

Criccieth Castle

Portmeirion

Chirk Castle

Plas Yn Rhiw

Harlech Castle

Dyfi Furnace

Dolgellau

Trewern Hall

Powis Castle

Glansevern Hall

map 4

Northern Ireland

Hezlett House

Londonderry

Gray's Printing Press

Templetown Mausoleum

Larne

Seaforde Garden

Springhill

Rowallane Garden

Wellbrook Beetling Mill

Belfast

The Argory

Ardress House

Enniskillen

Castle Coole

Florence Court

Aberystwyth

Strata Florida Abbey

Cardigan

Cilgerran Castle

Fishguard

St David's Cathedral

Dinefwr Park

Carmarthen

Careg Cennen Castgle

Brecon

Trebinshun House

White Castle

Tretower Court and Castle

St David's Bishop's Palace

Colby Woodland Garden

Llanwenarth House

Abergavenny

Raglan Castle

Carew Castle & Tidal Mill

Kidwelly Castle

Blaenavon Ironworks

Tintern Abbey

Pembroke

Tudor Merchant's House

Aberdulais Falls

Castle House

Chepstow Castle

Lamphey Bishop's Palace

Weobley Castle

Swansea

Penhow Castle

Caerphilly Castle

Castel Coch

Cardiff

Tredegar House

Folk Museum of Welsh life

Dyffryn Gardens

Cardiff Castle

▲ Accommodation/Hudson's Choice

10

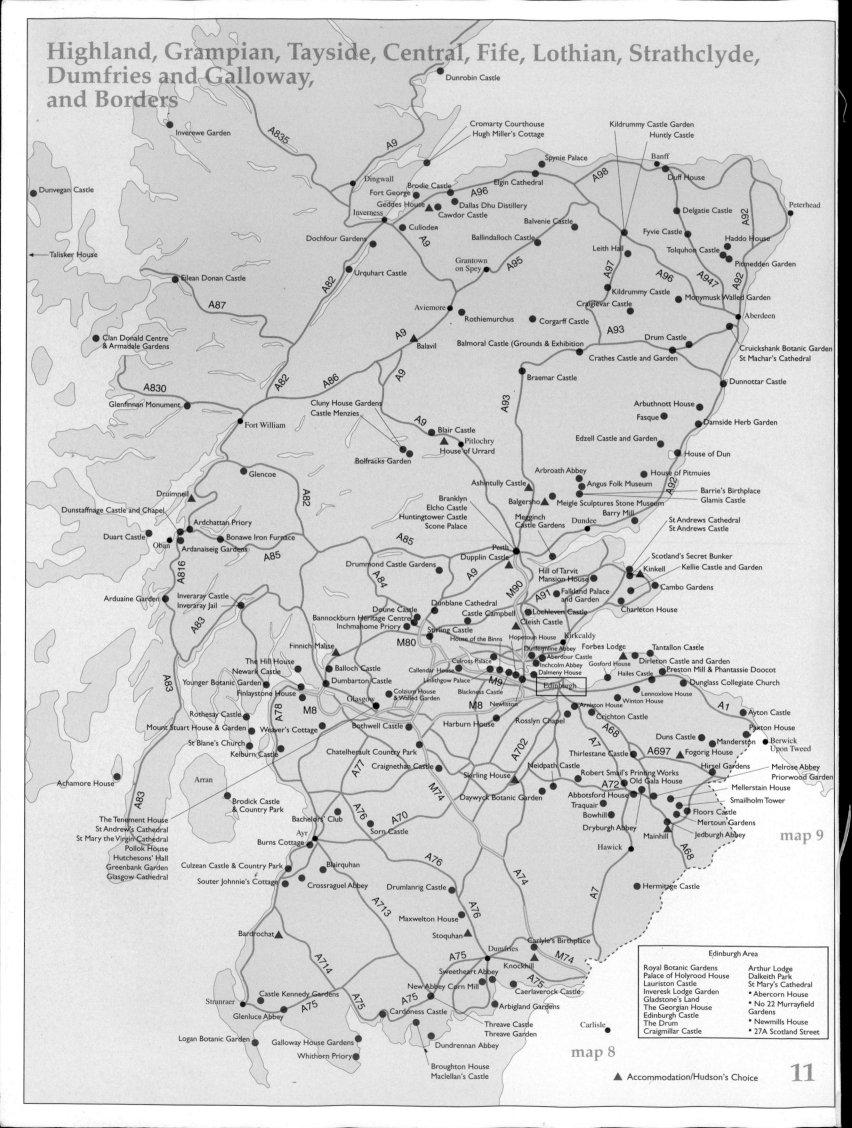

Highland, Grampian, Tayside, Central, Fife, Lothian, Strathclyde, Dumfries and Galloway, and Borders

Inverewe Garden

Dunvegan Castle

Talisker House

Eilean Donan Castle

A87

Clan Donald Centre & Armadale Gardens

A830

Glenfinnan Monument

Fort William

Glencoe

Druimneil

Dunstaffnage Castle and Chapel

Ardchattan Priory

Duart Castle

Oban

Bonawe Iron Furnace

Ardanaiseig Gardens

A85

A816

Arduaine Garden

Inveraray Castle
Inveraray Jail

A83

Achamore House

A83

The Tenement House
St Andrew's Cathedral
St Mary the Virgin Cathedral
Pollok House
Hutchesons' Hall
Greenbank Garden
Glasgow Cathedral

Bardrochat

A714

Stranraer

Castle Kennedy Gardens

Glenluce Abbey

A75

Logan Botanic Garden

Galloway House Gardens

Whithorn Priory

Dunrobin Castle

Cromarty Courthouse
Hugh Miller's Cottage

Dingwall

Brodie Castle

Fort George

Geddes House

Inverness

Culloden

Dochfour Gardens

Urquhart Castle

Aviemore

Balavil

A9

Spynie Palace

Elgin Cathedral

A96

Dallas Dhu Distillery

Cawdor Castle

Balvenie Castle

Ballindalloch Castle

Grantown on Spey

A95

Rothiemurchus

Corgarff Castle

Balmoral Castle (Grounds & Exhibition

Braemar Castle

A93

Cluny House Gardens
Castle Menzies

A9

Blair Castle

Pitlochry

House of Urrard

Bolfracks Garden

A82

A86

A82

A85

Drummond Castle Gardens

A84

Doune Castle

Bannockburn Heritage Centre
Inchmahome Priory

Stirling Castle

M80

Finnich Malise

The Hill House

Newark Castle

Younger Botanic Garden

Finlaystone House

Rothesay Castle

Mount Stuart House & Garden

St Blane's Church

Kelburn Castle

Weaver's Cottage

Balloch Castle

Dumbarton Castle

Glasgow

M8

Bothwell Castle

Chatelherault Country Park

A77

Craignethan Castle

Arran

A78

Brodick Castle & Country Park

Bachelors' Club

A76

Sorn Castle

A70

Ayr

Burns Cottage

Culzean Castle & Country Park

Souter Johnnie's Cottage

Blairquhan

Crossraguel Abbey

Drumlanrig Castle

A713

Maxwelton House

Stoquhan

A76

Dumfries

Knockhill

Sweetheart Abbey

New Abbey Corn Mill

Cardoness Castle

Caerlaverock Castle

Arbigland Gardens

Threave Castle
Threave Garden

Dundrennan Abbey

Broughton House
Maclellan's Castle

Kildrummy Castle Garden
Huntly Castle

Banff

Duff House

A98

Delgatie Castle

A92

Peterhead

Fyvie Castle

Haddo House

Leith Hall

A97

Tolquhon Castle

Pitmedden Garden

A96

A947

A92

Kildrummy Castle

Craigievar Castle

Monymusk Walled Garden

Aberdeen

A93

Drum Castle

Cruickshank Botanic Garden
St Machar's Cathedral

Crathes Castle and Garden

Dunnottar Castle

Arbuthnott House

Fasque

Damside Herb Garden

Edzell Castle and Garden

House of Dun

Arbroath Abbey

House of Pitmuies

Ashintully Castle

Angus Folk Museum

Balgersho

Meigle Sculptures Stone Museum

A92

Barrie's Birthplace
Glamis Castle

Branklyn
Elcho Castle
Huntingtower Castle
Scone Palace

Megginch
Castle Gardens

Dundee

Barry Mill

St Andrews Cathedral
St Andrews Castle

Perth

Dupplin Castle

Scotland's Secret Bunker

Kinkell

Kellie Castle and Garden

Hill of Tarvit
Mansion House

Cambo Gardens

A91

Falkland Palace
and Garden

Charleton House

Dunblane Cathedral

Castle Campbell

Lochleven Castle

Cleish Castle

M90

Kirkcaldy

House of the Binns

Hopetoun House

Dunfermline Abbey

Aberdour Castle

Inchcolm Abbey

Forbes Lodge

Tantallon Castle

Culross Palace

Callendar House

Linlithgow Palace

Gosford House

Dirleton Castle and Garden

Preston Mill & Phantassie Doocot

Hailes Castle

Dunglass Collegiate Church

M9

Edinburgh

Blackness Castle

Colzium House
& Walled Garden

M8

Newliston

Harburn House

Rosslyn Chapel

Arniston House

Winton House

Lennoxlove House

A1

Ayton Castle

Paxton House

Crichton Castle

Duns Castle

Manderston

Berwick
Upon Tweed

A702

A68

A7

Thirlestane Castle

A697

Fogorig House

Hirsel Gardens

Neidpath Castle

Robert Smail's Printing Works
Old Gala House

Melrose Abbey
Priorwood Garden

Skirling House

A72

Mellerstain House

Daywyck Botanic Garden

Abbotsford House

Traquair

Bowhill

Dryburgh Abbey

Smailholm Tower

Floors Castle

Mertoun Gardens

Mainhill

Jedburgh Abbey

Hawick

A68

map 9

M74

A76

Carlyle's Birthplace

A7

Hermitage Castle

Carlisle

map 8

▲ Accommodation/Hudson's Choice

11